Bottom Line's

The Best Years of Your Life

Everything you need to know now to plan for the years ahead

Bottom Line
Books
www.BottomLineSecrets.com

Contents

16 • SURVIVING MAJOR MEDICAL THREATS

17 • ALL ABOUT HOSPITALS, SURGERY, MEDICAL PROCEDURES AND TESTS

18 • MEDICATIONS AND VACCINES

19 • VERY, VERY PERSONAL

1

Preparing to Retire

The Simple Secrets of Planning for Your Retirement

All of us seek levels of comfort in our lives, perhaps more so when we retire. *That includes, along with other things...*

- **Living where we want to live.**
- **Doing what we enjoy doing.**
- **Having work that brings us satisfaction.**

Retiring successfully means staying within our comfort zone while making the transition from working full-time.

We can't rely on others to plan our retirement, because we all have our own unique realm where we want to be. Building retirement comfort zones is something you and your spouse must do on your own. *Key steps...*

- **Prepare for what comes after the honeymoon phase.** That begins with your retirement party. It will end six months to two years

later. You've done all the chores and played all the golf you want to play. Many of those who haven't prepared for what happens next become depressed. And they feel unimportant and unappreciated because they aren't doing anything that makes others appreciate them.

Challenge: Don't make vague retirement plans such as, "I'll catch up on jobs around the house," or, "I'll play golf whenever I want to."

Prepare for the end of the honeymoon by making specific, long-range plans to develop a second career, become involved in community service...or go back to school to learn what you didn't have time for when you were working.

Financial trap: The postretirement letdown can come from financial as well as emotional causes—a realization that your finances aren't providing the retirement you had anticipated.

Marion E. Haynes, retirement planning consultant, 3811 Valley View Dr., Springdale, AR 72762. He spent 35 years as a corporate human resources executive, retiring in 1991 as manager of pensioner relations for Shell Oil. He is a past member of the board of the International Society for Retirement Planning and author of the retirement planning book *Comfort Zones.* Crisp.

1

Be honest in your retirement planning, so you know exactly how far your nest egg will carry you.

Find your comfort zone, matching your retirement plans with your financial resources. Do that by taking inventory of your current financial reserves and by developing a realistic postretirement budget that allows for the impact of future inflation on your reserves.

●**Leave excess baggage from your working life behind.** One day you are president or general manager or a successful salesperson. The next day, you're retired and sitting at home. Suddenly, you're nothing. Your title, and the perks that went with it, are gone.

Retirement is a move into a new phase of life—just another member of the community. Acknowledge the reality of what you will have to deal with.

Prepare in advance by developing alternative activities that will provide the fulfillment you had been getting from your work life.

My experience: When I retired from Shell Oil, three companies offered me part-time assignments. I did consulting for one company for two years, working about 60 days each year. That proved an excellent transition for me—bridging the period between going to work every day and not going to work at all.

With that transition behind me, I felt comfortable and fulfilled devoting most of my time to community service with organizations in my area.

Be flexible and open to whatever postretirement opportunities come along. You may do consulting in your own field, but you may also find opportunities in areas far removed from what you did during your working life.

Don't assume that when you retire, you have to stop working for good.

Example: Our local newspaper carried an article about a man who had just gone back to work at 73. He said he had already carried out all his plans for retirement. "There's nothing left to do, so I decided to go back to work," he said.

●**Include your life partner in all your retirement planning, so that you reinforce each other.** Often, it's the husband who makes the retirement plans and the wife—who typically outlives her spouse—who must struggle to make them work.

Some people—including most women—still believe that only men retire. A working wife, however, will have the same problems in retirement as her husband. Less obvious, but still true, is that homemakers often find the transition to be more difficult than someone who has been working outside the home. Women who have been homemakers all their lives must insist on being a full partner when the working spouse retires.

Since retirement involves both husband and wife, all retirement plans must be made jointly. Each partner must agree on when to retire, where to live, the financial resources that will be needed in retirement and how each will deal with the emotional letdown that follows the end of the retirement honeymoon.

Differences: Postretirement living won't be precisely the same for both partners. One may become infirm before the other. One almost certainly will die before the other. That reality isn't easy to think about, but it must be planned for.

I suggest spouses practice some role shifting as they approach retirement. Women need to know how to do routine household repairs, get the car serviced, manage the couple's finances and investments. Men need to know how to prepare their own meals, wash their clothes, keep the house clean.

●**Anticipate the phases of retirement**— and plan ahead for each. Most people talk about retirement as a single phase—lasting from the day they stop working until they die. Even as we go through retirement, we tend to feel that whatever is happening to us now will last forever.

For most people, retirement will consist of four phases—with different comfort zones required for each. *Those four phases are...*

●**Transition.** That's the "honeymoon" phase, when you're first getting used to the idea of being retired. The main emphasis in this phase is to build the structure that will sustain you when the honeymoon ends and the posthoneymoon letdown begins.

●**Active living.** You're healthy, vigorous and over the "posthoneymoon" letdown. Now you can do the extensive traveling you always hoped to do. When my wife and I travel, we fly into a city, rent a car and spend two or three weeks of very busy sightseeing.

●**Slowing down.** You're still basically healthy, but now it's harder to get around. This is a time for catching up on such long-deferred activities as organizing and cataloging the family photographs, and writing your own memoirs so your grandchildren will learn about how you lived as a child. You can still travel, but tours are more your speed—where you sit and are taken from place to place.

●**Assisted living.** No one likes to think he/she will someday have to depend on others for help. In fact, most of us will need some assistance when we become old and truly infirm. Don't spend your retirement years obsessing about it. But think about it well in advance so you will know how to handle it when the time comes.

Much Longer Lives Require Shrewder Retirement Planning

Ruth L. Hayden, a financial educator and consultant based in St. Paul. She is author of *For Richer, Not Poorer: The Money Book for Couples.* Health Communications, Inc.

When the Social Security system was established in 1935, people, on average, lived to the ripe old age of 62.

Today, thanks to advances in medicine, greater awareness of the benefits of good nutrition and an increased awareness of the benefits of physical exercise, we can expect to live as long as 30 years beyond retirement age—into our 80s and 90s.

To avoid financial mishaps during these bonus retirement years requires careful planning. You must keep yourself healthy emotionally, physically, mentally *and* financially. *Take time now to...*

●**Imagine your future.**

●**Plan how you want to live.**

●**Practice making—and sticking to—a financial budget.**

SETTING GOALS

Resolve any fears you may have for your financial future by setting retirement goals. *To start...*

1. *Write down what you want to have*...to do...to be...and to see during your retirement years. *Ask yourself the following questions...*

●**What is my life going to be like** emotionally, physically, mentally and financially?

●**How will I continue to feel worthwhile** and valuable to society?

●**Will I continue working** part-time or volunteer for a charity?

●**Will I take care of my health** by exercising regularly and eating a healthful diet?

●**Do I have adequate health insurance?**

●**What will my finances be like** in retirement?

This goal-setting stage of planning is the time to fantasize and dream about the future.

Do you want to travel? Move to a different place? Spend more time with your grandchildren? Launch your own business or a new career? Take up a new sport or hobby?

Whatever it is you want to do in retirement, write it all down.

2. *Create a time frame for achieving your goals,* and write that down along the left-hand margin of a piece of paper.

Look at a calendar of years to come and choose actual dates by which each goal will be achieved. For every date, write down the age you'll be at that time.

3. *Fit the hopes and dreams you wrote down in Step One* into the time frame you created in Step Two.

Example: Make a column to the right of your "future dates" that asks, "What do I want?"

Then, add another column next to that one that asks, "What will I need to do by this date to make this goal happen?"

LESS MONEY

The steps you need to take to accomplish your goals may or may not involve the accumulation of money.

No matter what they involve, however, write them down. When you've got a clear picture of what you want to achieve during your retirement years, create a budget that helps you both achieve your goals and get used to the idea of living on a reduced income.

Most of us will find ourselves living on a reduced—if not fixed—income at some time during our three-decade-long retirement. By setting a budget now and sticking to it, you'll know that you can do it. You can trust yourself to plan your finances and, by extension, plan your life.

Software packages can help you create a budget. My favorite is Intuit's *Quicken*. If you need additional help, read a book on budgeting and/or talk to a financial planner.

BUDGETING

Things you'll want to take into account when creating a budget include…

●**Monthly fixed expenses.** Rent/mortgage, phone service, TV, Internet service, electric service, car payments, etc.

●**Nonmonthly fixed expenses.** Quarterly water service, car insurance payments, estimated taxes, etc.

●**Weekly flexible expenses.** Eating out, books, newspapers.

●**Nonmonthly optional expenses.** Gifts, theater tickets, movies, trips, etc.

The budget is your first step to financial security. You'll feel more in control of your finances, now and in the future, when you have your budget in place.

THE FUTURE

To help carry that sense of financial control forward into retirement, adopt the following model for planning and managing your finances.

As circumstances such as health and living arrangements change, adapt the model and your financial plan to address your needs.

●**Between the ages of 60 and 70,** continue accumulating money for retirement. Take a part-time job and use the money you earn for cash-flow needs—buying groceries, paying bills, etc.

If your part-time job offers a 401(k) plan, take advantage of it. Otherwise, invest money in a traditional IRA, a Roth IRA and/or the stock market.

●**Between the ages of 70 and 80,** your health-care costs may go up. You may have quit working altogether. To continue living comfortably, use the income from your investments, but—if at all possible—don't touch the principal. If you do use the principal, your money may not hold out.

●**In life's later years, from the age of 80 on up**, do whatever you need to do financially to maintain autonomy and make your life work.

This is the time to dip into the principal, if necessary, from your investments and enjoy yourself!

How to Be Prepared When Your Spouse Retires

Gloria Bledsoe Goodman, author of *Keys to Living With a Retired Husband.* Barron's Educational Series, Inc.

One of the greatest mistakes a couple can make is to assume that retirement will simply be a continuation of married life as they have known it.

Retirement has its own rhythm, just as the honeymoon years, child-rearing years and empty-nest years had theirs.

Most likely change: You will spend much more time together. *Result:* Trouble spots may arise in the smallest areas of daily life. Many newly retired couples, even those who agree on the major issues of their retirement—where to live, how to handle the finances—are surprised by how infuriating they may suddenly find their comfortable, cherished mate.

Most common trouble spots…

●**Lack of retirement planning.** Many a husband has been shocked to learn that his wife has no desire to move to the fishing village he always pictured as a retirement home. Failure to communicate expectations about retirement, or to do the pre-planning necessary to make your dreams a reality, can cause terrible conflict in retiring couples.

To offset clashes over major issues: Attend a retirement planning workshop at your local

Chamber of Commerce, community college or senior center.

● **Failure to appreciate the psychological impact of retirement.** Couples must realize that retirement can be a traumatic passage, particularly for men. Even men who look forward to retirement may feel fearful and "lost" when they no longer have a routine and the familiar identity of their working selves. Concerns with mortality and self-worth may loom large for the first time.

Best course for women: Respect the grieving period. Don't crowd or smother your husband with suggestions, opinions, questions or demands or push him into a full schedule before he is ready. But do let him know that you are there. This is a good time for extra cuddling, affection and reassurance. Let him percolate a bit, and shift the focus to your own feelings.

Many women feel that they have spent their entire lives deferring to the needs of their husbands and families. They expect retirement to be "their turn," and fear being trapped again by their husbands' needs.

Best course: Have compassion for your husband's feelings, but be very firm regarding your own needs.

Once the transitional period passes, women can help their husbands back into active life. Men are badly needed as community volunteers. Some may just want to "play" a while, others may enjoy part-time work or a second career.

● **Alcoholism/clinical depression.** Alcoholism is under-recognized and badly under-treated in seniors, even though treatment has a high likelihood of success in this age group.

Depression, with or without alcohol, can afflict either sex, but is especially common among those forced to take "early retirement." Depression can also be triggered by many medications. If you suspect either problem in your family, don't hesitate to seek professional help.

Small stuff—but major gripes…

● **Grocery shopping.** It sounds hilarious—but this is a top area of conflict cited by retired couples. Often the wife has been shopping for years, and finds it insulting when her husband suddenly questions every choice and examines every tomato.

I have met many couples who have had bitter arguments over who gets to push the cart!

Solution: Decide that one of you will do all the shopping. Or shop with two lists. He can select the produce, while she does the rest.

● **Territorial strife.** With two people in one house, problems often arise over rooms and routines.

Examples: She wants the spare room as a sewing room, he wants a den. He used to leave for work, so she could drink coffee and watch *Good Morning, America,* before starting her chores. Now he wants to watch CNN and complains when she starts the housework.

Solution: Communication, compassion and compromise. It's your retirement as well as your spouse's. Wives must be willing to cede some domestic territory—it's his kitchen, too. Husbands must face the necessity to "get a life," and not expect their wives to provide one.

● **Comings and goings.** Insecurity often manifests as controlling behavior…Where are you going? When will you be home? Who's on the phone?

Solution: Stay calm and considerate. Reassure your mate, but don't be bullied. *Essential:* Keep your sense of humor.

● **Division of labor.** He expects her to perform the same chores she always has, even if she's still working part-time. She expects that now that he's retired, he'll take on some household chores.

Solutions: It's time to be fair.

Men: You may have retired from work, but not from the partnership of a marriage. Offer to take on the vacuuming. Don't force her to ask.

Women: Acknowledge the work he does do —caring for the yard, garbage, car, etc. Then ask for the help you need from your spouse. But if you ask him to vacuum, let him do it his way. *Helpful:* List chores you each hate, and negotiate for the other to take them on. Hire help for chores you both hate.

● **Sex.** Many men find sex a means of self-proof as well as pleasure. So a pleasant side effect of the anxieties retirement can produce is that many men discover a renewed enthusiasm for sex. Older men often have a stronger sex drive in the morning—so don't be too quick to leap out of bed. You don't have to—you're retired!

Wives: Enjoy it, buy some new lingerie, be willing to try new things.

Caution: Some couples experience the opposite, and shy away from intimacy after retirement. If your sex life is unhealthy, this is a problem that needs to be resolved through frank discussion or counseling.

● **Television.** Get two!

Best Time to Retire Is Early July

A full-time worker will have accumulated the 1,000 hours required during a calendar year for full benefits. Summer retirement lowers stress—major lifestyle changes are easier to handle when days are warm, there is plenty to do outdoors and many people are away from work as well. *Caution:* Retirement in summer can eliminate a year-end bonus, and can have Social Security implications. Consult your financial adviser.

Lee Rosenberg, certified financial planner, Valley Stream, New York.

How to Have a Steady Income for Life

Robert M. Freedman, Esq., Freedman and Fish, 521 Fifth Ave., New York 10175. Mr. Freedman is former chairman of the elder law section of the New York State Bar Association and founder of the National Academy of Elder Law Attorneys.

The peace of mind that comes from knowing you'll have a steady income for life comes at a price—your assets will decline rather than grow. *But if lifetime income is your goal, there are a number of ways to achieve it...*

RETIREMENT PLANS

When you retire, you'll likely have a choice of how to take your money from the company pension plan.

Many financial advisers suggest rolling over a company retirement plan distribution into an IRA to retain maximum flexibility. When the money is in an IRA, you can invest it as you see fit. And you'll have full access to the funds at all times.

But if a steady income for life is your primary goal, you may want to have the pension money paid to you in monthly installments. If your spouse survives you, he/she can continue to receive a monthly income for life.

Caution: Once you've made the election to take pension distributions in the form of a monthly annuity, you can't change your mind.

Alternative: Roll over pension funds to an IRA, and, in effect, create your own fixed flow of income. Simply withdraw the IRA money in regular monthly installments.

Self-defense: Sit down with a financial planner who can work out a withdrawal schedule to provide for a monthly income from the IRA (based on your life expectancy).

While distributions from your IRA must begin by April 1 of the year following the year you turn 70½—you can start taking your annuity payments from the IRA at any younger age you choose. (If you're under age 59½, though, you'll be assessed a 10% early withdrawal penalty, unless payments are made in a series of substantially equal periodic payments.)

BUY A COMMERCIAL ANNUITY

Those who lack the experience of handling large sums of money may want to use insurance proceeds or other lump-sum payments to buy lifetime income from an insurance company in the form of an annuity.

Commercial annuities are investment products offered by insurance companies. They are bought directly from the company or through banks and brokerage firms.

The insurance company paying on the life insurance policy can provide an annuity, but shop around to find the best one for you.

From an investment perspective, commercial annuities may not appeal to you. You must consider the fees the company charges for the annuity in relation to the return.

But if you're prepared to pay the price and the insurance company is sound, then peace of mind can be yours with a commercial annuity.

INCOME OPTION

Annuities pay a fixed monthly amount to you during your lifetime and can be tailored to provide a continued flow of income to your surviving spouse.

TURNING ASSETS INTO INCOME

• **Reverse mortgages.** Older people of moderate means can convert the equity in their home into a monthly retirement income by using a reverse mortgage. Instead of paying principal and interest monthly, you receive a monthly check.

General qualifications...

• Generally you must be age 60 or older.

• There must be little or no other mortgage on the home.

• The home must be single family (or a one-unit condominium that is FHA-approved) and owner-occupied. Owners of mobile homes don't qualify for reverse mortgages.

The monthly income you receive is fixed according to the value of your home, the area in which you live (FHA-insured reverse mortgages set maximum loan caps for various areas) and your current age. There are different payment options to choose from, one being a monthly income for life (or the joint life of the home owners).

Caution: The reverse mortgage becomes due when the owner sells the home, moves or dies.

CHARITABLE REMAINDER TRUSTS

If you have substantial assets, especially appreciated assets such as securities, you can use them to obtain a fixed income for life *and* benefit charity by setting up a charitable remainder trust. *Benefits...*

• **Fixed income.** You receive a fixed monthly income based on the value of the assets in the trust—and the type of charitable remainder trust you use.

You can even obtain inflation protection by using a charitable unitrust. It pays a monthly income based on a percentage of the value of the assets annually. If the assets' value rises, you benefit accordingly.

• **Tax deduction.** You can claim a current income tax deduction for the value of the "remainder interest" of the money that the charity will receive when you die. This deduction is determined by IRS tables, which have recently been changed.

Caution: To achieve tax benefits, the trust must be set up carefully. Consult an attorney for this purpose.

OTHER CHARITABLE OPTIONS

Instead of using a personal charitable trust, consider...

• **Pooled income funds.** Your contribution to the charity goes into a pool with gifts from other donors. The money is invested by professional money managers.

Your income is based on the size of your gift and your age. You also receive an upfront tax deduction for the gift based on the value of what the charity will get upon your death.

• **Charitable gift annuity.** Some of the country's biggest charities will provide you with a monthly income and a tax deduction—in return for a hefty donation. The monthly income payments may not be as large as those from a commercial annuity, but you're providing a benefit to society rather than to an insurance company's shareholders.

Fewer Cars Mean More Retirement Money

Over a 40-year career, someone who buys a new car and keeps it for 10 years—instead of trading it in every three years—could have an extra $385,000 at retirement. *How to do it:* Take the savings in new-car payments and insurance and invest it—aim for an average annual return of 7.5%. Let it compound without withdrawals over the decades.

Jonathan Pond, president, Financial Planning Information, Nine Galen St., Watertown, MA 02472. *www.jonathan pond.com.*

Pension Traps— Annuity Opportunities

Glenn Daily, a fee-only insurance consultant and author of *The Individual Investor's Guide to Low-Load Insurance Products.* International Publishing Corp.

Before collecting checks from your company pension plan or a single-premium deferred annuity, it pays to investigate your options.

By choosing an immediate annuity, you may wind up with hundreds of dollars more per month in your pocket—at no additional risk.

An immediate annuity is an insurance contract that, in return for a one-time payment, starts paying a fixed sum for your lifetime or for some other period right away.

A single-life annuity, for example, pays the agreed-upon sum every month until the purchaser dies. The payment doesn't have to stop at the first death. It depends on the option you select: Joint and two-thirds survivor, joint and 50% survivor, and joint and 100% survivor. A joint-and-survivor annuity for a married couple, by contrast, pays one larger sum while both spouses are alive, and a lesser amount after the first spouse dies. Payments continue at the lower level during the lifetime of the surviving spouse and end only when that person dies.

IT PAYS TO SHOP

Comparison shopping in the immediate annuity market can pay off quite nicely.

Example: Recently, I checked out rates—which are expressed as monthly income per $10,000 of premium—for a 65-year-old woman. For a $100,000 investment, the monthly income ranged from a high of $915 to a low of $716—a difference of almost $200, or about 28%.

Trap: Don't automatically go for the highest monthly income figure. Given all the turmoil in the insurance industry these days, and the failure of Executive Life, in the example above I decided not even to consider the seven companies paying the top rates because I had reservations about their soundness. Bear in mind that you are purchasing something that you intend to last for the rest of your life.

I wound up recommending my client purchase an annuity that ranked 20th out of 100. It was offered by Northwestern Mutual, the solid, conservative, and well-run Minnesota company. The annuity provided monthly income of $839. The median income figure was $809 a month.

COMPARE CAREFULLY

Two common situations in which investigating what you'd receive with an immediate annuity makes sense...

●**When you're retiring from your company.** Before you automatically accept the monthly pension check your company plan offers, ask if the plan permits a lump-sum distribution instead. Many, but not all, plans do.

See what you can get in monthly income by purchasing an immediate annuity with some of that money. You may be surprised to discover that you'll get a much larger payment with the annuity than with your company pension.

●**When you're ready to start annuitizing, or receiving distributions,** from a single-premium deferred annuity that you purchased years ago. Just because you purchased the annuity from Company A, don't assume that it now offers the best deal in terms of monthly income. You may do better by switching to Company B or C.

Caution: In either case, don't sink all your money into an immediate annuity all at once. You may be purchasing at a trough, and annuity rates may subsequently shoot up. I recommend that people purchase several contracts over time and that they not annuitize more than 50% of their total investable assets.

It's vital that you do your comparative shopping right at the point when you are ready to make your purchase.

Reason: The immediate annuity market is a very fluid one, and rates can fluctuate widely, even within a given company, depending upon the details of your individual situation.

Example: A particular company may post attractive payouts one month, but not the next. Or, it may be competitive at some ages but unattractive at others.

To compare the different rates offered by different companies, you can check with a local broker or contact the following sources...

●**Web Annuities,** 800-872-6684, *www.immediateannuity.com.* An insurance-brokerage and research firm that specializes in immediate annuities. It also works on a commission basis.

•**TIAA-CREF,** *www.tiaa-cref.org.*

•**AnnuityNet,** *www.annuitynet.com.* Look for the inflation proofer immediate annuity.

Of course, there are some drawbacks to opting for an immediate annuity, rather than for your company pension. Rejecting your pension might be unwise, for example, if your company has a history of increasing its pension payouts from time to time in order to offset inflation. The annuity check you get the first month is the same amount you'll receive 20 years from now—assuming you're still alive to collect.

And—pensions are insured by the Pension Board Guaranty Corporation, while immediate annuities are only as good as the company that issues them.

Before you jump at the highest available rate, you should always very carefully investigate the issuing company's financial health.

Aim: To be reasonably sure it will be able to make those payouts as long as you live.

Caution: Some, but not all, insurers require annuity buyers to pay upfront policy fees or other charges, which can range from $150 to $500. And about 10 states impose premium taxes that amount to 1% to 3% of the amount invested.

How Safe Is Your Pension?

George E.L. Barbee, executive director of client services, Price Waterhouse, 1251 Avenue of the Americas, New York 10020. He is a contributor to the *Price Waterhouse Retirement Adviser.* Pocket Books.

More and more people are discovering—to their horror—that they can't rely solely on their company defined-benefit pension plan for retirement security. Some companies have even terminated plans. And sometimes plans fail because of a company's financial problems or problems with an insurance company that provided a guaranteed income contract.

What can you do? Not much, if a pension-plan failure catches you unprepared. You could write to the US Department of Labor, but in practice it can't be counted on to do much unless you're with a large company. Nor is the IRS likely to provide much help. The Pension Benefits Guaranty Corporation is supposed to pay when defined benefit plans fail, but it has payout caps that could be much less than what you were counting on, and some observers claim the organization is overextended. Nearly all lawyers with pension-plan expertise work for plan sponsors, not individual participants.

Avoid bad surprises...

Keep yourself informed about your company's pension plan. *Ask yourself fundamental questions (some of these can be answered by your pension plan's annual report)...*

•**What's the pension plan invested in?**

•**Is the pension portfolio heavily loaded with your company's stocks?**

•**Is the pension plan in sound condition?**

•**If your company offers a guaranteed income contract portfolio,** is it provided by a single insurer? If just one, how solid is it?

•**How sound is your company?** Monitor annual reports, quarterly reports and business news affecting your company.

•**What are the ratings of insurance companies involved with your guaranteed income contract portfolio?** Consider a B- (or lower) rating from A.M. Best, Moody's or Standard & Poor's as a warning flag.

SELF-DEFENSE

•**Consider a pension plan as one part of an overall portfolio.** Don't rely on a company pension plan to provide the bulk of your retirement assets. Put eligible funds into an IRA. Buy an annuity. Build your own portfolio of savings and investments.

Your portfolio should be properly diversified, enabling you to survive in the event that something goes awry. Diversification is especially important for the millions of people who acquired large chunks of their company's stock through employee stock-ownership plans. If you have more than 5% to 10% of your assets in a single stock, look to diversify your portfolio.

•**Think ahead about health care.** Because costs are escalating dramatically, more and more companies are curtailing dollar payouts in many ways. You might not be able to use the doctor or hospital of your choice unless you pay out-of-pocket. Set aside additional savings for adequate health care protection or consider other forms of health insurance appropriate for your circumstances.

When a Pension Dies With You

A pension can "die" with you—if the payout is limited to lifetime monthly benefits and you aren't married. Pensions provide a joint and survivor payout option *only* to married participants. So unmarried participants can't pass on benefits—and payments cease at death. *Good news:* Plans generally allow participants to take lump-sum distributions in lieu of monthly benefits—although spouses of participants must consent to this and waive survivorship benefits. A lump-sum distribution can be rolled over to an IRA, from which monthly benefits can be taken. Whatever remains in the IRA upon the owner's death can be left to heirs—spouse, child, life partner.

Robert S. Keebler, CPA, Virchow, Krause & Co., Green Bay, WI, and author of A CPA's Guide to Making the Most of the New IRA. *American Institute of CPAs.*

Truth About Cash-Balance Pension Plans

Cash-balance plans are a fairly new type of pension plan in which employers pay 4% to 7% of an employee's compensation into the employee's account in the plan. Most accounts have a guaranteed rate of return, often tied to the yield on 30-year Treasury bonds, although some companies give employees investment options.

The money in the account accumulates steadily over time, and when employees retire or change jobs, they generally can take a lump-sum payment from the plan. Or a retiree could elect to receive an annuity based on the amount in the account.

With a traditional defined benefit plan, retirees typically get monthly payments until they die based on how long they were with the firm and their highest level of pay during the five years prior to retirement. Employees have to stay with a company most of their careers for this type of pension to be worth much—one reason why younger workers, who tend to change jobs, prefer the cash-balance plan.

For details, read "Cash Balance Package," free from the Department of Labor, 866-4-USA-DOL or online at *www.dol.gov.*

Nancy Dunnan, editor, Travel Smart, *40 Beechdale Rd., Dobbs Ferry, NY 10522.*

New Strategy to Help You Grow Your 401(k)

William E. Donoghue, chairman of W.E. Donoghue & Co. Inc., registered investment advisers, and publisher of Donoghue's WealthLetter, *a monthly strategic mutual fund investment newsletter, Box 309, Suite 401, 100 Medway Rd., Milford, MA 01757.*

During the past 10 years, three trends have made traditional retirement savings assumptions obsolete...

• **The wave of corporate mergers and acquisitions** has concentrated more assets in fewer large-company stocks.

• **People in these large corporations are investing 30% of their 401(k) money in their own company stocks**...and 30% in large-cap index funds. This drives up demand for large-cap stocks.

• **People are living longer.** The cost of living comfortably into your 90s and beyond has increased dramatically.

Investors should be least conservative with tax-deferred retirement money and instead think long term. These accounts have the greatest compounding power. And with increased longevity, you're going to need a lot of money for a long time.

So—advice such as "diversify your 401(k) portfolio" and "play it safe" adds to your risk of running out of money before you run out of life.

Here are my new rules to boost your chances of saving enough for a long and happy retirement…

●**Focus on large-cap growth stocks.** Spreading your money equally among all your 401(k) plan's funds only dilutes long-term returns.

Better: Concentrate your assets in an S&P 500 index fund and other funds that invest mainly in large-cap growth companies. Large-cap stock funds have been the strongest performers over the past decade. Historically, they have out-performed, on average, small-cap stock funds 9.24% to 13.78%.

Large companies have performed well during this period because, on average, they do business more economically. They also attract the best talent while outperforming or acquiring their smaller competitors.

I haven't seen a scenario in which small-cap stocks will outperform large-cap stocks again. The trend toward investing in large-cap stocks is denying many smaller companies access to the capital markets.

My suggested 401(k) allocation: People in their 30s, 40s, 50s and even nearing retirement can put at least 50% of their 401(k) assets in funds that invest in large-cap domestic stocks.

Once you retire, keep two to three years of cash to cover spending needs in less volatile investments, such as money market funds and income-oriented stock funds. The rest of your assets can remain in large-cap stock funds. Remember, anyone with a 25-year time horizon is a long-term investor. If you are 65 and expect to live to 90, you are a long-term investor.

●**Don't overinvest in overseas stock funds.** International stock funds may offer great short- or intermediate-term investment opportunities. But overall, these funds have not proven to be sound long-term, buy-and-hold investments. Few foreign countries or regions have the long-term economic stamina and vitality to outperform US stocks.

Rule of thumb: If you wish to invest in an international fund, limit your investment to 10% of your portfolio.

Use new 401(k) plan contributions to buy shares of international funds rather than sell off large-cap investments to raise cash. To maximize returns, buy fund shares when bad news abroad sends share prices down and sell shares when good news pushes prices up. Be prepared to move quickly. It is better to keep small profits than to lose big ones.

●**Avoid money market and bond funds.** Unless you are retired, there is only a very limited role for a money market fund in a long-term 401(k) portfolio.

With 24-hour phone access to funds and brokers—and no adverse tax consequences of trading in a tax-deferred 401(k) portfolio—it's easy to sell shares to raise cash if you need it.

Parking cash in a 401(k) plan's money market fund while waiting for the right time to invest it is of little value.

Also, limit your investment in bond funds. In a rising interest rate market bond funds lose value.

If you want to buy fund shares, raise cash by selling shares in a fund that you feel has the worst prospects.

●**Maximize 401(k) plan contributions.** There are three big reasons for you to contribute the total allowable amount each year, which is $12,000 for 2003, or $14,000 for those age 50 and older ($13,000 or $16,000 respectively in 2004).

●You are receiving "free" money if your employer matches some or all of your contributions.

●Plan contributions reduce your current income taxes because contributions are withdrawn from your paycheck before your income is taxed.

●Most 401(k) plans offer low-cost loan programs that come in handy when you need to borrow cash in emergencies.

●**Beware of newly started funds.** Out of the 3,727 domestic stock funds, only 20 outperformed a low-cost S&P 500 index fund over the past five- and 10-year periods.

New funds are as likely to be in the bottom 100 as they are to fall into the top 100 each year.

Exception: Enhanced index funds, which are designed to beat index returns by investing a portion of funds in a futures-and-options strategy tied to the index and the balance in a money market fund.

Examples: The Rydex Index Trust and ProFunds fund families both offer funds that are designed to earn between 1.5 and two times the S&P 500 stock index or the NASDAQ stock index.

Enhanced index funds are likely to make more money in a rising stock market and lose more in a declining market than any managed stock fund.

Ask your employer to consider adding an enhanced index fund to your plan.

•**Make the most of a rollover IRA.** Most people aren't aware that when they change jobs and move their 401(k) plan assets into a rollover IRA, they have many more investments open to them. If you choose to roll over your IRA to a discount broker, you will have even more investment choices than traditional brokerage firms.

How to Check Up on Your 401(k)'s Performance

Treat your 401(k) as you would other investments—check its performance against comparable investments.

Example: If you have 401(k) money in a growth fund, compare that fund against other growth funds.

If your 401(k) is underperforming, contact the 401(k) administrator. Most companies are responsive to well-researched complaints…it is in their best interest to keep the employees satisfied. Ninety percent of 401(k) plans are at firms that have fewer than 100 employees.

Ted Benna, inventor of the 401(k) and president of The 401(k) Association, 155 Lingwood Ct., Bellefonte, PA 16823.

401(k) Plan Trap

If you borrow funds from your 401(k) retirement account and leave your employer before repaying the loan, the entire outstanding balance will be taxable income to you. If you are under age 59½, it will be subject to an early distribution penalty as well.

Self-defense: If you plan to retire or leave your employer and have 401(k) loans outstanding, repay them before you leave.

Whenever you take out a 401(k) loan, be aware of the tax risk should you leave your employer unexpectedly.

Terry Savage, a syndicated *Chicago Sun-Times* financial columnist and author of *The Savage Truth on Money.* John Wiley & Sons.

Answers to Your Toughest Questions About IRAs

Ed Slott, CPA, E. Slott & Co., 100 Merrick Rd., Rockville Centre, NY 11570. He is editor of *Ed Slott's IRA Advisor.* *www.irahelp.com.*

While the basic rules for IRAs seem straightforward enough, working with the rules is not always easy. Many questions continue to trouble individuals—about putting funds into and taking funds out of IRAs. *Some helpful questions and answers…*

ON CONTRIBUTIONS

Am I permitted to contribute stock to my IRA?

No. Only cash contributions are allowed. Once money is in the IRA, though, you can buy stock with it. And stock that you have in an IRA can be rolled over or transferred directly to another IRA.

Caution 1: The stock you purchase in your IRA must be publicly traded. If you buy stock in a closely held corporation—even a minority interest—you are considered to be "self-dealing." This is prohibited by the law that governs IRAs, and you will be subject to a penalty.

Caution 2: You cannot swap stock into or out of an IRA. For example, if *you* own stock in X

Co. and *your IRA* owns stock in Y Co., you cannot exchange one for the other (even though they are of equal value). Doing so would be treated both as a taxable distribution to you and a nonpermissible contribution.

ON DISTRIBUTIONS WHILE YOU'RE ALIVE

I own some great stock in my traditional IRA and must start taking distributions this year because I'm 70½. Must I sell the stock and take a distribution in cash or can the stock be distributed to me?

You can have the stock distributed to you. Since the stock must be publicly traded, it is easy to value it for purposes of taking the required distribution. The stock is valued on the date of the distribution. The dollar amount of the distribution is taxed to you as ordinary income.

I am 72 and took my first required minimum distribution last year. My two children are named as beneficiaries on the account. Since then, I've remarried. What effect does my remarriage have on my future IRA distributions?

None, unless you change the beneficiary, naming your new spouse rather than your children and your new spouse is more than 10 years your junior. Required distributions are smaller when there is a much younger spouse named as the beneficiary. Otherwise, your distributions under the new distribution rules remain the same—whether your children continue as beneficiaries or you name your new spouse (who is not 10 years younger than you are).

ON DISTRIBUTIONS AFTER DEATH

My father died, leaving me as beneficiary of his IRA. What should I do?

First, the title to the account should be changed to read: *(Your parent's name), IRA, deceased (date of death), FBO (for the benefit of) (your name).* Then take your required distributions.

One way to meet the distribution requirement is to withdraw the entire amount (and pay tax all at once). With this alternative, you must take all by the end of the fifth year following the year of your father's death.

Or, if you wish to keep money in the IRA as long as possible, you can spread distributions out over your life expectancy. Here, distributions must begin by the end of the first year following the year of your father's death.

You can name a new beneficiary (such as your own spouse or child) to inherit the IRA if you should die before exhausting the account. However, your naming a new beneficiary has no impact on your required distributions.

My mother named me and my two siblings as cobeneficiaries of her IRA. She died at age 68. What are our options?

The account can be split into separate shares, one share for each beneficiary. Then each of you can take distributions from the IRA based on your life expectancies.

If the account is not split, then distributions must be based on the age of the oldest sibling.

An itemized income tax deduction can be claimed by a beneficiary who is required to report as income distributions from an inherited IRA. The beneficiary can deduct the portion of federal estate tax allocable to the IRA distribution he/she received. How is this calculated?

There is no clear IRS guidance on this question. It would appear that first you allocate the portion of the federal estate tax to the IRA. This is based on the percentage of the estate that the IRA represents. For example, if the estate is $2 million and the IRA is $800,000, then 40% of the estate tax is applicable to the IRA. Then, of that amount, the portion of the account distributed each year is the same portion of the estate tax deduction used each year.

Example: If one-twentieth of the account is required to be distributed to the beneficiary, then one-twentieth of the 40% allocable portion of the estate tax deduction can be claimed as an itemized deduction in the year of this distribution.

ON ROTH IRAS

I'm 72 and want to convert part of my regular IRA to a Roth IRA. Can I include the required minimum distributions I started taking at 70½ in the conversion amount?

No. Required minimum distributions cannot be converted to a Roth IRA. Amounts in excess of the required distributions can be converted if income for the year is no more than $100,000 (including the required minimum distributions). Starting in 2005, required minimum distributions will not be taken into account in determining eligibility to convert to a Roth IRA.

ON OTHER MATTERS

Can I roll over my IRA into my 401(k)?

If your IRA is a "conduit" IRA, one that consists solely of funds transferred from a qualified retirement plan (and the earnings on those funds), then you can roll over the IRA to a 401(k)—assuming the plan will accept such rollovers.

However, if you also contributed other money to that IRA, then the conduit is considered "tainted" and cannot be rolled into a 401(k) or other qualified plan.

You can also roll over an IRA consisting of after-tax contributions if the plan accepts such a rollover. But you cannot roll over your deductible IRA account.

My IRAs are in New York. That state provides protection to IRAs from the claims of creditors. I now live in a state that does not appear to provide such protection. Are my IRAs protected or not?

It would seem that your IRAs are still protected by the laws of New York, since the accounts are still in that state. However, check with a tax attorney in your new state to determine the extent of protection, if any, afforded there.

Valuable Opportunities Playing Roth IRAs by the New Rules

Ed Slott, CPA, E. Slott & Co., 100 Merrick Rd., Rockville Centre, NY 11570. He is editor of *Ed Slott's IRA Advisor.* *www.irahelp.com.*

Roth IRAs are clearly a success for those who have them. Wise use of a Roth IRA helps individuals build tax-free, long-term wealth.

THE BASICS

Traditional IRA: Any individual younger than 70½ with earnings of $3,000 or more can contribute up to $3,000 of *pretax* income for 2003 and 2004 (plus $500 if the individual is at least 50 years old by the end of the year), although active participants in qualified plans can only make fully deductible contributions for the year 2003 if Adjusted Gross Income (AGI) is below $60,000 on a joint return…or $40,000 on a single return (in 2004, $45,000 and $65,000 respectively). Earnings grow tax-free until withdrawals begin after retirement—or by age 70½, whichever comes first. Withdrawals are taxed at ordinary income rates.

Roth IRA: You can contribute the same amount to a Roth IRA, but contributions are not tax-deductible. Earnings, however, are completely *tax-free* (not tax-deferred, as with a regular IRA). Withdrawals are never required, as they are with a regular IRA. You can begin to withdraw *earnings* after age 59½ without penalty if the account is owned for at least five years. You can withdraw *contributions* tax- and penalty-free at any time.

WHO QUALIFIES

Roth IRAs are better for lower-bracket taxpayers.

To qualify…

•**You must have earned income equal to the contribution amount.**

•**Allowable contribution starts to phase out at AGI of $95,000** and disappears completely when AGI reaches $110,000 for single individuals…$150,000 and $160,000 for married couples filing jointly.

Distributions are income tax-free to your Roth IRA beneficiaries, who can spread distributions over their life expectancies—possibly another 30 or more years of tax-free growth.

What to do: Your Roth IRA beneficiary should elect the life expectancy term by taking the first required distribution by December 31 of the year after you die. Otherwise, he/she will have to withdraw the proceeds over five years …and will lose a lifetime of tax-free earnings. When you leave a Roth IRA to your spouse, he can roll it over into an existing or new Roth IRA and be exempt from any required distributions.

Caution: A Roth IRA is part of your taxable estate. So when you open one, buy additional life insurance held by a trust or your beneficiaries. The insurance provides liquidity for paying estate taxes without forcing your heirs to make excessive IRA withdrawals to pay the tax.

CHANGES IN IRA CONVERSIONS

• **Converting to a Roth IRA.** When Roth IRAs were first created in 1998, you could pay the income tax owed when you converted a traditional IRA to a Roth IRA over four years.

If you are eligible and convert now, you must pay the tax in the year of the conversion. To simulate the four-year income spread, convert 25% of your traditional IRA to a Roth IRA over four years.

• **Converting from a Roth IRA.** When the market drops, you can save taxes by converting a Roth IRA back to a regular IRA.

Example: You converted a $100,000 regular IRA into a Roth IRA in 2003 that shrank to $30,000 in April 2004, because the market fell. If you recharacterize the Roth account as a regular IRA in April 2004, you'll remove the tax owed on the initial $100,000. You can then convert the $30,000 back to a Roth IRA as a Roth conversion next year—only one conversion is permitted per year. This way, you'll regain the Roth IRA benefits.

Only one "recharacterization" from a Roth IRA to a regular IRA is permitted per year. Filing Form 8606, *Nondeductible IRAs,* removes taxes that were owed when the Roth IRA was opened.

IRA Nightmares

Errors by brokerages, mutual fund companies and other financial institutions are increasing —resulting in costly tax penalties for investors. *Reasons:* The complex tax law and high volume of customer requests. *Self-defense:* Use an IRA-savvy tax adviser to plan retirement investments and payouts. Then send your requests in writ-

ing, giving the institution plenty of time to execute them.

Ed Slott, CPA, E. Slott & Co., 100 Merrick Rd., Rockville Centre, NY 11570. He is editor of *Ed Slott's IRA Advisor.* *www.irahelp.com.*

Don't rely on your IRA trustee to keep records of your beneficiary designations and distribution elections. These may well not be used for decades. In the meantime, the papers can and do get lost, as firms that serve as IRA trustees merge, move, reorganize their offices, etc. *Trap:* If your elections are lost, the trustee will distribute your IRA funds following its "default" options—which may be very different from what you elected. *Safety:* When making beneficiary designations and distribution elections, get acknowledged copies of them from the IRA trustee, and keep them with your will and other estate planning documents.

Seymour Goldberg, Esq., CPA, Goldberg & Goldberg, PC, 1 Huntington Quadrangle, Melville, NY 11747.

Doublecheck IRA Designations

Check that your IRA beneficiary designations are properly on file.

Trap: IRA trustees can lose the paperwork on elections that were made many years ago.

Horror story: A person named his daughter beneficiary of his $500,000 IRA. But when the bank that managed the IRA merged with another bank, the paperwork didn't carry over. Since there was no named beneficiary, his estate was named beneficiary by default.

Result: When he died, the IRA was liquidated, creating a $200,000 income tax bill and forfeiting an untold amount of tax-deferred growth.

Ed Slott, CPA, E. Slott & Co., 100 Merrick Rd., Rockville Centre, NY 11570. He is editor of *Ed Slott's IRA Advisor.* *www.irahelp.com.*

How to Find Forgotten Assets

One out of every eight Americans has forgotten some financial asset—bank account, utility deposit, etc. These unclaimed assets eventually go to the states. A free Web site, *www. missingmoney.com,* lets you look for assets in 24 states—Arizona, Colorado, Delaware, Florida, Kansas, Kentucky, Maine, Maryland, Massachusetts, Michigan, Minnesota, Missouri, Montana, New Hampshire, New Mexico, North Carolina, Oklahoma, South Carolina, South Dakota, Utah, Vermont, Virginia, West Virginia, Wisconsin, plus the District of Columbia. Check the site as new states are added periodically. (e.g., Nebraska will be added soon).

Joan Caplin, money writer, *Money,* Rockefeller Center, New York 10020.

2

Estate Planning Strategies

Estate Planning For an Increasingly Complex Future

 state planning today is more complex than ever before, and the need for attention to estate plans will grow and grow. *Three factors have come together to make this so...*

●**Greater longevity.** With lifespans increasing, more people are choosing to combine a program of lifetime gifts, trusts and family limited partnerships with their estate plans. A simple will or even a living trust is no longer sufficient for an estate plan.

●**The unlimited marital deduction,** which gives you the right to transfer any amount of property to your spouse free of gift and estate tax, came into effect in January 1982. It has made estate planning and estate tax deferral easy for many couples. But by now there are many widows and widowers

with large taxable estates. Preserving as many assets as possible for their heirs without access to the unlimited marital deduction requires a carefully crafted estate plan.

●**The booming financial markets of the last decade,** combined with a period of economic stability, have given far more people than ever before enough assets to almost guarantee that their estates are potentially taxable.

A TEAM BUSINESS

The best approach to an estate plan is to think of it as a business—one that is focused on people.

To be successful, a business needs a plan and a mission, and it needs a first-rate management team.

Indeed, these business essentials are doubly important for an estate plan.

If you make a mistake in business, you can generally cut your losses and regroup. But, if

Owen G. Fiore, Esq., CPA, a nationally recognized estate planning attorney and tax litigator. He is founder of The Fiore Law Group, 101 Park Center Plaza, Suite 1150, San Jose, CA 95113.

your heirs are squabbling after your death, there's obviously nothing you can do.

Your plan and mission: Develop clear ideas about what you're trying to achieve with your estate plan...

- **Keep a family business going.**
- **Provide funds for your grandchildren's educations.**
- **Provide financial security for a surviving spouse or parent.**
- **Set up a really long-term, or "dynasty," trust.**
- **Keep an undisciplined young adult from controlling money too soon.**

Once you've thought out the plan—communicate your goals to your team of advisers so they can set up strategies to implement them.

THE TEAM

You are the CEO of the business of putting together an estate plan. The team members should be able to communicate and work together well with you—and with each other. *The three key team members are...*

- **CPA** is the gatekeeper. He can provide a financial reality check. That goes along with doing the tax returns and supervising the books and records.
- **Attorney** draws up the will, trust documents, and perhaps family limited partnership papers and ought to be able to explain them clearly.

Often, diagrams help—showing what assets go to whom at each step of the plan. A simple outline of the legal documents can also help make a complex plan understandable.

- **Life insurance professional** decides how much coverage is needed and what type is best for an individual or couple to achieve particular goals.

Example: A second-to-die policy that provides cash to pay estate taxes may be useful if a family business is to be passed intact to the next generation.

Depending upon the individual circumstances, other team members may include...

- **Financial planner** or investment adviser, particularly when primary assets are marketable securities.

- **Business valuation expert**—who will be needed if there is a family business or family partnership. The IRS is militant about business valuations, and a detailed, up-to-date appraisal by an outside expert must be included with a gift or estate tax return, if the return is to pass muster.

- **Family counselor or clinical psychologist**—who is sometimes needed when family members do not see eye to eye.

Example: Siblings may vie as to who should be the next CEO of a family business, or even over whether to carry on with the business or sell it. Sort out problems as soon as they are apparent. Do not let them fester.

- **Representative of an institutional trustee,** such as a bank or trust company, who may be needed if there is no individual or family member who alone could serve as executor of an estate. *Caution...*

- Watch out for "trust mills," impersonal "cookie-cutter" packages and the like.
- Interview your attorney, not only about billing, but also about how he plans to achieve your goals and ask him to explain the plan. If the attorney says, "You won't understand it, just trust me," make for the exit.

TAX SAVINGS

Once the team is in place and the estate's goals set, the team can decide on the best way to achieve them while minimizing taxes. It's often possible to save 50% or more of the taxes that might be owed, if assets were simply bequeathed outright. *Frequently used strategies...*

- **Lifetime gifts** are often preferable to leaving assets at death via a will or trust. Of course, each person may give $11,000 in 2003 and 2004 to each of any number of recipients free of gift and estate tax consequences.

For more sizable gifts, a gift tax return must be filed, but there will be no tax owed until the gift tax-exempt amount of $1 million is exceeded.

In any event, if you give securities that are likely to appreciate, the tax will be based on their current value. If you hold onto them and your heirs receive them as bequests in many years, the value, and hence the ultimate estate—and state—tax, could be far higher.

●**Family limited partnership** is frequently an ideal way to make your gifts while retaining control as the general partner.

You can bring the younger generation into the business as limited partners, sharing the income and learning the business.

At the same time, considerable tax savings may be realized due to valuation discounts on the limited partnership units given to family members. Discounts are allowed precisely because the donees do not have control, which makes their shares less valuable than yours.

Example: You put $4 million worth of securities into the partnership. Discounted to 75% of value, only $3 million would be taxable. Because estates of $3 million or more are taxable at 49% in 2004, that's quite a tax savings, even after the $15,000 to $20,000 it might cost to set up the partnership. Also, all estate tax is saved on post-gift appreciation in value.

Tax avoidance cannot be the only reason for the partnership, or the IRS will disallow the valuation discounts. But keeping control out of the hands of people who are not yet qualified is a valid reason.

Caution: Proper accounting and representation by counsel will be needed if the IRS challenges a partnership or trust document.

How to Take Advantage Of the Tax Laws

Sanford J. Schlesinger, Esq., partner and head of the wills and estates department of the law firm Kaye, Scholer, Fierman, Hays & Handler, LLP, 425 Park Ave., New York 10022.

Americans will be transferring *trillions* of dollars worth of assets to family members and other beneficiaries and heirs over the next 50 years. Possibly as much as $136 trillion will be given away or bequeathed.

No doubt your wealth, like that of so many others, is rapidly building up. *Impact:* Planning has never been so important.

This is the right time to review plans for gifts and estates, making sure your planning takes full advantage of what the tax laws allow.

Do not fall prey to two widely held misconceptions...

Misconception 1: **Congress has eliminated transfer taxes, so there is no need to act now.**

The new tax law increases the estate tax exemption and cuts estate tax rates over the next decade. However, estate tax is repealed only for those dying in 2010. Thereafter old estate tax rules reapply.

Bottom line: There's a continuing need to plan for estate taxes.

Misconception 2: **My finances are fairly straightforward, so I don't need to worry about a lot of sophisticated planning.**

Even married schoolteachers in their 50s can have more than $1 million in assets today if they bought a home years ago and have contributed regularly to their retirement plans. They need a lesson in estate planning if they want those assets to go to their children without the IRS taking a big cut. *How to get started...*

LIST YOUR ASSETS

First: **Make a list of all your assets.** *Include...*

●**The equity in your home.**

●**Your investment portfolio.**

●**All retirement plans and IRAs.**

●**Investment real estate.**

●**Value of business interests.**

●**Other significant assets** such as artworks and collectibles.

Then: **Update your estate plan.** If total assets exceed $1 million, you should proceed to update your trust and estate plans.

BEST WAYS TO CUT ESTATE TAXES

●**Divide assets with your spouse.** A couple can double the $1 million that is exempt from estate taxes ($1.5 million in 2004) simply by dividing ownership of assets into his and hers, rather than owning them jointly. A his/hers division creates two estates instead of one, fully utilizes each spouse's exempt amount and drastically cuts taxes.

• **Get insurance out of your estate.** Generally, insurance should be owned by an irrevocable life insurance trust or ownership rights should be relinquished. Many people mistakenly think of insurance as tax free.

It is true that beneficiaries do not owe income taxes on life insurance proceeds, but if you—or a business of which you own more than 50%—own the policy, it will be subject to estate taxes, which can far exceed income taxes.

• **Make annual gifts.** Remember, the law allows you to make gifts up to a dollar limit per recipient per year ($11,000 in 2003 and 2004) to as many recipients as you wish with no gift or estate tax consequences. A gifting program can reduce taxable estates for people whose assets clearly exceed their needs. The best time to make the gifts is early in the year, to get a full year's benefit of unloading the money and its appreciation.

• **Make tuition gifts.** The law allows you to make gift-tax-free gifts—in addition to the annual gift limit—for tuition costs.

Say you want to pay your granddaughter's college expenses. You can pay an unlimited amount of tuition gift tax free as long as you make the payment directly to the university. In limited circumstances, you may even be able to take advantage of this tax break by *prepaying* your granddaughter's tuition.

UPDATE YOUR WILL

If your will was written before the *Taxpayer Relief Act of 1997,* it may use numbers pegged to the former law. That exempted $600,000 from gift and estate taxes and $1 million from the generation-skipping transfer tax. *New amounts…*

• **The estate tax and generation-skipping transfer tax exemption amounts** will rise to $3.5 million by 2009.

• **The gift tax exemption amount** is now $1 million and will not increase.

As a result of these changes, wills and trusts may need to be revised, using *formulas* rather than absolute numbers.

• **For the charitably inclined,** consider naming a charity as the beneficiary of an IRA, instead of bequeathing it to an individual via your will.

If the IRA goes to your child, say, up to 80% could be gobbled up in income and estate taxes. *Better:* Leave the child assets that are not subject to income taxes and give a charity the asset—the IRA—that would otherwise be subject to income taxes.

FAMILY-OWNED BUSINESSES

The family-owned business deduction, which (combined with the exemption amount) shielded $1.3 million in value of a family business, is repealed starting in 2004. Those owning such business interests need to make new plans to reduce or eliminate the estate tax.

INDIVIDUAL STATE CHANGES

Because many states have passed new laws concerning gift and estate taxes, it is advisable to check with your attorney as to whether your will or trust documents need to be updated because of state law.

• **Gift taxes.** Many states are repealing gift taxes. New York, for example, repealed its gift tax, effective January 1, 2000, and adopted a "soft" estate tax, effective February 1, 2000. A "soft" estate tax is one that is based on the federal return. The switch removes a tax incentive for moving to Florida, as many New York retirees now do. (North Carolina, Connecticut, Tennessee, Georgia and Puerto Rico still levy gift taxes.)

• **Dynasty trusts.** Many states have repealed what is known as "the rule against perpetuities," which prevented assets from being held in trust indefinitely. Now, if you want to put assets, or even a family business, into a long-term trust, you may be able to do so under the laws of your own state instead of setting up an Alaska or South Dakota trust. In practice, many people prefer to set a limit on how long trusts last.

• **Investing trust assets.** States are beginning to look at trusts' overall rate of return, recognizing capital gains as income, not just interest and dividends. Trusts are often set up to pay out income to beneficiaries with what's left over (the "remainder") going to someone else after a set period or upon the deaths of the beneficiaries. This state monitoring of a trust's return has profound implications on how assets are invested. Check with your attorney or trustee concerning the law in your state.

How to Eliminate Family Squabbles

Martin M. Shenkman, CPA, JD, tax attorney in New York and author of numerous books on estate planning, including *The Complete Book of Trusts.* John Wiley & Sons.

Many of the nasty battles that siblings wage over estates arise because their parents failed to consider their feelings when making plans.

While wills and trusts are necessary to protect assets, they very often neglect emotional issues and create long-lasting relationship problems for heirs.

Feelings don't have to be hurt when protecting assets. Changing the wording or softening language in those documents can make a crucial difference in how a parent's wishes are perceived by children.

To anticipate and avoid the biggest problems...

***Problem:* Failing to distribute noninvestment assets fairly.** Families have always battled over seemingly worthless items that are left in estates. But the recent jumps in prices for art, antiques and collectibles have raised the stakes.

Even though you have good intentions when you make up your estate plans, problems may arise.

Example: If you leave one child your collection of first-edition books and your other child your favorite desk, the two items may have vastly different values. One child could benefit at the expense of the other.

Fights also erupt when parents completely forget to include such assets in their estate plans or fail to specify which child gets which piece of property.

Solution: Make a list of all of your personal assets. Then let the oldest child choose one item from the list, followed by the next oldest child—all the way down to the youngest child.

Then, in the second selection round, let the youngest child choose first from the list. This list can be circulated by mail or by e-mail, with pictures of the assets if necessary. The children can also submit their selections to you by mail.

When all the children have had a chance to select first, get appraisals of the assets they've chosen. Appraisals can vary in cost, from several hundred dollars to many thousands of dollars.

Balance the value of assets by giving cash in addition to items of lesser value. Values of items in an estate can change over time. So the sooner it is handled and everything is distributed, the better.

If children are unable to agree on who gets what within 60 days, state in your will that everything will be sold at current market value, with each child receiving a share of the proceeds to equalize the value of items distributed.

***Problem:* Completely disinheriting a child.** By doing so, you guarantee that the child's only memories of you are bad ones.

Better: Acknowledge in your will that the relationship between the two of you was not the best. Then leave your child something—even if it is not as much as you left other children.

Leaving less-favored heirs something may prevent legal challenges to your will. Naming them makes it legally clear that you intentionally meant to leave to them smaller portions than to their siblings.

Avoid using language that will hurt them, such as, "I leave only $100 to my son Frank, who I hope one day will make something of himself."

Words like these can cause divisions within a family for generations. Use milder language that puts a positive spin on your wishes and urges your family to become closer.

Example: "I leave 10% of my estate to my son Frank. While our relationship was not as close as I had wished, I hope that this bequest will encourage him to remain close with the rest of the family."

Problem: Leaving one child more than the other. If one child is left more than another—despite the fact there may be good reasons for this move—you may ruin their future relationship.

Example: One of my clients was worried about how to divide her estate fairly between her two daughters. One daughter is wealthy...the other is divorced and struggling to bring up her young children without financial support from her ex-husband.

Many parents would leave more to the divorced daughter—but my approach is to treat siblings equally in estate plans to preserve their relationship.

Solution: Because the less fortunate daughter will likely need more support, I suggested that my client leave each daughter 30% of the estate outright. Then the client put the remaining 40% into something I call a *pot trust.*

A pot trust is like a pot of soup—allowing each daughter to ladle out the money that she needs.

It named both daughters as cotrustees, since they were on good terms. If they weren't on good terms, she would have named a bank as trustee.

Each daughter must get the other daughter's permission to withdraw money from the trust.

Once the youngest grandchild, who is the son of the divorced daughter, reaches age 25, the trust will be dissolved. Whatever is left will be equally divided between the two daughters.

Problem: A will that can't adjust to changes in children's circumstances. Your will needs to deal with the differing needs of each child while still making them each feel satisfied.

Sometimes a subtle change in language is all that's necessary.

Example: Recently, I helped a client solve a difficult situation involving his two adult children—one son was a successful businessman and one could never hold a job.

The father wanted to split his estate, giving half to the businessman outright and putting the other half into a trust for the other son, naming his brother as trustee.

I convinced him this was a mistake. Putting the responsible brother in charge of his brother's finances would forever doom their relationship.

Better: We split the estate 50–50, putting each brother's share into a separate trust for life. We also named each son as cotrustee—along with a bank—of his own trust.

Even though the documents looked identical on the surface, there was a crucial difference in the language.

The businessman has the right to independently withdraw some of the principal in the trust without getting prior approval of the bank trustee.

But the other son must first get the consent of the bank before withdrawing funds from the trust, although he is entitled to the income produced by the trust assets.

Grandchild Loopholes

Edward Mendlowitz, CPA, partner, Mendlowitz Weitsen, LLP, CPAs, K2 Brier Hill Ct., East Brunswick, NJ 08816. He is author of several books on taxes, including *IRA Distributions: What You Should Know.* Practical Programs, Inc.

Gifts to grandchildren—or great-grandchildren for that matter—help them and cut the family's overall tax bill. *Here are the best tax-saving gift strategies...*

Loophole: Pay a grandchild's tuition and medical expenses. Generally, you owe gift tax when you give a particular grandchild (or anyone) more than the annual gift tax limit ($11,000 in 2003 and 2004). In 2003 and 2004 the tax-free limit is $22,000 per grandchild per year for a married couple who join in making the gift.

In addition to an annual gift-tax-free gift, you can give an unlimited amount to help with education expenses as long as payments are made directly to a school, college or other educational institution.

On top of that, payments you make directly to hospitals or other medical providers to cover a grandchild's *medical* expenses are gift tax free.

Caution: You must make out the gift check directly to the institution (education or medical), not to your grandchildren.

Another form of giving: A married couple can contribute up to $110,000 in 2003 and 2004 to a qualified tuition program (QTP) with the money to be used for a grandchild's education.

The $110,000 can be offset with five years' worth of $22,000 joint annual gift-tax exclusions, making the contribution absolutely gift tax free. The election to apply the five years' worth of $22,000 exclusions is made on IRS Form 709.

Note: Distributions of earnings that are used to pay tuition, fees, books and supplies are now tax free.

Caution: A steep penalty applies to earnings that are distributed but not used to pay for higher education expenses.

Loophole: **Make your grandchildren partners in a family partnership.** The limited partnership interests that you transfer to your grandchildren are valued for gift tax purposes at less than the fair market value of the entire assets. A discount is applied because the partners/grandchildren have no control over the invested assets.

How to do it: Make yourself the general, or controlling, partner and your grandchildren limited partners. You will have complete control over the assets owned by the partnership. Income generated by the partnership assets will be paid to the grandchildren or accumulated for them.

Loophole: **Name your grandchild the beneficiary of your retirement plan.** You must start taking money out of your IRAs and other retirement plans by April 1 of the year after the year in which you turn age 70½. When you withdraw less than the IRS-required minimum amount each year, you owe a penalty.

While having your grandchild as beneficiary will not affect the amount of your required minimum distributions, it will mean that when you die, your grandchild can withdraw funds over his life expectancy. This will provide a lifetime of tax-deferred savings for him.

Loophole: **Set up a custodial account for the grandchild**—a Uniform Transfers (or Gifts) to Minors Act account with a bank or brokerage firm. The account will be owned by the grandchild and generally taxed at his/her lower tax rate. Transfer enough cash or assets to each grandchild so that they have $1,500 of investment income in 2003 ($1,600 in 2004).

Reason: Because of the kiddie tax, children under age 14 can earn only $750 of investment income free of tax in 2003 ($800 in 2004). The next $750 ($800 in 2004) of investment income will be taxed at their low 10% rate. Investment earnings above $1,500 ($1,600 in 2004) will be taxed at the parent's tax rate.

Best assets to give grandchildren under 14...

●**Index funds or growth stocks** that produce little or no current income. The shares can be sold after the children turn age 14, and the gains taxed at their low rate.

●**Series EE or I US savings bonds** that mature after your grandchild's 14th birthday. The taxes are deferred on these bonds until they are cashed in or mature.

●**Zero-coupon municipal bonds,** which don't generate any current income.

Best assets for grandchildren older than 14...

Take advantage of the children's low tax rate by giving them income-producing assets like high-dividend-paying stocks or bonds.

Alternative: Give appreciated assets and have your grandchildren sell them.

Trap: Grandparents who make gifts to custodial accounts should not act as custodians. If they do, any money left in the account when they die will be included in their taxable estates. Avoid this by having one grandparent make a gift to the other grandparent, who then gives the money to the grandchild. That way, the first grandparent can act as custodian without adverse tax consequences.

Loophole: **Put your grandchild to work** as a model or "actor" in advertisements for your business or its products. Children can earn income of up to $4,750 before owing any tax in 2003 ($4,850 in 2004). Above that, earnings of up to $6,000 are taxed at 10% and earnings above $6,000 but not over $28,000 are taxed at their low 15% rate (in 2004, $7,150 is taxed at 10% and up to $29,050 at 15%).

Strategy: Up to $3,000 of earned income a year can be contributed to a Roth IRA and never taxed there.

Caution: The business will owe Social Security and payroll taxes on salaries paid to your grandchildren.

Loophole: **Set up a life insurance trust** to hold policies on your life for the benefit of your grandchildren. When the trust is properly set up, the proceeds paid on your death will not be subject to estate tax.

Trap: Gifts to grandchildren that exceed an exemption amount are subject to the generation-skipping transfer tax. Avoid this tax by transferring $1 million into a life insurance trust. You may owe little or no tax on this gift, depending on your other lifetime gifts. Then direct the trust to buy a single-premium life insurance policy on your life. This should pay a benefit of $2 million to $5 million, depending on your age.

When you die, the policy proceeds will be paid to your grandchildren free of estate tax. *Result:* You have passed on $2 million to $5 million for the price of gift tax on $1 million.

Caution: If the trust is set up incorrectly, the full insurance proceeds could be subject to a generation-skipping transfer tax.

Estate Planning Loopholes

Here are two strategies to consider if you have a disabled family member…

Loophole: **Gift-tax-free gifts to disabled persons.** Expenses paid for medical care or tuition directly to the hospital, provider or school also are exempt from gift tax and the generation-skipping transfer tax.

Caution: You must write a check directly to the institution, not to the individual receiving the care.

Loophole: **"Special needs" trust.** Money can accumulate in a "special needs" trust to provide a disabled person with income without any gift or estate tax or Medicaid consequences.

Caution: You must follow the guidelines outlined in OBRA (Omnibus Budget Reconciliation Act of 1993), Section (d)(4)(c).

Wiser Bequests

Leaving a bequest of cash to charity can be a tax mistake. *Better:* Instead of leaving cash to a charity, have your will fund a charitable bequest with an item that would be subject to income tax if left to heirs.

Examples: Deferred compensation, nonqualified stock options, IRA funds.

Since charities are tax exempt, they can receive these items income tax free. And heirs can receive cash income tax free. So you effectively cut the IRS tax bite.

Contrast: Deferred compensation and IRA funds are subject to income tax at ordinary rates, as are nonqualified stock options when exercised. If you leave the charity cash and bequeath your heirs taxable items, you will be leaving your heirs a tax bill—and making a bequest to the IRS. (See IRS Letter Ruling 200002011.)

Martin M. Shenkman, CPA, JD, tax attorney in New York and author of numerous books on estate planning, including The Complete Book of Trusts. John Wiley & Sons.

The "Forever Trust"

David S. Rhine, CPA, regional director of family wealth planning, Sagemark Consulting, a division of Lincoln Financial Advisors Corp., a broker/dealer and registered investment adviser, 395 W. Passaic St., Rochelle Park, NJ 07662.

Stock options, stock market gains, life insurance, family businesses, appreciated real estate…and other new wealth has exposed many more families to the steep estate tax.

NEW LAW

Fortuitously, a new opportunity to escape estate tax now exists. New law in several states makes it possible to place family wealth in a perpetual trust. This trust can protect wealth—and let it accumulate—for the benefit of family members forever.

Moreover, the wealth will pass from generation to generation estate tax free forever into the future—even as it grows.

In the past, it wasn't possible to create a trust that would last forever because of the "rule against perpetuities." That rule generally limits the maximum term of a trust to the lifetime of a living person, plus 21 years.

But now 16 states have repealed the rule—Alaska, Arizona, Delaware, Florida, Idaho, Illinois, Maine, Maryland, Minnesota, Missouri, New Jersey, New York, Ohio, Rhode Island, South Dakota and Wisconsin. Several more states have legislation pending to do so.

OUT OF STATE

The rule does not have to be repealed in your state in order to use a perpetual trust. It's possible to fund a trust during your lifetime in a state other than where you live.

Competition between states for this trust business is a large part of what's driving the spreading repeal of the rule against perpetuities.

Over time, the power of compound interest can produce staggering gains.

Examples: If a trust grows 7% per year—the average long-run return from the stock market over inflation—$1 million will grow to $867 million in 100 years. Yes, $867 million!

And if a trust grows just 1% faster, at 8%, $1 million will become $2.2 billion in 100 years.

Growth much less than this would probably be enough to secure your family's financial welfare—and their gratitude to you—for generations to come.

ESTATE TAX RULES

The initial transfers that fund a perpetual trust are subject to gift and estate tax under normal rules—but there are ways to minimize or eliminate the tax.

The tax advantage of a perpetual trust is that future "layers" of estate tax between generations are eliminated.

Estate tax applies at rates up to 49% in 2003 and 48% in 2004 (45% by 2007). So, on transfers through two generations (to grandchildren), almost 80% of an estate can be consumed by

estate tax—and through three generations (to great-grandchildren), the figure is 90%.

It is these future layers of estate tax that are eliminated by a perpetual trust.

Two kinds of taxes must be planned for when establishing a perpetual trust...

●**Gift or estate tax.**

●**Generation-skipping tax.**

Every individual has a personal gift- and estate-tax-exempt amount of $1 million in 2003. The estate tax exemption rises to $3.5 million by 2009, which can be used to fund the trust. A couple can make use of two exempt amounts with proper planning.

To make your exemption more valuable...

●**Life insurance can be used to fund the trust** and with proper planning, the insurance proceeds can escape being part of your taxable estate. The premium going into the trust may be subject to transfer tax, but that's just a fraction of the proceeds, particularly if you use second-to-die insurance. Or use split-dollar life insurance to get the transfer costs even lower.

●**Make your gift before it appreciates.** Appreciating assets can be placed in the trust before you die, so future appreciation escapes estate tax.

●**Minority interests in private businesses** often can be valued at discounts of 30% or 40%. You may be able to cover $1.4 million or more of underlying value with your $1 million tax-exempt amount.

GST

The generation-skipping tax (GST) is a special consideration whenever a transfer is made across more than one generation—such as to grandchildren as happens with the perpetual trust.

In order to prevent persons from avoiding layers of estate tax with transfers across more than one generation, Congress created the GST.

It applies to such transfers in addition to any gift or estate tax. But the GST can be minimized as well. *Planning opportunities...*

●**Every individual has an exemption amount from GST** ($1.11 million in 2003 and $1.5 million in 2004, but the same as the estate tax exemption amount thereafter).

●**GST applies only once to funds left in a properly drafted trust,** even if the trust eventually benefits many generations.

Example: In 2004, you can fund a trust with up to $1.5 million with no GST. If you fund the trust with more, GST will apply to the excess —but after it is paid, trust funds will pass from generation to generation in the future with no estate tax or GST, so future layers of estate tax will still be eliminated.

TRUST RULES

A perpetual trust is irrevocable. Once created, it cannot be changed or modified by the creator.

You can give beneficiaries limited power over disposition of the assets for succeeding generations.

A trustee selected by the trust's creator becomes responsible for managing the assets. Distributions may be discretionary, or set as a percentage of trust assets or trust income. You should also give a roadmap for the appointment of successor trustees by the beneficiaries. Do the trustees appoint their own successors? Or some hybrid? Typically, a corporate trustee will also play a role.

Flexibility: You can even give each beneficiary the right to demand a distribution of up to 5% of principal annually. *Advantage:* If you split up the trust by family, and a beneficiary doesn't need the money, it will remain in the trust and pass tax free to his/her family.

A perpetual trust does owe income tax on its income, so trust investments typically will be geared toward appreciation—which fits well with holding an interest in a growing family business or growth stock portfolio.

In some states, a perpetual trust can also function as a charitable lead trust—combining tax and charitable benefits. To minimize transfer taxes, each year for a set number of years after the trust starts, funds are paid to charity. The value of this charitable income stream reduces the taxable gift.

FAMILY PLANNING

Setting up a perpetual trust requires far-reaching vision…faith on your part in the trustee, who will require a great deal of flexibility…and procedures for selecting a succession of trustees in the future.

The trust will last far beyond what you can foresee, so you must make provisions for the unexpected.

Example: The trust's investments may grow much more quickly or slowly than expected —and your family may grow more quickly or slowly than expected as well.

Thus, careful thought will have to go into designing distribution standards that will keep the trust from…

●**Being prematurely depleted** due to excess distributions during a time of slow growth.

●**Retaining funds and "growing for growth's sake"** when it could be helping family beneficiaries while investments are booming.

Important: Specific legal rules for perpetual trusts vary in each state. And these trusts have many legal, tax and estate planning considerations that must be carefully considered with experts.

But if you have accumulated wealth and wish to make it really last for your family, a perpetual trust is a new option to consider.

Congress Killed the Estate Tax…or Did It?

Gideon Rothschild, Esq., CPA, partner in the law firm Moses & Singer LLP, 1301 Avenue of the Americas, New York 10019.

Through 2010, the rules for passing on property change dramatically. But in 2011, all the new rules expire, with estate tax reverting to its 2001 status.

During this nine-year period, some individuals will no longer have their estates depleted by taxes. Others are not out of the woods entirely and still need to plan to minimize estate and gift taxes.

TAX RATES AND EXEMPTIONS

Estate taxes continue to drop in the following manner…

●**The top tax rate declined from 55%.** In 2004 it's 48%. It continues to fall by one percentage point each year until it reaches 45% in 2007. It stays at that rate until 2010, when the federal estate tax is repealed entirely.

Caution: In 2011, the repeal *expires.* It remains to be seen whether Congress will act before the expiration date to make the repeal permanent.

•**The amount exempt from estate tax**—$1 million in 2003—increases to $1.5 million in 2004, $2 million in 2006 and $3.5 million in 2009.

In 2010, there is no exemption amount because there is no estate tax that year. When the old rules take effect again in 2011, the exemption amount reverts to $1 million.

Impact of these changes: Wills and trusts must be reviewed. Revisions may be necessary.

Requiring special scrutiny: Wills that contain credit shelter trusts, trusts designed to fully utilize the exemption amount in the estate of the first spouse to die.

Why: Because of the escalating exemption amount, it may no longer be desirable in an estate of less than $5 million to funnel the maximum exemption amount to the credit shelter trust.

Example: A couple has a combined estate of $2 million ($1 million each) and wills requiring credit shelter trusts to be funded with the "maximum federal estate tax exemption amount." If one spouse dies in 2006, when the exemption amount is $2 million, his/her entire estate would be placed in the trust. In essence, the other spouse would be disinherited.

Gift taxes: The gift tax exemption amount for lifetime transfers is now $1 million and, unlike the estate tax exemption, increases no further.

The gift tax is *not* repealed in 2010. Instead, it becomes a flat tax at the highest individual income tax rate—35%.

Wealthy individuals who have already used up the $675,000 lifetime exemption amount should make additional tax-free gifts in view of the current $1 million exemption.

Gift tax exclusion: In 2003 and 2004, the annual gift tax exclusion of $11,000 per recipient (or $22,000 if married), and the exclusion for direct payments of tuition or medical expenses

were not changed by the new law. Thus, in addition to the lifetime exemption amount, wealthy taxpayers can continue to make these tax-free gifts year-in and year-out to reduce the size of their taxable estates.

FAMILY BUSINESSES

The special additional deduction for family-owned business interests currently available—up to $675,000—is repealed for individuals dying after 2003. Business owners whose estates fall below the increasing exemption amount are not adversely impacted by this repeal. Those with substantial holdings need to consider other transfer-planning strategies to minimize taxes.

Review succession plans with tax advisers. If you don't have a succession plan, make one now.

CARRYOVER BASIS

While the new law reduces or eliminates the estate tax burden, it potentially *increases* the income tax burden on heirs and can result in an overall tax increase.

Property inherited after 2009 no longer receives a stepped-up basis to its value at death. Instead, carryover basis rules are set to apply. Heirs take over the same basis that the decedent had. This may be substantially lower than the property's current value.

When heirs sell their inherited property, they'll have to pay tax on the resulting gain—the difference between what they've realized on the sale (current value) and the decedent's original basis.

Exceptions: Two exceptions allow stepped-up basis rules to be used...

•**Up to $1.3 million of basis increase** can be allocated to appreciated assets passing to any heir. This dollar limit is increased by unused capital losses, net operating losses and unused built-in losses.

•**Up to $3 million of additional basis** for appreciated assets passing to a surviving spouse.

Example: A married individual dies in 2010, leaving an estate of $5 million, $4 million of which is bequeathed to the surviving spouse. The assets have a basis of $1 million for the spouse's bequest and $500,000 for the remaining assets.

The executor can allocate $3 million of basis to the assets passing to the spouse and $500,000 of basis passing to other heirs. *Note:* The stepped-up basis allocation cannot exceed the fair market value of the assets.

In the absence of contrary instructions in a will, it's up to the executor to decide which property can enjoy the stepped-up basis. It may be helpful to revise wills to include guidance to an executor on allocating the stepped-up basis amount.

PLANNING STRATEGIES

Individuals whose estates do not become tax free despite the exemption increase should continue transfer planning to ease the tax burden for their heirs.

●**The generation-skipping transfer tax (GST) is modified by the new law.** Now the exemption amount is the same as that for estate tax purposes. The same estate tax rate applies to generation-skipping transfers until repeal of estate tax. Thereafter, the same 35% rate used for gift tax applies to lifetime generation-skipping transfers. Thus, GST is still a planning issue to address.

●**Flexibility will have to be written into estate-planning documents.** Wills and trusts should consider using "but if" clauses so provisions can be tied to tax changes. *Remember:* An existing formula clause may leave too much to the credit shelter trust and nothing to the spouse.

> *Example:* A will might say that *if* the exemption amount is $1 million (and the individual dies in 2003), property passes in a certain way, *but if* the exemption amount is $2 million (and the individual dies in 2006), property is distributed in another way.

●**Trusts** continue to play an important part in estate tax planning. Dynasty trusts allowing assets to pass from one generation to another and another have not lost their appeal. Similarly, asset protection trusts should not be overlooked for the protection they can offer from creditors' claims.

●**Don't assume** that life insurance to provide estate tax liquidity is no longer needed. Don't be quick to cancel—wait and see what ultimately happens to the estate tax.

●**Valuation discounts** (such as those associated with family limited partnerships) remain an important tool for reducing estate taxes when used in conjunction with lifetime gifts.

Minimize Estate Taxes

Family Limited Partnerships (FLPs) are becoming increasingly popular for minimizing estate taxes. *Caution:* If most of the assets you transfer are appreciated stocks and bonds, you may inadvertently trigger all unrealized capital gains. To avoid this huge cost, have your accountant run through the "investment company rule" calculations. If they are violated, either change the transaction or don't do it at all.

Martin M. Shenkman, CPA, JD, tax attorney in New York and author of numerous books on estate planning, including *The Complete Book of Trusts.* John Wiley & Sons.

Taking a Chance On an FLP

Setting up a family limited partnership (FLP) is the latest game of Russian roulette rich people play with the IRS. If your estate tax return does not get audited, your beneficiaries win with a family limited partnership. But—if there is an audit, your beneficiaries could lose. They'll probably end up in a lengthy court battle, facing steep legal bills and possibly IRS penalties and interest charges.

How the game is played: Cash and marketable securities are transferred to a limited partnership. Each year interests in the partnership are given to family members. The value attributed to the assets owned by the FLP is always less than the market value of the cash and securities that were transferred to it, since those assets are subject to restrictions that would not exist if the assets were owned outright.

Why You Must Review Your Will

Common mistake with wills: Most people update their will when something happens to their family—such as a birth, death or divorce. But they neglect to do so when the law that applies to them changes.

Examples: Numerous recent changes in the federal estate tax affect basic issues such as the amount that a person can leave tax free. And when you move your residence from one state to another, an entirely new set of state laws will govern your will. Key parts of your old will may simply become invalid.

Important: Review your will with your attorney and estate tax adviser periodically even if your personal situation does not change.

Sidney Kess, attorney and CPA, 10 Rockefeller Plaza, Suite 909, New York 10020. Mr. Kess is coauthor of *1040 Preparation, 2004 Edition.* CCH Inc.

Durable Power of Attorney

A durable power of attorney gives a trusted adviser the power to handle your financial affairs during any period in which you are incapacitated.

Important: The power of attorney should include specific authority for that person to deal with the Internal Revenue Service on your behalf. This is often overlooked but may prove vital if your adviser must take responsibility for your tax affairs.

Martin M. Shenkman, CPA, JD, tax attorney in New York and author of numerous books on estate planning, including *The Complete Book of Trusts.* John Wiley & Sons.

How to Avoid the Naming of an Administrator

Encyclopedia of Estate Planning by the late Robert S. Holzman and John J. Tuozzolo. Bottom Line Books.

To ensure that an executor of your selection will serve, this is what you should do:

● **Sound out your designated executor** to see whether he will actually serve if named in your will. Do this periodically. Is his health still satisfactory? Has he taken on full-time responsibilities elsewhere? Is he still interested in you and your beneficiaries? If not, replace him.

● **Seek to ensure your designated executor's agreement** to serve by recommending to him knowledgeable and able attorneys, accountants, and (where appropriate) appraisers and brokers who can help him to carry out his responsibilities without excessive detail work with which he isn't familiar.

● **Name one or more successor or contingent executors,** so that if the person of your choice doesn't serve, at least it will be your second or third choice, rather than an administrator that you would never have engaged.

● **Name a trust company as coexecutor.** This virtually assures the permanence and continuity of an executor you have seen fit to name.

● **Make certain that your will is valid so that the executor chosen by you will qualify.** Have an attorney familiar with state law check such requirements as the minimum number of witnesses required. State laws vary as to the technicalities to be met.

● **Be sure that your will can be found when the time comes to have it probated.** A perfectly executed and technically correct will is useless if nobody knows where it is. Have your will in your attorney's office, or with your federal income tax workpapers.

Wiser IRA Management

Consider setting up a separate IRA for each heir to maximize the accounts' value to your family. If you have one IRA with multiple beneficiaries, required payouts are determined by the age of the oldest person. That means more must be paid out each year, with less left to keep growing tax-free. But if you set up separate accounts—each with only one beneficiary—younger beneficiaries, such as grandchildren, can stretch out withdrawals much longer.

Caution: Calculations can be complex—be sure to consult a financial adviser.

Edward Slott, CPA, E. Slott & Co., 100 Merrick Rd., Rockville Centre, NY 11570. He is editor of *Ed Slott's IRA Advisor. www.irahelp.com.*

3

Investment Opportunities

New Income-Boosting Essentials

Yesterday's conventional wisdom held that as people neared or reached retirement age, they had to reduce risk by moving most of their savings into conservative investments, such as bonds.

Today's reality: You can't afford not to be invested in equities to some degree, even after you've retired. Stocks or stock mutual fund investments keep your income ahead of inflation. *Fact:* Stocks have outpaced inflation better than any other investment over time.

Best allocation: Keep at least 20% to 50% of your investments in stocks and stock mutual funds. The rest of your portfolio can be in less risky investments, such as bank CDs and government bonds.

For more conservative investments: Consider US Treasuries. Depending on how competitive bank rates are in your area, Treasury bills, notes and bonds will earn 1% to 4% more than bank savings products—particularly passbook accounts. And while earnings on Treasuries are subject to federal income tax like CDs, they are not subject to state and local income taxes. *Three kinds of Treasuries...*

• **Treasury bonds are sold in $1,000 increments with maturities up to 10 years.** These and other Treasury instruments are available from banks and brokerage firms for about a $50 transaction fee. Or you can purchase them directly from the Federal Reserve without a fee through a program called Treasury Direct. *For information:* 800-722-2678 or *www.treasurydirect.gov.*

• **Treasury bills are sold in one-, three- and six-month maturities** and cost a minimum of $1,000 from Treasury Direct, with additional increments of $1,000.

• **Treasury notes are sold in two- to 10-year maturities in $1,000 increments through Treasury Direct.**

Barbara O'Neill, PhD, CFP, a professor of family and consumer sciences at Rutgers University. She is author of *Saving on a Shoestring* and *Investing on a Shoestring.* Dearborn Financial Publishing.

Strategy: "Ladder" maturities when buying CDs and Treasuries.

Instead of buying a single $10,000 CD, say, buy 10 $1,000 CDs and stagger their maturities so that one comes due in year one, a second comes due in year two, a third in year three and so on.

Benefits: You won't tie up all your money in a single CD or bond—you will receive a regular check as each one matures—and you can more easily take advantage of changing interest rates.

How: If rates increase, you can move some of your money into a higher rate CD as soon as one matures, instead of having to wait until a longer-term CD matures.

INVESTMENT APPROACHES

●**Never put your money in an investment product you don't completely understand.** Too many people, while chasing high yields, put money into investments only because they've been told they'll get a high return.

●**Follow the "four-year-old-kid rule."** Don't invest in anything you can't quickly and easily explain in a way that a four-year-old would understand.

●**Don't avoid an investment simply because it has a duration longer than your life expectancy.** Just because someone is age 70 doesn't mean he/she shouldn't buy a 30-year Treasury bond. These long-term investments generally produce higher returns than ones with shorter terms. Remaining principal will become part of your estate and will be passed on to your heirs.

●**Continue to set financial goals.** Reaching retirement doesn't mean you've reached your financial goals. You may need more money in retirement than you had planned. *Retirement expenses may include...*

●Travel, which can be expensive.

●Unanticipated health-care needs plus long-term-care insurance.

●Building up your estate to leave more to your heirs.

●Helping grandchildren pay for college.

●One or more new cars.

Expenses such as these may require you to shift assets to higher producing, riskier investments.

Required: A sound financial strategy to increase the odds that these new goals will be met.

CONTINUE TO WORK

There's a growing sentiment in this country that retirement is a dead end. More and more people say they don't want to retire—ever. They want to continue to work, at least part-time, as long as their health holds out, well past age 65. *If this is your intention...*

●**Check with former employers about returning to work.**

●**Get a part-time job.**

●**Split a full-time job with somebody in a time-sharing arrangement.**

●**Turn a hobby into a business.**

CUT EXPENSES

One of the easiest ways to increase your retirement income is simply to spend less by cutting expenses. This will enable you to save more. *Some painless strategies for reducing costs include...*

●**Review your insurance policies** to make sure you're not paying for coverage you no longer need.

●**Play the "age card,"** and get a Senior ID through your local Office of the Aging. This card entitles you to a wide array of discounts.

●**Shift to a low-interest credit card.**

●**Join a co-op** to buy food in bulk.

●**Choose basic clothing styles** that can be dressed up or down. And build your wardrobe around a few colors that complement you.

●**Revive the lost art of letter-writing,** or better still, send e-mail, instead of making expensive long-distance telephone calls.

●**Call the local utility company** for an energy audit and take advantage of its cost-saving advice.

●**Consider low-cost entertainment options,** such as early bird dinners, college theater presentations and inexpensive adult education classes.

●**Swap services,** such as pet-feeding and house-sitting, with neighbors and friends.

Before Hiring a Financial Adviser...

Edward Mendlowitz, CPA, partner, Mendlowitz Weitsen, LLP, CPAs, K2 Brier Hill Ct., East Brunswick, NJ 08816. He is author of several books on taxes, including *IRA Distributions: What You Should Know.* Practical Programs, Inc.

When choosing a financial adviser, look for someone whose style meshes with your needs.

The best way to find an adviser is through referrals from friends or your accountant. Get at least three referrals.

All referrals should have a recognized credential, such as CFP (Certified Financial Planner) or PFS (Personal Financial Specialist). That tells you he/she has completed educational requirements...and follows a strict code of ethics.

Contact the Certified Financial Planner Board of Standards (888-237-6275, *www.cfpboard.org*) or The American Institute of CPAs, PFS Division (888-777-7077, *www.cpapfs.org*) for information about complaints that may have been filed against a potential adviser.

Questions to ask each referral...

●**How do you charge for your services?** "Fee-only" advisers charge by the hour. Others charge a percentage of your total assets...or earn commissions on financial products they sell to you. The best advice generally comes from those who make the same money, no matter what the investment.

●**What is your investment philosophy?** Ask for samples of investment policy statements he helped clients prepare. If you are 35 and have no dependents, you likely want to be more aggressive than someone who is 35 and has children.

●**Beyond providing financial advice, how do you earn money?** If an adviser also sells life insurance, he may be more interested in selling products than in creating a sound financial plan for you.

●**How do you keep up to date in the financial field?** Any adviser you hire should read trade journals and financial publications ...and attend conferences and seminars.

●**How do you keep your clients informed about important financial issues?** An adviser's style must suit you—and he must be able to explain matters to you clearly.

Who Needs a Full-Service Broker?

Full-service brokers still have value for investors who are uncomfortable making their own investment decisions but who do not want to pay recurring fees to an investment manager.

Also: People who are easily influenced by cocktail party conversation about stocks might be better off with a wise full-service broker.

Caution: Choose a broker only after calling several references. Avoid anyone who strongly encourages buying into high-commission investments—particularly load mutual funds and annuities.

William G. Brennan, CPA/PFS, CFP, Capital Management Group, LLC, Washington, DC 20036.

Switching Brokers

It takes two to three weeks to switch brokers after completing an account-transfer form. But delays can occur. *Reasons:* Incorrect information on transfer forms...use of an incorrect form...transfer includes a margin or retirement account...transfer between two different *types* of accounts...change in the account owner. *Self-defense:* Fill out transfer forms carefully...monitor the transfer process.

John Gannon, acting director, Office of Investor Education and Assistance, Securities and Exchange Commission, Washington, DC.

Social Security Savvy

When planning an investment portfolio for retirement, count Social Security benefits as an asset. *Example:* You retire with $500,000 in savings, and plan to invest half in US bonds for safety and half in stocks for growth. You also receive a $1,000 monthly Social Security benefit. *Key:* Social Security benefits are as secure as the interest paid on US bonds. If you expect to receive $12,000 annually for 20 years, that's the equivalent of $150,000 in bonds. So, if you invest half your savings ($250,000) in bonds, that's too much. Your best safety/growth mix is $375,000 in stocks, $125,000 in bonds—with the consideration that your Social Security is the equivalent of $150,000 in bonds.

John Markese, American Association of Individual Investors, 625 N. Michigan Ave., Suite 1900, Chicago 60611.

Safer than Banks

Investors suffering from high anxiety are turning more and more to the safest investment there is: US Treasury securities.

Treasury bills (maturing within six months), notes (maturing in two to 10 years) and bonds (maturing after 10 years) are actually safer than government-insured bank accounts. *Trap:* There's only pennies in government insurance for every dollar of insured bank accounts. *Even worse:* Some of the insurance funds aren't in cash, but in illiquid receivables accepted from troubled banks.

By contrast, every penny of a T-bill is guaranteed by the full faith and credit of the federal government. And the government has never failed to pay its obligations.

Bonus: Liquidity, especially if they're purchased through a mutual fund that offers check-writing privileges. *Special tax status:* T-bills, notes and bonds bought by individuals aren't subject to state income taxes. When these securities are purchased through a mutual fund, 25 of the 40 income-tax states levy a tax.

James M. Benham, chairman, Benham Capital Management Group, 755 Page Mill Rd., Palo Alto, CA 94304.

Dividends Can Mean a Lot

Investors who need income should take dividends seriously (Whether or not they become tax free). As more and more companies plow money into research and development instead of paying out earnings to shareholders, dividends may no longer be a market fixture. But they do provide investors with an important income stream. Dividends and interest should cover at least 60% of the income needs of anyone who lives on money from investments, with the balance coming from growth of assets, such as a program of systematic withdrawal from an equity mutual fund. That way, if the market drops, the income stream continues with less of a draw on assets.

Madeline Noveck, CFP, president, Novos Planning Associates, Inc., 120 E. 56 St., New York 10022.

Where to Park Your Money for the Short Term

Here are some suggestions for money you will need soon...

●**Money market accounts** pay more than bank accounts and are safe.

●**Ultrashort bond funds** yield slightly more at some increased risk. They invest in issues averaging six-month terms. Best for people who don't want to risk principal.

●**Short-term municipal bond funds** invest in issues with terms up to three-and-a-half years. They go up more than ultrashort funds when interest rates drop but fall more when rates increase.

●**Prime-rate funds** invest in floating-rate bank loans taken by corporations. Yields can be good. Withdrawals are usually allowed only once per quarter. Best for people who need withdrawals at predictable times.

Peter DiTeresa, senior editorial analyst, Morningstar.com, 225 W. Wacker Dr., Chicago 60606.

Warren Buffett's Focused Investment Strategy Made Easy

Robert Hagstrom, manager of Legg Mason Focus Trust, which is modeled on Warren Buffett's investment strategy. He is author of several books on Warren Buffett's investment strategy, including *The Warren Buffett Portfolio: Mastering the Power of the Focus Investment Strategy.* John Wiley & Sons.

I've known Warren Buffett for 15 years, and I have closely studied his investment strategies. One of the secrets of his success is that he owns a small number of stocks—and only those with brand names that are extremely strong and will attract consumer demand over the long term.

You don't need to be a financial wizard to succeed at focused investing. *Here are my rules, based on what I have learned from Warren Buffett...*

• **Limit your portfolio to between 10 and 20 companies.** The majority of Berkshire Hathaway's portfolio is invested in about seven stocks...and Buffett believes a portfolio of 10 stocks is plenty for most people. The focused fund I manage owns only 16 companies.

I realize this type of focused approach may seem counter to conventional wisdom, which preaches the virtues of diversification. But Buffett believes that owning too many stocks hampers, rather than improves, performance.

• **Understand each company's business.** The key stocks Berkshire Hathaway owns— American Express, Coca-Cola, Gillette, Freddie Mac, Walt Disney, The Washington Post and Wells Fargo—are all household names. They operate in industries they dominate.

Buffett says he doesn't understand technology so he doesn't own technology or Internet stocks...but people who can understand technology should consider investing in great technology companies. He also doesn't own startups with new products that haven't been tested in the marketplace.

• **Look for a long history of superior performance.** We pick companies whose five-year trends of earnings growth and returns on equity exceed those of the S&P 500. Right now,

the earnings growth rate of the average stock in the S&P 500 is between 13% and 16%, while its return on equity is between 15% and 20%.

I'm less concerned with how much a company's growth rate exceeds the S&P 500 average than with its *consistency.* I would rather own a company that I'm confident will continue to post 20% annual earnings growth than one with highly erratic annual earnings over the past 10 years that average out to 30%.

• **Use the annual report to assess management and cash allocation.** One way that anyone can gauge the quality of management is to read the chairman's letter in the company's annual report. Even the best companies face some market difficulties. I look for those whose annual reports contain frank discussions of what went right and—equally important—what went wrong over the past year. If there's no mention of problems and challenges facing the company—that's a red flag.

I also like companies that disclose in their annual reports exactly how they are allocating their capital. You can find this information by reading the narrative section usually titled "Management Discussion of Cash Flow Statement."

Example: We sold an alcoholic beverage company because it persistently took cash that is generated by its high-margin distilling operations and allocated the money to its low-margin china business. That just didn't make sense to us.

• **Reinvest in your most promising holdings.** Most people purchase new stocks when they invest rather than buying more shares of what they already own. In most cases, this strategy reduces returns.

If you believe the companies whose stocks you own have bright futures, continue to invest in them.

Important: Each time you invest new cash, concentrate most of your money in the one or two stocks you think have the most promising prospects at that time.

• **Don't trade often.** When you buy a company's stock, plan to hold it for at least five years. Buffett says you should pretend that you have only 20 investment choices available to you during your entire lifetime.

This will force you to be choosy about where you invest and also is an incentive to leave your investments alone once you've made them.

•Sell a stock if it becomes overpriced compared with the rest of the market. We don't hang on to expensive stocks if we think their estimated future returns will be less than that of the overall market. We sell when the stock's price rises to a level that makes its future rate of return equal to or below what the future rate of return of the market will be.

Investment Lessons

George Stasen, a venture capital expert and chief operating officer of Supra Medical Corp., and Robert Metz, a financial journalist. They are coauthors of *It's a Sure Thing: A Wry Look at Investing, Investors, and the World of Wall Street*. McGraw-Hill.

There's no shortage of financial advice on Wall Street. The problem is that much of this financial advice is conflicting and leaves individuals confused or stuck in bad investments. So what's an investor to do?

Decisions, decisions…

•"Buy low and sell high" is sound financial advice—but there are actually four decisions to make. Stock market experts like to say that timing is everything, and most investors strive to sell at the top of a market and buy at the bottom.

This strategy is also known as the "contrary opinion"—doing the opposite of what most other investors are doing at a given time.

But moving successfully against the crowd is very difficult.

Trap: Market cycles contain many small, deceptive movements—so the buy-sell phases aren't always clear. *Here are four decisions a contrarian investor must make…*

•When the market is approaching the bottom of a cycle, sellers no longer have the stomach to buy. This creates an opportunity for bargain hunters. To determine when the market has reached this point, you can evaluate stocks using historically low valuations of revenues, earnings and dividends. Or you can wait for an uptrend before buying.

•After you buy, don't sell immediately after the bull trend becomes obvious to everyone. Let the crowd join you as the movement upward progresses.

•When serious overvaluation is reached, go against the majority and sell. Determine this moment by setting a price objective beforehand. Or base your timing on the heat of the market. Wait for the first sign of market weakness.

•As the downward cycle advances, resist the temptation to buy back your stock at a lower price. Wait until the market approaches the bottom again before buying.

•Don't confuse portfolio activity with progress toward investment goals. A common mistake made by many investors is rapid portfolio activity. They regard time as the enemy and believe that if they wait too long, that is an invitation for something to go wrong.

It's unrealistic, however, to expect that instant profits are easy to grab. When too much attention is focused on achieving short-term goals, the real opportunity—which is long-term—is forgotten. Think of time as an ally, not as an enemy.

•Beware of the company that offers creative excuses for underachievement. Some companies have a talent for making excuses for problems. Be especially wary of companies that wrap bad news in good news. *Danger signs:*

•When shortfalls and disappointments come with good-news announcements, such as the introduction of a new product or overhead-reduction programs.

•When you find your mailbox jammed with "We love you, shareholder" letters from the company.

•When bad news is accompanied by an announcement of a management shake-up. Did the company also say what took so long for them to clean up the problem? If not, incompetents may still be in charge.

Once credibility has been destroyed, it takes a long time for a company to win it back. When management repeatedly says, "Things will be better next year," it's time to sell.

●**Focus on essentials…skip the merely interesting.** Experienced investors are humble. They've learned that they can't possibly know everything. Less seasoned investors, on the other hand, may feel that if they had only a few more hours to do research, their investment returns would be considerably better. Usually this is hogwash.

Save time by not seeking out the opinions of yet another expert. Formulating intelligent questions that you then go out and seek answers to is much more valuable than collecting opinions.

Focus on an industry's prospects, the strength and track record of a company, and the long-term implications of a new development.

●**Good corporate news can lead to a dangerous sense of euphoria.** When there's good news, companies can't wait to circulate it. Many ladle it out in advance, tipping off key stock-market analysts. The result is that these stocks often rise before the news hits the media and afterward rise only slightly—or even fall.

Reasons: Many pros "sell on the news"—or take profits as the news becomes widely known and the price rises—and companies often use good news as an opportunity to seek more equity financing.

Similarly, beware of remarkably upbeat presentations at investment conferences. Instead, wait a few weeks or a month, and you'll almost always be able to buy the stock cheaper.

Opportunity: Look at the volume in the weeks before an "announcement." If it's high, this tells you that you may be late in getting the word.

●**Study the composition of a company's board of directors.** The role of a company's board of directors is to represent the interests of all stockholders. One way to determine whether the directors are representing your interests is to look at the people who make up the board. *How to tell a good board from a bad one…*

●**Determine how many directors come from the company and how many are from the outside.** If most are from the inside, the board may not be independent enough to resist undue pressure from top management.

●**Examine the credentials of the outsiders. If they are not particularly distinguished,** they may have been chosen as "good buddies."

●**If the board is small—fewer than five members—it's likely that outside directors were chosen for their cooperative attitude toward management preferences.** On the other hand, a large board—more than 10—is probably too unwieldy to support much independence on the part of outside directors.

●**The company's proxy statement will reveal the extent of each director's stock ownership and options and interest in the future of the company.** Token holdings are danger signs.

●**Learn to distinguish the truly underappreciated stock from the real losers.** *Key question:* Is the stock misunderstood by Wall Street or is it more likely that management misunderstands what's happened to its market?

Don't be fooled by a company's aura or unduly impressed by its past glories. "What have you done for me lately?" is a legitimate question to ask. "What do you plan to do tomorrow?" is an even better one.

Don't jettison a stock simply because it's the biggest loser in your portfolio. That's a short-term balm that usually turns into a long-term mistake.

How to Find Hot Stocks At Bargain-Basement Prices

Wallace Weitz, manager of Weitz Partners Value Fund and one of the country's shrewdest value investors, Wallace Weitz & Co., 1125 S. 103 St., Omaha 68124.

Value stocks are attracting more and more investors. *Wallace Weitz, a leading value investor, offers his investment secrets…*

Much of my approach to value investing I learned from Benjamin Graham, the master of finding stocks selling for less than their true business values. This approach made him a millionaire at age 35.

Graham was more concerned with a company's true value as a business, not the price the market put on its stock. Once you know the business's value, you know whether it is selling at a discount in the market.

Most people think that value investing means using their computers to screen for some stocks that sell at low price-to-earnings ratios (P/Es) or low price-to-book ratios.

But while seeking a low P/E and price-to-book ratio may eliminate some expensive stocks, ratios do not measure business value.

HOW I MEASURE VALUE

Business value is a function of how much discretionary cash a company will generate for its owners over the next 10 to 20 years.

Discretionary cash flow is the cash the business has left over at the end of the year—after paying taxes and interest and after spending on maintenance. It is also the amount of cash the company can take out of the business—to pay to shareholders or invest in the future—without wrecking the company's ability to function.

The more discretionary cash flow a company holds, the more valuable its business is to you, "the owner."

If you can buy that cash flow at a discount to the market price, you have a true value investment.

SIZING UP CASH FLOW

Start by adding the company's reported earnings per share and its depreciation and amortization. You can find these figures in the company's published income and cash-flow statements. However, distinguishing between maintenance, which is required, and expansion or acquisition, which is optional, can be difficult. The cash-flow statement sometimes gives clues.

Rule of thumb: Companies with lots of plants and equipment require lots of maintenance and replacement.

MANAGEMENT MATTERS, TOO

Not all value shows up on the balance sheet. Management quality adds or subtracts value. I want managers whose goals for the company are consistent with the long-term goals of shareholders. I won't buy a company whose management aims for quick but unsustainable profits just to please financial analysts.

Helpful: Look for senior management that demonstrates its commitment to the business by owning substantial amounts of company stock. This information can be found in annual reports.

Price Earnings Ratios

Price earnings (P/E) ratios have little to do with whether a stock is a good or bad buy. Many analysts recommend stocks with low P/Es as "cheap" and warn that stocks with high P/Es are "expensive." But history shows otherwise.

Study: During the 33 years from 1953 to 1985, the stock market had an average P/E of 15. But the top-performing stocks of this period started their market run-ups with an average P/E of 20 and ended with an average P/E of 45.

Reality: Firms with low P/Es often have them simply because they are poor stocks, while firms with high P/Es usually have demonstrated superior prospects. The simple truth is that most firms have P/Es that fairly reflect their value.

How to Make Money in Stocks: A Winning System in Good Times or Bad by William J. O'Neil, publisher, *Investor's Business Daily*. McGraw Hill.

Adding International Stocks to Your Portfolio Reduces Risk

Every monitored investment newsletter that recommends a blend of US and international investment has increased its return and lowered its risk by doing so.

Why: International stock markets do not move in lockstep with US markets, so when US markets are down, foreign ones are likely to be up and vice versa. Thus, buying international stocks reduces the risk that your whole portfolio will decline in value at one time. And international markets have equaled or surpassed the performance of the US market in recent years. Investments in international stocks are easily made through high-quality mutual funds.

Mark Hulbert, editor, *Hulbert Financial Digest,* 316 Commerce St., Alexandria, VA 22314.

Shift Investments From Stocks to Bonds

Shift investments from stocks to bonds at a gradual rate as you grow older.

Rule of thumb: The percentage of your portfolio invested in stocks should equal 100 minus your age. So if you are 55, you should be 45% invested in stocks and 55% invested in bonds or cash.

Rationale: Stocks are risky in the short run, but over the long run they consistently outperform bonds. You'll need this extra income for retirement. The money you keep in bonds will meet your short- and medium-term cash needs, letting you maintain your stock investments long enough for them to recover from any short-term market drop and protecting you from ever having to cash in your stocks while the market is low.

It's Never Too Late to Get Rich by James Jorgensen, editor, *It's Your Money* newsletter. Dearborn Financial Publishing.

Bonds vs. Stocks

Bonds are riskier than stocks much of the time—contrary to the belief of conservative investors. For much of this century, bonds have been poor investments because of losses in purchasing power, drops in value and low returns compared with other assets. *Important:* Look at a bond's total return—the change in its value plus its coupon amount—to compare it

fairly with other investments. The results may surprise bond buyers.

Kenneth Fisher, founder and CEO, Fisher Investments, a money management firm, Woodside, CA.

Bond Investment Trap

Before investing in bonds check to see if they are subject to a call provision that lets the issuer pay them off before maturity.

Key: Bonds go up in value when interest rates go down. But if bonds are subject to a call provision when interest rates decline, you can expect the issuer to redeem them and refinance at a lower rate. Thus, the call provision limits the potential for gain from a bond while leaving you with the full downside risk of loss if interest rates go up.

Point: While a call provision is onerous on bonds, it is especially so on high-yield "junk" bonds because of the greater risk involved in owning them.

Ben Weberman, financial columnist, *Forbes*, 60 Fifth Ave., New York 10011.

About Munis

Tax-free municipal bonds usually have better after-tax returns than US Treasury bonds for those in the 25% tax bracket—or higher. And there is minimal risk on AA or better municipals. Munis can be a great place to put profits from the stock market when you rebalance your portfolio. *Muni funds:* Look for low expense ratios and administrative costs. And check which munis they invest in—higher yield comes with higher risk.

James Lynch, editor, *Lynch Municipal Bond Advisory*, Box 20476, New York 10025.

Redeem E Bonds or Lose Interest

Barbara Weltman, an attorney with offices in Millwood, NY, and author of *J.K. Lasser's Small Business Taxes 6th ed.* (John Wiley & Sons) and *Bottom Line's Very Shrewd Money Book* (Bottom Line Books).

You may have been given US Series E or EE Savings Bonds as an anniversary gift or when you were married. Or maybe you even bought them through a payroll savings plan at work many years ago.

You probably stashed the bonds in the back of a drawer and then forgot about them, as so many people do.

Problem: E and EE bonds stop paying interest when they reach their final maturity date. The Federal Reserve says there are now billions of dollars worth of unredeemed savings bonds that are no longer paying interest.

What to do: Dig out your savings bonds and turn them in if they've matured. Put the money in something that pays interest.

E bonds issued before December 1965 have a 40-year final maturity, so a bond issued in March 1963 stopped paying interest in March 2003.

E bonds issued from December 1965 through June 1980 and EE bonds issued from January 1980 onward have a final maturity of 30 years, so a bond issued in March 1973 stopped paying interest in March 2003.

Deferring taxes: When you redeem the bonds, instead of paying tax on all the interest that has accrued, you can roll them over into US Government Series HH bonds.

HH bonds pay interest semiannually, but you will put off paying tax on your EE bonds until the HH bonds mature. HH bonds reach their final maturity after 20 years.

All About Cash

William E. Donoghue, chairman of W.E. Donoghue & Co. Inc., registered investment advisers, and publisher of *Donoghue's WealthLetter,* a monthly strategic mutual fund investment newsletter, Box 309, 100 Medway Rd., Suite 401, Milford, MA 01757.

When financial experts talk about allocating a portion of your assets in cash, they usually mean cash equivalents, such as brokerage money market accounts, bank money market deposit accounts and taxable and tax-free money market mutual funds.

These cash equivalents can be liquidated quickly, can earn a competitive money market rate of return (interest or daily dividends) and offer a high degree of safety from loss of principal.

There are several sound reasons for using these safe and convenient accounts…

● **To park money when you are between stock or bond investments.**

● **To maintain a reserve for short-term cash needs.**

● **To reduce the risk of your portfolio by allocating a portion to nearly risk-free investments during periods of heightened market risk.**

That is fine if you need the money in the short term, but these cash equivalent accounts should not be considered for long-term investments of a year or more, unless you intend to use them for checking accounts. There are more profitable places to park your money.

● **Always the best choice is to pay down your high outstanding credit card balances.** Some credit cards still charge as much as 19% interest annually. For many, eliminating this high nondeductible interest cost is the equivalent of finding a risk-free investment yielding as much as 30% before taxes. That's one of the best investments you will ever discover.

● **A well-managed, high-yield bond fund account is often an excellent choice for investors.** Principal losses can occur during periods of rising interest rates or market instability. Some advisers can demonstrate track records of up to 15% total return with conservative trading discipline. You could do this yourself if you wish.

Avoid load (sales commission) bond funds. There are plenty of no-load bond funds available to investors. Paying a 3% or 4% commission to buy a bond fund often defeats the purpose of investing, which is to earn 3% or 4% more than a money fund.

Be especially wary of insured municipal bonds, which are only as good as the insurance companies that back them. A study of these insurance companies indicates that they are grossly overrated. If the insurance companies are overrated, the bonds that rely on their ratings for credibility are overpriced. A realistic evaluation by the marketplace could cause these investments to lose market value, an uninsured loss.

Bottom line: There are several strategies for managing cash balances that can provide you with extra returns and lowered risks.

What to Look For In a Fund

Check a fund's cash position before deciding whether or not to invest. A fund that has more than 10% in cash may have more money than the portfolio manager can handle—unless the fund's prospectus specifically calls for it to maintain a large cash position. And it may signal trouble if a fund you already hold has a growing cash position—so watch its performance carefully. *Best:* Check the fund's cash position quarterly. A fund that can't put its cash to work over a 12-month period is out of step with today's market. Also watch out if a fund grows too quickly—the manager may be unable to invest new money without compromising the investing style that led you to buy into the fund in the first place.

Don Phillips, president, Morningstar, Inc., 225 W. Wacker Dr., Chicago 60606.

When It's Year-End Portfolio Review Time

Madeline Noveck, CFP, president, Novos Planning Associate Inc., 120 E. 56 St., New York 10022, and past president for the Institute of Certified Financial Planners.

It's important to review your portfolio well before the end of the year. Mutual fund distributions are taxable even if they are reinvested. You may consider realizing capital losses to offset these taxable gains by selling stocks or funds that have proved disappointing. But don't let the end-of-year urge to save taxes govern your investment decisions. Instead, identify those funds or stocks that have proved disappointing and evaluate them on their merits.

SELL? HOLD? BUY MORE?

If your shares in a mutual fund have been declining, it's time to reevaluate the holding, but not necessarily to sell. *Before unloading a fund that has been declining in value, consider the following...*

•**How has the fund performed relative to its peers?** It could be that the whole asset class is suffering—as has happened with Real Estate Investment Trusts, even though fundamental real estate values have been improving. Make your decision based on the fund's relative performance and the fundamentals of the asset class.

•**Have other investors been pulling out?** This isn't easy to learn, but you can often get leads from the financial press or the mutual fund tracking services. Or call the fund and inquire about monthly money flows. Are they positive or negative?

•**What is the impact of other shareholders withdrawing from the fund?** It is not easy for a fund manager to maintain his/her strategy when the crowd is pulling money out of the fund. In addition, if stocks need to be dumped to meet redemptions, this will create capital gains and add to your tax bill.

•**What has the fund returned on your investment?** A lower net asset value is a clue, but factor in dividends and capital gains distributions to determine total return. Compare your initial investment with the current value of your holding.

● **Has the manager stuck to the fund's investment goals?** If the prospectus promised small undervalued companies but the manager bought midsized growth companies, that's called "style drift." It's not bad if the stated strategy of the fund is to seek opportunities among small and midsized companies. But, if you don't want more mid-cap exposure, you might prefer another purely small-cap fund.

Caution: Before switching to a new fund, be sure you know its expected capital gains distributions and when they will come. These days, most funds are better prepared to give this information and many are being run more tax efficiently.

● **Are there any surrender charges?** If you bought B shares of a load fund and are selling within the first five years, you probably have surrender charges. These increase your loss. However, you can avoid them by switching within the same fund family if there is an appropriate fund. *Note:* You can still report your losses for tax purposes.

REBALANCING

Year-end is also a good time to rebalance your portfolio, which may have strayed from your original asset allocation due to the market's ups and downs.

Example: If large-cap growth stocks, which have done very well in recent years, have grown to, say, 44% of your portfolio instead of the allotted 30%, sell 14% and reinvest the money in an asset class that is now short of its allocation due to poor performance.

Benefit: This strategy leads to buying low and selling high. When an asset class is out of favor and with lower prices, underweighted in your portfolio, it may be a fine time to buy more.

Similarly, when an asset class becomes overweighted because prices are high, it may be appropriate to take some profits. Prices may go higher (or lower), but over the long run you'll be well served by using this discipline— it helps remove emotion from investing.

Understand that markets tend to go too far up or down in response to temporary factors (sometimes irrational). Then they're apt to reverse in the future.

Wash sale trap: You lose the tax benefits if you buy back the same holding you sold within 30 days, but you can buy a similar fund immediately to maintain your allocation. Just be sure to keep transaction costs to a minimum.

Do not let year-end tax-saving motives dictate your investment decisions. Change your asset allocation strategy only when your investment outlook changes, not to save a few dollars in taxes.

If you conclude that an investment is a loser, get rid of it. If a winner has become too prominent in the portfolio or you think it may be topping out, don't let taxes stop you from doing what is smart from an investment standpoint.

Example: Investors who were overweighted in IBM as it reached $139 earlier this year and didn't lighten up because of the tax bite, have ended up with a stock that went down as low as $90 shortly after.

There are nontaxable ways to get out of an investment. You can donate it to charity or give it to a family member in a lower tax bracket.

Trap: Watch out for gift taxes when you give assets to family members. The limit on gift-tax-free gifts is $11,000 per recipient in 2003 and 2004— $22,000 if your spouse joins you in making the gift.

Netting gains and losses: Add up all of your losses for the year, short-term and long-term. Then match them up against your gains. For tax purposes, net capital losses can be used to offset otherwise taxable capital gains dollar for dollar—there's no limit to the amount. Up to $3,000 of excess capital losses can then be applied against salary and other ordinary income. Additional losses are carried forward to future tax years to offset capital gains and other income.

How to Get Money Out of A Mutual Fund...Quickly

Sheldon Jacobs, editor and publisher of *The No-Load Fund Investor,* 410 Saw Mill River Rd., Suite 2060, Ardsley, New York 10502.

Most mutual fund investors don't think about getting their money out of a fund when they put it in. Too often, when financial markets dip and they want to redeem their shares, they find that getting their money back is time-consuming, frustrating and sometimes costly. *Reasons:*

●**The phones are tied up.** Mutual fund offices can be so inundated with orders to buy and sell shares that their switchboards may be busy at critical times. When you call requesting information about how to redeem shares, you may have to let the telephone ring for a few minutes before someone answers.

●**The procedures for redeeming shares are bureaucratic.** With most funds you must not only write a redemption letter requesting a check for the value of your investment, but you must also have your signature guaranteed by a commercial bank or by your broker. That can be time consuming, especially if you bought your shares directly from the fund instead of through a broker, and you don't happen to have an account with a commercial bank. Notarized signatures aren't acceptable and most funds will refuse to accept guarantees from savings-and-loan institutions. If your personal bank is an S&L, you'll have to go to a commercial bank that your bank has established a relationship with to have your signature guaranteed.

To avoid these obstacles:

●**Make a copy of the section of the fund prospectus that refers to redemption procedures—and keep it handy.** That way you won't have to make a phone call to get information on redemption procedures.

●**Prepare a redemption letter in advance. Have your signature guaranteed by your broker or commercial bank so you can simply date the letter whenever you decide to pull out of the fund.** Follow prospectus instructions for writing a redemption letter (usually, all you need to do is request that a check be sent to your home address, and give the number of shares owned and your account number).

●**Consider buying shares only in stock or bond funds managed by firms that also have money market funds to which you can switch part or all of your account by telephone.** That way you have access to the money via money market account checks, usually

within two days. *Caution:* It's always a good idea to call in a switch as early in the day as possible, because after 3 pm on heavy-volume days, many fund offices can be especially busy.

●**When you fill out the forms to purchase fund shares,** complete the section for authorizing wire transfers of redemptions to your bank. That service allows you to have shares redeemed and the proceeds deposited directly in your checking or savings account, usually on the same day you make the request. If you need the money fast and you have trouble getting through by phone, you can request a bank transfer in a redemption letter sent by overnight mail.

Five Rock-Bottom Investment Truths

Sheldon Jacobs, editor and publisher of *The No-Load Fund Investor,* 410 Saw Mill River Rd., Suite 2060, Ardsley, New York 10502.

In 2000, mutual funds had their first down year since 1994 and registered their worst performance since 1974. No wonder so many investors are questioning their basic strategy.

I've been reexamining my own beliefs, trying to isolate a few market basics that are always true, no matter what is happening in our economy or the world. *I've come up with five rock-bottom truths...*

1. It's hard to predict which way the market will go. Over the past 120 years, the stock market has done well in years ending in five. Does that mean that you should predict a good year in 2005? I don't believe so, because it seems to be coincidence.

On the other hand, the first year of a presidential cycle is traditionally a bad year for the stock market.

All those TV prognosticators can't predict the future any more than you can.

The goal is to invest sensibly even though you can't know which way the market is headed.

2. The stock market is reasonably efficient. There used to be any number of theories about how investors could make millions by finding undiscovered bargains. That's a lot harder to do today, with so many sophisticated computer programs sorting through the data.

For most of us, the best way to profit from market efficiency is to invest in total market index funds.

3. Diversification is critical. The wisdom of this old saw was driven home to many investors who went too heavily into tech and Internet stocks.

Throughout the 1990s, big-cap growth stocks were the clear winners. Now, value stocks are getting more attention. Small-cap value is doing particularly well. Investors who neglected fixed income lived to regret it, as bonds handily outperformed stocks.

Lesson: Don't overinvest in any one sector of the market.

4. It's vital to keep transaction costs low. There's no need for investors to pay sales loads when buying mutual funds. Also—it's important to pay close attention to funds' annual fees.

Studies have shown dramatic differences in long-term returns between high- and low-cost funds. This is a strong argument for low-cost index funds. These are tax efficient, too, because they have relatively low turnover—so you don't get big unexpected capital gains.

5. Take full advantage of compounding. Time is essential here—the longer you hold an investment, the more your money grows. To get the full benefit of compounding, you must also reinvest dividends.

4

Tax Savvy

Best States to Retire to In Terms of Taxes

Gone are the days when retirement meant whiling away the hours sitting in a rocking chair. Americans are retiring younger, living longer and planning full, active lives. Many are moving to locales where sunny weather, old friends, family or amenity-filled planned communities beckon.

KEY TAX BREAKS

Now, thanks to laws in recent years, even more Americans may be moving to another state to pursue their retirement dreams.

● **Source taxing forbidden.** What was known as "source taxing" has been generally banned.

Example: New York (or California) would tax payouts from a pension earned there, even though the taxpayer had moved to another state.

● **Tax-free home sales.** An exclusion in the tax law makes it unlikely that you'll owe capital gains tax on the sale of your home.

●Gains of up to $500,000 for a couple or $250,000 for a single person on the sale of a principal residence are tax free.

●Even those who have already taken the former one-time exclusion of $125,000 can take the new $500,000/$250,000 exclusion.

This change will free many people who have been staying in too large a home because they did not want to incur capital gains taxes. It could also make it possible for retirees—people who are widowed, for example—to move again without worrying about the tax consequences of selling their homes.

OTHER TAX ISSUES

In addition to these issues, people should consider a number of other tax matters when moving to another state. *Consider these also…*

Stanley Hagendorf, JD, estate and tax attorney, Hagendorf Law Firm, 2000 S. Jones Blvd., Las Vegas 89146.

- Income tax
- Sales tax
- Domicile
- Estate tax
- Property tax

INCOME TAX

Income tax is generally the biggest worry retirees have. Most people rank Nevada and Florida as the best states to retire to—two states with no income tax.

Contrast: Residents of New York City, for example, pay state and local income taxes that often are equal to one-third of their federal income taxes.

Florida does have an intangibles tax. This is a tax on the value of stocks, bonds, mutual funds and certain other items an individual brings into the state. But the intangibles tax is small in comparison with income taxes. It is only two-tenths of a cent per dollar.

Very few people—if any—pay a higher tax in Florida than in New York or in the Midwest.

Other states without income taxes: Alaska, South Dakota, Texas, Washington and Wyoming.

New Hampshire and Tennessee do not tax earned income (salary, etc.), but they do tax interest and dividends—an important source of money for many retirees.

DOMICILE

It is not unusual for people who retire to a new state to keep some ties to their former state—a business or investment property, for example, or even a house or an apartment, just in case they want to go back and visit. They think they have moved, but legally they may now be residents of two states, and liable for taxes in both.

High-tax states like New York, California and Massachusetts are aggressive in trying to collect taxes from such people, and the burden of proof is on the taxpayer to prove that he/she has abandoned the old state.

Remedy: When you move, really move…

- **Sever all ties to the former state.**
- **Sell off all your real estate there.**
- **Move your physical assets.**
- **File federal and state tax returns with your new address.**

- **Join social, civic or religious organizations** in your new state and resign membership in such groups in the former state.
- **File an affidavit of domicile in the new state.**
- **Change your driver's license, bank and brokerage accounts** to the new state.
- **Register to vote in the new state as soon as you can.**
- **Buy a new cemetery plot.**

To establish your new domicile, do as many of these things as possible.

ESTATE TAX

Estate tax is generally due at the federal level on estates that exceed $1 million in 2003 ($1.5 million in 2004). The exemption amount will rise over the next decade.

To calculate what your estate is worth, add up the value of your home, retirement accounts, securities portfolio, real estate or business interests that you own, and any other valuables.

Some states model their estate tax laws on the federal rules, but others levy taxes on much smaller estates.

So, if you want your assets to go to your heirs after your death instead of being gobbled up by taxes, it is important to check on the rules and rates of the state to which you are moving.

A will or trust documents written in one state may be valid in another. Even so, it could prove costly for your executor to have to track down witnesses who live in another state.

The prudent thing to do when you move is consult a local attorney who specializes in trusts and estates to find out if any legal changes are needed.

If you own property in two or more states, each may try to levy estate taxes on the whole estate. This gets back to the issue of domicile, and each state is free to set its own rules. However, the Supreme Court has ruled that total state estate taxes cannot exceed 100% of the value of an estate—but they can go that high.

Avoidance: The simple way to avoid handing your heirs this problem is to sell all property in one state when moving to another. That is not always possible, however. A property may be listed with a broker but take a while to sell. The sale of a business can be very complex.

Bottom line: If you move and still own property in another state, be sure to consult a local attorney who specializes in trusts and estates.

If you own property in two states, it may be wise to set up a trust in your lifetime, so a trustee can transfer property in the event of death.

SALES TAX

Sales taxes are often levied by both states and localities. *Important:* Check into the sales tax rates of a particular community before moving to it. Sales tax is of particular importance for people who spend a high portion of their income.

PROPERTY TAX

Property tax is nearly always a local issue, so again, check the property tax rates in a particular municipality before buying a new house or condominium there.

The Big, Bad Retirement Tax Traps

Stephen Pennacchio, partner, KPMG, LLP, 345 Park Ave., New York 10154.

People who are charting retirement finances better watch out for the minefield of tricky IRS rules. Here are the ones that are apt to trip you up and strategies to help you negotiate around them...

Trap: Mandatory withholding on retirement plan distributions. Plan sponsors must withhold 20% of any money that is not directly rolled over into a traditional IRA or another company's plan. *Double trouble:* The IRS views the withheld amounts as premature withdrawals if you're under 59½, so you owe a 10% penalty plus income tax on those amounts.

Example: You take $10,000 from your company plan when you leave the firm, but the plan sponsor only gives you $8,000 in cash. You owe a $200 penalty plus tax on $2,000.

Avoidance: If you replace the $2,000 with your own money and roll this amount over within 60 days of receipt into an IRA or other qualified plan, you can sidestep the penalty and tax. That

money is returned to you by the IRS at tax time in the form of a tax refund. But there can be a significant delay. If you withdraw money from the plan in February, you won't receive the refund until April of the following year, or 14 months later.

Better: Ask the plan sponsor to roll the money directly into another qualified plan or into an IRA. That way, no money will be withheld and no penalties will apply.

Strategy: If you're not sure which investment is best for your plan money, or you haven't found another job yet, have the plan sponsor roll the money into an IRA money market fund.

Strategy: If you need to use part of the money, have your company directly roll the entire sum into an IRA first. That way, you avoid withholding on the entire amount and just owe the early withdrawal penalties of 10% plus tax on the money that you take out. If you replace the money in 60 days, you won't owe anything at all.

Trap: Failing to take the required minimum distributions from IRAs. You must begin withdrawing money from traditional IRAs by April 1 following the year in which you turn 70½. The penalty for people who fail to do so is steep—50% of the amount that should have been distributed, but wasn't. When these amounts are ultimately distributed they are subject to income tax. Some banks and mutual funds alert their investors when distributions must begin, but the final responsibility rests with you.

The minimum required to be withdrawn is now based on a joint life expectancy of you and a beneficiary who is automatically treated as 10 years younger than you (whether or not you've named a beneficiary and whether that beneficiary is older or younger than you). *Exception:* You can reduce required distributions if your spouse is more than 10 years your junior—here distributions are figured over your actual joint life expectancy.

You do not need to begin required minimum distributions from company retirement plans until April 1 following the year in which you turn 70½ or when you retire, whichever is later. (This alternative does not apply if you own more than 5% of the business.)

Trap: Not making the most of tax-free compounding. When you retire, use your investments and other money held outside retirement plans first. That way, you defer taxes on the money inside the plans longer.

Example: You have a large sum inside an IRA and smaller amount in other investments. If you had used the after-tax money to cover living expenses for two years, your IRA would have grown at the rate of return you invested it, with the additional benefit of tax-free compounding.

Trap: Paying too much tax on retirement plan distributions. If you were born before 1936, you can elect more favorable tax treatment called 10-year forward averaging when you take a lump sum from a retirement plan. This method treats the money as if it had been taken in 10 equal installments rather than all at once, thus taxing more of the money in the lowest tax brackets.

Caution: Remember to factor in the impact of state taxes when you do the calculations.

Caution: Generally, as the lump-sum distribution is larger, rolling the money into an IRA and delaying distributions is more beneficial than averaging.

Simple Tax Mistakes That Can Be Very, Very Costly

Edward Mendlowitz, CPA, partner, Mendlowitz Weitsen, LLP, CPAs, K2 Brier Hill Ct., East Brunswick, NJ 08816. He is author of several books on taxes, including *IRA Distributions: What You Should Know.* Practical Programs, Inc.

The mistakes you make with tax filings, paperwork and elections can cost you big tax dollars.

RETIREMENT SAVINGS ERRORS

Many families have *most* of their wealth saved in retirement accounts.

●**Self-employed qualified retirement plan mistake.** Not filing a form in the 5500 series. The exact form depends on the number of participants and assets in the plan. These information returns must be filed for all plans that provide benefits to employees and for one-person plans that had more than $100,000 of assets in any year after 1993. The late-filing penalty is up to *$1,000 per day.*

Trap: With a booming stock market over the last decade, owners of one-person plans may not realize their accounts are now worth more than $100,000.

Self-defense: If you are behind on filing the 5500 form, consult a retirement plan expert *immediately*. File the form, and have your adviser ask that penalties be waived. You have a *much* better chance of reducing potentially huge penalties if you correct the delinquency before the government catches it.

●**401(k) plan mistake.** Taking a distribution of employer stock from a 401(k) and rolling it over into an IRA.

Snag: When you finally cash in the stock and withdraw the proceeds from the IRA, they will be taxable as ordinary income. You will lose favorable capital gains treatment for the shares.

Better: If you intend to hold the shares, take a distribution so you own them. You'll owe a current tax on their appreciation since your 401(k) account acquired them. All further long-term gain will be taxed at a rate of up to 20%.

●**IRA mistake #1.** Not naming beneficiaries—either your estate will become your beneficiary or default provisions established by your IRA's trustee will go into effect. *Either case is bad...*

●If your estate becomes your beneficiary, you forfeit your ability to have your heirs stretch out the distribution.

●If default provisions go into effect, your IRA probably won't be distributed as you wished.

●**IRA mistake #2.** Changing the name on the IRA to that of the beneficiary when the owner of an IRA dies. This accelerates IRA distributions.

Better: Keep the IRA in the name of the deceased owner to extend the IRA distribution period.

FILING ERRORS

●**The worst mistake anyone can make is not filing.**

●If you are owed a refund, the statute of limitations expires after three years. After that, you lose the ability to collect your refund.

●If you owe tax, the statute of limitations *never* expires. You will accumulate nonfiling penalties, plus late-payment penalties and interest. Even if you can't afford to pay the tax, file a return to avoid nonfiling penalties. Use the IRS's new installment payment option by filing IRS Form 9465, *Request for Installment Agreement.*

● **Filing a joint return when one spouse owes a bill for the past year and the other is due a refund.** The IRS may take the refund to pay back taxes.

Better: File separate returns to protect the refund. While this may increase the overall tax rate for the couple, if the back tax bill is paid within three years, you can file an *amended* return claiming joint filing status for that year. This lowers the tax rate, and you can file for a refund.

● **Not completing the tax return and filing all required supporting documents.** Such mistakes cost you deductions...or increase your risk of being audited. *Examples...*

● For charitable gifts of property valued at more than $500, you must file Form 8283, *Noncash Charitable Contributions.* You will need qualified appraisals for donated property worth more than $5,000.

● When claiming a home-office deduction, you must file Form 8829, *Expenses for Business Use of Your Home.*

● On Schedule B of Form 1040, check a "yes" or "no" box for the question asking if you have a foreign bank account.

● **Not filing the IRS's Form 8822, *Change of Address,* when you move.** If you don't, IRS notices sent to your old address may be deemed effective even if you never receive them...and you may lose a tax case by default.

FAMILY ERRORS

Errors in family finances that can boost the tax bill...

● **A grandparent puts money in a child's name** in a Uniform Gifts to Minors Act (UGMA) or Uniform Transfers to Minors Act (UTMA) account...then acts as custodian of the account.

Trap: Because the grandparent retains control over the funds, they remain taxable to the grandparent's estate in spite of the gift.

Better: Name someone else as custodian of the UGMA/UTMA account.

● **A couple separates,** and one spouse voluntarily pays support to the other until they work out a formal separation or divorce agreement.

Trap: The payments are not deductible as alimony because they are not made under a written agreement.

Better: Have a written agreement covering such payments from the start.

● **A will doesn't specify the account from which estate taxes are to be paid.**

Trap: A conflict over who pays the tax may arise. The *entire* cost of estate tax may fall on beneficiaries paid from the "residual estate"—the amount left after bequests of specific items and amounts—with other beneficiaries paying *nothing.*

Better: Have your will explicitly state how estate tax will be paid.

Avoiding The Biggest Mistakes Investors Make

Ted Tesser, CPA, Waterside Financial Services, 30 Waterside Plaza, #9G, New York 10010, which assists clients with tax, investment and retirement plan strategies. He is author of *The Serious Investor's Tax Survival Guide.* Traders' Library.

Mistake: **Not considering taxes until you begin preparing tax returns.** By then it's often too late to adopt strategies that could have cut the tax bill. Monitor the tax implications of your investments throughout the year, and periodically consult with your accountant.

Mistake: **Failing to take responsibility for tax and investment strategies.** Some investors rely completely on accountants, brokers, lawyers or other advisers. Of course, you should seek advice from tax and investment professionals, and use their expertise when implementing the strategies you decide upon. But it's important to remember that you are the person who will have to live with the results, so take responsibility and begin planning ahead now to make the most of your investments.

***Mistake:* Not quantifying tax consequences when comparing investment options.** This means looking at the dollar numbers earned after taxes from investments that receive different tax treatment.

Example: Consider the after-tax returns paid out over 10 years by a 10% taxable investment and an 8% tax-free or tax-deferred one. *Let's assume the investments were made by a person paying both a combined federal/state tax rate of 46%.*

	Before taxes		After taxes	
	10%	8%	10%	8%
Starting value	$10,000	$10,000	$10,000	$10,000
After 10 yrs.	$25,937	$21,589	$17,690	$21,589
Net return	$15,937	$11,589	$7,690	$11,589

Without working through the numbers, you are likely to be surprised that taxes cut the return from the higher-yielding investment by more than half (from $15,937 to $7,690)—and that the "lower" yielding investment in fact pays over 50% more after taxes ($11,589 vs. $7,690).

This example is simpler than most real cases. Some investments are partially taxable—for example, US Treasury issues are exempt from state tax but not from federal tax. Also, your own tax bracket will vary according to local law, income level, and the deductions and credits available to you. Although this calculation appears to be complicated, it is made simple with the worksheets I provide in my book.

In some cases, it may pay to increase tax exposure.

Example: If you live in a low- or no-tax state, it may pay to move funds from Treasury bonds to a portfolio of AAA-grade corporate bonds, to receive more income after taxes with almost the same safety, even though more total tax will be due.

The way to know which investment plan is best for you is to work through the numbers illustrating different options.

***Mistake:* Not making full use of retirement plans.** Tax-favored retirement programs let you obtain the higher returns offered by taxable investments in a tax-deferred environment. Today, personal retirement accounts such as IRAs, Simplified Employee Plans (SEPs), SIMPLEs and other qualified retirement plans can invest in almost anything except collectibles, mortgaged rental properties or a business in which you own an interest of 5% or more.

Many employer-provided 401(k) savings plans also offer self-directed investment options.

Common error: Thinking the main tax benefit from a retirement-plan contribution is the deduction for it, and making contributions at the last minute each year. In fact, over the long run, the tax-deferral obtained for compound retirement-plan earnings can be more valuable than the contribution deduction.

Example: A $3,000 IRA contribution saves $1,200 for a person in a 40% combined federal and state tax bracket. But a contribution made early in the year will also earn tax-deferred income within the account during the year. If the IRA earns 10%, $3,000 contributed a year before the deadline for just one year will earn $300, and over 30 years this $300 will compound to over $5,000—all of which is forfeited if you make your contribution at the last minute instead. If this contribution is made early each year, the increase in total retirement funds available is significant.

Make plan contributions as early in the year as possible. Also consider making contributions to a Roth IRA to obtain tax-free returns. While there's no deduction for contributions, the potential tax-free returns make this a great investment strategy.

ESTATE-PLANNING MISTAKE

Not averting estate taxes is a big mistake. Many people put off estate planning simply because thinking about death is not pleasant. Others underestimate the cost of estate taxes because they believe the applicable exemption amount ($1 million in 2003, rising gradually to $3.5 million by 2009) will protect them, or because they know they can pass assets tax-free to a spouse. *Traps:*

● **Your estate may be pushed far over the applicable exemption amount** by assets that you don't think of—such as life-insurance proceeds, the value of retirement accounts or appreciation in the value of your home.

● **Passing all your assets to your spouse can be a costly mistake,** because he/she will be able to pass no more than the applicable exemption amount to the next generation tax-free—while the two of you could plan together to pass double that amount.

Self-defense: Have the insurance on your life owned by your spouse, a child or a trust benefiting family members. You can provide the money needed to pay the premiums through annual tax-free gifts. When you die, the insurance proceeds will not be part of your taxable estate.

Self-defense: If your assets exceed the applicable exemption amount, pass up to that amount of your assets to children directly. *Alternative:* Use a trust that pays income to your spouse for life and then distributes its assets to your children, while leaving the remainder of your assets to your spouse. The applicable exemption amount will be available both for your disposition of property, and for your spouse's disposition of property inherited from you.

Self-defense: Use gifts to cut your estate. You can make gifts of up to $11,000 each to as many separate recipients as you wish in 2003 and 2004, free of gift tax. The limit is $22,000 if the gift is made jointly with your spouse. You can also make larger tax-free gifts by using part of your applicable exemption amount. Although this will reduce the amount that will be available to your estate, it can pay off if you expect the gift assets to appreciate in value before you die.

Gifts of income-producing assets to family members in lower income-tax brackets, such as children over age 14, can cut family income taxes as well. And gifts of appreciated assets to low-bracket family members can be cashed in by these family members with less gains tax resulting.

Strategy: When older family members have less than the applicable exemption amount in assets, a reverse gift can save big taxes. You can make gifts to them of assets that have appreciated in value. When they die, the assets will pass back to you or to other family members with stepped-up basis—revalued for tax purposes at market value—so potential gains tax on their appreciation is eliminated.

MORE TAX-CUTTING IDEAS

●**Earmark stock and mutual fund shares to maximize the tax advantage when shares are sold.**

Example: Say you bought shares in a stock or mutual fund at different times at different prices, and now wish to sell some. If you have price records for specific shares, you can sell the particular shares that produce the optimal gain or loss—perhaps to minimize taxable gain, or to maximize a capital loss that will protect other gains

from tax. If you do not have price records, the IRS will treat the first shares bought as the first sold.

●**Get the IRS to absorb part of the sales load on a mutual fund.** Do this by buying shares in a money fund offered by a family of funds. After three months or more, transfer out of the money fund and into one of the other fund options (stocks, bonds, etc.). The sales load will produce a loss on the sale of the money fund shares, which you can deduct or use to shelter other gains from tax.

●**Look for losses in your portfolio that can be used to offset gains or generate deductions.**

Tactic: Use tax swaps to produce paper losses that can shelter gains from tax. *How:* Sell a security to produce a loss, then immediately buy back a similar security.

Example: You can sell a bond and then buy back a bond from a different issuer that pays the same interest and has the same maturity date and credit rating. You get a loss deduction while maintaining your investment position. You cannot buy back the same security within 30 days to produce a tax loss.

The 30-day time limit does not apply if you sell a security to produce a gain. So if you already have a loss, you can sell a security at a gain, shelter the gain with the loss, then immediately buy back the same security, avoiding future tax that would otherwise have been due on its appreciation.

●**Consider "trader" status.** If you actively manage your portfolio to profit from market swings—instead of profiting from appreciation, and dividend and interest payments—you may qualify as a professional stock trader and become eligible to deduct investment costs on Schedule C as business expenses. This enables you to fully deduct items that provide only limited deductions to investors, such as interest and investment expenses.

Although you cannot make deductible contributions to SEP, SIMPLE or other qualified retirement plans from trading gains, trading gains are not subject to self-employment taxes either. Consult your tax adviser about how the rules may apply to your situation.

Leaving-the-Nest Loopholes

Edward Mendlowitz, CPA, partner, Mendlowitz Weitsen, LLP, CPAs, K2 Brier Hill Ct., East Brunswick, NJ 08816. He is author of several books on taxes, including *IRA Distributions: What You Should Know.* Practical Programs, Inc.

When your children have all moved out and you're huddled in an empty nest, give some thought to the tax breaks that await you...

Loophole: **Use the home sale exclusion to downsize your living space on a tax-free basis.** If you don't need the size home you now have, consider selling it and buying or renting a smaller place.

Break: You don't pay any tax on the profit you make when you sell your home unless the profit exceeds $500,000 on a joint return or $250,000 if you're single.

Requirement: You must have owned and used the home as your principal residence for at least two out of five years preceding the date you sell it. If you're married, it does not matter that the title is in one name as long as both spouses lived in the home for the requisite two years.

Use the proceeds from the sale of the house to buy a smaller home or to create income used to pay rent on a smaller home. Invest the balance for retirement income.

Loophole: **Modify your investment strategies.** You no longer are saving for your child's college education but instead for your own retirement. With this long-term focus, you can concentrate on tax-deferred investment vehicles, such as growth stocks and bonds and CDs maturing in five or more years.

Caution: In making personal investments, coordinate your holdings with assets in company 401(k) plans and your IRAs. Remember that distributions from these retirement plans are taxed as ordinary income at rates as high as 39.6%, regardless of the underlying investment producing that income.

Thus, concentrate bond holdings and dividend-paying stock inside these plans, while holding growth stock and stock mutual funds in personal investments. This will allow sales of these personal investments to yield capital gains taxed to you at no more than 20% (top IRS rate).

Loophole: **Rethink life insurance needs.** You may have been carrying life insurance as a vehicle to replace income if you died while your child was still in school. You may no longer need the same amount of coverage. *Consider the following...*

• **Reduce the level of coverage** and save on future premium costs.

• **Convert an existing policy** to a paid up policy and stop paying premiums altogether.

• **Donate the policy to charity** (for example, to set up a scholarship at your alma mater) and obtain a tax deduction. Without making a formal agreement to do so, continue donating cash each year to the school to cover the premiums and claim a deduction for your cash donations.

Caution: Before canceling a policy, consider whether it's needed for liquidity for your estate. If you die, make sure your estate has sufficient liquid assets—cash and securities—to pay administrative costs and estate taxes (due nine months after death).

Loophole: **Review your will.** Update your will to delete references to guardians you had named to care for your child in the event both you and your spouse died while he was a minor. Now that your child is grown, you may also want to consider eliminating trusts used for bequests to him and/or name him as your executor or coexecutor.

Loophole: **Review beneficiary designations.** When your child was young, you may have named custodians or trustees of trusts for his benefit as beneficiary of various assets. Now that he's mature, change your beneficiary designation to his name alone. *Review the following for designations you may have made...*

• **Company retirement plans.**

• **IRAs.**

• **Life insurance** (including company-provided coverage).

• **Annuities.**

Loophole: **Buy a long-term-care insurance policy.** If you're in your mid-50s or older, have assets you want to protect (especially if you need to protect a spouse), but don't have millions of dollars, then you should consider a long-term-care policy. The policy will pay for care in your home or in a nursing home if you have a condition or disease requiring custodial care (the type of care not covered by Medicare).

Without such coverage, you'll be forced to deplete the assets you built up over your lifetime before you'll qualify for Medicaid (a needs-based federal–state benefit program).

While odds are you won't need this care until you're much older, the younger you are when you take out the policy, the lower your premiums for life. Expect to pay about $2,000 annually, depending on the extent of the coverage you take.

Tax benefit: You can reduce your out-of-pocket cost for coverage by taking a deduction for premiums. Long-term-care premiums are deductible as itemized medical expenses (subject to the 7.5% floor) according to your age.

Deduction Limits for Long-Term Coverage Premiums for 2003

Age before year-end	Deduction limit
40 or younger	$250
41 through 50	470
51 through 60	940
61 through 70	2,510
71 and older	3,130

Caution: In buying a long-term-care policy, make sure it has a cost-of-living adjustment (inflation rider) to keep pace with increased medical costs over the years.

Loophole: **Do old age and estate planning for your parents.** Every suggestion for your estate planning review applies with equal force to your parents. *Make sure your parents have...*

●**Reviewed their wills and had them updated,** if necessary.

●**Reviewed the beneficiary designations they've made for IRAs,** insurance policies, etc.

●**Prepared and signed health-care proxies and living wills.** A health-care proxy will let you make medical decisions if your parent can't speak for himself. A living will sets out the kind of care your parent would want should he become seriously ill.

●**Purchased long-term-care insurance** to cover the cost of nursing-home care.

If your parents fail to get matters in order, you'll have additional problems when they become ill or die.

Retirement Plan Loopholes

Edward Mendlowitz, CPA, partner, Mendlowitz Weitsen, LLP, CPAs, K2 Brier Hill Ct., East Brunswick, NJ 08816. He is author of several books on taxes, including *IRA Distributions: What You Should Know.* Practical Programs, Inc.

Those who take full advantage of tax-deferred retirement plans have a real chance of living out their golden years in financial comfort. *Consider these tax-wise strategies...*

Loophole: **Shelter part-time business income with tax-deferred retirement plans.** People with sideline businesses can build big retirement nest eggs. They can set up a qualified retirement plan and effectively contribute up to 20% of "self-employed earned income." There's a limit—contributions to a defined contribution plan can't exceed $40,000 in 2003.

Alternative: A Simplified Employee Pension (SEP) plan is easier to administer than a qualified plan, requires no government filings and, in 2003, has the same limit as above.

Deadlines: Contributions to SEPs and qualified plans can be made as late as the return's extended due date—and still be deductible. *Catch:* A qualified plan must have been set up by December 31 for you to make deductible contributions to the plan next year.

New alternative: Companies that are making large amounts of money might want to consider a combination of defined benefit and defined contribution plans. The plan is complex, so consult your tax adviser.

Loophole: **Consider a SIMPLE retirement plan if your business earns $40,000 or less.** When your net income from a part-time or start-up business is less than $40,000, you may be better off with a Savings Incentive Match Plan for Employees (SIMPLE).

Reason: Assuming you're under age 50, you can put away the lesser of earned income or $9,000 in 2004 and make a matching contribution of as much as $9,000, depending on your income. With net income of $40,000, the match would be limited to $1,200. (The match is 3% of net income.)

You must set up a SIMPLE by October 1 to take deductions. After the plan is in place, you can make contributions up until the time you file your tax return.

Your Health And Your Taxes

Medical deductions have been allowed for the following items…

●**Apartment rent when the apartment was rented for an ailing dependent, because it was cheaper than hospitalization.**

Sidney J. Ungar, TC Memo 1963-159.

●**Elastic stockings recommended by a doctor for a person with varicose veins.**

Bessie Cohen, TC Memo 1/21/51.

●**Fluoridation device installed at home on the recommendation of a dentist.**

Revenue Ruling 64-267.

●**Stop smoking programs and prescription drugs to alleviate nicotine withdrawal.**

Revenue Ruling 99-28.

●**Hair removal through electrolysis performed by a licensed technician.**

Revenue Ruling 82-111.

●**Mattresses and boards bought solely to alleviate an arthritic condition.**

Revenue Ruling 55-261.

●**Mobile phone installed in a car to enable a person who has heart disease to immediately call a doctor in an emergency.**

George M. Womack, TC Memo 1975-232.

●**Telephone calls made long-distance to a therapist for psychological counseling.**

Letter Ruling 8034087.

●**Reclining chair bought on a doctor's advice to alleviate a heart condition.**

Revenue Ruling 58-155.

●**Transportation to AA meetings.**

Revenue Ruling 63-273.

John J. Tuozzolo, associated with the law firm Collins, Hannafin, Garamella, Jaber and Tuozzolo, PC, 148 Deer Hill Ave., Danbury, CT 06810.

Medical Deductions for Nursing Home Expenses

William G. Brennan, CPA/PFS, CFP, Capital Management Group, LLC, Washington, DC 20036.

Deductions for nursing home care fall into various areas of the tax law. There are different types of expenses that can be taken as medical deductions.

GUIDELINES

●**Long-term care services.** Costs of care in a nursing home for someone who is chronically ill that are not otherwise covered by insurance are treated as medical expenses deductible to the extent they exceed 7.5% of Adjusted Gross Income.

●**Long-term care insurance.** Premiums are treated as deductible medical expenses (the dollar amount depends on the insured's age for the year and is adjusted annually for inflation).

●**Lump-sum payments.** In some cases, a lump-sum fee is paid for lifetime care in a nursing home. The home should be able to provide you with a statement detailing the portion of the fee that will be required for the patient's future medical care, based on the nursing home's past experience. This amount is generally deductible in the year it is paid—even though it is for future medical care.

●**Dependents' medical expenses.** You may deduct medical expenses that you pay for your spouse or a qualifying dependent. Your parents or other relatives generally qualify as your dependents if you could claim a personal exemption for them on your tax return.

Note: The gross income test, which says that a dependent must earn less than $3,050 for 2003 ($3,100 in 2004), does not apply when claiming a dependent's medical expenses. The person must be your dependent either at the time care was received or when the expenses were paid.

●**Nature of services.** Whether or not an expense is deductible is determined by the nature of the services provided, not by the qualifications or experience of the provider.

Example: Assume you broke your hip and hired domestic help. If that person also helped with your in-home physical therapy, you could claim as a medical expense the charges for the time spent on your exercises. It wouldn't matter if the provider were not a qualified medical professional, as long as the physical therapy program was for legitimate medical reasons and was prescribed by a doctor. However, the cost of having the same person do housework would not be deductible. The fact that your injury made you unable to do the housework yourself is irrelevant.

Reminder: Medical expenses are only deductible to the extent that they have not been reimbursed by insurance and exceed 7.5% of your Adjusted Gross Income.

What the IRS Won't Tell You About Audits

Frederick W. Daily, Esq., tax attorney, 302 Warren Dr., San Francisco 94131. He is author of *Stand Up to the IRS* and *Tax Savvy for Small Business.* Both from Nolo Press.

Most taxpayers who face an IRS auditor fear how much the IRS knows about them. Auditors use this fear to intimidate taxpayers into making concessions and revealing more.

With the right tactics, you can keep the IRS auditor from learning any more...and help move the audit to its best possible conclusion.

WHAT THE IRS KNOWS

When you appear for an IRS audit, the auditor will have a file on your case that typically contains only three sources of information about you...

●**Tax return being audited.**

●**Your tax-filing history for the past six years.** This tells whether you filed tax returns ...were audited...or had a tax bill adjusted for those years. It does *not* include copies of prior years' tax returns.

●**List of third-party payments made to you** that were reported to the IRS on W-2 and 1099 forms or other information returns.

In 90% of cases, that's all the information the auditor will have about you before the audit begins.

If information that could cause you audit problems is not contained among these three items, the overwhelming odds are that the auditor doesn't have it.

Then the only way the auditor can get it is from you or by issuing a summons on the record keeper.

The auditor will not have: Copies of bank statements, motor vehicle records, property deeds or police records.

Nor will the auditor have copies of 1099s or other information returns sent to the IRS under a Social Security or taxpayer ID number other than yours.

Key: Don't volunteer any information to the IRS auditor that you aren't legally obligated to give—even if he/she asks for it.

THE BIGGEST MISTAKE

By far the most common audit mistake is providing copies of your other years' tax returns just because the audit notice asks you to do so.

Doing so greatly expands audit risk by giving the auditor many things to look at that he otherwise would not see.

Patterns of income and deduction amounts reported over multiple years may raise questions that would not arise when looking at just a single year's return.

The fact that an auditor doesn't have information doesn't mean he won't ask for it. So it's important to know what you are legally required to provide to an auditor...and what you aren't.

Rule: You are required to provide an IRS auditor only the information relating to the specific tax year listed in the audit notice. You are not required to provide information relating to any other tax year, except as it might relate to the year under audit—as carryover items might.

SAYING NO

Most people never imagine saying no to an IRS auditor for fear the auditor might retaliate by expanding the audit.

This fear is greatly exaggerated—retaliation is unlikely. IRS auditors have no incentive to expand an audit. They are evaluated by how quickly they close cases and work through their caseloads. And those caseloads are very heavy.

Inside secret: An auditor who feels there is good reason to examine another year's tax return can obtain it from the IRS's own files, but it may take weeks or months for the IRS to retrieve that old return. One who doesn't take the trouble to do so probably is "just fishing" for the taxpayer to reveal something.

The way to say *no* safely to such an auditor is to respond politely, "I don't believe that this relates to the year or issues being examined." Almost always, that will end the matter.

THE RIGHT REPRESENTATION

If there is information you want to protect from the IRS, consider being represented at your audit by a tax professional—instead of attending the audit personally. They are experienced at dealing with auditors.

A professional representative will not have the answers to some of the auditor's questions —including any information that you might reveal unintentionally.

Your representative will ask the auditor to put the request in writing. Then, in responding to a written request, your representative can discuss things with you and draft as narrow an answer as possible.

The whole process will slow the audit, which the auditor doesn't want. So attempts by the auditor to "go fishing" will be frustrated.

The IRS cannot conduct a "lifestyle or economic reality audit," asking questions that are unrelated to the preparation of the return being examined, unless it already has a reasonable indication that income has been understated.

A professional representative will also prevent your emotions or personal factors from complicating an audit. No matter how difficult the audit may be, your representative should be able to deal with the auditor in a calm and professional manner.

The fee you pay may be a bargain for both the taxes it saves and the anxiety you avoid by not dealing with the auditor personally.

And, last but not least, fees paid to a tax professional for defending an audit are deductible.

5

Your Insurance Edge

Early Retirement & Social Security Benefits

The age at which you can begin to collect full Social Security retirement benefits is going up. It will rise gradually, in two-month increments, from age 65 for persons born in 1938 and later, to age 67 in the year 2027.

Ultimate impact: Persons born in 1960 and later won't be able to collect full benefits until they reach age 67. (Refer to the chart below).

Retirement Age Increases

The full retirement age will increase in stages to 66 through 2009, and then, starting in 2022, gradually to 67 by 2027.

Year of Birth	Age for Full Benefits
1937 and earlier	65
1938	65 & 2 months
1939	65 & 4 months
1940	65 & 6 months
1941	65 & 8 months
1942	65 & 10 months
1943 through 1954	66
1955	66 & 2 months
1956	66 & 4 months
1957	66 & 6 months
1958	66 & 8 months
1959	66 & 10 months
1960 and later	67

The *early retirement age,* however, will *not* change. You'll still be able to begin collecting *reduced* Social Security benefits at age 62.

REDUCED BENEFITS

Quandary: When you opt for early retirement, your monthly benefits are reduced from what you'd get if you waited until the full retirement age to start collecting Social Security.

The benefit reduction for taking early retirement at 62 is 20% of what you'd get if you waited until age 65. Those who retire early

Peter J. Strauss, Esq., a partner in the law firm Epstein Becker & Green, PC, 250 Park Ave., New York 10177. He is a fellow of the National Academy of Elder Law Attorneys and coauthor of *The Elder Law Handbook—A Legal and Financial Survival Guide for Caregivers and Seniors.* Facts on File.

must take a percentage reduction for each month that they retire before their "full" retirement age. A percentage of the full benefit is lopped off.

The percentage of full benefits lost is five-ninths of 1% for the first 36 months of retirement before full retirement age and five-twelfths of 1% for each additional month. (The chart below spells out the reductions for various ages.)

Reduction in Retirement Benefits
Depending On Early and Full Retirement Age

EARLY RETIREMENT AGE	PERCENTAGE BENEFIT REDUCTION...		
	for those with full retirement age of 65	for those with full retirement age of 66	for those with full retirement age of 67
62	20%	25%	30%
63	13⅓%	20%	25%
64	6⅔%	13⅓%	20%
65	—	6⅔%	13⅓%
66	—	—	6⅔%

Example 1: A person who opts for early retirement at age 62 would have his/her monthly Social Security benefit check permanently reduced by 20% of the full retirement benefit. So, if benefits at 65 would be $1,000 a month, taking retirement at 62 will reduce benefits to $800 a month.

Example 2: Someone born after 1959 who takes early retirement at age 62 (when the full retirement age has gone up to 67) will have benefits reduced by 30%. If full benefits are $1,000 a month, early retirement benefits will be $700 a month.

If you're thinking about early retirement, you need to get an estimate of your benefits. This is sent to you automatically about three months before your birthday if you are 25 years old or older. If you don't receive it, request it from the Social Security Administration at 800-772-1213 or from its Web site at *www.ssa.gov.*

SHOULD I TAKE EARLY RETIREMENT?

Opting for early retirement means that benefits commence early, before age 65, even though at a reduced rate.

Advantage: This gives you additional years of collecting benefits.

Bottom line: Suppose your full retirement age is 65 years, four months, but you take early retirement at 62 with reduced benefits. In terms of total benefits, you'll be ahead of what you would have received had you waited until age 65 to start collecting, until you reach a "crossover

point" at age 77. Beyond that point your total benefits would be greater if you retired at age 65.

As the full retirement age increases to age 67 (and the reduction in early retirement benefits also increases), it will take about 14 years (until the same age of 77) before the later retiree can catch up with the early retiree in total benefits received.

WORKING WHILE COLLECTING

• **Under current law, retirement benefits are reduced** for those *under the full retirement age* if their earnings from employment exceed a set amount ($11,520 in 2003). Then, Social Security benefits are reduced by $1 for each $2 of excess earnings.

• **Those who have attained the full retirement age** and still working are not subject to an earnings penalty and can earn any amount without a reduction in benefits.

Note: The earnings limit does not change even though the full retirement age has been increased.

If you plan to work full time or otherwise earn more than the modest earnings limit for those under age 65, it may not make sense to commence benefits before retirement.

MEDICARE

Benefits under Medicare do not start before age 65. This is so even if you opt for early retirement at age 62.

However, the Medicare starting age does not change. This is the case even though the Social Security full retirement age will increase. The Medicare eligibility age remains 65.

DECISIONS, DECISIONS

Whether or not to start receiving Social Security benefits at the early retirement age depends on your personal situation. *Questions to ask yourself...*

• **Life expectancy.** What is your personal health history (and family health history)? If you do not anticipate a long life, then opting for early commencement of benefits may prove more financially rewarding than waiting until your normal retirement age.

• **Capacity for work.** If you are planning to continue at a job or to work at your own business, then waiting until you cease working—or, depending on your earnings, at least attain age 65—may make much more sense for you than starting benefits early.

●**Deduct losses.** At year-end, take "paper" investment losses to offset income from gains and up to $3,000 of ordinary income. You can repurchase the loss investment after 31 days, or a similar, but not identical one, immediately.

Social Security Tax-Saving Strategy

Barbara Weltman, an attorney with offices in Millwood, NY, and author of J.K. Lasser's New Rules for Small Business Taxes *(John Wiley & Sons) and* Bottom Line's Very Shrewd Money Book *(Bottom Line Books).*

Social Security recipients lose a significant portion of benefits to taxes if their income exceeds certain limits. More specifically, when Modified Adjusted Gross Income (MAGI) —which is Adjusted Gross Income increased by tax-free interest on municipal bonds, certain exclusions and a portion of Social Security benefits—exceeds…

●**$32,000 on a joint return or $25,000 on a single return,** up to 50% of Social Security benefits are included in taxable income.

●**$44,000 on a joint return, $34,000 on a single return or zero if married filing separately,** up to 85% of Social Security benefits are included in taxable income.

TAX-SAVING STRATEGY

Reduce tax on your Social Security benefits by reducing your MAGI. *How…*

●**Defer income.** Invest for growth rather than income. Postpone realizing gains on investments and taking discretionary distributions from IRAs and other retirement plans.

●**Make tax-free investments.** Roth IRA payouts of earnings are tax free if certain conditions are met, so fund a Roth IRA rather than a regular IRA.

Interest from tax-free municipal bonds is included in MAGI for purposes of determining tax on Social Security benefits—but municipals pay a lower interest rate than taxable bonds.

●**Shift income.** Make estate-tax-reducing gifts of property to younger family members by shifting income-producing property.

Social Security Rip-off

There are now four million illegal users of fake Social Security numbers. *Result:* Someone else may be receiving your benefits.

Self-defense: Call the Social Security Administration (800-772-1213) to request your summary statement of earnings. Compare it with your past W-2 statements. Lower annual figures may mean benefits are being misdirected. Higher figures could mean your number has been stolen and could attract the IRS, which scans this data to uncover hidden income.

Statute of limitations for an appeal: Three years, three months, and three days from the contested year.

How You Can Make the Most of Medicare Coverage

David S. Landay, Esq., president of NVR, Inc., a New York City company that provides financial counseling to people who have serious health conditions. He is author of Be Prepared: The Complete Financial, Legal and Practical Guide to Living with Cancer, HIV and Other Life-Challenging Conditions. *St. Martin's Press.*

As you may already know, Medicare has two key advantages over private health insurance. It costs little (or nothing) and is available to every US citizen or legal resident age 65 or older—even those with preexisting conditions that would make them ineligible for private insurance.

Eligible people can receive an enrollment form in the mail a few months before turning 65. Once they fill it out and send it back, they're in the program.

But like most federal programs, Medicare is enormously complex. To help you take full advantage of it, we spoke with David S. Landay, a lawyer specializing in counseling people with serious illness…

•I know that Medicare has two parts. Could you please explain them? Part A covers in-patient hospital care and—under some circumstances—home health care, treatment in a nursing facility and hospice care.

This part of the program is free to any Medicare enrollee who has accumulated—or whose spouse has accumulated—about 40 credits. That generally means 10 years of full-time work.

Part B covers doctors' fees, outpatient medical and surgical services, diagnostic tests and more. This part is optional. It costs $58.70 per month in 2003.

You'll automatically be enrolled in Part A if you complete the Medicare application. When you enroll in Part A, you're automatically enrolled in Part B, unless you check a box on the enrollment form.

•Is Part B worth the expense? For most people, the answer is yes. Otherwise, unless you're covered by private insurance, you'll be responsible for paying doctors' fees as well as the costs of diagnostic tests. Compared with other insurance plans, the monthly premium is very reasonable.

Some people decline Part B because they're covered by a group insurance plan at work and feel they don't need additional coverage.

This may be unwise, particularly for people who have a medical problem or who come from a family with a history of medical problems, since Part B picks up many of the co-payments and deductibles.

•Where does Medigap coverage fit in? Since Medicare doesn't cover everything, many people get additional coverage through a so-called Medigap policy.

Medigap policies are sold by private insurance companies, but the benefits they offer are standardized. This makes it easy to compare prices and coverage levels among companies.

There are 10 Medigap policies, designated by the letters A through J. Plan A provides the most basic coverage, Plan J the most comprehensive. Each policy covers some or all of Medicare's coinsurance payments. A few pay the deductibles as well.

Which plan makes sense for you depends upon your health, the cost of any prescription medications you take and, of course, what you can afford to pay in monthly premiums.

Medigap policies can be confusing, and there's a great deal of overlap among them. For free help in picking one, call your state health insurance assistance program. Look in your phone book in the state government section under "Insurance" or "Department of Insurance."

•Can I switch Medigap policies if my health starts to decline? Yes, but try to do so within six months of the time you first enroll in the program. Otherwise, you'll have to pay a higher premium because of your preexisting condition.

By law, every Medigap policy comes with a money-back guarantee. If you're dissatisfied with the coverage, ask for a refund and switch to another insurer.

•What's the best policy for covering prescription drugs? The most comprehensive Medigap policy, Plan J, pays 50% of the cost of prescription drugs up to an annual maximum of $3,000. Plans H and I also pay 50% of the cost, but the annual cap will be lower.

Except for medications you receive in the hospital and some cancer drugs, Medicare does not pay the cost of medications.

•What is Medicare managed care? It's an arrangement whereby an HMO or another managed-care program provides Medicare coverage.

Signing your benefits over to an HMO typically extends your coverage to things not traditionally covered by Medicare—dental care, hearing aids, prescription medications, etc. And the fees with a Medicare HMO are more predictable than those in fee-for-service coverage.

The disadvantages with this arrangement are the same as those you would face in any managed-care organization. You'll have to choose a primary-care physician from the plan's roster, and you'll have to get all of your care within the plan. The plan—and not you—will be managing your care.

If you sign up for managed care and decide you're unhappy with your treatment, you can switch back to standard Medicare at any time.

• **How do I protect myself in case I need long-term care?** Neither Medicare nor the various Medigap policies pay for indefinite nursing home care. Review your policies carefully to determine exactly what's covered, and then decide whether you need extra insurance. Consult a lawyer, social worker or your insurance broker if you need assistance.

A companion program to Medicare, Medicaid does provide long-term nursing care.

Ordinarily, only low-income people and those who meet certain financial criteria are eligible for Medicaid. But home owners and others with substantial financial assets who anticipate that they may need extended long-term care should consult a lawyer. In many cases, it's possible to take advantage of the Medicaid safety net without liquidating all of your assets.

To Find a Good Archer Medical Savings Account (MSA)...

Shop around. Fees and interest rates for Archer MSAs vary widely. Carefully review the details of the savings account part of the MSA. Think of it as a money market account. Compare interest rates...enrollment fees...monthly membership fees...withdrawal process. *Also:* Check with Independent Insurance Agents and Brokers of America, 800-221-7917 or *www.iiaa. org,* for a free comparison of offerings. Check separately with insurers that sell exclusively through their own networks of agents.

Edward Slott, CPA, E. Slott & Co., 100 Merrick Rd., Rockville Centre, NY 11570. He is editor of *Ed Slott's IRA Advisor. www.irahelp.com.*

How to Choose the Best Health Insurance

Bruce Pyenson and Jim O'Connor, principals with Milliman & Robertson, a consulting firm that works with insurance companies and health-care providers, Two Pennsylvania Plaza, New York 10121. Mr. Pyenson is author of several books, including *J.K. Lasser's Employee Benefits for Small Business.* Prentice-Hall.

Most health insurance is provided through group policies in the workplace. But there are millions of people who are self-employed or between jobs who have to find individual coverage on their own. Medicare also offers different coverage options.

While there are plenty of good policies out there, finding one that fits your needs takes some digging.

SIZE UP YOUR NEEDS

The health-care needs of families with young children are different from those of singles starting new jobs...couples without children...and empty nesters. Families with infants want a full range of care that covers everything from routine vaccinations to ear infections. Healthy singles may only need bare-bones coverage for unexpected catastrophes.

In these days of managed care, there are four basic types of coverage...

HEALTH MAINTENANCE ORGANIZATIONS (HMOs)

A very prevalent type of group coverage, HMOs provide comprehensive medical care through networks of physicians. Typically, you pay $5 or $10 per in-network doctor visit and don't have to fill out forms after each appointment or worry about meeting a deductible requirement.

If you have a special health problem, you typically must first consult your primary care physician—also known as the *gatekeeper.* This physician may treat you or may refer you to a specialist. If you decide to use an out-of-network specialist or hospital, coverage—if any —is limited.

With limited choice about which doctors and hospitals to use and limited access to specialists, these plans are usually the most economical. Your out-of-pocket costs are fairly low for the wide range of coverage you get.

Best for: People with children who are new to a community—they have no relationships with physicians or hospitals. Also good for people with children whose current physician and hospital are part of the HMO network.

PREFERRED PROVIDER ORGANIZATIONS (PPOs)

These types of policies—which are more expensive than comparable HMOs—give you the ability to go outside the plan network for your medical care. Most PPO plans don't have a gatekeeper system, so you usually don't need approval to see specialists.

If you see a physician within the network, you get one level of benefits (usually 80% of a claim is covered). If you see a physician outside the network, you get another, lower level of benefits (only 60% to 70% of the claim might be covered).

Best for: People who want more choice about health-care providers...and whose doctors are part of the PPO network.

INDEMNITY POLICIES

These plans pay benefits for most services no matter what doctor or hospital you go to. Such traditional policies appeal to people who have lived in the same community for a long time and have established ties to physicians and hospitals. While they guarantee you the most latitude in terms of choosing your health-care providers, indemnity plans are also the most expensive. Sometimes people who want the flexibility of an indemnity policy opt for high deductibles of as much as $10,000 to reduce monthly premiums.

"ANY DOCTOR" POLICIES

These hybrid plans use a PPO approach for hospitals but allow you to see any licensed physicians you wish. They are cheaper than indemnity policies but more expensive than full-fledged PPOs.

Best for: People who feel comfortable with the hospitals in the PPO network but want the flexibility of using any doctor they choose.

FINDING THE BEST PLAN

●**Research what is available in your state.** Because each state regulates insurance, choices will be limited. Not all insurance companies offer policies in all states. And a company's policies may be different in different states.

If your car and homeowner's insurance is with a company that sells through a network of agents, start by calling your agent.

If you belong to a professional or trade group or a college alumni association, find out if these organizations offer special health policies for members. Such policies often cost less than individual policies but more than group policies. If you have chronic health problems, these policies can be a good deal since you may not be able to get an affordable policy on your own.

●**Determine what different types of policies will cost you.** Call two major companies that write health insurance nationwide.

For HMOs: Aetna (*www.aetna.com/index. htm,* 800-872-3862)...United Health Group (*www.unitedhealthgroup.com,* 877-311-7848).

For PPOs, "Any Doctor" and indemnity: Fortis Health (800-211-1193)...Mutual of Omaha (*www.mutualofomaha.com,* 800-775-6000).

Simplify your search by using the Internet. Two sites that provide up to 20 different premium quotes are *www.insure.com* and *www. insweb.com.*

Be sure to get the answers to some crucial questions...

●**Does the plan cover maternity, mental health and substance abuse?**

●**What are the rules concerning preexisting conditions** (health problems you had before taking out the policy)?

●**Ask the insurer about rate increases.** You want to know how often and by how much insurers boost their premiums each year. Ask what the increases have been for the past several years. Some companies charge very low initial rates but then raise premiums by a large amount. Rate increases are currently running 10% to 15% a year. If your insurer is boosting rates by 30% or more annually, it's time to shop around.

●**Find out if customers are satisfied.** Get the names of current HMO members. Ask if they've experienced delays in obtaining membership cards, problems communicating with physicians, difficulty getting pharmacies to accept their coverage, trouble getting doctor's appointments quickly or trouble getting prompt referrals to specialists.

You can also call your state insurance or health department (they usually are listed in the state government pages of your telephone directory). Some states develop statistics that indicate complaint ratios of HMOs.

If you have an established doctor, you might also call him/her for feedback on the plan you are considering, particularly for HMOs.

How to Outsmart Your Managed-Care Organization

Bruce A. Barron, MD, PhD, associate professor of clinical obstetrics and gynecology at Columbia–Presbyterian Medical Center and a former senior medical director at Empire Blue Cross/Blue Shield, both in New York City. He is author of *Outsmarting Managed Care: A Doctor Shares His Insider's Secrets to Getting the Health Care You Want*. Times Books.

Before the era of managed care, people who sought medical care were known as patients.

Nowadays many of us are customers of a health-maintenance organization, preferred-provider organization or another managed-care organization (MCO).

Customers of MCOs don't always get what they pay for...

•**Some MCOs deny patients key diagnostic tests.**

•**Some MCOs refuse to pay for costly medications.**

•**Some MCOs push customers into surgery with a surgeon who has substandard training**—in a second-rate hospital.

There's really no need to be a victim of managed care. *Here's how to fight back...*

PLAIN FACTS ABOUT MCOs

Managed care is big business. Your doctor may focus on easing symptoms and healing disease, but MCOs inevitably focus on the *bottom line*. This may be especially true of for-profit MCOs, which now constitute the majority of plans. Whatever their fancy brochure says, their allegiance is to their shareholders—not to you.

Like all businesses, MCOs try to maximize revenues while minimizing expenditures. Raising premiums is one way MCOs improve their bottom lines. They also reduce the *medical loss ratio*. In plain English, that means delivering as little health care as possible.

CHOOSING A DOCTOR

In most MCOs, customers must choose a primary-care physician from a roster of participating doctors. These doctors are listed by medical specialty.

Trap: Just because a doctor is listed as an internist, cardiologist, etc., does not mean he/she has had the extra training and has passed the rigorous tests required for board certification.

It's common for MCOs to hire doctors who are not board-certified, even though board certification has long been considered a mark of medical expertise.

What to do: Call your MCO or the doctor's office to find out about board certification.

For a list of board-certified physicians in the US, consult the *Directory of Medical Specialists*. This book—available at most public libraries—also details doctors' training, experience, etc.

The American Medical Association offers similar information on its Web site, *www.ama-assn.org.* Or you can contact the American Board of Medical Specialties at 866-ASK-ABMS. *www.abms.org.*

Important: If a doctor you are considering practices as part of a group, check the credentials of his partners, too.

The doctor you select must be your ally. Will he help you fight for proper medical care? Will he help you get critical tests, treatments and referrals even if the MCO doesn't want to provide them?

Although it is hard to know how a doctor will behave until a problem arises, it is important to find out his general feelings on the subject.

GETTING FIRST-RATE CARE

Some doctors like to joke that managed care is fine—as long as you don't get sick. Unfortunately, the joke contains a kernel of truth. And the more serious your illness, the harder it can be to get state-of-the-art medical care.

Example: An endoscopic examination of the stomach is often the best way to check for a peptic ulcer. But an MCO may refuse to cover endoscopy, arguing that this $1,200 procedure falls outside its "practice guidelines."

Each time you discuss treatment options with your doctor, ask whether his recommendations are constrained by rules set down by the MCO.

If so, ask what he *would* do—which tests, procedures, medications, etc., he would recommend—if there were no such constraints.

If this recommendation differs from his original one, ask that he explain his position *in writing*. That way, you'll have a record if you need to appeal an MCO decision.

If you need a specialist, do the ones affiliated with the MCO have the best qualifications? Or are there better specialists outside of the MCO's network?

If you need surgery, how do the surgical track records of hospitals affiliated with the MCO compare with the track records of hospitals unaffiliated with the MCO?

Death rates tend to be much lower in hospitals that do a high volume of a given procedure.

If you believe the MCO's rules will adversely affect your health, the MCO is required *by law* in some states to review your case. But you'll have a battle on your hands.

TAKING IT TO THE TOP

When you telephone the MCO to appeal a decision, you'll probably talk first to a "case manager." In many cases, this person is a nurse who simply explains the MCO's treatment guidelines.

If the case manager rejects your appeal, insist on speaking to a "medical director"—a doctor who works for the MCO.

Do *not* let yourself be intimidated. Nonphysicians tend to be deferential around medical doctors. That's inappropriate here. You're dealing not with Marcus Welby, but with a representative of a giant corporation.

Find out the medical director's specialty. If he's a dermatologist and you have cancer, he may know less about your condition than you do. In such a case, ask to speak to a medical director who has training in oncology.

If this medical director rules against you, ask to speak with the MCO's "medical director for policy." This company official has greater power to help you.

Crucial: Each time you speak with a representative of the MCO, ask for a report of the conversation or ruling *in writing*. It's essential that you create a paper trail. That way, you'll have all the documentation needed if you choose to get an external review, in which an expert outside the MCO evaluates your case.

At some point as you make your way up the hierarchy, the MCO will probably give in to your demands.

If the MCO does not give in, file a complaint with the agency that regulates insurance companies. In some states, it's the department of consumer affairs.

Another option: Contact the media. When TV or newspaper reporters cover cases in which an MCO customer has been denied care, the MCO almost always capitulates.

Long-Term-Care Insurance And Your Taxes

Thomas Orr, CPA, partner with the accounting firm Bregante & Co., 180 Howard St., San Francisco 94105. The head of his firm's insurance tax practice, he has published opinions on the taxability of long-term-care insurance.

The *Health Insurance Portability and Accountability Act* (HIPAA) of 1996 divided the world of long-term-care insurance (LTC) into two types of policies—tax-qualified and non-tax-qualified.

Tax-qualified policies' major benefits...

•**Premiums may be tax deductible.** The deductions for long-term-care insurance range up to set limits, depending on your age each year, according to the following schedule for 2003...

Age	Maximum Deduction
40 or under	$250
41–50	470
51–60	940
61–70	2,510
71+	3,130

●**Benefits you receive won't be taxable.** This exclusion applies to amounts received up to $220 per day in 2003, indexed for inflation, on long-term-care contracts that pay a per diem benefit.

Bonus benefit: Amounts over $220 per day also will be excluded if the money reimburses the policyholder for LTC expenses.

TESTS FOR TAX BENEFITS

In order to qualify for these tax benefits, LTC policies must meet certain key standards…

●**The insured individual must be unable to perform** at least two of the following "activities of daily living" (ADLs)—eating, bathing, dressing, getting out of bed, toileting and continence.

●**A licensed health-care professional** must certify that these conditions will last for at least 90 days.

BARRIERS TO BENEFITS

Even with tax-qualified policies the tax benefits aren't certain.

Example: Premiums are deductible only if you itemize.

Trap: Premiums on a tax-qualified policy are added to other medical expenses and only those expenses that exceed 7.5% of your AGI are deductible.

Example: Frank Fisher is a 61-year-old single taxpayer with $70,000 in AGI. Assume he's in the 27% tax bracket. Only those medical expenses over $5,250 per year are deductible and then, only if he itemizes deductions.

Suppose Mr. Fisher has $4,588 in total medical expenses this year, not counting long-term-care premiums. If he pays a $2,200 premium for a tax-qualified LTC policy, he'd raise his total medical expenses to $6,788. His federal tax savings from his deductible LTC policy would be less than $415.

If Mr. Fisher had $100,000 in AGI, the LTC deduction would have no value, because his total medical expenses would be well under 7.5% of his AGI.

The age limits given in the chart on page 64 further restrict deductions for LTC insurance premiums.

As a result, many taxpayers won't be able to deduct all or part of their LTC premiums, even if they have a tax-qualified policy.

Tax professionals generally believe that the premiums on a tax-qualified policy will be deductible, as long as all the conditions are met. Premiums on a nonqualified policy won't be deductible.

CONTROVERSY

However, the taxability of policy benefits is a controversial issue.

Example: Mary Adams, an elderly widow, goes into a nursing home and collects benefits of $100 per day under her LTC policy. That's $36,500 a year. Will those benefits be considered taxable income? *Some answers…*

●**They won't be taxable income if Mary owns a tax-qualified policy.**

●**They won't be taxable income if Mary has an LTC policy** bought before 1997, because such policies were grandfathered by HIPAA.

Strategy: If you have such a policy, don't exchange it or modify it without careful consideration.

If Mary owns a post-1996, nonqualified policy, though, her $36,500 is not specifically excluded from income—it is not included in income either.

TRACKING THE TAX CODE

It is likely that such benefits are not meant to be included in income. Prior to the passage of HIPAA, benefits received under an LTC policy were treated as nontaxable and the premiums paid for such coverage were not deductible.

Accordingly, benefits received now under a nonqualified LTC contract probably should not be included in income. This is especially true for those benefits that reimburse the policyholder for the expenses of qualified long-term-care services.

IRS position: Informally, an IRS spokesman has declared that benefits from a nonqualified LTC policy likely will be considered income if the money was spent to help an elderly individual go shopping—but benefits used for custodial care won't be taxed.

Paper trail: Insurance companies must report LTC benefit payments to the IRS, noting whether or not the policy is tax qualified. This will make it easier for the IRS to pinpoint such benefits.

However, the federal tax return doesn't have a line specifically for the inclusion of LTC benefits and the instructions for the "other income" line of Form 1040 are unclear, to say the least, when it comes to benefits from a nonqualified LTC policy.

Key: In most cases, the after-tax cost of paying tax on LTC benefits would wind up being modest, in relation to the benefits received.

WEIGHING THE ALTERNATIVES

As indicated, not all long-term-care policies meet these standards. *However, some nonqualified policies may provide more benefits than tax-qualified policies...*

•**Nonqualified policies may pay if policyholders can't meet the two-activities-of-daily-living test** but are unable to perform other functions, such as walking around or getting to a doctor's appointment.

•**Nonqualified policies generally don't include a 90-day test,** so they may pay off in cases of shorter term disabilities.

•**Some require only that a doctor state a patient can't care for himself/herself** any more and that care is "medically necessary."

Thus, buying a nonqualified LTC insurance policy means you won't be able to deduct your premiums—which you might not be able to deduct anyway. In a worst case scenario, you might owe some tax on any benefits received.

Trade-off: In return for such tax disadvantages, you might be getting a policy that provides better coverage.

Faced with a choice between safer tax benefits and more comprehensive coverage, how should you or your elderly parents decide?

One option is to buy a nonqualified policy that includes an option to convert to a tax-qualified policy if the tax situation becomes clearer—and such a conversion seems desirable. That may prove to be a prudent hedge against another round of "tax simplification."

If you do buy a policy with a conversion feature, make sure...

•**You won't have to pay a higher premium** because of your age at the time of conversion.

•**You won't incur tax consequences** due to a policy exchange.

Long-Term Care ...New Option

A problem with obtaining long-term-care insurance is that most people won't need long-term care, in which case the expensive premiums are wasted.

But new combined life insurance/long-term-care policies address this problem. The policies pay a standard life insurance benefit, but should you need long-term care, you can tap the policy benefit tax free. The life insurance benefit may be reduced by amounts spent on care needs. Whether you eventually need care or not, your premiums will earn a return. Ask your insurance adviser for details.

Lee Slavutin, MD, CPC, CLU, principal of Stern Slavutin-2 Inc., insurance and estate planners, 530 Fifth Ave., New York 10036.

Give Your Life Insurance Policy a Checkup

Glenn Daily, a fee-only insurance consultant and author of Life Insurance Sense and Nonsense, *available from the author.*

A fter a life insurance policy is purchased, most people put the papers in a file and just pay the premium when the bill arrives.

Problem: A family's life insurance needs may change every few years.

Depending upon the type of policy you own, performing a life insurance checkup might take as little as an hour or so and save you big, big money.

Before you begin...

•**Understand the policy you already own.** Many people don't know what type of insurance coverage they have. *Questions to ask yourself...*

•Do you have a term...whole life...universal...or variable universal policy? If you're uncertain, review your policies—or ask your life insurance agent for in-depth explanations.

In short, term insurance provides coverage for a set period of time—such as 10 years. The other three types are cash-value policies, meaning that in addition to a death benefit, part of your premium is placed in a savings vehicle and can be withdrawn or borrowed. Each type has different fees and investment returns. The checkup process is different for each one.

●How much insurance coverage do you have currently? Chances are you've forgotten the amount, so verify it with the company or agent. Coverage levels that seemed appropriate even four or five years ago may look out-of-date when compared with your family's current financial realities.

Important: If you also receive life insurance coverage from your employer, add that to any personal policies you own to obtain your total coverage level.

●**Gather all relevant policy documentation.** If you own a cash-value policy—whole life, universal or variable life—pull your most recent annual statement and ask your agent for an up-to-date, in-force illustration that estimates your future premium and policy values based on current assumptions. For term policies, the illustration will show you estimated premiums.

●**Compare existing total coverage with your family's actual insurance needs.** A family's insurance needs keep changing. Many financial planning books have worksheets to estimate insurance needs.

Key events that signal more coverage is probably needed: Birth of a child…purchase of a home…new job with a higher salary.

Key events that signal less coverage is probably needed: Child's college graduation…divorce…retirement.

●**Start thinking about adjusting your coverage levels to suit your family's current needs.** If you don't need as much coverage as you did in the past, cutting your annual premiums can be as simple as calling your agent and asking to reduce your coverage.

Opportunity: If your insurer permits you to reduce the face amount of an existing policy, you'll be able to skip new application fees and a medical exam. Find out if there are any changes or tax consequences before you act.

If your insurance needs have increased, it may be possible to reduce your costs. *Here's how to tell, depending on the type of insurance you own…*

●**Term insurance.** This is the quickest, easiest checkup to perform. *Goal:* To determine if your premiums are attractive compared with those offered by your insurer's competitors.

Strategy: Call Quotesmith (800-556-9393) for free comparisons. If competitors' prices are lower, it may be time to switch to another insurer. *It may be time to switch if…*

●Your family's insurance needs change.

●Your insurer raises your premiums unexpectedly.

●You own a level-premium term policy—which means you are charged the same premium for a set number of years—and the term is about to expire.

●**Cash-value insurance.** With cash-value policies—which provide coverage plus a savings account or investment—the checkup process is more complicated but not impossible. *Whether you own a whole life, universal or variable universal policy, start with these two steps:*

●Order a rate-of-return analysis from the Consumer Federation of America (CFA) (202-387-6121). CFA takes the values from your in-force illustration and computes a rate of return you can compare with other policies and investments.

Mistake: Automatically canceling a cash-value policy because you learn that it is underperforming the market. You have paid a lot in commissions, and there is going to be a charge to forfeit the policy.

Better: Consult with your agent about other options if you're unhappy with your policy. Such options may include repaying a loan, using dividends to buy paid-up additions or shrinking the face value of your policy.

●Evaluate your current insurer's financial stability. Ask your agent to send you current, full-scale reports on your insurer from rating agencies—A.M. Best, Standard & Poor's, Moody's and Duff & Phelps. If the ratings look shaky, consult your agent about your options.

●**Whole life insurance.** If you determine that your insurer is stable and your policy's investment returns are competitive, look for ways to get better value from your policy.

Helpful: Pay premiums annually rather than paying them semiannually...quarterly...or monthly. *Savings:* 8% to 12% in interest charges.

Use dividends to buy paid-up additions. This is one of the best bargains offered by insurers—equivalent to making a single-premium, no-commission addition to your coverage.

Scrutinize policy riders. If you can eliminate extra cost benefits that you no longer need, you'll lower premiums.

●**Universal life insurance allows policyholders to pay more or less than the suggested premium.** If they pay less, the policy will last for fewer years than established at the outset because less money is going to maintain the policy.

Key: Determine whether the amount you plan to pay in premiums is sufficient to keep your policy going as long as you'll need it.

Ask your agent when the policy will expire under various assumptions about premium payments and interest rates.

Important: You're particularly vulnerable if you bought your policy during the 1980s, when interest rates were higher than today. If your insurer anticipated a much higher rate of return than your policy has actually earned, your coverage may expire sooner than you expect or desire unless you take steps now to increase the premium or reduce coverage.

●**Check competitors.** If you need to increase coverage, make certain that what your insurer is offering still seems competitive. In addition to the Consumer Federation of America, call the Wholesale Insurance Network to get comparisons with new low-load policies. They charge lower commissions so more of your premium goes toward insurance.

Life Insurance If You Can't Pass a Physical

Can't pass the life insurance physical? Don't give up—there may be a way.

Find an agent who knows his way with insurance companies. Their standards vary on overweight, blood pressure, smoking, and other medical conditions. *Example:* Six-foot middle-aged man weighing 270 pounds—many companies would add a big surcharge premium for his weight. But one company will insure him with no surcharge at all.

The agent's job is to find the exceptional company and know how to present the application in the most favorable light. Few agents do this well. You've got to insist the agent shop for you.

If an individual policy isn't available (or only at very high cost), group policies can be found in clubs, fraternal orders, religious orders, volunteer firemen. It may pay to join a club just for the group insurance. The saving on the premium is usually more than the dues.

Frank J. Crisona, attorney and principal of the Crisona Agency, Box 130, Carle Place, NY 11514.

You Can Fight Insurance Companies...and Win

William M. Shernoff, a consumer-rights lawyer who practices in Claremont, CA. He is author of *How to Make Insurance Companies Pay Your Claims and What to Do If They Don't.* Hastings House.

I hear horror stories every day from families whose insurance companies refused to make timely payments on legitimate claims. Individuals are inhumanely hounded by collection agencies because their insurance companies haven't paid the bills they are legally obligated to pay. The disabled are forced to go on welfare. Some people have even been driven to attempt suicide.

Very few people—fewer than 1% of those with insurance claims—question claim denials. By not questioning a denied claim, there's a good chance you're letting the insurance company cheat you out of money that rightfully belongs to you.

Good news: Most of those who do challenge insurers either win their cases or significantly improve their positions.

WHAT IT TAKES TO WIN

●**Positive attitude.** Don't assume "they" must be right and take the first no for a final answer. Insurance companies count on the fact that most people simply accept their decisions.

●**Persistence.** The adage, "a squeaky wheel gets the grease," is true when it comes to dealing with a claim denial.

●**Knowledge.** Educate yourself on specific issues and the tools available to help you fight a large insurance company.

YOU BE THE JUDGE

On any claim refusal, exercise your rights as a consumer…

●**Insist on a written explanation.** Most state laws require an insurance company to give you one.

●**Compare the explanation you get from the company with the language of the policy.** Insurers notoriously write policies that are difficult to understand and then interpret them to their own advantage. But in court, where language is unclear, the meaning is construed against the insurance company. Some courts have even held that the reasonable expectation of the policyholder governs the meaning of policy language.

●**Rely on your own common sense. Judge for yourself "what is fair" and "what you expected."** If what the insurance company offers doesn't seem fair, there is a good chance that it isn't.

●**Don't be put off if your claim is denied for technical reasons.** An insurer cannot deny benefits because you filed late or filled out a form improperly unless the company can show it has been harmed by your failure. That's very, very rarely the case.

●**Use intermediaries to press your claim.** The agent who sold you the policy, or if you have a group policy, the administrator who handles claims for your company, can often give a decisive nudge to the insurer.

●**Always put your claim in writing.** Arm yourself with supporting evidence. One of the most common reasons insurers give for rejections is that a bill exceeds regular and customary charges. But some companies use outdated fee schedules or averages that don't apply to your case. Get written estimates from other doctors for the same treatment to prove your point.

Example: One woman who received much less than she expected for a Cesarean delivery called 27 doctors in her area and asked what they charged for a C-section. Only three charged less than her gynecologist, 10 charged more. Faced with these figures, the insurer paid up.

●**Pursue your claim up the company's chain of command.** Keep written notes of every conversation—who you talked to, his/her telephone extension, what was said.

GO THE EXTRA MILE

If the insurer continues to stonewall, seek outside help. *Sources:*

●**States' department of insurance.** Most try to identify and prevent unfair claims practices. Strong ones—like California, New York and Illinois—will even act as a referee between you and your insurance company.

●**Small claims court.** Sue the insurer yourself if the claim does not exceed the maximum recovery amount for small-claims court, usually between $1,000 and $2,500. Rather than spending their time and money to defend themselves against you, the company may well settle.

●**Lawyer.** It isn't hard to find one who will work on a contingency basis if you have a really strong case. You may end up collecting not just the claim amount, but additional sums for economic loss, emotional distress and—if the company has been really unscrupulous—punitive damages for wrongful conduct.*

Example: A client of mine had a $48 gripe against his insurance company, which refused to pay for medicine. After we proved the company had fraudulently changed its basic policy coverage, the jury awarded him $70,000 in compensatory damages—and $4.5 million in punitive damages.

*Group policyholders governed by Employee Retirement and Income Security Act (ERISA) regulations can recover only policy benefits from successful lawsuits.

Whichever routes you take, the important thing is to keep pushing to get the benefits you rightfully deserve. Don't be a victim.

Mistakes When Filing Insurance Claims

●**Failure to accurately calculate losses.** It's hard to believe, but many people can't accurately determine their losses—whether by damage or theft.

Reason: They fail to maintain effective accounting and record-retention procedures to document the losses. It's not uncommon to hear of a situation in which a theft loss amounted to $250,000 but the claimant could substantiate only $100,000 of the loss. It's important to plan ahead with your accountant to determine the best procedures for demonstrating what you own in case you have to make a claim.

●**Overstating the loss.** This is a subtle problem. If a claimant purposely overstates the loss to the point where the insurance company could question his integrity, the latter will take a hard line. Generally, if the claimant takes a fair position, the insurer will still bargain over the loss claim but will be more reasonable.

●**Underestimating the loss.** This sounds like a contradiction of the above, but it's not. Immediately after losses are claimed, the adjuster will ask the claimant for an estimate of the damage, not an accurate, justified number. The insurer requires such a rough estimate, but be wary of providing a number before taking the time to get a reliable estimate. If the adjuster reports a number that's too low and then must go back later to the insurer and restate it much higher, both his credibility and yours are hurt. He looks foolish. Those hurt feelings can make future loss negotiations tricky. So tell the adjuster about any problems you have in coming up with a number.

6

Smart Banking

Your Bank Is Still Ripping You Off

The average American family is paying far more than it should in bank fees, including ATM charges and mortgage interest. *Some of the latest bank rip-offs and how you can avoid them…*

LOAN RIP-OFFS

•**Interest rates.** Two customers walk into a bank and ask for loans. One has a great credit rating and a 20% down payment. The other has an okay credit rating and a 10% down payment. Which customer gets the better deal from the bank? *Neither!* Both get the same quote.

Banks will not offer below-standard rates without some prompting. But they generally will when good customers push.

The best customers have clean credit ratings, ongoing relationships with the lender and adequate collateral. These customers should ask for the loan rate to be lowered by one-half to one percentage point.

On a typical 30-year, $100,000 mortgage, that's a saving of up to $25,000 over the life of the loan.

•**Loan type.** When you're ready to accept the rate offered, tell the loan officer you want to borrow on a *simple-interest, single-payment note* that allows for monthly payments or an *installment note calculated by simple interest.* Do not take the standard front-end loaded installment note that is usually offered.

With a standard installment note, the borrower pays interest on the entire loan amount through the life of the loan—despite the fact that an increasing portion of the loan is paid off over time. With a simple-interest, single-payment note, you pay interest on only the amount of the loan outstanding.

Edward F. Mrkvicka, Jr., former chairman of a national bank and current president of Reliance Enterprises, Inc., a national financial consulting firm, 22115 O'Connell Rd., Marengo, IL 60152. He is author of Your Bank Is Ripping You Off. *St. Martin's Griffin.*

Example: For a $10,000, four-year loan at 10.25% Annual Percentage Rate (APR), you'll save $140 by requesting a simple-interest note.

Also tell the loan officer that you don't want *Credit Life and Disability Insurance* on your loan. This coverage protects the bank's interests—not yours. While not required, such insurance is often slipped into the loan—increasing its cost—without the customer knowing or understanding that he/she could have refused coverage. The premium is then subject to hidden finance charges.

You can get better coverage at less cost from your insurance agent.

FEE RIP-OFFS

● **Overdraft checking.** With this type of account, if you write a check that exceeds your balance, the bank automatically lends you the money to cover it. But it's not as good as it sounds. The bank lends this money at a high interest rate, and these accounts often carry additional charges, such as transaction fees—even if you pay off the overdraft right away.

Better: Ask to have your checking account *red flagged*. Many banks—particularly small ones—allow such no-cost arrangements, under which customers are called if they overdraw. If the customer can cover the checks that day, the bank waives the overdraft fees.

● **Unadvertised account options.** Don't assume the checking and savings policies in a bank's literature are the only ones available.

Example: Free low-balance checking accounts often are available for senior citizens, students and the disabled—but only if you ask.

● **Bank consolidation.** The number of banks continues to fall, from a peak of nearly 15,000 in 1983 to roughly half that today. Less competition is never good for consumers. Large banks generally charge more and provide less than small banks. Whenever two banks merge, they inevitably adopt the fee structure and charges of the more expensive bank.

Better: If you're currently shopping for a new bank, consider a credit union. These institutions typically offer better rates than banks and are less likely to be taken over. Contact the Credit Union National Association (CUNA) to find credit unions in your area that you are eligible to join. 800-358-5710…or *www.cuna.org.*

CREDIT CARD RIP-OFFS

● **Disappearing grace periods.** Not long ago, credit card users could be relatively confident that if they paid off their bills within 30 days, they wouldn't pay interest. But more credit card companies are doing away with "grace periods" and charging interest from the *moment* of purchase.

Today, the top priority for those not carrying balances should be a grace period, not interest rates or special features.

● **Debit card downsides.** *Two problems to be aware of…*

● Debit cards withdraw funds from your account immediately.

● Married couples are more likely to incur overdraft fees when using debit cards. Before debit cards were introduced, if both partners wrote big checks on the same day, one could run to the bank with a deposit to cover the shortfall. But today the immediacy of debit cards means that overdrawn is overdrawn.

How to Protect Yourself from Your Banker

Edward F. Mrkvicka, Jr., former chairman of a national bank and current president of Reliance Enterprises, Inc., a national financial consulting firm, 22115 O'Connell Rd., Marengo, IL 60152. He is author of *Your Bank Is Ripping You Off.* St. Martin's Griffin.

Reality: While there are certainly some smart and some honest bankers in the United States, as an industry, bankers have not run their business at all well. *In the past 10 years…*

…on average, more than 100 banks a year have failed. Taxpayers may have to bail out savings and loans to the tune of up to $500 billion or more before it's over. And many individuals have lost all of their life's savings.

…bank insurance reserves dwindled from $18 billion to a deficit of $7 billion before being rebuilt.

Self-defense: Ask questions and look out for your own interests in any dealings with your bank.

COMPARISON SHOP

No matter how convenient your bank may be or how long you've done business there, it's important today to at least call around and see what's available from other banks in the area.

Example: All banks today are trying to increase their earnings through added fees. Just the fees for an average checking account can cost you several hundred dollars annually, net of any interest you may earn on that account. So, it pays to shop around for the bank with the lowest fees.

Bargains: If you qualify as a senior citizen by whatever standards a given bank uses, it will often give you free checking. But most banks don't advertise this. You must ask for it. If your bank doesn't offer free checking, it may pay to switch to another bank.

Ask around, too, to see whether other banks have senior citizen clubs that offer discounts on local restaurant meals, transportation, travel, etc.

WHAT'S REALLY INSURED?

Of course it's comforting to know that your deposits are insured for up to $100,000, but don't make the mistake of thinking that just because there's an FDIC symbol on the door, all transactions with your bank are protected. They're not...and often bank employees don't know (or don't tell you) that.

Safe-deposit box contents, for example, aren't considered deposits and may or may not be insured by the bank.

Any mutual funds that you may have with a bank's broker don't fall under FDIC insurance either.

At best, they're covered by the Securities Investor Protection Corporation (SIPC), which protects brokerage accounts against fraud, but not market declines.

Rule: If a bank tries to sell you anything other than a Certificate of Deposit, which is covered under FDIC protection, find out whether it is insured. What happened in the notorious Charles Keating (Lincoln Savings & Loan) bank failure was that investors had been switched out of CDs and into bank bonds that were not insured.

Don't simply take the word of bank employees. They may have been told that bank products are insured in order to sell them.

Better: Verify the information with the FDIC in your region, the state banking authority or—for banks with "National" in their names—the US Comptroller of the Currency. If investments are not insured and the bank gets into trouble, it could take years to get your money back, if you ever do.

FORM A RELATIONSHIP

It's important for everyone—especially seniors—to get to know their banker by name. When your banker knows you, he/she can be helpful if an emergency arises.

Many banks are now charging $25 to $35 per bounced check, for example, and it can cost even more for overdraft protection. Once you're known, instead of buying expensive overdraft protection, ask to speak to the bookkeeper and request that he/she red flag your account and call you immediately if there's an overdraft. Then, at no cost, you have until the end of the business day to add funds. Again, if your bank won't do this, find one that will.

Don't trust trust departments: If you must deal with a bank trust department, pick a big bank. I have real reservations about using bank trust departments, especially when you don't have enough money to command adequate attention from senior officers. Banks are known more for their mismanagement of trust moneys than for astute investment advice. You can probably do better with a smart trust accountant, trust attorney or trust company.

WHAT TO AVOID

●**ATMs.** Young people may swear by them, but most seniors are not comfortable with automatic teller machines (ATMs). That's fine because it's becoming more and more costly to use the machines and, since they can be a magnet for criminals, elderly people could easily become victimized.

●**Bank-sponsored mutual funds.** Many banks are now pushing to sell mutual funds to depositors. But you should be aware that almost all of what they sell are load funds that carry a sales commission of up to 8%. And most banks offer a very limited universe of funds with only one or two selections in each category. By doing a little research at your library and reading financial publications, you can easily find many well-managed funds with good histories and invest in them directly without paying a sales load.

● **Reverse mortgages.** With so much current emphasis on getting the equity out of your home, more banks can be expected to offer some form of reverse mortgage financing—an annuity-like upside-down mortgage—to seniors. I don't recommend it because essentially you're giving away your home—at least a big share of the equity you've built up over the years—to the bank in order to stay there. Diluting your (and your heirs') hard-earned equity in your home should be a last resort.

For younger seniors with a longer life expectancy, the monthly income from a reverse mortgage probably won't be enough to make much difference and, because the interest compounds over a long period, it becomes a very expensive way to borrow.

Better: Sell your home to your children and let them pay you $300 to $400 a month. Or sell to an outsider under an arrangement that allows you to live there as long as you wish.

Check with your state information office. There are many programs to help with real estate taxes, repairs and maintenance, and assistance for health reasons. These programs may be enough to ensure you don't have to move.

Bank-Failure Loophole

If your bank fails and your deposits exceed $100,000 (the maximum amount insured by the FDIC), you may be able to use the uninsured portion to pay off any outstanding debt to the bank you may have.

Self-defense: Request a "voluntary offset" from the bank's claims agent.

Example: Someone with $120,000 in deposits and a $50,000 bank loan can ask that the $20,000 not covered by the FDIC be used to pay down the loan.

Rationale: You probably won't see the $20,000 for some time, and when you do, you aren't likely to receive the full amount. Meanwhile,

your debt would be reduced by the amount offset, dollar for dollar.

Cody Buck, former senior executive of the FDIC's division of liquidation. He is author of *The ABCs of FDIC: How to Save Your Assets from Liquidation.* CoStarr Publications.

Bank Safe-Deposit Box Trap

In effect, many banks don't insure safe-deposit boxes for theft. If there is insurance, it is very difficult to collect because you can't prove the box's contents. You could have a bank officer sign a safekeeping receipt each time you visit to confirm the contents…but this sacrifices your confidentiality and doesn't guarantee coverage.

Best: A home safe. Models that exceed the fire safety of a bank vault cost less than $250 and losses are covered by your homeowner's insurance. List each item in a policy rider.

Edward F. Mrkvicka, Jr., former chairman of a national bank and current president of Reliance Enterprises, Inc., a national financial consulting firm, 22115 O'Connell Rd., Marengo, IL 60152. He is author of *Your Bank Is Ripping You Off.* St. Martin's Griffin.

Beware of Bank IRAs

Edward F. Mrkvicka, Jr., former chairman of a national bank and current president of Reliance Enterprises, Inc., a national financial consulting firm, 22115 O'Connell Rd., Marengo, IL 60152. He is author of *Your Bank Is Ripping You Off.* St. Martin's Griffin.

Retirement planning: One cannot overstate the importance of it. And…in investigating all of your Individual Retirement Account (IRA) options, I believe you'll find that a bank IRA is one of the least acceptable alternatives.

In fact, a bank IRA could be the most unrewarding investment you ever make.

Some banks advertise how you can "easily" accumulate a million dollars in your IRA.

Unfortunately, a Government Accounting Office study revealed that if inflation continues at its historical pace, your million dollars may be worth, in buying power, only $50,000. In other words, you'll be lucky to get back exactly what you put in.

There are other investments that could return much more for your retirement—even if you have to pay taxes on them.

Problem: Banks like IRAs for one reason and one reason only—they are cheap money for the banks. Bank IRA interest rates are historically one to three percentage points below those of other market IRA vehicles available from brokers and mutual fund families. In later years, when your IRA balance is substantial, that could mean tens of thousands of dollars in interest lost every year.

Bigger problem: The banks' below-market IRA interest rates can be even more unfavorable. Under some plans, the bank also maintains the right to change the basis on which it pays interest, at its own discretion.

The insurance trap: Too many older investors say to me, "Never mind that I may be sacrificing some interest—at least I know that my retirement funds are insured by the full faith and credit of the US government."

For many years investors could have confidence in government insurance, at least up to the maximum insured limit—currently $100,000 (IRA balances in excess of $100,000 are not insured). But in the past 10 years, everything has changed.

We should have learned from the savings-and-loan disaster about the questionable value of government-backed deposit insurance.

Sooner or later there will be failures of major money-center banks—banks that have been getting away with privatizing their profits—and socializing their losses by claiming they're "too big to fail."

As with the savings-and-loan bailout, this means that US taxpayers—you and I—will pay for those bank losses caused by illegal behavior, greed, incompetent regulatory agencies and a Congress that looks the other way.

Don't invest in a bank IRA because of bank insurance that is coming right out of your pocket.

Checkbook Checklist

Your check register is a good record of deposits and spending if you record all transactions in it. Be sure to include date, check number, name and invoice number or date of invoice. *More ideas...*

●**Keep a spare check or two in your wallet.**

●**Paper clip the checkbook on the page you are working.**

●**Write check numbers in the register ahead of time.**

●**Color code in the register.** Use red for tax-deductible items.

●**Round up check amounts to the nearest dollar.**

●**Cut addresses off extra deposit slips for address labels.**

●**Keep a small,** thin calculator in your register.

●**Use black or blue ink.** Light colored ink doesn't copy as well.

●**Keep track of monthly expenses at the back of the book.**

Heloise, whose syndicated column Hints from Heloise *appears in more than 500 newspapers internationally. She is author of a number of books, including* Heloise: Household Hints for Singles. *Perigee Books.*

Beware of Playing The *Float* on Checks

The time between writing a check and having it clear keeps shrinking. Most checks now clear in three business days or less...and mortgage and car payments may go through immediately. *Trap:* If several of your checks reach the bank at the same time, the largest one may be sent through first—hitting you with multiple "insufficient funds" fees if the first check wipes out your balance. *Self-defense:* If your bank offers overdraft protection free or at low cost, sign up. Checks that would otherwise bounce are advanced by the bank or charged to your credit card. Just be sure to pay off your balance immediately. *Also helpful:* Accounts that allow you to transfer money by phone.

Edward F. Mrkvicka, Jr., former chairman of a national bank and current president of Reliance Enterprises, Inc., a national financial consulting firm, 22115 O'Connell Rd., Marengo, IL 60152. He is author of *Your Bank Is Ripping You Off.* St. Martin's Griffin.

More from Ed Mrkvicka...

ATM Self-Defense

Discarding your ATM receipt at the bank may help thieves loot your account. High-tech bandits are using video cameras to observe/record customers punching in ID numbers at teller machines. Then they match it to the account numbers on receipts left behind.

Self-defense: Guard your PIN number... retain receipts to match up against monthly bank statements. If there's a withdrawal discrepancy, report it immediately to the bank.

Save ATM Fees

To avoid ATM surcharges, open an account at a bank that gives rebates when you use the machines. *Example:* USAA Federal Savings, 800-531-2265, will refund up to 10 ATM charges per month. *Alternatives:* Switch to a bank that has many ATMs in your area, and use only that bank's machines...pay with ATM cards at supermarkets—many markets let you take out extra cash with no fee.

Jean Sherman Chatzky, financial writer, *Money,* Rockefeller Center, New York 10020.

Do-Gooder Credit Cards Do Little

So-called affinity cards claim to give a portion of what you charge to a cause in which you believe. Cards are available with tie-ins to environmental and family-oriented organizations. But charities get very little money from your use of the cards. *Example:* If you charged $800 a month for a year—a total of $9,600—on one major bank's do-good card, its tie-in fund would get only $48. *Also:* Affinity cards often carry high interest rates.

Robert McKinley, president and publisher, CardWeb.com, Inc., which closely follows the credit card industry, Frederick, MD.

Cosigner's Trap

To obtain credit for their children, parents often cosign credit cards or other loans for them. But parents should be aware that creditors in some states are not required to notify cosigners when a borrower exceeds a credit limit or falls behind on loan payments. So a cosigning parent can become liable for overdue payments and penalties without ever knowing there is a problem. The parent's credit rating may be harmed as well.

Defense: If you cosign a child's borrowings, monitor payments and monthly statements closely.

Better: Consider having the child cosign your credit card. That way, the child will have access to the credit line and build a credit history while monthly statements come directly to you.

Gerri Detweiler, consumer advocate and president, Ultimate Credit Solutions, Sarasota, FL.

Dangers of Cosigning A Loan

You will be listed with credit bureaus as responsible for the loan—and your credit could be damaged if payments are missed. Since the amount of the loan appears as your debt, you may find it harder to qualify for a loan of your own. If payment trouble develops, you may not find out until the borrower has defaulted and your credit has been damaged. *Extra danger:* Cosigning on credit cards. Since credit lines may be increased periodically, you may end up being responsible for much more than you planned.

Gerri Detweiler, consumer advocate and president, Ultimate Credit Solutions, Sarasota, FL.

Credit Card Traps

Credit card balance-transfer traps can make some low-rate offers almost worthless. *Examples:* The low-rate introductory period may start when you open an account, not when the transfer is made—and may end shortly after the transfer is done. Card issuers may charge high fees—up to 4%—for balance transfers that then have a low interest rate. Missing a single payment date on any card—not necessarily the low-rate one—can cause the low-rate card company to increase your rate significantly. Low rates may apply only to transfers—new purchases may still incur high rates.

Also, when you cancel a credit card, be sure it's listed as closed on your credit report. If the report still lists the account as open, your ability to borrow may be reduced. After canceling a card, ask for written verification that it has been canceled. A month later, ask for a copy of your credit report. If the report still shows the account as open, inform the credit bureau and send it a copy of the verification letter showing the account to be closed. By law, credit bureaus must verify disputed information with the source within 30 days.

Gerri Detweiler, consumer advocate and president, Ultimate Credit Solutions, Sarasota, FL.

Don't Pay Too Much

Nearly three out of four mortgage holders pay too much into escrow accounts—set up by lenders with a borrower's money to pay real estate taxes and home-insurance costs.

Self-defense: Check monthly payments carefully against copies of all tax and insurance bills. If what's due in taxes is less than the funds in escrow—seek a refund immediately.

Bottom line: While you pay monthly, the lender might pay only quarterly—or even annually. Any funds held in escrow until those payments come due are the equivalent of giving the lender a no- or low-interest loan.

Edward F. Mrkvicka, Jr., former chairman of a national bank and current president of Reliance Enterprises, Inc., a national financial consulting firm, 22115 O'Connell Rd., Marengo, IL 60152. He is author of *Your Bank Is Ripping You Off*. St. Martin's Griffin.

Smarter Home Loans

You'll find that when applying for a home-equity loan, home appraisals are almost always lower than the *market-value* appraisal of a home. The bank does this for protection in case of a default on the loan. If you want a larger loan than the original appraisal would allow, there is recourse. Have your home independently appraised—this can usually be done through a real estate agent. Ask for a *Comparative Market Analysis,* which reports on your home in relation to others in your area, and for an estimate of your home's fair market value. Then call the bank with the new information and ask it to reconsider. If the bank is still uncooperative, go to a new bank with your appraisal. The second bank will likely be more flexible than the first because its appraiser won't feel comfortable deviating greatly from the information you provided prior to his appraisal.

Edward F. Mrkvicka, Jr., former chairman of a national bank and current president of Reliance Enterprises, Inc., a national financial consulting firm, 22115 O'Connell Rd., Marengo, IL 60152. He is author of *Your Bank Is Ripping You Off*. St. Martin's Griffin.

Auto Financing

Those who have to take out a five-year car loan in order to afford the payments probably can't afford the car.

Better: A less expensive model that can be paid off in three or four years.

David L. Scott, PhD, professor of accounting and finance, Valdosta State University, GA. He is author of *The Guide to Managing Credit: How to Stretch Your Dollars Through Wise Credit Management.* The Globe Pequot Press.

Internet Banking... Consider This

Internet banks operate without retail outlets and big staffs, so they often offer higher interest rates and lower fees than traditional banks. *But consumers may pay a high price in other ways...*

• **Poor service.** Internet banks are often bad at dealing with problems.

Example: If an improperly recorded deposit causes checks to bounce, it is nearly impossible to set things straight, according to customers with whom I've spoken.

Resolving problems is a hassle at any bank— but when you have a location, you can meet with a real person.

• **Lack of insurance.** Not all Internet "banks" have FDIC insurance, yet some claim they do.

Alternative: Consider a brick-and-mortar bank that also has an Internet presence.

There are several Web sites you can use to research a bank. Both *www.bankrate.com* and *www.gomez.com* focus on E-banks.

Edward F. Mrkvicka, Jr., former chairman of a national bank and current president of Reliance Enterprises, Inc., a national financial consulting firm, 22115 O'Connell Rd., Marengo, IL 60152. He is author of *Your Bank Is Ripping You Off.* St. Martin's Griffin.

7

Stretching Your Dollars

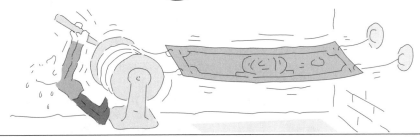

Be Sure You Collect All the Benefits to Which You're Entitled

Don't let ignorance or false pride prevent you from getting all you're entitled to in the way of aid. Some of the benefits may surprise you.

Some benefits are provided on the basis of age alone...others depend on financial need.

AGE-BASED BENEFITS

These benefits are yours simply because you've reached a certain birthday. *Included...*

•**Social Security benefits.** As a general rule, provided you've worked for a certain number of years over your lifetime, you qualify for Social Security benefits starting at age 62... though the benefits are reduced at that age.

Full benefit checks don't begin until your full retirement age—age 65 years, four months, but it will increase to 67 over the next several years.

Spouses, former spouses and widow(er)s may be entitled to benefits based on the other spouse's (or former spouse's) earnings and may start as early as age 60.

•**Medicare.** Unless you receive Social Security disability benefits for 24 months, your Medicare coverage doesn't start until age 65, even if you elected to begin receiving Social Security benefits at age 62.

Once you turn 65 you're covered under Part A of Medicare (hospital, skilled nursing facility, home health and hospice coverage) if you worked a certain length of time.

To receive Part B of Medicare (doctors' coverage, some home health and other outpatient services), you must pay a monthly premium.

LOCAL BENEFITS

Check local papers for seniors' activities and the minimum age for participation. Also look for discounts and other help. *What you'll find...*

Judith A. Stein, an attorney and executive director of the Center for Medicare Advocacy, Inc. She is past president of the National Academy of Elder Law Attorneys.

●**Clubs, trips and programs for seniors.** Local governments generally help seniors' groups that meet for social and recreational purposes.

Examples: Daily recreational facilities…bus trips to a wide variety of places…field programs.

●**Senior discounts.** Retailers may offer discounts to seniors of a certain age. Many places provide senior ID cards to those as young as age 50 (for example, members of American Association of Retired Persons) that can be used to cash in on discounts in the area.

●**Help with local transportation.** Cities and counties, in many places, run bus services for seniors.

BENEFITS BASED ON NEED

A number of benefits for seniors can only be obtained if there is a financial need. The eligibility requirements may change from year to year. *Included…*

●**Supplemental Security Income (SSI)** provides income to seniors.

●**Food stamps.** Monthly allotments are available for the purchase of food items. The amount depends on household size and income. *Note:* The right to food stamps is not dependent on age.

●**Meal programs.** Homebound seniors may be entitled to receive daily meal deliveries.

●**Medicare beneficiary programs** provide assistance with premiums, deductibles and copayments.

These Medicare programs are entitled QMB, SLMB, QI-1 and QI-2—depending on the benefits provided. They are limited to those age 65 or older with financial need.

●**Medicaid** pays for medical costs for those age 65 or older who have income and assets below a certain level (which varies by state). It also provides coverage for the blind and disabled, regardless of age.

●**Prescription aid.** In some states, low-income prescription drug programs help those age 65 or older who do not have Medicaid or other insurance to cover drug costs.

●**Property tax relief** lets senior home owners reduce their property tax bill. Rules differ in each locality, but may provide relief of up to 50% of the bill for those age 65 or older with income below a certain amount.

●**Rent subsidies.** As with property tax relief, some localities provide rent assistance for those in need.

●**Home energy assistance** for both renters and home owners gives cash (or makes payments to energy suppliers) in some localities if monthly income is below a threshold amount.

No minimum age: There may not be any minimum age for eligibility for the following…

●**Emergency assistance cash** for food, rent, moving, etc., for those with income below SSI limits.

TO FIND OUT ABOUT BENEFITS

There's an elder network operating in every state that can provide information and assistance. You can tap into this network by contacting your local agency on aging or state department on aging.

Note: If you're investigating benefits for someone else, you can obtain general information without authorization. But if you need to discuss confidential information with a particular governmental agency, you may need authorization from the person you're helping.

●**Departments on Aging.** Every state has some administrative agency or subdivision for the elderly. It may go by a different name in your location—Office of Aging, Commission on Aging, Division of Senior Services, etc. Some state departments have regional offices. This is your first contact point. *This state office can provide…*

●Information about benefits and eligibility requirements.

●Referral services to agencies providing specific types of assistance.

●**Federal resources.** The Social Security Administration can provide information and help on Social Security benefits, Medicare and more. 800-772-1213 or *www.ssa.gov.*

●**The Health Care Financing Administration (HCFA)** also provides information and help with Medicare. 800-633-4227 or *www.medicare.gov.*

●**Access America for Seniors Web site** makes it easier to connect with various federal agencies. *www.seniors.gov.*

●**Administration on Aging** provides information for older Americans about opportunities and services. *www.aoa.dhhs.gov.*

●**Department of Veterans Affairs** provides information about VA programs for veterans and their families. 800-827-1000 or *www.va.gov.*

●**Private seniors organizations.** They can give you information on assistance programs. *These organizations include…*

●American Association of Retired Persons (AARP) at 800-424-3410 or *www.aarp.org.*

●Gray Panthers at 800-280-5362 or *www.graypanthers.org.*

●Older Women's League (OWL) at 800-825-3695 or *www.owl-national.org.*

●**The Center for Medicare Advocacy** provides assistance regarding Medicare and healthcare rights. 860-456-7790 or *www.medicare advocacy.org.*

●**Other organizations.** The National Academy of Elder Law Attorneys (NAELA) distributes brochures to explain various benefit programs for the elderly. 520-881-4005 or *www.naela.org.*

Frugality Secrets from An Expert

Amy Dacyczyn, author of *The Complete Tightwad Gazette: Promoting Thrift as a Viable Alternative Lifestyle.* Random House. She lives in Leeds, ME, with her husband and their six children.

Frugality is nothing to be ashamed of. Frugal people are just making choices—the trade-offs necessary to reach their financial goals.

Wealth is not how much you earn…it is how much you accumulate. Wealthy people tend to be those who work hard, save and thoughtfully invest money.

Golden rule of penny-pinching: Use materials you have before you spend money on new items. *Here are the best ways to do that, along with my favorite money-saving strategies…*

BEST BARGAINS EVER

●**Toothpaste and dental floss.** Next time you're at the dentist, think about how much toothpaste and floss you could buy for the cost of that filling.

●**Paper and crayons**—they are still the best gifts for any child.

●**Noncable television.** People like to bash TV, but there are plenty of worthwhile programs.

●**Postage stamps.** The sheer volume of material that can be included in a one-ounce letter is amazing—and the post office will carry it thousands of miles for only 34 cents.

And e-mail, of course, is a great bargain for computer owners.

●**Potatoes.** Pound for pound, potatoes offer more nutrients for lower cost than any other food.

My favorite cheap-and-easy meal: Baked potato (cooking in the microwave costs less than the oven) topped with chopped, steamed broccoli and cheese sauce. Sprinkle with bacon bits. I feed my entire family for about $1 because I buy economy-size bags of potatoes and make my own sauce.

Other tasty-but-tightwad topping combinations: Chili and cheese…sour cream and chives…cheese and mushrooms…meat sauce.

FREEBIES

●**Free attractions.** Look in your local paper for museums, gardens, historical buildings, etc. They are often listed in the calendar section. Check the library for *Guide to Free Attractions, USA* and *Guide to Free Campgrounds.*

●**Free information.** The federal government publishes hundreds of free consumer guides, from *College Handbook* to *Understanding Social Security.* For a free catalog of publications, call 888-878-3256 or 800-FED-INFO…or go to *www.pueblo.gsa.gov.*

●**Free posters.** The US Postal Service sends promotional posters for new stamps to every post office in the country. If you see one you like, ask the postmaster if you can have it when the office is done with it.

Also ask at your video store for outdated movie posters.

●**"Free" health club membership.** See if you can work part-time in exchange for free membership. Many clubs have child-care rooms and are looking for moms to staff them.

●**Freebies from your congressperson.** Elected officials occasionally offer free calendars and other items. If you're planning a trip to Washington, DC, ask your congressional representative for free passes to restricted Senate and House galleries.

IN YOUR CAR

●**Car repairs.** Inquire at a local vocational school—students may need cars to fix. Most schools charge only for paint and parts.

●**Obey the speed limit.** This saves on gasoline, of course, but it also reduces wear on tires, brakes and other car components. And it reduces your risk of costly (and dangerous) accidents and speeding tickets—and the increased insurance premiums that go along with them.

IN THE KITCHEN

●**Save energy when cooking.** When preparing rice or pasta, bring water to a boil...add noodles or rice...bring back to a boil...and turn off the burner. Leave covered for 10 to 20 minutes, stirring occasionally to prevent sticking.

Many other foods can be prepared using residual heat, rather than keeping the burner on the entire time.

●**Watch what you drink.** Tap water is the cheapest thirst quencher. Homemade iced tea costs five cents per eight-ounce glass...Kool-Aid, 13 cents...apple juice, 25 cents.

If you must have a soft drink, a serving from a one-liter bottle costs about 20 cents, versus 30 cents for the same amount from a can.

AROUND THE HOUSE

●**Carpeting.** When replacing wall-to-wall carpeting, cut out sections from under the beds and sofas where the carpet is not worn. Take them to your carpet dealer for binding and use them as area rugs.

Opportunity: Ask your carpet store for old samples, which are often thrown out. Use them in the car, bathroom, doorways or basement.

●**"Free" paint.** Don't throw out old, half-empty cans of paint. Instead mix them together, and use to repaint the basement, garage or toolshed—someplace where you're not picky about the color.

Caution: Don't use paint from before 1980—it may contain lead. And never mix oil-based paint with latex paint. But you can mix interior paint with exterior...and flat with semigloss.

20 Easy Ways to Save Hard Dollars... Year In...Year Out

Amy Dacyczyn, author of *The Complete Tightwad Gazette: Promoting Thrift as a Viable Alternative Lifestyle.* Random House. She lives in Leeds, ME, with her husband and their six children.

Small changes in your lifestyle can add up to significant savings over the course of a year. *If you adopt just half of these suggestions, you'll save over $1,000 a year...*

●**Switch from a bank to a credit union.** The average checking account now costs $185 a year in service charges to maintain. Credit unions are nonprofit organizations that return surplus funds to members in the form of low-cost services. Larger credit unions offer free checking, low or no annual fees on credit cards and excellent rates on car loans.

Disadvantages: Fewer branch offices, and the branches may not have automatic teller machines. But, remember, not very long ago, we all survived without ATMs.

●**Buy your home heating oil in the summer.** In my area, prices drop 20¢ a gallon during the off-season, so filling a 275-gallon tank in the summer saves $55. If you are a do-it-yourselfer with extra space, you can buy a used second tank, so you'll have two tanks that can be filled in the off-season. Check local laws about installation and inspection of the second tank. You will have to monitor prices for some weeks to get the best deal in your area, but the bottom should hit some time between July and early September.

Caution: Don't wait until November, when prices go back up, to get your first fill-up.

●**Change the oil in your car yourself.**

●**Review your insurance policies.** Take higher deductibles where you can afford them, and eliminate coverage you don't need for your lifestyle.

Examples: Many people past childbearing age are still paying for maternity benefits. Most car insurance policies cover car rental reimbursement when the car is in the shop—but will you use this? Maybe you have a second car or friends who will help out. Are there extra drivers listed on your insurance who no longer live with you? Many homeowners' policies cover furs, jewelry, computers or other items you may not own.

Also, check with your agent to make sure you are getting any discounts you qualify for.

Examples: Nonsmoking on health insurance, alarm systems or safe driving records on car insurance, owning multiple policies with one company.

●**Make your own popcorn.** A family that pops two batches of traditional generic popcorn a week instead of an equivalent amount of microwave popcorn will save $100 in a year. And it can take less time to make popcorn in a hot-air popper than in a microwave.

●**Reduce your smoking by three cigarettes a day.** (Or give up smoking altogether and save even more.)

●**Rent videos instead of going to the movies.** Even better, check them out of the library.

●**Make pizza from scratch instead of having it delivered.**

●**Give personal services rather than store-bought presents.** Offer to garden, clean bathrooms or baby-sit for your friend in the hospital. Bring your hostess potted herbs from your kitchen or a homemade casserole. Give the new graduate "free résumé service" or 100 pages of thesis typing. Fill out change-of-address forms for your friend who just moved. Refinish a chest of drawers for newlyweds. And don't forget to make your own greeting cards.

●**Share a newspaper subscription with your neighbor.** Are you finished with the paper before you leave for work in the morning? Does your neighbor read the paper before supper? Share magazine subscriptions, too. Many public libraries microfilm, then discard magazines every six months. Request the outdated issues be held for you. Raid recycling bins.

●**Hang four loads of laundry a week instead of running the dryer.**

●**Drink four fewer cans of soda per week—saves at least $100 a year.**

●**Tape 10 pieces of music from the radio rather than buying commercially recorded audiotapes.**

●**Cut your family's hair yourself.** A child's haircut costs as much as $8 to $10 every six weeks. An adult haircut at $25 every six weeks adds up to $217 a year. If you learn to trim it yourself you will only need to have a professional job at the hairdresser half the time. This will save you $100.

●**Bake one batch of bread (two loaves) once a week.**

●**Write one good letter a month instead of making an $8 long-distance telephone call.**

●**Use half your usual amount of cleaning and personal care products.** Find the minimum effective level of shampoo, conditioner, laundry detergent, bleach, dishwasher detergent, toothpaste, shaving cream, lotion, perfume, etc. You may find you can make do with less than half your usual amount.

●**Buy articles of clothing from thrift shops and yard sales rather than paying store prices.** This is also a fun way to shop.

●**Barter for one regular service.** Handy with graphics? Arrange to make fliers and do an advertising layout for your massage therapist in return for monthly sessions. Want help cleaning? Offer to take your cleaning person's kids for a weekly activity in return for two hours of housecleaning. Are you an accountant? Trade tax preparation for lawn care or TV repair.

Consider three-party trades to get what you need.

Example: You want ten $10 computer lessons, the computer instructor needs a $100 repair on her car, so you prepare the mechanic's tax return in exchange for fixing the car, in exchange for your lessons.

Be creative!

●**Use dry milk.** A gallon of whole milk costs up to $2.59 per gallon. Dry milk, purchased in the 20-quart store-brand box, costs $1.60 per gallon. Dry milk is 100% fat-free, while whole milk contains 4% fat. By mixing the two kinds of milk, half dry milk and half whole milk, you can make your own 2% milk. If you use a gallon of milk every three days, you will easily save $100 in a year by substituting dry milk in cooking, homemade cocoa mix and in using the half-and-half mixture for drinking.

Secrets of Big-Time Food Bill Savings

Linda Bowman, professional bargain hunter and author of *The More for Your Money* series of guides, including *Free Food…& More* and *Freebies (& More) for Folks Over 50.* Probus Publishing Co.

Most of us have had the thought, "I can't believe I'm paying this much for one bag of stuff," as the supermarket cashier finishes ringing up the "few things" we ran to the store for.

"Did I really buy that much?" we wonder. Usually, we haven't bought that much—just paid too much. Here are some ways to save big on the family food bill…

SUPERMARKET SAVINGS

● **Shop with a list…or you'll spend more than you save.**

● **Clip coupons—and keep them organized.** Don't throw money away with the garbage. Coupons can easily save you $1,000 a year.

Be willing to give up brand loyalty in favor of a meaningful discount. One brand of tomato paste or dish detergent is much like another.

File coupons in envelopes by category—canned goods, cereals, pet foods, paper products, etc. Put coupons you plan to use right away and those with short expiration dates in the front. Take them with you to the store, along with an empty envelope to put coupons in for the items you select, so you don't have to sort them at the checkout counter.

Shop at a supermarket that honors double the value on the face of coupons. You can also increase your savings by combining in-store sales with coupons. Be sure to calculate the per-unit price of products when using coupons.

Example: A six-ounce jar of instant coffee may cost $3.29, or 55¢ an ounce, and a 10-ounce jar $4.99, or 50¢ an ounce. Normally, the larger size is the better buy. But with a 75¢ coupon, at a double-coupon store, the six-ounce jar costs $1.79, or 30¢ an ounce, while the 10-ounce jar is $3.49, or 35¢ an ounce.

● **Companion product offers.** Companies and supermarkets often issue coupons for a free item, with the purchase of a companion item.

Examples: A free gallon of milk with the purchase of a breakfast cereal…a free box of pasta with the purchase of spaghetti sauce.

● **Refund and rebate offers.** You may need to clip UPC symbols or save register receipts as "proof of purchase" to send for these offers. They are worth the trouble—and can be very lucrative, whether you get a cash rebate, additional coupons or free products.

● **Senior discounts.** Many large chain stores and some independent markets issue senior discount cards that allow cashiers to subtract as much as 5% to 10% off the final bill.

● **Generic brands.** Not only are they here to stay, they are growing and growing. Generics can provide substantial savings, especially on grooming products, cereals and canned goods.

● **Track savings.** Most supermarkets total the amount saved with coupons at the bottom of the register receipt. You can deposit monthly savings from coupons, refunds, etc., in an account earmarked toward a goal.

SUPERMARKET ALTERNATIVES

● **Join a wholesale or warehouse shopping club.** These huge operations are in metropolitan and suburban areas nationwide. Shopping is a no-frills enterprise, and products must often be purchased in bulk or large sizes. Brand selection may be limited and may change at any given time. But savings can be excellent. *Key:* Know your prices. Some warehouse club prices are not significantly better than prices at the discounters.

● **Shop at farmers' markets,** where vegetables and fruits are fresher, tastier and cheaper. Buy in bulk in-season, then can or preserve.

● **Shop at bakery outlets and "thrift stores."** Thrift stores are one-brand outlets for companies such as Entenmann's, Pepperidge Farm, Arnold's Bakery, Sunbeam Bread and

Wonder Bread/Hostess. Prices run 30% to 50% off retail for day-old goods.

●**Food co-ops and buying clubs.** Consumer cooperatives are run by members and usually buy food in bulk and then repackage it for buyers. Members can save 15% to 50% on most items, because brokers, middlemen and costly packaging are eliminated from the exchange.

●**Do it yourself.** Grow a vegetable garden, make your own frozen dinners from leftovers.

RESTAURANT SAVINGS

●**Happy hour buffets.** Between 4 pm and 6 pm, for the price of a drink—not necessarily alcoholic—many restaurants provide free buffets. If you don't mind eating early, many people find these feasts to be filling, fun dinners and a change in daily routine.

●**Early bird specials.** Many restaurants offer much lower prices for those who order dinner between 4 pm and 6 pm. You get the same food as on the dinner menu, often with dessert and beverage included, for less than you'd pay for the entrée alone during peak hours. To find specials, check local newspapers or call the restaurants that you are interested in.

●**Senior menus.** Some restaurants, particularly large chains, have senior menus, which offer smaller portions at lower prices. Carry your identification.

●**Two-for-one or free item coupons.** Check newspapers and circulars for coupons from area restaurants for "buy one entrée, get the second of equal or lesser value free" or "free wine or dessert with entrée" offers.

●**Restaurant discount books.**

Examples: Entertainment Publications publishes regional guides, with about 200 coupons for 2-for-1 meals and discounts at restaurants, fast-food chains and specialty shops. 2125 Butterfield Rd., Troy, MI 48084, 888-231-SAVE. The Dinner on Us Club qualifies you for 2-for-1 or other discounts at member restaurants nationwide. 300 W. Schrock Rd., Westerville, OH 43081. 800-346-3241.

INVEST IN SAVINGS

Other companies publish local or regional discount books as well. These can be a wise investment if you like to dine out a lot—but shop around. Prices and services vary substantially.

Key: Make sure the book contains enough discounts you will really use to pay for itself.

Saving Money With Coupons

Linda Bowman, professional bargain hunter and author of *The More for Your Money* series of guides, including *Free Food…& More* and *Freebies (& More) for Folks Over 50.* Probus Publishing Co.

Most of us pay more than we should for groceries, household products and other goods and services. The biggest mistake we make is failing to take full advantage of cents-off coupons, refund offers, two-for-one deals and other money-saving offers. Compared with the billions of coupons issued every year, not that many are actually redeemed.

Reasons: Many shoppers are too embarrassed to present coupons to checkout clerks. Others are not aware or interested in the available deals, or they feel that clipping coupons is too time-consuming.

Today, however, more consumers are looking to cut weekly costs and stay on a budget. There are several ways to clip coupons and save up to 25% on your supermarket bill. *How I do it…*

●**Set up a system.** Spend a few minutes each week looking over newspaper inserts and other likely sources of coupons. Clip the ones you think you might use and toss them into a shoe box, then separate them by category. Mark each grouping of coupons with its own labeled note card. Be as general or as specific as you like with your categories.

Just prior to each trip to the grocery store, review your shopping list. Transfer the coupons you plan to use from the storage box to an envelope labeled "unused." Take this envelope and a second, empty one (labeled "used") along to the store. As you toss each item on your list into your shopping cart, transfer its coupon from the first envelope to the second.

●**Be choosy.** Coupons should be used to buy only two types of products—those you use regularly and those you'd like to try. Don't let coupons entice you to buy products you neither need nor truly want. Don't be trapped by brand loyalty. Buy whatever brand you have coupons for.

●**Accumulate as many coupons as possible.** Today coupons are available from a wide variety of sources, including product labels and cartons, supermarket ads, inserts in your Sunday newspaper and displays placed along supermarket shelves. Coupons may also be distributed directly through the mail, on airline flights and at movie theaters.

●**Save unused coupons.** Take them along to the supermarket. *Reason:* Some markets maintain informal coupon-exchange bins where customers can exchange coupons they don't want for those they do.

●**Join a coupon-exchange club.** There are several large clubs to choose from, all offering the same basic service.

How they work: Upon joining, members fill out a form specifying which products they use. Periodically, members mail in coupons they don't need…and the club mails back coupons they do.

●**Shop at "coupon-friendly" supermarkets.** Some markets accept coupons only grudgingly. Others not only accept them, but will give you twice their face value.

●**Use coupons in conjunction with other savings offers.** When reading through your local newspaper's supermarket ads, watch for "double plays"—items discounted by both coupons and special sale prices.

Even better: Triple plays. These occur when prices are reduced not only by coupons and specials, but also by a mail-in refund offer.

To keep track of the thousands of refunds being offered at any given time, there are refunding newsletters. They not only list all the offers, but also detail the often Byzantine regulations governing how to obtain the refunds.

My favorite: Refundle Bundle, Box 140, Centuck Station, Yonkers, NY 10710, *www.re fundlebundle.com.*

●**Bank your savings.** Because coupons net you only a few dollars each time you shop, it's easy to squander the money saved by using them. *Solution:* Open a savings account specifically for your coupon savings. Decide on a particular item to save for. Don't dip into the account until you've accumulated enough to make the purchase.

Wintertime Money Savers

Andy Dappen, author of *Cheap Tricks: 100s of Ways You Can Save 1000s of Dollars.* Brier Books.

Winter is the season of higher electricity and gas bills, car maintenance and repair bills, bills for cold and flu medications and so on. But there are several ways that you can cut down on expenses without sacrificing great comfort.

AVOID COSTLY CAR REPAIRS

●**Keep your gas free of water.** The most frequent problems mechanics see in winter are caused by water in the gas. To prevent problems, add a drier (such as Prestone Gas-Drier or Heet) to your gas every few fill-ups.

●**Check your radiator fluid and the condition of the radiator hoses.** If the fluid is low, add a 50/50 mixture of antifreeze and water. In the coldest parts of the country or when an extreme cold snap strikes, you may want to alter this by using more antifreeze. *Best:* Use a mixture of 70% antifreeze and 30% water. Muddy-looking fluid should be changed. Make sure that the rubber hoses leading from the radiator to the engine are not cracked, brittle, bulging or mushy when they are squeezed.

●**Keep your battery terminals clean to avoid starting problems (and costly towing bills).** Clean the battery terminals occasionally with baking soda and then reduce the corrosion problem by smearing them with a thin coating of petroleum jelly.

●**Promptly repair any nicks in your windshield.** Stop those smaller than a quarter from spawning spider legs and ruining the windshield by covering them on both sides with transparent tape (duct tape works too). Then get the car to a windshield-repair specialist. Cost for a nick ranges from $30 to $50, compared with the $300 to over $600 it can cost to replace the whole windshield.

●**Check tire inflation every few weeks with an accurate gauge.** Changes in temperature alter tire pressure, and under-inflation increases tire wear and gas consumption by as much as 5%. *Important:* Check the pressure while tires are cold. Know how many pounds of pressure they require. Then check them again at the gas station (after they've warmed from being driven on) and add the pounds of pressure that were needed when they were cold.

SAVE ON HEATING

●**Put on an extra sweater and modify your heating habits.** Keep the daytime thermostat at 65 degrees Fahrenheit (rather than 70) and the nighttime temperature at 55 degrees Fahrenheit (rather than 60 or 65). This can reduce your heating bill 15% or more. And turn down the heat when you leave to run errands.

●**Keep fireplace dampers closed when not in use.** Install glass fireplace doors. Then heat won't escape through the chimney.

●**Have your home's insulation checked by your utility company.** Many utilities perform this inspection service free or for a nominal fee. Make sure your home's insulation meets the US Department of Energy's recommendations.

●**Wrap fiberglass insulation around heating ducts and hot water pipes in basement,** attic and crawl space. Putting 2½ inches of insulation around these ducts and pipes will pay for itself in one season.

SAVE ON LIGHTING

●**Replace incandescent lights with fluorescent lights in areas that need light for hours each day.** Today's fluorescent tubes produce warmer hues that won't make your home feel like a factory, and they're three to four times more efficient. If you don't want to install the tubes, use compact fluorescent bulbs. They screw into standard sockets.

●**Use outdoor light fixtures that turn on and off by means of built-in heat/motion detectors and timers.** They're far more economical than those that burn nonstop.

●**Don't turn lights on and off frequently.** Turning the lights out every time you leave the room for a few minutes may seem like it's doing good, but it shortens the life of the bulbs. So don't turn out the light unless leaving for more than a few minutes.

GRANDMA'S REMEDIES

●**Get an annual flu shot if you're 65 or older or suffer from cardiac or respiratory problems.** It's cheap insurance against the major problems a flu can precipitate.

●**Have prescriptions filled at a discount drugstore.** It is much cheaper than using your hospital's pharmacy.

MISCELLANEOUS MONEY SAVERS

●**Freeze your credit.** This is a good idea any time of year, but works especially well around the holiday season. Put your credit cards in a bowl of water and place them in the freezer. It sounds crazy, but by the time the ice melts enough to retrieve the cards, the urge to buy may have passed. And writing checks or paying cash for items forces you to do a "reality check" on how much you really have to spend.

●**Put rubber half-soles on the bottom of your shoes.** In damp or wet weather, the leather soles of your shoes are constantly absorbing water, which slowly damages the leather and reshapes the shoe. Half-soles cost $12 to $15 and add years of life to your shoes. *Also:* Alternate the shoes you wear each day. Having a day to dry and air between uses greatly extends shoe life.

Big, Big Money to Be Saved by Making the Most of Rebates

Tim Duffy, private legal investigator in Covina, CA, who works on product liability and advertising practices cases. His Web site, *www.timduffy.com*, features 50 rebate links as well as consumer stories and alerts. He is a former consultant to the US Department of Agriculture's Division of Weights and Measurement Standards on matters of consumer fraud.

Only 8% of the people who buy products that offer cash rebates ever take advantage of them. That leaves stores and manufacturers sitting on millions of dollars they were prepared to hand out. Here's how to make the most of rebate offers...

●**Keep an eye on the deadlines.** Before you buy a product for its rebate, search the small print on the packaging, in the rebate certificate and in ads for the rebate's expiration date.

Helpful: Check one of the many Internet resources available that list manufacturer rebates and deadlines, including...

● *www.rebateplace.com* for computer-related manufacturer rebates.

● *www.freakyfreddies.com/rebate.htm* and *www.mycoupons.com,* which offer details on coupon and rebate offers.

If you're considering a specific product rebate, also check for details on that company's Web page.

Another good source is *Refunding Makes Cents,* Box 969, Bountiful, UT 84011 *(www. refundcents.com).* It lists hundreds of major manufacturer rebates, contact addresses, qualifications and deadlines.

●**Shop on Sundays.** Many stores offer rebates on products only while supplies last. Some stores even purposefully keep low supplies of products that have the best rebate offers. But nearly all stores first announce their rebate offers in local Sunday newspaper ads. Once you've circled the items you want, shop early that day.

Trap: Stores that offer rain checks on their rebates often won't offer extensions on products with manufacturer rebates.

●**Shop at stores that brag about their low prices.** Many of these stores have underutilized policies that guarantee instant rebates if you find their products sold for less elsewhere.

Examples: Three large office-supply chains —Office Depot, Office Max and Staples—back their low-price guarantees. If you find a lower price advertised locally on their merchandise, they will match that price. Office Depot and Office Max may also offer a rebate of up to $55. (The exact amount varies with the difference between the prices.) Check with individual stores for their requirements.

Once you confirm a store offers such a guarantee—and you've decided on what you want —call a few other local retailers or drop in to compare prices. If their price is even $1 less

than the store with the rebate guarantee, pick up a store ad or flyer that shows the lower price. Or ask the store to write down the price on its stationery or fax a written quote to you as proof of the lower price.

●**Hold the store accountable if a manufacturer fails to pay up.** If a rebate check has not arrived within the time stated in the rebate—usually six to eight weeks—and you followed the rebate's rules, politely ask the store manager for the cash amount. Or call the store's customer service line.

A recent court case in Palm Springs, California, decided that a major retail chain that had advertised a manufacturer's rebate was responsible for the rebate amount—plus damages— when the consumer complained because he had not received it more than two months after the promised date.

Important: You may be asked to provide copies of the original materials you mailed in to claim the cash offer.

Avoid firms that sell rebate offers. Most of these offers are scams. They are for products that too few want...the offers have expired or involve hidden charges, such as excessive shipping costs...or they duplicate information in coupons mailed for free by the millions.

Guerrilla Shopper's Guide To Outlet Malls

Elysa Lazar, author of *Outlet Shopper's Guide.* Lazar Media. Her Web site, *www.lazarshopping.com,* includes a database of factory outlets nationwide and mail-order companies.

Hundreds of factory-outlet stores have popped up around the country—all claiming to offer great bargains.

Careful...many of those bargains can be buried under loads of inferior merchandise.

Here's how to avoid the big traps and how to find the best deals...

● **Order coupons to maximize savings.** *With very little effort, you can cut your bill at outlet stores by an extra 25%...*

• Visit *www.outletbound.com* (888-OUT LET-2) before you shop, and request a free VIP Voucher. It is redeemable for coupons or special offers worth hundreds of dollars at more than 160 participating outlet centers nationwide. The site also lets you search outlets by location, store, brand or product category.

• Request a coupon book from the store manager. These books are presented to members of bus tours, not to individuals. But the store will usually let you have a coupon book as a gesture of goodwill. Another place to find these books is at an outlet center's information desk or management office.

● Ask for "early markdowns." Most stores will give you the sale prices on any items you're buying that will go on sale within the next two weeks. Ask the store what its policy is.

● Sign up for the store's mailing list. You will receive advance notices of special sales, as well as vouchers for 5% to 15% off.

My favorite outlet-store mailing lists: Donna Karan...Joan & David.

● Ask for a "volume discount" from store managers if you're buying a large amount of merchandise at once.

● **Beware of items that were never sold in retail stores.** Many popular stores create lower-priced lines, with the same brand name and style, and sell them through their outlet stores.

Examples: I've seen outlet coats and sweaters with plastic buttons instead of the leather ones on the retail versions. Other garments lack quality work, such as reinforced stitching around the sleeves.

How to spot the difference: Most inferior made-for-outlet merchandise has "factory store" stamped on its label or tag. Items from the designer's retail stores will have labels that are sliced in half or are marked with ink. When in doubt, ask a salesperson.

● **Give clothing the quality test before buying.** I perform a wrinkle test on every garment I buy. I grab a fistful of the fabric, squeeze it, then release. Except for linen, the item should retain its shape and wrinkle very little.

Many outlet stores post charts that decode the flaws in the merchandise. *But you can do your own quick check...*

Bath towels: Are the hems even? Are the stitches near the borders tight?

Belts: Does it say "full-grain" leather? Full-grain is almost twice as thick as "split-grain" leather, which is brittle and wears out quickly.

Dress shirts: Turn the shirts inside out to see if the lining at the collar and armholes is sewn well. Pay more for 100% two-ply cotton. It stands up much better to repeated washings than polyester blends.

T-shirts: Is there strong, close stitching around the neck, shoulder seams and armholes? If not, the shirt will lose its shape quickly.

● **Consider items that fail to meet manufacturers' standards.** These are marked off by up to 70%. The items that are worth buying are labeled "irregular." They have minute flaws, such as crooked waistband seams or missing buttons.

Usually not worthwhile: Clothes that are labeled "seconds." They typically have serious flaws, such as stains or seams that pull. Clothes made of 100% silk rarely hold their color or shape more than one season.

● **Ask about the store's refund and exchange policy.** They vary greatly, especially during the holidays.

Before you buy, find out if you can return outlet items through the mail...or to full-price retail stores. *Examples...*

● Ann Taylor outlets let you return items to their full-price branches.

● Levi's outlets will take back an irregular garment—even after you've washed it.

Self-defense: Save the tags. If you purchase an "all-sales-are-final" item and then discover you want to return it, look for a defect. If the garment wasn't specifically marked imperfect, you can bargain to get a refund.

Or find a substitute garment in the store that costs a bit more. Ask the manager if you can use your "final sale" purchase as partial payment for the new one you chose.

● **Don't assume outlet stores have the lowest prices.** Many stores mix in full-price items with discount merchandise. So—an item on sale at the company's retail store can be priced less than in the outlet. Research prices at retail stores. Then look to pay at least 25% less for the same item at the outlet store.

Also, ignore the "suggested retail price" listed on the merchandise tag at outlets. It is usually inflated to make the saving look big.

Focus on quality rather than the discount. If you don't love a garment, you won't wear it, no matter how much you've saved.

Formula: Before I buy, I ask myself a simple question—*If the item was full price at the retail store, would I still buy it?* If I hesitate when answering, I put it back.

●**Shop from home or online before making the trip to the outlet.** Some stores allow you to make purchases over the phone with a credit card if you describe what you're looking for. Others offer a catalog of their outlet merchandise.

Resource: OutletsOnline has a complete listing of names, locations and phone numbers of outlet centers and their stores in the US by state. It indicates which ones will let you shop online. *www.outletsonline.com.*

Bargaining Secrets at Flea Markets, Tag Sales And Antique Shows

Susan Dresner, president, Ways & Means, wardrobe-management and retail consulting firm, New York. She has been dubbed "The Blackbelt Shopper" by *Money* magazine.

Bringing home bargains from flea markets, antique shows and yard sales is very satisfying, but negotiating prices can be intimidating for many people.

Vendors, on the other hand, expect haggling. It is a time-honored tradition in markets throughout the world. Prices are padded for haggling. I find bargaining a lot of fun—a dance of wills and knowledge.

Using these strategies will help you feel more in control during the trading process.

BARGAINING BASICS

●**Make a quick circuit of the area to see if anything is of interest,** no matter the price. If nothing "tugs at your heart," leave. There will always be another opportunity with a better payoff for your time and money.

●**Calculate your price.** If you spot a *must-have,* mentally calculate the most that you would be willing to pay to acquire it. Consider the item's value in the real world...what you think the vendor will want for it...and its value to you.

Scenarios: You spot a battered World War II medal. In better shape, it might go for $50, but the way it has been just tossed in a pile of costume jewelry, the seller might accept $10. You decide you would love it for your collection even if you had to spend $15.

If you do not know an object's worth: Compare prices around the market for similar pieces...or bid at another time, after you have done some research.

●**Engage the vendor.** First, hang around the vendor's stall to watch how the vendor operates. Does he/she set firm prices? How far does he budge from his asking price? Is he pleasant? Knowledgeable? Or scattered and careless?

Once you have sized up the situation, eye the object you want. Pick it up. Examine it carefully for defects. Look for a manufacturer's mark, which makes it more desirable, etc. The vendor will notice your interest, and the courtship game begins.

THE DIALOGUE OF TRADE

For those embarrassed or intimidated by the thought of bargaining, here's how a typical bargaining session progresses. *Use it as a basic script to guide you through the process...*

You make eye contact with the vendor and eye the object to acknowledge you are interested in a deal.

How much? you ask casually. He responds firmly with a dollar amount. You examine the object again, taking your time.

If you decide to continue, make a counteroffer—usually one-half to one-third lower than the initial price. Say hesitantly, *I don't know. I don't really need it. How about $____?*

The vendor might communicate *nothing doing* by shaking his head or muttering something like, *It's worth more to me to just cart it away.*

If the vendor appears unwilling to play (he walks off or doesn't respond), move on.

If, on the other hand, he studies you and/or the item and maybe relates a tale about it, you might then ask, *What's your best price?*

For good measure, suggest that you may sell it to someone else. Doing so drives home the point that you need a competitive price. At this juncture, you rejoin with, *My absolute ceiling figure is $____!* Choose a number that is just a bit lower than your real limit…or wait for the vendor's final offer.

CLOSURE

While the bargaining process might seem confrontational, closure should be a win-win situation.

Once you agree on a price, handshakes, a joke or two and smiles all around are in order. As the vendor wraps your prize, tell him how much you love the object and what a treasure trove his stall is. Along with your cash, this cements the deal and opens the door for future trading.

BARGAINING SAVVY

Not all outdoor markets are the same. Modify your tactics for where you are and what is being sold.

•**Roadside flea market.** A regularly held market where anybody can sell anything— soap, household gadgets, handmade items, baked goods, old books, etc.

Prices are marked, but bargaining is expected. If you buy two or more things from a dealer, always get a special deal.

Make sure you want what you buy and are not just swept up in the "high" of trading. This year's prize can land in your garage sale next season.

•**Outdoor antique show.** For serious collectors of old postcards, quilts, antique furniture, etc. Trade publications, which can often be found in antique stores, and Web sites, such as *www.openair.org* or *www.collectors.org*, post details about these fairs.

Arrive before the show opens (admission fees may be higher at that time) when antique dealers are searching for finds.

•**Estate sales.** The contents of an upscale property must be disbanded. The sales are often professionally run. Find out about them from local newspapers or roadside signs.

Offerings can range from antiques and rugs to linens and kitchen items. My best deals have come from these.

Example: A green-painted armchair, for which I paid $25, turned out to be a 19th-century mahogany piece worth $800 once the finish had been restored and the seat re-covered.

Prices are marked, but negotiations are always in order. At the end of the tag sale or flea market, things fly out at unbelievable bargains.

•**Garage sales/yard sales.** Basically offer other people's "junk." Chances to mine diamonds in the rough improve when you confine yourself to nicer neighborhoods.

Heirlooms picked up for a song can be sought-after antiques…and throwaway doodads can be transformed into treasures for your home with some imagination.

Much Shrewder Car Buying

No matter what car price you have negotiated, a salesperson typically will make at least three more attempts to raise the price.

He/she will tell you that the manager won't approve the deal—but in reality he won't talk with the manager until he has tried to bump up the price several times. *Self-defense…*

•**Before shopping,** use the Internet to find the "true" best price for the car you are considering at Web sites such as *www.carsdirect.com* and *www.kbb.com*.

•**Use prices from one dealer** (or the Internet) to work against the others. This improves your chances of getting the best deal.

•**Not happy?** Leave your number and walk out. Many salespeople will call within 24 hours to match the price quoted by the competition.

David Solomon, president, Nutz & Boltz, automotive information membership organization, Box 123, Butler, MD 21023. *www.motorminute.com.*

How to Cut the Cost Of Car Insurance

Jack Gillis, director of public affairs at the Consumer Federation of America, 1424 16 St. NW, Washington, DC 20036. He is author of *The Car Book*. HarperCollins.

Despite declining auto insurance rates, 75% of car owners haven't changed their insurance policies—or even inquired about doing so—within the last five years.

How can you pay less for your insurance coverage…

● **Compare policy rates on the Web.** This process takes about a half hour. First look at the sample rates charged by all insurers that do business in your state.

● *www.insure.com* provides a link to every state insurance department. At the home page, enter your state in the box labeled "insurance in your state."

Once you have a benchmark rate, visit a site that can locate policies with the lowest rates.

● Insweb *(www.insweb.com)* and Quicken Insurance *(www.insweb.com/quicken)*. You type in the information about your driving history. Then these Web sites sift through the insurance companies in their databases to find the ones that have the lowest prices. These services are free.

● **Shop aggressively every two years.** Different insurers target certain types of drivers at different times and then offer lower rates based on how closely you fit their preferred "top tier" profiles.

You're a candidate for a lower rate whenever…

● Points are removed from your license.

● One of your cars is removed from your policy.

● Your kids no longer drive your car.

● Your car is no longer used for commuting.

● **Maximize your policy's discounts.** Discounts can cut your premium in half. Most insurers offer as many as 20 different discounts. Most don't tell you about all of them unless you specifically ask. *Helpful…*

● Air bags

● Antilock brakes

● Antitheft devices

● Car-pool drivers

● Graduates of driver-training courses

● Low mileage

● Multiple policies

● No accident in three years

● Nonsmokers

● Older drivers who don't drive at night

● **Ask groups if they offer low-rate policies.** More insurers now offer organizations group policies that have discounted rates for members.

Examples: Retirement organizations, alumni associations, credit unions…and some credit card issuers, too.

● **Eliminate unnecessary coverage.** Increasing your monthly deductible from $200 to $500 could reduce your collision and comprehensive premiums by as much as 30%.

Consider eliminating collision and comprehensive coverage if your car is paid off…more than four years old…or worth less than $4,000.

To research car values: National Automobile Dealers Association *(www.nada.com)*…or Kelley Blue Book *(www.kbb.com)*.

● **Buy a less desirable—or safer—car.** Buying a model that is a favorite with thieves or statistically in frequent accidents can send your premiums sky-high.

For cars with low theft rates: The National Insurance Crime Bureau *(www.nicb.com)*.

For cars with the highest safety ratings: Insurance Institute for Highway Safety *(www.highwaysafety.org)*.

Car Buying Trap

Used fleet and rental cars are rarely good bargains for personal transportation. While these cars are maintained by the fleet or rental-service garage, only the *normal* service maintenance schedule is followed—even though the cars experience severe usage and should receive extra maintenance. *Result:* They are more likely to develop mechanical problems than used cars purchased from individuals. *Self-defense:* Ask to see documents of previous ownership before buying a used car. Have your mechanic check for neglect, abuse, odometer rollback or flood damage.

David Solomon, president, Nutz & Boltz, automotive information membership organization, Box 123, Butler, MD 21023. *www.motorminute.com.*

Slash New-Car Costs

Car buyers can save hundreds of dollars by *factory-ordering* a car. *Reasons:* You pay only for options you want…and can negotiate with multiple dealers for *precisely* the same car. *Downside:* Delivery may take six weeks or longer…and if a major incentive is due to expire before you take delivery, the deal may not be extended. *To get the best deal:* Determine the precise model, options, etc. that you want …research prices at such free Web sites as Kelley Blue Book *(www.kbb.com)* and Edmunds *(www.edmunds.com)*…then check the average transaction price at *www.autoadvisor.com.* Use the lowest Internet price as leverage with local dealers.

Ashly Knapp, CEO of AutoAdvisor.com, nationwide vehicle buying and consulting service.

Free or Almost Free Health Care

Matthew Lesko, a syndicated columnist based in Kensington, MD, who specializes in advice on receiving free services. He is author of *Free Health Care!* Information USA. His Web site is *www.lesko.com.*

There are many ways to get free or low-cost checkups…vaccinations…drugs… even surgery and dental care.

To receive this care, it's not necessary to be unemployed, elderly or in a low-income bracket. Nor is it essential to have some rare disease. In many cases, all that's required is the willingness to do a little detective work on the phone or on the Internet…

● **Visit a government health clinic.** Free checkups, vaccinations and other kinds of care are offered at clinics operated by state and municipal governments. Some clinics provide free prenatal and well-child care, too.

More information: Call your state public health department. The number should be listed in your phone book's "blue pages." Or call your state medical association.

Hint: Bring along a book or magazine. Government health clinics are busy—and noisy—places and they don't make appointments. Expect to spend more time than usual in the waiting room.

● **Get free medications.** Most pharmaceutical manufacturers have programs that provide medicine for free. These are often called "indigent programs." In fact, however, the income requirements are often quite lenient. People with an annual household income of up to $45,000 are sometimes eligible.

The request for the medication must come from the patient's doctor.

More information: Visit the Web site of the Pharmaceutical Research and Manufacturers of America at *www.phrma.org.* The site lists companies that provide free medication, types of medication available and information about applying.

● **Get care at a dental school.** There are 53 dental schools in the US. All operate clinics that provide basic services at great savings. That includes checkups, cleaning, X rays and fillings.

More advanced services such as fitting bridges, dentures and implants may also be available.

Student dentists do the work but are closely supervised by their professors.

Bonus: Care may be free for conditions the professors are studying.

More information: To locate a nearby dental school, visit the American Dental Association Web site at *www.ada.org.* Click on "Education" and follow the links. Or call local universities and ask if they have dental schools.

● **Join a clinical study.** The National Institutes of Health (NIH) spends billions of dollars annually to study cutting-edge treatments for every imaginable ailment. Physicians conducting these studies always need patients to participate.

The NIH conducts some studies at its Clinical Center in Bethesda, Maryland. But most are conducted at academic medical centers across the country.

Important: Some NIH studies compare the effectiveness of new treatments with placebos and/or standard treatment. Participants are assigned randomly to study groups and they cannot choose the treatment they will receive.

More information: Visit the NIH Web site at *www.clinicaltrials.gov*. It lists studies by condition, explains requirements for joining and identifies researchers to contact.

If you lack access to the Internet, call the NIH Clinical Center at 800-411-1222 or *www.cc. nih.gov*.

• **Get a free "second opinion."** The proliferation of Web sites devoted to health and medicine makes it easy to learn about virtually any condition. *Some reliable sites...*

• MayoClinic.com, the site of the Mayo Clinic *(www.mayoclinic.com/index.cfm?)*.

• CBS Health Watch, the consumer health Web site maintained by Medscape, a comprehensive site for physicians *(www.cbsnews.com,* then click on "Health Watch").

• Intelihealth, featuring Harvard Medical School's consumer health information *(www.inteli health.com)*.

Another option: For nearly every condition, there's an organization and/or government agency that provides printed material for no more than the cost of a stamped, self-addressed envelope.

More information: Contact the National Health Information Center in Washington, DC. *www.health.gov/nhic*. 800-336-4797. It will direct you to the appropriate organization for your condition.

8

Secrets of Living Longer and Better

It's Important to Take Charge of Old Age Now

It's no longer news that more Americans are living longer—the 75-plus and 85-plus age groups are the fastest growing segments of the US population. But for the first time, we can benefit from studies that tell us not only who is living longer, but why—and what we can do to enrich and lengthen our lives.

Research consistently shows that there is more to healthful aging than just staying physically fit. Maintaining strong social ties plays an essential role. And a third factor, less frequently discussed, is also important…a sense of personal purpose. *Bottom line:* People who lead purposeful lives live longer than those who do not.

PHYSICAL HEALTH: BASIC LIFE-EXTENDERS

● **Eliminate tobacco,** regardless of your present age and health status.

● **Drink alcohol in moderation,** if at all. If you are one of the nation's 10 million alcoholics, get help. There are very, very few elderly alcoholics.

● **Lower the amount of fat in your diet.** Most Americans get up to 40% of their calories from fat. *Better:* 10% to 20%.

● **Mediate the effects of stress with exercise and other techniques.**

● **Exercise for a half-hour daily, five days a week.** Choose a solid cardiopulmonary program. Fast walking is inexpensive and effective.

Caution: Golf is not recommended. It is not an aerobic exercise, and can be stressful if combined with business.

MENTAL HEALTH AND ABILITIES

Contrary to popular belief (and barring disease), intelligence does not decline with age.

Robert N. Butler, MD, chairman of the department of geriatrics at Mount Sinai School of Medicine, Mount Sinai Hospital, New York. He is coauthor of *Aging and Mental Health*. Macmillan.

While reaction speed does slow, some abilities such as judgment, accuracy and general knowledge may actually increase as learning continues. *Important:* Ongoing stimulation.

In terms of human development, one of the essential tasks of old age is to find ways to understand and use the lessons of one's lifetime. This entails learning to apportion one's strengths and resources, and to adapt to changes and losses as they occur.

Key: People must continue to adapt to stay healthy, both mentally and physically. Failure to adapt to changing circumstances can result in physical or mental illness at any age.

A comprehensive Seattle study found wide variation in intellectual changes among individuals as they aged. A large number showed little decline, even in their 80s. *What they had in common:* These people had no cardiovascular disease, were not poor, were actively involved in life...and their attitudes and behavior were already flexible in midlife, and remained so.

Expect some emotional changes with aging. *Most common:* Family authority roles begin to reverse, usually in the mid-50s. Women tend to grow more active and assertive, while men tend to become more nurturing. This pattern occurs in many cultures, and should be supported, as each sex explores potentials that may have been neglected in earlier life.

Recommended: Encourage men to share and network, women to be more self-determining and active in the world beyond their families.

Helpful to men: Beginning to recognize and develop your nurturing side now, whatever your age, can help prevent or alleviate the common syndrome of stress, coronary disease and shortened life expectancy associated with overidentification with work and subsequent "retirement shock."

OTHER CHANGES TO EXPECT—AND SUPPORT

•**Desire to leave a legacy.** *This can take many forms:* Artwork, fortune, grandchildren, possessions, family recipes, memories in the minds of others. Many older people find the role of "elder" (counselor, mentor, teacher) to be particularly enriching.

•**Altered sense of time.** Older people tend to lose both "time panic" and boredom, in favor of a sense of time based on the appreciation of the truly important things in life... human relationships, nature, etc. *Result:* An ability to live in the moment that can make old age a richly enjoyable time, filled with emotional and sensory awareness. Older people also experience a personal sense of the cycle of life and one's place in the cycle...for many, a deepening of spiritual beliefs.

•**Creativity and curiosity.** Most older people stay productive and active their entire lives, barring ill health or social problems, such as poverty. *Less well known:* Many older people become creative for the first time in their lives. *Keys:* An attitude of curiosity and the ability to be surprised throughout one's lifetime.

•**Feelings of serenity, wisdom, fulfillment.** As older people come to accept the inevitability of death, feelings of satisfaction with one's life, of having done one's best, of having survived life's challenges, are more common than generally believed—though not as common as possible. The process of reminiscence that characterizes old age is essential to the emotional well-being of older people, as they work to resolve past conflicts and find significance in their life history.

Recommended: Make examining personal conflicts and reviewing your life a habit. Listen and support the process in the elderly. It can be hurtful, even devastating, for an older person to be told his/her life story is boring or unimportant.

SOCIAL HEALTH

People who have healthy social networks have less disease and live longer than those who do not. A study of men and women over age 65 conducted at Duke University Medical Center found the risk of mortality to be four times greater in people who had little social support, even when other factors, such as gender, health, smoking, economic status, depression, etc., were considered.

A Swedish study found that social isolation is one of the best predictors of mortality from all causes. Other studies have found that individuals who are "self-starters," able to initiate new social contacts and activities, have the least disease and the longest survival rates.

Researchers are just starting to appreciate the importance of friendship at all phases of life. In addition to immediate family, friends are seen as "family" by many older persons, and they lend important support in times of need.

Studies are beginning to show that one reason women may outlive men is their greater skill in seeking and maintaining friendships. Mortality following the loss of a spouse is also lower in women, due in part to their better social networks.

Recommended: Use the telephone, write letters and cards, attend reunions. Nurture friendships with people of all ages throughout your lifetime. While many consider retirement communities to be artificially segregated environments, studies show older people who live among other older people make more friends than those who live among the young.

Caution: American cultural beliefs about independence and "doing for oneself" can foster a sense of isolation in people who resist help when it is needed. By contrast, people in group-oriented societies (Israeli kibbutzim, for example) can accept the support of others with no loss of self-esteem or feelings of dependence.

Recommended: Make use of support groups in the times of grief, stress or loss that are an inevitable part of life: Illness, widowhood, family crisis. *Also very useful:* Humor, a healing mechanism and coping skill that is underused in the elderly.

A SENSE OF PURPOSE

One's goal or purpose in later life (or any other time) need not be lofty. A sense of purpose can be derived from volunteer work, one's role as a grandparent or an attachment to the New York Yankees. Retirees who organize their daily lives to accommodate their goals live longer than those who do not.

Example: A University of Michigan study found that men who did volunteer work at least once a week were two-and-a-half times less likely to die than those who did none.

Caution: The highest suicide rate in America is among white men in their 80s. *Reason:* This group suffers the greatest loss of power, influence and status, and can therefore experience the greatest sense of helplessness and impotence.

Essential: Maintaining the deep sense of self-esteem that is derived from inner purpose.

Recommended: Begin now to make good use of your time…tutor, fund-raise, work for a cause you admire. *Key:* Choose a regularized activity that is outside yourself.

Make Your "Real Age" Younger

This is the age that reflects your health and life expectancy, rather than chronological age. An analysis of hundreds of factors in numerous health studies identifies how they affect your "Real Age"—some very surprisingly.

Example: Flossing regularly reduces "Real Age" by 6.4 years because bacteria that attack gums can trigger an immune reaction that harms arteries and leads to stroke, heart disease and memory loss.

Over two million people have taken the comprehensive "Real Age test" on the Internet at *www.realage.com,* a site which also has many other useful health resources.

Michael Roizen, MD, dean of the College of Medicine and vice president for biomedical sciences, State University of New York, Upstate Medical University, Syracuse.

Living Life to the Fullest… In the Later Years

Phillip Berman and Connie Goldman, authors of *The Ageless Spirit: Reflections on Living Life to the Fullest in Our Later Years.* Ballantine Books.

Aging is so often thought of in our society as an entirely negative experience. So—we spoke with 40 people over the age of 60 about their experiences in aging.

We asked each person: "What can you say in praise of age?" *Their answers were inspiring...*

Maturity turns out to give us a chance to do many new things and to develop ourselves in new ways. *Suggestions from the people we interviewed...*

●**Develop a new avocation.** It's important to develop a vital, challenging interest that you can take up when you retire. This is especially important for people who, after years of work, have grown tired of their jobs. They look forward to retirement and then find themselves bored, with too much time on their hands, and they become depressed or even ill.

If you develop an avocational interest that's an alternative to your work well in advance of retirement, you will be able to make the transition with much less stress and sense of loss.

Example: Radio and television broadcaster Art Linkletter has used his "retirement years" to start a new career as a writer, using his personal experiences of aging as the basis for his work. His book, *Old Age is Not for Sissies,* which focuses on the joys and pains of late life, became a national best-seller.

●**Retirement is a full-time job.** A regular job consumes 35 or 40 hours a week—more if you factor in commuting. But if you're retired, you're retired 24 hours a day, seven days a week. And you alone have the responsibility for how your day turns out. Structuring your own time is a skill that has to be learned. That's particularly so if you've spent your life in a corporation, where a lot of structure was provided. Some retired people can't find enough activities they enjoy to fill their time, while others, like former Time Warner executive Dick Munroe, find retirement to be busier than full-time work. "I love what I'm doing. I love not doing what I used to do," explains Munroe, "I'm just doing too many things and I should fix that!"

So find things you love to do and learn to say no to anything else.

●**Value your own experience.** Americans undervalue experience. We're so hooked on youth that we haven't yet recognized that inexperience isn't always a virtue, and knowing what you're doing isn't a handicap.

For people who stay open to change and growth throughout their lives, the mature years can prove to be unexpectedly rewarding.

The late writer May Sarton told us she was glad to be old. She had solved a lot of problems that are very anguishing for young people, and she had come to terms with her own life in ways that made life much easier.

The late Norman Cousins spoke very specifically about being in the harvest years. He told us that he was using everything he had ever learned, everything he had ever done or known, and using it better than he ever had before. He could accomplish things with greater economy of effort than when he was younger.

The more you learn, the more you will ultimately be able to do. In a long life, you will have time to develop skills you don't have now but would like to. And when you have assembled them you will be able to use and truly enjoy them.

●**Become wise.** You don't necessarily grow wise as you grow old. Wisdom isn't part of the biological process of aging. But you can work to develop it. Wisdom comes from wrestling with our experiences, making sense out of them...enjoying life's pleasures, letting go of its sorrows and mistakes, and moving forward.

Many of the people that we interviewed found great security in the knowledge gained through aging of what their moral values were and what's valuable in life. Dancer and choreographer Bella Lewitsky told us, "As I've aged I've grown more confident in my own values and at the same time more tolerant of differences."

●**Take time to enjoy the simple things in life.** We have the idea as we come into the later years that if we do nothing, or very simple things, we're not using our time very well.

The late writer Eve Merriam talked about how she relished the change of seasons, particularly the coming of spring, finding what she called daily joy in the colors and fragrances of the trees and flowers.

●**Explore your inner life.** Young adulthood and middle age don't leave us much time to explore the heart and spirit deeply. As the outer life shrinks, there's room for a great deal of inner growth for most people. Although we continue to need the nourishment of other human beings of all ages in our lives, we also need quiet and solitude to explore the inner self.

Through this self-exploration, many of the people we interviewed developed a strong spiritual sense as they grew older—and found that to be one of the richest aspects of aging. This spirituality was often connected with a reverence for nature.

Clarinetist Rosario Mazzeo finds his spiritual connection in nature and takes long walks in the woods every day.

●**The challenge of physical changes.** There's general agreement that the worst thing about aging is the physical erosion that often accompanies the later years—the slowing up of the body.

The attitude that you take toward your physical aging is extremely important. Actor Hume Cronyn spoke about the lines on his face, "Let them get deeper—particularly the laugh lines!"

Important: Deal with physical limitations and needs to care for yourself. Then move past them and focus on the many satisfactions that are possible out there.

While the body is subject to deterioration, the person inside has a continued capacity for growth, whatever the body's age.

●**Understand the value of life.** The best way to get the most out of life is to come to terms with mortality. The late actor Jason Robards once told us that to him, life is like a hotel—everybody checks in and everybody checks out. Once he fully grasped this, he was able to truly savor each day.

It is in fact the sense of the preciousness of time that we acquire as we get older which should fill our later years with a new richness and intensity.

The late songwriter and singer Burl Ives found that contemplating death gave him a renewed sense of joy in life.

●**Forget the myths.** If we want a richer later life, we have to take responsibility for achieving it. We can't accept the myths that "old is over," and that only youth matters. We must learn to appreciate and give thanks for the many gifts that aging brings us.

How We Can Slow Our Aging Processes

Deepak Chopra, MD, executive director for the Institute for Mind/Body Medicine, San Diego, CA. He is author of *Ageless Body, Timeless Mind: The Quantum Alternative to Growing Old*. Harmony Books.

Today, people are living longer, but enjoying it less. Many of us fear old age as a period of declining powers and failing health. But if we learn to replace that fear by a positive attitude, an enhanced physical and spiritual awareness of our bodies and a sensible pattern of activity, we can expect to enjoy the blessings of a vigorous and healthy old age.

A century ago, less than one person in 10 reached the age of 65. Most of those who did live that long had been worn out by a lifetime of inadequate nutrition…widespread disease …backbreaking physical labor. Their remaining years were difficult not because they were old, but because their bodies were in a state of breakdown.

Today, relieved of those harsh external pressures, most of us will live well into our 60s and 70s…and the physical disease and mental breakdown we fear in old age is largely a result of internal stress we can learn to avoid.

PEOPLE AGE DIFFERENTLY

Your well-being depends far less on your chronological age—how old you are according to the calendar—than on two other indicators…

●**Biological age tells how old your body is** in terms of critical life signs and cellular processes.

Every individual is affected differently by time…in fact, every cell and organ in your body ages on its own timetable.

Example: A middle-aged marathon runner may have leg muscles, heart and lungs of someone half his age, highly stressed knees and kidneys that are aging rapidly and eyesight and hearing declining on their own individual paths.

Most 20-year-olds look alike to a physiologist...but at 70, no two people have bodies that are remotely alike.

●**Psychological age indicates how old you feel.** Depending on what is happening in your life and your attitude to it, your psychological age can change dramatically within a very short period.

Examples: An old woman recalling her first love can suddenly look and sound as if she has just turned 18...a middle-aged man who loses his beloved wife can become a lonely old man within a few weeks.

AGING IS REVERSIBLE

It is not news that psychological age can decrease. *We all know the old proverb:* You are as old as you feel. And—now scientists have learned that biological aging can be reversed.

Example: Muscle mass is a key factor in the body's overall vitality...and it was believed until recently that it inevitably declined with increasing age. But Tufts University researchers discovered that isn't so. They put 12 men, aged 60 to 72, on a weight-training program. After three months, the men could lift heavier boxes than the 25-year-old workers in the lab...and milder weight-training programs proved equally successful for people over 95!

That's not all the good news for aging bodies. *The Tufts team found that regular physical exercise also reverses nine other typical effects of biological age...*

● **Reduced strength**
● **Lower metabolic rate**
● **Excess body fat**
● **Reduced aerobic capacity**
● **Higher blood pressure**
● **Lower blood-sugar tolerance**
● **Higher cholesterol/HDL ratio**
● **Reduced bone density**
● **Poorer body temperature regulation.**

To get optimum benefits from exercise, the type and amount have to be expertly tailored to your individual constitution. You don't have to

be a fitness freak to gain from exercise...just 20 minutes of walking three times a week improves the cholesterol/HDL ratio. No expert advice is needed to benefit from another important route to longevity...a balanced lifestyle.

A study of 7,000 Southern Californians found that the longest-lived followed seven simple rules:

● **Sleep seven to eight hours a night.**
● **Eat breakfast.**
● **Don't eat between meals.**
● **Don't be significantly over- or under-weight.**
● **Engage in regular physical activity**...sports...gardening...long walks.
● **Drink moderately**...not more than two alcoholic drinks a day.
● **Don't smoke.**

The study found that a 45-year-old man who followed these rules could expect to live another 33 years...but if he followed only three of them or less, he would probably die within 22 years.

ROLE OF STRESS

The human body reacts to stress by pumping adrenaline and other powerful hormones into the bloodstream. This "fight or flight" response provides energy for taking rapid action and is vital when you are actually faced with pressing external danger.

But it makes your metabolism work in the direction of breaking your body down instead of building it up.

If it occurs too often or continues too long it produces lasting harmful effects including muscle wasting...diabetes...fatigue...osteoporosis...hypertension...effects typical of aging.

That is why a major contribution to the aging process in modern life comes from situations that do not present real physical dangers but produce dangerous levels of stress.

Example: Our cities are full of unavoidable noise, a serious source of stress. Studies have shown increased levels of mental disorder in people who live under the flight paths near airports... elevated blood pressure in children who live near the Los Angeles airport...more violent behavior in noisy work environments.

Fortunately, we have discovered a number of measures that can reduce the aging effects of stress and other hazards of modern life.

To reduce stress and slow the aging process...

●**Experience silence.** Research has shown that people who meditate have higher levels of DHEA, a hormone that protects against stress and decreases with age. Spending 20 minutes twice a day in calm silence pays great benefits in detaching you from the mad bustle of the world and finding your true self.

●**Avoid toxins**...not only foods and drinks that stress your system, but relationships that produce anger and tension.

●**Shed the need for approval by others** ...it's a sign of fear, another stress factor that promotes aging.

●**Use relationships with others to learn your own self.** People we love provide something we need...those we hate have something we need to get rid of.

●**Change your inner dialogue.** Change from *What's in it for me?* to *How can I help others?* Selfishness is bad for you. Psychologist Larry Scherwitz found that people who used the words *I, me, mine* most often in their conversations had the highest risk of heart disease.

●**Be aware of your body's needs.** You will be healthier if you learn to respond to its signals.

Example: Don't eat by the clock...eat when you're hungry...stop when you're full.

●**Live in the moment.** Much stress comes from living in the past or the future instead of the present.

Example: If you're angry at something that already happened...or fearful of something that may happen...your stress can't produce any useful result now. When those feelings occur, bring yourself back to the present.

●**Become less judgmental.** Don't get stressed by other people's decisions...your viewpoint may not be right for them.

●**Stay in contact with nature.** It will make you feel you want to stay around to enjoy it longer...and your body will respond.

How to Change Your Biological Age

William J. Evans, PhD, chief of the human physiology lab at the Human Nutrition Research Center on Aging, a Boston-based facility operated jointly by the US Department of Agriculture and Tufts University. He is coauthor of *Biomarkers: The 10 Keys for Prolonging Vitality.* Fireside Books.

G ray hair, wrinkled skin, growing flabbiness, loss of vitality and reduced resistance to injury and disease...

To most Americans, these are harbingers of old age, unwelcome but inevitable milestones along a path that leads inexorably to the grave.

In fact, research suggests something quite different—that the body's gradual decline stems not from the passing of years but from the combined effects of inactivity and poor nutrition. So no matter what your present health status or your chronological age, regular exercise and improved eating habits will lower your biological age.

Benefits: Reduced body fat...increased muscle mass...strength increases of 200% to 300%...increases in aerobic capacity by 20% or more...and reduced risk of heart disease, diabetes, osteoporosis and other age-related ailments.

To lose fat and gain muscle: Be sure to combine a low-fat diet with regular exercise.

●**Aerobic capacity.** To gauge fitness, doctors often measure the body's ability to process oxygen during exercise. The greater this aerobic capacity, the faster oxygen is pumped through the body—and the fitter the individual. Like other biomarkers, aerobic capacity often declines with age. Typically, by age 65 it is 30% to 40% below its level in young adulthood.

●**Blood-sugar tolerance.** For most Americans, aging brings about a gradual decline in the body's ability to metabolize blood sugar (glucose). So common is this problem that by age 70, 20% of men and 30% of women are at an increased risk of diabetes, a potential killer.

At special risk for problems: The overweight, the sedentary and those who eat a fatty diet.

Good news: A low-fat, high-fiber diet, combined with regular exercise, will cut your diabetes risk. Be sure to include both strength-building and aerobic exercise in your routine.

•**Cholesterol ratio.** As most of us already know, a high cholesterol level boosts your risk of heart disease. But total cholesterol isn't the only thing that counts.

Very important: The ratio of total cholesterol to HDL (good cholesterol). For older people, the ideal ratio is 4.5 or lower. A person whose total cholesterol is 200 and whose HDL is 50, for example, has a ratio of 200/50, or 4.0.

To lower your ratio: Stop smoking, lose weight, reduce your intake of fatty, cholesterol-rich foods (especially animal products) and exercise regularly.

•**Blood pressure.** In many countries, advancing age brings little, if any, change in blood pressure. In the US, however, where older people tend to be overweight and sedentary, blood pressure does rise with age.

To keep pressure in check: Stay slim, don't smoke, get regular exercise and limit your consumption of fat, salt and alcohol. If these steps fail to regulate pressure, pressure-lowering drugs may be necessary.

•**Bone density.** As we age, our skeletons slowly become weaker and more brittle. While some mineral loss is inevitable, the severe and potentially deadly condition known as osteoporosis is not.

Prevention: Although consuming adequate amounts of calcium a day will retard the loss of bone, that alone rarely does the trick. *Also needed:* Weight-bearing exercise, such as walking, running or cycling.

Not helpful: Swimming and other forms of exercise that do not subject the long bones to the stress of gravity do not build bone strength.

•**Body temperature regulation.** Compared with young people, old people sweat less, get less thirsty and excrete more water in their urine. These seemingly minor changes, which are a part of aging—plus the loss of muscle tissue needed for efficient shivering—hinder the body's ability to regulate its internal temperature, which raises the risk of dehydration in summer and hypothermia in winter.

Important: Force yourself to drink during exercise and in hot weather, even if you're not thirsty.

Sleep Deprivation Danger

While chronic sleep deprivation doesn't make you age *faster,* it appears to increase risk for age-related chronic disorders —such as hypertension and diabetes—earlier in life. *Bottom line:* Adequate and restful sleep is as important for your health as proper nutrition and exercise.

Karine Spiegel, PhD, a research assistant at Free University of Brussels in Belgium. Her study of young men and the impact of sleep debt on metabolic and endocrine function was published in *The Lancet,* 84 Theobald's Rd., London WC1X 8RR.

When researchers deprived 11 young men of four hours' sleep a night for six nights, they found deteriorations in the men's carbohydrate metabolism and endocrine function. These are effects that normally occur with aging, suggesting that sleep deprivation may increase the severity of disorders related to age. *To get a better night's sleep:* Don't eat large meals or drink a lot or exercise close to bedtime...don't smoke...avoid caffeine and alcohol before bed...establish a regular bedtime schedule.

Eve Van Cauter, PhD, research professor, department of medicine, University of Chicago.

Optimists Live Longer

Healthy elderly people living in the community who rated their health as "poor" were two to six times more likely to die within the next four years than those who said their health was "excellent."

Study of individuals 65 and older, and a review of earlier studies by Ellen L. Idler, PhD, associate professor, Institute for Health, Health Care Policy and Aging Research, Rutgers University, New Brunswick, NJ.

Your Ever-Growing Brain

Biologists at Princeton University have found that brains continue to grow new cells throughout life. The study, done on monkeys, whose brains are very similar to humans, showed that no matter how old the brain, new cells are added daily to the cerebral cortex—the part of the brain that controls advanced functions such as learning and memory. It seems likely that this is also true for humans. If so, it reverses previous thinking that the cerebral cortex of adults cannot produce new cells.

Margery Hutter Silver, EdD, associate director, New England Centenarian Study, Harvard Medical School Division on Aging/Beth Israel Deaconness Medical Center.

The Seniors Win!

Older people score higher than younger people on some mental tests. In a recent study, two groups of people, one aged 18 to 39 and the other aged 65 to 85, were asked to press a button when they saw a particular sequence of two letters on a computer screen. The reaction time of both groups was comparable, but the older group made fewer errors, particularly when more distracting letters were added to the test. Researchers theorize that the older people made fewer errors because the age-related decline in memory function makes them less likely to be led astray by misleading contextual information.

Todd Braver, PhD, assistant professor of psychology, Washington University, St. Louis.

You & Your Brain— Your Brain & You

Vernon H. Mark, MD, FACS. He is coauthor, with Jeffrey P. Mark, MS, of *Brain Power.* Houghton Mifflin.

We've all been taught to take care of our bodies so we can live longer, healthier lives. But mere physical survival does not guarantee quality of life. A meaningful life requires the use of a healthy brain.

Although today's Americans live longer than ever, we fill nursing homes at a record rate. *Reason:* It's not loss of physical function that forces most people into a nursing home…it's the loss of mental faculties.

Good news: Barring severe injury or progressive disease—Alzheimer's, Parkinson's, etc.—much loss of brain function is preventable.

AGING AND THE BRAIN

Failing brain function is not normal. It is a sign of disease, injury or neglect.

Although we may lose brain cells as we age, maturing brains compensate for cell loss in ways that increase brain function.

How: The sheath around the nerve fibers grows thicker, improving the transmission of electrical signals in the brain. And the nerve fibers, or dendrites, grow new branches. *Result:* More interconnections for richer, deeper thinking.

Certain kinds of intelligence, however, do decline as we age.

Example: People slowly lose their ability to work out complex problems in theoretical mathematics…although their ability to do simple calculations isn't impaired.

Applied skills—law, medicine, engineering, architecture, etc.—do not deteriorate with age. And areas that depend on interpretation—art, music, drama, etc.—are actually enhanced as wisdom and judgment deepen. The ability to speak and write also improves from age 50 to 70. And philosophers don't hit their stride until they reach 70 or 80.

PREVENTABLE BRAIN DRAINS

For every patient I see with Alzheimer's or another serious brain disorder, I see 20 who are impaired by something that is preventable or treatable. *Common culprits:*

•**Depression.** The number-one reversible cause of memory loss in the elderly.

People who are depressed enough to warrant professional attention suffer from reduced attention span and poor concentration. *Result:* Impaired performance and a loss of the ability to form new memories.

In severe cases, depressed brain function lessens a person's ability to retrieve old memories. In the elderly, depression can mimic Alzheimer's disease.

●**Medication.** Many of the medicines that a lot of older people take—for high blood pressure, sleep disorders, anxiety, emotional problems, etc.—have side effects, some of which can impair the brain.

Older people are often overmedicated, a result of seeking relief from pain and other problems. Most do not tolerate drugs in the same doses they once did. And certain medications—that are perfectly safe on their own—can cause trouble when combined with others.

●**Alcohol.** The number-one brain poison in our society, it's abused by six million Americans. Alcohol breaks down the blood-brain barrier—a built-in defense that normally protects our brain cells from poisons that enter the bloodstream. A person who is alcohol-poisoned can suffer as much disability as a person with a stroke, tumor or brain injury. The difference is in duration, not degree.

Alcohol abusers run a 30% greater risk of suicide than the general population. *Other risks:* Memory loss, vitamin B1 deficiency, seizures, Korsakoff's psychosis (a brain disorder with severe memory loss).

●**Cocaine and other illicit drugs.** Opiates, stimulants, depressants and hallucinogens all penetrate the blood-brain barrier and alter brain function. Cocaine can cause convulsions, stroke and outbursts of violence.

●**Lack of stimulation.** This alone can seriously depress brain function.

Example: A partially blind stroke victim spent two years in a bed positioned so her sighted side faced a blank wall. It appeared her mental faculties were failing, until she was turned to face the world. *Result:* Remarkable improvement.

An interesting, challenging environment promotes increased brain function. Lacking stimulation, brain function and development are interrupted.

Other potential brain drains are physical illness, including stroke, pain, stress, head injury and poor nutrition.

BUILD A BETTER BRAIN

Our brains improve with stimulation. We can enrich our thinking, sharpen our response time and improve our memory with simple techniques of diet and exercise.

●**Diet.** For optimum brain efficiency, avoid excessive salt, saturated fats and sugar. Breakfast should be the big meal of the day. Eat a full breakfast high in protein such as fish, chicken, turkey or soy products. The last meal of the day should be light, and several hours before bed.

Although many doctors do not think that vitamin/mineral supplements are necessary, I do recommend them. *Reason:* Most recommendations are based on what our body needs to avoid vitamin-deficiency-induced diseases, such as scurvy, rickets and pellagra. That's not enough to keep the brain healthy. Various studies correlate increased vitamin intake with improved verbal and nonverbal intelligence, behavior, memory and visual acuity. *Note:* Check with your doctor before you take any supplements.

●**Exercise.** The brain benefits from mental exercise the same way the body does from physical activity. *Suggested:*

●Balance your checkbook without using a calculator. The mathematical centers atrophy with disuse. Math exercises maintain skills and improve concentration and attention.

●Practice printing with your nondominant hand. Start by making large letters. Don't worry if they're not perfect. *Goal:* To develop speech abilities in the nondominant side of your brain. This will facilitate quicker recovery in the event of a stroke.

●Draw geometric figures and designs. You can do this while you're on the phone. Then copy the drawings with your nondominant hand. *Goal:* Improved perception of complex spatial relations and integration of both brain hemispheres.

●Put information you want to remember in a verse or song. Melody and versification are generated in the nondominant hemisphere. Combining melody with lyrics employs the whole brain and improves retrieval.

●Read challenging material. Good choices include histories, technical information, biographies, quality novels by writers with a good grasp of language (Proust, Austen, Stout, etc.). Read aloud. Listen to books on tape.

•Punctuate brain activity with brain rest. Brain rest is not the same as napping or watching TV. Brain rest requires temporarily shutting down some brain function.

Example: Sit quietly, close your eyes and progressively relax the parts of your body that use the brain most—the lips, tongue, thumbs, index fingers and big toes. Learn this exercise when you are not stressed.

•Stay active. Doing is more rewarding and enriching than watching. Sensory stimulation in its active rather than passive forms is terrific brain food. *Suggested:* Don't just look at art—paint...don't just listen to music—play an instrument...don't just read—write.

How to Sharpen Your Memory as You Grow Older... Nine Simple Strategies

Cynthia R. Green, PhD, director of the memory enhancement program at Mount Sinai School of Medicine in New York. She is author of *Total Memory Workout: 8 Easy Steps to Maximum Memory Fitness.* Bantam.

Research suggests that the popular herb *ginkgo biloba* is moderately beneficial in cases of Alzheimer's disease or other forms of dementia.

But there is little indication that ginkgo—or any other herbal or nutritional supplement—boosts mental function in individuals who are healthy.

Memory expert Dr. Cynthia Green shares her strategies for boosting memory and mental function as you grow older...

•**Make a conscious effort to remember.** The brain sorts information by routing it to short-term memory and then either discarding it or storing it in long-term memory.

Memories held in short-term storage are fleeting. Unless you make a conscious effort to remember new events, names, etc., they won't make the transition to long-term storage.

Suppose you're meeting someone for the first time. You may be a bit anxious about making a good impression. If so, you're probably *not* paying close attention to the person ...and you're likely to forget his/her name the instant you hear it.

Better approach: Run the name through your mind several times as soon as you hear it. Repeat it aloud to the person. Also—once it's convenient to do so, you might even jot the name down on a piece of paper.

This process of focusing will help shift the information from short-term storage to long-term storage.

•**Give meaning to information you'd like to remember.** It's easier to recall new information if you embed it with meaning. *There are several ways to do this...*

•Chunking. This involves grouping different bits of information into manageable—and meaningful—groupings.

Consider telephone numbers. They're easy to remember because they're written in chunks. There are three digits for the area code, three for the exchange and four final digits. Remembering an "unchunked" 10-digit number is much more difficult.

Chunking can be used for any number. You can also chunk information in lists. For instance, you might try mentally categorizing the items on a shopping list—produce, cleaning supplies, grain products, etc. That should make it easy to remember them.

•Mental images. Information is easier to remember if you create a mental image to go along with it.

Suppose you meet someone named Chris. You might envision a Christmas tree as a way of giving the name meaning. If you meet a Laura, you might think of a laurel leaf.

•Connections. Grammar school pupils are taught to spell "principal" by mentally connecting it with the word "pal." You can form analogous links for almost any new bit of information.

Say you've been assigned to locker #84 at a health club. To remember your place, consciously take the time to connect it with something already stored in your long-term memory—Orwell's classic novel *1984*, for instance.

•**Commit information to writing.** Date books, calendars and electronic organizers are invaluable memory tools. If you use one, make it a point to consult it at the same time each morning and evening—to make sure things aren't overlooked.

Often, the mere act of writing something down makes it easier to recall—even if you never refer back to what you've written. Of course, if you do forget, you'll have a written record.

•**Create "forget-me-not" spots.** To keep track of car keys, wallets, sunglasses and other easy-to-misplace items, choose a special place in your home where you'll always put them.

Examples: Bowl on a tabletop...kitchen drawer...drawer near the door.

Forget-me-not spots can also be used to hold your to-do lists, letters to be mailed, videotapes to be returned and receipts.

•**Talk to your doctor about your medications.** Memory can be disrupted by certain common medications, including the heartburn drug *cimetidine* (Tagamet) and the antianxiety drug *diazepam* (Valium).

In many cases, memory trouble can be minimized simply by changing to a different drug or lowering the dosage. If you are taking numerous drugs (polypharmacy) ask your doctor whether this could be affecting your memory.

•**Get regular exercise.** In addition to boosting cardiovascular fitness, taking a brisk walk or doing some other form of aerobic exercise every day enhances blood flow to the cerebral cortex. That's the part of the brain most involved in memory and other cognitive skills.

Exercise also reduces the risk for cardiovascular disease, high blood pressure and diabetes. These conditions are risk factors for *vascular dementia,* a memory-robbing condition caused by multiple tiny strokes.

•**Limit caffeine and alcohol intake.** A little caffeine can help you stay alert, but too much can cause anxiety and make it difficult to concentrate. Alcohol can affect the ability to focus.

•**Boost your consumption of fruits and vegetables.** Individuals with high levels of

vitamin C and beta-carotene in their blood score better on tests of memory than do similar people with low levels of antioxidants.

Researchers theorize that antioxidants—which are abundant in fruits and veggies—guard against memory loss by helping to deactivate cell-damaging substances known as *free radicals.*

Good sources of antioxidants: Broccoli, kale, oranges, red peppers and strawberries.

•**Take a daily multivitamin.** Over time, there's a gradual decline in the small intestine's ability to absorb nutrients—vitamin B-12 in particular. Along with thiamine and other B vitamins, B-12 plays a key role in memory and mental function.

To counter this problem, take a daily multivitamin containing 100% of the RDA for vitamins B-6, B-12 and folic acid, in addition to the minerals zinc and boron.

Myths About Memory... And the Realities

Myth: **You can improve your memory by taking dietary supplements**—ginkgo biloba, choline, DHEA, phosphatidylserine, L-carnitine, vinpocetine, etc.

Reality: For most of us, our memory is neither sick nor broken, so it doesn't need to be "cured." You don't need to take a magic potion to have a good memory.

Myth: **Memory lapses are a sign of growing old age.**

Reality: More often than not, they're simply a sign of the times we live in—the Age of Information Overload.

Myth: **Some people just don't have a good memory.**

Reality: There's no such thing as having a "bad" memory. Like other functions, most people have strengths and weaknesses. Some people have good visual memory while others have good aural memory.

Myth: **Memory is a purely intellectual skill.**

Reality: Our memory is an integral part of ourselves, affected by many aspects of our daily lives.

***Myth:* Serious memory loss is an inevitable consequence of aging.**

Reality: Only about 15% of adults age 65 and older develop a degenerative memory disorder such as Alzheimer's disease.

Cynthia R. Green, PhD, director of the memory enhancement program at Mount Sinai School of Medicine in New York. She is author of Total Memory Workout: 8 Easy Steps to Maximum Memory Fitness. *Bantam.*

Predicting Longevity

Childhood personality predicts longevity. Children described as being conscientious and dependable were 35% more likely to live to age 70 than those described as being optimistic and having a sense of humor. The reason for this difference in longevity is unknown.

Howard Friedman, PhD, professor of psychology, University of California, Riverside. His review of data from a study of 1,178 children begun in the early 1920s was published in the Journal of Personality and Social Psychology, *750 First St. NE, Washington, DC 20002.*

Most Causes of Death Are Preventable

Officially, the top 10 causes of death in the US, in order, are heart disease, cancer, stroke, accidental injury, lung disease, pneumonia/influenza, diabetes, suicide, liver disease and AIDS.

But these categories camouflage the true, underlying causes of death—most of which are preventable.

In a single year…

…tobacco kills 400,000 people. Causes cancer, heart disease and stroke.

…diet/inactivity kills 300,000 people. Causes high blood pressure, diabetes and cancer of the colon, breast and prostate.

…alcohol kills 100,000. Causes cirrhosis of the liver, cancer and unintentional injury from car wrecks and other mishaps.

…infections kill 90,000. Includes meningitis, encephalitis and other parasitic diseases.

…toxic agents kill 60,000. Includes contaminated food and water, chemical additives, asbestos, lead and radon.

…motor vehicles kill 47,000. Using seat belts, air bags, child car seats and motorcycle helmets would halve this number.

…firearms kill 36,000.

…sexually transmitted diseases kill 30,000. Includes AIDS, hepatitis and cervical cancer.

…illegal drugs kill 20,000. Drugs account for a large portion of the deaths officially attributed to suicide, homicide, car accidents, AIDS and more.

J. Michael McGinnis, MD, deputy assistant secretary for health (disease prevention and health promotion), US Department of Health and Human Services, Washington, DC. His research on the actual causes of death was published in the Journal of the American Medical Association, *515 N. State St., Chicago 60610.*

Grains for Longevity

In a recent 10-year study, the death rate among people who ate at least one serving of *whole* grains a day was 15% to 20% below the death rate among those who ate only white bread, white rice and other refined grains.

Whole grain foods include whole-wheat, pumpernickel and oatmeal breads…whole-wheat pasta…bulgur…and oatmeal.

David Jacobs, PhD, professor of epidemiology, University of Minnesota School of Public Health, Minneapolis. His study of 38,000 women was published in the American Journal of Public Health, *800 I St. NW, Washington, DC 20001.*

 # Learning Not To Smoke

The American Way of Life Need Not Be Hazardous to Your Health by John Farquhar, MD. W.W. Norton & Co.

Kicking the cigarette habit has less to do with willpower than with acquiring the skills to stop smoking. One widely successful treatment uses a gradual, self-directed learning program.

First, plan to stop smoking during a relatively stable period in your work and social life. Understand your smoking habits by keeping a simple diary that records how many cigarettes you smoke daily and how badly you want each one. Score the craving on a scale of one (automatic, boredom) to four (powerful desire). Firm up your commitment by enlisting a nonsmoking buddy to call up and encourage you several times a week.

Phase out the cigarettes in three stages:

1. Taper. Heavy smokers should reduce to 12 to 15 cigarettes daily. If that's your present level, then reduce to eight or nine a day. Use a smoke suppression drill, a mental learning process, each time you have an urge to smoke. Begin by focusing on the craving; then immediately associate it with a negative effect of smoking, such as filthy lung passages, clogged, fatty arteries or skin wrinkled and aged by carbon monoxide and nicotine. *Next:* Relax and imagine a peaceful scene. Follow up with a pleasant image associated with nonsmoking (smooth skin or greater vitality).

2. How to withdraw. One week before your scheduled quitting date, smoke only four cigarettes a day. Smoke two cigarettes in a 15-minute period. Wait at least an hour, and then smoke the other two. While gulping down the cigarettes, concentrate on the negative sensations: Scratchy throat and lungs, foul breath. Keep up negative thoughts for at least five minutes after finishing the last cigarette.

3. Quit. When a smoking urge arises, conjure up the negative image, relax and follow it with a pleasing fantasy. Also, call your nonsmoking buddy for moral support.

Note: Never label yourself a failure. If you have a relapse, return to the tapering phase, and try the procedure again.

9

Family and Friends

How to Enjoy the Birth Of a New Grandchild

To fully experience the special event, plan to be there for the delivery. If that's not possible, make a trip to see the infant—and the *parents,* of course—as soon as you can.

Why is it so important? Because a grandchild's birth brings the family together. With you on the scene to welcome the baby, the occasion becomes a family celebration. *Special reasons for doing special things...*

- **You can be the family reporter,** recording the birth and accompanying celebration with a camera or a videocamera.

- **Your presence can be a great help to the parents.** Chances are the new parents will have their hands very, very full.

- **The new baby's siblings** will need the kind of attention and support that loving grandparents can provide so well.

A new birth in the family is an important enough event for you or your spouse to take time off work to attend. When you look back on it, a few days of missed work will seem inconsequential by comparison.

PLAN AHEAD

- **Discuss the visit with the parents-to-be** so you'll be able to comply with their wishes.

- **If travel will be necessary,** schedule your vacation for the time of the expected birth—but keep a bag packed, in case your grandchild makes an early arrival.

- **Coordinate your plans with those of the other grandparents** to avoid any conflicts.

- **Find out the hospital rules** from the doctor who'll be performing the delivery. Sometimes grandparents (even grandfathers) are allowed in the delivery room, perhaps in the background to respect the mother's modesty.

Arthur Kornhaber, MD, psychiatrist and president, Foundation for Grandparenting, 108 Farnham Rd., Ojai, CA 93023. He is author of *Grandparent Power: How to Strengthen the Vital Connection Among Grandparents, Parents, and Children.* Crown.

CLOSE ENCOUNTERS

You don't have to be looking over the doctor's shoulder when the baby comes. Indeed, hospital policy or the new parents' wishes may prohibit such an intimate presence. *Exception:* Grandmothers may be allowed in the delivery room, especially if it's their own daughter who's giving birth.

One grandmother who was fortunate enough to help her daughter in the delivery room put it this way: "Helping my daughter give birth was truly an incredible experience. She had a beautiful, unmedicated birth...love and her family surrounded her."

The moment of truth: My own experience delivering babies has shown me that the emotion flowing between new mother and new grandmother at the moment of birth is especially powerful, a time both will cherish forever.

If you can't witness the birth, you can be in the waiting room. Then you can hold the newborn, and present your new grandchild with his/her first teddy bear.

Key: Not only should you be there to welcome the new baby, you should thank the new parents for the incredible gift of a grandchild.

Sometimes, the new parents won't want anyone—even grandparents—in the hospital at all. The thought of relatives sitting impatiently in the waiting room may add to the expectant mother's stress. If that's the case, let the parents-to-be decide how to keep you posted.

SAFE AT HOME

Today, hospitals don't encourage long maternity stays. In most cases, Mom and Baby will be home within a day or two. That's when Grandma and Grandpa are *really needed.*

The new parents may not have provided anything to eat for their return home. If that's the case, why not bring in something special for the happy couple, so they'll have meals for several days?

Grandparents can help in countless ways, from basic housekeeping to making sure that older grandchildren get to and from school and playdates, etc. If there's no live-in housekeeper, one grandparent may actually move in for a while to ease the burden.

Just keeping your eyes open may provide some insights as to how you can help. "I noticed how gingerly my daughter-in-law eased herself into the maple rocker she sat in to nurse my grandson," one grandmother wrote. "I brought her a doughnut pillow and she said it was the best present she received, aside from the baby himself."

Most important: Be sensitive to the wishes and comfort level of the new parents, yet make it clear that you want to provide meaningful support.

In particular, first-time parents may not know what they will need until that need actually arises. Exercise resourcefulness, creativity and good judgment in suggestions you offer.

If you do so, your presence can add immeasurably to this memorable event. The happiness, fulfillment and spiritual joy that every baby brings reach far beyond the new parents to resonate within the hearts of all family members—and that goes double for grandparents!

How to Be a Better Grandparent

Eda LeShan, educator and family counselor. She is author of *Grandparenting in a Changing World.* Newmarket Press.

Those of us who are grandparents grew up in a world far different from today's world.

It was a world of stable families...strict rules of behavior...conventional ideas about the roles of men and women...little concern about crime and environmental destruction. As children, we led a slower paced and far less-stressed life than our grandchildren.

With a more complex world full of more choices, only one thing has not changed...the unconditional love and support grandparents can give their grandchildren.

PARENTS AND GRANDPARENTS

To be good grandparents, we need to accept that our experience bringing up our own children does not entitle us to second-guess them in their current adult role as parents. They have the right to decide how to run their household and bring up their children.

When your children raise their children differently from the way you raised them, it is because they think their ways are better.

If you are uneasy about their choices, make sure you make any suggestions in a diplomatic fashion...and if they still think their way is right, accept it.

Example: Edna insisted her daughter Gloria follow formal rules of behavior from a very early age. Gloria did not want to be so strict with her own child, Antoinette. Edna feels that Gloria has gone too far in the other direction.

She should not say, "Antoinette is never going to learn how to behave herself unless you teach her some manners!"

A better approach: "Do you feel she's too young to learn to say 'please' and 'thank you'? I know there's a difference of opinion whether to teach children by example or by reminding them."

When you "take out" your grandchildren, don't be afraid to spoil them a little bit. Most parents fondly remember similar experiences with their own grandparents and regard it as part of the grandparents' role.

Exception: Be very strict about following health and safety rules set by your children. Grandchildren have to learn that their parents set the rules to protect them and that unconditional love does not mean dangerous permissiveness.

HOW MUCH HELP?

A basic fact of life is that grandparents are older than their children. It is often hard to cope with the demands of lively grandchildren, but it is well worth making an effort to find creative ways to help.

Example: When Eric's wife had to go to the hospital, he called his mother to ask her if he could bring his three young children to stay in her house. Grandma agreed on the spot...and immediately called a nanny agency and hired a full-time baby-sitter.

Later, she told me, "I love the children, they're very cute. I played with them 10 minutes here, 10 minutes there—and it worked out just fine!"

A DEVELOPING RELATIONSHIP

If you live close to your children, they may expect you always to be ready to drop everything and baby-sit at a moment's notice. Don't feel guilty about saying no if it's too much for you.

The most exciting part of being a grandparent is watching a new generation grow up, without all the worries and responsibility you had with your own children.

WHAT TO EXPECT AT DIFFERENT STAGES

•**Infancy.** Small babies need lots of attention...and the new parents need relief. Grandparents can give some by baby-sitting or providing financial aid and moral support.

•**Preschool.** The years from two to five are critical to children's development. Grandparents can help them learn to cope with the complexities of language, feelings and relationships. *Key message to communicate:* Accept feelings, but learn to control behavior.

Example: If your three-year-old grandson calls you a dope, don't just tell him, "It's naughty and rude to say that!" *Better:* "If you're angry at me, you can tell me, but calling me 'dope' hurts my feelings."

•**School age.** Children become more interested in their peers than their grandparents ...but they still enjoy educational adventures. You can read to them...take them to museums and zoos...go on special trips. Show interest in their everyday activities...celebrate their birthdays...express joy at their successes but not disappointment at their failures.

•**Teenagers.** At 12 or 13 they are likely to feel they have outgrown you and may refuse to come along with the family to visit you. Don't despair...they will come back later. You can provide sympathetic reactions to their problems and gently give advice they will accept more easily than their parents'.

•**At all ages.** Tell your grandchildren tales about how you grew up. They will be fascinated to learn what the world was like in a different era...and develop a sense of where they came from.

GRANDCHILDREN WITH DIVORCED PARENTS

With divorce more prevalent than ever before, grandparents can provide the emotional support that their grandchildren need to cope with the emotional damage.

Your grandchildren love both their parents. Avoid taking sides in front of the children, regardless of your opinion of who is at fault.

Try to do your best to maintain a good relationship with your child's ex-spouse, particularly if he/she has custody of your grandchildren.

When divorce is followed by remarriage, you may find yourself with a new set of step-grandchildren. You will help keep the new family stronger if you don't demonstrate favoritism to your own grandchildren.

The most important thing you can teach your grandchildren...

According to a Puerto Rican saying: "If someone has to boast about himself, other people say, 'I guess he has no grandmother.' "

By providing unconditional love to our grandchildren just because they were born, we give them a sense of high self-esteem, the key to a worthwhile life.

Very Tax-Wise Ways to Help Your Grandchildren

Edward Mendlowitz, CPA, partner, Mendlowitz Weitsen, LLP, CPAs, K2 Brier Hill Ct., East Brunswick, NJ 08816. He is author of several books on taxes, including *IRA Distributions: What You Should Know.* Practical Programs, Inc.

Grandparents who are in a financial position to help out their grandchildren may be rewarded for doing so with special tax breaks. *Ways to be of help...*

●**Pay for college.**

Options...

●Fund a Qualified Tuition Plan (QTP). All states now offer some form of qualified tuition plan that allows you to contribute on behalf of your grandchild, and private institutions may also offer prepaid tuition plans. If you're married—and your spouse consents to the gift—gifts up to $110,000 can be fully tax free. *Here's how...*

For example, you can elect on a gift tax return to treat the $140,000 as having been made over five years. You won't pay gift tax because $110,000 spread equally over five years is $22,000 a year, and that's the maximum amount you and your spouse can jointly give a grandchild annually without owing gift tax.

Impact: The estate tax savings potential to you is enormous if you have several grandchildren and can afford to make this gift to each.

Bonus for some: You may be entitled to a state income tax deduction for a portion of your contribution.

●Contribute to a Coverdell education savings account. Depending on your Adjusted Gross Income, you may be able to put up to $2,000 per grandchild into a Coverdell education savings account (ESA). Your grandchild isn't taxed on contributions you make to the ESA, nor on the earnings on the contributions. And—withdrawals for qualified education costs are tax free.

●Pay tuition directly to the school. You can pay tuition for grandchildren or other relatives of any age, in any amount, directly to the school at no gift tax cost to you. This gift tax benefit is in addition to the annual gift tax exclusion (in 2003 and 2004, $11,000, or $22,000 for a married couple who join in making the gift).

●**Pay medical expenses.** Like direct payments of tuition to schools, direct payments of medical expenses on behalf of a grandchild are exempt from gift tax.

●**Make interest-free loans.** As a general rule, if a lender fails to charge interest of at least the applicable federal rate (AFR)—an interest rate set by the IRS and published monthly on *www.irs.gov*—then the lender must report "imputed interest income." This is the interest that would have been earned using the AFR rate.

Exceptions: There's no imputed interest income on loans of up to $10,000. And loans up to $100,000 are free of imputed income if the grandchild's net investment income (investment income minus investment expenses) is $1,000 or less.

If net investment income is more, then imputed interest charged to *you* is limited to the extent of your grandchild's net investment income.

●**Make grandchildren beneficiaries of your IRAs and pensions.** When you die, amounts remaining in your plans will belong automatically to your grandchildren.

Naming a grandchild as beneficiary will allow you to reduce your required post-70½ minimum distributions from the plan.

When you name your grandchild as beneficiary, you can figure your minimum annual distributions based on the longer joint life expectancy of you and your beneficiary/grandchild, minimizing payouts.

● **Transfer assets to grandchildren.** By giving assets to them you may be able to turn income that would be taxable to you at your high tax rate into tax-free income to the grandchildren. Income earned by your grandchildren on the assets may be shielded by their income tax exemption or taxed at their low rates.

● If your grandchild is under age 14, then he/she can receive investment income up to $750 tax free in 2003 ($800 in 2004).

The next $750 ($800 in 2004) of investment income of a child under age 14 is taxed at 10%. Investment income over $1,500 ($1,600 in 2004) is taxed to the grandchild at his parents' top income tax rate.

● If he is 14 or older, he can have investment income up to $750 tax free ($800 in 2004). Investment income over this amount is taxed at the grandchild's tax rates.

● If he is taxed at the 10% or 15% rate on regular income, the rate he pays on capital gains is only 5%.

● **Set up custodial accounts.** Even if your grandchild is just a baby, you can start him off with savings through the use of gifts to custodial accounts. You can set up these accounts with banks, brokerage firms or mutual funds under the *Uniform Transfers (or Gifts) to Minors Act.* Use these accounts to put money aside for your grandchild.

Since the grandchild's Social Security number is on the account, the income is taxed to him under the rules discussed above—the under 14 years of age, over 13 rules.

Caution I: Don't act as the account's custodian yourself. Doing so can result in the money being included in your estate when you die, even though the funds are owned by your grandchild.

Caution II: Before you give money to your grandchild, consider the impact it might have on college financial aid he may be entitled to later on. Funds in a grandchild's name count heavily against grants of aid.

● **Set up a trust fund.** If you want to give substantial assets to your grandchild, it's generally wise to use a trust. This will provide greater control over assets. As long as the trust meets certain requirements, gifts to the trust will qualify for the annual gift tax exclusion even though the grandchild can't touch the money immediately.

Caution: Consult a tax expert to ensure that the trust is a Section 2503(b) or Section 2503(c) trust. These are special trusts endorsed by the Tax Code that allow money put into the trust to qualify for the annual gift tax exclusion.

● **Use life insurance.** Give your grandchild substantial amounts through life insurance. If your child doesn't need the money (he's already got an estate of his own), consider naming a grandchild as beneficiary of your life insurance policy.

If the policy is owned by a trust that's properly set up, your estate will escape tax on the proceeds.

Caution: Consider the impact of the generation-skipping transfer tax.

● **Bring your grandchildren into the business.** You can provide income to your grandchildren while reducing your estate on favorable tax terms. *Here's one way...*

Set up a Family Limited Partnership (FLP). Transfer stocks, real estate or other appreciated assets into the company. Give interests in the FLP to your grandchildren at a discount to the value of the underlying assets of about 30%.

● **Put business assets in a trust for your grandchildren.** If your business is about to buy an asset, consider setting up a trust to buy the asset. Make your grandchild the trust beneficiary and have the business lend the trust the funds to buy the asset.

Charge the trust the AFR to avoid gift tax issues. *Result:* The grandchild will obtain the benefit of the asset's future appreciation—which will be kept out of your estate.

Variation: Instead of using a trust, the same objectives can be accomplished through an FLP.

How to Organize A Family Reunion

Harry McKinzie, author of *Family Reunions: How to Plan Yours.* McKinzie Publishing Co.

You want to reunite with relatives you haven't seen in years, and meet some you've never even heard about.

You want to have a chance to reestablish relationships—even mend some bridges—and make new friendships. That's what a family reunion is all about...and it's worth the effort to organize one.

KEEP IT SIMPLE

Since putting together a reunion takes lots of time and you must pay attention to detail, it is important that you start off right at the beginning with the motto: *Keep it simple.* In order to keep it simple, you need a plan and must be organized. *Here's how to begin...*

GOAL: A BIG TURNOUT

One of the easiest ways to generate enthusiasm for a family reunion is to plan it around a 50th wedding anniversary or the 75th (or 100th) birthday of an older, much-loved family member. Knowing that a great-grandmother or grandfather or the family's oldest living great-aunt will be holding court at the reunion adds excitement to the event and attracts the mature—and the younger—family members to be part of what will be a historic family event.

PULLING YOUR TEAM TOGETHER

Once you have selected the family relative whom you will fete and a date for the reunion, you'll need to plan three initial mailings:

First mailing: Write to every family member and announce the date and occasion for the reunion...and ask for nominations for chairperson, secretary and treasurer for a Family Reunion Executive Committee.

Enclose a form for each position that includes full name, address, date of birth, phone number and qualifications of nominees.

Request that the form be returned within two weeks so a decision can be made quickly. Don't be surprised if you, as the driving force behind the reunion, wind up as chairperson.

Second mailing: Send everyone the names of the nominees, and include a ballot due back in two weeks. This democratic process will imbue the newly elected with legitimate authority.

Third mailing: Announce the names of the Executive Committee, and begin to get the entire family involved by calling for volunteers for the following committees:

●**Communications Committee.** Develops the mailing list. Keeps track of all the correspondence and forms that will be sent to and received from a growing list of family members, including the introductory letter, mailing list, family address and telephone numbers, birthday list and reservation forms.

●**Host Committee.** Chooses the ideal location for the reunion, such as an inn, dude ranch, spa, resort or family home.

●**Travel Committee.** Works with a travel agent to coordinate travel and accommodations...and gets the best price.

●**Welcoming Committee.** Greets and directs family members upon arrival in the host town.

●**Events Committee.** Plans raffles, scholarship awards, family member achievement awards.

●**Meals Committee.** Organizes the food for formal and informal indoor and outdoor events such as picnics, lunches and dances.

How to Help Yourself Heal from Your Spouse's Serious Illness

Rachael Freed, MSW, founder of Minneapolis-based Heartmates, Inc., which provides resources for heart patients and their families.

After a heart attack, life changes forever. We mourn our old innocent ways and our lost certainties. And—we face changes in lifestyle, financial security, retirement and our spouses' physical capabilities.

Learning to live with uncertainty is one of the greatest challenges for the partner of a person with heart disease.

Over the years, you have developed an idea of security. Now the rules have changed.

Important: Give yourself permission to break with family protocol and do whatever it takes to get all of you through. The task of a cardiac couple is to develop a "new normal" that incorporates heart disease.

The upside: A brush with mortality can reorder a couple's priorities for the better.

You don't have the power to eradicate your spouse's heart disease or to eliminate its effects on your life. Your goal is to be prepared to support his/her recovery—*and yours.*

Years after a cardiac event, people expect the heartmate to be a constant cheerleader.

My experience: During the crisis period, friends asked only about the patient. When the emergency was over, they were too uncomfortable to rally around. But I needed help—a lot of help.

GRIEF AND LOSS

After my husband's heart attack, I was coping, but I felt overwhelmed by strong feelings that took months to define. It was the grief that accompanies loss.

Since my husband was alive, how could I be feeling grief and loss? Because our life together had changed forever.

During an early presentation I made to spouses of heart attack survivors, I said, *"You are feeling grief."* Their tears and thanks convinced me that I was on the right track.

YOU'RE A TOP PRIORITY, TOO

The most important person in a heart patient's recovery is not the doctor, but the spouse. To maintain your role as a positive caretaker, you must pay attention to your own recovery.

Example: Airplane travelers are instructed to put their own oxygen masks on before helping someone else.

Taking care of yourself helps you come to terms with a life-changing crisis. *Steps to take…*

●**Make a list.** It should contain actions that would nourish your body, feelings, mind and spirit. Write one on your calendar every day—and do it.

Examples: Listen to music…sit in a chapel …take a walk.

●**Gather information.** Learn how diet, exercise and stress affect heart patients.

●**Confide in someone.** To reduce your sense of isolation, share your concerns with a nonjudgmental sibling, close friend or neighbor.

Many people find great relief by communicating with others in similar situations. *Good resource:* The Heartmates Web site at *www. heartmates.com.*

TAKE YOUR TIME

The nagging fear of another attack always churns below the surface. The fear never disappears entirely, but you'll begin to believe that your mate won't collapse every time he coughs.

Healing is a process, not an event. It takes at least a year, often two, to recover from a spouse's heart attack or cardiac event. No one but you can know the limits of your grieving period.

EMBRACE YOUR HEALING ROLE

Take these steps to reinforce family bonds and your vitality as a couple…

●**Involve the whole family.** The patient and family members may experience different realities. Learn what your family is feeling. At weekly problem-solving meetings, ask each person to describe his greatest concerns. Then discuss them.

Example: If your children are grown and living elsewhere, performing this exercise even once during a visit can break the tension and be extremely helpful.

115

•**Fight your guilt and fear of stressing the patient.** Use caution in all things, but be aware that the patient won't die if you accidentally sprinkle a little salt on his food...use a noisy vacuum cleaner...take some time for yourself...or cry.

•**Repair the heartmate connection.** Fear of communicating is common after the hospital stay has threatened the marriage bond.

The trauma pulls some cardiac couples apart, intensifying existing conflicts. For others, the crisis provides an opportunity for enriching the relationship.

Honest confrontation of the changes in your relationship is a step toward deepening the marriage connection. *Avoid these traps...*

•Concealing your concerns from the patient.

•Thinking you can reduce stress by withholding your anger and other negative feelings.

•Assuming you must always agree with the patient.

•Disregarding your own emotional needs.

•Letting TV preempt precious time to communicate with each other.

SEX: THE UNASKED QUESTION

At my group presentations, people almost never ask about sex. Privately, they are distraught by the silence, isolation and lack of information about impotence.

These misconceptions contribute to spouses' fear and apprehension...

Myth: Sexual activity is hazardous for heart patients.

Reality: For most, not so. The amount of energy expended during sex is roughly equivalent to climbing two flights of stairs. A patient who can do the latter can probably do the former safely.

Myth: Heart disease decreases sexual drive and impairs sexual functioning.

Reality: Fatigue, depression and medications for angina, high blood pressure or palpitations can cause impotence. Fatigue and depression can be treated. If medications are the problem, the doctor may be able to prescribe a different one.

Myth: Heart disease signifies the end of normal sexual activity.

Reality: After a few weeks of recuperation, the overwhelming majority of cardiac couples can resume their sexual relationship...and mend their bond through affection and physical intimacy.

How to Choose Support Groups

Audrey Gartner, director of the National Self-Help Clearinghouse in New York.

Whether you're coping with chronic illness, the loss of a loved one or any of a hundred other problems, chances are there's a support group to help you.

Getting support from people facing the same problems is reassuring...and therapeutic. Studies suggest that participation in a support group lowers psychological stress ...reduces depression...and raises self-esteem. It can also improve the prognosis for a range of ailments, from cancer to heart disease to infertility.

Recent finding: Women with metastatic breast cancer who belonged to a weekly support group survived 18 months longer than similar patients without peer support.

Support groups also provide their members with useful information about diseases and treatment options. That makes these groups more popular than ever in today's managed-health-care-environment, where time with doctors is limited.

INSIDE SUPPORT GROUPS

Groups generally range in size from a few members to about 25. Meetings are held anywhere from once a day to once a month. They usually last an hour or two.

Groups are led by trained lay members or by medical or mental health professionals. Some groups pass the hat or ask for nominal dues.

At meetings, members share feelings and coping strategies. Some groups also enlist experts to talk about relevant topics.

Examples: A diabetes support group asks a doctor to discuss blood sugar management…a phobia group brings in a psychologist to talk about desensitization techniques.

FINDING A GROUP

The nonprofit National Self-Help Clearinghouse (NSHC)* refers callers to one of about 50 regional self-help clearinghouses. Each of these keeps a directory of local support groups.

If there's no regional clearinghouse in an area, the NSHC refers callers to an appropriate national organization, such as the American Cancer Society or the American Heart Association.

Caution: Clearinghouses cannot vouch for every organization in their directories. A referral is not necessarily an endorsement. The responsibility is on the individual to determine if a group is appropriate and likely to be a productive source of help.

ONLINE SUPPORT

Self-help through the Internet can be a godsend for people who are housebound… geographically isolated…lack transportation… or have a condition so rare that their community doesn't have enough potential group members.

It's also appealing to people who want anonymity when discussing embarrassing topics. Internet support groups are great equalizers, too. Members know nothing of each other's age, ethnicity or economic status.

Online support group members may "meet" in chat rooms, post messages to public newsgroups or forums or e-mail other members.

Caution: In the largely unregulated realm of cyberspace, people are free to post inaccurate advice—with none of the accountability inherent in face-to-face group encounters.

As with all information you find on the Web, consider the source. Groups affiliated with well-known national organizations are safe bets, although these account for relatively few of the thousands of online self-help options.

*The NSHC can be reached at 212-817-1822 or *www.selfhelpweb.org*. Or mail a request for information, along with a self-addressed, stamped, business-sized envelope, to the NSHC at 365 Fifth Ave., Suite 3300, New York 10016-4309.

For the remainder, it's a good idea to visit a new group several times to get a feel for its content and members before joining.

Whenever possible, send an e-mail to the group's administrator, whose address may be posted on the Web site. He/she can give you basic information about the group (group size, focus, etc.) before you decide to sign on.

FINDING ONLINE HELP

Three Web sites can be especially helpful in locating an online group that is right for you…

●**drkoop.com** *(www.drkoop.com).* Headed by former Surgeon General C. Everett Koop, MD, this site hosts message boards on a range of physical and mental ailments.

●**Mental Help Net** *(www.mentalhelp. net).* This site provides links to dozens of groups focusing on topics from anxiety to depression to eating disorders.

●**Psych Central** *(www.psychcentral. com).* This site has links to hundreds of live chats and newsgroups on psychology and general mental health topics.

QUALITY CHECKS

As you assess an online or face-to-face group to decide if it's right for you, watch for these signs of potential trouble…

●**One or two people monopolize the conversation.** Every participant should feel free to contribute—or not. Groups should not become sounding boards for a few members' troubles.

●**The advice seems inappropriate.** Group members may insist, for instance, that other members take a particular action or use a certain medication or therapy. If you feel bullied, leave the group.

●**Members are urged to substitute self-help for professional diagnosis and treatment.** Self-help is a valuable adjunct to proper medical care—never a replacement for it.

Funeral Planning Trap

Prepaying for a funeral is a bad investment. *Problems:* It locks in arrangements that do not take into account that the person's wishes may change—such as after a divorce or remarriage. Also, the funeral industry is undergoing significant restructuring as more low-cost funeral operations are opening. The cost of a funeral may be significantly less in the future than it is today. *Better:* Fund funeral expenses within your estate assets unless you are applying for Medicaid. *Average funeral cost today:* $500 to $1,500 for a basic cremation...and $5,000 to $10,000 for an elaborate funeral.

Lisa Carlson, executive director, Funeral Consumers Alliance, a nonprofit group that monitors the funeral industry, Hinesburg, VT, and author of *Caring for the Dead.* Upper Access Publishers.

Lessons from Widowhood

Dr. Joyce Brothers, noted psychologist and author of *Widowed.* Ballantine Books.

My husband, Dr. Milton Brothers, died several years ago. As a psychologist, I knew that bereaved people pass through a predictable series of stages in the normal course of grieving, but this knowledge did not make my personal emotional turmoil any less.

EMOTIONAL RECOVERY

For months after losing Milton, after almost 40 years of an intensely happy marriage, I was in a state of despair...even though I was financially secure and my career kept me constantly busy. All my lecturing, writing and traveling seemed meaningless without my husband to share it. I was overcome by agonizing loneliness.

Today, the loneliness is still there, but it is much less intense. Life has recovered its meaning. Once again, I am able to look forward to new experiences and when I think of my husband, most of the time it brings not tears but smiles because of the legacy of happy memories he left me.

STAGES OF GRIEF

British psychiatrist Dr. Colin Parkes discovered the predictable stages of grief following the loss of a spouse or other close relative.

First stage: Immediately following the death is shock...followed by numbness.

Even though Milt had been struggling for 18 months with terminal cancer, his death still came as a dramatic shock to me.

In the immediate aftermath, I was kept so busy notifying relatives and friends and arranging the details of the funeral that I was essentially operating on autopilot, feeling nothing.

To this day, I still cannot remember the details of those days immediately following Milt's death...not even what I wore to the funeral.

Second stage: Suffering. When the numbness wears off, the pain begins.

Every person's pain is different...a different blend of emotions...a different period of time needed to recover.

The pain seems to be least for those who have suffered a lot in life and learned to accept the vicissitudes it brings.

I was not one of those people, because my life had been full of love, happiness and achievement...all shared with Milt.

Now I recognize that my major emotional problem was self-pity. *I cried...*

- **When someone asked how I was.**
- **When I reached out for Milton**—and once again—I remembered him in his absence.
- **Whenever I passed our favorite restaurant.**
- **When I saw Milt's car.**
- **When I recognized Milton's signature.**

Value of tears: When someone cries, it makes others uncomfortable and they usually try to make the person crying feel better. But research has shown that crying fulfills a valuable physiological function.

Tears of sadness or anger contain leucine enkephalin, a natural pain reliever, and prolactin, a hormone that encourages the secretion of tears. These chemicals are produced in the brain at times of stress. This has led biochemists to suggest that crying is an emotionally helpful process that relieves stress by washing out the chemicals that stress builds up.

So I believe that tears are really a widow's friend, helping her deal with the frustrations and difficulties of life without her helpmate.

As I began to emerge from the stage of intense suffering, the nature of my tears began to change. One day, on the farm where my husband and I had spent so many of our favorite hours together, I noticed the coffee pot. I touched it, remembering how much pride Milt always took in the coffee he made, and I cried.

But this time, I realized that I was not shedding tears for myself and my constant loneliness...they were for Milt, dead at only 62, missing out on decades of vibrant life he should have continued to enjoy. I was emerging from the depths.

OTHER REACTIONS

•**Anger.** Along with sadness, I was full of anger, like many widows. I was angry at Milt for leaving me alone to deal with many unfamiliar aspects of life. I was angry at him for continuing to smoke even though he, a physician, certainly knew the association between smoking and disease, including the cancer that killed him. And I was angry whenever I saw couples together, enjoying what I had lost.

It is natural for widows to be angry. The loss of emotional security accompanied by loneliness produces tremendous stress. Stress, say experts like Dr. John Larson of the Institute of Stress Medicine at Norwalk Hospital, deprives brain cells of essential nutrients and leaves the victim irritable and angry.

•**Insecurity.** Widowhood lowers a woman's social status and leaves her feeling insecure in many different ways.

Even though I am something of a celebrity, professionally successful and financially comfortable, I was not immune from insecurity.

One afternoon, a major talk show failed to call me back to confirm the date I was tentatively scheduled for. Normally, I would not have been concerned. But, just six months after Milt's death, I felt they didn't want me on their show...and nobody else would, ever again.

I was only reassured when the scheduler called me again the next morning, explaining that she hadn't been able to speak to the producer earlier.

COPING WITH LOSS

My experience has taught me that nothing can prepare you for the devastating experience of the loss of a loved one. I was not able to manage my grief better than anyone else. *But I have learned firsthand a number of ways a widow can help herself...*

•**Stay in control of your life.** It is very helpful if a child or other close relative offers to take care of all your bills, taxes and financial matters...but don't let the person do it for more than a month or two.

It shouldn't take long to learn how to take care of basic bill paying and check balancing yourself. For tax expertise, you may want to hire an accountant or other professional...but you make the decisions.

•**Avoid hasty decisions.** If possible, a widow should not make any major decisions for at least a year after her husband's death. If you cannot avoid it, get the best advice you can from a variety of sources.

I regret that a few weeks after Milt died I sold his big farm tractor to a neighbor, thinking I would never need it. Now I regret that I didn't keep it and learn to operate it, so that every time I used it, Milt's memory would have ridden along with me.

•**Maintain your regular routine.** Losing a husband is such a shock that it seems hard to do anything. If you succumb to that, you may end up in a long-term state of depression. Pushing yourself to continue your regular activities serves as an early therapy for grief. Later, when the grief has eased, you will find it easier to make changes.

•**Plan anniversaries and holidays**—they are more painful because of the memories they evoke.

Helpful: Surround yourself with people. The first Thanksgiving after Milt's death, I invited 18 people to the farm for Thanksgiving weekend. I was far too busy to feel miserable. If you can't do it with your own family, invite people you know who will be alone otherwise. You will do good for them as well as yourself...always a rewarding experience. Weekends are also times

119

of potential loneliness, so be sure to plan ahead so you have something worthwhile to do…religious services…sports or hobbies.

●**Be good to yourself.** Widows need coddling…so coddle yourself. Get your hair done …have a facial or massage…and be sure to exercise.

●**Check your progress.** Every three months, see how you have progressed. Do you feel better? Are you less depressed? The answer will not always be yes. But as the months pass, you will notice signs of improvement. There is no timetable, but if you see no progress after a year, it may be a good idea to consult your doctor or therapist for advice and reassurance. You will always feel your loss, but with time you should be able to smile once again. I know that I do, especially when the many happy hours I spend with our grandchildren remind me what a joyous legacy Milton left behind.

How to Make New Friends

To create opportunities to strike up new friendships:

●**Carry an interesting book or pamphlet with you.**

●**Wear an unusual T-shirt.**

●**Walk a dog.**

●**Go window shopping.**

●**Have a party and invite each guest to bring a friend, too.**

Take active steps to meet new people…and to become closer to people you already know.

Suggestion: Get more involved with people who share some of your interests.

●**Always attend large family gatherings.** You will find that your relatives are more interesting than you thought when you were a kid.

●**Find out more about the people at work.** Take every opportunity to attend trade shows and conventions where you will have the chance to meet new people.

●**Join service, sports or volunteer organizations.** The other people there all share at least one of your interests. When you get to know them better, you will find some who have even more in common with you.

●**Join specialty clubs such as chess and card clubs.**

●**Enroll in continuing education classes** in subjects you want to learn more about.

●**Visit libraries and bookstores,** especially for author readings and literary discussion groups.

Getting started…

Make a list of specific things you might do to make a friend. If you have trouble thinking of any, begin with some of the suggestions above. Then choose one from your list—*and do it.*

Two weeks later, go back to your list and choose another reaching-out activity.

Perry Treadwell, PhD, a consultant on relationships. He is author of *Making Friends, Leaving Loneliness Behind.* Health Communications.

An Openhearted Hug

When you hug someone you love, take hold of the person and in the first breath, in and out, be totally present with him/her—no place else in the world.

Then hold the person for three breaths.

Nothing more.

Nothing less.

Thich Nhat Hanh, Nobel Peace Prize nominee from Plum Village, France, and author of more than 75 books, including *The Miracle of Mindfulness.* Beacon Press.

The Astounding Healing Power of Pets

Gail Vines, PhD, a science journalist based in Cambridge, England, and author of *Raging Hormones.* University of California Press.

Animals, like babies, can do wonders for the image, which is why politicians try to be photographed with both as often as possible. Every American president in living memory has exploited his pet's electoral appeal.

Millie Bush, the former president's Spaniel, wrote a best-seller and Socks Clinton, former First Cat of the White House, had his own newsletter. But are companion animals as good for your health as they are for the profile?

Public health experts have long been skeptical. After all, dogs bite and pass on parasites, pigeons and parrots cause lung disease, cats can provoke asthma and tortoises can transmit salmonella. Yet animal lovers should take heart from several findings.

In 1991, researchers at the University of Cambridge discovered that just months after acquiring a cat or a dog, some Britons suffered less from perennial health problems such as headache, backache and flu. And Australians who keep pets were found to have less cholesterol in their blood than non-pet owners with comparable lifestyles, making them less likely to develop heart disease.

These findings may be little more than puzzling correlations. Why should owning a pet make you less likely to suffer from backache? Why should it reduce your cholesterol level? But many researchers suspect that the answers are in the subtle links between mental and physical well-being.

PETS AND LONGEVITY

The first hint that pets could help some people to live longer came from a discovery made by Erica Friedmann, at the time a graduate student at the University of Maryland and later at the City University of New York. She investigated whether a person's social life and degree of social isolation might influence his/her ability to survive a heart attack.

Friedmann interviewed 92 convalescing male patients and quizzed them in detail about their lifestyle, a few questions touching upon pets. A year later 14 of the 92 men had died. Friedmann went back to her data to look for differences between those who had and those who had not survived. She found that socially isolated people were more likely to succumb, and that those who had pets were more likely to recover.

So unexpected was this finding that Friedmann began to look for other explanations.

Perhaps the benefits came from the extra exercise dog owners took walking their pets. Yet she found that people with other sorts of pets that needed no exercise were also more likely to survive. She then investigated the possibility that pet owners were healthier to start with and so had less severe heart attacks. This theory also proved to be false.

Nor did pet owners appear to have different psychological make-ups from those without pets, at least judging from their responses to a wide range of standard psychological tests. Friedmann concluded that owning a pet really did help people to recover after a heart attack.

The benefit she found was small: A 3% decline in the probability of death. But given that more than a million people in the US die of heart disease every year, that means that pets could help 30,000 Americans to survive in any given year.

In another study by Warwick Anderson at the Baker Medical Research Institute in Prahran, Australia, 5,741 people attending a heart disease risk clinic were questioned about their lifestyle and whether they had any pets. Researchers found that the average cholesterol level of the 784 patients who owned pets was 2% lower than those who did not own pets. Epidemiologists estimate that this might lower the risk of heart attack by 4%. Pet owners also had lower levels of triglyceride fats in their blood and lower blood pressure, which indicated that owning a pet was as efficient at reducing blood pressure as eating a low-salt diet or cutting down on alcohol.

FISHY EXPERIENCE

No one has yet suggested a mechanism by which pets could lower levels of cholesterol or triglyceride fats. But Friedmann and her team have at least established that people sometimes produce physiological responses to animals. They measured the blood pressure of volunteers who were either resting, talking, reading out loud or greeting their dogs. As expected, blood pressure levels rose as the volunteers performed the slightly stressful tasks of talking or reading to the experimenters. But when the volunteers talked to their dogs, their blood pressure fell to resting levels or below.

What's more, it seems that such responses do not necessarily depend on stroking or talking to a pet. In various tests involving psychological questionnaires and standard observational checks of anxiety levels, adults and children proved to be more relaxed simply in the presence of a friendly dog. Aaron Katcher, a psychiatrist at the University of Pennsylvania, showed that people who watch an aquarium full of tropical fish experience a fall in blood pressure greater than those who merely stare at a blank wall.

Yet such studies do not prove there is anything special about our reactions to animals. It has long been known that anything that distracts our attention from our preoccupations has a calming effect on the body. In another experiment by Katcher, watching a videotape of tropical fish proved more absorbing and relaxing than watching a tankful of real fish, judging from measurements of blood pressure. Could pets improve human health simply by distracting and absorbing us?

Many researchers think this is unlikely. According to advocates of "pet therapy," animals can also make us feel better indirectly, by making strange settings or people seem less threatening. It is hard to design experiments to test this theory rigorously, but anecdotal evidence abounds. In the late 1960s, for example, Boris Levinson, an American psychiatrist, noticed that severely withdrawn children who were afraid to communicate with people made rapid contact with his dog Jingles. By carefully insinuating himself into the child-dog relationship, Levinson found he was able to reach his child patients.

Animals can even promote social contact between strangers. Peter Messent, a British zoologist, spent days hanging around public parks watching people strolling through. Those with dogs were much more likely to experience positive encounters with other people, including prolonged conversations with people who were alone or with children.

Pets may thus be "confirming cultural symbols of harmless respectability," says James Serpell, formerly director of the Companion Animal Research Group at the University of Cambridge and later at the University of Pennsylvania. But his research shows that they are far more than

this. According to questionnaire responses, pet owners value their pets "as distinctive personalities with whom they have affectionate relationships." And it is here, in friendship, argues Serpell, that we find the real explanation for pets' beneficial effects on our health.

Study after study has shown that people who feel isolated and depressed are more likely to succumb to illness than people who claim to be content. And Serpell and his colleagues were the first to show that pets could improve an ordinary person's general health. They recruited three groups of people. At the start, there was no significant difference between their scores on a questionnaire monitoring minor health problems. Then one group of people were given dogs, another cats.

A month later, they filled in the questionnaire again. Those who owned new pets reported a marked improvement in their general health, which lasted throughout the 10-month study. In contrast to Friedmann's earlier study, dog owners fared slightly better than cat owners, perhaps partly because they also increased the amount of exercise they took. Serpell then repeated the study over 18 months, with three times as many people, all of whom had the same socioeconomic status. He also had access to doctors' assessments of their patients' health. The results supported the conclusions of the earlier study.

GOOD LISTENERS

Part of the explanation, argues Serpell, is that pets can provide owners "with a special kind of emotional support which is lacking, or at least uncommon, in relationships between people." He claims that an animal's muteness is a boon, not a burden. The problem with language is that although we use it to communicate our deepest thoughts and emotions, we also use it to deceive, misinform, criticize and insult others. The fact that pets listen and seem to understand but do not question or evaluate may be one of their most endearing assets as companions, says Serpell. It resembles the relationships some psychotherapists try to build.

Dogs and cats are the most cherished animal companions, largely because they are adept at feeding us with nonverbal signs of affection, argues Serpell. They make us feel respected, admired and wanted. The typical feline expression of slightly detached contentment is enormously appealing to humans, while the way dogs' facial muscles are arranged enables them to express a wide range of human-looking emotions.

"Our confidence, self-esteem, ability to cope with the stresses of life and, ultimately, our physical health depend on this sense of belonging," says Serpell. The sense of responsibility involved in caring for an animal is especially significant. Such nurturing gives meaning to our lives, a sense of being needed that can deeply sustain an ability to set personal goals. "Far from being perverted, extravagant or the victims of misplaced parental instincts, most owners are normal rational people who make use of animals to augment their existing social relationships," says Serpell.

CHILDHOOD EXPERIENCES

Why, then, doesn't everyone keep pets? Serpell has found that childhood experiences with pets are the key. Children brought up with pets are much more likely to have them as adults. Those who went without pets as children seem to remain indifferent to companion animals throughout their lives.

Childhood experience also seems to direct preferences for animals in specific ways. People brought up with dogs remain dog lovers, those with cats, cat lovers. Only those who had both as children remain fond of both. No one has yet found consistent personality differences between cat and dog lovers, nor between pet owners and nonpet owners.

Yet people who have, or have had, pets do tend to have something distinctive about them. In a survey of undergraduates, Serpell's colleague Elizabeth Paul found that people who have had experience with pets tend to have a more positive and humane attitude to animals and the environment, and a tendency to have greater "emotional empathy" for people, too.

Pet ownership has its disadvantages, however, not least of which is the risk of catching something from your companion animal. Britain's canine population deposits about 4.5 million liters of urine and one million kilograms

of feces every day, some of it in public places where it can be a health hazard.

Dogs can transmit *toxocariasis* (visceral larva migrans)—infection by a roundworm parasite—which can cause blindness in children. But the condition remains rare—about 10 cases of toxocariasis are reported each year in England and Wales—and can be prevented by giving puppies and nursing bitches antiworm drugs.

More common is *toxoplasmosis,* with symptoms like glandular fever, caused by a parasitic protozoan. About 700 cases are reported each year in Britain, and most people catch it by eating undercooked meat from sheep, goats and pigs, or by coming in contact with cat feces. The parasite can be avoided by wearing gloves when gardening or handling cat litter, and washing hands after handling raw meat. Bird-fanciers need to be on guard for *psittacosis,* caused by a viruslike organism inhaled in the dust from the droppings or feathers of infected birds. The flulike symptoms can be treated with antibiotics.

Pet animals also cause significant injury to people: In Britain alone, more than a quarter of a million dog bites are registered each year. Yet many of these problems could be minimized by public education and restrictions on dogs in recreation areas, according to the report of a working party on companion animals in society, set up by the Council for Science and Society in London.

There are more grounds for concern, perhaps, from the pets' point of view—not all pet owners are good for their animal's health.

Every summer, animal shelters run by charities fill up with pets abandoned as their owners go on holiday. New forms of exploitation may emerge if the health benefits of keeping pets becomes widely accepted. According to Nicholas Tucker, a psychologist at the University of Sussex, "pet burnout" (tiredness and irritability) has been recorded among some of the dogs and cats acting as four-footed therapists among the mentally ill or socially deprived. In the US, castrated, de-toothed monkeys have been trained to act as domestic servants to paraplegic patients. "Being de-clawed or un-voiced may be fairer on the furniture or the neighbors,"

Tucker says, "but what might it be doing to the pets?"

 **Canine Tips**

To cure dogs of pulling without jerking or tugging them, simply stop in your tracks whenever you feel tension on the lead from the dog pulling. Do not move until the dog turns around or backs up to get slack in the leash. Then praise the dog and continue walking. Most dogs will quickly learn that they get to keep moving forward only when the leash is slack, not when they pull on it and make it tight.

Dennis Fetko, PhD, dog trainer and applied animal behaviorist, San Diego, quoted in *Your Dog,* Box 2626, Greenwich, CT 06836.

Feline Tips

Danger to cats: Dog flea products. Cats are very sensitive to high concentrations (45% to 65%) of the chemical *permethrin,* which is found in some dog "spot-on" flea products. Severe illness or death can result when cats are exposed to this ingredient. *Self-defense:* Protect cats from fleas only with products made specifically for cats. Don't use even small amounts of products made for dogs. Follow all usage instructions carefully. Contact your veterinarian at any sign of a problem. *Caution:* Products with identical brand names may contain different ingredients, depending on whether they are designed for dogs or cats. Be sure to buy the right formula.

E. Kathryn Meyer, VMD, coordinator, US Pharmacopeia Veterinary Practitioners' Reporting Program, Rockville, MD.

10

Home Smarts

Safety for Seniors

Each year many older Americans are injured in and around their homes. The kitchen and bathroom are two of the areas in which accidents are most likely to occur. Here's some advice that can keep you from paying a visit to a hospital emergency room...

IN THE KITCHEN

Keep anything that might catch fire away from the range—that includes flammable and combustible items, towels and curtains.

Don't wear garments with loose long sleeves when cooking; besides the likelihood of catching fire, they are apt to catch on pot handles, overturning pots and pans and causing scalds.

Avoid shocks or even electrocution by keeping electrical appliances and power cords away from the sink and hot surfaces. *Precaution:* Move appliances closer to wall outlets or to different outlets so you won't need extension cords.

Low lighting and glare can be contributors to burns or cuts. *Remedy:* Improve lighting by opening curtains and blinds (unless this causes too much glare); use maximum wattage bulbs allowed in each fixture; reduce glare by using frosted bulbs, indirect lighting, shades or globes or partially closing blinds; install under-cabinet or countertop lighting.

Guard against falls. Don't stand on chairs or boxes to reach high shelves. Buy a step stool (preferably one with a handrail). Before climbing on a step stool, make sure it's opened and stable. Tighten screws and braces on step stools. Discard any step stool with broken parts.

IN THE BATHROOM

Equip bathtubs and showers with nonskid mats, abrasive strips or surfaces that are not slippery.

Grab bars can help you get into and out of your bath or shower, and can help prevent falls. *Warning:* Test existing bars for strength

Consumer Product Safety Commission, Washington, DC 20207.

and stability. Attach grab bars, through the tile, to structural supports in the wall, or install bars specifically designed to attach to the sides of the bathtub.

Keep your hot water heater set to "low" or 120 degrees. Water temperature above 120 degrees can cause tap water scalds.

Always check water temperature by hand before entering bath or shower.

Tip: Taking baths, rather than showers, reduces the risk of a scald from suddenly changing water temperatures.

Financing a Retirement Home

Maureen Tsu, CFP, San Juan Capistrano, CA, quoted in *Where to Retire,* 1502 Augusta Dr., Suite 415, Houston 77057.

When buying a retirement home, a key decision is whether to purchase it with cash or finance it with a mortgage. Many people prefer the security of buying with cash and not owing any debt on their home.

Drawback: Using so much cash may leave you cash poor and limit the lifestyle you can afford in retirement.

Contrast: Buying a home with a mortgage can leave you with more spendable cash. The debt on the home can be paid off or refinanced upon your death.

Issues if you decide to finance with a mortgage…

●**Can you obtain tax benefits** from deducting mortgage interest? Do you have enough total deductions to itemize deductions? Are you in a high enough tax bracket to make it worthwhile?

●**Can you invest the cash saved** by buying with a mortgage to earn a higher after-tax rate of return than you will pay on the mortgage?

●**Are you willing to have your estate deal** with the debt on your home by selling it, or by having heirs refinance it at your death?

Issues if you buy with cash…

●**Will you have a way of tapping your equity in the home** to raise cash in an emergency?

●**After spending cash on the home,** will you have enough money to enjoy a comfortable retirement lifestyle?

●**Will your estate eventually sell the home for cash**—so that you might as well take the cash while you are alive by financing the home?

Best: Consider these issues before you retire, while you are still working. You will have more options and a stronger credit standing to make any arrangement you finally choose.

Simple System to Help You Find the Right Retirement Community

Deborah Freundlich, copublisher of *Briefing,* a restaurant marketing newsletter from American Express, and author of *Retirement Living Communities.* Macmillan.

While you are strong and healthy, energetic and living comfortably in a community where you have good support services, friends and family, you probably give little thought to the prospect of moving to a full-service retirement community.

But—this is precisely the time to investigate possible future living arrangements. You don't want to delay the search until you are sick, injured or have lost a helpful spouse.

Look for a retirement living community (RLC) leisurely and carefully. The search can be very enjoyable.

●**Start with a paper search.** Think of it as gathering information for a vacation spot. Ask friends…and the children of people you know who have moved to such communities…and senior citizen groups in your community what places they know of *both good and bad.* Send for literature on RLCs located in areas you might find attractive.

Try to be open about location. Don't think only about how convenient a place is to your children or other family members. You will be there 100% of the time and that's what counts most.

●**Review your finances.** This will be your first opportunity to analyze the financial implications of a move to an RLC. You will have to make a substantial advance payment—in many cases more than $100,000—to qualify for most RLCs.

Be realistic about what you can afford. Above all, ask lots of questions and compare the costs of your prospective RLC with your current expenses.

CHECK THEM OUT

Visit as many RLCs as you can. Arrange short excursions or vacation travel so that you can spend some time at a prospective RLC. Call ahead in plenty of time to arrange a stay— at least one night but preferably longer—in a guest house or guest room in the community. *Check out...*

●**The food and ambience of the communal dining facilities.** Meals tend to be a focal point of your life at any such facility.

Opportunity: The dining room is the best place to meet and talk with the residents to get an idea of whether they are people you would like to spend time with.

●**Nursing and custodial services and facilities.** *Preferable:* A special wing for residents with Alzheimer's or other forms of dementia. Such people need special care and may disrupt other residents who require health care.

Extras: Be sure to get a clear—preferably written—explanation of what extra costs might be involved if one spouse needs special nursing care while the other is well enough to live independently in the RLC with minimal care.

●**Transportation.** Even if the RLC has its own golf course, swimming pool and other sports and community facilities, you will probably want the ability to travel easily to nearby shopping malls, theaters, concert halls and houses of worship. Make sure there is regular, convenient and economical van or bus service. Use it during your visit even if you have your own car.

WHAT IT COSTS

Once you narrow down your prospects, talk seriously about finances with staff members of the RLC.

Don't be pushed into a premature discussion of a contract and finances by overeager staffers during your visit. The most desirable RLCs have waiting lists. In fact, beware of those with an occupancy rate under 85%—*and* hard-sell tactics. *Ask about...*

●**Advance payments.** What is refundable, partially refundable or nonrefundable.

●**Monthly charges.** And what they cover— specifically. Ask what the guarantee is that the charges will not increase—or how such increases will be determined.

●**Added charges.** Charges that might be added if you need more intensive nursing or medical services...or if you have to be moved to an affiliated hospital, rehabilitation facility or medical center.

●**All special fees.**

●**Special benevolent funds.** Should you or your spouse live well beyond any reasonable life expectancy, you could run out of money and you may need to rely on these special funds.

Once a particular RLC begins to seem like an attractive possibility, ask for a complete package of its financial statements. The RLC must make them available to you.

Be sure the statements are recent and audited by a reputable professional. Even if you feel comfortable making sense of balance sheets and profit-and-loss statements, have a CPA evaluate them. You don't want to make a substantial advance payment and then find yourself in a community that begins to skimp on services because of financial problems.

If you decide to sign a contract and get on the waiting list, you can be confident that you've done all that you can to assure yourself the best of care for the last years of your life.

The Very Best Mortgage

Avoid a 30-year mortgage if you do not expect to be in the house for anything close to 30 years. The shorter the time period for which you borrow, the lower the interest rate. So if you plan to stay in a house for only five or so years, you are overspending by taking out a 30-year mortgage. *Alternatives:* Balloon mortgages, which have a fixed rate for five or seven years and then jump to a higher rate…or adjustable-rate mortgages if you plan to stay just a few years.

Robert Van Order, chief economist, Freddie Mac, McLean, VA.

Moving Does Not Have to Be Traumatic

Cathy Goodwin, PhD, author of *Making the Big Move: How to Transform Relocation into a Creative Life Transition.* New Harbinger Publications. She has moved more than 12 times in her life and is currently professor of marketing at Nova Southeastern University in Fort Lauderdale, FL.

Whether you are moving to a smaller space in the same city…to a retirement community in another state …or to an apartment across the country, there are steps you can take to minimize the disruption that relocation invariably causes.

First, make sure moving is something you want to do. People who feel forced to move often experience anger and resentment on top of all the normal relocation-induced feelings of loneliness, anxiety, excitement and expectation.

PSYCHOLOGICAL ISSUES

If moving is something you've decided is right for you, make it easier on yourself by working through some of the psychological issues ahead of time.

•**List the activities you most enjoy doing.** Think of the roles you play in life that define you. Ask yourself what it is about your home environment that energizes you.

It's often the seemingly trivial routines and comforts—like a morning cup of cappuccino at the local coffee shop—that we miss most in a new location. If you make careful note of these comforts, you'll be able to duplicate them in your new home.

•**Prepare for moving by deciding who you are.** Decide what you need around you in order to fully express your identity.

Exercise 1: Who are you? As quickly as you can, complete the sentence, "I am a _____" 10 times.

Examples: I am a mother, I am an artist, I am a gardener, etc.

Review what you've written and think about what it reveals about you. What, if anything, will change if you move to a new location?

Exercise 2: Which routines are important to you? You will gain an understanding of the importance of your daily routines by writing them down. *As thoroughly as possible, write down…*

1. What you do on weekday mornings.

Example: Wake up without an alarm clock …walk the dogs…drive to the local newsstand for the paper…stop at the corner coffee shop.

2. What you do to relax in the evening.

3. How you spend Saturday mornings.

When you've completed this exercise, ask yourself how you'd feel about interrupting these routines.

Though the details you record may seem trivial, it's often these little changes and losses that increase the psychological trauma of moving.

PRESERVING COMFORTS AND ROUTINES

By understanding which routines and comforts are important to you, you'll more easily develop replacements in your new community. *Do some homework before the move…*

•**Learn all you can about your prospective community.** Use the Internet to research the community and learn about its character/culture.

By typing in the city and state you're considering, you can learn about museums and theater programs…local businesses and restaurants …opportunities for continuing education… medical services…transportation, etc.

Use the library to research the archives of the local newspaper.

Better: Make a premove visit to the area you're considering and talk to people of all ages about what it's like to live in the area.

●**Visualize how you'll spend a day in the new location.** Begin by visualizing your new home for 15 to 20 minutes. Relax, close your eyes and get comfortable.

Ask yourself: What is my ideal home? Where does the sun rise and set? Are there skylight windows? Lamps? Overhead lighting? What is the shape of each room, and what kind of furniture do I see in each? Who or what do I see in the home with me (spouse, dog, cat)?

After you've pictured your new home in your mind, visualize a day in your new community. See yourself waking up. What will you do next? What familiar roles might be useful in your new location? What new roles or activities might you engage in? What problems might you encounter (e.g., no coffee shop!) and how will you deal with these problems?

When you've completed this exercise, write down any insights you've gained, then compare your notes with your real life in the new location after you've moved.

FOR RENTERS

If you choose to rent, place a "Rental Wanted" classified ad in the local paper. I've done this twice. As a result, I've learned about really fine properties that are typically only rented by word-of-mouth.

And, contrary to what many people think, I didn't get any crank phone calls.

Sample ad: *Model tenant with steady income seeks single-level, three-bedroom apartment. References provided.*

PLANNING A NO-TEARS MOVE

●**Use checklists provided by moving companies as well as lists found in books, such as...**

●*Moving: A Complete Checklist and Guide for Relocation* by Karen G. Adams (Silvercat Publications, Limited Availability).

●*Steiner's Complete How-to-Move Handbook* by Clyde Steiner (Dell).

●**Put together an emotional first-aid kit.** Your kit can include coping statements such as, "I will just let go and relax"..."I can deal with this"...or "I've survived this before...I can do it again."

Add to the kit meditation and visualization books and tapes. Also include the phone numbers of old friends—at least one to laugh with, one to listen to you and one who moved recently and can give good advice. Pick up a journal in which you can record your thoughts, concerns and feelings.

Moving to a New State

Get expert advice from a local real estate broker and a local real estate attorney before looking at any houses. *Reason:* Real estate laws and prevailing practices can be different among states and mistakes can be costly. *Questions to ask...*

●**What is the customary spread between list and sale prices?**

●**How much inventory is on the market?** And what is the average time a house stays on the market?

●**Do I need a lawyer to close?**

●**How much are transfer taxes?** When real estate is bought and sold, a tax is paid to transfer the property. This may be paid by the buyer or the seller...or split between them.

●**How long am I committed to a broker with which I sign?**

●**How have property taxes increased over time?** How are they evaluated? Sometimes, the property tax increases upon the completion of a purchase.

●**How much money do I have to give when the offer is made?** How much when the contract is written?

●**What if I want to back out after signing an agreement** and paying a deposit?

Useful resources: Relocation Directors Council (312-726-7410 or *www.rdcrelo.org*) ...Employee Relocation Council (202-857-0857 or *www.erc.org*).

Marge Fisher, management and relocation consultant in Riverside, CT.

Pitfalls When Buying a New Condominium

Dorothy Tyrnon, author, *The Condominium: A Guide for the Alert Buyer*. Golden-Lee Books.

Buying a condominium is more complicated than buying a house. *Reason:* The purchase is really for two separate pieces of property—your unit and the property held in common. *Before signing any contract for a new condominium, which is harder to check out than an established condominium, buyers should study the prospectus for any of these pitfalls:*

• **The prospectus includes a plan of the unit you are buying,** showing rooms of specific dimensions. But the plan omits closet space. *Result:* The living space you are buying is probably smaller than you think.

• **The prospectus includes this clause:** "The interior design shall be substantially similar." *Result:* The developer can alter both the size and design of your unit.

• **The common charges set forth in the prospectus are unrealistically low.** Buyers should never rely on a developer's estimate of common charges. *Instead:* They should find out the charges at similarly functioning condominiums.

Common charges include: Electricity for hallways and outside areas, water, cleaning, garbage disposal, insurance for common areas, pool maintenance, groundskeeping, legal and accounting fees, reserves for future repairs.

• **Variation on the common-charge trap.** The developer is paying common charges on unsold units. But these charges are unrealistically low. *Reason:* The developer has either underinsured or underestimated the taxes due, omitted security expenses or failed to set up a reserve fund.

• **The prospectus includes this clause: "The seller will not be obligated to pay monthly charges for unsold units."** *Result:* The owners of a partially occupied condominium have to pay for all operating expenses.

• **The prospectus warns about the seller's limited liability.** But an unsuspecting buyer may still purchase a condominium unit on which back monthly charges are due, or even on which there's a lien for failure to pay back carrying charges.

• **The prospectus makes no mention of parking spaces.** *Result:* You must lease from the developer.

• **The prospectus is imprecise about the total number of units to be built.** *Result:* Facilities are inadequate for the number of residents.

• **The prospectus includes this clause: "Transfer of ownership (of the common property from the developer to the home-owners' association) will take place 60 days after the last unit is sold."** *Trap:* The developer deliberately does not sell one unit, keeps on managing the condominium and awards sweetheart maintenance and operating contracts to his subcontractors.

• **The prospectus specifies that the developer will become the property manager of the functioning condominium.** But the language spelling out monthly common charges and management fees is imprecise. *Result:* The owners cannot control monthly charges and fees.

Is Your Property's Assessed Value Too High?

The effective real estate tax is the tax rate multiplied by the assessed value. There's not much an individual can do about the tax rate, but assessment can often be challenged successfully. *Requirements:* Proof that either the property is overvalued or the assessment is higher than on comparable property in the same area. *When to ask for a reduction:*

• **Just before making necessary repairs of damages that have lowered the value.**

• **Local tax records err in description by overstating size or income.**

• **Net income drops due to factors beyond owner's control.**

• **When the price paid for the building in an arm's length transaction is lower than the assessed value.**

What to do:

●**Determine the ratio of the assessed value to the present market value.** Compare with average ratios of similar properties recently sold in the same area. *Sources:* Ratios are available to the public in tax districts. Real estate brokers or professional assessors can also be consulted.

●**Check tax records for a description of the property.**

●**Consult a lawyer on the strength of the case,** whether it can be handled by an informal talk with the assessor, and how much it will cost if a formal proceeding and appeal are necessary.

When the New House Is a Lemon

A home buyer may be able to get out of the entire purchase contract if the seller has misrepresented a house with many serious defects.

Normally, when defects show up after the buyers move in, they can sue for damages. Some state courts have ruled that two reasons for suing may void the entire sale: (1) Misrepresentation of an important aspect of the house. (2) The presence of many serious defects.

One case: The builder had assured the buyer that there would be no water problem. But the house was flooded soon after the closing. The court said the related damage would be impossible to repair.

Chastain v. Billings, 570 SW2d 866.

When to Watch Your Broker Closely

A company or individual listing property for sale with a real estate agent may find it's no longer listed after an offer is turned down.

Reason: The agent is trying to make the commission by temporarily taking the property off the active list in the hope the owner will give up and accept the offer. The agent may keep other agents from sending around prospects by removing the file or spreading the word that the property has been sold.

How to Sell Your Own Home Fast

William Supple, Jr., publisher of *Picket Fence Preview,* for-sale-by-owner real estate magazines serving Vermont, New York and New Hampshire. He is also co-founder of the National For Sale By Owner Association, a nonprofit group that helps home owners sell their own property. Mr. Supple is author of *How to Sell Your Own Home.* Picket Fence Publishing.

When my wife and I wanted to sell our home several years ago, we found that real estate agents weren't for us.

Agents typically charge a commission of around 6%. That means they'll take $9,000 of your equity from the sale of a $150,000 home.

In fact, the biggest myth in real estate is that you need an agent to sell your home.

Selling your house yourself often means selling it faster, and saving thousands of dollars in the process. Since you don't have to inflate your price by the amount of the commission, you'll sell sooner than a comparable agent-listed property.

Almost 60% of all real estate agent listings don't sell during the listing period. Many of these home owners then take matters into their own hands and sell by themselves. *Here's how to sell your own home...*

●**Set the right price.** Few home sellers know the market value of their property. Get a professional appraisal ($200 to $300). This will tell you the highest possible price to expect for your home in the current market.

Price your home using the appraisal and the market's supply and demand. *Example:* If you're in a tough buyer's market (with many similar homes on the market), price your home at or below appraised value. Our experience shows us that buyers are more likely to make a reasonable offer on a fairly priced home, and no offers on an overpriced one.

●**Fix and clean everything.** A potential buyer expects a home to be in move-in condition. Buyers will tolerate a little wear and tear, but you're more likely to get a full price offer when the buyer falls in love with your immaculate home.

Pay particular attention to your home's exterior. If the exterior is not in good condition, potential buyers will drive right by without stopping to go inside.

●**Use a multipronged approach to advertise your house.** A classified ad in the local paper is the traditional route, and sometimes these ads are effective.

But if you want to sell your home fast, yard signs and for-sale-by-owner publications are the way to go.

According to a survey of home buyers by *USA Today,* an astounding 49% of them found their future residence simply by noticing a sign in the front yard.

The most effective way to find buyers is by advertising in magazines that exclusively feature homes for sale by owner. Many regions of the nation now have these widely distributed publications. Also consider making a fact sheet about your house with a photo.

Internet sites are another relatively new—and inexpensive—way to reach potential buyers. *Our favorite: www.nfsboa.com,* a national network of for-sale-by-owner Web sites.

Fast Home Fix-Ups Attract the Right Buyers

Patricia MacDonald, owner of Innovative Interior Design, a consultation firm in Orange County, CA, that specializes in helping homeowners prepare their property for sale.

First impressions are critical when it comes to winning over undecided home buyers. *Before putting your house on the market...*

●**Give the front of your home a "haircut."** Look at your home from the street. Trim hedges and overgrown landscaping. Add a coat of semigloss paint to the front door. Buy a new doormat.

●**Make the entryway look big.** When I enter a house, the first thing I like to see is a table with a mirror above it. That makes the entryway feel spacious. Setting a lamp on the table—perhaps with a vase of flowers—also helps.

Remove coat stands, keys and mail from the entryway.

●**Open up first-floor traffic patterns.** Rearrange furniture to create more spacious walkways. *Examples...*

●If you have a sofa dividing your living room from the dining area, move it against a wall.

●Take a piece of furniture out of the room if you have to make more space. Store the furniture in the garage or attic, where clutter won't come as a surprise.

●Remove the leaves from your dining room table.

●**Shine up the kitchen.** Put away large countertop appliances. Take down the magnets and kids' drawings from the refrigerator.

Place a big wooden bowl on the counter, and fill it with lemons or oranges.

No plants should be hanging from the ceiling. They clutter kitchens and block window views. The windows should be clean and offer a clear view. Get rid of any leftover hooks on the walls or ceiling.

●**Clean up the patio.** If your furniture is missing some parts, either repair the items or throw them out.

Put bikes and toys in the garage, and move your grill against the exterior wall of your home.

Garage Sale Before Home Sale

Get rid of as much clutter as possible before putting your house on the market. An uncluttered house looks larger and is more attractive to buyers. Clear out everything you no longer use or do not expect to need when you move. The cleaning-out process may reveal things you should fix or clean before selling your home. After the garage sale and a sprucing-up, list your home for sale.

Robert Irwin, real estate investor and broker in Los Angeles, and author of the *Tips & Traps* home book series. McGraw-Hill.

Simple Secrets Of a Chemical-Free Lawn

Warren Schultz, author of *The Chemical-Free Lawn*. Rodale.

There is no doubt that Americans love their lawns—all of our five million acres of lawns. And so we spend $6 billion a year on lawn care and cultivation.

Problem: The excessive—and largely unnecessary—use of pesticides, herbicides and fertilizers could be avoided. They are damaging our soil, contaminating our water systems and exposing our families to hazardous chemicals.

A healthy lawn has no need for chemicals. It can keep out weeds, disease and insects by itself. Think of your lawn as a garden of grass, and simply follow the principles of good gardening. Consider climate, soil and available light. And—select plant varieties with care—and learn to feed, mow and water correctly.

GRASS GARDENING MADE EASY

If you are planting a new lawn: Consult a reputable garden center for recommendations on grass varieties and advice on sowing or sodding. Many new grasses are resistant to insects and disease.

Grasses are bred to thrive in specific climates and conditions. You may want to have a soil sample analyzed by your state's agricultural college or cooperative extension service. When choosing a grass, consider how you use your lawn. Color is important for perfect vistas, whereas toughness (the ability to bounce back from wear) is crucial in heavy traffic areas such as children's play areas.

To convert to and maintain a chemical-free lawn:

●**Fertilizers.** Use a slowly soluble organic fertilizer, with no more than two pounds of nitrogen per 1,000 feet per year.

Fertilize only once a year, in the fall. Then you won't be fertilizing your weeds…they are not programmed to germinate and grow strongly in the fall. But grass leaves and roots both grow vigorously well into the fall. Fertilizing before winter sets in allows the roots to build up carbon reserves that carry over to spring.

●**Weeds.** Weeds are crowded out by healthy turf. They appear only when a lawn is suffering. *Usual culprit:* Wrong type of grass in the wrong place. *Best approach:* To avoid damage to the surrounding turf, weed by hand. Many of the new, long-handled weeding tools are excellent. Then go back to the bare spots and reseed.

Note: Just because it doesn't look like a blade of grass doesn't mean it's a weed. Enjoy the many plants, such as violets and speedwell that were brought to this country as ornamentals. They add color and attract beneficial insects.

●**Mowing.** Most people mow too often—and too low. *Problem:* When grass is cut too short the roots stop growing. Longer grass shades out weeds—and has deeper roots. *Best:* Raise mower blades to maintain grass at three to four inches high. Never cut more than 40% of the height of grass at one time. Keep mower blades sharp to avoid shredding the grass. Mow higher and less often in hot, dry weather. Let grass grow one inch higher in the shade for increased photosynthesis. To cut back on mowing, plant ground cover around trees, on banks, etc.

●**Watering.** Most people water too often—and too lightly. Sprinkling induces roots to stay near the surface. *Best:* Allow water to soak six to 10 inches deep into the soil. Hold off watering again until the grass begins to wilt. This forces roots to grow deeper, for a healthier lawn. Too much water on the surface can encourage disease. So water in the morning after dew has dried, or in the afternoon—not at night.

●**Insects.** Insects are rarely troublesome when turf and soil are healthy. *Best:* Add shrubs and trees to encourage grub-eating birds. Plant wildflowers and herbs to encourage beneficial insects. If your lawn is actually being damaged by a specific pest, consider reseeding with a resistant strain of grass. *Last resort:* Apply an organic pesticide at the risk of also killing useful bugs.

●**Diseases.** Diseases are usually a symptom of grass that has been overwatered and overfertilized. Most are caused by fungi. *Solutions:* Improve drainage, overseed with resistant strains of grass, stop using chemicals.

Lawn care companies…

Negotiate with your lawn service to do less. Ask them to set mower blades higher. Look for an organic fertilizer program. Discontinue routine weed-spraying, pest treatments, etc. Then, tell your neighbors how you got your lawn to thrive.

Is That House Environmentally Safe?

Gary T. Deane, EdD, executive director of the National Society of Environmental Consultants, a fee-based group that trains realtors, bankers and appraisers to detect environmental hazards of commercial and residential properties, 303 W. Cypress St., San Antonio 78212.

Does the neighborhood in which the property is located appear on any government hazards lists? This is not something that the owner of the property is likely to know. The information is available by calling your regional Environmental Protection Agency (EPA) Superfund office. It will tell you whether the EPA has targeted the area for cleanup.

In some cases, you must rely on the Freedom of Information Act,* a process that often takes six weeks or more. If the EPA is unable to help you, there are several fee-based information groups. *They include:*

●**Fidelity National Information Solutions.** This fee-based firm in Santa Barbara has

*Contact your local EPA office for more information.

developed residential reports that are available by mail and overnight delivery. *Information:* 888-934-3354.

●**How has the property been used during the past 40 or 50 years?** Not all hazardous sites are listed in state or federal records. Check with the city's or town's zoning records. Speak with people who have lived there for a long time.

Harmful: Was the property ever used as an auto-repair facility…a pottery, art or photo studio …a dry cleaner…a printer…a farm…or a junkyard? The chemicals used by these businesses may have leached into the ground, raising the chances of health hazards from contaminated soil.

●Is the property—or adjoining properties—built on a former landfill? Landfill dirt can contain asbestos and other outlawed substances. Over time, these substances can create harmful gases or contaminate the surrounding land or ground water. Check with your state's Solid Waste Management Office or Landfill Office.

●Is there, or was there ever, a gas station, chemical plant or factory within one-quarter mile of the property? The underground storage tanks for facilities built in the 1950s and 1960s are prone to leakage. There have been cases in which leaks went undetected for years and gasoline or chemicals permeated the soil of entire neighborhoods.

The locations of such facilities will appear on a Fire Insurance Map—available at most public and university libraries, at your fire department, in the databases of ERIIS and Vista, in city or county site records or on the federal government's Leaking Underground Storage Tanks list.

●**Has a radon screen been performed on the property?** Many states require the seller to do a radon test on behalf of the buyer. Your state or regional radon office will tell you if radon is a problem in your area. Home test kits, available in hardware stores, are adequate. *Cost for a kit:* $10 to $50. Or hire an EPA-certified radon inspector. The EPA will send you a free list of all certified radon inspectors in your state. *Cost for an inspection:* $100 to $300.

Dangerous Chemicals Are in Our Homes

Ruth Winter, author of *A Consumer's Dictionary of Household, Yard, and Office Chemicals*. Crown Publishers.

According to the Environmental Protection Agency's estimates, the average household contains between three and 10 gallons of hazardous chemicals—and many of them are organic compounds that vaporize at room temperature.

In the effort to save money by sealing our homes to reduce heating and air-conditioning bills, and by becoming do-it-yourselfers for many tasks once left to professionals, we expose ourselves and our families to high levels of these toxic substances.

READ THE LABEL

"We are all guilty of not thoroughly reading labels," according to Charles Jacobson, compliance officer at the US Consumer Products Safety Commission.

If vapors may be harmful, it doesn't do much good to read the label after you have used the product and inhaled the vapors.

Important: Read the labels before buying a product to select the safest in a category. If you find any of the 11 ingredients listed below on a container, avoid buying it. If you must buy it, use extreme caution when working with…

1. Methylene chloride. A widely used solvent, it is in pesticide aerosols, refrigeration and air-conditioning equipment, cleansing creams, and in paint and varnish removers. Some paint strippers are 80% methylene chloride. Its toxic effects include damage to liver, kidneys and central nervous system. It increases the carbon monoxide level in the blood, and people with angina (chest pains) are extremely sensitive to the chemical. Methylene chloride has been linked to heart attacks and cancer.

2. Dichlorvos (DDVP). Used to control insects. It has a wide range of uses in the home, agriculture and commercial establishments. Currently, dichlorvos is undergoing a special review by the EPA on the grounds that exposure to this compound may pose an unreasonable risk of cancer as well as present other dangers. People may be exposed to dichlorvos by consuming foods with residues of the chemical.

3. 2,4-D. A weed killer related to Agent Orange—which allegedly caused health problems in exposed Vietnam veterans—2,4-D is widely used by home gardeners and farmers. It does not cause acute toxicity, but its long-term effects are scary—much higher incidence of non-Hodgkin's lymphoma and other cancers have been associated with its use among farmers. The National Cancer Institute also reports that dogs whose owners use 2,4-D on their lawns have an increased rate of a type of cancer closely related to human non-Hodgkin's lymphoma.

4. Perchlorethylene. The main solvent employed in the dry-cleaning process, metal degreasing, and in some adhesives, aerosols, paints and coatings, it can be absorbed through your lungs or your skin. The most common effects of overexposure are irritation of the eyes, nose, throat or skin. Effects on the nervous system include dizziness, headache, nausea, fatigue, confusion and loss of balance. At very high exposure it can cause death. California has banned the use of perchlorethylene.

5. Formaldehyde. An inexpensive and effective preservative used in more than 3,000 household products. They include disinfectants, cosmetics, fungicides, preservatives and adhesives. It is also used in pressed-wood products—wall paneling, fiberboard and furniture, and in some papers. There are serious questions about its safety. It is estimated that 4% to 8% of the population is sensitive to it. Vapors are intensely irritating to mucous membranes and can cause nasal, lung and eye problems.

6. Benzene. Among the top five organic chemicals produced in the United States, this petroleum derivative's use in consumer products has, in recent years, been greatly reduced. However, it is still employed as a solvent for waxes, resins and oils and is in varnish and lacquer. It is also an "antiknock" additive in gasoline—thus, make sure your house is well ventilated and insulated from vapors that arise from an attached garage.

Benzene is highly flammable, poisonous when ingested and irritating to mucous membranes. Amounts that are harmful may be absorbed through the skin. *Possible results:* Blood, brain and nerve damage as well as cancer.

7. Cyanide. One of the most rapid poisons known, it is used to kill fungus, insects and rats. It is in metal polishes (especially silver), art materials and photographic solutions.

8. Naphthalene. Derived from coal, it is used in solvents, fungicides, toilet bowl deodorizers and as a moth repellent. It can be absorbed through the skin and eyes as well as through the lungs. It may damage the eyes, liver, kidneys, skin, red blood cells and the central nervous system. It has reportedly caused anemia in infants exposed to clothing and blankets stored in naphthalene mothballs. This chemical can cause allergic skin rashes in adults and children.

9. Paradichlorobenzene (PDB). Made from chlorine and benzene, it is in metal polishes, moth repellents, general insecticides, germicides, spray deodorants and fumigants. PDB is also commonly found in room deodorizers. Vapors may cause irritation to the skin, throat and eyes. Prolonged exposure to high concentrations may cause weakness, dizziness, loss of weight and liver damage. A well-known animal cancer-causing agent, the chemical can linger in the home for months or even years.

10. Trichloroethylene (TCE). A solvent used in waxes, paint thinners, fumigants, metal polishes, shoe polish and rug cleaners. Tests conducted by the National Cancer Institute showed TCE caused cancer of the liver. A combination of alcohol ingestion with exposure to trichloroethylene can cause flushing of the skin, nausea and vomiting.

11. Hydroxides/lye products. These include automatic dishwasher detergents, toilet-bowl cleaners, fire proofing, paint remover and drain cleaners. Ingestion causes vomiting, prostration and collapse. Inhalation causes lung damage. Prolonged contact with dilute solutions can have a destructive effect upon tissue, leading to skin irritations and eruptions.

Smoke Detector Alert

The most popular type—an *ion detector*—will detect fast-developing fires, such as wastepaper basket or kitchen grease fires. It won't detect the more common smoldering fires, such as those started by cigarettes in mattresses. Every home needs two types—ion and photoelectric.

B. Don Russell, PhD, associate vice chancellor of engineering and deputy director, Texas Engineering Experiment Station, Texas A&M University, College Station. He has researched smoke detectors for more than a decade.

Bug Zapper Alert

Bug zappers do more than kill mosquitoes and other flying bugs. They shower the area with allergy-causing insect parts…and with disease-causing viruses and bacteria carried by the bugs. *Best bet:* Get rid of zappers in and around the house and keep bugs away with a repellent containing DEET. *Next best:* Position zappers away from areas where food is served and people congregate.

Alberto B. Broce, PhD, professor of entomology, Kansas State University, Manhattan. His study was presented at a meeting of the American Society for Microbiology.

Very Carefully Researched Ways To Clean Your Home

Cheryl Mendelson, Esq., a graduate of Harvard Law School and author of *Home Comforts: The Art & Science of Keeping House*. Scribner.

Eight years ago, when my home was undergoing major renovations, I found myself with some knotty cleaning questions. I couldn't find effective information for removing many stains or getting all the different surfaces of my home as clean as I wanted.

For answers, I consulted manufacturers, private businesses and craftsmen around the country. *Here is what I learned...*

KITCHENS

•**Sweeping.** Use a broom with even nylon or synthetic bristles. It collects dirt better than corn brooms.

Start sweeping at the walls, and move dirt toward the center so you push it the shortest distance. Don't lift the broom high off the floor after a stroke—this flings dirt into the air.

Store brooms with the bristles up. Otherwise bristles break or bend.

•**Coffee or tea stains on china, plastic and glassware.** Mix one-eighth cup of regular chlorine bleach with one cup of water. Pour into the bottom of your dishwasher before starting the wash cycle.

Important: Make sure nothing aluminum or silver is in the machine—it can become discolored.

BATHROOMS

•**Hardened soap scum on tiles.** Coat the entire surface with undiluted liquid detergent, and allow it to dry overnight. Wet the surface and scrub with a stiff brush and scouring powder. Rinse and buff with a bath towel.

•**Nonslip treads on bathtub floor.** Try Naval Jelly or KRC-7, a porcelain and tile cleaner (both available at plumbing supply stores). These cleaners may remove mineral stains without eating away at the treads.

•**Rust around faucets and fixtures.** Use a powder containing oxalic acid, such as Barkeeper's Friend or Zud (both available at hardware stores).

Important: Never mix these rust removers with chlorine bleach. The fumes are toxic.

•**Concentrate on the spots where fingerprints accumulate**—if you want to disinfect your bathroom in addition to just cleaning it.

Examples: Toilet handles, light switches and knobs on the shower door, medicine cabinet and door.

FURNITURE

•**Water rings on hardwood surfaces.** Try mildly abrasive substances, such as mayonnaise mixed with a bit of ashes or toothpaste. The secret is to rub gently for a long time—as long as 45 minutes—so you remove the stain without scratching the finish.

Afterward, wax the whole surface to even the finish. Use paste wax (sold at home centers and hardware stores). It is more protective than oils or liquid waxes.

•**Minor scratches on wood.** I use Old English Scratch Guard (sold at hardware stores). If in doubt about which color to use, start with a lighter color. Apply the product to your wiping cloth, not directly on the furniture.

•**Use the right dust rag.** Soft white flannel or cheesecloth is best because dust adheres to it so well. Dampen the cloth very slightly with water. For heirlooms and valuable antique woods, use distilled water to dampen rags. For carved furniture, china, ceramics, chandeliers and vases, use a small artist's paintbrush made from natural- or hog's-hair bristles.

UPHOLSTERY

•**Stains from eggs, milk, chocolate.** Rub with a solution of one tablespoon household ammonia and one-half cup of water.

•**Coffee, cola and beer stains.** Rub with a solution of one-third cup of white vinegar mixed with two-thirds cup of water. Avoid soap, which can set the stain permanently.

•**Ink stains.** Sponge with rubbing alcohol.

WALLS

•**Nonwashable wallpaper.** For grease stains, place an absorbent towel over the stain and cover it with an iron set at low for several seconds. For ink or pencil marks, try rubbing with cleaning putty such as Absorene (available at home centers) or a wadded-up piece of fresh, soft, white bread.

- **Washable vinyl wallpaper.** For stubborn stains, such as crayon, tar or adhesives, use WD-40 (available in hardware stores).
- **Painted walls.** Mix a thick paste of baking soda and water. Dip your cloth in it, and rub marks very gently to remove fingerprints, crayon, etc.

CARPETS

- **Spills.** Use as little water as possible. Blot as much of the spill as possible with paper towels. Then, in a bowl, whip up a sudsy foam using water and mild detergent. For delicate carpets, I use Orvus WA paste from Procter & Gamble (available at antique stores, or call 800-332-7787).

Dip your brush into the *foam,* not the water. Brush stain lightly, then wipe off excess foam with a clean cloth. Rinse with a 50/50 solution of white vinegar and water. Then rinse with plain warm water. Blot thoroughly.

- **Use a vacuum with low dust emissions.** If you have asthma or other allergies, consider investing in a vacuum with a HEPA filter—I use the Miele White Pearl (800-694-4868).

WOOD FLOORS

- **Scuffs and heel marks on hard-finish or urethane-type floors.** Dampen a cloth with a small amount of mineral spirits (available at hardware stores). Rub gently in the direction of the grain.
- **Oil or grease stains on natural-finish floors.** Saturate a cotton ball with hydrogen peroxide, and place over the stain for several minutes. Saturate a second cotton ball with ammonia, and place over the stain for several minutes. Repeat until the stain is removed. Let the area dry, then buff with a soft cloth.

COMPUTERS

- **Keyboards.** Try rubbing alcohol or degreaser sprays (available at electronics stores) to clean off the grime.
- **Computer screens.** Make sure screen is off. Use a slightly damp cloth. Avoid those special-purpose towelettes sold in office-supply stores. They leave a soapy residue.

Best Home Water Filters

Richard P. Maas, PhD, professor of environmental studies at the University of North Carolina, Asheville. He is codirector of the university's Environmental Quality Institute, a leading center for research on tap-water purity.

With regular news reports about water contamination—even in the best communities—more and more people are turning to home water filters to protect their families' health...

DETERMINE YOUR NEEDS

To choose the best filter for you, have your tap water tested.

Larger water utilities are now required to send an annual report to customers with the results of tests for about 80 different contaminants. If you haven't received one, call your local utility.

If you have well water—or if you want to do more extensive testing—look in the *Yellow Pages* under "Water Testing" or "Laboratories–Testing." Test price depends on what contaminants you look for. The range is wide—between $17 and $800. The most likely contaminant is lead (20% of US households), which can be picked up by the household plumbing system.

Clean Water Lead Testing (828-251-6800) provides a two-sample, mail-in test (first drawn and after running water for one minute) for $17. *Warning:* Home testing kits may be unreliable.

CARAFE FILTERS

Water flows by gravity, and there's plenty of the filtering medium with which it interacts to remove lead, reduce chlorine byproducts and improve taste and smell. Inexpensive (less than $30).

Drawbacks: Slow...holds only two to three quarts...filters must be changed often, generally every 50 to 100 gallons, depending on the level of contaminants in the water.

Top carafe filter: **Pur Pitcher CR-500.** Half-gallon pitcher uses carbon and an active agent to improve water taste while reducing levels of lead, chlorine, copper and zinc. Safety gauge indicates when filter needs replacing. $20. *Replacement filters:* $8 each. 800-787-5463.

FAUCET-MOUNTED

Inexpensive (less than $50)...easy to install and change filters.

Drawbacks: Units are small, and water pressure forces water through the filter too quickly to thoroughly remove all impurities.

Top faucet filter: Pur Plus FM-3000. Removes microorganisms, such as giardia and cryptosporidium, as well as contaminants, including lead, chlorine and mercury. Automatic shut-off stops water flow when filter needs replacing. Filters last for 100 gallons. $30. *Replacement filters:* $15 each. 800-787-5463.

UNDER-SINK FILTER

Contains a reservoir so water has more time to pass through the filtering mechanism...long-lasting filters.

Drawbacks: Costs $100 or more...may require a plumber for installation.

Top under-sink filter: Waterpik IF-100A. Dual-filter unit removes lead, chlorine and some pesticides—such as lindane—while improving water odor and taste. Installs easily and comes with extra-long tubing and a movable base for quick filter changing. Filters last for approximately 1,200 gallons. $159. *Replacement filters:* Lead filter/$38.59...chlorine/pesticide/taste and odor filter/$12.49. 800-525-2774.

WHOLE-HOUSE FILTER

For homes on well water and not connected to a municipal water system.

Contains sophisticated filtering material tailored to meet the home's specific needs...removes hardness...neutralizes water...removes bacteria. Filtered water is supplied to the whole house, including taps, showers and washing machine.

Drawbacks: Expensive ($1,000 to $3,000 installed plus filtering materials)...requires monthly maintenance...changing filters and/or adding filtering materials.

There is no *best* whole-house system—it depends on your water-treatment goals. Leading manufacturers include Culligan, Flek and Hauge. The company that services your well can provide guidance following a comprehensive water test. Or look in the *Yellow Pages* under "Water Purification & Filtration Equipment."

Stress-Free System to Unclutter Your Home

Donna Smallin, Troy, New York-based author of *Unclutter Your Home: 7 Simple Steps, 700 Tips and Ideas.* Storey Books. She writes for several major manufacturers and retailers and has contributed articles to *Bridal Guide* and *Running Times* magazines.

Too much stuff in your house? Many of us are troubled by the clutter...and overwhelmed by the imposing task of doing something about it. Here is a no-stress system to unclutter your home. *Key questions...*

If I had 20 minutes to evacuate my home, what would I take? That's when you realize that most things aren't very important.

How much is enough? On a scale of zero to 10—with 10 being everything you now own and zero being nothing—what amount of stuff would you prefer to own? Nine? Eight? Five? If five seems about right, your goal should be to eliminate half of your belongings.

If that seems like a lot, remember—you'll be getting rid of things you don't want, use or need.

TOSS OBVIOUS JUNK

Walk around your house with a plastic garbage bag. Toss out expired coupons or packages of food no one will eat...single or worn socks...old, rusted tools and utensils. Do this the night before garbage pickup so you aren't tempted to retrieve anything.

SORT YOUR THINGS

Now comes the hard part—deciding what to keep. Bring a laundry basket or large box into a room, and gather everything that doesn't belong there. Carry these items into the rooms where they belong, and put them away properly.

When you're done with the last item, look around the room you're in. Repeat the process, gathering all the things that don't belong and taking them where they do belong. Keep going until all your rooms are clutter-free.

For items that belong in a room, you need to make some decisions.

If you haven't used an item for a year or you don't like it anymore—get rid of it. If you really want it—put it back.

If it's hard for you to toss things, organize a cleaning party. Find a few people willing to help—in exchange for you helping them another time.

Touching an item increases your attachment. So ask a friend to hold each item while you decide whether to keep it.

Place items you're unsure of in a box. Seal the box and date it. After six months, if you haven't gone back to retrieve anything from the box, get rid of it or have a tag sale. Bring items to a church sale or donate them to the Salvation Army or another charity.

STAYING AHEAD OF CLUTTER

Organizing is a process, not a one-time event. If you spend 15 minutes a day on the task—while watching TV or waiting for dinner to cook—you'll stay ahead of the clutter. *Other strategies...*

- **Watch what you bring home.** When you buy something, get rid of something else. If you get two new sweaters for your birthday, get rid of two old sweaters.

- **Stay current.** Open, sort and file your mail every day. After you read a newspaper or a magazine, get rid of it. If you want to save an article, tear it out and file it. Clean up the kitchen every night. Hang up your clothes or put them in the hamper when you take them off.

11
Looking Good

Cosmetic Surgery Dos and Don'ts

These days with so many people undergoing some kind of cosmetic surgery—whether it's a face-lift, a nose job or a tummy tuck—it's important to remember that plastic surgery is, after all, surgery. It is not to be taken lightly. *Here are my dos and don'ts for people now considering a cosmetic-surgery procedure...*

● **Choose a doctor you trust.** First, you want a surgeon who's competent—he/she should be board-certified or at least board-eligible. If you're not sure, ask the surgeon directly—or check with your local medical society. But equally important is the way you feel about this doctor.

● **Ask the surgeon for references**—former patients who can testify to his competence. Choose a doctor you feel comfortable with. If you know former patients, talk to them. If you are uncomfortable with your doctor, it may affect your willingness to approach him with questions.

● **Ask questions.** Informed patients make good patients. You're paying good money to talk with an expert, so get your money's worth by asking everything you want to know about the procedure—the anticipated outcome, recovery time, costs...

If you don't understand something, ask to have it explained again. Write down the responses. During an initial consultation there's usually so much technical information discussed that the average patient retains only about 50% of it. Having written answers in hand will be a tremendous plus after you leave the office.

● **Keep an open mind.** People often come in to see the surgeon already loaded down with information—so many statistics and anecdotes from friends, relatives and magazine articles that they don't tune in to what the doctor is saying.

It's okay to challenge the surgeon's remarks with something you may have read or heard,

---

Stephen Cotlar, MD, a Houston-based plastic surgeon certified by the American Board of Plastic Surgery.

but remember that everyone responds to procedures differently—your neighbor's experiences may not be the same as yours. Put aside your own beliefs and preconceptions long enough to really focus on what the doctor is telling you.

• Don't ignore the risks. Too many people assume that a nose job, say, or liposuction is so common that it's risk free. All surgery carries risk.

Examples: It's very rare, but it's possible for a facial nerve to be damaged during a face-lift and result in partial paralysis of the face. And TV talk-show host Jenny Jones went public with the serious problems she experienced with her breast implants, which she subsequently had removed.

The doctor should explain what your risks are—and if he doesn't, you should ask.

• Be wary of doctors who recommend procedures you didn't ask for. It's quite possible that a surgeon will give you a good suggestion you never considered. For instance, you might come in for a nose job, and the doctor might suggest that you also have a chin implant, to better balance your entire face.

But be alert to someone who suddenly tries to encourage you to have, say, breast implants when you're there for a face-lift.

• Answer all questions honestly. During the initial consultation, the surgeon will—and should—ask you a lot of questions involving your health, your habits and even your personal life that may seem irrelevant or nosy...but they're not. They will help him assess whether you're a good candidate for surgery, as well as how well the procedure will turn out.

These questions may include:

- Do you smoke?
- Do you take any medications?
- Do you have a heart condition?

For whatever reason, you may not want to answer the questions, but it's critical that you do so.

Examples: You might not want to admit that you smoke or when you had your last cigarette. But smoking can compromise the circulation to the skin, and smokers who have face-lifts have a higher incidence of complications, so I generally tell patients to stop smoking six to eight weeks prior to surgery.

Or, a doctor may tell you to stop taking aspirin for a week before surgery, because aspirin has a blood-thinning effect—and you want your blood to clot properly during the operation. If the surgeon doesn't ask, volunteer any information you think might be important.

• Don't assume you know the best solution to your particular problem. The surgeon should, of course, consider any procedure you request, but he might recommend an alternative that may work better for you.

Example: You want surgery done on your eyelids to help correct a tired look, but what you might actually need is a forehead lift to raise your eyebrows.

Or you believe that liposuction will "cure" your obesity, but liposuction is not a weight-reduction operation—it's a procedure designed to improve certain parts of the body that can't be trimmed any other way, such as "saddlebags" on an otherwise slim person.

The professional doctor will steer you in the right direction.

• Don't assume you can't have plastic surgery because you're "too old." The age of the patients coming to the operating table these days is getting older and older. Although the optimum age for a first face-lift is from about 48 to 60 years old, people in their 80s are having them now.

The state of your health is more important to a plastic surgeon than your age, and if you're in generally good health, you may be a fine candidate for surgery.

• Examine your reasons for having surgery. During the initial consultation the doctor will probably ask, "Why are you having this surgery done?" If you're having a face-lift because you think it'll enhance your chances to get a job, or simply because you want to like what you see in the mirror better, those are valid reasons.

But if you're doing it to win back a wife who left you for a younger man or because your new girlfriend wishes you would, those are poor reasons.

Plastic surgery should never be done to solve an emotional crisis or because you expect it to make you a different person. If you're doing it for someone else, rather than for yourself... reconsider.

Plastic Surgery Problems

Linton A. Whitaker, MD, chief of the division of plastic surgery, the Hospital of the University of Pennsylvania, and professor of surgery, University of Pennsylvania School of Medicine. Dr. Whitaker specializes in facial surgery.

Whether it's an ordinary nose job or the removal of a rib to achieve a smaller waistline, cosmetic surgery performed by a qualified surgeon is usually safe and effective.

As with any medical procedure, however, cosmetic surgery occasionally results in complications—in a small portion of all procedures. And when complications occur, the results can be devastating.

COSMETIC SURGERY RISKS

•**Persistent infection.** The most common complication—and usually the easiest to correct. Antibiotics are effective in most cases, although implants sometimes have to be removed.

Exception: Cartilage infections, especially those following a nose job (rhinoplasty), rarely may persist for a year or longer even with aggressive antibiotic treatment...and they can destroy the nose's shape.

Self-defense: Choose a qualified surgeon—one who has performed the same procedure dozens of times.

•**Bad nose job.** Nose jobs involving excessive cartilage removal can cause big trouble later in life. As the patient ages, the skin thins, and the nose appears to shrink—sometimes to little more than a tiny nubbin.

In extreme cases, a nubbin nose causes not only acute embarrassment, but also breathing difficulties. The only way to correct the problem is to transplant cartilage taken from elsewhere in the body.

Self-defense: The less tissue removed during any cosmetic surgery, the safer.

•**Lumpy skin.** Surgeons performing liposuction must wield the cannula (fat-sucking instrument) very deftly, since uneven removal of fat results in lumpy or rippled skin. These defects are difficult or impossible to fix, even with additional liposuction or fat transplantation.

In very rare cases, fat cells liberated during liposuction cut off the supply of blood to the heart or brain. Although rare, some fat embolisms are fatal.

Also in rare cases, liposuction can result in inadvertent damage to the spleen or other internal organs. A ruptured spleen usually necessitates emergency surgery to control bleeding.

Self-defense: Use an experienced surgeon. Check out the doctor's reputation, enlist word-of-mouth recommendations and directly ask the doctor questions about his/her background.

•**Distorted eyes.** Surgeons performing eye tucks (blepharoplasties) must be careful to remove just the right amount of tissue around the eyes. Otherwise, the patient may be left with eyes that seem to turn downward or outward, or with an exposed mucous membrane around the eyes.

Sometimes the eyelids are stretched so tight by surgery that the eyes cannot fully close. Botched eye jobs can also result in acute glaucoma...even blindness.

Self-defense: Choose a highly experienced surgeon.

•**Lopsided face.** In rare instances, face-lifts damage the facial nerve. *Result:* Diminished muscle tone or even partial paralysis. The patient may develop a crooked smile, sagging cheeks or may have difficulty blinking.

Similarly, implants in the chin, cheeks and other parts of the face must be firmly attached to bone, or over time they may be mobile. More than an annoyance, mobile facial implants can result in a lopsided appearance.

Self-defense: Make sure the surgeon plans the implants so they are placed on bone.

•**Rashes and redness.** Collagen used to fill in acne scars and other skin defects can cause severe rashes and persistent redness. Theoretically, collagen injected directly into a blood vessel rather than just under the skin could interrupt the flow of blood to an eye—resulting in blindness.

Self-defense: The doctor should make sure the patient is not allergic to collagen before large quantities are injected. This can be done by test injections, introducing a small amount of collagen into the body in an inconspicuous place.

• **Too-tight face-lift.** This usually occurs on repeat face-lifts and strictly skin lifts. Newer face-lifts include both deeper layers and skin and give a more natural look.

Self-defense: Ask what technique the surgeon uses and how much experience he/she has with the procedure. Ask to see other patients ...or their photographs.

Fat Removal Technique And Its Pitfalls

Liposuction—surgery performed to remove excess fat from various parts of the body—is now the most popular cosmetic operation in the United States. The doctor inserts a thin tube called a cannula through a small incision in the skin and moves it back and forth to break up a fatty deposit. The dislodged fat is then evacuated through this tubing by strong suction.

In cases where a person has good skin elasticity—up into their early 40s for most people—a double chin can be fixed without undergoing a face-lift. Liposuction can remove fat from a full neck, giving the patient a clean jawline and only a tiny scar.

Dr. Henry Zackin, a plastic and reconstructive surgeon in private practice in New York City.

Liposuction is safest when performed as an outpatient procedure under local anesthesia—in a doctor's office, not in a hospital. The doctor should be a board-certified dermatologic surgeon. Avoid doctors who plan to extract large amounts of fat at one time...and those who perform multiple procedures at the same time. Liposuction is usually safe, but serious complications do occur in rare cases—usually when general anesthesia is used. *These include:*

Shock, blood clots, infection, bowel perforation in abdominal procedures.

William Coleman III, MD, clinical professor of dermatology, Tulane University, New Orleans, and leader of a study of 257 liposuction-related insurance claims, published in *Dermatalogic Surgery.*

Simple Exercises for a Nonsurgical Face-Lift

Judith Olivia, national spokesperson for Advanced Dermatology Care, an organization that lectures to medical professionals on advancements in the field, and creator of the videos *Face Aerobics* and *Advanced Face Aerobics* (available through her company, Judith Olivia Inc., Box 181706, Casselberry, FL 32718).

Face-lifts make the skin tighter, but the benefits are often temporary because the underlying muscles continue to sag. Then a second—or even a third—face-lift is often necessary.

Free and painless alternative: Strengthen and firm the facial muscles. Facial exercises pull the muscles upward so that the skin looks firm and youthful.

These exercises hit the main trouble spots. Do each exercise once a day for two weeks. After that, weekly workouts are fine. Facial muscles are small, so you'll see improvements quickly.

UNDER-EYE BAGS

Using both hands, gently place one forefinger under each eye, just below the lower lid. Use the muscles of the lower lids to try to lift the weight of your fingers. Do this exercise 20 times, twice a day.

SAGGING JOWLS

Lift your bottom lip so it covers the top lip. Tilt your head up slightly, and smile toward the tops of the ears. Hold for a count of 10, then relax. Repeat five times.

You'll know you're doing it right when you feel a tingle in the muscles of the jaw and throat.

Male advantage: Men move their faces around almost every day when they are shaving, so this exercise is less important for men than it is for women.

DOUBLE CHIN

Lie on your back, with your knees slightly bent and feet flat on the floor. Slowly raise your head and tuck your chin against your chest. Hold this position for a second, then slowly lower your head. Try to repeat it 10 times at first…and gradually work up to 50 repetitions.

DROOPY EYELIDS

Using both hands, put a forefinger on each eyebrow, exerting enough pressure so the eyebrows won't move easily. Try to close your eyes, working against the resistance of your fingers. Don't scrunch your forehead—just try to push the upper lashes into the lower ones as hard as you can. Repeat between five and 20 times, holding for a count of five each time.

FOREHEAD LINES

Cover your forehead with the palm of one hand, holding it firmly. Try to push the forehead muscle toward the top of the head, pushing against the resistance of your hand. Hold for a second, then relax. Repeat 10 times.

Bonus: This exercise not only tightens skin on the forehead—it also helps smooth frown and worry lines. It trains the forehead muscles to work together, instead of rippling.

LOOSE THROAT

Flex throat muscles—as a weight lifter's neck would look straining to lift weights. Hold for a minute, then relax.

Wrinkle Magic

Egg whites smooth facial wrinkles by temporarily tightening the skin.

Directions: Beat an egg white until frothy, then apply it to wrinkles. Let it dry for five minutes, then rinse—first with warm water and then with cool water.

Important: Use fresh egg whites.

Seth L. Matarasso, MD, associate clinical professor of dermatology, University of California, San Francisco, School of Medicine.

Secrets of Youthful-Looking Skin

Nicholas V. Perricone, MD, assistant clinical professor of dermatology at Yale University School of Medicine in New Haven, CT. He is author of *The Wrinkle Cure: Unlock the Power of Cosmeceuticals for Supple, Youthful Skin*. Rodale. For more on skin care, see Perricone's Web site at *www.nvperriconemd.com*.

In their quest to keep a youthful appearance, growing numbers of men and women are using costly—but ineffective—wrinkle creams and undergoing painful procedures like face-lifts and dermabrasion.

There is an effective alternative. It's not a quick fix, but a science-based change in the way you eat and live.

OXIDATION AND INFLAMMATION

What we call "aging" of the skin—wrinkles, age spots, etc.—is *not* the fault of time. It's the result of inflammation. In fact, you might say that aging *is* inflammation…and that if you want to attack the first, you must defend against the second.

Inflammation is usually thought of as something obvious—the redness of sunburn, for instance, or painful swelling associated with infection. Actually, inflammation goes on invisibly—and constantly—at the cellular level.

Oxidation is a cause of underlying inflammation. You may have heard that this cell-damaging process is caused by highly reactive molecular fragments known as free radicals.

Ultraviolet radiation from sunlight creates free radicals in the skin. So does air pollution. And so do the natural metabolic processes that the body uses to convert food into energy.

Free radicals are especially damaging to the membrane that encases every cell. As each cell membrane oxidizes, inflammation-promoting compounds known as *prostaglandins* and *leukotrienes* are created. With its membrane damaged, the cell can't bring in essential nutrients…or expel wastes.

The key to stopping or reversing "aging" is to minimize oxidation—and inflammation.

ANTI-INFLAMMATORY DIET

• **Cut back on sugar.** It's responsible for 50% of skin aging. Sugar molecules react with *collagen,* the protein that gives texture to the skin. That makes skin saggy instead of resilient. And each time sugar reacts with collagen, it releases a burst of free radicals.

In addition to cake, candy and other sweets, it's best to avoid pasta, potatoes, white rice, fruit juices, grapes and cooked carrots. These foods have a high glycemic index—meaning that they are converted into blood sugar very rapidly.

Most fresh fruits and vegetables like broccoli, eggplant, tomatoes and greens are okay because they are absorbed slowly.

●**Eat more protein.** The skin needs a constant supply of amino acids to repair cellular damage. But not all of us get enough of the proteins that supply these amino acids.

Daily protein intake should be 35 g to 60 g for women, 70 g to 80 g for men. Men tend to get enough protein, but the average woman gets just 20 g of protein a day.

Protein comes from dairy products, beans and peas, poultry, etc. But from the perspective of skin health, the best protein sources are cold-water fish like sardines, anchovies and especially salmon.

Cold-water fish are rich sources of omega-3 fatty acids, which exert a potent anti-inflammatory effect. These fish are also rich in a little-known compound called *dimethylaminoethanol* (DMAE). DMAE is the raw material used by the body to synthesize acetylcholine, the chemical that carries messages from nerve endings to muscles. By boosting acetylcholine synthesis, DMAE keeps the muscles that support the skin well-toned.

If you don't like fish, fish oil supplements are an alternative. But they contain only omega-3s, not protein or DMAE.

●**Take supplements.** Vitamins C and E, the mineral selenium and other antioxidants work in concert to inhibit free radical activity.

Because it's difficult to get enough antioxidant protection from foods alone, ask your doctor about taking the following daily supplements…

●Vitamin C…1,000 mg to 2,000 mg.

●Vitamin E…400 international units (IU) of *natural* vitamin E.

●Coenzyme Q10…30 mg for people under age 40…60 mg for people in their 40s…100 mg for people age 50 or older.

●DMAE…50 mg to 100 mg.
●Lipoic acid…50 mg.
●Selenium…200 micrograms.

SUNLIGHT AND THE SKIN

To get a sense of just how significant sun exposure really is, compare your facial skin with skin on a part of your body that's always covered.

To minimize damage: Use sunscreen every day. SPF 15 is okay for day-to-day sun exposure. Use SPF 30 and a hat and other protective clothing if you plan to be out for an extended period.

THE ROLE OF EXERCISE

Exercise dilates blood vessels, bringing nutrients to the skin. And sweating expels toxins from the skin. Exercise also promotes synthesis of growth hormone. High levels of growth hormone are linked to youthful-looking skin.

Running, brisk walking, cycling or using a stair-climber for 30 minutes, five times weekly should suffice. If possible, fit in two or three days per week of strength training. Concentrate on shoulders, back, arms, legs and abdominals. Each session should last about 30 minutes.

AVOIDING IRRITANTS

Avoid contact with cosmetics, soaps, etc., that cause redness or irritation. Prescription retinoic acid preparations like *tretinoin* (Renova) are generally okay, though they may cause temporary pinkness. If severe pinkness lasts for more than four weeks, consult a physician.

Retin-A Repairs Damaged Skin

Retin-A doesn't just smooth wrinkles—it repairs damaged skin. In a study, 29 people with sun-damaged skin applied either 0.1% tretinoin (Retin-A) or a placebo cream once a day. After one year, those using tretinoin showed an 80% increase in formation of collagen, the protein that gives skin its elasticity.

Those receiving the placebo cream had a 14% decrease in collagen synthesis.

Albert M. Kligman, MD, PhD, professor of dermatology, University of Pennsylvania, Philadelphia. His study was published in *The New England Journal of Medicine*, 10 Shattuck St., Boston 02115.

Help for Irritated Skin

Soothe irritated skin by adding one to two cups of milk and one-half to one cup of oatmeal to your bath water. You can also use equal parts of milk and water as a face wash or cold compress...or make an oatmeal face mask for skin inflamed by sunlight or an allergic reaction. *Caution:* Those with food allergies should test a small amount on the skin and wait 48 hours for a reaction.

Diane Berson, MD, assistant clinical professor of dermatology, New York University School of Medicine, New York.

Hair Dye/Cancer Connections

Black hair dye may boost the risk of some cancers. In a study, women who used black dye for 20 years or longer faced an increased risk of death from non-Hodgkin's lymphoma and multiple myeloma. Other colors were found to be safe—even with long-term use.

Good news: Less than 1% of hair-dye users have used black dye for more than 20 years.

Michael J. Thun, MD, MS, director of analytic epidemiology, American Cancer Society, 1599 Clifton Rd. NE, Atlanta. His study of hair dye use among 570,000 American women was published in the *Journal of the National Cancer Institute*, 9030 Old Georgetown Rd., Building 82, Room 209, Bethesda, MD 20814.

Blow-Dryer Alert

Daily blow-drying *can* damage hair, especially dyed or permed hair.

Problems: The heat may cause strands to break or may lead to the development of little pimples (called *folliculitis*) on the scalp. It can also worsen facial acne.

In rare cases, if hair is often pulled tightly to straighten it during drying, hair may fall out, leaving bald spots. Frequent tight braiding/cornrows and constant twirling of hair can also lead to baldness.

Self-defense: If you must use a blow-dryer, dry hair on a medium setting, not hot...keep the dryer at least eight inches from your head and face...don't pull hair tight while drying...use a cream rinse or detangler after shampooing and prior to drying.

Deborah S. Sarnoff, MD, assistant clinical professor of dermatology, New York University School of Medicine, New York. She is author of *Beauty and the Beam: Your Complete Guide to Cosmetic Laser Surgery*. St. Martin's Griffin.

For Men Only

New hair-transplant procedures—*mini-* and *micro*-grafts—give a more natural look than older techniques. Risk is minimal as long as antibacterial ointments are used to prevent infection. *Cost:* About $2,000 to $8,000. *Also very popular for men:* Liposuction—surgical fat removal—to eliminate double chins, "love handles" and other bulges. *Cost:* $1,500—and up. Using local instead of general anesthesia greatly reduces both the risks and postsurgical "downtime" of liposuction. More men are turning to cosmetic surgery to stay competitive in the youth-oriented workplace.

Bruce Katz, MD, dermatologist and director, Juva Skin and Laser Center, New York.

What Causes Teeth to Become Yellowed

Yellowed teeth are usually caused by coffee, tobacco or *gastroesophageal reflux disease* (GERD). In this condition, corrosive stomach acids back up into the esophagus and mouth …eroding teeth and eventually causing them to break off. GERD can often be controlled with *omeprazole* (Prilosec) or other prescription or over-the-counter medications.

Pat Schroeder, MD, gastroenterology fellow, University of Alabama School of Medicine, Birmingham.

Secrets of Exercise Stick-to-it-iveness

Seventy-five percent of people who start an exercise program quit within a year. *To be an exercise veteran…*

●**Choose a program that is fun for you.** *Best:* Lifetime sports—hiking, swimming, walking, dancing, gardening, volleyball, tennis, golf (no golf carts please). Add appropriate conditioning exercises once you are comfortable with the regime.

●**Pick a motivating role model**—someone you've seen on the tennis court or in your aerobics class.

●**Join—or create—a team** to add fun, competition and socializing.

●**Treat exercise times like "appointments."** Those who miss three consecutive exercise sessions are more likely to abandon the program altogether.

Robert Hopper, PhD, gives seminars on health and fitness nationwide. He is based in Santa Barbara, CA.

Walking Boosts Brainpower

In a recent study, sedentary adults 60 to 75 years of age started walking briskly three times a week, gradually increasing the length of the walks from 15 to 45 minutes. After six months, their mental function had improved by 15%. Similar adults who did stretching and toning exercises for one hour three days a week showed no improvement. *Theory:* By increasing oxygen flow to the brain, walking averts the earliest mental changes that occur with aging.

Arthur Kramer, PhD, professor of psychology, University of Illinois, Urbana-Champaign.

Exercises to Do in the Car

Double chin: Lift chin slightly and open and close mouth as though chewing. *Flabby neck:* Move head toward right shoulder while looking straight ahead at the road. Return head to center, then toward left shoulder. *Pot belly:* Sit straight with spine against back seat. Pull stomach in and hold breath for count of five. Relax, then repeat. The exercise also relieves tension and helps fight sleepiness.

Exercise and Your Immune System

Brisk walks strengthen your immune system—but too-strenuous workouts can lower immunity to colds and flu. Exercising near your maximum capacity for just 45 minutes—or more—produces a six-hour "window" of vulnerability afterward. *Better:* Exercise at a moderate level—the equivalent of a brisk walk —if not training for competition.

David Nieman, DrPH, professor of health, department of health and exercise science, Appalachian State University, Boone, NC.

Tai Chi Helpful for Older People

Tai chi improves balance and may help reduce the risk of falls in elderly people. The ancient Chinese exercise—which involves gentle turning and pivoting—teaches participants to focus on how their weight is distributed. Older women who did tai chi three times a week for six months, along with leg presses and brisk walking, experienced a 17% improvement in their ability to balance on one leg. Those who only stretched and practiced tai chi once a week had no significant improvement.

James Judge, MD, assistant professor of medicine, University of Connecticut School of Medicine, Farmington. His study of 21 women was reported in *Physical Therapy,* American Physical Therapy Association, 1111 N. Fairfax St., Alexandria, VA 22314.

Treadmill Traps

Setting the speed too fast or the incline too steep...keeping your ankles too stiff, which can lead to shinsplints...flailing your arms, which can twist your torso and stress the back ...locking your arms in one position, which prevents your body from making subtle adjustments to better absorb impact.

Helpful: Keep your gait smooth, upper body loose and arms close to your torso, moving them back and forth in a relatively straight line.

Mike Motta, president, Plus One Fitness, New York, quoted in *American Health,* 28 W. 23 St., New York 10010.

Real Cause of Flabby Muscles

Lack of exercise—not aging. Muscle mass does decline between ages 30 and 70. But isotonic—strength-building—exercises can reverse the decline. Half an hour of isotonics two or three times a week can increase strength within two weeks and double it in 12 weeks—by changing the ratio of muscle to fat. *Bonus:* Increased bone density—helping prevent fractures caused by osteoporosis.

William J. Evans, PhD, director of Noll Laboratories of Human Performance Research, Pennsylvania State University, University Park, and coauthor of *Biomarkers: The 10 Determinants of Aging You Can Control.* Simon & Schuster, Inc.

Exercise and Lactic Acid

Lactic acid builds up during exercise and may contribute to the uncomfortable burning sensation that many exercisers feel.

To remove lactic acid faster: Have an active recovery period after a workout, like walking after running...instead of a passive one, like lying down.

Karen Segal, PhD, associate professor of physiology in pediatrics, director of exercise physiology lab, Cornell University Medical College and New York Hospital, New York.

Elderly and Weight-Lifting

Weight-lifting exercise boosts muscle strength and size as well as mobility in the elderly. Nutritional supplements, on the other hand, have no benefit on these outcomes—either alone or in conjunction with exercise.

Maria A. Fiatarone, MD, chief of the human physiology laboratory, Human Nutrition Research Center on Aging, Tufts University, Boston. Her 10-week study of 100 frail nursing home residents was published in *The New England Journal of Medicine,* 10 Shattuck St., Boston 02115.

Smarter Running

Many seniors cannot run because of joint or other problems. For those who can, running may be a good choice. You can do it anywhere, cost is low and health benefits are significant. *Smart runners...*

●**Run every other day to give your body a day to recover.**

●**Invest in good running shoes,** the one essential item of equipment a runner needs. Running places great stress on feet, knees, hips and lower back. So consult a physical therapist who specializes in sports medicine.

●**Replace shoes when they lose shape,** even if the soles aren't worn.

●**Take care of your feet.** Check them daily for blisters and calluses, and remedy other small problems before they become big ones.

Arthur Safalow, PT, CPed, director of Nassau Rehabilitation and Sports Therapy, Mineola, NY.

Exercising for Weight Loss

John Jakicic, PhD, assistant research professor of psychiatry and human behavior at Brown University School of Medicine, Providence, RI. His study of the role of exercise in weight loss was published in The Journal of the American Medical Association, 515 N. State St., Chicago 60610.

If you're exercising primarily as a way to lose weight, you may have read that 30 minutes three to five times a week is all that's needed. *Not true.* A study recently published in *The Journal of the American Medical Association* suggests that a total of at least 40 minutes —and preferably 60—is needed *each* day of the week to lose weight and keep it off.

An hour a day probably sounds pretty daunting. But that's mainly because few of us exercise as effectively—or as creatively—as we could. *Here are some helpful suggestions...*

●**Find a form of exercise that you truly enjoy.** That way, you're more likely to stick with your exercise routine. If you like bicycling, for example, don't try to become a runner. If you like swimming, don't commit yourself to long sessions on a stair-climbing machine.

Structured exercise isn't the only way to lose weight. You can burn calories just by increasing the intensity of everyday activities.

Shoveling snow burns about 400 calories an hour. That's four times as many calories as you would burn off with an hour of walking. An hour of raking leaves burns about 270 calories.

You probably wouldn't shovel snow or rake for a solid hour. But that's not the point. The idea is that any kind of movement done at moderate intensity can help with weight loss.

●**Put exercise on your calendar.** Individuals who pencil their workouts into their calendar are much more likely to follow through.

Give exercise the same priority as you would a business meeting or lunch with a friend.

●**Exercise early in the day.** Morning workouts burn no more calories than workouts late in the day. But they do give you more options if your schedule changes.

If an unforeseen circumstance forces you to cancel a workout that you've scheduled for the morning, you'll still have the rest of the day to break a sweat.

If you're forced to cancel an evening workout, you've lost your chance for the entire day.

●**Break up your workouts.** If you cannot fit a 60-minute workout into your daily schedule, do several shorter workouts throughout the day. You might go for a 30-minute walk in the morning, then take three 10-minute walks later on in the day.

Helpful: If there's any concern that weather or darkness might keep you from working out, invest in a treadmill. Recent research suggests that it's the most effective exercise machine for weight loss.

Whatever exercise you do, it should keep your heart rate elevated to at least 60% of its theoretical maximum capacity for at least 10 minutes at a time, for a total of 40 minutes a day.

To calculate your theoretical maximum heart rate, the old formula still holds true: Subtract your age in years from 220. A 60-year-old, for instance, has a theoretical maximum heart rate of 160 (220 minus 60).

●**Use a heart monitor.** This electronic device—typically consisting of an electrode-studded strap that's worn around the chest and a wristwatch-like digital display—gives a continuous readout of your heart rate.

With a heart monitor, there's no need to stop exercising to take your pulse. That's something you must do if you take your pulse using a finger held against your wrist.

Bonus: Heart monitors give you a clear target heart rate to shoot for, so they can be a tremendous source of motivation.

Heart monitors sell for $50 and up. They're available at sporting goods stores and via mail order.

One good mail-order source of heart monitors is Road Runner Sports, 800-636-3560, *www.roadrunnersports.com.*

•**Exercise to music.** When people listen to fast-tempo music, research shows, they tend to exercise more vigorously than they otherwise would. They also tend to keep at it longer.

Caution: Listening to headphones when running or walking outside can be dangerous.

How to Take Weight Off And Keep It Off

Kathleen Thompson, coauthor of *Feeding on Dreams: Why America's Diet Industry Doesn't Work & What Will Work for You.* Macmillan.

Each year, Americans spend billions on commercial diet programs—and much of that is essentially wasted.

Reason: The premise on which these programs are based—cut calories, and you'll lose weight—is out of date. In study after study, it's been thoroughly discredited.

Weight loss just isn't that simple. As we all know, the hard part isn't losing weight, but *keeping* it off. Unless you're willing to eat frozen dinners and drink low-cal shakes for the rest of your life, keeping the weight off is almost impossible on most of the commercial weight-loss programs.

Not surprising, then, that many dieters shuffle unsuccessfully from one diet plan to the next—losing weight on one program, putting it back on and then moving on to another plan.

In fact, counselors working for the leading commercial diet plans freely admit that perhaps nine of 10 people who try one commercial diet program wind up trying two or three or more.

WEIGHT-LOSS PRINCIPLES

How do you take weight off and keep it off —once and for all? *There are three fundamental principles for effective and lasting weight loss...*

Principle #1: **Take control of your life and your weight.** Turning responsibility for what you eat and what you do over to anyone else is deadly. You need to design a program for yourself. You also need to open up your life to self-inspection.

Often, eating is a survival skill. It's a way of coping with frustrations and disappointments. Life can be very difficult. Eating can get you through it.

Overeating becomes a way to maintain emotional health—although, of course, physical health is jeopardized as a result.

To overcome this self-destructive approach to food, you must learn to separate food itself from its emotional symbolism. You may need the help of a psychologist specializing in weight problems.

For referrals to a psychologist in your area, contact the National Association of Anorexia Nervosa and Associated Disorders, P.O. Box 7, Highland Park, IL 60035. 847-831-3438.

Principle #2: **Accept your body.** Focus not upon how your body looks, but on what it enables you to do. And don't compare yourself with the ideal body put forth in sexy movies or magazine ads. After all, body shape is determined largely by heredity. We tend to look like our mothers and fathers—and that persists even if we're successful at losing weight.

Principle #3: **Make food a pleasure.** Avoid thinking of food as a moral issue. "Good" foods are those you think you should be eating— fruits, vegetables, beans, pasta, etc. "Bad" foods taste good but are fattening—cakes, candy, sugary soft drinks, etc.

Substituting good foods for bad sounds like a good idea, but odds are it's just setting you up for failure. *Problem:* Even if you could steer clear of "bad" foods for several months, you'd give in to temptation—possibly by going on an eating binge.

Better way: If you like cheesecake, allow yourself the freedom to eat it on occasion. By removing this cheesecake "taboo," you reduce your obsession with it.

DIETING VS. YOUR SET-POINT

The only way to ensure lasting weight loss is to lower your set-point. That's the weight your body "thinks" it should be.

When people overeat, they generally gain weight only temporarily, returning to their usual weight, or "set-point" when they resume their previous eating habits.

Similarly, when you go on a low-calorie diet, your body wants to keep you from starving. As a result, your metabolism slows to maintain your set-point. *Result:* Weight loss occurs very slowly. When you resume your normal eating patterns, your weight quickly rises to its former level.

To lower your set-point, you must reduce your intake of dietary fat *and* increase your lean muscle mass. In other words, lighten up your eating habits and get enough exercise to build muscle.

CUTTING OUT DIETARY FAT

•**Start small.** You're not going on a diet—you're changing the way you eat for the rest of your life. So there's no need to cut out dietary fat all at once.

You might start by switching to milk instead of cream in your coffee, then switching to low-fat mayonnaise on your sandwiches, etc.

•**Eat what you like. If you already enjoy certain low-fat foods,** make them staples of your diet. Make a list of your favorite high-fat foods, and find a way to substitute low-fat versions for some of them.

•**Keep track of your fat intake.** Buy a nutritional guide that lists the fat content of each food. Use it to calculate how many grams of fat you consume each day.

The maximum number of grams of fat you can eat each day and still lose weight is determined by your age, sex (men burn fat faster than women) and medical condition, among other things.

A woman over 30 should probably consume no more than 20% of her calories in the form of fat. A man over 30 can probably get away with up to 25%. (One gram of fat equals about nine calories.)

•**Make sure the whole family adopts healthful eating habits.** If your spouse has an ice cream sundae for dessert, you probably won't feel satisfied with a pear. But if everyone in the family starts eating healthfully, there's less temptation.

THE IMPORTANCE OF EXERCISE

The more you exercise, the more muscle you build. And because muscle cells burn dietary fat more efficiently than fat cells do, gaining muscle mass speeds your metabolism. *Payoff:* A thin person can eat much more fat than a fat person without gaining weight.

If you've been inactive for a long time, begin by exercising just five or 10 minutes a day. Gradually build until you're exercising at least 20 minutes a day, three to four days a week.

The point is to do what you like. Otherwise, you'll quickly give up exercising. If you used to thrive on volleyball or softball, for example, try to work these activities back into your schedule. If you're joining a gym, look for one where you feel comfortable. One reason people stop going to the gym is that they feel they don't measure up. If you feel intimidated by a chic club, try the local "Y" instead.

Consider hiring a personal trainer (for $15 to $50 per session). If you can't afford one, pool your money with a few friends and hire a trainer to come to one of your homes. Invest in headphones and a few good exercise tapes.

Dieting Magic

Barbara Rolls, PhD, professor of nutrition and head of Laboratory for the Study of Human Ingestive Behavior, Pennsylvania State University, University Park. She is coauthor of *Volumetrics: Feel Full on Fewer Calories.* HarperCollins.

Diets that work don't require you to follow drastic eating regimens or feel guilty if you sneak a brownie.

The real secrets: Portion control…moderation…and variety. Use these secrets to trim calories. General strategies…

●**Make small changes over time.** Eating habits are the hardest ones to change. But small, gradual changes are fairly easy.

Examples: If you drink 2% milk (121 calories/eight ounces), switch to 1% (102 calories) and then to skim (86 calories) over several months. Use reduced-fat sour cream and cottage cheese.

●**Substitute lower-calorie ingredients** in your favorite recipes and still enjoy the taste. You can make healthful, low-calorie foods tastier by adding spices.

●**Don't avoid treats completely.** Quite simply, sugar tastes good. And it doesn't make you fat unless you eat a great deal of it. So— use sugar to your advantage.

Examples: Add one teaspoon of sugar to a bowl of oatmeal if that's the only way you'll eat it. If you want chocolate, eat it at the end of a meal, when you are less likely to overindulge.

NEW WAY TO LOOK AT FOOD

One way to reduce your calorie intake is to eat the same volume as usual—but choose foods that are lower in calories than your regular high-calorie favorites.

●**Eat "high-water" foods.** Fruits, vegetables, nonfat milk and broth-based soups contain a lot of water—so you get a lot of volume and few calories.

Other high-water foods: Hot cereal… boiled eggs…pasta.

Eat less of "low-water" foods, which have a lot of calories by volume.

Examples: Most meats, cheeses and bread …most snack foods (including dried fruit)…oil… crackers…nuts…cookies…candy.

Myth…you'll eat less if you drink a glass of water before a meal. *Reality:* Water alone doesn't satisfy hunger. But thick water-rich drinks, such as tomato juice or milk, will.

●**Choose proteins carefully.** A 2.9-ounce serving of lean sirloin steak is comparable in calories to a 4.8-ounce serving of perch or 3.9 ounces of turkey breast. The larger portions of fish and turkey are more satisfying. Beans, low-fat milk and yogurt are also low-calorie, high-volume ways to eat protein.

HEALTHFUL WAYS TO FILL UP

●**Adjust the balance of foods.** Change the fat and calorie content of sandwiches by using low-fat meat, more garnish—dark lettuce, tomato and sprouts—with reduced-fat mayonnaise and spicy peppers or mustard for punch.

Increase the amount of vegetables in stir-fries, soups and stews. Use lean ground turkey breast in chili instead of ground beef.

Add extra vegetables, such as spinach, mushrooms and eggplant, to lasagna—and use less cheese. Take larger helpings of healthful "side" dishes and smaller portions of meat.

Healthful alternative to sugary soft drinks: Fill a glass with one-quarter juice and three-quarters club soda.

●**Add air to pump up food volume.** Food filled with air tricks your senses into thinking you're eating more than you are.

The longer you blend a fruit smoothie, the frothier it becomes. A large glass filled to the brim has more appeal than the same ingredients that fill only two-thirds of the glass.

For a low-fat frozen dessert, blend low-fat whipped topping with fruit, flavored yogurt or fruit-flavored extract…then freeze.

●**Choose snacks carefully.** Try a high-volume bunch of grapes rather than a comparable handful of raisins. Eat reduced-fat versions of your favorite snack foods—but watch the portions.

PORTION CONTROL

●**Make servings look more plentiful.** At home, eat on small plates rather than on dinner plates. At restaurants, order half servings—or ask that half be wrapped before the meal is served and take it home.

●**Freeze foods in single-serving portions,** so you can easily control how much you eat when you reheat.

●**Serve yourself**—rather than letting others serve you.

●**Buy the smallest packages available of snacks such as cookies or chips**…or buy the more economical size and repackage right away into single servings. Big packages encourage you to eat more.

●**Keep a daily food diary.** Most people underestimate how much they eat. By keeping a log, you'll discover ways to change mindless snacking habits.

Certain Aromas Promote Weight Loss

Certain aromas, including banana, peppermint and green apple, "fool" the brain into thinking the stomach is full. *Result:* Diminished appetite and significant weight loss. *To promote weight loss:* Sniff food before eating…chew food thoroughly…and if your tablemates can tolerate it, blow air through your carefully chewed food before swallowing. Hot food produces more odor—and therefore is more filling—than the same food eaten cold.

Alan R. Hirsch, MD, neurologic director, Smell & Taste Treatment and Research Foundation, 845 N. Michigan Ave., Chicago 60611.

Spotting Fraudulent Weight-Loss Programs

Dieters would be wise to avoid weight-loss programs that:

• **Promise rapid weight loss** (substantially more than 1% of total body weight per week).

• **Try to make clients dependent on special products** rather than teaching how to make good choices from conventional foods.

• **Do not encourage permanent, realistic lifestyle changes.**

• **Misrepresent salespeople as "counselors"** supposedly qualified to give guidance in nutrition and/or general health.

• **Require a large sum of money at the start,** or require clients to sign a contract for an expensive, long-term program.

• **Fail to inform clients** about the various health risks associated with weight loss.

• **Promote unproven or spurious weight-loss aids.**

• **Claim that "cellulite" exists in the body.**

• **Claim that the use of an appetite suppressant or bulking agent** enables a person to lose fat without restricting caloric intake.

• **Claim that a weight-control product** contains a unique ingredient or component, unless that component really is not available in other weight-loss products.

William T. Jarvis, PhD, president of the National Council Against Health Fraud, quoted in *Nutrition Forum,* George F. Stickley Co., Philadelphia 19106.

Good News for Dieters

Yo-yo dieting does not increase overall body fat or permanently slow the body's metabolism…so it doesn't make future weight loss more difficult. Previous studies had suggested just the opposite.

Lesson: If you are overweight, it's a good idea to lose weight—even if there's a chance you'll gain it back. Of course, it's better to maintain a healthy weight via regular exercise and a balanced diet.

Susan Yanofsky, executive secretary, National Task Force on the Prevention and Treatment of Obesity, Bethesda, MD. For more information, write to Weight Control Information Network, One WIN Way, Bethesda, MD 20892.

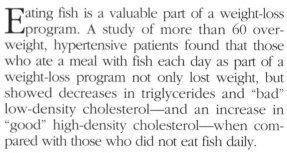

A Fish a Day…

Eating fish is a valuable part of a weight-loss program. A study of more than 60 overweight, hypertensive patients found that those who ate a meal with fish each day as part of a weight-loss program not only lost weight, but showed decreases in triglycerides and "bad" low-density cholesterol—and an increase in "good" high-density cholesterol—when compared with those who did not eat fish daily.

Lawrence J. Beilin, MD, FRCP, FRACP, professor of medicine, University of Western Australia, Perth.

12

Eating Right ...and Wrong

The Foods and Nutrients That Protect the Heart

There's now compelling evidence that certain foods contain special nutrients that guard against heart disease. The most important of these so-called "nutraceuticals" is *carnitine,* an amino acid found in red meat and in smaller amounts in chicken, fish, dairy products and certain fruits and vegetables.

Carnitine's primary function in the body is to ferry fatty acids from the foods we eat into the mitochondria. These microscopic "furnaces"—found inside every cell—convert fatty acids into the chemical energy that is put to use throughout the body.

CARNITINE SUPPLEMENTS

Biologists have been studying carnitine since the 1940s. Recent studies suggest that high levels of carnitine improve cardiac function in people suffering from coronary artery disease.

Other studies have shown that carnitine given immediately before or after a heart attack helps stabilize the heart rhythm. That improves the heart's pumping efficiency.

Carnitine has also been shown to minimize damage to the heart in the aftermath of a heart attack.

No one can predict when a heart attack will strike. For this reason it's often a good idea for people age 35 or older to take a daily carnitine supplement—to ensure that carnitine levels in the body are sufficient to protect the heart. Consult your doctor.

Carnitine supplementation is especially important for individuals with one or more risk factors for heart attack—obesity, family history of heart disease, elevated cholesterol level, high blood pressure and diabetes.

Stephen L. DeFelice, MD, chairman of the Foundation for Innovation in Medicine, *www.fimdefelice.org,* in Cranford, NJ, and former chief of clinical pharmacology at Walter Reed Army Institute of Research in Washington, DC. DeFelice coined the term "nutraceutical" and was among the first researchers to study carnitine's effects on the heart. He is author of *The Carnitine Defense.* Rodale.

155

Carnitine supplements are sold over the counter in drugstores and health food stores. Check labels carefully. Animal studies suggest that carnitine *fumarate* is more cardioprotective than other forms of carnitine.

Typical daily dosage: 1,500 mg to 3,000 mg. Taking carnitine twice daily—in divided doses 12 hours apart—helps keep blood levels consistent.

At this dosage, carnitine is extremely safe. Any excess is simply excreted in the urine.

BEYOND CARNITINE

Carnitine isn't the only heart-healthy nutraceutical. Vitamin E, magnesium, folic acid and other B vitamins, chromium and alcohol *in moderation* are proven to reduce heart attack risk.

Since these compounds are present in food only in small quantities, it's sometimes hard to get enough of them from food alone. For this reason, supplementation is often a good idea.

VITAMIN E

Vitamin E helps neutralize free radicals, helping keep these highly reactive molecular fragments from triggering the buildup of fatty deposits in coronary arteries.

Typical daily dosage: 400 international units (IU). To get that much vitamin E from food alone, you'd have to eat 48 cups of wheat germ or 100 cups of spinach.

One recent study of patients at high risk for heart disease seemed to suggest that vitamin E supplementation did not protect the heart against a lack of oxygen. This study contradicts numerous other studies showing that the supplements are heart-protective.

It may turn out that vitamin E is more effective at *preventing* high cholesterol and high blood pressure than at reducing heart attack risk in individuals who already have these risk factors.

Decades of clinical experience suggest that vitamin E supplementation is safe.

Caution: Check with a doctor if you've had a stroke or are on daily aspirin therapy and/or are taking *warfarin* (Coumadin) or another prescription anticoagulant. In such cases, vitamin E supplementation can thin the blood to the point that hemorrhage is likely.

MAGNESIUM

Magnesium prevents platelets from clumping together and clogging coronary arteries. It also stabilizes heart rhythm, reducing the risk of damage to the heart muscle during a heart attack.

Typical daily dosage: 400 mg to 500 mg. Divide into two doses and take twice a day to keep blood levels up all day.

Dietary sources of magnesium include artichokes, beans, shellfish, nuts and whole grains.

B VITAMINS

The B vitamin folic acid cuts blood levels of *homocysteine,* a blood protein that's been linked to heart disease. Folic acid's homocysteine-busting effect is especially pronounced when it's taken in combination with vitamins B-6 and B-12.

Typical daily dosages: 400 micrograms (mcg) folic acid...400 mg vitamin B-6...500 mcg to 1,000 mcg vitamin B-12.

ALCOHOL

Moderate drinking fights heart disease three ways. It boosts levels of HDL (good) cholesterol...helps rid the body of LDL (bad) cholesterol...and helps prevent platelet clumping.

Typical daily "dosage": The equivalent of one drink for women...one or two drinks for men. One drink equals 12 ounces of beer, four ounces of wine or 1.5 ounces of distilled spirits.

If you have a family or personal history of alcohol abuse: Consult a doctor before using alcohol. Pregnant women should not drink alcohol.

CHROMIUM

Chromium has been shown to reduce insulin resistance, in which cells' increasing resistance to insulin causes glucose levels to rise. This is a significant problem for people with diabetes.

Typical daily dosage: 500 mcg to 1,000 mcg.

Dietary sources of chromium include brewer's yeast, liver, egg yolks, wheat germ and whole-grain cereal.

MAKING IT WORK

If it's too hard to keep track of which supplements to take once a day and which twice a day, divide all the doses in half and take all your supplements twice a day.

Caution: Consult a doctor before taking any nutritional supplement. Like prescription medications, supplements can interact with other drugs you take.

Your doctor should carefully monitor the effects of the supplements...and, if necessary, adjust dosages.

Guidelines for Eating Right

Suzanne Havala, RD, MS, FADA, registered dietitian based in Chapel Hill, NC. She is author of several books, including *The Complete Idiot's Guide to Being Vegetarian* (Macmillan) and *Good Foods, Bad Foods: What's Left to Eat?* (John Wiley & Sons).

The word is out. A government-appointed panel of scientists has issued the fifth edition of *Dietary Guidelines* for Americans, the federal government's official word on the best nutritional practices. *Here is what they say...*

1. Aim for a healthful weight. There are a variety of ways to assess your weight. Check with your doctor to determine if you have excess abdominal fat. This puts you at a higher risk for a variety of diseases.

2. Be physically active every day. Greater emphasis is placed on the importance of regular physical activity and its role in weight control.

3. Let the Food Pyramid guide your food choices. The old guidelines said simply to "eat a variety of foods." Now people are encouraged to refer to the US Department of Agriculture's Food Pyramid for specific advice about what to eat. *www.nal.usda.gov/fnic/*, click on "Food Guide Pyramid."

4. Eat a variety of grains daily—especially whole grains. Previous recommendations lumped grains together with fruits and vegetables. The new guidelines emphasize grains as the foundation of a healthful diet.

5. Eat a variety of fruits and vegetables daily. Along with grains, fruits and vegetables are considered the pillars of a healthful diet. They are linked to lower rates of all types of disease, including diabetes, heart disease, some types of cancer, high blood pressure, etc.

6. Keep food safe to eat. For the first time, the guidelines address safe handling of foods to prevent food-borne illnesses.

Examples: Cooking and reheating food thoroughly...keeping preparation surfaces clean ...keeping raw and prepared foods separate.

7. Eat a diet that is low in saturated fat and cholesterol...and moderate in total fat. No more than 30% of daily calories should come from fat.

8. Limit your intake of foods with added sugars. Foods and beverages that contain added sugar displace nutrient-dense foods from your diet. Cut down on sweets and junk foods.

9. Choose and prepare foods with less salt. Americans continue to be advised to limit their sodium intake. *Heaviest sources:* Processed foods...salt added in cooking.

10. If you drink alcoholic beverages, do so in moderation—no more than one drink per day for women...two per day for men. The new guidelines acknowledge a heart-health benefit to moderate amounts of alcohol —particularly in women over age 55 and men over age 45. Alcohol consumption in younger women is associated with an increased risk of breast cancer.

The full text of Dietary Guidelines for Americans can be viewed online at *www.ars.usda. gov/dgac.*

Elderly People May Need More Protein

Elderly people may need more protein— 25% to 50% more—than the familiar recommended daily allowance (RDA).

Current guidelines call for 0.36 gram of protein per pound of body weight per day (equaling 61 grams for a 170-pound person and 51 grams for a 143-pound person). But in a study, healthy subjects 56 to 80 years of age who ate a diet containing the RDA for protein excreted more protein than they ate. Inadequate protein intake may result in muscle mass loss, which can lead to frailty.

Self-defense: Elderly men of average build should consume at least 93 grams of protein a day, elderly women at least 78 grams.

Food	Grams of protein
One cup of 1% fat milk	8
One cup of lowfat yogurt	10
Three ounces of tuna	24
One cup of cooked lentils	39

Wayne Campbell, PhD, research associate, Noll Physiological Research Center, Pennsylvania State University, University Park.

Poor Nutrition in The Elderly

Eating alone is the leading factor behind poor nutrition among old people. Women who eat alone tend to eat too few calories...while men who eat alone tend to eat too much fat.

Other contributors to poor nutrition: Low education level...belonging to a racial minority...living in a low-income neighborhood...smoking...wearing dentures...taking multiple medications.

Katherine Tucker, PhD, assistant professor, Tufts School of Nutrition, Boston. Her study of 700 people ages 60 to 89 was published in *Food & Nutrition Research Briefs,* US Department of Agriculture, 6303 Ivy Lane, Fourth Floor, Greenbelt, MD 20770.

Caffeine and Your Health

Timothy McCall, MD, a Boston internist and author of *Examining Your Doctor: A Patient's Guide to Avoiding Harmful Medical Care.* Citadel Press.

Over the years, conflicting information has been written about the risks of caffeine. Studies have shown that drinking coffee has been tied to pancreatic cancer...high cholesterol...heart attacks...and birth defects.

Reality: The results of these studies have been called into question by health experts. That's because people who drink a lot of coffee tend to have other bad habits as well, such as smoking or not exercising—which may be the culprits.

CAFFEINE AND OSTEOPOROSIS

While caffeine in coffee, tea, cola, chocolate and some medications can cause jitteriness, trembling, irritability and insomnia, studies have not substantiated most of the claims about caffeine's negative *long-term effects.*

Exception: There appears to be a connection between consuming high levels of caffeine and osteoporosis—the thinning of bones that can lead to hip fractures, especially in older women. Risk factors for osteoporosis include being female, thin, white—particularly of Northern European or Asian ancestry—not exercising, smoking and having a family history of the disease.

Self-defense: If you are at high risk for developing osteoporosis, you should significantly reduce your caffeine intake and be sure to include enough calcium in your diet. In one study, women who drank at least one glass of milk per day were protected from the bone-thinning consequences of caffeine.

If you can't drink milk, take a calcium supplement. Calcium carbonate, sold in supermarkets, drugstores and health food stores, is an inexpensive and effective source.

Premenopausal women should take 1,200 mg/day...postmenopausal women, 1,500 mg/day. For best absorption, take no more than 500 mg at one time.

CAFFEINE WITHDRAWAL

People who are accustomed to drinking several cups of coffee a day may develop headaches, have difficulty concentrating, and experience fatigue and depression if they eliminate caffeine from their diets.

If you decide you want to cut down on caffeine, it's best to do so slowly. Cut back by about 20% a week over a month—or more.

Slowly reducing the amount of caffeine in your system prevents withdrawal reactions. If headaches or other symptoms develop, increase your consumption slightly, then continue to slowly lower it over time.

Skim Milk Alert

Drinking skim milk deprives you of a powerful cancer fighting substance. Recent studies have found that conjugated linoleic acid, a compound present in milk fat, is one of the most potent of all natural substances in fighting colon and breast cancers in animals. While human studies have not yet been performed, the research suggests that milk drinkers seeking to reduce fat consumption without losing milk's many nutritional benefits might try 1%-fat milk rather than fat-free milk.

Dale E. Bauman, PhD, Liberty Hyde Bailey professor of animal science, Cornell University, Ithaca, NY.

Chili Pepper Danger

Eating too many hot peppers may boost your risk of stomach cancer. Those who identified themselves as "heavy" consumers of chili peppers were 17 times more likely to develop stomach cancer than those who did not consume chilies. *Possible culprit:* Capsaicin, the hot-tasting component in chili peppers.

Robert Dubrow, MD, PhD, associate professor of epidemiology and public health, Yale University School of Medicine, New Haven, CT. His study of 220 stomach cancer patients and 752 healthy individuals was published in the *American Journal of Epidemiology*, 2007 E. Monument St., Baltimore 21205.

Green Tea Fights Disease

Green tea fights heart disease, cancer, flu—even tooth decay. It's rich in a class of natural antioxidant compounds called *polyphenols*. Green tea is derived from the same plant as the more common black tea, but it's processed differently. Black tea is fermented before drying—green tea is not. The fermentation process reduces the levels of polyphenols.

Hasan Muktar, PhD, professor and director of research, Case Western Reserve University School of Medicine, Cleveland.

Green tea eases arthritis—at least in rodents. In a recent study, mice drank water containing *polyphenols*—antioxidant compounds derived from green tea—or plain water.

After 10 days, the mice were injected with a compound that ordinarily triggers a rheumatoid arthritis-like disorder.

Result: Less than half of the mice that drank water with the polyphenols developed the disorder. In contrast, 94% of the mice that drank plain water developed the disorder.

Human trials are being planned. In the meantime, there's no downside to drinking green tea. Black tea contains lower levels of polyphenols, and so may not provide the same benefit.

Tariq M. Haqqi, PhD, associate professor of medicine and rheumatology, Case Western Reserve University School of Medicine, Cleveland. His study of green tea and arthritis in mice was published in the *Proceedings of the National Academy of Sciences,* 2101 Constitution Ave. NW, Washington, DC 20418.

One More Reason to Eat Green Leafy Vegetables

They seem to help prevent *age-related macular degeneration,* the leading cause of blindness among elderly people. In one study, people who ate the most of certain types of carotenoids—found in spinach and other dark, leafy greens—had a 43% lower risk of developing the eye disorder than those who ate the least.

Johanna M. Seddon, MD, associate professor of ophthalmology, Harvard Medical School and Harvard School of Public Health, and director of the epidemiology unit, Massachusetts Eye and Ear Infirmary, all in Boston. Her study of 356 men and women, age 55 to 80, with age-related macular degeneration and 520 healthy people with normal vision was published in the *Journal of the American Medical Association,* 515 N. State St., Chicago 60610.

Garlic Danger

Fresh garlic mixes can cause botulism if stored at room temperature. The preservatives found in *commercial* garlic preparations retard spoilage only when refrigerated. Because they lack preservatives, *homemade* garlic mixes may spoil even if stored in the refrigerator. After two weeks, throw them out.

Joseph M. Madden, PhD, strategic manager for microbiology, Center for Food Safety and Applied Nutrition, Food and Drug Administration, Washington, DC.

All About Genetically Engineered Foods

Sheldon Krimsky, PhD, professor of urban and environmental policy at Tufts University, Medford, MA. He is author of *Hormonal Chaos: The Scientific and Social Origins of the Environmental Endocrine Hypothesis* (Johns Hopkins University Press) and *Agricultural Biotechnology and the Environment* (University of Illinois Press).

Some nutrition experts and geneticists have expressed concern that genetically engineered foods will have unintended, and dangerous, side effects.

●**What exactly is genetic engineering?** It's a technique for snipping individual genes from one organism—plant, animal or microbe—and slipping them into another. This is done to introduce new traits or to enhance existing traits in crops.

One common goal of genetic engineering is to render crops resistant to attack by insects and the herbicides applied to control weeds.

Another goal is to lengthen the timespan that fruits and vegetables stay fresh. The *Flavr Savr* tomato, which made headlines when it was introduced in 1993, contained a gene that suppresses *polygalacturonase,* an enzyme that causes ripening.

●**Are genetically engineered foods safe to eat?** There's no evidence to suggest that genetically altered foods are harmful—or that they're less nutritious than their unaltered counterparts.

However, there is no compelling evidence that they're safe either. That's because food producers are not required to conduct safety tests on genetically engineered foods that they deem to be equivalent to the natural foods from which they are derived.

Perhaps of greatest concern is the use of genetically engineered *bovine growth hormone* (BGH), which is widely used in the dairy industry to increase cows' milk production.

Cows given BGH are more likely than other cows to develop mastitis, an infection of the udders.

Preliminary research involving animals suggests that drinking milk from cows treated with BGH causes high levels of *insulin-like growth factor* (IGF-1), which are linked to higher cancer risk.

Also, since infections are more common among cows that have been given genetically engineered BGH, they receive more antibiotics.

If dairy farmers could ensure that these powerful drugs didn't get into the human food supply, this might not matter. But antibiotics do slip through.

Widespread use of antibiotics—by doctors as well as food producers—has contributed to the surge in antibiotic-resistant streptococcal infections and other bacterial infections.

●**What can I do to protect myself?** Given what we now know, it's prudent to buy dairy products from producers who don't use BGH.

This information is sometimes included on carton labels. I look for it when I buy milk.

•Which other foods are likely to have been genetically modified? Today, more than 60% of soybeans sold in the US have been genetically modified using gene-splicing techniques.

Other crops whose DNA has been altered include apples, broccoli, cranberries and peanuts. These are not yet on the market, but may be soon.

Except for soybeans, corn and some varieties of tomatoes and potatoes, few "whole" foods on the market have been genetically modified.

It's difficult to avoid genetically modified soybeans because they're an ingredient in so many different products. I don't even bother looking for it on the label.

I do try to avoid genetically engineered foods when doing so is feasible. I buy organic produce because I know that federal regulations prohibit labeling genetically altered foods as organic. And I buy free-range chicken because I know that it hasn't been treated with hormones.

If you don't have access to organic foods—or prefer not to pay the premium price—consider buying produce at a local farmers' market.

Small farms are less likely than large growers to use genetically modified seeds.

•Isn't gene-swapping a problem for those with food allergies? It can be. The FDA now requires food producers to alert consumers when a genetically engineered food contains a known allergen.

In one highly publicized case, a company was considering transferring a gene from a Brazil nut into a soybean. Then a study showed that individuals allergic to Brazil nuts also became allergic to the genetically modified soybeans. Ultimately, the company did not market the soybean.

Currently, there is no required testing for new allergens created by genetically modified foods. Consequently, as genetic engineering becomes more common, people may find themselves experiencing allergies to foods that never gave them problems before.

•Do genetically engineered foods taste different? Food producers say there's no difference, but I'm not so sure.

Once I asked my students to do a blind-folded taste-test on two tomatoes, one of which had been genetically modified. The genetically engineered tomato looked fantastic, but it wasn't nearly as tasty. Some students said it tasted like cardboard.

With other foods, you may never notice the difference.

Salt Substitute Danger

Salt substitutes containing a mixture of sodium chloride and potassium chloride can be dangerous for those on sodium-restricted diets.

Danger: Used liberally by such individuals, these products can result in a potassium buildup, leading to irregular heartbeat or even a fatal heart rhythm disturbance.

Better way: Instead of salt substitutes, add flavor to food with garlic, onion, lemon juice or herbs. Salt substitutes are generally safe for healthy individuals.

Randall Zusman, MD, associate professor of medicine, Harvard Medical School, and director, division of hypertension and vascular medicine, Massachusetts General Hospital, both in Boston.

Margarine Problem

Semisolid, hydrogenated fats are less healthful than the oils they're made from. A group of people with high cholesterol went on a cholesterol-lowering diet that contained corn oil...and their LDL (bad) cholesterol fell an average of 17%. But LDL fell only 10% when researchers replaced the corn oil with corn oil margarine in stick form.

Alice Lichtenstein, DSc, assistant professor of nutrition, lipid metabolism group, Human Nutrition Research Center on Aging, Tufts University, Boston. Her study of 14 men and women ranging in age from 44 to 78 was published in *Arteriosclerosis and Thrombosis*, 7272 Greenville Ave., Dallas 75231.

All About Antioxidants

Kenneth H. Cooper, MD, founder of the Cooper Aerobics Center, 12100 Preston Rd., Dallas 75230. *www. cooperaerobics.com*. He is author of *Dr. Kenneth H. Cooper's Antioxidant Revolution*. Thomas Nelson, Inc.

Antioxidants may be a popular health catchword, but many people are confused about what antioxidants are and what the conflicting data imply about their usefulness.

To clear up the confusion, we spoke to Dr. Kenneth H. Cooper, whose book *Aerobics* revolutionized America's attitude toward fitness more than 25 years ago. He continues to direct research into exercise, diet, health and fitness at The Cooper Aerobics Center in Dallas.

●**What are antioxidants, and why are they important?**

To understand antioxidants, you must first understand the concept of free radicals.

A free radical is an unstable type of oxygen molecule. It lacks one of its electrons, and must therefore "steal" an electron from another molecule. When that unstable oxygen molecule seeks to replace its missing electron, it causes a chain reaction that can damage cell membranes and DNA.

Free radicals are unavoidable: They're a by-product of normal metabolism, as well as a response to environmental factors like air pollution, cigarette smoke, radiation, pesticide residues and other food contaminants, physical injury, excessive exercise and possibly emotional stress.

Another source of free radicals is ischemia, the cutoff of oxygen to cells, such as during surgery, followed by *reperfusion,* when blood rushes back into the deprived organ.

Free radicals aren't all bad: They're thought to help the immune system and are necessary for the proper function of organs and blood vessels. *But when these renegade molecules get out of control, they can be very destructive...*

●Free radicals promote cancer.

●Free radicals change LDL (bad) cholesterol into the harmful form that clogs arteries.

●Free radicals promote signs of aging, such as deterioration of the skin and other organs.

●Free radicals have also been linked to a variety of medical problems, from cataracts to stroke to rheumatoid arthritis and Parkinson's disease.

Fortunately, the body has weapons to keep free radicals under control—the antioxidants. These molecules prevent and repair free radical damage by sacrificing their own electrons ...and by "mopping up" unstable molecules before they do damage.

Some antioxidants are endogenous, meaning they are produced within the body. The most important of these are superoxide dismutase, catalase and GSH. Others are exogenous, or taken from outside in the form of nutrients.

The primary exogenous antioxidants are vitamin C, vitamin E and beta-carotene.

●**Can you get enough of these exogenous antioxidants from food?**

Researchers are still trying to answer this question. A diet high in vitamin-rich fruits and vegetables—especially greens and cruciferous vegetables like cabbage and broccoli—is associated with a lower incidence of cancer and many other diseases. This may well be due to the foods' antioxidant properties, although the connection has yet to be proven.

Theoretically, it's possible to get all the vitamin C and beta-carotene you need from your diet—if you consume seven to nine servings of fruits and vegetables a day, prepared with minimal cutting, peeling, trimming and cooking so as to minimize vitamin loss.

But most Americans simply don't eat that many fruits and vegetables every day.

As for vitamin E, it's found primarily in fatty foods like nuts and seeds—making it virtually impossible to get enough of this vitamin through diet alone and still keep calories and fat under control.

Vitamin supplements are not a substitute for a healthful diet, regular exercise or controlled weight. But they probably enhance what we're getting from other sources—and at very little financial cost or physical risk.

Think of them as a kind of insurance policy in our stress- and pollution-filled world.

•Didn't a Finnish study find that taking vitamins increases health risk?

This study did find that subjects who took beta-carotene supplements were more likely to develop lung cancer—a result trumpeted in the media around the world.

Since then, however, a number of experts have pointed out flaws in the research. The subjects had all smoked heavily for many years. The cases of lung cancer and heart disease that occurred might well have already been present—undiagnosed—before the study began. (Antioxidants are thought to have a protective, not a curative, effect.) The effects of supplements on nonsmokers weren't studied at all.

To say that beta-carotene is dangerous based on that one study is irresponsible. Far more research suggests that beta-carotene supplements protect against lung and other types of cancer.

Example: A study in China found a 13% reduction in all cancers, and a 9% reduction in overall mortality, among subjects who took supplements of beta-carotene, selenium and vitamin E.

The Finnish study did find that even minimal doses of vitamin E—50 international units (IU) per day—were linked to a 34% reduction in death from prostate cancer, a 16% reduction in death from colon cancer and a 5% reduction in death from heart attack. Yet the press ignored these encouraging findings.

•What doses of vitamin supplements do you recommend?

Based on the existing research, *I believe that most adults should take a daily antioxidant "cocktail" containing...*

•1,000 milligrams (mg) vitamin C. That's 500 mg taken twice a day. Costly sustained-release capsules seem to be no more effective than regular tablets.

•400 IU vitamin E. The natural form—d-alpha tocopherol—is preferable to synthetic dl-alpha tocopherol.

•25,000 IU beta-carotene. Beta-carotene is a precursor of vitamin A, which can be toxic in large doses.

•What role does exercise play in the free radical/antioxidant equation?

Moderate exercise appears to enhance the activity of the body's own antioxidants. However, excessive exercise—such as training for a marathon—seems to increase free radical production.

While I wouldn't presume to tell a marathon runner to stop training, I do think it makes sense to take higher levels of antioxidant supplements.

•3,000 mg vitamin C.

•1,200 IU vitamin E.

•50,000 IU beta-carotene.

•Can these vitamins have toxic side effects?

Not at the above doses, in most cases. *Exceptions...*

•Don't take beta-carotene within four hours of drinking an alcoholic beverage. The interaction of alcohol and beta-carotene can cause liver damage. Heavy drinkers probably shouldn't take beta-carotene at all.

•People on anticoagulant therapy should avoid vitamin E, since it can cause excessive bleeding.

•People with kidney stones should avoid large doses of vitamin C.

•Pregnant women should check with their doctors before taking vitamin supplements or any other type of medication.

Even if you are not in any of the above categories—but especially if you are—check with your doctor before beginning a vitamin regimen. And whenever you're asked about the kinds of medications you're taking, remember to include the supplements on your list.

•Do you recommend any other antioxidant supplements?

The compound Coenzyme Q10 and the mineral selenium help neutralize free radicals. However, Coenzyme Q10 hasn't yet been studied extensively. And excess selenium can cause hair loss, fatigue and other toxic effects. I need more data before I can recommend either of these as supplements.

•What else can I do to head off free radical damage?

Avoid sources of environmental stress. If you exercise outdoors, do so early in the morning or after sundown, when pollution levels are low. Stay away from major highways.

Limit your exposure to sunlight. Give some thought to the other environmental hazards you're likely to encounter—then think of ways to minimize them.

Don't try to change your whole life all at once, however. Pick one factor, address it— and once you've got it under control, start on another.

•What about aspirin?

Aspirin is not an antioxidant, but it has been recommended as protection against heart attacks. Yet most of the research indicates that aspirin is most beneficial to individuals who already have cardiovascular disease…and it may sightly increase the risk of hemorrhagic stroke.

Consequently, for healthy people with no known history of heart disease, I do not recommend taking aspirin regularly.

Prostate Cancer Risk

In a study of 48,000 men, those who ate the most red meat, butter and chicken with skin were two-and-a-half times more likely to develop late-stage prostate cancer than men who ate the least of these foods. By age 80, two-thirds of men have prostate cancer. But whether the cancer lies dormant for years or quickly becomes life-threatening may depend upon the amount of animal fat in the diet.

Edward Giovannucci, MD, ScD, instructor of medicine, Harvard Medical School, Boston.

Save on Vitamins

Nearly all vitamin supplement makers buy their raw vitamins from the same suppliers.

Just three major manufacturers—Roche, BASF and Rhone-Poulenc—produce 90% of the world's vitamins. So, no matter which brand you buy or how much you pay, and regardless of the appearance of the vitamin pill, you are getting the same basic vitamin product. You can save a lot of money if you buy the drugstore's house brand.

Caution: How the raw vitamin is formulated for use—tablets, gel caps, capsules, etc.—can affect how well it dissolves in your body. Look for "USP" on the label to be sure the product meets US Pharmacopeia standards for dissolvability.

V. Srini Srinivasan, PhD, director, dietary supplements division, US Pharmacopeia, 12601 Twinbrook Pkwy., Rockville, MD 20852.

Myths About Minerals

Mia Parsonnet, MD, a member of the clinical faculty of the New Jersey College of Medicine and Dentistry. She is author of What's Really in Our Food? Fact and Fiction about Fat and Fiber, Vitamins and Minerals, Nutrients and Contaminants. *Shapolsky Publishers, Inc.*

Thanks to everything we've read and heard lately about fat, fiber and food additives, we've all become much smarter about what we're eating—and that's great.

However—a surprising number of myths remain concerning the minerals we take in, both in our daily diets and in the form of supplements. And that misinformation can be dangerous…even deadly.

What we do know for certain is that minerals are essential for life. To a large extent, the body is composed of minerals. For example, our blood carries significant amounts of sodium, potassium and chloride. And our bones and teeth are rich in calcium, phosphorous and magnesium.

The news about minerals is generally good: If you eat a healthy, varied diet—including adequate amounts of milk, fruits and vegetables—your body should get all the minerals it requires. Special needs do arise, however.

Example: As people age, calcium is less well utilized, and extra amounts are recommended, especially for women. Prolonged gastrointestinal illness, and certain drugs, may also change requirements.

Minerals are an often-misunderstood category of nutrients, and you may do well to let go of some of the myths:

Myth: A salty taste is a reliable indicator of salt content.

Truth: Food-content labels must be read very carefully—some items that you would never suspect to be high in sodium are. For example, ounce for ounce, certain dry cereals contain more salt than potato chips.

As most of us now know, too much salt in the diet can promote high blood pressure—and possibly strokes in susceptible individuals. We require only a tiny amount of salt to maintain good health—just 500 milligrams daily, or the equivalent of a quarter-teaspoon. Chances are you're getting more than that amount naturally from the foods you eat each day—you need never go near a salt shaker. In fact, the average American consumes closer to 4,000 to 5,000 milligrams per day—10 times what's needed.

If you're a salt-lover, you'd be wise to wean yourself off it. Our taste for salt (or any other flavor) is acquired and thus can be unlearned at any age.

To keep your kids from getting hooked on salt, don't serve them salty food or snacks.

Myth: Calcium deficiency is really only of concern to women approaching menopause.

Truth: Women are never too young to step up their calcium intake to help ward off future osteoporosis. Even teenage girls should start taking calcium supplements to build bone strength, especially if they don't drink milk. Bones that are strong at an early age are less likely to leach out calcium, a process that leads to fractures and other problems later on.

Between the ages of 19 and 24, women (and men) should be sure to get 1,200 milligrams of calcium per day—the amount provided by approximately a quart of milk. If you know you're not taking in sufficient quantities of calcium from your food—and most people's diets are imperfect—by all means take a calcium supplement.

Myth: "Health" foods are better sources of minerals than ordinary foods.

Truth: Some so-called "health" or "natural" foods can in fact be harmful.

Example: Health food fans will often buy "natural" calcium supplements. These supplements are generally produced from limestone and are rich in calcium and magnesium, but they can also contain dangerous impurities, including lead.

In general, it's unwise to buy foods that haven't been carefully inspected and analyzed by government agencies. *Problem:* Many products found in health food stores have not undergone rigorous inspection. If you choose a food or a supplement that hasn't been government-approved, you run the risk of ingesting impurities. While some of them are harmless, others are not.

Myth: Minerals lost through sweat during strenuous exercise should be replaced via a mineral-rich drink such as Gatorade or by taking salt tablets.

Truth: Gatorade, a dilute solution of some of the minerals found in the body, is a perfectly fine product, but you rarely need it. Your body will restore its lost minerals on its own.

It's far more important to replenish the water your body has lost in sweat.

As for salt tablets, athletes used to rely on them, but nowadays we know that these tablets can do more harm than good. Again, it's best to stick to plain water after your workout, unless the salt loss was truly excessive.

Exception: Pedialyte is a solution that pediatricians may give to children who've become dehydrated from excessive vomiting or diarrhea. That's because youngsters have a much more delicate constitution than adults, and so their water and mineral levels must be restored quickly and completely.

MINIMUM DAILY REQUIREMENTS

●**Sodium.** 500 mg. (¼ teaspoon of table salt). *Sodium-rich foods:* Those that have been pickled, canned, smoked or cured...soy sauce...luncheon meats...salted snack foods.

●**Potassium.** 2,000 mg. *Some potassium-rich foods include:* Bananas (four)...orange juice (four 8-ounce glasses)...carrots (six).

●**Chloride.** 750 mg. (or ¼ teaspoon of table salt). *Chloride-rich foods:* Most processed foods.

●**Calcium.** 1,200 mg. (ages 19 to 24)...800 mg. (age 25 and over). *Some calcium-rich foods:* Milk (three 8-ounce glasses)...plain yogurt (three 8-ounce cups)...cheddar cheese (6 ounces).

•**Phosphorus.** 1,200 mg. (ages 19 to 24)... 800 mg. (age 25 and over). *Phosphorus-rich foods:* Same as those rich in calcium.

•**Magnesium.** 350 mg. (men), 280 mg. (women). *Some magnesium-rich foods:* Green beans (five cups)...Brazil nuts (12).

•**Sulfur.** A daily requirement has not been established. *Sulfur-rich foods:* Cheese, eggs, milk, meat, nuts, vegetables.

Some essential trace elements—needed by the body in miniscule amounts...

•**Iron.** *Daily requirement:* 10 mg. (men)... 15 mg. (women ages 19 to 50)...10 mg. (women 51 and over). *Some iron-rich foods:* Liver (4 ounces)...breakfast cereal, such as Cheerios or Raisin Bran (2 ounces).

•**Selenium.** *Daily requirement:* 70 micrograms (men)...55 micrograms (women). *Some selenium-rich foods:* Canned tuna (2½ ounces) ...molasses (2 ounces).

•**Iodine.** *Daily requirement:* 150 micrograms. *Some iodine-rich foods:* Iodized salt...haddock (4 ounces)...milk (8 ounces)... plain yogurt (two 8-ounce cups).

How Herbs Can Keep You Healthy

Sandra McLanahan, MD, director of the stress management training program at Dr. Dean Ornish's Preventive Medicine Research Institute in Sausalito, CA, and executive medical director of the Integral Health Center and Spa, Buckingham, VA. For more information on herbs or for information on starting an herb garden, Dr. McLanahan recommends *The Healing Herbs,* by Michael Castleman. St. Martin's Press.

I never stop being amazed by the remarkable healing power of herbs. As a practicing physician, I've been recommending them to my patients for more than 25 years. Unfortunately, few physicians have taken the initiative to learn enough about herbs.

Herbs have several advantages over conventional drugs. They're inexpensive, potent and—if you take care not to overdose—far less likely to cause allergic reactions or other side effects. (Some potentially dangerous herbs, including sassafras and chaparral, have been taken off the market.) Herbs are readily available without a prescription at health food stores—although it's best to check with your doctor before using herbs.

HERE ARE HERBAL REMEDIES I FIND MOST USEFUL

•**Aloe vera is wonderful for soothing minor burns and preventing subsequent infection.** Although it's available in gel form, research suggests that fresh aloe vera leaves are more potent in their anesthetic and antibacterial properties. I urge my friends, family and patients to keep an aloe vera plant in the kitchen and use its leaves to dab on minor burns.

•**Chamomile tea contains oils that have antispasmodic and anti-inflammatory effects.** It's good for indigestion, anxiety, insomnia and exhaustion. Babies given chamomile tea in their bottle fall asleep faster.

•**Comfrey contains allantoin,** a compound that speeds healing by promoting growth of muscle and connective tissue. It helps prevent bruising and swelling associated with muscle sprains and strains. Applied to the skin as a paste...not to be taken by mouth.

•**Echinacea**—sometimes blended with the natural antibiotic goldenseal—stimulates the body's production of the virus-fighting compound interferon and boosts the number and activity of white cells. That makes it a perfect all-around remedy for colds or flu. It's also good for urinary tract infections. Often taken as drops mixed in a glass of water.

•**Garlic lowers cholesterol,** boosts the immune system and kills disease-causing germs. People who eat lots of garlic get fewer colds. *Important:* Deodorized garlic preparations—used by individuals worried about bad breath—are somewhat less potent than fresh garlic. Parsley helps eliminate bad breath.

•**Ginger tea relieves nausea caused by motion sickness,** morning sickness, influenza or radiation therapy. In tincture form, ginger is also effective against flatulence and indigestion. It may also be useful for lowering serum cholesterol, although at this point the data is preliminary.

•**Milk thistle is widely used in Japan to treat liver problems, including hepatitis A,**

B and C. It contains compounds that promote the flow of bile and stimulate production of new liver cells. Taken in capsule form.

●**Nettle contains the compounds choline, acetylcholine and histamine.** Together, they reduce inflammation, helping to relieve runny nose, watery eyes and other allergy symptoms. It also stimulates the immune system. Studies at the National College of Naturopathic Medicine in Portland, Oregon, demonstrated that two nettle capsules a day reduced symptoms of hay fever. Taken as capsules or brewed as a tea.

●**Saw palmetto contains liposterol,** a compound that inhibits action of the male hormone *dihydrotestosterone*. It's an extremely potent remedy for prostate problems, including frequent urination, prostatitis (prostate inflammation) and benign prostatic hypertrophy (prostate enlargement).

●**St. John's Wort contains an antibacterial oil.** It's good for treating stubborn colds or coughs—and possibly flu and other viral infections. A study found it to be an effective treatment for mild to moderate depression. Taken as capsules or drops.

What to Eat to Prevent Cancer...and What Not to Eat

Leonard A. Cohen, PhD, head of the section of nutritional endocrinology, the American Health Foundation, One Dana Rd., Valhalla, NY 10595. Dr. Cohen's specialty is in the area of nutritional carcinogenesis.

Although scientists continue to debate the role specific foods play in the development of cancer, there's now a consensus that Americans could dramatically lower their cancer risk by altering their eating habits—specifically, by eating less fat and more fiber.

THE FAT CONNECTION

Most Americans consume 38% to 40% of their total calories in the form of fat—well above the 25% to 30% fat consumption considered desirable.

This appears to make us more susceptible to cancer of the colon, breast, pancreas and prostate.

No one knows exactly why eating too much fat promotes the development of cancer, but the evidence—drawn from studies on both animals and humans—is compelling.

Different foods contain different types and quantities of fat...

●**Saturated fats are found in beef and other meats, fried foods and poultry skin.**

●**Monounsaturated fats are found in peanuts, olives and a few other foods.**

●**Polyunsaturated fats are found in corn, safflower and other cooking oils.**

●**Omega-3 fatty acids are found in cold-water fish,** such as herring and salmon.

It's important to keep track of what kinds of fats you eat because nutritionists now recommend that these fats be eaten in equal amounts. In other words, each day we should eat equal portions of polyunsaturated, monounsaturated and saturated fats. For most of us, this means cutting down on saturated fats while increasing intake of monounsaturated and polyunsaturated fats.

To reduce your consumption of saturated fats, eat fewer fried foods, trim the fat off beef and other meats, and remove the skin from poultry. These small sacrifices have big health payoffs.

About fish: Although fish contains oils that are highly unsaturated, it's still unclear what, if any, role this oil plays in preventing cancer. There is some evidence, however, that eating large amounts of fish reduces cancer risk and lowers serum triglycerides—lipids that may be associated with heart disease.

THE FIBER CONNECTION

While we're eating too much fat, we're also eating too little fiber. On the average, Americans consume only 10 to 12 grams of fiber a day. Instead, we should be eating 25 to 30 grams of fiber every day.

Big problem: Our diet consists of highly refined, easy-to-chew foods instead of high-fiber fruits, vegetables and grains.

There are two basic kinds of fiber...

●**Insoluble fiber, found primarily in wheat bran,** is fiber that is not broken down

167

by bacteria in the intestine. By helping waste pass quickly through the colon, it helps prevent colon cancer, diverticulitis and appendicitis.

• **Soluble fiber,** found in oat bran and in most fruits and vegetables, is fiber that is broken down by bacteria. It helps to prevent heart disease (by lowering cholesterol) and diabetes (by lowering the blood sugar).

Nutritionists now recommend that Americans should double their intake of dietary fiber...fruits and vegetables as well as grains. Pears, for instance, at 4.6 grams of fiber each, contain more fiber than any other fruit. *Other good fiber sources:* Red kidney beans (7 grams), lentils (4 grams), apples (3.3 grams), bananas (2.7 grams) and grapefruit (1.5 grams per half).

Caution: Don't consume more than 40 grams of fiber a day. Too much can be almost as bad as too little. In animals, excessive consumption has been found to cause bulky stools that can result in a form of constipation.

There also is some early evidence that alfalfa and certain other grains may actually increase the risk of developing colon cancer. *Self-defense:* Until the final verdict is in, don't rely just on grains for your fiber...eat a wide variety of fiber-rich foods.

BEYOND FAT AND FIBER

Other than increasing fiber and reducing fats, evidence linking dietary choices to cancer is less reliable.

Still, there are things to do that probably will help prevent cancer...and which won't hurt in any case.

• **Eat a wide variety of foods.** This limits your exposure to any carcinogens that might be found in a particular food...and eliminates the need for vitamin and mineral supplements.

• **Increase your consumption of vitamin A.** A powerful antioxidant, it keeps our cells from being attacked by oxygen, and thus prevents cancer. Vitamin A seems particularly effective in helping prevent lung cancer in smokers. To a lesser extent, it also seems to help stave off colon cancer, breast cancer and lung cancer. *Best vitamin A sources:* Carrots, squash and other orange and leafy vegetables.

• **Increase your intake of selenium.** Selenium is a trace element found in most vegeta-bles. To get more into your diet, eat more vegetables. *Alternative:* Selenium supplements.

• **Limit your consumption of smoked and pickled foods.** They have been tied to stomach cancer. An occasional dill pickle won't hurt you, and neither will an occasional barbecued meal. But a daily regimen of pickled vegetables and smoked meats is imprudent.

Evidence: At the turn of the century, stomach cancer was common in the US. Now that refrigeration is almost universal—and we rely less on pickling and smoking to preserve our foods—it is a rarity. In Japan, however, where pickled and smoked foods remain common, stomach cancer rates are among the highest in the world.

• **Avoid obesity.** Obesity is clearly linked to cancer of both the endometrium (the lining of the uterus) and the breast. Also, obese women with breast cancer are far more likely to succumb to the disease than are normal-weight women diagnosed with similar breast cancer.

Keeping track of your diet is one step toward controlling your weight. *Also extremely helpful:* Exercise.

Watching TV, working in an office and other aspects of a sedentary lifestyle all are associated with cancer.

Although it's not yet clear exactly how exercise helps prevent cancer, the incidence of colon cancer is much higher in men with sedentary occupations than men who are active. Women athletes have lower rates of reproductive-tract cancer than sedentary, out-of-shape women. And animal studies have demonstrated that moderate exercise cuts the risk of breast, pancreas, liver and colon cancer.

Caution: Too much exercise may actually be almost as bad as too little. Several studies have indicated that extreme exertion (like that necessary to complete a marathon) temporarily weakens the immune system, opening the way for infectious bacteria and viruses—and possibly the development of cancer.

• **Limit your consumption of simple carbohydrates (sugars).** Evolving man ate very little sugar. As a result of this, our bodies are not set up to properly digest it.

Problem: Simple carbohydrates cause the pancreas to produce a large amount of insulin very rapidly, and there is now some evidence suggesting that this can have a harmful effect on the pancreas. *Better:* Complex carbohydrates—found in pastas and breads.

•**Limit your caffeine consumption.** Caffeine has been tied to a variety of cancers, including those of the pancreas and bladder. More recent data suggests caffeine does not cause cancer. Nonetheless, caffeine is very clearly a potent drug, and it makes sense to consume it in moderation.

•**Limit your alcohol consumption.** Drinking to excess (more than a couple of drinks a day) has been linked to cancer of the mouth and throat. People who drink and smoke are at high risk. Most patients with head or neck cancer are alcoholics or near-alcoholics with poor nutritional habits who smoke regularly.

Vegetarianism vs. Calcium

Strict vegetarianism can lead to a calcium deficiency. A so-called "vegan" diet—which excludes dairy products as well as meat and eggs—is unlikely to provide enough calcium for the average adult. That's true even for vegans who avoid salt, protein, caffeine and other substances that trigger calcium loss...and for those who eat plenty of calcium-rich vegetables, such as broccoli and kale. Vegans should bolster their calcium intake with calcium-fortified foods and calcium supplements, after checking with a doctor about their specific calcium needs.

Connie Weaver, PhD, head, department of foods and nutrition, Purdue University, West Lafayette, IN.

Seafood Savvy

Lisa Y. Lefferts, an environmental-health consultant in Hyattsville, MD, who specializes in food safety, environmental policy and risk assessment.

Seafood and fish are excellent sources of protein and are low in saturated fat, light on calories, and high in vitamins, minerals,

and the omega-3 fatty acids that help reduce the risk of heart disease.

But there are risks. More than 80% of the seafood eaten in the US has not been inspected for chemical or microbial contaminants. *Fortunately, there are things that you can do to enjoy maximum health and minimum risk...*

•**Avoid chemical contaminants.** When you buy fish, choose younger, smaller ones, since they've accumulated fewer contaminants. Low-fat, offshore species like cod, haddock and pollack are especially good choices. Always trim the skin, belly flap and dark meat along the top or center, especially when it comes to fatty fish such as bluefish. Don't use the fatty parts to make sauce. Don't eat the green "tomalley" in lobsters or the "mustard" in crabs.

•**Avoid natural toxins.** When traveling in tropical climates, avoid reef fish such as amberjack, grouper, goatfish or barracuda, which are more likely to be contaminated. Buy only seafood that has been kept continuously chilled, especially mahimahi, tuna and bluefish, which produce an odorless toxin when they spoil.

•**Avoid disease-causing microbes.** Bite for bite, raw or undercooked shellfish is the riskiest food you can eat.

Self-defense: Don't eat shellfish whose shells remain closed after cooking. Do not eat raw fish or shellfish if you are over 60, HIV-positive, pregnant, have cancer or liver disease or are vulnerable to infection. Cook all fish and shellfish thoroughly. Raw clams, oysters and mussels should be steamed for six minutes.

•**Don't buy fresh fish that has dull,** sunken eyes, or fish that smells "fishy." Do not buy ready-to-eat seafood that is displayed too close to raw seafood.

Fish-Dish Danger

Ciguatera fish poisoning is a hard-to-diagnose illness caused by consumption of fish that carry a hard-to-detect toxin. *Symptoms:* Nausea...vomiting...diarrhea...cramps... numbness or tingling of the lips, tongue and throat...reversal of hot and cold sensations...blurred vision...low blood pressure...labored breathing...depression.

Danger: There is no diagnostic test for the toxin, and symptoms are easily confused with those of other ailments. The only known remedy—large doses of the sugar mannitol—must be administered within 48 hours.

Self-defense: When traveling in tropical areas, avoid grouper, red snapper or any dish containing unspecified fish...never eat barracuda...avoid fish liver, where the toxin is most concentrated. *Usually safe:* Yellowtail snapper and mahimahi.

Donna Blythe, MD, a ciguatera expert from Coral Gables, FL.

Food Additives Appear Safe for Most People... But Not All

Richard W. Weber, MD, staff allergist, Allergy Respiratory Institute of Colorado, 5800 E. Evans Ave., Denver 80222. Dr. Weber has also served as director of allergy training programs for the US Army and the University of Michigan.

Although food additives are safer than many people imagine them to be, certain additives can cause allergic reactions, including hives, childhood hyperactivity—and worse.

MOST COMMON CULPRITS

•**Antimicrobials,** including benzoates like sodium benzoate and benzoic acid, are used to fight growth of yeasts and bacteria in many canned or pickled foods and some cereals.

Problem I: Benzoates can cause asthma and hives.

Problem II: They may cause hypersensitivity in some children. Other problems, including joint pain and diarrhea, have also been reported.

•**Antioxidants,** such as BHA and BHT, are used to retard spoilage of cereal, margarine, potato chips, pastries and other packaged foods.

Problem I: Some people have developed contact dermatitis after handling products treated with antioxidants. In rare cases, people sensitized through skin contact with antioxidants later become sensitive to these additives in foods.

Problem II: Like benzoates, antioxidants may cause hives.

•**Azo dyes are colorfast dyes used in pills,** foods and clothing. One azo dye—tartrazine (FD&C yellow #5)—was dubbed the *yellow peril* 20 years ago when it was suspected of causing asthmatic reactions, hives and hyperactivity.

In fact, tartrazine and other azo dyes, such as sunset yellow (FD&C yellow #6), *do* cause hives in susceptible people—but not asthma as previously thought.

Azo dyes, including tartrazine, can cause hyperactivity but not as commonly as once suspected.

Most vulnerable: Children of preschool age—especially boys.

•**Monosodium glutamate** (MSG) is used as a flavor enhancer in Chinese and Japanese cooking, soup bases and convenience foods. It has been linked to *Chinese restaurant syndrome.*

This ailment—marked by flushing, headache, nausea and a feeling of warmth across the shoulders—typically occurs an hour or so after eating food that contains MSG. Chinese restaurant syndrome is not thought to be dangerous.

MSG also has been blamed for fullblown asthma attacks, which have occurred up to 12 hours after eating food that contains this flavor enhancer. We don't yet know what percentage of the asthmatic population is affected by this susceptibility...but it is thought to be quite small.

•**Sulfites are used to prevent food discoloration**—and to retard growth of mold and bacteria.

Sulfites are often found in dried fruits, wines, some beers and shrimp. At one time they were sprayed on the produce in salad bars. In most localities, legislation now restricts this use.

At highest risk: Asthmatics. For them, ingesting sulfites can cause shortness of breath—and in very sensitive people, a potentially fatal asthma attack.

Inhaling sulfites—which might occur when sulfur dioxide gas is released upon opening a bag of dried fruit—can temporarily irritate the mouth and nose of asthmatics and nonasthmatics.

DO RESTRICTED DIETS HELP?

Asthmatics should avoid sulfites and possibly MSG. For others, however, there is no good evidence that dietary restrictions are necessary or helpful.

Some people susceptible to hives have shown improvement after several months on a diet free of dyes and preservatives as well as natural salicylates (the active ingredient in aspirin, which also occurs naturally in apples and lingonberries).

Important: Because drastically restricted diets may be deficient in key nutrients, check with a doctor or nutritionist before attempting to eliminate additives from your diet.

How You Cook Has a Lot to Do With Fiber Content

How much fiber a food gives you depends considerably on the method of preparation. Leaving the skins on vegetables and fruits enhances their fiber content. Browning bread increases its fiber (which is why crusts have more fiber than the interior of a loaf). Stir-frying or sautéing vegetables adds fiber more than boiling because less soluble fiber is removed. Deep-frying increases fiber, too, but at great cost in fat and calories. On the other hand, puréeing food decreases fiber, and reducing foods to juice almost completely destroys fiber content.

Cookware Alert

Stainless steel cookware boosts the iron content of some foods an average of 14%.

Recent study: Iron leached into scrambled eggs, hamburgers, stir-fried chicken breast and pancakes...but not into rice, green beans or medium-thick white sauce. Six percent of Americans are believed to have too little iron in their bodies, while 1% are believed to have too much. Either condition can be dangerous. If you're unsure of your iron status, ask a doctor about getting tested.

Helen C. Brittin, PhD, professor of food and nutrition, Texas Tech University, Lubbock. Her study of 10 foods cooked in stainless steel and glass pots was published in the *Journal of the American Dietetic Association*, 216 W. Jackson Blvd., Chicago 60606.

Happier and Healthier Restauranting

Theresa Henkelmann, co-owner of the Thomas Henkelmann restaurant at The Homestead Inn, Greenwich, CT.

Dining out shouldn't mean deprivation if you're trying to eat healthfully. *What* you eat is not as important as *how much* you eat. *To control portion size...*

• **Request a half portion or one to share.** Restaurants will often do this for appetizers or desserts—but rarely for entrées other than pasta.

• **Ask for a doggie bag.** Never feel embarrassed to do this, even at gourmet restaurants. Whatever you pay for is yours to take home and savor a second time.

• **Make special requests.** *Best:* Call the restaurant in advance to find out whether the chef can customize a dish—or a meal.

Second best: When you arrive, inform the captain or maître d' of your preferences—avoiding fats, salt, cream sauces, etc.

Upscale restaurants can do the most customizing because most dishes are prepared to order. Most other places will grill fish on request.

Chicken dishes are less flexible—they are often prepared in advance.

Surprising: Sauces may be more healthful than you suspect. Many chefs make them through reduction—slow cooking to develop the richness that used to come from butter or cream.

Excellent choices when dining out: Veal, sautéed lightly in a trace of oil (the meat is very lean)...steamed vegetables...salad with vinaigrette dressing or lemon juice and oil on the side—most people don't feel satisfied if their dressing contains absolutely no oil.

Special-Order Food

You can special-order food at practically any fine restaurant. Dining out can be troublesome for people on special diets—to cut fat or salt...if you are a vegetarian...if you have a food allergy, etc. Most chefs will modify dishes at your request. If your needs are very specific or you want to be sure of getting what you need, call the chef. *Note:* If you're calling,

remember that chefs are busiest from 12 pm to 2 pm and 6 pm to 9 pm. Call the restaurant during off hours prior to your reservation.

Tim Zagat, president of Zagat Survey, which publishes the best-selling guides to restaurants in major US cities, Four Columbus Circle, New York 10019.

Best Time to Eat in a Restaurant

Late-afternoon restaurant meals can be great bargains—with much better service than at lunch or dinner. Some expensive, hard-to-get-into restaurants in major cities are now serving during mid-to-late afternoon, from about 2:30 pm to 5 pm. Portions tend to be smaller and lower-priced than at regular mealtimes, and service is very attentive since few people dine during these hours. Call in advance—not all restaurants offer late-afternoon service.

New York Magazine, 755 Second Ave., New York 10017.

13

The Mind/Body Connection

Healing and the Mind/Body Connection

Over the past century, physicians have learned much about the workings of the various organs in the human body...and have also found effective treatments for many diseases.

This focus on the machine-like aspects of the human body has led many doctors to ignore the many natural ways people can heal themselves when they are aware of the connection between the mind and the body.

THE MIND/BODY CONNECTION

The human body is a complex mechanism that regulates itself using naturally occurring chemical substances. When something is wrong in one organ, messenger molecules of various kinds flow through the body and cause the release of other chemicals that help correct the situation.

Example: When you cut your finger, your body reacts by releasing chemical clotting factors, which thicken the blood in the vicinity of the cut, preventing you from bleeding to death from a cut.

Blood clotting occurs unconsciously, but every process that happens in our bodies, including thought, involves chemical reactions.

Scientists have learned about important chemicals such as peptides—chains of amino acids that transmit chemical messages. And they've learned about endorphins—proteins that are powerful natural painkillers.

Peptides are found throughout the body, not just in the brain. It has become evident that there is no clear distinction between mind and body.

Since antiquity, we have known that chemicals like drugs and alcohol affect both the mind and the body. Changes in the balance of the chemicals in our bodies also affect the way we feel.

Example: When we have a problem in just one part of the body...like a toothache...our whole self tends to feel down.

Bernie S. Siegel, MD, a surgeon and writer. He is author of *How to Live Between Office Visits: A Guide to Life, Love and Health*. HarperCollins.

More surprisingly, the mind/body connection also works the other way. We are finding more evidence every day that the way we feel about life does not simply reflect the state of our health—it also affects it.

Doctors long ago observed that about 30% of patients respond positively even when given a placebo—an inert pill with no curative properties.

The placebo effect occurs because those patients believe that they are being given a useful medicine...and their bodies follow that belief by fighting their sickness better than they would have otherwise.

Unfortunately, many doctors themselves encourage a reverse placebo effect. By emphasizing that a certain treatment has only a small statistical chance of success, they encourage patients to expect failure...and their bodies are likely to get the message.

Better way: Doctors should discuss procedures more positively, encouraging patients to adopt a hopeful attitude, so their bodies will be more likely to react favorably. Patients should not let themselves be convinced by statistics... because every person is a unique human being, not a statistic.

THE BODY'S NATURAL WISDOM

Today, a growing number of physicians recognize that their patients have an ally in the body's natural wisdom. Sensitivity to signals sent by our bodies helps us detect emerging health problems before standard medical tests reveal them.

Example: Journalist Mark Barasch had a terrifying dream that he was being tortured by hot coals beneath his chin and thought he had cancer in his throat. Months later, he felt symptoms and went to a doctor, but his blood tests were normal. However, during a later and more complete examination, a thyroid tumor was found.

And, conversely, by sending hopeful signals back to the body, we encourage our bodies to respond with their surprising self-healing capabilities.

Example: In December, Mary was told she had only a few weeks to live. Her daughter, Jane, tried to cheer her up by buying her a new winter nightgown. Mary, who had always been very frugal, said she didn't want the gown, but would like a new summer purse.

This reaction surprised Jane until she interpreted it as a signal that her mother thought she could survive another six months. Jane demonstrated that she shared that belief. Mary recovered enough not only to enjoy her new purse but was active enough to wear it out...and a half dozen more.

One of the most striking examples of the mind/body connection is susceptibility to disease. Many years ago, researchers at the University of Rochester found that people who adopted an attitude of helplessness and hopelessness were those most likely to contract a variety of diseases.

Other studies have found that people who repress their emotions because of unhappy childhood relationships with their parents are prone to suffer heart disease, hypertension, mental illness and cancer.

Mental attitudes also affect the ability to overcome disease.

Patients who take an active part in treatment ask doctors and nurses many questions, insist on finding out what lies behind every request before complying and want to be given a choice between a variety of treatment options. They want to be told what the choices and the priorities are for each. A Yale study showed that these most "difficult" patients were those with the most active immune systems. They survived longer than "good" patients who were quiet and submissive.

HOW TO SURVIVE

You are most likely to survive serious illness if you can answer "yes" to the following questions:

- **Does your life have meaning?**
- **Do you express your anger appropriately—in defense of yourself?**
- **Are you willing to say "no"?**
- **Do you make your own choices?**
- **Are you able to ask for help?**
- **Do you have enough play in your life?**

People who answer "yes" are survivors because their minds give their bodies a good reason to fight for survival. Everyone is eventually going to die. I see life as a labor pain. But like a mother willing to suffer labor pains to give birth to a child, survivors accept the pain of fighting back against disease as part of giving birth to their own renewed life.

Your Imagination And Your Health

Martin L. Rossman, MD, clinical associate professor of medicine, University of California, San Francisco, and codirector of the Academy for Guided Imagery, Mill Valley, CA. He is author of *Healing Yourself: A Step-by-Step Program to Better Health by Imagery.* Pocket Books.

One key to better health lies not with proper nutrition or regular doctor's visits…but with your imagination.

More than a tool for daydreaming or creativity, your imagination can affect your body as well as your mind.

See for yourself: Imagine quartering a lemon. See the bright yellow. Smell the citrus. Now imagine biting into a piece and swallowing the juice.

By now, you're probably starting to salivate. Your jaw may ache. Clearly, what you think affects your body as well as your mind—and this demonstration gives only the tiniest inkling of the vast potential of the mind/body link.

IMAGINATION IS POWERFUL

With practice, you'll be conjuring up images that help you ease psychological stress and alleviate the symptoms of many disorders. Imagery may even be able to heal these disorders.

Mental imagery can also help you change destructive habits or behavior patterns.

Imagery is how we represent things to ourselves—mentally. It's the natural way our nervous system processes information. Memories, dreams, daydreams, planning and creativity are most readily available to us through images— essentially thoughts that you can see, taste, smell and/or feel.

IMAGERY FOR RELAXATION

The most basic use of imagery is for relaxation…

The imagery used in relaxation and stress reduction is really a directed daydream. In fact, it's the reverse of creating tension by worrying and imaging all the things that frighten you— and make you anxious.

What to do: Close your eyes. Breathe deeply and focus on each body part from head to toe. Invite each one to relax. Then imagine a place that's beautiful and serene—a stress-free "hideaway."

Some people imagine a windswept mountaintop. Others see a field full of wildflowers… or a warm, sunny beach.

Whatever you imagine, immerse yourself in the sights, sounds, aromas and feelings of being in this hideaway. After doing this for five to 15 minutes, you'll probably feel very peaceful and relaxed. Practiced regularly, this technique can be used to help alleviate a variety of medical problems—pain, allergies, high blood pressure, etc.

Caution: Imagery can change your body's need for—and tolerance of—certain medications. So if you're taking medications, make sure you're closely monitored by your doctor.

HELP HELPS

Most people can master simple visualization techniques on their own. Others do best when they use a guided-imagery audio- or videotape.

For especially complex problems, it may be necessary to seek the guidance of a professional "guide"—a psychotherapist experienced in the use of guided imagery.*

Such a guide can quickly lead you into a "quiet place" where it's possible to create an identity for the particular problem that's troubling you…and to confront this identity.

HOW IMAGERY HELPED BEAT STOMACH PAIN

One of my patients asked me to help her overcome the chronic pain in her chest and abdomen.

This woman—who had already received treatment for an ulcer—had been imagining her pain as a fire burning inside her stomach. She had visualized dousing this fire with water. That worked for a while, but the pain always came back.

*While many hypnotists, psychotherapists and social workers may be able to help you apply visualization techniques, few professionals are trained in guided imagery. For more information, and to locate guides in your area, call the Academy for Guided Imagery, 800-726-2070.

I suggested that she let another image come to mind, and she saw a little hand pinching her stomach. She asked the hand why it was doing that. It angrily shook a fist at her.

She didn't understand what this meant. So I told her to ask. When she did, the fist opened up and a finger pointed directly at her heart.

Then she got an image of her heart encased in a burlap sack filled with sharp objects. These objects were piercing her heart. The hand, she concluded, wanted to protect her heart.

With my help, she went on to visualize opening the sack and releasing each object. One of the first images to emerge was of her stepfather, who had been very violent. We eventually discovered that her current pain flared up in situations where she was treated abusively by her employer and where she felt powerless.

Creating awareness of this relationship between her emotions and her pain helped her develop assertiveness and ultimately relieved her pain.

So working with receptive imagery as above can be a form of education or psychotherapy that can help teach us about ourselves, expand our problem-solving abilities and train our minds to promote healthy bodies.

Like any other skill, guided imagery can be mastered only after considerable practice. Also, some people are more gifted at it than others. But almost anyone who pursues imagery derives deep relaxation and comfort. Most people also gain spiritual and possibly physical healing.

How to Use Your Mind To Heal Body Pains

John Sarno, MD, professor of clinical rehabilitation medicine at New York University School of Medicine, and attending physician at Howard A. Rusk Institute of Rehabilitation Medicine, New York University Medical Center. He is author of *The Mindbody Prescription—Healing the Body, Healing the Pain.* Warner Books.

My early work in the treatment of back, neck and shoulder pain was unpleasant and frustrating. I found that the conventional diagnoses and therapy methods yielded inconsistent and disappointing results.

THE SPINE

Usually, the pain was attributed to a variety of abnormalities of the structure of the spine such as a herniated or narrow disk and other aging or congenital defects.

These normal deviations were easy to spot on X rays—which show the bones and, indirectly, the general disk structure, but reveal nothing about soft-tissue changes in muscles, nerves or tendons.

In the early 1970s, I began to doubt the validity of these conventional diagnoses, and the spinal "treatments" that went with them—manipulation, acupuncture, stretching, other physical therapy and the most drastic of all, surgery.

Studies of people without back pain have shown that such spinal abnormalities have no connection with back pain itself. The abnormalities are blamed for this pain simply because they are in the same general location.

THE REAL PROBLEM: TMS

My growing experience, along with my study of the medical literature, suggested to me that the primary sites of the pain were the muscles running from the back of the head to the buttocks. Usually pain occurred in one part of the neck or back, often associated with pain in an arm or leg due to nerve involvement as well.

I call this malady *Tension Myositis Syndrome,* or TMS. Myositis refers to a physiologic alteration of muscle tissue.

TMS is a painful but harmless change in the muscles brought on by emotional factors, which set off a reaction in certain tissues of the body, resulting in pain and other neurological symptoms.

HOW IT WORKS

The circulation of the blood is controlled by a part of the central nervous system known as the autonomic nervous system.

When confronted with threatening unconscious feelings, the autonomic nervous system reacts in milliseconds, reducing blood flow to the involved muscle tissue to create a state of mild oxygen deprivation.

CURING TMS

I frequently see patients who have been suffering chronic pain for years—and yet their symptoms often disappear in a matter of days, after just a 45-minute consultation followed by two lectures on TMS.

Understanding the nature of TMS is key to thwarting the brain's avoidance strategy.

Caution: First, make sure you have nothing serious like cancer or a tumor. Consult with your regular doctor.

My therapeutic program involves three key steps...

●**Repudiating the structural diagnosis.** The first thing I tell each patient is that the structural abnormalities identified by doctors are not the cause of his/her symptoms. Instead, the pain, stiffness, burning, pressure, numbness, tingling or weakness he feels is caused by mild oxygen deprivation in the muscles, nerves and tendons.

By themselves, these symptoms are harmless. Even though they may cause severe pain, this pain leaves no residual damage once it vanishes —meaning there's no need for you to "baby" your back or take any special precautions.

●**Acknowledging the psychological basis of the pain.** When back pain or other symptoms occur, instead of concentrating on where the pain is and how bad it feels, I encourage patients to begin thinking about any repressed rage. Even though you may consciously prefer to be angry than to feel pain, your unconscious mind is terrified by rage, and reacts accordingly. *Sources of rage...*

●Rage from trauma in infancy or childhood that has never dissipated.

●Internal rage resulting from self-imposed pressure to be "good" or "perfect" or "successful."

●Rage as a reaction to the very real pressures of everyday life.

It's important to realize that this internal rage is a universal part of the human condition—we all put pressure on ourselves to accomplish tasks and be a "good person," and we all have negative feelings from childhood that reside in our unconscious minds.

When a lifetime of stored anger reaches a critical level and threatens to erupt into consciousness, the brain creates back pain or some other physical symptom as a distraction. This prevents a violent emotional explosion.

In other words, the symptoms of TMS are a strategy for avoiding painful emotions, by diverting attention to your physical body.

●**Accepting the psychological basis for pain and dealing with it.** To counter this built-in tendency, you need to use your conscious mind to "talk to" your unconscious...

●First, tell yourself, *It's all right to be enraged, unconsciously and illogically, like a child having a tantrum. That's part of being human.*

●Next, whenever you feel pain, try to think consciously about repressed rage and its possible reasons. Remember, you are contradicting what your brain is trying to do. But it's essential to focus on threatening thoughts to deny your pain its purpose, which is to divert attention from these feelings.

When your pain is severe it's hard to concentrate on emotions, but think of this process as a contest—pitting your conscious will against the unconscious reactions of your brain.

Example: When you feel a twinge of pain, talk or shout at yourself—tell your mind that you know what it's doing, that you know the physical pain is harmless and a distraction from repressed rage and that you no longer intend to be diverted and intimidated. You might even tell your brain to increase the blood flow to the affected areas.

By becoming aware of what's going on in your body physically and psychologically, you can learn to frustrate your brain's strategy and lead a full, pain-free life.

Once you change your focus of attention from your body to your psyche, you will render your pain useless—taking away its purpose, and revealing what it was trying to hide.

The Taoist Principles Of Preventive Medicine

Kenneth S. Cohen, MA in psychology, a master scholar of Chinese healing arts. A former faculty member of Boulder Graduate School psychology department, he is currently director of the Taoist Mountain Retreat in Nederland, CO.

M any Chinese follow a way of life called Taoism. Its goals are to promote balance and harmony…in both the immediate environment and the universe. Taoists believe that anyone can reach a state of enlightenment called *hsing ming shuang hsiu*, the balance of mind and body. *Required:* Great self-discipline and personal effort, including the cultivation of health and longevity.

Interesting: The Taoist emphasis on preventive medicine is so strong that in old China people paid their physician only when they were well. If they got sick, the treatment was free.

THE BREATH OF LIFE

Taoists believe in an internal energy called *Qi*, the breath of life. Qi corresponds closely to Western concepts of bioelectricity, the body's electrical program. By changing this inner program, people can influence their metabolism in a way that actually strengthens the immune system.

Taoists believe that Qi flows through a system of subtle veins, called meridians. If the Qi is blocked anywhere in the body, you'll have too much Qi—too much energy—on one side of the blockage, and too little on the other.

To open the blocked areas along the meridians so the Qi can flow freely, the Chinese use a series of exercises that involve breathing, gentle movement and visualization.

Called *Qi kung*, these exercises are based on five animals—the crane, bear, monkey, deer and tiger. Each exercise affects a specific internal organ and bodily system. Qi kung exercises, which resemble tai chi exercises, are easy to learn.

THE THREE TREASURES

In addition to the meridian system, Taoists believe that the human body contains three basic forms of energy that create health when they are in balance with each other.

● **Qi is breath energy.** It resides in the chest and lungs.

The three sources of Qi are the air we breathe, the food we eat, and the energy and strength of the immune system that we inherit from our parents. The more Qi you accumulate, the greater your vitality and better your health.

Exercise: Stand with your feet about shoulder-width apart, legs slightly bent, back straight but not stiff, chest relaxed, abdomen loose, with your palms at waist height, facing downward. Inhale and allow the lower abdomen and back to expand as though you were filling a balloon. When you exhale, the lower abdomen and back should contract. Continue to do this exercise as long as you can comfortably. If there's pain there's no gain.

This exercises the diaphragm, gently massaging the internal organs. And because the lower lobes of the lungs are stretched downward, the body can take in more air…and more Qi.

● **Jing is sexual energy,** which is believed to be stored in the lower abdomen and cultivated through balanced sexual relationships.

Exercise: To enhance Jing, stimulate the endocrine system, and improve sexual health, men should contract the muscles of the perineum (the soft band of muscles located between the scrotum and anus) when they inhale and release when they exhale. Women should contract and release the anal and vaginal muscles while continuing to breathe naturally. These exercises, known in the West as Kegel exercises, also help solve sexual problems, including prostate enlargement in men and irregular menstruation in women.

● **Shen is spiritual or intuitive energy.** Shen, which means clarity of mind, requires the ability to temporarily shut off the interference of constant thinking. Most people's minds are like a TV that they can't turn off. Without the clarity and fullness of Shen, which is developed through meditation, none of the other techniques are possible.

Exercise: Sit upright in a chair and breathe at a natural pace. At the same time, observe any thoughts that pass by, as if you were watching passing clouds. Make no judgments and don't try to control or manipulate your thoughts. I call this being an open window of awareness. And although it may sound quite easy, it is very difficult for most Westerners, who always have to be doing something.

BASIC TAOIST PRINCIPLES

There are two underlying principles of Taoist philosophy that tell us how to live in a manner that promotes health and well-being.

•**Tzu jan** involves things that grow from the inside out rather than being created outside. *Translation:* Spontaneity, which shouldn't be confused with impulsiveness. Spontaneity means sensing what is coming from inside you and allowing it to express itself.

•**Wu wei,** or effortlessness, involves going with the flow, lacking artifice, using only those muscles needed for the task at hand.

Taoists think that these two principles should be applied consistently on every level—lifestyle, relationships, exercise, movement, etc.

Example: Unless sexual partners surrender completely to the experience, there can be no exchange of energy. *Result:* None of the elaborate Taoist sex techniques will work until both partners are willing to go with the flow of the experience and express whatever they feel.

Everyday Soul-Soothing

Soul-soothing objects you place where you will see them regularly can boost your spirits when stress starts to get you down.

When creating your own personal "shrine," consider just how much of your inner self you want to reveal. It may be seen by coworkers or visitors to your home, too.

Display the meaningful object(s)—such as an intriguing stone, a shell or a baby's shoe—in a way that evokes inspiration, memory or reverence. Pick objects that remind you of people and places that lift your spirit. You can change shrines frequently or leave them untouched for years.

Jean McMann, PhD, architectural historian and professional photographer, and author of *Altars and Icons: Sacred Spaces in Everyday Life.* Chronicle Books.

Stress/Cancer Connection

Long-term psychological stress can cause cancer of the colon and rectum. Patients who had serious job problems in the previous 10 or more years were 5.5 times more likely to develop colorectal cancer than adults without such problems.

Theory: Stress-induced hormonal changes boost production of tissue-damaging substances called *free radicals.* The higher the concentration of free radicals, the greater the cancer risk. *Also:* Stress weakens the immune system. This limits the body's ability to kill cancer cells, allowing them to grow into tumors. Further, stressful life events may lead to poorer diets and reduced levels of physical activity, also raising risk.

Joseph G. Courtney, PhD, research epidemiologist, University of California, Los Angeles, School of Public Health.

Stress Reliever

Proper breathing reduces stress and helps you relax. It slows your heart rate and lowers blood pressure. *Technique:* Rapidly blow out all the air in your lungs...slowly breathe in through your nose. *Helpful:* Think of it as caressing your lungs with air...relax your stomach muscles...when lungs are full and without stopping to hold your breath, breathe out slowly and completely...repeat six times.

Sexual Pleasure: Reaching New Heights of Sexual Arousal and Intimacy by Barbara Keesling, PhD, sex therapist and teacher at Pepperdine University, Malibu, CA. Hunter House, Inc.

Depression Fighter

To fight depression, exercise can be just as effective as drugs. In a recent study, volunteers diagnosed with major depressive disorder were divided into three groups. One group participated in 30-minute exercise sessions three times a week...another took the antidepressant *sertraline* (Zoloft)...and the third did both. Patients in the medication-only group improved fastest—but after 16 weeks, all three groups showed similar significant improvement.

James Blumenthal, PhD, professor of medical psychology, Duke University Medical Center, Durham, NC. His study of 156 men and women was published in *Archives of Internal Medicine,* 515 N. State St., Chicago, 60610.

Sleeplessness and Depression

Sleeplessness—a common problem among people with depression—can be controlled with supplements of the hormone melatonin. *Recent finding:* Depressed people who took a slow-release formulation of melatonin for four weeks reported marked improvements in sleep quality, compared with similar individuals who took a placebo. If you suffer from depression, check with your doctor to see if melatonin is right for you.

Ornah T. Dolberg, MD, director, division of psychiatry, Sheba Medical Center, Ramat Gan, Israel. Her four-week study of 24 people with major depression was published in *The American Journal of Psychiatry,* 1400 K St. NW, Washington, DC 20005.

Dealing with "Blue" Moods

Richard O'Connor, PhD, a psychotherapist with practices in Canaan, CT, and New York City. He is author of *Undoing Depression: What Therapy Doesn't Teach You and Medication Can't Give You.* Berkley Books.

Sadness is as much a part of life as happiness—there are times to cry as well as smile. But in the course of their lives, one American in five suffers dark moods that deepen and linger. This includes six million older folks.

In the past, depression was often accepted as a "natural" part of aging. After all, sickness often strikes in later life, careers may come to

an end, those we love pass away. No wonder older people get depressed, it was thought.

But we now know that even in the face of such losses, most people mourn, recover and move on. When a blue mood settles in and remains severe, it needn't be endured.

Modern treatments with medication and psychotherapy can help the vast majority of depressed people. But these treatments only go so far. If you feel so persistently "down" that it's hard to enjoy life, *you must take an active role in your recovery.*

THE HABIT OF DEPRESSION

Depression may be caused by a shift in the chemicals that carry messages between brain cells (which is why antidepressant drugs are effective)—or it can be triggered by a major loss. Once it takes hold, it can establish a self-defeating pattern that's hard to escape.

Most depressed people develop a cluster of habits that make it hard to maintain a healthful, positive mood. Even after successful treatment, they may remain somewhat down and are prone to another severe episode of depression a few months or years down the road.

These habits include ways of thinking, feeling and behaving that protect people from their own painful emotions. Instead of being open to experiences that may leave them emotionally vulnerable, they live closed off from other people, and ultimately become emotionally paralyzed—unable to participate in their own lives.

Overcoming these habits means following a program of recovery. This demands effort, self-discipline and courage. *Among the most important steps...*

UNDERSTAND YOUR MOODS

When blue moods strike, they often seem to come out of nowhere...feeling you're at their mercy creates a sense of helplessness and hopelessness.

But in fact, a bad mood is almost always triggered by events or thoughts that you can identify.

Helpful: Keep a *mood journal* to track your ups and downs. Note the circumstances (where you were, with whom, what you were doing) that surround each drop in spirits.

Try to catch and record the internal events that preceded them—thoughts, memories, fantasies. Then imagine how a nondepressed person might feel in these circumstances—remembering the difference between a feeling (it passes quickly) and a mood (it lasts).

FEEL YOUR FEELINGS

Emotions that we refuse to feel don't just go away. When we avoid experiencing the anger that we may have been taught is bad, or insulate ourselves against the acute pain of grief, these emotions turn into less intense, but more lasting, negative moods.

Getting in touch with your feelings is a skill you can develop. As a first step, try to be alert to the slightest glimmer of emotion—a surge of rage, spasm of fear, pang of sadness. Instead of avoiding it, amplify it...allow yourself to feel it more fully.

Also helpful: Talk about your feelings with people you trust, with a therapist or in a support group. Or write them out...many people find that when they sit down for 15 to 20 minutes and write quickly and spontaneously about events of the day, memories or whatever comes to mind, feelings begin to emerge, and become stronger as the words flow to describe them.

CHALLENGE DISTORTED THOUGHTS

People who are prone to depression tend to think in ways that make their moods worse. They dismiss positive events as "flukes" or only temporary...when they feel bad, they're sure it will last forever. They tend to blame themselves and overgeneralize ("I never do anything right") and to believe they are powerless to make things better.

Not only are such thoughts depressing, they're unrealistic. A person who thinks, "I never do anything right" is forgetting the vast majority of things he/she has done that turned out well. To believe that you'll always be alone or unhappy implies fortune-telling powers that you don't have.

With practice, you can catch yourself thinking negative, self-defeating thoughts that darken your mood. When you do, challenge them.

Example: A friend fails to return your phone call and you think, "She doesn't like me. No one cares." Ask yourself: "What other explanation could there be?" Your friend could be busy...forgetful...out of town. And is it really true that you have no other friends?

TAKE CARE OF YOURSELF

When you're depressed, it's hard to get involved in pleasurable activities. Your energy is low and you can't believe that anything will bring you enjoyment. It's a self-fulfilling prophecy—doing nothing is virtually guaranteed to keep you from feeling better.

Instead: Plan activities that are likely to improve your mood, and do them whether you want to or not. Schedule times when you'll visit friends...listen to music...go to the movies... take a long walk in the park.

Almost always, once you've overcome lethargy and put yourself in action, you'll enjoy yourself more than you expected.

Exercise is especially beneficial. It produces natural chemicals—endorphins—that actually elevate your mood, in addition to giving you energy.

BE OPEN-HEARTED

Giving your time, energy and concern to others keeps you from ruminating on your own problems. It boosts your self-esteem to know that you've done something to make someone else feel better.

Generosity can begin close to home. Open your heart to friends and their troubles. Beyond that, time spent in volunteer work—serving the homeless in a soup kitchen, tutoring, reading to children in a hospital—is such a potent mood lifter that researchers have called it "the helper's high."

KNOW WHEN TO SEEK HELP

Depression severe enough to interfere with your life (you sleep poorly, lose your appetite, can't enjoy activities that used to give you pleasure) for more than a few weeks may need more than self-help alone.

Ask your doctor for a referral to a therapist and/or psychiatrist. Particularly if you've been treated for depression in the past, taking prompt action can save you a lot of unnecessary suffering.

Anxiety Disorder

Anxiety disorder is our nation's most prevalent psychiatric problem. At some point in their lives, nearly 15% of the population will suffer from panic attacks, obsessive-compulsive disorder or some other anxiety disorder.

Steve Dager, MD, associate professor of psychiatry and bioengineering, University of Washington, Seattle.

Healing with Life Force

Julie Motz, an energy healer who works in major hospitals across the country and teaches energy healing to inner-city teenagers. She is author of *Hands of Life.* Bantam Books.

Every living thing exudes energy—and this energy can be manipulated to improve your health and to heal both your body and your mind.

A system to explain the body's energy and utilize it in healing exists in every major culture.

•**The Chinese believe that the body's vital life force,** or *qi* (pronounced *chee*), is an energy —think microwaves—that flows unseen and connects all organs and systems.

When qi is disrupted and out of balance, illness results. Qi can be toned, through meditation and exercise. And it can be adjusted, if necessary, by acupuncture.

•**From India comes the concept at the heart of Ayurvedic medicine that there are seven chakras,** or centers of energy located along the spine, that govern a person's emotional and physical well-being.

•**In Western medicine an electrocardiogram (EKG),** for example, measures electrical signals from the heart to tell a doctor a variety of information about heart function.

THE CAUSES OF PAIN

The body's energy correlates with four of the most powerful emotions a human can feel— fear…anger…pain…love. These forces manifest themselves on a physical level, because emotions are a kind of energy.

Anger is the most important because it's the emotion that is so often suppressed. One powerful way to control someone else is to suppress that person's anger.

Parents control their children by not honoring their anger or by not allowing it to be expressed. Most children learn early to hide their feelings of anger. Instead, they're trained by their parents to cry, which is more acceptable.

But the feeling behind the tears is rage. Even when a child does have a temper tantrum, some parents are unlikely to intervene. Instead, they ignore this outburst, so the emotion behind it goes unheard.

THE HEALER'S JOB

As an energy healer, I can "receive" these emotional messages from specific parts of the body, even parts of a cell, which are related to whatever ailment the patient is suffering.

How it works: I scan the body, lightly touching it with my hands, to find where the energy is strong, where it is weak and where it is "blocked." I don't physically "manipulate" the energy—instead I send it a silent "message" to move where it's needed and relieve the blockage. Once it begins flowing smoothly, healing can begin.

This sometimes involves enlisting the patient's help.

A large part of my job as an energy healer is to convince the patient to let go of all of this stored emotion.

While I long ago found myself endowed with the power to feel what others are feeling, it is something that can be learned.

HOW TO HELP YOURSELF

•**Follow your instincts.** When you hurt yourself, say, by catching your thumb in a closing door, your instinct is to grab it and hold it. You should continue holding or touching that body part until you feel some kind of change come over it. This can be the disappearance of the pain, a change in temperature, a tingling that stops or a return of what I call "lost energy." *Helpful:* You have to really concentrate on the thumb to understand what I mean.

Also: Convey to the body part, either verbally or silently, that it is loved and appreciated. This may sound strange at first, but too often people reject and isolate a part of the body that becomes injured or afflicted with a disease. *Better:* Take time to concentrate on the part, to embrace it with the rest of your body and bring it "home."

• **If the problem is internal, place your hand over the area to attract ambient energy to where it's needed.** I often ask patients to visualize themselves entering the organ to tell me what it looks and feels like. Then I ask them how old they are in that place. This often reveals the root cause of their disease.

• **Enlist the help of others.** Others can help us heal. It's a mistake to think we have to be strong when we're ill.

Let yourself be taken care of. When friends and family offer themselves, allow them to do so.

Ask them to send their thoughts, prayers and good feelings to you. People are pleased to help and this positive energy will help you overcome the illness.

• **Additional education.** To learn more about energy healing, attend a class in any of the healing arts, including Reiki…polarity… healing touch.

Good health food stores usually have information about local classes. You'll also find ads in the back of alternative medicine magazines such as *New Age Journal* and *Natural Health*.

You'll find that, once you're with others who understand these techniques, energy healing is relatively easy to learn—and can help you live a healthier, happier, more productive life.

Music & Healing

Postoperative pain can be minimized by listening to soft, soothing music.

Surgical patients who listened to music for as little as 15 minutes a day while recovering reported significantly less pain than did those who relied only on painkillers.

Also helpful: Relaxation techniques such as slow, rhythmic breathing. Music and relaxation

should be considered adjuncts to painkilling medication—not replacements for it.

Marion Good, PhD, RN, associate professor of nursing, Case Western Reserve University School of Nursing, Cleveland. Her study of 500 surgical patients was published in *Pain*, 666 W. Baltimore St., Room 5E-08, Baltimore 21201.

The Healing Power Of Plants

Diane Relf, PhD, assistant professor of horticulture, Virginia Polytechnic Institute and State University, Blacksburg. She is the former president of the American Horticultural Therapy Association, 362A Christopher Ave., Gaithersburg, MD 20879.

You've probably heard that keeping a pet is good for your health. Close contact with animals has been shown to lower blood pressure, ease feelings of depression, boost feelings of self-esteem—and more.

Now we know that you can get many of the same health benefits by tending a garden. Studies have demonstrated that plants…

• **Reduce stress.** A study of college students worried after taking an exam found that the simple act of viewing plants increased positive feelings and reduced fear and anger. Other studies showed that viewing plants lowers blood pressure and reduces muscle tension.

• **Boost self-esteem.** As plants grow, so do their owners' feelings of self-worth. That's why plants are often used in psychiatric rehabilitation. Plants are also used in physical therapy. Caring for them requires balance, flexibility and coordination.

• **Raise job performance.** Studies have shown that workers whose offices afforded a view of trees and flowers experienced less job stress, enjoyed greater job satisfaction and experienced fewer ailments and headaches than those who could see only man-made elements from their windows.

• **Speed recovery.** In another study, gallbladder surgery patients whose rooms looked out on greenery had shorter postoperative hospital stays than patients without a view. Those with the view also used less painkilling medication, suggesting they were in less pain.

If you're intrigued by the idea of using plants for therapy, I recommend filling your home with plants. Just be sure not to buy more than you can comfortably care for. Neglected, sick plants are depressing.

Beware: Plants sold at discount stores tend to have more problems than those bought at a reputable nursery.

To derive maximum health benefits from your plants, I recommend caring for them yourself. If you don't have the time, consider hiring someone else to care for them for you. Simply being around plants is better than not being around them—even if you're not the gardener.

If you're a novice gardener, choose easy-to-raise plants, such as pothos, philodendron, cactus or dracaena marginate.

Rosemary, basil and thyme also do well inside, but they need more light.

Despite their popularity, ficus trees, scheffleras and corn plants are often tricky to care for.

If you'd like to derive physical as well as psychic nourishment from your plants, plant tomatoes, lettuce, etc., in pots on your patio—where you can enjoy watching them grow.

Prayer Heals

Four-hundred and sixty-six heart patients who were the object of other people's prayers during their hospital stay had 11% fewer complications than did 524 patients who were not prayed for. Patients did not know prayers were said for them. Those who did the praying knew only the patients' first names...and prayed only for "a speedy recovery with no complications." The researchers note that, statistically, such a difference between the groups would occur by chance only one in 25 times.

William S. Harris, PhD, heart researcher, Lipids and Diabetes Research Center, Saint Luke's Hospital, Kansas City, MO. His study of 990 coronary care unit patients was published in the *Archives of Internal Medicine*, 515 N. State St., Chicago 60610.

Secrets of Self-Hypnosis To Overcome Bad Habits

C. Roy Hunter, a certified hypnotherapy instructor in Tacoma, WA. He is author of *Master the Power of Self-Hypnosis* (Sterling) and *The Art of Hypnosis* (Kendall/Hunt).

Finding it hard to quit overeating? Smoking? Drinking? You're not alone. As we all know, the vast majority of people who try to break a bad habit fail at first. Many fail repeatedly.

You can remind yourself a hundred times a day that your habit is bad for you. Unfortunately, it's the *unconscious* mind that fuels bad habits. It doesn't care about logic. All it wants is the physical and emotional satisfactions your habit supplies.

Hypnosis helps you let go of the negative unconscious desires...and replace them with positive, habit-breaking emotions.

Hypnosis isn't magic. You will still have to work hard at breaking your bad habit. But hypnosis can give you the edge you need to succeed.

MYTH vs. REALITY

Hollywood has given hypnosis an unrealistic image. The hypnotic trance is not a mystical state in which you lose all self-control. You cannot be forced to quack like a duck or do other humiliating things when you're under hypnosis. In fact, you won't do anything you don't want to do.

The hypnotic trance is nothing more than a state of very deep relaxation.

This state is similar to the one that exists just before you fall asleep, when the beta brain waves that predominate during consciousness are replaced by alpha waves.

You're still fully conscious, but your rational mind is less active than usual...and your imagination is more active. This shift is critical because imagination is the language of the unconscious.

With practice, the emotions you generate during each hypnosis session become permanently embedded in your unconscious. That gives your willpower a much-needed boost.

DO IT YOURSELF

Many psychologists practice hypnosis, but it's also effective when done on your own. *Here's how to do it...*

●**Carefully consider the emotional benefits associated with breaking your habit.** Odds are you've already given a great deal of thought to the physiological benefits—reduced risk for heart attack, stroke, cancer, etc.

But you must also consider all the *emotional* reasons you have for changing. These might include feeling more in control...pleasing your family...having more energy...looking better.

●**Put yourself in a trance.** Find a comfortable and quiet place to lie down or sit. Unplug the phone and turn off the lights.

Take several deep breaths as you imagine your cares slipping away. Then imagine a beach at sunset, a mountain meadow or some other relaxing scene.

Tell yourself, "My toes are relaxed...my breathing is relaxed...I'm getting more and more relaxed."

You've entered a trance when you feel totally relaxed and your mind starts to wander. For most people, this takes about five minutes.

●**Imagine the pleasure you will feel upon successfully breaking your habit.** Once you've entered the trance, imagine that you have already reached your goal. Savor the emotions that thought triggers.

You might think, "My family is so proud of me"..."I look great"..."I feel so much better."

Over time, these feelings will become part of your unconscious...and will stay with you even when you're fully awake and going about your business.

●**Replace old "triggers" with new ones.** Still in the trance, imagine new ways of behaving.

Perhaps you tend to have a cigarette each time you relax with a cup of coffee. During the trance, imagine that having the coffee triggers a *different* response from you.

You might say, "I don't *really* want a cigarette with my coffee. I'd rather focus on reading that novel I just started."

Repeat this scenario again and again.

●**Come out of your trance.** Count slowly from one to five. When you reach five, say, "Fully awake."

Most people notice a diminution in their cravings after just a few sessions of self-hypnosis.

For the first three weeks, it's best to do self-hypnosis for about 20 minutes each day. After that, you can cut back to 20 minutes once or twice a month.

Of course, you can always intensify your self-hypnosis schedule if you find your resolve weakening.

Simple Secrets Of Better and Sounder Sleep

William C. Dement, MD, PhD, director of the Sleep Disorders Center at Stanford University School of Medicine, Palo Alto, CA. He is author of three books, including *The Promise of Sleep*. Delacorte Press. For more information about sleep disorders, contact the National Sleep Foundation at 888-673-7533...or at *www.sleepfoundation.org*.

L ying awake at night. Waking up too early. Feeling drowsy during the day. As we grow older, these and other sleep problems can become more than major annoyances. They can jeopardize our health.

Sleep deprivation can cause diminished performance, apathy and drowsiness. Falling asleep at the wheel is now known to contribute to an estimated 4% of all fatal automobile accidents.

What can be done to curb sleep problems? You may have heard that it's important to cultivate good sleep habits. But few people realize just how important proper "sleep hygiene" really is. *The basics...*

●**Go to bed at the same time each night.** Wake up at the same time each morning.

●**Take a hot bath or perform some other relaxing ritual 30 to 60 minutes before bedtime.**

●**Make sure that your pillow, blanket and mattress are comfortable**...and that your bedroom is dark and quiet. Most people sleep best when the room temperature is around 65°F.

●**Banish computers and other reminders of work from your bedroom.**

- **Avoid caffeinated beverages for six hours before bedtime.** Have no more than three alcoholic drinks in the evening.

- **Avoid exercise for three hours before bedtime.** Working out early in the day is relaxing, but working out before bed boosts alertness.

If revamping your sleep hygiene fails to improve your sleep, try these strategies...

- **Take steps to alleviate worry.** Worry has a way of descending at bedtime. To keep this from happening, spend a few minutes after supper jotting down your concerns—and composing your "to do" list for the next day. Then relax until you go to bed.

- **Go to bed *only* when you feel sleepy.** Your biological clock sends out wake-up messages twice a day—one in the morning, another in the late afternoon. Trying to sleep before the second message has worn off—a process that can take an hour or more—can result in insomnia.

If you tend to fall asleep early and wake up before dawn, your biological clock may be running fast. To overcome this problem, try taking melatonin in the morning or exposing yourself to bright light late in the day.

- **Spend less time in bed.** If you typically spend eight hours in bed—but spend two of those worrying about being awake—try staying in bed for six hours instead. Odds are you'll get the same amount of sleep—but will feel less frustrated.

That's significant, since insomnia-related frustration often sets the stage for even greater sleeplessness.

- **Watch out for too much sleep.** If you pay off your entire "sleep debt" each night, your sleep drive is weakened and you may sleep poorly the next night.

Getting slightly less than a full night's sleep means that you carry some sleep debt into the next day—and sleep more soundly that night. Ten to 20 minutes of sleep debt should keep you sleeping well. More than that leaves you drowsy the next day.

- **Consider physiological causes of sleep trouble.** Thirty million Americans suffer from obstructive sleep apnea, a condition marked by repeated pauses in breathing during sleep. These pauses—up to 200 a night—make it impossible to get deep, restorative sleep.

Most cases of sleep apnea are caused by excessive tissue in the back of the throat. At night, this tissue collapses onto the trachea, shutting off the flow of air until the sleeper gasps and then resumes breathing normally again.

Apnea sufferers tend to snore heavily—and to snort periodically as they sleep. If you suspect that you have sleep apnea, consult a doctor.

In many cases, apnea can be controlled with *continuous positive airway pressure* (CPAP), in which an air mask worn at bedtime continuously pumps air and regulates pressure. For those unable to tolerate the mask, surgery may be necessary.

- **Take steps to control restless legs.** Restless legs syndrome (RLS) causes a creeping, pulling sensation in the legs, particularly at night. The urge to move the legs makes it almost impossible to fall asleep. If you think you might have RLS, ask a doctor about *carbidopalevodopa* (Sinemet) and *gabapentin* (Neurontin). These prescription medications are highly effective at curbing RLS.

- **Consider the possibility that you're depressed.** Early morning awakening is a hallmark of depression and, to a lesser extent, of anxiety. See your doctor if symptoms of these disorders, including hopelessness and worthlessness, persist.

- **Watch out for drug-induced insomnia.** Many different medications, including some antidepressants and heart drugs, can cause insomnia.

If you take any medication regularly, ask your doctor if it might be interfering with your sleep. If so, he/she may be able to alter the dosage or switch you to another medication.

- **Consider sleeping pills.** Short-term use of a sleeping aid is often helpful—especially during periods of stress. The prescription drug *zolpidem* (Ambien) is highly effective and is far less likely to cause addiction than other prescription sleeping pills.

Over-the-counter sleeping aids seem to be effective but have not been carefully studied.

14

Take Charge of Your Medical Needs

Wisest Ways to Treat Home Medical Emergencies

It is difficult to stay calm when you are confronted with a health emergency, such as a bad cut...a serious allergic reaction...or sudden and debilitating back pain.

Don't panic. Even if you are waiting for an ambulance or driving to the emergency department, taking the appropriate action right away—and avoiding common mistakes—will improve the chances of a complete and fast recovery.

The most common home emergencies—and what you should do for them immediately...

ALLERGIC REACTIONS

Some people suffer a life-threatening allergic reaction called anaphylaxis. It can follow insect bites or stings...eating certain foods...or taking a medication to which you are sensitive.

Prime symptoms: Difficulty breathing, dizziness, nausea or a sudden and severe rash.

Do: Take Benadryl *(diphenhydramine)* right away. Follow dosage recommendations on the label. If you have a known allergy and carry an epinephrine self-injector, use it right away. Then get to an emergency department.

Don't: Wait for a serious allergic reaction to go away on its own. It can escalate very, very quickly.

HEAD INJURIES

Head trauma is responsible for more than two million emergency department visits a year. If you or someone you're with loses consciousness—even briefly—following a head injury, get emergency treatment. There could be a concussion or other type of brain damage.

Do: Be alert for symptoms like lethargy or sleepiness...nausea...weakness...changes in vision, etc. These are signs of brain injury that require immediate attention.

Don't: Assume the worst. Most people recover quickly from head injuries. As long as

Ted Christopher, MD, chief of the division of emergency medicine at Thomas Jefferson University Hospital in Philadelphia.

187

you're not feeling dazed, weak or disoriented, you can treat the discomfort at home with an ice pack and by taking acetaminophen. Do not take aspirin or ibuprofen, which may increase bleeding.

HEART ATTACK

Chest pain, often accompanied by sweating, shortness of breath or nausea, is the most common symptom of a heart attack. Call an ambulance if the discomfort doesn't go away promptly or if you have a history of heart problems.

Do: Take an aspirin at the first sign of symptoms. It can help prevent heart damage.

Don't: Wait to get medical attention, even if the discomfort improves. Intravenous medications that are used to dissolve blood clots are most effective when given within just a few hours of symptom onset.

DEEP CUTS

Get help right away for any cut that is longer than one inch or in which you can see underlying tissue.

Do: Use a lot of water pressure when cleaning deep cuts. It spreads the tissues apart and provides more thorough cleaning. Use cool or tepid water, and flood the cut for two to three minutes. Wash with soap (regular bath soap is fine) to prevent infection. Apply pressure with gauze or a clean cloth to stop the bleeding.

Don't: Wash cuts with hot water. It dilates blood vessels and may increase bleeding. And don't use hydrogen peroxide to disinfect cuts—it can damage the tissue.

Warning: If the area surrounding the wound is numb or turns blue, a nerve or major blood vessel may have been damaged. Get to an emergency department right away.

PUNCTURE WOUNDS

Cuts from animal bites or stepping on a nail and other puncture wounds are always serious. The wounds are narrow and deep—they are difficult to wash and there is little bleeding—so bacteria can get trapped inside.

Do: Get to an emergency department quickly. Puncture wounds have a high infection rate. You'll probably need prescription antibiotics and a tetanus shot.

Don't: Remove nails, pencils, etc. that have penetrated deeply into the body. Pulling them out may increase the damage.

Better: Fasten the object in place with a clean bandage and tape...and get to an emergency department.

SUDDEN BACK PAIN

Most cases of back pain are caused by muscle strains. Acting quickly can mean the difference between a fast recovery and spending days—or even weeks—in bed.

Do: Take aspirin or ibuprofen right away. These medications block the action of prostaglandins—chemicals in the body that cause inflammation after an injury. Or try acetaminophen, a good pain reliever. However, seek medical attention immediately for back pain associated with fever or loss of control of your bladder or bowels. Do not self-medicate.

Do: Apply a cold pack or ice cubes wrapped in a cloth to the area for at least 20 minutes, every few hours. The cold will constrict blood vessels and help prevent swelling.

Don't: Apply heat right after a back injury—it may increase swelling. After 24 hours, however, applying heat may help relax muscle spasms.

Warning: Back pain is rare in children. In the absence of an obvious injury, it may be a symptom of a more serious illness. Get it checked out right away.

Also, persistent back pain in the elderly should be checked by a physician. It could be a symptom of a serious medical problem.

HEAT BURNS

Even small burns can be slow to heal, and infections are common.

Do: Flood the area with cool water for five minutes. It lowers the temperature in the skin and helps prevent damage from residual heat. Cool water also acts as an anesthetic to reduce the pain.

Pat the area dry, and apply a triple antibiotic ointment. Then loosely cover with a gauze pad.

To reduce swelling and pain, take aspirin or ibuprofen.

Don't: Apply ice or very cold water to burns—extreme cold damages the skin. Also, don't "protect" the burn with petroleum jelly or butter.

The oils trap heat and restrict air circulation. Do not pop burn blisters intentionally. Intact blisters help prevent infection.

POISONING

If you or someone you're with has ingested a toxic substance (including a large amount of over-the-counter or prescription medicine), get to an emergency department right away.

Do: Call an emergency department or your local poison control center for advice while you're waiting for help. If possible, have the product container in front of you so you can describe exactly what was taken.

Don't: Induce vomiting without medical advice. Many substances will cause additional damage on the way back up. There's also the risk that the vomit will be aspirated into the lungs.

FIRST-AID KIT/ESSENTIALS

- **Several sizes of gauge pads**
- **Rolls of bandage tape**
- **Aspirin, acetaminophen and ibuprofen**
- **Benadryl** (diphenhydramine)
- **Triple antibiotic ointment**
- **Elastic bandage**
- **Chemical ice pack**
- **Epinephrine self-injector** for serious allergy sufferers (requires a prescription)

Do Your Own Medical Research

Gary Schine, president of the medical research agency Schine On-Line, Providence, RI. He is author of *If the President Had Cancer....* Sandra Publications.

A doctor's advice is usually accepted at face value. Yet when it comes to treating a serious illness, that advice should be given close scrutiny.

Reason: Even the most caring, compassionate physician is ultimately performing a job. He/she has less at stake than the person who's sick—and whose life may be on the line. In a world where medical breakthroughs occur on an almost daily basis, no doctor can be expected to be up-to-date on every new treatment for every illness.

If you assume that your doctor has all the pertinent information, and accept his suggestions about the "best" course of action without providing any input of your own, you're behaving dangerously.

When your well-being is at stake, you must be your own best advocate. To do that, you must educate yourself about your condition—the various treatment options...and what the latest research reveals about new and possibly experimental treatments. You must then work with your caregivers to assure optimal care.

HOW I SAVED MY LIFE

Four years ago my doctor told me I had a rare and incurable form of leukemia. What he did not know—and what my own research revealed—was that a new anti-leukemia drug had become available three months before my grim diagnosis.

This new drug was especially effective against the rare form of leukemia I was suffering from—80% of those treated achieved a complete and lasting remission. Because of that new treatment I am alive and cancer-free today. *Here is how you or a loved one can learn what you need to know about a serious illness...*

SECOND OPINIONS

If you heed no other advice in this article, be sure to get a second opinion. It can literally spell the difference between life and death.

Example: Six years ago, a friend of mine was diagnosed with advanced liver cancer. My friend's doctor offered him no treatment and gave him only months to live. But on the advice of his brother-in-law, a hospital administrator, Frank sought a second opinion from a major cancer research center. The doctors there recommended a new type of surgery. Frank got the surgery—and he is now healthy and cancer-free.

Moral of this story: Medicine is an inexact and rapidly evolving science. Doctors vary widely in their knowledge. Some are diligent about keeping up with advances in their field. Others aren't. By seeking out a second or perhaps even a third or fourth opinion, you boost your odds of finding a practitioner knowledge-able about every form of therapy that might prove beneficial to you.

Caution: The choices garnered from multiple opinions aren't always clearly black or white, right or wrong. One doctor might recommend a treatment that has an 80% cure rate—but a 20% risk of serious long-term adverse effects. Another might recommend a treatment with a 50% cure rate—but with only a 5% chance of serious side effects. Which is the better option? It's up to the patient to decide.

USING A MEDICAL LIBRARY

Medical information—including information on the latest developments in treatment for virtually every illness, is readily available. The key is knowing how—and where—to find it.

Libraries affiliated with medical schools or major hospitals tend to have the most complete information.

If you're already hospitalized, federal law requires that you be given access to the hospital library—and that the hospital librarian respond to your requests for help in doing research.

If you're not hospitalized, call the library and find out if it's open to the public. If not, ask which local medical libraries are. If none are, ask about exceptions to the restricted access policies. In most states, at least one health library is open to the public.

In addition, at least two medical libraries in the US are geared specifically to lay people...

●**Center for Medical Consumers,** 237 Thompson St., New York 10012.

●**Planetree Health Resource Center,** 2040 Webster St., San Francisco 94115.

PINPOINTING INFORMATION

Pinpointing information in a medical library can be a daunting task to the uninitiated.

To start, ask the librarian to help look up relevant studies in the *Index Medicus,* the master index of medical information. Copy down the names of relevant articles in respected medical journals—such as *The New England Journal of Medicine,* the *Journal of the American Medical Association* and *The Lancet,* a British periodical.

What are you looking for? A general overview of your illness, plus details of the latest research. In particular, you'll want to know dif-ferent methods of treatment—including their success rates and their possible complications—and whether there's been any recent development that your primary physician may not yet know about.

You also want to know about clinical trials—experiments that test new treatments at the cutting edge of medicine. Participating in these experiments carries some risk, but it also offers hope where previously none existed. Despite the risks, far more people have been helped than hurt by clinical trials in this country.

If you find an article that details a promising new treatment, call the author of the article—or ask your doctor to call for you. Some researchers prefer talking to other medical professionals rather than to patients.

ONLINE MEDICAL DATABASES

Thanks to powerful computers and high-speed modems, medical information is now readily available via the Internet.

Benefit: Research that might take days of labor in a library can now be compiled in a matter of minutes.

Useful resources: Medline, a vast compilation of medical articles and Physician's Data Query (PDQ), a database that provides detailed information about new drugs and other treatments for all types of cancer.

If you are not familiar with the Internet or are having difficulty searching for the information you need, consider hiring a medical research firm to do the research for you. *Three excellent services:*

●**The Health Resource,** 564 Locust St., Conway, AR 72032. 501-329-5272.

●**Planetree,** 2040 Webster St., San Francisco, CA 94115. 415-923-3681.

●**Schine On-Line,** 39 Brenton Ave., Providence, RI 02906. 800-346-3287 or 401-751-0120.

The Homeopathic Medicine Chest

Asa Hershoff, ND, DC, a naturopathic doctor and chiropractor who practices homeopathy in Santa Monica, CA. He is author of *Homeopathic Remedies: A Quick and Easy Guide to Common Disorders and Their Homeopathic Treatments*. Avery.

Many Americans are returning to *homeopathy*. This 200-year-old system makes use of more than 2,000 preparations that are designed to support the body's innate healing powers.

These remedies are derived from herbs… animal products, such as snake venom and cuttlefish ink…and mercury, sulfur and other minerals.

LIKE CURES LIKE

The basic idea behind homeopathy is that the symptoms of an illness represent the body's attempt to repair itself or rid itself of disease.

By extension, homeopaths argue, any substance that would cause similar symptoms when taken by a healthy person would bolster the body's healing powers in someone who is sick.

This philosophy is often summed up as: Let like be cured by like.

Example: Raw onion can irritate the eyes and cause a runny nose. The homeopathic remedy for hay fever—which causes similar symptoms—is an extract of onion called *allium cepa.*

Why don't homeopathic preparations exacerbate symptoms? Because the active ingredient is present in an extremely dilute form.

In fact, the concentration is typically so low that not a single molecule of the active ingredient is present.

What's left, homeopaths say, is the *information* contained within the original substance. This "blueprint" instructs the body how to cure itself, much as software tells a computer what to do.

Mainstream physicians contend that this explanation violates laws of chemistry. But centuries of experience suggests that homeopathic remedies really do work.

And recent studies demonstrate that the effectiveness of homeopathy cannot be explained by the placebo effect.

In 1997, the British medical journal *The Lancet* published a study that analyzed more than 100 controlled trials on homeopathy. The study's authors concluded that homeopathic remedies—applied for a range of ills including dysentery and hay fever—were significantly more effective than placebos.

NO SIDE EFFECTS

One clear advantage of homeopathy over conventional drug therapy is the absence of side effects.

What's more, homeopathic remedies do not interact with prescription or over-the-counter drugs…and they are compatible with herbs, surgery and even chemotherapy.

In its purest form, homeopathy involves close collaboration between the homeopath and the patient. The doctor takes a thorough medical history, zeroing in on the exact nature of the symptom, when it occurs, what causes it, etc. He/she also assembles a detailed psychological and physiological profile of the patient.

HOMEOPATHIC SELF-CARE

Homeopathic remedies can also be self-administered. The preparations are readily available in health-food stores and drugstores. Reliable manufacturers include B&T, Boiron, Dolisos and Standard.

Preparations come in liquid or pellet form, at various concentrations. For do-it-yourself use, use 6c, 12c and 30c concentrations. The higher the number, the more dilute the preparation—and the greater its potency. Follow dosage directions carefully.

Useful homeopathic remedies to keep on hand include…

● **Allium cepa.** The onion extract is good not only for hay fever, but also for the early stages of a cold.

● **Arnica.** An extract of the mountain daisy, this anti-inflammatory preparation speeds relief from aches and bruises. Taken just before exercise, it increases stamina and helps prevent muscle soreness. It can also speed healing if taken before surgery or dental work.

● **Arsenicum.** Derived from arsenic—but containing none of it in the final preparation—

arsenicum is an effective remedy for stomach flu...mild food poisoning...diarrhea...and hypochondria and other forms of anxiety.

●**Belladonna.** Derived from a nightshade plant, belladonna is a powerful remedy for inflammation of all sorts. It's good for bursitis, sore throat and arthritis as well as styes and skin inflammation. It's also effective for pounding headaches and for fever.

●**Bryonia.** This anti-inflammatory agent—derived from the cucumber plant—is effective for migraine, joint pain and other conditions made worse by movement. It can also be used to treat early symptoms of flulike illness.

●**Carbo veg.** This charcoal preparation is a classic remedy for belching, bloating and flatulence. It's also an effective adjunct to conventional medical treatment for serious respiratory disorders such as asthma and emphysema.

●**Nux vomica.** This remedy, derived from an east Indian plant known as Quaker's buttons, is a natural sedative. In addition to relieving anxiety and irritability, it helps alleviate back pain and muscle tightness.

Nux vomica is also an antidote for the edginess caused by overindulgence in coffee and tobacco. It can ease a hangover in minutes. Taken at bedtime, it can help prevent a hangover the following day.

Homeopathic preparations should be used only for acute or minor conditions. Contact a homeopath and your doctor to see if a homeopathic approach is right for you.

To locate a homeopath in your area, contact the National Center for Homeopathy at 703-548-7790 or *www.homeopathic.org.*

Steering Clear of Incompetent Doctors

Martin L. Gross, an investigative journalist and social critic. He is author of The Medical Racket: How Doctors, HMOs and Hospitals Are Failing the American Patient. *Avon.*

Too many health-care workers are either incompetent or dangerously sloppy. Here are the threats consumers face—and what we can do to protect ourselves...

●**What sorts of incompetence are you talking about?** American doctors are generally well-trained, but a surprisingly large number are woefully inept in one way or another.

Consider these disturbing findings...

●**Poor stethoscope skills.** In a study involving 453 medical residents, only one in five heart abnormalities that should have been easily diagnosed with the stethoscope was correctly diagnosed.

●**Bad care for diabetes.** The most important diagnostic tool for the treatment of adult-onset diabetes is the *glycosylated hemoglobin* test. Yet in a Medicare study of 97,000 diabetics, 84% of doctors failed to administer the test.

●**Misread mammograms.** Radiologists fail to spot malignant breast tumors that are present on mammograms 46% of the time, a Yale study found.

●**Bad care for people with pneumonia.** Doctors often fail to follow crucial guidelines when treating older pneumonia patients.

In a study of more than 14,000 pneumonia patients, many doctors failed to take blood cultures and to give antibiotics correctly and on a timely basis.

●**How can I tell if a particular doctor is competent?** There's no easy way for a lay person to tell. The best you can do is look for evidence that other *medical experts* have judged the doctor competent.

In addition to a medical school diploma and admitting privileges at an accredited hospital, your doctor should be board-certified in his/her specialty.

To learn if he is board-certified, consult the *Directory of Physicians in the US* and the *Directory of Board Certified American Medical Specialists.* These references are available at most municipal libraries.

Another helpful resource is the American Medical Association. Visit its Web site—*www.ama-assn.org*—and go to "Doctor Finder."

For most people, the best bet is to find a private practitioner who has a faculty appointment at a medical school. Such doctors tend to be more up to date than other doctors.

If you have a particular medical problem, call the nearest medical school. Speak with the chair of the appropriate department or one of his colleagues. Many take private patients.

• **Is there any way to find out if a doctor has been disciplined?** Citizens must write to the agency that oversees the licensing of physicians—this varies from state to state—and ask for information on a particular physician.

The Washington, DC-based consumer advocacy group Public Citizen publishes *20,125 Questionable Doctors*. This book lists physicians who have run afoul of their licensing boards or who have been hit with disciplinary actions by state medical boards or by the federal government.

Some doctors whose names appear on the list may be perfectly competent. But inclusion on the list should lead you to question your doctor closely about why he has this dubious distinction.

If you can't find a copy of the book at your library, you can call Public Citizen at 202-588-7780 to order a report covering your home state.

Friends or relatives who are doctors may have privileged access to information about doctors in your area. Ask what they know.

• **What should I look for in a hospital?** The best hospitals are those that have been accredited "with commendation" by the Joint Commission on Accreditation of Healthcare Organizations (JCAHO). "Regular" accreditation is virtually meaningless.

On request, this not-for-profit agency will send a free report on any hospital. It can be reached at One Renaissance Blvd., Oakbrook Terrace, IL 60181, 630-792-5800. *www.jcaho.org*.

If no nearby hospital has the top JCAHO ranking, opt for the nearest university (teaching) hospital. For serious medical problems at least, teaching hospitals tend to offer better care than community hospitals.

• **What threats do hospitalized patients face?** There are two primary threats—medication errors and infections.

To avoid being given the wrong drug and/ or the wrong dosage, take pills only if they are offered to you by a registered nurse (RN), licensed practical nurse (LPN) or physician.

Your doctor should tell you the generic and trade names of any drug he prescribes, the size and color of the pills, how many pills you should take and how often—and any possible side effects, too.

For intravenous (IV) drugs, you should know the drug's name and how often the bag should be changed.

Medication errors and side effects kill an estimated 50,000 Americans each year.

---

6 Ways Doctors Let Older Patients Down

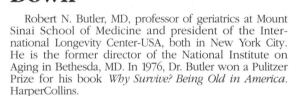

Robert N. Butler, MD, professor of geriatrics at Mount Sinai School of Medicine and president of the International Longevity Center-USA, both in New York City. He is the former director of the National Institute on Aging in Bethesda, MD. In 1976, Dr. Butler won a Pulitzer Prize for his book *Why Survive? Being Old in America.* HarperCollins.

As we grow older, we're more likely to have health problems that require first-rate medical care.

Unfortunately, as many seniors have learned, it can be hard to find a doctor suited to care for *their* special needs.

How can older people be sure to get good medical care? Dr. Robert Butler, a well-known crusader for elder rights, explains how important it is to watch out for mistakes doctors sometimes make when treating elderly patients…

Mistake: **Failing to appreciate the physical changes that come with age.** A disease that causes one set of symptoms in a young person may manifest itself quite differently in an older person. Not all doctors realize that. And an unwary doctor can easily miss the diagnosis.

Example I: If a 30-year-old man suffers a heart attack, he is likely to experience severe chest pain. But chest pain affects fewer than 20% of older heart attack victims. Instead, older victims may simply seem weak or confused.

Example II: An older person suffering from an overactive thyroid may exhibit apathy instead of hyperactivity, the classic symptom.

Mistake: **Urging older people to "take it easy."** Even if you've been disabled by a stroke or another medical problem, leading an active lifestyle helps keep you healthy—and happy.

Even people in their 80s and 90s can develop big, powerful muscles with a program of weight lifting. Such a program can literally put a bedridden patient back on his/her feet.

Mistake: **Being too quick to blame health problems on old age.** Doctors often assume that health problems are inevitable in older people, exhibiting a defeatist "what-can-you-expect-at-your-age?" attitude.

They order fewer diagnostic tests and generally treat disease less aggressively in old people than in young people.

Example: An elderly woman seems confused and disoriented. Assuming that she has Alzheimer's disease, her doctor neglects to order tests that might show the real culprit to be an easily correctable drug reaction.

Mistake: **Not giving the patient enough time.** A good physician takes the time to ask about your work status and lifestyle as well as your medical problems…and, in general, makes you *feel* taken care of.

At each office visit, the doctor should ask about symptoms you have reported in the past. He should also review your response to medications… and ask about new problems.

Your first visit to a new doctor should be devoted to giving a thorough medical history and undergoing a physical exam and lab tests. This can take more than an hour. Once this comprehensive exam is completed, you probably won't need another exam for a year—unless there's a health crisis.

Mistake: **Failing to advocate preventive measures.** Some doctors seem to think, "Why bother trying to lower an elderly patient's cholesterol level. He's just going to decline anyway."

We now know that heart patients of *any* age can benefit from a program of dietary modification, lifestyle change and—if necessary—medication or surgery.

Mistake: **Giving inappropriate prescriptions.** Doctors are too quick to order tranquilizers and antidepressants for their older patients, thinking—incorrectly—that psychotherapy is of no use. And they often fail to realize that older bodies respond differently to drugs.

Example: It can take an older person twice as long to "clear" *diazepam* (Valium) from his body as a young person. A dose that would be appropriate for a young person could make an older person drowsy.

If you're not sure that your doctor knows about all the drugs you're taking, put all of your medications (including nonprescription drugs and herbal remedies) in a paper bag and bring them with you to your next office visit.

For referral to a certified geriatrician in your area, call the American Geriatrics Society at 800-247-4779.

Your Doctor's Doctor

Fewer than one-third of US doctors have a personal physician. These doctors are less likely to go for regular checkups or undergo routine screenings for cancer and other diseases. They're also less likely to discuss such preventive health measures with their patients.

Gary Gross, MD, associate professor of medicine, Yale University School of Medicine, New Haven, CT.

Assessing Your Doctor

Ask yourself these questions to gauge the level of care you're getting…

●**Do I have the chance to express comfortably all that I feel?**

●**Does the doctor really listen to me?**

•**After communicating with my doctor, do I feel relieved or frustrated?**

●**Do I share with my doctor the responsibility for my own well-being?**

●**Am I given the freedom of choice among different treatment plans?**

• **When in doubt, do I feel comfortable in voicing my need for a second opinion?**

• **Does the doctor share his/her knowledge without intimidation?**

• **Do I follow my doctor's instructions, or do I use my own judgment?**

• **Do I perceive that my doctor is doing everything possible to help me?**

• **Does the relationship with my doctor fulfill my expectations and needs?**

Holistic Medicine, 4101 Lake Boone Trail, Raleigh, NC 27607.

How to Be a Better Patient

David Biro, MD, PhD, assistant clinical professor of dermatology at State University of New York Downstate Medical Center and a dermatologist in private practice, both in Brooklyn. Biro has recovered fully since his bone marrow transplant in February 1996. He is author of *One Hundred Days: My Unexpected Journey from Doctor to Patient.* Pantheon.

At age 31, having earned an MD from Columbia University and a PhD from Oxford University in England, my life seemed too good to be true.

I was finishing my first novel and working in my father's dermatology practice. And I was happily married.

But the "good life" was about to go bad. I was about to become…a desperately ill patient.

SHOCKING TEST RESULTS

After noticing a strange flashing sensation in my right eye, an ophthalmologist found a clot in the retinal vein. Blood tests showed that I was anemic and suffering from leukopenia—a condition in which there are dangerously low levels of infection-fighting white blood cells. I also had thrombocytopenia—low levels of platelets.

Four doctors and numerous diagnostic tests later, I was finally diagnosed with *paroxysmal nocturnal hemoglobinuria* (PNH), a rare and often fatal bone marrow disease.

MY DIFFICULT DECISION

I was told that medication might keep my PNH under control. But the only *cure* for the disease was a bone marrow transplant. Only about 70% of patients survive this procedure, in which the marrow—which generates blood cells—is destroyed with drugs and radiation and then replaced with marrow from a donor. Faced with a lifetime of coping with a deadly disease, I opted for the transplant.

Five years later, life is good again—I'm writing another novel, practicing dermatology and still happily married. But having seen medicine as a seriously ill patient as well as a doctor, I have a new perspective on all things medical.

Here's what I learned…

• **Don't expect an immediate diagnosis.** Most patients seem to think that doctors know everything. I certainly felt that way before I got sick.

In fact, doctors often have a hard time making an accurate diagnosis. You'll cope better with the inevitable uncertainty if you anticipate it—if you realize that doctors don't always have all the answers.

• **Learn all you can about your illness.** When I learned that I had PNH, I read all I could about the disease.

Do the same for any condition you might have. Go to a medical library at a local hospital or university…buy a book about the problem…and search the Internet. Knowledge of your condition gives you a sense of control over it. And as an informed patient, you can ask your doctor better questions about your care.

Caution: Information is not expertise. You're educating yourself so that you can ask better questions, not answer them.

• **Get additional opinions.** One doctor was unable to diagnose me. He said we should test my blood regularly and "wait and see" what developed.

Another doctor made an accurate diagnosis —and recommended drug therapy.

It wasn't until I talked with a third doctor that I understood all my options and could make a rational decision.

Tell your doctor you want additional opinions—and ask for referrals. If a second opinion doesn't settle things, go for a third. Don't stop asking until you're satisfied.

●**Decide how much you want to know about side effects and complications.** Yes, I read about PNH. But I did not want to know about *all* the possible side effects of the drugs I'd be taking and *all* the possible complications of the medical tests and procedures I'd undergo.

As a doctor, I'd always felt that reciting a list of possible side effects and complications — most of which happen to only a tiny percentage of patients—was more frightening than useful. So, when I became a patient, I didn't press my doctors to tell me about every risk I faced. I didn't want to worry needlessly.

Best: Ask your doctor about the *likely* problems associated with your medical care. That way, you'll be informed about the important risks without being scared to death.

●**When making a decision, trust your "gut."** I had three main treatment options, and my doctors couldn't agree on what was right for me.

I could have had infusions of *antithymocyte globulin* (ATG), a drug that corrects some of the problems associated with marrow failure. But ATG requires transfusions—which might have increased the risk for complications had I gone on to have a marrow transplant.

I could have taken cyclosporine. But having prescribed it for my patients suffering from psoriasis, I knew it could cause serious side effects, including kidney damage.

My third option was the marrow transplant. But there were two types to consider—and doctors disagreed about which one was right for me.

In the end, I realized that no doctor can make a decision for his/her patients. Yes, there are some conditions for which every doctor makes the same recommendation. But in many cases, there is a "conservative" option and a "radical" option—and you have to choose.

The best way to make a tough medical decision is to evaluate all the facts, become as informed as possible and then choose the option that feels right—the one that best fits with your personality and lifestyle.

●**Fight pessimism.** *Believing* that your treatment will prove effective helps lift your spirits

—and that kind of attitude gives you the best chance of recovery.

To stay "up," I used a support network that included my wife, Daniella…my family—one of my three sisters wound up being the marrow donor…and friends.

I exercised every day—even with an armful of intravenous needles. I covered the walls of my hospital room with photos of loved ones and favorite places.

Whatever it takes to make you feel that everything will turn out all right—that's the most important thing to do to see you through a medical ordeal.

Complexities Of At-Home Nursing Care

Peter J. Strauss, Esq., a partner in the law firm Epstein Becker & Green, PC, 250 Park Ave., New York 10177. He is a fellow of the National Academy of Elder Law Attorneys and coauthor of *The Elder Law Handbook—A Legal and Financial Survival Guide for Caregivers and Seniors.* Facts on File.

Only the very rich can afford not to be concerned about the likelihood that some day they will need home care or nursing home care.

But the rest of us do have to worry about becoming incapacitated. And most of us would prefer to be cared for at home. *Questions we all have…*

●**How much does home care cost?**

●**Will Medicare pay for some of it?**

●**What quality of care can one expect from the government?**

●**Do I need a Medigap policy?**

●**What about a long-term-care insurance policy?**

MEDICARE

Medicare generally covers a very limited portion of the cost of care provided in the home. Although home care typically follows a hospital stay, Medicare does not make hospitalization a prerequisite for coverage.

As long as the care is necessary for treatment of an illness or injury, Medicare coverage applies. This coverage, however, includes only the items defined as "home health care benefits." *These include…*

- **Medical social services.**
- **Nursing care** (part-time or intermittent).
- **Medical supplies/equipment.**
- **Physical therapy.**
- **Occupational therapy.**
- **Speech therapy.**
- **Home health aides** (part-time or intermittent), but only if a skilled service—such as therapy—is provided also.

The benefits *must* be prescribed by a doctor and provided by a home-care agency that has been certified by Medicare.

Your share: You pay an annual $100 deductible and copayments for benefits under Medicare Part B. You must also make a 20% copayment for medical supplies—hospital beds, walkers, wheelchairs, etc.

Exception: People under a managed care type of Medicare do not have to make a copayment for benefits received under Medicare Part B.

- **Medicare does not cover everything.** For instance, Medicare limits coverage for part-time or *intermittent* home care—fewer than five days a week on an infrequent basis—to 35 hours per week. If continuing care is needed—care for a period of up to 21 days—then coverage can be for up to seven days a week, but only for up to 56 hours a week.

If a home health aide and nursing services are needed, the amount billed must be kept under 35 hours a week to be considered intermittent.

- **Medicare does not cover the cost of long-term care or personal assistance care.** These are considered custodial-type care rather than medical care. This kind of care applies to those with chronic conditions, such as Alzheimer's disease, Parkinson's disease, etc., who need assistance with daily living activities (eating, bathing, getting in and out of bed, going to the bathroom, etc.).

- **Medicare does not cover the cost of housekeeping.** This is often needed by a person with a chronic condition.

MEDIGAP COVERAGE

Supplemental Medicare insurance—Medigap insurance—picks up only the amounts of Medicare *covered expenses* that Medicare does not pay for, such as copayments and deductibles.

Medigap *does not* cover the cost of long-term care, since Medicare doesn't provide this coverage.

MEDICAID

The cost of custodial care provided in the home may be covered by Medicaid in a few states.

Medicaid is designed to pay only for those who are "poor." So, to be eligible for Medicaid, a person's income and assets must be below limits set by law. Only a few states have a broad home-care program.

Loophole: In most states, people who transfer assets so that Medicaid will pay for *in-home care* are *not* subject to the federal government's 36-month look-back rule. That rule disqualifies people who unload assets within that time period from getting Medicaid to pay for their stay in a nursing home.

Beware: Individual states may impose look-back rules that bar people who transfer assets from getting government assistance for in-home care.

LONG-TERM-CARE INSURANCE

A growing number of older people are buying private insurance policies—long-term-care insurance—to cover the cost of nursing care. The policy should cover both care in a nursing home *and* care in their own home.

You can also buy policies that cover only in-home care or only nursing home care, but this is usually not wise.

Caution: Make sure a policy labeled a "nursing home policy" also covers at-home care.

These policies are expensive: They get more expensive the older you are when you buy them. *Best:* Buy them by the time you are in your 60s. Make sure you take an inflation rider!

CONSIDERATIONS

- **What is the extent of insurance coverage?** Some policies pay for home care only a fraction of what they pay for nursing home care.

●**What is the "triggering event" for payment** of expenses under the policy? Some policies pay much more quickly than others. Find out what the lag time is in policies you're considering.

Bottom line: Make sure that the level of coverage and the event that triggers payment are clearly spelled out in the policy.

TAX INCENTIVES

The tax law now provides breaks that defray some custodial care costs. A person needing home care can take an itemized deduction for "qualified medical expenses" to the extent that total expenses exceed 7.5% of Adjusted Gross Income (AGI). *Deductible medical expenses include...*

●**Out-of-pocket medical costs,** including out-of-pocket payments to home health aides.

●**Medicare copayments and deductibles.**

●**Long-term-care insurance premiums up to a dollar limit** (depending on age).

●**"Long-term-care services"**—up to any amount—provided to a person who is chronically ill. The meaning of "long-term-care services" is liberally interpreted to include rehabilitative services and personal care services. This is so even though personal care service probably would not qualify as a deductible medical expense were it not a *long-term-care* service.

Taxes: Some part of the benefits provided under a long-term-care policy may be taxable.

How to Get the Care You Want When You're Too Sick to Ask for It

Susan H. Evans, PhD, research scientist, Institute for Health Promotion and Disease Prevention, University of Southern California School of Medicine, Los Angeles. She is coauthor of *Surviving Modern Medicine: How to Get the Best from Doctors, Families & Friends.* Rutgers University Press.

If you're like most Americans, you've failed to sign an *advance medical directive*—a living will and/or a medical power of attorney.

A *living will* is used to spell out in detail what sort of health care you wish to receive should you become incapacitated—unable to communicate in *any* way—and doctors judge that you are near death.

A *medical power of attorney* is used to appoint a health-care agent. That's a person who makes medical decisions on your behalf if you are incapacitated—whether you are near death or not.

Having an advance medical directive brings peace of mind for you and your loved ones. It frees them from the burden of having to make tough medical decisions at a time of great upheaval and psychological distress.

Having a directive can also help avoid the family conflict—and protracted legal battles —that often arise when there is disagreement about what sort of treatment you should get.

No one knows when an illness or accident may strike, so every person age 18 or older should complete an advance medical directive—either a living will or a medical power of attorney.

LIVING WILL

A living will specifies your wishes regarding health care at the end of life. It takes effect only if you are terminally ill or permanently unconscious.

If you recover, of course, you're free to make your own decisions. You may also revoke a living will at any time as long as you are able to communicate your wishes.

The living will covers decisions about the use of feeding tubes, respirators and antibiotics. Pain medications would still be administered, even if your living will called for life support to be withdrawn in case of terminal illness.

MEDICAL POWER OF ATTORNEY

A medical power of attorney for health care—also known as a durable power of attorney for health care or a health-care proxy—is broader and more flexible than a living will. It lets you designate as your agent someone close to you—a friend, relative, member of the clergy, etc.

This person legally makes medical decisions for you if you become incapacitated.

Unlike a living will, a medical power of attorney applies to survivable illnesses, such as a stroke, as well as to terminal ones.

Also unlike a living will, a medical power of attorney does not generally state such specifics as whether doctors should attempt to prolong your life by administering cardiopulmonary resuscitation (CPR), placing you on a respirator, etc.

Instead, your health-care agent will express your wishes.

MEDICAL DIRECTIVE

Statutes governing advance directives vary from state to state. A few states recognize only a single basic form known as a medical directive. In this document, you can explain what you want in terms of life support...and appoint a spokesperson. It takes effect only in cases where a living will would apply.

To obtain copies of the appropriate documents for your state, contact Partnership for Caring, 1620 Eye St. NW, Suite 202, Washington, DC 20006 (800-989-9455/*www.partnershipfor caring.org*). None of the medical directives requires a lawyer's help.

PICKING A HEALTH-CARE AGENT

Your health-care agent must be at least 18 years of age. To prevent conflicts of interest, avoid picking your primary-care physician or any other health-care professional involved in your care. Many states prohibit you from doing this—unless the practitioner is related to you by blood, marriage or adoption.

Discuss your wishes with your health-care agent before you execute the medical directive. Be sure the person you select is psychologically resilient enough to make critical decisions under stressful circumstances.

Good idea: Designate an alternate health-care agent, just in case your first choice is unable to fulfill the role.

As you consider potential agents, ask yourself...

●**Is this person comfortable talking about death?**

●**Is he/she assertive enough to see to it that I get the care I want** even in the face of opposition from my doctors or members of my family?

●**Does he understand and respect my values?**

●**Is he capable of exercising good judgment** in case an unforeseen situation arises?

Once you decide whom you'd like to be your agent, spend some time rehearsing how you'll broach the subject. Many people find it best to begin the discussion when the whole family is present.

Whatever you say, make sure to explain things in detail. Many people complete advance directives too hastily, without considering all their options and without describing fully their wishes for end-of-life care. Don't try to cram everything into a single discussion. Several may be necessary.

During these conversations, tell your agent just what you think about "extreme measures" doctors might use to prolong your life. Do you want every treatment available, no matter how limited the benefit might be? Or would you rather forgo treatment once it becomes clear that death is inevitable?

After considering these questions, you may find that there is no one you trust sufficiently to become your health-care agent. If so, it's probably best to stick with a living will—which does not require you to appoint an agent.

WHERE TO KEEP THE DOCUMENT

Whichever advance medical directive you choose, be sure that key family members and/or friends have a copy.

Your loved ones should be able to press photocopies of the document into the hands of your doctors and nurses.

Your physicians and your HMO should also have a copy—just in case. Many hospitals and nursing homes also request copies upon admission.

If you have multiple residences: Prepare an advance medical directive for each location.

If you spend half the year in one state and half in another, have forms filed with your doctors in both states. Make sure each document conforms to the requirements of that state.

Medical Directives: The Legal View

An adult has the right to decide on the type of medical treatment to receive—or not receive. Advance "medical directives," such as living wills and health care proxies, ensure that your wishes are followed if you can't speak for yourself.

•Is refusing medical treatment the same as suicide?

No. From a legal view, the refusal of medical treatment, which in turn results in your death, is not considered by law to be suicide.

When treatment is refused, the US Supreme Court has held that the cause of death is the underlying medical problem, not the refusal.

•Does one need a living will to enforce the right to die?

No. As long as you can speak or express your wishes regarding medical treatment, your doctors must follow them. But having a living will or other advance medical directive will protect your wishes when you can no longer communicate them.

Peter J. Strauss, Esq., a partner in the law firm Epstein Becker & Green, PC, 250 Park Ave., New York 10177. He is a fellow of the National Academy of Elder Law Attorneys and coauthor of The Elder Law Handbook—A Legal and Financial Survival Guide for Caregivers and Seniors. *Facts on File.*

Secrets of Happier Recuperation

Regina Sara Ryan, a Prescott, Arizona, wellness consultant. She is author of After Surgery, Illness or Trauma: 10 Practical Steps to Renewed Energy and Health. *Hohm Press.*

Convalescing after illness, surgery or injury can be frustrating and tedious—or productive and life-affirming. Much depends on how you spend your time during your period of forced confinement.

Here's how to flourish while you're recovering...

FACING YOUR EMOTIONS

Illness or injury can spark strong emotions like anxiety, anger and grief. Painful though they may be, these emotions are normal and healthy responses to what you've been through. *To express them...*

•**Keep a personal healing journal.** Record your feelings, sketch, write poetry, compose letters you'll never send. Don't edit yourself. Accept the full range of your emotions.

•**Let go by yelling.** Scream into a pillow. Or practice "silent screaming": Open your mouth... let out your breath...contort your face...and gesture as if you were shouting at the top of your lungs.

•**Enlist a sounding board.** Choose one or two people who agree to let you vent—uninterrupted—without advising, reassuring or judging you.

STRESS REDUCTION

Breathing and relaxation techniques reduce stress, aiding your body's efforts to heal. *Useful exercise...*

Focus your gaze on something you find soothing, like a painting or a vase of flowers. Silently count "one thousand," "two thousand," "three thousand," "four thousand" as you inhale through your nose. Then exhale through your mouth, repeating the same slow count. Keep breathing this way for three minutes.

Next, tense every muscle in your body—jaw, fists, abdomen, calves—whatever your condition allows. Hold for a count of 10, then slowly release the tension. Breathe deeply again.

Finally, make a loud noise such as "bah" or "dah" over and over until you start to relax. Stop and repeat to yourself, "I am here, I'm alive, I can cope, I survive."

EXERCISING THE BODY

It's important to keep moving to improve muscle tone, blood flow, digestion and sleep. Do what you can. Wriggle and stretch your fingers and toes. *Or, if your doctor permits, try these in-bed exercises...*

•**Inner leg isometrics.** Lie flat on your back, knees bent, feet a few inches apart. Put a pillow between your thighs. Inhale, then squeeze the pillow with your legs, holding for a count of five. Exhale and release. Repeat five times.

● **Glute sets.** From the same starting position (but without the pillow), inhale, squeeze your gluteal (buttocks) muscles and hold for a count of five. Exhale and release. Repeat five times.

● **Head and neck.** Imagine that you have a pencil protruding from your chin. Inhale, turn your head left and begin to draw the biggest circle you can. At the halfway point, exhale slowly but continue to draw.

Make three circles to the left, rest, then turn to the right and make three circles.

● **Total body stretch.** Lying on your back, raise your arms above your head. Extend your feet and hands in opposite directions as if you were being stretched. Hold this position for 10 seconds, being sure to breathe normally. Repeat three times.

EXERCISING THE MIND

Nothing is more frustrating than feeling as if you're wasting time. *But time recuperating can be time well spent...*

● **Read about countries you'd like to visit or heroes who inspire you.**

● **Delve deeply into a subject that's always fascinated you**—art, astronomy, politics, economics, etc.

● **Use audiotapes to practice a foreign language.**

● **Master chess, backgammon or bridge.**

● **Draw or paint.** If you don't want to draw freehand, use a coloring book. Terrific ones made for adults are available at book and art supply stores.

● **Listen to music.** Now is the time to enjoy entire symphonies, operas or albums.

Trap: Television can be a harmless escape... or an energy-depleting crutch. Before tuning in, ask yourself, "Does TV make me laugh more? Does it leave me feeling better about myself and my life? Does it distract me from my pain or problems?" Should you answer "no" to any of these questions, explore other, more energizing pastimes.

A HEALTHFUL ENVIRONMENT

Where you heal affects how you heal. Your immediate environment should make you feel calm and uplifted—not agitated or depressed.

● **Declutter your room.** Clear off surfaces ...ask a friend to remove excess furniture... and toss old magazines and newspapers.

● **Use incandescent lights, not fluorescent ones.** Experiment with rosy lightbulbs that cast a soothing glow.

● **Give yourself new vistas.** Have new paintings or posters hung or old ones rearranged.

● **Surround yourself with mood-enhancing color.** Drape beautiful fabric over an old table or nightstand. Festoon windows with bright curtains.

● **Add fragrance to the room with incense or fresh flowers.**

● **Fill your room with plants** or grow an herb garden in an ice-cube tray on a window ledge.

WELCOMING VISITORS

Illness and injury can make visitors uncomfortable. Family and friends may be unsure of what to say or do. Put your guests at ease by voicing your wants and needs. *Be very specific...*

● **If talk is tiring, ask your visitor to hold your hand** and pray, meditate or do a breathing exercise with you.

● **Suggest a game of cards** or ask your guest to read to you.

● **Request a back or foot massage** from a close relative or friend.

● **Ask to have groceries picked up or library books returned.** Most loved ones appreciate having concrete ways to help you.

If you're too tired for visitors or need to cut a visit short, say so. Be gracious but firm. Your guests will understand.

Secrets of Better Living With a Terminal Illness

Ed Madden, a columnist for the *Dorchester Reporter,* a weekly newspaper in Dorchester, MA, and author of *Carpe Diem: Enjoying Every Day with a Terminal Illness.* Jones and Bartlett Publishers.

Several years ago, my doctor told me that the excruciating back pain that had plagued me for six months was caused by *multiple myeloma,* a rare bone marrow cancer that was attacking my spine and ribs.

Multiple myeloma accounts for only 1% of all cancers—and it's incurable. I was 53 years old, and I knew it was unlikely that I would survive more than a few years.

I hate the cancer, and there have been times that I railed against it. But I decided early on to try to put my disease in its place and go about my business.

Today is the only day I have. I'm going to enjoy it. This philosophy can benefit not only people with terminal or chronic illness, but also those who are healthy. *Here are some of the other lessons I've learned...*

•**View terminal illness as the key that opens the vault to unknown treasures.** Since I got sick, I've experienced more love, concern, compassion and care on a single day than I used to experience in an entire year.

Even though I know my days are numbered, I really enjoy life. I have a good time with my family and friends. I realize that I am one of the richest people in the world.

•**Accept help.** My close friends and relatives all felt powerless when I told them I had cancer. They wanted to help, but there wasn't much they could do. So they did what they could. Some came and did yard work for me. My brother-in-law put up a banister. A friend dropped by once a week to have dinner with me.

They couldn't cure my cancer or take away my pain, but they could help in other ways. And their help has helped me not only in practical terms, but also emotionally.

My friends all say, "You'll beat this." Of course, I won't. They're in denial, but I don't let that bother me. It's their way of coping. It's also their way of trying to be kind to me.

•**Don't worry about the things you can no longer do.** Instead, try to focus on what you still can do.

My cancer has caused my bones to deteriorate. As a result, I now have severe osteoporosis. If I attempt heavy physical labor or try to lift more than 20 pounds, I risk a fracture.

It would be easy to feel sorry for myself. But I'm not in pain, and I've been able to resume gardening and biking—two pleasures I'd thought were history—so I'm content. Sure, it would be safer to avoid these activities, too, but I refuse to wrap myself in a protective sheath.

•**Don't view yourself as a patient.** When you do, you see yourself sick, lying in a hospital bed with tubes sticking out of your body. That's not a pleasant concept, and it's certainly not one you have to dwell on.

Although I might be a bit more physically flawed now than I used to be, I'm really not too different from you or anyone else. We're all flawed. It's the daily struggle to better ourselves physically, spiritually, intellectually and emotionally that makes life interesting and challenging. Illness is just another imperfection that we can strive to overcome.

•**Take charge of your health care.** If you're used to being "in control" of your life, suddenly being diagnosed with an uncontrollable illness can be overwhelming.

I've always been a take-charge person. While I can't control the course of my illness, I refuse to give up power over the one thing that I do have control of—my treatment.

I've become a partner in my health care. My doctor and I decide on all treatments together. I stay on top of the latest medical advances. I read medical journals and I discuss the things I read about with my doctor.

If you or a close friend or family member has a serious illness, you should do the same. Hospital libraries are an excellent place to start your search for helpful information.

•**Decide what you want in a hospital.** Many of us have a choice between teaching hospitals and community hospitals. Teaching hospitals tend to offer the most up-to-date care, *but they have certain drawbacks...*

- **You'll often be seen by a medical resident instead of your regular doctor.**
- **You may have to wait a long time before you're seen.**
- **You may have to commute to get to the hospital.**

I decided to go to a local four-doctor practice because I wanted to get individualized care. Each of these doctors knows who I am and what my condition is. I don't have to reeducate them each time I come in for a checkup.

- **Practice positive thinking.** The latest research shows that the mind has at least some control over the body. And how you feel can control the mind. To keep myself optimistic, I focus on all the great things in my life—especially my family and close friends.

When my cancer was diagnosed, one of my greatest disappointments was that I wouldn't live to see my 25th wedding anniversary. But I did! Joy is great medicine.

- **Decide whether the side effects of treatment are worth its benefits.** For cancer that's curable, you go ahead with chemotherapy or radiation regardless of the side effects. But some people with incurable cancer decide against chemo and radiation because they don't want to suffer the nausea, fatigue and other side effects that often accompany these treatments.

I take chemotherapy treatments that don't abuse my body terribly but suppress the cancer sufficiently to give me some more and better days.

I know that eventually my cancer may destroy my kidneys. But I've decided not to go on dialysis. Getting hooked up to a machine three times a week and knowing I'll never quite feel well again is not the sort of life I can bear to live. If you want to maintain your quality of life, you must know when to say no to treatment.

- **Root your hope in reality.** People living with terminal illness need hope, but a hope that denies reality is a false one. It makes you prey to charlatans who seek to profit off your suffering.

I know that I'm going to die in a few years. I can't keep thinking that maybe there's some-

thing out there to cure me. If my bones start breaking, if I get pneumonia and my kidneys are going...then it's time to say good-bye.

- **Join a support group.** I've always hated meetings. And I never thought I needed any psychological counseling. But support groups are different. They let you share your concerns and feelings with others who are just like you.

Midway through the first meeting of my support group, I realized something very powerful—that I was able to help everyone in the room—and that everyone was helping me. Some people say they don't feel comfortable opening up. If you're one of them, realize that in a support group, nobody forces you to talk.

If you'd like information on cancer support groups in your area, contact a hospital social worker or the American Cancer Society at 800-227-2345.

- **Plan for your future.** Tending to the business of dying is not easy. But it's something that we must do—both for ourselves and for our loved ones. I've made a living will. It says that when I'm near the end and I can no longer express myself, I want to die as quickly as possible.

I also have a durable power of attorney, which gives another person—my wife—the right to carry out my wishes. If you don't get your affairs in order, hospitals and doctors are liable to use mechanical marvels to keep you alive—even if you'd simply prefer to die.

- **Appreciate the spirituality of illness.** A terminal illness forces you to look inward and find what's important in your life. It's comforting to know that if your priorities have been misplaced, you can correct them for whatever days remain.

Those of us who believe in God can make ourselves fit for the journey to come. That might mean squaring ourselves with people with whom we've quarreled in the past.

Those who do not believe in a divinity probably feel even more strongly about leaving behind favorable and healing memories.

- **Seize the day.** My motto is the Latin phrase *carpe diem* (literally "seize the day"). I think of it as "enjoy today." Those of us with terminal illness have had life's brevity impressed upon us.

Yet because our tomorrows are limited, our todays become much more important. In reality, of course, we all have a limited number of days. We should enjoy each one as if it were our last.

My wife and I are very much living in the moment. Recently, after dreaming of seeing Rome for years and years, we finally made the trip. We also visited Nova Scotia, where my maternal grandparents were born.

I'm storing up great memories, not so much for myself but for my wife and daughter. My attitude is, *Let's get on with the good times.* You may not be able to have them later.

Getting the Government Aid You Are Entitled to For Health Care and Medical Bills

Charles B. Inlander, president of the People's Medical Society, a nonprofit consumers' health organization, 462 Walnut St., Allentown, PA 18102. He is coauthor, with Karla Morales, of *Getting the Most for Your Medical Dollar.* Pantheon.

Given the skyrocketing costs of medical care and health insurance, it is particularly important to make sure you receive the benefits you're entitled to…and to minimize the expenses for which you are liable.

The primary federal health-care programs are Medicare…and Medicaid—for the needy.

Other government programs, for which fewer people are eligible, include Veterans Administration (VA) benefits and Supplemental Security Income (SSI).

Medicare and Medicaid aren't charity programs. They are tax-funded insurance programs you have paid premiums for—through Social Security—and that you are entitled to. Most beneficiaries of Medicaid, which now covers half of the US nursing-home population, have paid premiums for most of their working lives.

Even with an employer-provided health insurance plan—and we recommend you keep any plan you have—you should enroll in Medicare Part A (hospital insurance), when you turn 65…and purchase Part B (doctor insurance) within three months of your 65th birthday. Otherwise, you will have to pay an additional 10% premium for every year you wait. Enrolling keeps that cost to your employer down and maximizes the benefits of your existing plan.

Medicare was never intended to cover all of its beneficiaries' health costs. Everyone's share is rising. Today, the elderly spend up to 20% of their income on health care, even with Medicare.

Money-saving solutions: Make sure you have supplemental private insurance ("Medigap" coverage)…and try to keep all medical costs as low as possible.

HOW TO GET THE MOST FROM MEDICARE

Maximize your coverage by tuning into Medicare's best-kept secrets…

• **Doctors' fees are very negotiable.** A doctor who accepts Medicare assignments agrees to accept the fee that it pays for the procedure or treatments provided, and handles the paperwork. You remain responsible for your deductible and 20% co-payment.

Seventy-five percent of physicians and other limited licensed practitioners accept assignments for all of their Medicare patients. Ninety percent of all Medicare-allowed charges are now billed by participating practitioners. This shows how consumers have used their power to persuade providers to accept assignment.

If your physician does not accept assignment, you can try to persuade him. *Helpful approach:* "I believe that Medicare pays a fair rate, and I hope you will respect my request, as I cannot afford more than the 20% co-payment. However, if you do not accept assignments, perhaps you could refer me to another practitioner who does." Most people who take the trouble to negotiate assignments are successful.

• **You never have to pay more than the balance billing limit for any service,** even if your doctor does not take assignments.

Medicare has set a maximum fee of 115% above the Medicare-approved amount for all services that doctors who do not take assignments may charge Medicare patients. (Some states have set lower limits.) To find out a specific balance billing limit, call the Medicare carrier in your area. If your doctor bills you for more than the balance billing limit, neither you nor your insurance company has to pay the difference.

Example: Your doctor charges $3,000 for a procedure. Medicare pays $2,000 for the same procedure, and has set the balance billing limit at $2,300. Medicare will pay 80% of the $2,000 "reasonable cost," or $1,600. If your doctor accepts assignments, you would only have to pay the 20% co-payment, or $400. If the doctor does not take assignments, you must pay the difference between $1,600 and the $2,300 balance billing limit, or $700, and the doctor must absorb the other $700. (The difference between the doctor's charge of $3,000 and the balance billing limit of $2,300.) But if you didn't check the balance billing limit, you may be billed for the full $3,000, less Medicare's $1,600, and unknowingly pay the $1,400 difference.

• **The fact that Medicare refuses payment does not necessarily mean that you must pay.** You are not responsible for any medical bill that you could not reasonably have been expected to know wasn't covered. You must be informed in writing from an official source, such as a Medicare notice or pamphlet, that a service isn't covered. If your doctor tells you something is covered by Medicare and it isn't, then the doctor—neither you nor your insurer—is responsible.

• **You cannot be discharged from the hospital before you are medically able to go.** You cannot be discharged because your Medicare payments or "DRG" (Diagnosis-Related Group system) days have been used up. When you are admitted to the hospital, you will be issued a form outlining your rights as a Medicare patient. If you think you are being discharged too soon, request a review by your state's PRO (Peer Review Organization), a group of doctors who review Medicare cases. The PRO will decide if your Medicare coverage can be extended, based on medical necessity.

SHOPPING FOR "MEDIGAP" INSURANCE

Employer-provided retiree health insurance is usually as good as the available high-option Medigap policies, and often better. But several million Medicare beneficiaries continue to purchase duplicate policies to supplement their Medicare coverage. Changes in the law prohibit an insurance company from *knowingly* selling a second or third Medigap policy to a Medicare beneficiary. *Unfortunately,* these companies are not prohibited from selling *disease-specific* insurance (such as cancer, heart, accident) to Medicare beneficiaries. If you have an employer-sponsored plan you may not need more coverage. If you don't, consider supplemental insurance.

WHAT TO LOOK FOR

The federal government certifies insurance policies as meeting the standards established for Medicare Supplemental Insurance or "Medigap" policies. As a result of reforms in the Medigap insurance market, one basic policy and nine optional plans have been approved for sale. It is illegal for an insurance company to sell you a policy as a Medigap plan if it does not conform to these standards.

Key: Since the coverage offered by each plan is the same regardless of the insurance company selling it, the only difference is the premium. Comparison shop on premium once you have determined which plan best meets your needs. Also, be aware that all 10 policies may not be available in your state. Check with your state insurance department to learn which policies are approved in your state, and which companies are authorized to sell policies.

If you have had a Medigap policy for at least six months and you switch policies, the replacement policy may not impose a waiting period for any pre-existing conditions. *The only exception:* Your new policy offers a benefit that was not in the old policy. However, some states prohibit any exclusions.

Rule of thumb: Don't change an existing policy unless you know that your new policy will cover your existing conditions.

SAVING ON OUT-OF-POCKET EXPENSES

You can minimize your co-payments and keep premiums down by trying to keep your medical expenses as low as possible.

• **Take advantage of low-cost or free health services** offered by counties, organizations, or health fairs.

Examples: Inoculations, screenings.

●**Make sure you are aware of your health plan's limits and exclusions.**

Example: Number of chiropractic visits.

●**Shop around for prescription prices,** and buy generic drugs when possible.

●**Guard against unnecessary or excessive testing.** Many physicians have adopted new, costly tests while continuing to administer the old ones—often less expensive and just as effective.

●**Avoid hospitalization and surgery unless absolutely necessary.** Avoid for-profit hospitals—they're up to 23% more costly. Avoid weekend admission.

●**Bring your own food, vitamins, and drugs.**

●**Specify in writing that surgery or invasive procedures must be done by the person you are paying,** i.e., your fully-trained physician, not a resident or intern.

●**Keep track of all bills and services** while hospitalized.

Common errors to check for: Additional services not covered by the DRG for your condition, physician visits that actually occurred, as opposed to those routinely billed. Report any irregularities to the Medicare Inspector General at 800-447-8477.

Cold Defense

Avoid colds this winter by being active. A study of middle-aged adults found that those who were most active throughout the day had fewer colds.

Men with the highest levels of physical activity accumulated at work, at home and in regular exercise experienced a 35% reduction in risk of colds compared with less active men. Highly active women experienced a 20% reduction in risk.

Any kind of activity, as long as it was at least moderately intense and performed for two to three hours per day, provided cold-reducing benefits—from structured exercise to gardening and yardwork to brisk walking.

Chuck Matthews, PhD, research assistant professor, department of epidemiology and biostatistics, University of South Carolina, Columbia.

Weight Control and Aging

Beginning in their mid-30s, most people begin losing one-third to one-half pound of muscle each year.

Muscle burns calories and drives metabolism. As you lose muscle, you'll begin to accumulate fat even if your diet is unchanged.

This sequence affects both men and women—but after age 35, women tend to lose twice as much muscle, and accumulate twice as much fat, as men.

Result: Effective weight control requires exercise as much as diet—to combat age-related muscle loss. By maintaining muscle mass or restoring lost muscle, one can maintain a desired weight—or get back to it—without "deprivation" dieting…and be stronger and healthier overall as well.

Good news: It's possible to restore lost muscle with moderate exercise. Studies show that even women in their 70s can restore their muscles to what they were when 40 years younger, with only two exercise sessions per week.

Required: Building muscle mass requires resistance training—lifting weights or working on an exercise machine—in addition to aerobic exercise such as walking or jogging. Get inexpensive advice on strength training at your local YMCA or seniors center.

Miriam Nelson, PhD, director, Center for Physical Fitness, Tufts University, Boston, www.strongwomen.com, and coauthor of Strong Women, Strong Bones. Putnam.

15

Medical Problems And Solutions

Lifesaving Breakthroughs In Asthma Care

Asthma is a growing problem in the US. Today, more than 15 million Americans suffer from the disease, and 5,000 die of it each year. That's more than twice as many as died from asthma 20 years ago.

Here's what asthma sufferers should be doing to gain control of the disease...

•**Control allergies.** More than half of all cases of asthma are associated with allergies to food or environmental factors, such as pollen, mold, pet dander and microscopic dust mites.

A doctor can perform a "prick" test—dotting the skin with small amounts of suspected allergens—to show which substances cause trouble for you.

Armed with this knowledge, you can avoid environmental allergens...and avoid foods that might cause an attack.

Minimizing the allergens in your home is critical to asthma control. If you have an allergy to pet dander, for instance, it's best to find a new home for any dog or cat you might have. If that's impossible, keep the animal out of your bedroom and off upholstered furniture. Bathe your pet weekly to reduce dander.

To control your exposure to dust mites and their feces—the leading culprit in allergies—encase your mattress and pillows in zippered, airtight covers.

Covers range in price from $2 to $80. Two reputable mail-order sources of the covers are National Allergy Supply (800-522-1448)...and Allergy Asthma Technology Ltd. (800-621-5545)

Leather furniture is unlikely to harbor mites. If your furniture is upholstered in fabric, cover it with a sheet that can be removed and washed every week.

Betty B. Wray, MD, chief of allergy and immunology, and professor of pediatrics and medicine at the Medical College of Georgia in Augusta, and former president of the American College of Allergy, Asthma and Immunology. She is author of Taking Charge of Asthma: A Lifetime Strategy. *Wiley.*

207

For allergies that interfere with work, school or daily living, allergy desensitization injections may be needed.

The injections contain tiny doses of the substances that cause allergic reactions. Over time, the body adjusts and reacts less strongly.

Initially, shots are given once or twice a week. Once the maintenance dose is reached, shots are given every two to three weeks. Improvement may take six months to be apparent.

●**Make sure heartburn is under control.** Asthma is sometimes caused by spasms of the bronchi, the tubes that connect the lungs to the windpipe.

Bronchospasms are often triggered by gastroesophageal reflux (heartburn), in which stomach acid flows "upstream" from the stomach to the esophagus. Reflux is especially likely to occur when you're lying in bed. To control heartburn, lose weight, eat smaller meals and avoid trigger foods. Common triggers include caffeine, alcohol and fatty or spicy foods.

●**Avoid medications that aggravate asthmatic symptoms.** Twenty percent of asthma sufferers experience an attack after taking aspirin or another nonsteroidal anti-inflammatory drug (NSAID), such as *ibuprofen* (Motrin) or *naproxen* (Aleve). NSAIDs can cause airways to narrow. *Acetaminophen* (Tylenol) does not have this effect. It's often a better choice for people with asthma. Ask your doctor.

Beta-blockers such as *propranolol* (Inderal) —often prescribed for high blood pressure or congestive heart failure—can cause the bronchi to constrict. If your doctor prescribes a beta-blocker, ask if you can take a diuretic, an ACE inhibitor or another alternative instead.

●**Take vitamin C.** Recent studies suggest that vitamin C supplementation boosts lung function in people with asthma. *Usual dosage:* 1,000 mg a day.

●**Do breathing exercises.** Deep breathing exercises, tai chi, qi gong and yoga are all good for breath control—and strengthening the diaphragm. That's the sheet-like muscle between the chest and abdomen that is used to draw air into the lungs.

Breathing exercises are taught by respiratory therapists and speech therapists.

Tai chi, qi gong and yoga are best learned from an instructor. Check with a local hospital, college or health food store for classes in your area.

●**Be careful about taking your asthma medications.** If other methods don't work, medication can help you prevent an attack—or short-circuit an impending one.

Several medications are used, depending on the severity of your asthma…

●Nonsteroidal inhalers, such as *cromolyn* (Intal) and *nedocromil* (Tilade) can help prevent asthma attacks—if used before you exercise or encounter an allergen. Because these prescription drugs have few side effects, they're often the first line of defense.

Caution: Over-the-counter inhalers, such as Primatene Mist, should be used only in a breathing emergency. Most contain epinephrine, a compound that can cause rapid heart rate, increased blood pressure and dizziness.

●Antihistamines control histamines, the body chemicals that are released in an allergic reaction. Histamines can cause bronchospasm.

Mild asthma can often be controlled by using *loratadine* (Claritin), *fexofenadine* (Allegra), *cetirizine* (Zyrtec) or another prescription antihistamine.

●Inhaled beta-agonists, such as *albuterol* (Ventolin) and *terbutaline* (Brethine) can be used to stop an attack that is just beginning…or on a regular basis to prevent attacks.

These prescription drugs work by relaxing bronchial muscles, opening air passages.

●Steroids are the most potent asthma drugs. Inhaled steroids, such as *fluticasone (Flonase)* and *beclomethasone* (Vanceril), are used mainly to prevent attacks.

After a few weeks of regular use, these prescription drugs cause the lungs to become less reactive to allergens.

Oral steroids, such as *prednisone* or *dexamethasone,* are used to treat severe attacks.

Since long-term use of oral steroids can lead to osteoporosis, high blood pressure and heart trouble, these drugs are generally a good idea only if no other medication has worked.

Caution: If you must rely on long-term oral steroids to control your asthma, ask your doctor if you are taking the lowest possible dose.

• Leukotriene modifiers—the newest asthma drugs—prevent asthma attacks by blocking *leukotrienes*. Those are substances released from cells during an asthma attack.

Taken in tablet form, leukotriene modifiers, such as *zafirlukast* (Accolate), *zileuton* (Zyflo) and *montelukast* (Singulair), have few side effects but may interact with other drugs. Rare complications include joint pain or shortness of breath.

• **Use a peak flow meter.** This handheld device is used to measure how forcefully you can exhale. A low reading might suggest that an asthma attack is imminent.

Using a peak flow meter twice a day—when you first wake up and then again at bedtime—will enable you to predict attacks and tailor your medication accordingly.

Look for meters with both high and low ranges. They're sold in drugstores for about $35.

Natural Year-Round Allergy Remedies

Richard Firshein, DO, physician practicing in complementary medicine in New York. He is author of *A Guide to Nutritional Therapies: The Nutraceutical Revolution* (Riverhead) and answers health-related questions at *www.drcity.com*.

More than 20 million Americans suffer from springtime allergies. Over-the-counter and some prescription antihistamines can cause drowsiness. Decongestants can raise blood pressure and steroid nasal sprays may cause nasal bleeding and may have other yet unknown effects.

Here are some natural remedies that can often be used instead of—or in conjunction with—medications. Consult a doctor before trying any of these, especially if you are pregnant, planning surgery or taking other medications.

• **Quercetin.** This supplement is a bioflavonoid—the component in fruits and vegetables that gives them their vibrant color. It has natural antihistamine and anti-inflammatory effects.

Typical dosage: If you have spring allergies, start taking quercetin when spring weather begins, and continue through the end of June. Take 300 mg twice a day for one week. If that doesn't work, increase to 600 mg.

If you also suffer from fall allergies, begin again in mid-August and continue through the first frost. In hot climates, you may need to take quercetin year-round.

• **Stinging nettle.** Like quercetin, this plant extract is an excellent antihistamine and anti-inflammatory. It can be used in conjunction with quercetin or on its own.

Typical dosage: 400 mg twice a day during allergy seasons.

On-the-spot treatment: If you find yourself in the throes of an allergy attack despite taking quercetin and/or stinging nettle regularly, take an extra dose. I tell my patients to reach for these remedies whenever they would take an antihistamine.

Most allergy sufferers find quercetin and/or stinging nettle highly effective. But if they don't work for you, one of the following natural antihistamines and anti-inflammatories may help—either in conjunction with each other or alone. Try them in this order—but, of course, talk with your doctor first.

• **Vitamin C.** Take 1,000 mg once or twice a day during allergy season. This should be reduced or eliminated during the off-season. Recent studies suggest vitamin C in high doses may cause thickening of arteries and interfere with certain cancer therapy. Caution is advised for patients with these conditions.

• **Pycnogenol.** An antioxidant derived from the bark of pine trees. Take 50 mg twice a day.

• **Ginkgo biloba.** Take 60 mg twice a day. Once symptoms subside, stop taking this herb. Used in excess (more than 200 mg per day), it can cause diarrhea or sleeplessness.

Caution: People using blood thinners should avoid ginkgo biloba.

• **Feverfew.** Buy a product standardized to contain at least 0.7% parthenolide. That is the component of this herb that reduces swelling in the sinuses. Take 500 mg two or three times a day.

MORE ALLERGY DEFENSES

● **Rinse pollen out of your nasal passages before bedtime.** Use a saline nasal spray, or make your own nasal wash by dissolving one-half teaspoon of salt in one-half cup of water. Place a few drops of the solution in your nose with a dropper, then blow your nose.

● **Keep home and car windows closed**—to keep pollen outdoors. Run an air conditioner continuously to filter air and fight allergy-causing molds.

● **Run a HEPA filter all the time during allergy season**—to purify your air of pollen and other allergens. A HEPA vacuum cleaner may also help.

● **Shampoo your hair, eyebrows, eyelashes, mustache and beard** at bedtime and after outdoor activities. Dust mites and other allergens cling to hairs. Change clothes when you come inside.

● **Strengthen your immune system.** Better overall health means reduced allergy symptoms. Take a daily multivitamin/mineral supplement…eat healthfully…get adequate rest…exercise regularly…and don't smoke.

New Weapon for Fighting Sinus Congestion

Sinupret, a highly effective German herbal remedy, is available in the US under the name Quanterra Sinus Defense. It is a combination of five herbs—gentian root…elder flower…European vervain…primrose flower… and sorrel. *Best for:* Persistent mild-to-moderate sinus congestion brought on by changes in weather. It may be used in place of a decongestant. Consult your doctor before using any herbal treatment.

Andrew L. Rubman, ND, adjunct professor of clinical medicine, Florida College of Integrative Medicine, Orlando, and medical director, Southbury Clinic for Traditional Medicines, CT.

Stopping a Nose Bleed

If your nose starts bleeding, blow it gently to remove any blood clots…sit upright with your head leaning forward…and pinch both nostrils below the nose bridge for 15 minutes, using your second and third fingers of both hands. *If bleeding doesn't stop:* Go to the hospital emergency room. The ruptured blood vessels may need to be treated by a physician.

Ronald Charles, MD, assistant professor of emergency medicine, University of Texas Southwestern Medical Center, Dallas.

Inhaling Steam Doesn't Help Get Rid of a Cold

Previous studies suggested that steam inhalation kills the cold-causing rhinovirus in the respiratory tract. But in a newer study, volunteers who breathed steam long enough to raise the temperature inside their nostrils to 109° Fahrenheit—the minimum needed to inactivate the virus—reported no differences in their symptoms compared with those who simply inhaled warm air.

G.J. Forstall, MD, assistant professor of medicine and staff physician, department of infectious disease, McLaren Regional Medical Center, Flint, MI.

Treating Chronic Coughs

Chronic coughs should not be treated with over-the-counter remedies. Most short-term coughs clear up on their own within a week or two. A chronic cough may signal an allergy, asthma or another more serious condition—which should be evaluated by a doctor.

Steven Lamm, MD, clinical assistant professor of medicine, New York University School of Medicine, New York.

Heartburn Help

Two promising treatments for chronic heartburn have been approved by the FDA. Both were successful when tested on approximately 200 patients with moderate chronic heartburn. *How they work:* Each treatment involves passing a tiny device through an endoscope—a tube inserted into the esophagus—to fix the faulty valve that allows acid to escape from the stomach and cause heartburn. The Stretta System emits pulses of radio-frequency radiation to burn spots on the muscle that controls the valve. The endoscopic suturing system tightens the valve with tiny pleats.

James C. Reynolds, MD, chief of gastroenterology at MCP Hahnemann University, Philadelphia.

Beat Heartburn Without Drugs

Avoid foods that can trigger heartburn—alcohol, chocolate, peppermint, spearmint and fat. Avoid caffeine in foods and over-the-counter pain medications. Avoid carbonated drinks. *Also:* If you are overweight, lose weight ...if you smoke, quit smoking.

For nighttime heartburn: Raise the head of your bed on four- to six-inch blocks, or use a wedge-shaped support to elevate the upper half of your body. Do not lie down with a full stomach.

Marvin Lipman, MD, chief medical adviser, Consumers Union, writing in *Consumer Reports on Health,* 101 Truman Ave., Yonkers, NY 10703.

How to Beat Dizziness

Brian Blakely, MD, PhD, associate professor of otolaryngology and director of the dizziness clinic at Wayne State University School of Medicine in Detroit. He is coauthor of *Feeling Dizzy: Understanding and Treating Dizziness, Vertigo and Other Balance Disorders.* Macmillan.

In the absence of other symptoms, occasional mild dizziness is nothing to worry about. But see a doctor right away if dizzy spells recur ...if they're severe enough to force you to lie down...*or if they're accompanied by...*

- **Double vision.**
- **Incontinence.**
- **Arm and/or leg weakness.**
- **Difficulty with speaking or swallowing.**
- **Severe headache.**

These symptoms are suggestive of stroke, brain tumor, aneurysm or another potentially life-threatening problem.

COMMON TYPES OF DIZZINESS

- **A mild turning sensation.** Caused by almost any systemic ailment, including transient ischemic attacks, multiple sclerosis...even AIDS.

Some women have mild turning during menstruation—or as a side effect of hormone replacement therapy or menopause.

- **Imbalance.** This swaying or wobbling feeling can be caused by flu, infection, arthritis, compression of the spinal cord, diabetes or another metabolic disorder.

Imbalance can also be caused by alcohol abuse, depression or anxiety (rapid breathing reduces the flow of oxygen to the brain)...or by certain medications, including cough medicines and blood pressure drugs.

- **Vertigo.** This sensation of spinning often accompanies migraine headaches and many diseases.

- **Presyncope** (feeling of faintness). This is often a result of *postural hypotension,* the brief period of reduced blood pressure that occurs when someone abruptly stands or sits up.

Several medications can contribute to postural hypotension, including antihypertensives, antihistamines, sedatives and antipsychotics.

EAR AND BRAIN DISORDERS

Persistent dizziness not linked to an underlying illness usually involves brain or inner ear trouble. *Most common forms of inner ear/ brain dizziness...*

- **Benign paroxysmal positional vertigo** (BPPV) occurs when a person moves his head in a certain position—typically when he lies on his back, then rolls quickly to one side.

BPPV itself isn't life-threatening, but it can be deadly if it occurs while driving an automobile or standing up.

BPPV in people under 50 is often caused by head trauma. Even a light bump can be enough. In people over 50, BPPV can occur after illness, or be caused by degeneration of the nerves in the middle ear. In some cases, BPPV appears for no apparent reason.

•**Vestibular neuronitis** is sudden vertigo that occurs a few days or weeks after recovery from a viral infection. Often it's accompanied by nausea and/or vomiting. *Likely cause:* Inflammation of the vestibular nerve, which connects the brain and inner ear.

•**Ataxia** is a loss of coordination. It's usually caused by the death of brain cells, although it can also be caused by vitamin deficiencies or heavy drinking. Most common among elderly people, it often comes on gradually, and is generally irreversible.

•**Méniére's disease** is a set of related symptoms, including vertigo attacks...roaring, ringing or hearing loss in one ear...a feeling of fullness in the ear. Most cases are caused by fluid buildup in the inner ear.

Méniére's usually strikes between the ages of 30 and 50. Symptoms tend to recur, lasting an hour or more at a time. They range from mild to debilitating.

•**Ear infection** that causes fluid to accumulate in the middle ear can cause everything from mild imbalance to severe vertigo.

GETTING GOOD TREATMENT

There's no easy way to test the balance mechanisms in the ear and the brain, so your doctor may have trouble pinpointing the cause of your dizziness.

If he/she fails to take a complete medical history...or does not take your dizziness seriously...or has little experience with dizziness, find another doctor.

Best: An otolaryngologist or neurologist working in a dizziness clinic. For the name of an otolaryngologist near you, call the American Academy of Otolaryngology-Head and Neck Surgery, 703-836-4444. For a neurologist, call the American Academy of Neurology, 651-695-1940.

Doctors use several tests to check for inner ear damage. The tests I use most often are the hearing test (audiogram) and two more specialized tests, *electronystagmography* (ENG) and the *rotary chair exam.*

ENG looks at eye movements caused by electrical stimulation of the vestibular system. The rotary chair exam measures eye movements as the patient sits in a computer-controlled rotating chair.

The best antidote for inner ear ailments is time. Inner ear damage usually heals within a few weeks or months. Fluid buildup from ear infection also tends to disappear in a few weeks.

Even persistent nerve damage usually stops causing dizziness after several months. The brain simply learns to re-sort incoming information (much as it adjusts to the rocking of a ship).

Vestibular neuronitis often persists until the underlying inflammation clears up. That can take years—though medicine, bed rest and rehabilitation exercises are helpful.

Dizziness may be permanent in those suffering from ataxia, multiple sclerosis or other central nervous system disorders.

Treatment for Méniére's disease may involve surgery to relieve accumulation of fluid, but diuretics and/or steroids can provide significant relief.

If you do have surgery, make sure the surgeon is board certified in otolaryngology. *To check credentials:* Call the American Board of Medical Specialties, 866-275-2267.

Dizziness usually subsides within eight weeks of surgery. In some cases of dizziness, the mild sedative *meclizine* (Antivert) brings short-term relief. *Scopolamine* is even more effective...but also causes more side effects, including drowsiness and dry mouth. *Caution:* These drugs should be used for no more than a week or two, during severe episodes.

Causes of Trembling Hands

Hand and head tremor are often attributed to Parkinson's disease, the debilitating neurological disorder. But tremor can also be the result of a condition known as essential tremor. *Telling the two apart:* Parkinson's-related tremor is typically seen at rest. Essential tremor is typically seen when the afflicted body part is in use. Alcohol has no effect on Parkinson's, but a drink can reduce the severity of essential tremor for a couple of hours. *Good news:* Most essential tremor sufferers can be helped by the beta-blocker *propranolol* (Inderal) or the anti-seizure drug *primidone* (Mysoline).

William C. Koller, MD, president, International Tremor Foundation, P.O. Box 14005, Lenexa, KS 66285-4005. *www.essentialtremor.org.*

Shingles Alert

Pain from shingles can be relieved very effectively by the Lidoderm patch. Nerve injury from a shingles outbreak often causes postherpetic neuralgia (PHN), excruciating pain that continues for months or years, particularly in people over age 60. The most effective topical method of easing the pain is the Lidoderm patch, an adhesive patch about 4" by 5.5" that releases the analgesic lidocaine directly onto the affected area. Recently approved by the FDA, the patch relieves PHN pain without causing numbness or any of the side effects caused by other methods of relief. *Caution:* People with a history of drug sensitivity should be cautious in using the patch.

Michael C. Rowbotham, MD, associate professor of neurology and anesthesia at the School of Medicine at the University of California, San Francisco.

Chicken Pox Vaccine May Prevent Shingles In Older People

And—those over age 60 are especially prone to shingles. A study of 200 people aged 55 to 80 who were inoculated with chicken pox vaccine were found four years later to still have their immunity boosted to the virus that causes shingles. A pilot study of the vaccine's effec-tiveness against shingles is currently being conducted nationwide.

Myron J. Levin, MD, professor of medicine and chief of pediatric infectious diseases, University of Colorado Health Sciences Center in Denver.

Fight Bug Bites ...Naturally

To protect yourself from bug bites, take a multi–B-vitamin complex twice daily. A preliminary study indicates that riboflavin, one of the B vitamins, causes the body to emit an odor that repels mosquitoes, stinging ants, wasps, yellow jackets and bees.

Important: Use one that contains an average of 50 mg of most B vitamins.

Also: Apply a sports rub or an aromatic compound that contains menthol or eucalyptus. These odors temporarily scare off bugs.

Natural remedies: Sprinkle monosodium glutamate (MSG) powder—available in super-markets and pharmacies—on the bite as often as needed. Or use After Bite, a penlike device that delivers a safe amount of sodium hydrox-ide (lye). Both penetrate the skin and break down the offending compounds that cause stinging and itching.

Andrew L. Rubman, ND, adjunct professor of clinical medicine, Florida College of Integrative Medicine, Orlando, and medical director, Southbury Clinic for Traditional Medi-cines, CT.

About Lyme Disease

Deer ticks usually require 24 hours or more to transmit Lyme disease. If you remove a tick promptly, you shouldn't have a problem. Always check yourself and your children care-fully for ticks after leaving a potentially infested area. *Hot spots:* Armpits, groin and hairline.

Ticks that carry Lyme disease are tiny—as small as a poppy seed—so they can easily be missed.

Allen Steere, MD, chief of rheumatology and immunology, New England Medical Center, Boston.

West Nile Virus Update

State and local health departments and the Centers for Disease Control and Prevention are closely monitoring mosquitoes, which carry the virus, and bird populations, which are the first to be afflicted, for early signs of the return of the potentially deadly virus along the eastern seaboard and Gulf Coast. Currently there is no treatment. *Self-defense:* Curb outdoor activities during the early morning and early evening hours, when mosquitoes are most likely to be feeding…wear long-sleeved shirts and long pants when outdoors…use insect repellent that contains DEET…and remove any standing water, such as birdbaths, near your home—it attracts mosquitoes.

Tom Skinner, Centers for Disease Control and Prevention, Atlanta.

Leg Cramp Reliever

Nighttime leg-cramp relief: "Acupinch." How it works: With thumb and forefinger, pinch your upper lip—yes, lip—just below the nose for 20 to 30 seconds. This works about 80% of the time.

Donald Cooper, former US Olympic team doctor, quoted in *Minute Health Tips: Medical Advice and Facts at a Glance* by Thomas G. Welch, MD. DCI/Chronimed Publishing.

Foot Pain Relief

To relieve foot pain from high arches, a protruding bone or a nerve or tendon injury, try leaving a space in your shoelaces. Skip the eyelets at the painful point and draw the laces to the next set of eyelets.

Carol Frey, MD, chief, foot and ankle clinic, University of Southern California, Los Angeles.

Knee Pain Relief

Knee pain associated with arthritis can be eased with injections of *hylan G-F 20* (Synvisc).

The drug curbs pain by increasing the viscosity of synovial fluid, which cushions the knee joint.

Treatment: Three injections, spaced one week apart.

Knee pain sufferers who got the injections reported less pain while walking. Some needed less pain medication.

Others were able to resume participation in sports that they had abandoned.

Jane Servi, MD, a sports medicine specialist in private practice in Fort Collins, CO. Her study of 43 arthritis sufferers 34 to 94 years of age was presented at a meeting of the American Medical Society for Sports Medicine.

A Sign of Osteoporosis

An unexplained foot fracture may be an early sign of osteoporosis. A bone-density study of 21 men and women who suffered from small fractures of their foot bones found that 19 of them had significant bone loss. Nine of those tested, mostly women in their 50s and 60s, had osteoporosis in their hips and spine. Researchers suggest that people who suffer foot fractures that are not due to accidents or repeated stressful motion should ask their physicians to consider giving them a bone-density test for osteoporosis.

Rodney L. Tomczak, DPM, EdD, assistant professor of orthopedics, Ohio State University, Columbus.

Osteoporosis Warning

Osteoporosis can be a complication of chronic illnesses. That includes chronic obstructive pulmonary disease (COPD) as well as asthma and other chronic diseases treated with steroids. At-risk patients should ask a doctor about bone-density testing and calcium supplements. Men may need to have testosterone levels tested.

Jeffrey Michaelson, MD, senior research fellow, pulmonary and critical care division, Emory University School of Medicine, Atlanta.

Drug Fights Fractures

Bone-boosting drug makes sense for women who already have osteoporosis as well as for those at risk for the disease. In a new study, the prescription medication *raloxifene* (Evista) cut risk for additional fractures by up to 50% in women who had already sustained one fracture. In previous studies, raloxifene was shown to help prevent breast cancer. The drug may be a good alternative for women at risk for osteoporosis who fear the increased breast cancer risk associated with hormone-replacement therapy (HRT). HRT can be used to prevent osteoporosis.

Bruce Ettinger, MD, senior investigator, division of research, Kaiser Permanente Medical Care Program, Oakland, CA. His three-year study of 7,705 women 31 to 80 years of age was published in *The Journal of the American Medical Association,* 515 N. State St., Chicago 60610.

Tranquilizers and Hip Fractures

Elderly people who take tranquilizers that remain in the body for more than 24 hours are 70% more likely to fracture their hips in falls than those taking tranquilizers that remain in the body for less than 24 hours or those who don't take any at all.

Long-acting: *Diazepam* (Valium), *flurazepam* (Dalmane), *chlordiazepoxide* (Librium).

Short-acting: *Alprazolam* (Xanax), *lorazepam* (Ativan), *oxazepam* (Serax).

T. Franklin Williams, MD, director, National Institute on Aging, Bethesda, MD.

You Can Beat Arthritis

Hani El-Gabalawy, MD, clinical investigator with National Institute of Arthritis and Musculoskeletal and Skin Diseases in Bethesda, MD.

Osteoarthritis (OA)—the most common form of arthritis—affects nearly 21 million Americans.

It primarily strikes the hands…knees…hips…feet…and back. It occurs when cartilage in the joints begins to wear down after injury—usually after age 45.

Here are answers to some frequently asked questions about the best ways to prevent and treat this troubling condition…

How can I prevent osteoarthritis if I have a family history of the disease?

The best way is to maintain an ideal body weight. Excess weight stresses the joints—especially hips and knees.

How can I slow the progression of OA if I already have it?

There are no medications currently available to stop OA, but the over-the-counter supplement glucosamine sulfate may. A recent three-year Belgian study of 202 people with OA of the knee found that taking 1,500 mg of oral glucosamine daily slowed joint deterioration and eased pain and stiffness.

There's also limited evidence that antioxidant vitamins may retard OA. I suggest my patients take the same daily doses recommended for prevention of heart disease—1,000 mg of vitamin C...400 IU of vitamin E...and 15,000 IU of beta-carotene.

What other drugs are available?

Most other OA medications minimize pain. They include *aspirin, acetaminophen* (Tylenol) and non-steroidal anti-inflammatory drugs (NSAIDs)—*ibuprofen* (Advil)...*naproxen* (Aleve, Naprosyn)...*nabumetone* (Relafen)...*piroxicam* (Feldene)...and *etodolac* (Lodine).

The safest drug is acetaminophen. NSAIDs can cause stomach upset, gastrointestinal bleeding and ulcers.

Other agents, including *misoprostol* (Cytotec) and *omeprazole* (Prilosec), can be prescribed along with NSAIDs to protect the stomach from these side effects.

Newest agents: *Celecoxib* (Celebrex) and *rofecoxib* (Vioxx). Compared with other NSAIDs, these "COX-2 selective inhibitors" are just as effective and seem to have a less harmful impact on the gastrointestinal tract. But not all insurers will pay for them.

Have any alternative therapies proven to be effective?

Besides glucosamine and antioxidants, the alternative remedy for which there is good data is acupuncture. Several trials indicate it alleviates pain that originates from extremities, such as legs or arms. So it's worth a try.

It's possible you could benefit from using magnets or another alternative remedy. Even though there's no proven reason they should work, they may work for you.

If you try an alternative remedy, tell your doctor to make sure it won't interfere with your conventional treatment.

What foods are associated with increased or decreased arthritis problems?

Foods that contain high levels of antioxidants, such as fruits and vegetables, may reduce risk of arthritis. Eat as much of those as you can. There's no scientific evidence to support the common belief that nightshade plants —tomatoes, potatoes, peppers and eggplants —exacerbate arthritis.

I always wake up feeling stiff. What can I do to get my day started faster?

Ask your doctor about taking a long-acting NSAID or Celebrex at night. The drug's effects will carry over into the morning, when you take your next dose.

Performing some stretches and range-of-motion exercises in the morning can also help.

Sleep on a firm mattress and pillow that support your neck and back. Avoid caffeine, nicotine and alcohol, which can prevent you from sleeping well.

What are some particularly useful products for people with arthritis?

The Arthritis Foundation (800-283-7800 ...*www.arthritis.org*) offers a wealth of well-balanced, scientifically validated information and products.

Reliable companies that have useful catalogs...

- **Aids for Arthritis, Inc.,** 800-654-0707.
- **MOMS Home Healthcare,** 800-232-7443.
- **Rolyan,** 800-323-5547...*www.rolyan.com.*
- **Center for Assistive Technology and Environmental Access** (404-894-4960... *www.catea.org*), an information clearinghouse for people with disabilities.

When should I consider joint replacement?

Most orthopedic surgeons recommend arthroplasty (joint replacement) only when there is no cartilage left in the hip or knee and you're experiencing pain even when at rest. Some people who have great problems with the pain have it done sooner.

Disadvantage: The prosthesis will loosen in about 10 years and will need to be replaced.

If you have arthroplasty before age 70, ask your surgeon about getting an *uncemented* prosthesis, which is easier to replace than a cemented one.

What about injectable drugs for arthritis? Do they work?

They certainly are worth trying. You're probably referring to *Hyalgan* and *Synvisc*. These products contain hyaluronic acid to lubricate the joint. I've used these devices often, with mixed results.

Cost: $200 to $300 for a full course of treatment—usually three injections given one week apart. Few insurance companies cover it.

Corticosteroid injections are also used. But unlike hyaluronic acid, they are proven to work. Three or four injections per year seem to be safe.

What does the future of arthritis treatment hold?

There's a tremendous amount of research. *Most exciting:* There are specialized stem cells in the body that make all sorts of connective tissue, such as bone, cartilage and tendons. We're hoping to use these cells to replace the damaged cells and "fix" the joint.

How to Overcome Headaches, Arthritis, Backache and Other Common Sources of Chronic Pain

Norman J. Marcus, MD, president, International Foundation for Pain Relief, and medical director of the New York Pain Treatment Program at Lenox Hill Hospital, both in New York City. He is author of *Freedom from Chronic Pain*. Simon & Schuster.

Our brains are programmed to interpret pain as a sign of acute injury. Almost instinctively, we stop what we're doing...we limit our movement...and we get help. When pain is chronic, however, these instincts are counterproductive. Inactivity won't heal a bad back, constant headaches or arthritis—it just creates more problems.

People come to our pain center seeking total relief. But that isn't always possible. What they must really learn is to *manage* their pain, to focus on quality of life. That way, they can learn to live happily, even with pain.

OVERREACTING TO PAIN

One of the first things I ask new patients to do is to describe their pain. More often than not, they describe not the sensation of pain, but what the pain means to them.

Typical responses: "Pain makes my life miserable...pain drives away my friends...it means that something is terribly wrong...it consumes my whole life...it makes me irritable and angry."

Such negative thoughts can be more devastating than the pain itself. This "pain-button thinking" turns every twinge into a catastrophe. Do any of these "catastrophizing" thoughts sound familiar?

- **Things are bad and getting worse.**
- **This pain will destroy me.**
- **My body is falling apart.**
- **Poor me.**

Thinking that severe pain must mean some dreadful disease adds mental anguish to physical discomfort. Many people experience pain as a form of punishment—like being spanked as a child. That only makes it worse.

None of these negative thoughts makes sense. Becoming aware of your pain-button thinking is the first step to getting rid of it.

ENDURING DISCOMFORT

One of the most important strategies for coping with chronic pain is to develop a capacity to endure discomfort.

Modern Americans are so accustomed to comfort and convenience that we expect it. As a result, we're less able to withstand pain than people were a century ago. A minor ache that our ancestors might not have given a second thought to can debilitate us.

To have a full life, you must be willing to tolerate some discomfort.

THE REAL CAUSE OF CHRONIC PAIN

Although few pain sufferers are aware of it, chronic pain usually goes hand in hand with tense, weak muscles.

Example I: Most chronic headaches are the result of muscular tension. You may feel the pain in the front of your head, but it's really coming from tight muscles in your neck and shoulders.

Example II: Pain blamed on osteoarthritis sometimes comes not from the joints themselves but from stiff muscles around the joints. Exercising to strengthen those muscles and make them more limber will diminish your pain—even if your joints remain stiff.

217

Example III: Weakened or tense muscles are responsible for at least 80% of chronic back pain. Even when a high-tech test like magnetic resonance imaging (MRI) shows evidence of herniated disks, there's no proof that these are causing the pain. In fact, 40% of people who display spinal abnormalities on an MRI (including herniated disks) have no pain.

Perhaps the most effective way to tame chronic pain is to relax, stretch and strengthen your muscles.

PAIN-RELIEF STRATEGIES

●**Breathe from your belly.** Most people move their chests in and out when they breathe. *Problem:* This type of breathing places constant strain on the muscles of your neck and shoulders, exacerbating headaches and back pain.

Better way: Place your hands on your belly or over your head and relax your shoulders. Breathe so that your abdomen goes in and out while your chest remains still. Once you get the hang of it, practice belly breathing without using your hands—and try to breathe that way all the time.

●**Get regular exercise.** If your pain is too severe to permit aerobics classes, jogging or weight-lifting, try walking or swimming. They will increase the flow of blood and oxygen to muscle cells without causing more pain.

Pacing is essential. Plan to finish your walk or swim before you become tired. If necessary, start off by going only a very short distance. Increase the distance gradually. Concentrate on gentle, stress-free motions.

●**Reduce psychological stress.** Stress intensifies pain by restricting blood flow and tightening muscles. And negative feelings speed the transmission of pain impulses from the body to the brain. Pleasant emotions help block the transmission of pain signals.

Learn to recognize the links between tension and pain. Notice the situations that cause back pain or headache to flare up. Consider what role might be played by your thoughts and emotions. Once you've tuned in to the triggers, look for better ways to solve problems and eliminate hassles.

Helpful: Keep a "pain diary" that details what you're doing and thinking when pain strikes.

If you notice that you can sit for 45 minutes before your back starts to hurt, for example, you can then make it a point to get up before that time is up.

Once you break the association between a specific activity and pain, you'll avoid the anticipation that makes pain a self-fulfilling prophecy. This way, you'll gradually increase your endurance.

●**Be more assertive.** If chronic pain limits your energy, you must learn how to set limits —to say "no" in a reasonable way, without anger or guilt.

Also important: Good planning skills. Each morning, make a list of what needs to be done that day. Recognize that focusing wisely on the top 20% of your list will fulfill 80% of your needs. Intelligent management of your time prevents the fall behind/catch-up spiral that exacerbates chronic pain.

●**Get enough sleep.** Go to bed and get up at the same time every day...and avoid caffeine, alcohol, sleeping pills and naps. Use your bed for sleeping and sex only.

If you're not sleepy—or if you wake up in the middle of the night—get out of bed. Read or listen to music until you're drowsy.

Essential: A firm mattress. If your body "gels" into position on a soft mattress, you'll wake up in more pain than if you had moved around throughout the night.

●**Steer clear of painkillers.** While they're helpful for acute pain, long-term use often causes severe side effects. Regular use of painkillers can actually *cause* some forms of chronic pain.

As your ability to tolerate discomfort grows, cut back gradually—under your doctor's supervision, of course.

Migraine Prevention

Magnesium and vitamin B-2 can help prevent recurrent migraines. In separate studies, migraineurs who took 400 mg a day of either supplement reported fewer headaches—

often within a couple of weeks. *Helpful:* An over-the-counter product called *Migra-Lieve.* It contains magnesium, vitamin B-2 and feverfew, an herbal remedy that has also been shown to be effective against migraines.

Alexander Mauskop, MD, director, New York Headache Center, New York.

Hidden Cause of Stomach Problems

Bloating and stomach pain may be caused by *tight pants syndrome.* The "condition" was named by a doctor who treated a male patient who complained of mysterious abdominal pains. After a series of tests proved negative, the doctor discovered that the man's waist size was at least three inches greater than his pants size.

Octavio Bessa, Jr., MD, clinical assistant professor of medicine, New York Medical College, Valhalla, and an internist practicing in Stamford, CT.

An Often Undiagnosed Disease

Celiac disease affects one million Americans—and many have no idea they have it. The disease is caused by an intolerance to gluten—the main protein in wheat, barley, rye and oats. The resulting intestinal inflammation hampers absorption of nutrients and can lead to diarrhea, cramps, anemia, osteoporosis, infertility and seizures. Because many different conditions can cause these same symptoms, the average individual with celiac disease goes 11 years before receiving a diagnosis. *Good news:* Once celiac disease sufferers eliminate bread, pasta, beer and other gluten-containing foods from their diets, most begin improving in as little as one week.

Peter Green, MD, clinical professor of medicine, Columbia University College of Physicians and Surgeons, New York. For more information, contact the Celiac Disease Foundation, 13251 Ventura Blvd., #1, Studio City, CA 91604. 818-990-2354.

Epilepsy and Aging

Epilepsy in elderly people often goes undiagnosed. The condition's incidence rises steeply in people age 60 or older. But the symptoms of the most common seizure type in the elderly—the complex partial seizure—are often blamed on dementia. These include facial movements such as chewing or lip-smacking, memory loss, wandering, intermittent altered mental status and clumsiness. *Self-defense:* Call your doctor at once if you or a loved one experiences an apparent seizure.

A. James Rowan, MD, professor of neurology, Mount Sinai School of Medicine, New York.

It May Not Be Carpal Tunnel Syndrome

A numb wrist does not necessarily mean that you have carpal tunnel syndrome (CTS). A recent study of 2,500 people reporting numbness and tingling in the wrist or hands found that 80% of the cases did not have carpal tunnel syndrome, which comes from compression of the median nerve in the wrist. If your doctor cannot diagnose your problem quickly, ask for a carpal compression test. The doctor presses the median nerve with his thumb. If this does not reproduce tingling in your fingers within 60 seconds, CTS is unlikely to be the cause.

Robert A. Werner, MD, associate professor and chief of physical medicine and rehabilitation at the Ann Arbor VA Medical Center at the University of Michigan.

The Mint/Gallstone Connection

In England, gallstones are often treated with an over-the-counter mint preparation called *Rowachol.* In a recent study, 42% of gallbladder patients who took Rowachol were stone free after four years, compared with 73% of those who took Rowachol plus a stone-dissolving prescription drug, which can cause diarrhea and liver damage. Rowachol is hard to find in the US. *Instead:* Ask your doctor about taking one or two enteric-coated 0.2 ml peppermint oil capsules three times daily, with meals. The capsules are sold in health food stores.

Melvyn R. Werbach, MD, a physician in private practice in Tarzana, CA. He is author of *Nutritional Influences on Illness*. Third Line Press.

Lower Your Risk of Kidney Stones

Kidney stone risk can be lowered by consuming less protein. It has long been known that high protein intake boosts risk for stones. But in one of the first studies of its kind, researchers found that moderate protein reduction lowers levels of urea, calcium, uric acid, phosphate and oxalate in the blood and urine. All of these are considered markers for kidney stone formation. *If you have kidney stones:* Limit your daily intake of protein to 1g per kilogram of body weight daily (with a maximum of 90 g). To calculate your weight in kilograms, divide your weight in pounds by 2.2.

Sandro Giannini, MD, PhD, assistant professor of medical science and surgery, Institute of Internal Medicine, University of Padova, Padova, Italy.

Accident Complications

Car crash survivors can develop post-traumatic stress disorder (PTSD).

Most often associated with combat veterans and victims of natural disasters, PTSD can cause vivid, crippling memories, disabling anxiety, severe anger, depression and guilt.

Helpful: Talk with friends and relatives about the accident…stay active physically and mentally…get back to your daily activities …consider taking a defensive driving class to bolster your confidence.

If necessary, your doctor should be able to refer you to a psychotherapist and/or prescribe an antidepressant or another helpful medication.

Dennis J. Butler, PhD, director of behavioral science, Medical College of Wisconsin, Milwaukee.

Good News for Those with Macular Degeneration

There is a breakthrough drug treatment for vision loss to slow progress of macular degeneration, the leading cause of blindness in the elderly. The FDA has approved the prescription medicine *Visudyne,* which is injected into the arm and then light-activated, so it should act only in the eye and have limited side effects. Visudyne is for the *wet form* of macular degeneration—not for the more common, but less serious, dry form.

Jennifer I. Lim, PhD, is associate professor of ophthalmology, Keck School of Medicine, University of Southern California, Los Angeles.

For Better Vision

Vision-enhancement "goggles" improve vision dramatically in those with very poor eyesight. The Low Vision Enhancement System (abbreviated LVES and pronounced "Elvis") contains three separate black-and-white video cameras. A control unit worn on the belt allows the user to adjust contrast and magnify images from three to 10 times. The LVES is available to individuals who have experience using low-vision devices. Obtaining the LVES requires a low-vision evaluation and individual training. *Cost:* $4,000–$5,000. *Information:* Call the Lions Vision Center at Johns Hopkins Wilmer Eye Institute, 410-955-0580.

Robert W. Massoff, PhD, professor of ophthalmology, Johns Hopkins Wilmer Eye Institute, Baltimore.

All About Dry Eyes

Dry, red eyes aren't always caused by irritation or lack of sleep. *Another possibility:* Rosacea, a progressive skin disease marked not only by facial redness, but occasionally by burning, stinging or a feeling that there's something in the eye.

Danger: Severe cases of ocular rosacea can cause scarring and even vision loss. Although the condition cannot be cured, it can be managed and controlled with oral antibiotics and possibly corticosteroid eye drops.

See an ophthalmologist about any eye rash associated with redness, burning or itching that lasts for more than a couple of days.

Jerome Z. Litt, MD, assistant clinical professor of dermatology, Case Western Reserve University School of Medicine, Cleveland.

Custom eyeglasses offer relief for severe eye dryness (Sjögren's syndrome). This condition can be very painful, particularly when outdoors. The custom glasses have plastic "moisture chambers" that hug the wearer's face to slow the evaporation of tears from the eye surface. Customizing a pair of eyeglasses takes at least three visits to the optometrist. The work is covered by some insurance plans. For more information on moisture-chamber glasses, write Dr. Dean Hart at 185 Woodbury Rd., Hicksville, NY 11801.

Dean E. Hart, OD, associate research scientist, Harkness Eye Institute, Columbia University, New York. His report on moisture-chamber eyeglasses was published in the *Journal of the American Optometric Association,* 243 N. Lindbergh Blvd., St. Louis 63141.

Glaucoma—Prevention And Treatment

Martha Motuz Leen, MD, assistant professor of ophthalmology, glaucoma specialist, University of Washington, Seattle.

A leading cause of blindness,* glaucoma afflicts approximately two million Americans—half of whom may not even know that they have the disease.

*The other two leading causes of blindness in the US are *age-related macular degeneration* and *diabetic retinopathy.*

Glaucoma occurs when the *optic nerve*—the nerve in the back of the eye that transmits visual information to the brain—is damaged by an abnormal rise in the pressure of the fluid filling the eyeball.

Normally, this fluid—called *aqueous humor*—drains out of the eye as new fluid is produced. In some individuals, however, the drainage system can become blocked.

Result: Increased *intraocular pressure* (pressure inside the eye).

Some people think that abnormal pressure itself constitutes glaucoma. But a patient is usually considered to have the disease only once the optic nerve is damaged.

Some people with high intraocular pressure, as measured by eye exams, have no nerve damage. Other patients with normal pressure readings, but a more vulnerable optic nerve, suffer vision loss.

There are two major types of glaucoma...

●**Closed-angle glaucoma** occurs when drainage becomes blocked. This can happen suddenly or gradually. Sudden (acute) closed-angle glaucoma is usually accompanied by eye pain or redness, seeing colored halos around lights and/or nausea. With this type of glaucoma, permanent vision damage can occur within a few days. See an ophthalmologist immediately if you notice any combination of these symptoms. The disease is usually treated with laser surgery. Gradual (chronic) closed-angle glaucoma is usually asymptomatic.

●**Open-angle glaucoma** is much more common. Unlike the acute closed-angle type, open-angle glaucoma rarely causes symptoms until the disease has caused a significant amount of damage to the optic nerve. Loss of peripheral vision may occur during the early stages of open-angle glaucoma—but so gradually that the person fails to notice it.

RISK FACTORS

People in their 60s are six times more likely to develop glaucoma than those younger than 60. But the elderly aren't the only ones at increased risk for the disease. *Also at risk:*

●**People with a family history of glaucoma.**

●**African-Americans.**

- **People who use steroids in any form**—including drops, creams and inhalers.
- **Nearsighted people.**
- **Those with a past eye injury.**
- **Migraine sufferers.**
- **Diabetics.**

DETECTING GLAUCOMA

By the time glaucoma starts to produce symptoms, it may already be in an advanced stage. For this reason, every adult at increased risk for glaucoma should have annual eye exams.

A thorough glaucoma exam will include…

- **Intraocular pressure measurement.** Some doctors still measure pressure using a device called an air-puff tonometer. More accurate, however, is the *applanation tonometer*. It touches the eye directly, after the eye has been numbed with anesthetic drops.
- **Visual field testing.** This procedure checks for loss of peripheral vision, which is often an early sign of glaucoma. Usually, patients are asked to spot tiny lights as they appear on a screen.
- **Optic disk exam.** The most important part of the three-part exam because it can detect glaucoma in the earliest possible stages. The ophthalmologist uses a special lamp or viewing scope to peer into the back of the eye. The instrument does not actually come in contact with the eye.

TREATMENT

Although glaucoma has no known cure, it can be arrested—usually with drug therapy. *Essential:* Early treatment.

Glaucoma medications—taken in drop form or as pills—are designed either to decrease the rate of aqueous humor production or improve the flow of the fluid out of the eye. A combination of drugs may be needed to achieve the correct fluid balance. In most cases, the medication must be taken indefinitely.

If drug therapy fails, laser surgery may be required to open up the eye's drainage system. A third treatment alternative—incisional surgery—involves creating a completely new drainage system. This system bypasses the eye's own blocked system. This treatment is now quite effective, thanks to medications that prevent scar formation.

You Don't Have to Put Up With Hearing Loss

Donna Wayner, PhD, clinical director of The Hearing Center at Albany Medical Center in Albany, NY, and director of science and education for the Deafness Research Foundation's National Campaign for Hearing Health (*www.drf.org*). She is author of *Hear What You've Been Missing: How to Cope with Hearing Loss.* John Wiley & Sons.

It's a shame. Despite the availability of highly effective hearing aids, many of the 28 million Americans with hearing loss are failing to get help for their frustrating—and potentially dangerous—condition.

Many hearing loss sufferers aren't even aware that they have a problem. But if you've been having trouble making out what others say—or if you've been told that you speak too loudly or watch TV with the sound turned up too high—stop making excuses. Effective help is available.

What should I do if I suspect that I have hearing loss? Have your doctor check your ears for wax blockages, infection or some other easily treatable problem.

If no such problem is found, consult an audiologist for a comprehensive hearing exam. The exam takes about 45 minutes and costs about $150.

If your doctor is unable to refer you to an audiologist, call the American Academy of Audiology at 800-222-2336 for a referral.

Generally, hearing aids are appropriate if you're having trouble hearing the telephone or a car horn. That can be dangerous. Hearing aids are also a good idea, of course, if you cannot make out speech clearly.

Hearing aids are now sold on a 30-day trial basis, so there's little downside to trying them out.

How effective are hearing aids? The newest "digital" models are custom-programmed to amplify the frequencies that trouble you most. They're much more effective than the standard "linear" models that were popular just five years ago.

Some people think that hearing aids are useless for so-called "nerve deafness." In fact, more than 80% of all hearing aid users have nerve-related hearing loss—and most of them get substantial help.

Which kind of hearing aid is best? Behind-the-ear models are more powerful and more versatile than the inside-the-ear models that have become popular in recent years. They can correct a wider range of hearing loss.

The only drawback to behind-the-ear models, of course, is that they're a bit more conspicuous than inside-the-ear models.

Ask the audiologist which type of hearing aid is most suitable given your problem.

Besides using a hearing aid, what else can I do to hear better? Turn off the TV, radio, etc., if it's not the focus of your attention…and do your best to avoid loud restaurants.

In conversation, try to have your partner's full attention. Watch his/her face carefully.

Doing so not only helps you read his lips but also helps you pick up facial expressions that can clue you in to what's being said. If you find yourself having trouble understanding someone, don't ask him to speak more loudly. Ask him to speak more slowly. That gives your brain more time to interpret the meaning.

If trouble persists, ask the other person to reword what he's saying rather than simply having him repeat himself.

Hearing loss often involves problems with the brain's ability to process spoken language. So if one wording causes trouble, another might be easier for your brain to process.

What about phones that flash and other assistive devices? If your hearing loss is particularly severe, the audiologist can equip you with assistive listening devices and systems —lights that flash when the phone or doorbell rings, vibrating alarm clock, telephone amplifier, etc.

Don't forget to take advantage of the captioning available for many TV programs—and, in some cities, theatrical movies.

To protect yourself against additional hearing loss, avoid exposure to loud sounds.

If you must be in a noisy environment, pick up a pair of $1 sound-dampening earplugs at a drugstore. Better yet, buy a pair of sound-deadening ear muffs. They're better at protecting against hearing loss. They're sold by sporting goods stores and audiologists for $15 to $25.

Free Hearing Test

Free hearing test identifies hearing problems in your own home.

How it works: Call 800-222-3277 from 9 am to 5 pm, EST, Monday through Friday. Request your local Dial-A-Hearing-Screening-Test number. Call that number from a quiet room using a corded telephone (not a cordless or cellular phone). A recording will play four tones for each ear. If you don't hear all eight, see a doctor or audiologist.

Occupational Hearing Services, Box 1880, Media, PA 19063.

Best Way to Get Rid of Earwax

Most of the time, earwax dries up and falls out on its own. Using a swab to clear out wax can push it against the eardrum. That can interfere with hearing—or damage the eardrum. If earwax does accumulate, use a rubber bulb to flush your ears gently with warm water. If that doesn't work, see a doctor.

M. Lee Williams, MD, associate professor of otolaryngology and head and neck surgery, Johns Hopkins University School of Medicine, Baltimore.

Controlling Tinnitus

Ringing in the ears (tinnitus) can, in many cases, be controlled with the antianxiety drug *alprazolam* (Xanax). After three months on the drug, 75% of tinnitus sufferers reported a lessening of symptoms.

Caution: See a doctor to rule out any underlying problems.

Robert M. Johnson, PhD, professor of otolaryngology, Oregon Health Sciences University, Portland.

Protect Yourself from Gum Disease

Robert J. Genco, DDS, PhD, professor and chair of oral biology and director of the periodontal disease research center at the State University of New York in Buffalo.

Four out of five American adults have some form of periodontal (gum) disease —from swollen gums to bleeding gums to loose teeth.

The damage isn't limited to the mouth. Gum disease contributes to heart disease and can cause trouble for diabetics and pregnant women, recent studies show.

HOW GUM DISEASE DEVELOPS

Gum disease is caused by bacteria that breed in plaque. That's the substance formed by food debris that accumulates around the gum line.

If it's not removed by brushing, plaque eventually turns into tartar *(calculus).* Tartar roughens tooth surfaces, making plaque adhere even more tightly to teeth.

Toxins produced by the bacteria in plaque inflame gums, making them red, swollen and prone to bleeding. This condition is called *gingivitis.*

Unless inflammation is arrested, gums eventually pull away from teeth. Bacteria then collect in the resulting pockets, further promoting tissue destruction.

Over time, the infection and inflammation destroy bone and tissue. Teeth then loosen and fall out.

Although gum disease usually has obvious symptoms, it can lurk in the mouth even if gums don't bleed. *Among the lesser-known warning signs:* Persistent bad breath...a change in the way teeth fit together when they bite...a change in the fit of partial dentures.

Anyone can develop gum disease. But some factors put people at special risk. These include smoking...diabetes...stress...and low bone density.

THE THREATS TO YOUR HEALTH

Severe gum disease (periodontitis) poses serious health risks...

•**Heart disease.** People with periodontitis have nearly twice the risk for fatal heart attack as do those without the disease.

However, recent studies suggest that the milder form of gum disease—gingivitis—is not associated with heart disease.

How does gum disease harm the heart? The same bacteria that cause gum disease may also raise heart attack risk by provoking a barrage of inflammatory substances that exacerbate coronary artery plaques. They're the sticky deposits that clog blood vessels and lead to heart attack.

•**Diabetes.** Diabetics are more likely to develop gum disease. And, for unknown reasons, diabetics with gum disease have more trouble controlling their blood sugar than do other diabetics. The more severe the gum disease, the worse their blood sugar control.

REVERSING GUM DISEASE

The same oral hygiene regimen that prevents gum disease can reverse it if it's caught early.

•**Brushing.** Twice a day, brush gently for three minutes with a soft-bristled brush. Don't brush side-to-side or in circles. Hold the brush at a 45-degree angle to the gums and sweep from the gum line to the tip of the tooth. Brush the back of each tooth, too.

What about the special grips and bristles common in toothbrushes nowadays? They're frills. Use them if they make brushing more enjoyable. But they're no more effective than straight-handled, straight-bristled versions.

Electric toothbrushes are not necessarily better than manual ones. But they can be useful for people who have difficulty brushing properly because of arthritis or other conditions.

The newest devices—sonic toothbrushes—use sound waves to dislodge plaque and debris. These brushes can help with plaque removal. But good flossers do just as well with old-fashioned manual toothbrushes as with sonic ones.

•**Flossing.** Floss at least once daily. Guide the floss between each set of adjacent teeth in sequence, so you don't miss any. Slide the floss gently down the side of one tooth, then up the side of the other.

Some flosses are waxed or Teflon-coated. Some are flavored. Some are thin filaments. Others are broad ribbons or tapes. None is inherently better than the others. Use the type you prefer.

To make sure you remove all plaque and debris between teeth, add at least one of these strategies to your flossing routine…

●**Use a rubber-tipped stimulator or an interproximal brush**—a tiny flexible brush perched atop a metal wand. The brush is useful for people with spaces between their teeth. Insert the brush or stimulator between teeth at the gum line and move gently back and forth.

●**Try an irrigator such as a Water Pik.** The stream of water dislodges debris caught between teeth.

●**Mouthwash.** Some mouthwashes have been proven to fight gingivitis. Look for the American Dental Association seal of approval.

●**See your dentist.** Even if you're doing everything right, regular dental checkups and professional cleanings are essential. Twice-yearly cleanings suffice for most people. But some need more frequent attention, no matter how scrupulous their home regimen.

Ask your dentist what schedule is right for you. Make sure he/she examines your mouth for signs of bone loss at every visit.

FIGHTING ADVANCED DISEASE

Periodontitis is most often treated with root "scaling" and "planing." Scaling removes plaque and tartar below the gum line at the tooth's root. Planing smooths the root to keep plaque from accumulating along rough surfaces.

In especially severe cases, surgery is needed to cut away detached gum tissue and regenerate bone.

Treatment for periodontitis usually includes antibiotics. New strategies have been developed to deliver antibiotics and germicides directly to gum tissue. These include a gel that hardens in the gum pocket…and a tiny chip that's inserted into the pocket.

Surprising Causes of Dental Problems

●**Cough drops, antacids and chewable vitamin C tablets.** These typically contain lots of cavity-causing sugar.

●**The antiseizure medication *phenytoin* (Dilantin)…**and calcium channel blockers *nifedipine* (Procardia) and *diltiazem* (Cardizem) used to treat blood pressure. They can cause gums to swell, increasing the risk for periodontal disease.

●**Chemotherapy drugs.** These can cause dry mouth, which encourages growth of decay-causing dental plaque.

If you take any of these drugs, be especially careful to practice good oral hygiene.

See a dentist at least three times a year for a cleaning and checkup. Tell him/her if you are taking a drug that can affect teeth and gums.

Alan Winter, DDS, a periodontist in private practice in New York.

Answer for Chronic Pain

Dharma Singh Khalsa, MD, founding director of the Acupuncture Stress Medicine and Chronic Pain Program at the University of Arizona College of Medicine in Tucson. He is president and medical director of the Alzheimer's Prevention Foundation in Tucson, and is author of The Pain Cure. Warner Books.

Twenty-five million Americans are bedeviled by some form of chronic pain—sciatica, migraine, arthritis, muscle pain, etc. There are effective ways to curb chronic pain, but these aren't the ways typically recommended by mainstream physicians.

Here are 10 pain-relieving strategies that really work…

●**Eat more fish and poultry.** Doctors often prescribe *fluoxetine* (Prozac) for chronic pain. This prescription antidepressant helps curb pain by boosting levels of the neurotransmitter *serotonin* in the brain. Serotonin blocks synthesis of *substance P,* one of the main chemical messengers involved in chronic pain.

But many people can keep serotonin levels high simply by eating foods rich in *tryptophan,* an amino acid that the body converts into serotonin.

Two excellent sources of tryptophan are poultry and fish. If you have chronic pain, try eating three ounces of either one five days a week.

225

In addition to blocking substance P, serotonin helps make people less aware of pain by improving mood and regulating disturbed sleep cycles.

• **Eat a banana every day.** Most chronic pain stems from arthritis, muscle pain or another inflammatory condition, which invariably goes hand in hand with muscle spasms. These spasms contribute to chronic pain.

Eat one banana a day—along with a bit of the lining of the peel that you've scraped off with a spoon. Doing so will supply you with lots of magnesium and potassium. Both minerals help control spasms.

• **Get regular exercise.** Exercise triggers the synthesis of natural painkillers known as *endorphins.*

If you're experiencing severe pain, of course, you probably don't feel like doing vigorous exercise. That's fine. Endorphin synthesis can be triggered by any form of activity that pushes the body a bit harder than it's accustomed to.

If you've been sedentary for a long time, something as simple as rotating your arms for a few seconds can work. So can sitting in a chair and raising your legs a few times.

• **Take steps to control psychological stress.** Stress plays a central role in chronic pain. Meditation and other relaxation techniques reduce muscle spasms, limit the release of pain-causing stress hormones and improve breathing. Each of these helps reduce pain intensity.

One recent study found that pain sufferers who meditated for 10 to 20 minutes a day visited a pain clinic 36% less often than did their nonmeditating peers.

What to do: Carve out at least 15 minutes of quiet time each day. If you aren't comfortable meditating, use the time to pray...visualize a tranquil scene...or sit quietly.

• **Avoid harmful fats.** Red meat and cooking oil stimulate production of *arachidonic acid,* a compound that the body converts into hormone-like substances that trigger inflammation. These substances are known as *prostaglandins.*

Chronic pain sufferers should avoid red meat entirely...and use cooking oil sparingly.

• **Take omega-3 fatty acid supplements.** Taking 1,000 mg to 3,000 mg of fish oil or flaxseed oil each day helps block synthesis of prostaglandins.

In addition to blocking prostaglandin synthesis, a type of omega-3 fatty acid known as *eicosapentaenoic acid* (EPA) improves circulation by making the platelets—cell-like structures that are responsible for blood clotting—less "sticky." This helps keep blood from pooling and causing inflammation and irritation.

Fatty acid supplements are unnecessary for individuals who eat cold-water, dark-flesh fish several times a week. Salmon, tuna, mackerel and sardines all fit the bill.

• **Take a vitamin B complex supplement.** Chronic pain is often accompanied by fatigue. When you feel more energetic, your pain is more manageable.

Ask your doctor about taking a daily supplement that contains at least 50 mg of B complex vitamins.

Vitamin B helps increase energy levels by facilitating the production of ATP, the high-energy compound found in mitochondria, the "power plants" inside cells.

• **Season food with turmeric.** Its primary constituent, *curcumin,* has been shown to be as effective at relieving pain as cortisone or ibuprofen—without any risk for side effects. A pinch or two a day is all you need.

• **Try acupuncture.** There's now solid evidence that acupuncture can be more effective than drug therapy for relieving many types of chronic pain.

Acupuncture that is done by a physician seems to be especially effective. So-called medical acupuncture often involves the application of electrical current to needles inserted into the skin. This variant of traditional acupuncture is called electroacupuncture.

For referral to an acupuncturist in your area, call the American Academy of Medical Acupuncture at 800-521-2262.

• **See a chiropractor or osteopath.** Most physicians rely upon drug therapy and surgery for controlling pain. Chiropractors and osteopaths incorporate physical manipulation into their treatments. For back pain especially, manipulation often works better than drugs or surgery.

16

Surviving Major Medical Threats

All You Need to Know About Alzheimer's and Other Age-Related Dementias

**M**any people who dread the idea of getting older are especially worried about dementia. For about four million Americans, dementia is not a fear but a reality.

Alzheimer's disease accounts for 60% of all cases of dementia, and at least 30% more are attributable to vascular dementia—the type caused by a major stroke or a series of small "mini-strokes." The remainder of cases are caused by other brain diseases, such as Parkinson's and Huntington's.

●**What's the difference between dementia and normal age-related mental changes?** Some slowdown in the formation of new memories—and some memory loss—is a normal part of aging. By contrast, dementia involves not just forgetfulness but also declines in language, visual and spatial skills...and impaired judgment and problem-solving ability. These grow steadily worse.

Example: A healthy person might forget where he/she left the house keys. But he would solve the problem by calling a neighbor or a locksmith. Someone with dementia would have no idea what to do.

●**Is dementia preventable?** We don't know how to prevent Alzheimer's. All we have are some studies that point to possible Alzheimer's risks and suggest ways to lower them.

On the other hand, strong evidence indicates that vascular dementia *is* preventable.

High blood pressure is the main cause of the strokes that cause this type of dementia. To prevent strokes, get your blood pressure checked

---

Muriel R. Gillick, MD, associate professor of medicine and director of the geriatrics fellowship program at Harvard Medical School and staff physician at the Hebrew Rehabilitation Center for the Aged, both in Boston. She is author of *Tangled Minds: Understanding Alzheimer's Disease and Other Dementias*. Dutton.

regularly. Your systolic pressure (the upper number) should be 120 or less. If it's higher, work with your doctor to lower it through diet, weight loss, exercise and medication.

•If Alzheimer's can't be prevented, what can be done to minimize the risk? Inflammation is thought to play a key role in Alzheimer's disease, and a recent study suggests that non-steroidal anti-inflammatory drugs (NSAIDs) such as *ibuprofen* (Advil) and *naproxen* (Naprosyn) have a small protective effect. The study compared sets of identical twins in which one twin had Alzheimer's and one didn't. It found that the healthy twin was more likely to be taking NSAIDs for another condition—such as arthritis—or to have taken them recently.

I don't think the data are strong enough to recommend that everyone take ibuprofen in the hope of preventing Alzheimer's. NSAIDs can cause side effects ranging from gastrointestinal bleeding to kidney problems. But for people who have recently been diagnosed with Alzheimer's, it might be worth taking 400 mg of ibuprofen three times a day.

•What about estrogen supplementation and Alzheimer's risk? Postmenopausal women on estrogen replacement therapy are less likely to have Alzheimer's than women who don't take estrogen.

The problem is that it's hard to separate estrogen's effect from that of other factors. Women who take estrogen tend to be better educated—and for some unknown reason, higher levels of education are associated with lower Alzheimer's risk.

•Is aluminum exposure a risk factor for Alzheimer's? Studies in England conducted in the mid-1980s showed higher rates of Alzheimer's in areas with a high concentration of aluminum in drinking water. But the increase was slight. I do *not* make any recommendations based on the studies.

•What are other risk factors for Alzheimer's? Serious head injury is one. Several studies have shown that injury resulting in a loss of consciousness is associated with a two-fold increased risk of developing Alzheimer's.

•How much does family history matter? Up to 15% of Alzheimer's cases have a clear hereditary basis. Most of these involve a particular version of a gene called *ApoE*. For people with this form of the gene, the lifetime risk of developing Alzheimer's is 29%. For the general population, the risk is 15%.

Having this specific version of the gene does *not* guarantee that you'll get Alzheimer's...and not having it doesn't ensure that you won't get it. That's why I don't recommend genetic testing for Alzheimer's. It won't tell you anything certain and might cause needless anxiety.

Genetic testing *can* be useful to help confirm a diagnosis of Alzheimer's after an individual begins to show symptoms of dementia.

•How effective are the medications used to treat Alzheimer's? The FDA has approved *tacrine* (Cognex) and *donepezil* (Aricept). These prescription drugs work by preventing the breakdown of acetylcholine, a neurotransmitter essential for nerve signaling.

Both drugs lead to slight improvement on tests of memory and language in the early stages of Alzheimer's.

Donepezil, the newer of the two drugs, is taken once a day and has few side effects. Tacrine can cause vomiting and liver damage and must be taken three times a day.

•Do any alternative treatments work against Alzheimer's? In one recent study, Alzheimer's patients who took high doses of vitamin E or the prescription antioxidant drug *selegiline* (Eldepryl) stayed out of nursing homes longer. This suggests that the antioxidants may have delayed the disease's progression by mopping up cell-damaging "free radicals."

Unfortunately, the study didn't measure the patients' cognitive function, so we don't really know what impact vitamin E had. It may or may not be effective, but at low dosages of 200 to 400 international units (IU) a day, it probably won't hurt.

Some studies also suggest that *ginkgo biloba* boosts memory in patients with Alzheimer's and other forms of dementia. It does not work as well as donepezil or tacrine, but it might be an alternative for people who can't tolerate even donepezil's minimal side effects.

Ginkgo can interact with other medications, so check with a doctor before taking it.

• **What's the outlook for future Alzheimer's treatments?** The most promising research involves *amyloid*. That's the protein that forms abnormal deposits in the brains of Alzheimer's patients. One line of research aims to find medicines that halt production of amyloid. Researchers also hope to create a vaccine that would prevent amyloid deposition. But such a vaccine probably won't be available for at least a decade.

Alzheimer's Care Basics

Establish a daily routine for the person suffering from Alzheimer's...remove items that might encourage the person to wander, such as a coat rack near the door...have the person wear an ID bracelet in case he/she does leave home unattended...plan at least one regular daily outing, such as a walk or trip to the grocery store...reduce clutter so that misplaced items can be more easily found...respond to agitation by distracting and reassuring rather than arguing or correcting the person...make others a part of the regular care routine.

Rebecca Logsdon, PhD, clinical psychologist, University of Washington, Seattle.

Parkinson's Hope

New Parkinson's drug quells the characteristic tremors and muscle rigidity with few side effects. In a recent study, *ropinirole* (Requip) was just as effective at relieving symptoms as *L-dopa* (Sinemet). That's been the main drug used to treat Parkinson's for more than a decade. Only 20% of the ropinirole group developed sudden, involuntary twisting motions (dyskinesia) compared with 46% of the L-dopa group.

Carl Clarke, MD, associate professor of neurology, University of Birmingham, Birmingham, England. His study of 268 Parkinson's patients was presented at an International Congress on Parkinson's Disease in Vancouver.

Staying Healthy Despite Diabetes

Peter Lodewick, MD, medical director of the Diabetes Care Center in Birmingham, AL. A diabetic himself, Dr. Lodewick is author of *A Diabetic Doctor Looks at Diabetes—His and Yours.* Lowell House.

Have you developed diabetes without realizing it? If so, you've got lots of company. One in three individuals with the more common form of the disease—adult-onset, or type 2 diabetes—has never been diagnosed.*

Even more alarming, more than half of those who have been diagnosed with type 2 diabetes aren't getting adequate treatment. As a result, their blood sugar (glucose) levels remain perilously high. That places them at risk for heart disease, blindness and other complications of diabetes.

There's no excuse for this. As a diabetes specialist—and as a diabetic myself—*I've found that most cases of type 2 diabetes can be controlled if the following key steps are taken...*

• **Be on the lookout for symptoms.** In its early stages, type 2 diabetes causes only subtle symptoms—fatigue...increased thirst and/or hunger...frequent urination...weight loss...blurred or double vision...anxiety...faintness or irritability.

If you suspect you have diabetes, ask your doctor about having a blood glucose test. This in-office test checks your glucose level before and after eating. You probably have diabetes if your fasting blood sugar level exceeds 126...or if your blood sugar level after eating exceeds 200.

IF TESTING REVEALS DIABETES

• **Adopt a low-carbohydrate diet.** Just how far diabetics should cut back on carbohydrates remains a matter of debate among diabetes specialists.

The American Diabetes Association recommends a diet in which 50% to 60% of daily calories come from carbohydrates. But I've found that my diabetic patients fare much better if they limit carbohydrates to 30% of their total calories—maybe as little as 30 g a day.

*The other form of diabetes, juvenile or type 1, typically requires a lifetime of insulin injections.

This is especially true during the first few days of treatment, when glucose levels are still very high.

To cut back to the 30% level, you must limit your consumption of corn, rice, wheat, barley, potatoes and pasta. Fruits and fruit juices should be avoided completely. So should breads and other baked goods, including bagels, pancakes and waffles...sugary drinks and candy...and milk, yogurt, cottage cheese and dairy substitutes.

You can eat liberal amounts of fowl, fish, meat, cheese, eggs, green vegetables (including broccoli, asparagus, spinach and brussels sprouts), cabbage, avocado, mushrooms, sauerkraut, zucchini, yellow squash, peppers, almonds, walnuts, tea and coffee.

Caution: A very-low-carbohydrate diet should be undertaken only with a doctor's help. The doctor should carefully monitor your cholesterol and triglyceride levels and your kidney function until cholesterol and blood sugar levels are acceptable.

●**Get aerobic exercise every day.** Walking, bicycling, swimming or jogging—or doing some other form of aerobic exercise—for at least 30 minutes a day is even more important for diabetics than for nondiabetics.

A recent study of 70,000 nurses published in *The Journal of the American Medical Association* found that those who exercised aerobically for 30 minutes a day had a 41% reduction in risk for diabetes.

●**Be vigilant about blood sugar testing.** During the initial stages of diabetes treatment—when glucose levels are still fluctuating—I recommend doing a finger-stick blood test just before and two hours after your morning and evening meals. That's a total of four times a day.

Even more frequent testing may be helpful if blood sugar levels are not optimal.

Your blood sugar should fall between 70 and 100 before eating...and below 150 two hours after eating.

Once your blood sugar has stabilized, ask your doctor about cutting back on testing.

●**Get a hemoglobin A-1C test every three months.** This $30 test, performed in your doctor's office, lets you know your average blood sugar over the previous three months. We now know that average glucose levels are much more significant than any single spot reading.

Ideally, hemoglobin A-1C should be 6.2% or lower.

●**Take antioxidant supplements.** Tissues exposed to high glucose levels undergo oxidation, a process in which free radicals are formed. Free radicals can damage cells, nerves and blood vessels.

To minimize oxidation, take a daily multivitamin supplement such as *Alpha Betic* along with five additional supplements...

- ●Alpha lipoic acid . . . . .200 mg divided into two 100-mg doses
- ●Chromium . . . . .200 mcg
- ●Folic acid . . . . .400 mcg
- ●Vitamin C . . . . .500 mg
- ●Vitamin E . . . . .400 international units (IU)

●**Take oral diabetes medication if necessary.** Few people with type 2 diabetes need insulin injections, but some do require oral diabetes medication.

If your blood sugar level remains high after several weeks on a low-carbohydrate diet, your doctor should prescribe one or more hypoglycemic agents.

Examples: Glyburide (DiaBeta)...*metformin* (Glucophage)...*pioglitazone* (Actos)...and *repaglinide* (Prandin).

New diabetes medications are being introduced every few months. Discuss with your doctor which medication is right for you.

Drinking and Diabetes

Moderate drinking is beneficial for people with diabetes. Diabetics who routinely had one or more drinks a day had one-fifth the risk of dying from heart disease than that faced by nondrinking diabetics, a study found. *However:* This finding does *not* necessarily mean that all diabetics who don't drink should start. Nor does it mean that those who already drink should drink more. But if you have diabetes, ask your doctor about the potential benefits of moderate drinking.

Ronald Klein, MD, MPH, professor of ophthalmology and visual sciences, University of Wisconsin, Madison, Medical School. His study of 983 diabetics was published in *The Journal of the American Medical Association,* 515 N. State St., Chicago 60610.

If Lyme Disease Just Won't Go Away…There Are Things to Do

Joseph J. Burrascano, Jr., MD, an internist in East Hampton, New York. He has treated Lyme disease patients and conducted research on the illness for more than 15 years.

L yme disease is the most common tick-borne illness in the US, infecting about two million Americans in the past 20 years. No one knows the exact number of Lyme cases because the usual blood test used to diagnose it is unreliable.

While most medical authorities question the notion of chronic Lyme disease and its treatment with repeated courses of antibiotics, some doctors do believe it. They believe that up to half of all Lyme patients still have symptoms after they undergo the standard treatment—a one- to two-month course of antibiotics. Of those, 20% are believed to suffer from chronic Lyme disease (post-Lyme syndrome).

One prominent proponent of this theory, Joseph J. Burrascano, Jr., MD, has treated more than 7,000 Lyme patients. *His advice:*

•**See a specialist.** While an internist or family practitioner can treat you, a select group of physicians—primarily in the Northeast, where the disease is prevalent—specializes in Lyme disease care.

To find a specialist, contact the Lyme Disease Foundation referral program (*www.lyme.org* or 800-886-LYME).

Lyme specialists are more likely to know about the latest in treatments, medications and clinical trials.

•**Keep a daily diary of your symptoms and treatment.** This will help your doctor identify the most effective therapies.

Track any pain, confusion or other symptoms. Also note what you were doing when the symptoms occurred.

This helps to rule out other conditions, such as neurological disease, arthritis and depression.

•**Get tested for other tick-borne diseases.** Like Lyme, ehrlichiosis, babesiosis and bartonella cause chills, high fever, headache and fatigue.

When Lyme is combined with another tick-borne illness, symptoms include sudden severe headache…drenching sweats…and high fever (above 101°F).

Of 100 ticks recently collected in Hunterdon County, New Jersey, 43 carried Lyme…17 carried ehrlichiosis…and five carried babesiosis. Ten ticks carried two of the three diseases.

Antibiotics that help relieve Lyme disease symptoms do not fight babesiosis.

•**Ask your doctor about other antibiotics.** There is no universally effective antibiotic for treating Lyme. The choice of drug depends on many factors, such as age…body size…and how long you've had the disease.

•**Have a polymerase chain reaction (PCR) test after each round of antibiotic treatment.** This $100 blood test detects the DNA of the Lyme bacterium.

You may need to repeat the test because the Lyme bacterium, though present in your body, may not appear in each blood sample.

A negative test result doesn't prove that the disease has disappeared. A positive result means that it still exists.

•**Adjust your lifestyle.** Stop smoking… avoid alcohol and caffeine…get enough rest… avoid stress, which weakens immunity.

•**Eat right.** That means low-fat, low-carbohydrate foods.

Each day, eat eight ounces of yogurt containing active cultures. Or take two acidophilus capsules after each meal to control the overgrowth of yeast that antibiotic treatment can cause.

•**Exercise.** If you're sick with Lyme disease, you may be spending too much time in bed. This can leave you stiff and weak.

Work with a professional trainer to develop a program that stretches and tones your muscles.

Avoid aerobic exercise until you have recovered. High-intensity exercise actually weakens immune function. Your doctor can recommend a physical therapist or exercise physiologist.

●**Ask your doctor about helpful herbs and supplements.** In addition to a multivitamin/mineral, consider taking…

●*Cordyceps.* This herb from Tibet has been shown to improve stamina, enhance lung function and reduce fatigue.

●*Essential fatty acids (EFAs).* Derived from plant and fish oils, EFAs curb achiness, depression, fatigue, memory loss and poor concentration.

Take four plant oil capsules (borage oil, evening primrose oil or black currant seed oil) and four fish oil (omega-3) capsules a day.

Caution: See your doctor before taking plant or fish oil if you already take a blood thinner. The combination can cause bleeding.

●*Coenzyme Q10.* Lyme patients may be deficient in this naturally occurring compound (also known as *ubiquinone*). Take 200 mg to 300 mg daily of a standardized brand.

Warning: Do not take coenzyme Q10 if you take *atovaquone* (Mepron). This antibiotic may negate the effect of coenzyme Q10.

●*Vitamin B complex.* Supplemental B vitamins help relieve neuropathy, poor memory and mood disorders. Take one 50-mg B-complex capsule every day.

●*Magnesium.* Lyme patients may be deficient in this mineral, which eases headaches, tremors, twitches, cramps, sore muscles and irregular heartbeat. The best source is magnesium L-lactate dihydrate. Take 168 mg every 12 hours.

●**Treat symptoms even if you can't cure the disease.**

●*Depression.* Nearly 75% of Lyme patients are depressed. Ask your doctor about antidepressants and psychotherapy.

●*Fibromyalgia.* This related disorder causes stiff, sore muscles. Ask your doctor about anti-inflammatories, such as ibuprofen (Motrin), and low-dose tricyclic antidepressants, which restore sleep patterns and relieve muscle pain.

New Treatment for Multiple Sclerosis

Severe attacks of multiple sclerosis (MS) and similar neurological disorders that fail to respond to the usual treatment may be eased by treatment with plasma exchange. In a recent study, half of MS patients who underwent this new therapy regained their ability to move their limbs and speak. During plasma exchange, the fluid portion of blood is replaced with a synthetic substitute. Seven two-hour treatments are given over a two-week period. Plasma exchange is *not* a cure for MS.

Brian G. Weinshenker, MD, consultant, department of neurology, Mayo Clinic, Rochester, MN. His study of 22 MS patients was published in *Annals of Neurology,* 5841 Cedar Lake Rd., Suite 204, Minneapolis 55416.

Up to 70% of Cancers Can Be Avoided

Melanie Polk, MMSc, RD, director of nutrition education, American Institute for Cancer Research, 1759 R St. NW, Washington, DC 20009.

People often assume that cancer is out of their hands because it is "genetic." In fact, lifestyle decisions are much more important in determining who gets cancer—and who doesn't.

Even if your genes place you at risk for cancer, 60% to 70% of all malignancies can be avoided by paying attention to four lifestyle factors—diet, weight control, physical activity and not smoking.

IF YOU MAKE JUST ONE CHANGE

Eating a plant-based diet is the single most important thing you can do to lower your cancer risk.

Foods should be minimally processed and as close to their natural state as possible. Processed foods may have lost some of their nutritional value.

Example: Eat a potato rather than potato chips.

Also limit intake of foods with added sugar, such as soft drinks and sweetened cereals.

If you eat red meat, have no more than three ounces per day.

Eating at least five servings—about one-half cup each—of fruits or vegetables every day can decrease your risk of cancer by 20%.

OTHER IMPORTANT STEPS

●**Maintain a healthful weight, and be physically active.** Try not to gain too much weight after reaching your full height (at about age 18 for women…24 for men).

Start by walking every day—working your way up to a brisk, one-hour walk daily. In addition, work up a sweat by engaging in some form of vigorous physical activity for at least one hour each week.

●**Drink alcohol in moderation—if at all.** There is no evidence that alcohol reduces cancer risk, though some evidence suggests that moderate alcohol consumption helps prevent coronary artery disease in men and possibly women. If you do drink, limit your consumption to one drink a day for women…two drinks a day for men.

Avoid alcohol entirely if you are a woman with an increased risk of breast cancer.

●**Select foods that are low in fat and salt.** Limit your intake of fatty foods. Use a moderate amount of monounsaturated oils, such as olive and canola.

Avoid animal fat and hydrogenated fat, which are commonly found in shortening, margarine and bakery items.

Watch those snack foods, salty condiments and pickles.

●**Prepare and store foods safely.** Keep cold foods cold and hot foods hot.

If you eat meat, avoid charring it. Limit cured or smoked meat. Take precautions when grilling —trim fat from meat, marinate it, microwave it for half the cooking time before grilling.

●**Avoid tobacco in any form.**

CANCER RISK FACTORS

Anticancer precautions are particularly important for individuals at increased risk for cancer.

These risk factors include*…

●**Family history of genetically linked cancers,** such as breast, ovarian and colon cancers.

●**Inflammatory bowel disease.**

●**Human papillomavirus (HPV) infection.**

●**Alcoholism.**

●**Hepatitis B or C virus (HBV/HCV).**

Additional risk factors for women…

●**First menstrual period before the age of 12.**

●**First child born after age 30.**

●**Childless and over age 50.**

●**Postmenopausal and on hormone-replacement therapy.**

*This information is based on a major study by the American Institute for Cancer Research that reviewed more than 4,500 studies to determine the relationships among diet, lifestyle and cancer risk.

Colon Cancer Prevention Secrets

Samuel Meyers, MD, clinical professor of medicine at Mount Sinai School of Medicine in New York. He is coauthor of the medical textbook *Bockus Gastroenterology.* W.B. Saunders.

Colon cancer is diagnosed in 130,000 Americans each year…and 50,000 die of the disease. That makes colon cancer second only to lung cancer as the leading cause of cancer deaths in this country.

These statistics are doubly tragic because colon cancer can almost always be prevented.

Tumors in the colon—and rectum—usually begin as tiny mushroom-shaped growths. Most of these *polyps* are harmless, but a small percentage turn cancerous.

The progression from benign polyp to cancerous tumor takes at least five years. That's ample time for detecting and removing any polyps before they threaten your health.

If cancer cells are detected in the colon, removal of the polyps is curative in 92% of all cases.

Unfortunately, only one in four Americans undergoes the periodic screenings necessary to check the colon for growths.

Not smoking and getting regular aerobic exercise help cut your risk. *Here's what else you can do to prevent colon cancer…*

●**Have periodic colonoscopies.** Colonoscopy is an outpatient procedure in which a long, flexible viewing tube inserted through the rectum is used to examine the entire length of the large intestine. If polyps or tumors are detected, they often can be removed on the spot—the colonoscope doubles as a cutting tool.

People are understandably reluctant to undergo colonoscopy. If you are properly sedated, however, you should not feel any discomfort.

There is a small risk of complications—about one in 1,000. The most common complication is a perforated intestine, which requires immediate surgery.

The test is extremely accurate. When you have periodic colonoscopies, there's no need for sigmoidoscopy, barium enema or any of the other tests often recommended by doctors.

If you're in good health and have no family history of colon cancer, ask your doctor about having a colonoscopy once every 10 years, starting at age 50.

If you have a family history of colon cancer, have your first colonoscopy no later than age 40…and perhaps even earlier.

The starting age—and the frequency of exams—depends on how many of your first-degree relatives had colon cancer…and the age when it was diagnosed. A first-degree relative is a parent, sibling or child. Ask your doctor which schedule is right for you.

An experimental technique called *virtual colonoscopy* uses X rays and computer technology to create a 3-D view of the colon's interior. Less invasive, virtual colonoscopy is a bit like having a computed tomography (CT) scan.

Virtual colonoscopy should be available within the next few years. Whether it will prove as accurate as the real thing remains to be seen.

●**Consume at least 25 g of dietary fiber a day.** Fiber binds to special digestive juices known as *bile acids* in the intestine and carries them out of the body in the stool.

This is critical, because the interaction of bile acids with intestinal bacteria releases carcinogenic by-products.

It's fine to boost your fiber intake with fiber supplements such as Metamucil. But research suggests that it's more effective to have at least five servings a day of fruits, vegetables, beans, peas and whole grains.

Unlike fiber supplements, these food sources of fiber contain vitamins and minerals that reduce your risk for cancer.

Examples: Yellow, orange and dark-green vegetables and fruit are rich in vitamins A and C. Peppers, squash, broccoli and cauliflower are rich in vitamin E, folic acid and selenium.

Colon cancer occurs much less often in parts of the world where people eat lots of plant-based foods. Fiber is found only in plant foods.

●**Eat less fat.** Fiber gets most of the attention, but cutting back on dietary fat may be even more critical for preventing colon cancer. That's because bile acids are produced largely in response to the presence of fat in the small intestine.

Reducing fat consumption to 20% of total calories is ideal. If that level is unrealistic for you, keep your fat intake under 30% of total calories. That means roughly 45 g of fat a day.

Cutting back on or eliminating red meat, butter and snack foods—and switching to non-fat dairy foods—is often enough to lower fat to the right level.

●**Don't eat charred meats.** When animal fat is exposed to barbecuing with charcoal or to a direct flame in the broiler, carcinogens similar to those in tobacco are created.

Self-defense: When broiling or grilling, don't let the flames touch the meat. Avoid grilling with charcoal.

●**Eat fish three times a week.** Fish contains fatty acids that the body uses to reduce the potency of *prostaglandins* and other tumor-promoting chemicals in the body. Salmon and mackerel have the most fatty acids.

People who don't like the taste of fish sometimes take fish oil supplements. There isn't enough research to show they work, however, and they can give perspiration a fishy odor. Eating fish is better.

●**Get 1,000 to 1,500 mg of calcium a day.** Three servings of low-fat milk or other dairy foods supply about 1,000 mg. Calcium fights colon cancer by preventing rapid growth of cells in the colon.

Helpful: Antacids such as Tums contain more than 500 mg of calcium per tablet. They're a less costly source of calcium than calcium supplements. Use the sugar-free kind.

•**Ask your doctor about taking aspirin.** Aspirin, *ibuprofen* (Motrin) and other non-steroidal anti-inflammatory drugs (NSAIDs) seem to help keep polyps from forming by inhibiting prostaglandin production.

These drugs seem to have a cancer-inhibiting effect when taken over the course of many years—even at low dosages.

Caution: Regular use of NSAIDs can cause ulcers and other problems, especially in people with a history of gastrointestinal bleeding and those over age 65. NSAID therapy should be implemented only with your doctor's okay.

Beating Pancreatic Cancer

Ordinarily one of the fastest-growing malignancies, pancreatic cancer can be slowed dramatically. In a pilot study, pancreatic cancer patients lived an average of three times longer than would otherwise have been expected when they ate a vegetarian diet...took vitamin, mineral and pancreatic-enzyme supplements...and had twice-daily coffee enemas, which are thought to clear the body of metabolic wastes. In light of these impressive results, the National Cancer Institute has funded a new, larger trial to study the regimen. *More information:* 800-4-CANCER.

Nicholas J. Gonzalez, MD, an immunologist in private practice in New York. His study of 11 pancreatic cancer patients was published in *Nutrition and Cancer,* 12433 Galesville Dr., Gaithersburg, MD 20878.

Lung Cancer Treatment

Certain lung cancer patients in remission live longer when they receive radiation therapy to the brain. *Background:* Treatment for lung cancer has improved, decreasing the risk for recurrence in the lung. Ironically, this good news means that a spread (metastasis) of lung cancer to the brain has become one of the main types of relapse. In a recent study of 987 patients whose small-cell lung cancer was in remission, "prophylactic cranial irradiation" cut the death rate 16% by reducing the risk that the cancer would later spread to the brain.

Jean-Pierre Pignon, MD, PhD, senior statistician, department of biostatistics and epidemiology, Institut Gustave-Roussy, Villejuif, France. His study was published in *The New England Journal of Medicine,* 10 Shattuck St., Boston 02115.

Drinking More Water Reduces Risk Of Bladder Cancer

A 10-year study of almost 48,000 men found that those who drank six glasses of water a day had only half the chance of developing bladder cancer as those who drank only one glass...and those who drank 10 glasses of fluids (including water) had an even lower risk.

Dominique Michaud, ScD, is a research fellow at the Harvard School of Public Health in Boston.

Better Bladder Cancer Therapy

Conventional surgery for bladder cancer that invades surrounding muscle tissue calls for removing the entire bladder along with the tumor. Without a bladder, patients who undergo this treatment must—for the rest of their lives—use an uncomfortable and inefficient urine-collection bag.

Now: An experimental treatment spares the bladder. The surgeon simply cuts out the tumor using instruments attached to a slender fiber-optic scope that's passed through the urethra. The operation is followed by chemotherapy and radiation.

Outlook: Half of patients who underwent this procedure were still alive after four years with no signs of the cancer spreading. That's the same cure rate as obtained via the old method.

Donald S. Kaufman, MD, associate clinical professor of medicine, Harvard University Medical School, and oncologist, Massachusetts General Hospital, Boston. His study of 53 bladder cancer patients was published in *The New England Journal of Medicine*, 10 Shattuck St., Boston 02115.

Cancer Pain Problem

One-fourth of all cancer patients fail to get adequate pain relief.

Reason: They assume that pain is inevitable …they don't complain because they want to be "good" patients…they fear addiction…and they are afraid that pain management will distract the doctor from treating the disease.

Reality: Pain management is an integral part of cancer treatment. Patients should not hesitate to communicate their needs.

Jamie H. Von Roenn, MD, associate professor of medicine, section of medical oncology, Northwestern University Medical School, Chicago. Her survey of 897 cancer doctors was published in *Annals of Internal Medicine*, Independence Mall West, Sixth Street at Race, Philadelphia 19106.

Good News About Irritable Bowel Syndrome

Gerard Guillory, MD, clinical professor of medicine at the University of Colorado Health Sciences Center in Denver and an internist in private practice in Aurora, Colorado. He is author of *IBS: A Doctor's Plan for Chronic Digestive Troubles*. Hartley & Marks. He maintains the Web site *www.ibsinformation.com.*

Thirty million Americans have irritable bowel syndrome (IBS). The condition is characterized by bloating…abdominal pain…urgent need to defecate…mucus in the stool…and episodes of diarrhea or constipation —or alternating bouts of both.

Only a few years ago, IBS sufferers awaiting diagnosis endured months of fear as doctors first ruled out other conditions like cancer and Crohn's disease.

When these patients finally got their diagnosis, all too often doctors told them that the ailment was "all in their head"—due simply to stress or emotional problems.

Today, IBS is usually diagnosed after just one doctor's visit. Patients have more treatment options…and no longer have to endure put-downs from skeptical doctors.

DIAGNOSING IBS

IBS experts now agree on a set of criteria to diagnose the condition without first excluding many other possibilities. *These criteria include…*

•**Presence of abdominal pain** and at least two of the following symptoms for at least 12 weeks in the preceding year…

•Unusually frequent or sporadic defecation during periods of abdominal pain.

•Unusually hard—or soft—stools during periods of abdominal pain.

•Relief of abdominal pain with defecation.

•**Absence of the following: Fever, weight loss, abdominal pain at night, blood in the stool or anemia.** These signs and symptoms are suggestive of another diagnosis, such as colon cancer or Crohn's disease.

WHAT CAUSES IBS?

Recent research shows that certain nerves in the colons of IBS sufferers are overreactive. These are the nerves that control sensation (what is felt in the colon) and motility (how colon muscles move).

Result: Mild stimuli that would not bother most people cause the colon to spasm. These stimuli include the pressure of intestinal gas…colon contractions triggered by eating *(peristalsis)*…and psychological stress.

GETTING RELIEF

Self-help strategies can be remarkably effective in easing IBS symptoms…

•**Prevent excess gas.** People with IBS are intolerant of even normal amounts of intestinal gas. *To minimize it….*

•Avoid gum and candy. They stimulate salivation, which increases the number of swallows.

With each swallow, a little air goes into the intestine.

•Eat slowly. Quick eaters gulp their food… and swallow more air.

•Avoid carbonated drinks.

•**Avoid trigger foods.** IBS symptoms often occur after consumption of sugary and/or fatty foods. Undigested sugar ferments in the colon, causing more gas. Fat causes the body to release *cholecystokinin,* a hormone that stimulates colon contractions.

Other common food triggers are caffeine, nicotine and alcohol. *Monosodium glutamate* (MSG) and *aspartame* (NutraSweet) can also trigger IBS symptoms.

Sources of MSG include commercially prepared soups, bouillon, low-fat salad dressings and most restaurant foods.

Products that contain aspartame or MSG must say so on the labels.

To identify triggers: Keep a "look-back" diary. After every IBS attack, jot down a list of all the foods you consumed in the previous 12 hours. You should spot patterns that point to foods you should avoid.

•**Get more fiber.** Fiber helps IBS sufferers who are constipated or whose constipation alternates with diarrhea. It's not helpful for diarrhea-predominant IBS.

Gradually add fiber-rich foods such as fruits, vegetables and whole grains to your diet. Add foods one at a time to make sure they're not trigger foods.

Another option: Use psyllium seed supplements such as Konsyl or synthetic fiber supplements such as FiberCon. Take them at mealtime so they mix with foods. This produces a soft stool that is easy to pass. Avoid supplements that contain sugar or aspartame.

•**Reduce stress.** Eliminate as many stressors as you can…and increase your use of stress-reduction techniques. Good ones include exercise and yoga.

MEDICATION

If self-help strategies fail to alleviate symptoms, medications may help.

Historically, doctors have treated IBS using muscle relaxants, laxatives, antidiarrhea drugs and antidepressants.

A new generation of drugs block serotonin, a neurotransmitter that stimulates supersensitive nerves in the colon.

Unfortunately, *alosetron* (Lotronex) was recently pulled from the market due to side effects.

Treatment for Ulcerative Colitis

Ulcerative colitis that fails to respond to steroids may respond to cyclosporine, a drug long used to prevent organ rejection.

Study: Nine of 11 patients taking the drug had relief from bloody diarrhea and other symptoms—within a week. The drug was so effective that researchers cut the study short—they felt it would be unethical not to treat those subjects taking placebos.

Payoff: Cyclosporine therapy may eliminate the need for intestinal surgery.

Simon Lichtiger, MD, assistant professor of medicine, Mount Sinai School of Medicine, New York.

What You Should Know About Hepatitis A, B…and C

Suzanne Cotter, MD, epidemiologist in the Hepatitis Branch of Centers for Disease Control and Prevention in Atlanta. For more information on hepatitis, go to *www. cdc.gov/ncidod/diseases/hepatitis.*

Millions of Americans are infected with hepatitis, a highly contagious inflammation of the liver…yet many don't know it.

Symptoms of the three most common forms—A, B and C—are the same. They include vomiting…fever…abdominal pain…lethargy… loss of appetite…yellow eyes and skin…and dark-yellow urine.

However, many people with hepatitis don't experience any symptoms.

A vs. B vs. C

●**Hepatitis A is transmitted primarily by the fecal-oral route** by either person-to-person contact or ingesting contaminated food or water. The only treatment is bed rest and a healthful diet. Symptoms may last up to two months.

●**Hepatitis B is transmitted through blood or body fluids via sexual contact** …contact with contaminated equipment (such as syringes)…and from mother to child during delivery (perinatal transmission). Symptoms usually last up to two months. Ten percent of infected adults may become virus carriers, meaning they can infect others and can have chronically inflamed livers. There are antiviral drug treatments available (such as *lamivudine*) for chronic carriers.

●**Hepatitis C is transmitted predominantly via blood**—through cuts or needle sticks…via sexual contact…and from perinatal transmission. Combination antiviral drug therapy with interferon and ribavirin is sometimes effective.

Up to 70% of infected people develop chronic hepatitis, making them vulnerable to cirrhosis (scarring of the liver) and liver cancer or liver failure. Then the only cure is a liver transplant.

At greatest risk: People who had blood transfusions before 1992…intravenous drug users (even those who experimented just once)…hemodialysis patients before 1992…organ transplant recipients…infants born to infected mothers.

PREVENTING HEPATITIS

Vaccines are available for hepatitis A and B. Speak with your doctor about whether the vaccine or screening is appropriate for you. There is no vaccine for C. *Other self-defense strategies…*

●**Wash your hands after going to the bathroom and changing diapers.**

●**Follow precautions for safe food preparation.**

●**Bandage cuts and wounds.**

●**Practice safe sex.**

●**Don't share personal-care products,** such as razors, toothbrushes, toothpaste tubes, nail clippers, etc.

Syndrome X—The Little-Known Cause of Many Heart Attacks

Gerald M. Reaven, MD, professor of medicine at Stanford University School of Medicine in Stanford, CA. He is coauthor of *Syndrome X: Overcoming the Silent Killer That Can Give You a Heart Attack.* Simon & Schuster.

It's well known that a high cholesterol level—especially a high level of LDL (bad) cholesterol—is a major risk factor for heart attack. Now, another risk factor is finally getting the attention it deserves as a major contributor to heart disease. That factor is insulin resistance.

Insulin—produced by the pancreas—is the hormone that ushers blood sugar (glucose) into cells. Cells can become resistant to insulin's action. When they do, the pancreas pumps out more insulin in an attempt to "force" sugar into the cells.

Excess insulin directly damages coronary arteries. It also triggers an array of metabolic abnormalities that contribute to the development of artery-clogging fatty plaques and to blood clots.

The constellation of abnormalities, which affects 70 million Americans, is called "syndrome X." *It includes…*

●**Excess fibrinogen,** a substance that promotes blood clots.

●**Excess plasminogen activator inhibitor-1 (PAI-1),** a substance that slows clot breakdown.

●**High levels of triglycerides,** the body's main fat-storage particles.

●**Low levels of HDL (good) cholesterol,** which sweeps fat out of arteries.

Many people with syndrome X also have high blood pressure. And they're likely to have glucose intolerance—a condition characterized by slightly elevated blood sugar levels.

Important: Glucose intolerance is not diabetes. But up to 5% of people with syndrome X go on to develop type-2 diabetes annually. That's the form that occurs later in life among people, typically overweight, who become increasingly insensitive to the effects of insulin.

DIAGNOSING SYNDROME X

The results of five simple tests point to a diagnosis of syndrome X. Risk for heart attack rises with each out-of-bounds test score.

- **Fasting triglyceride level in excess of 200 milligrams per deciliter (mg/dl).**
- **Fasting HDL cholesterol level under 35 mg/dl.**
- **Blood pressure higher than 145/90.**
- **Being overweight by 15 pounds or more.**
- **Fasting blood sugar level higher than 110 mg/dl**...or a level higher than 140 two hours after drinking a glucose solution.

FIGHTING SYNDROME X

- **Eat the right diet.** Americans are besieged by a glut of high-concept diets, all of them purporting to be best for weight loss and health.

The American Heart Association diet counsels cutting down on fat and boosting consumption of carbohydrates. *The Zone* diet advises boosting protein intake and lowering fat.

These diets may work for people who don't have syndrome X. But protein and carbohydrates stimulate insulin production—which is a dangerous outcome for people with the syndrome.

The Atkins diet counsels consumption of low levels of carbohydrates and as much fat as desired. But that diet is too high in artery-clogging saturated fat.

The ideal diet to combat syndrome X supplies 45% of calories from carbohydrates...15% from protein...and 40% from fat.

Key: Emphasize beneficial mono- and polyunsaturated fats. These should supply 30% to 35% of the diet. Only 5% to 10% should come from saturated fats.

Good sources of healthful fats include avocados...fatty fish (such as sea bass, trout, sole and salmon)...natural peanut butter...nuts and seeds...canola, corn, olive, safflower, peanut, soybean, sesame and sunflower oils.

- **Lose weight.** Shedding pounds improves insulin resistance. *Recent study:* Insulin resistance fell an average of 40% in overweight individuals who lost 20 pounds.
- **Exercise.** People who exercise daily use insulin 25% more efficiently than those who do not exercise. Forty-five minutes of aerobic exercise a day is ideal.
- **Stop smoking.** Smoking promotes insulin resistance.

MEDICATION

If lifestyle changes alone don't overcome syndrome X, medication can help...

- **Triglyceride-lowering medication.** Three drugs can lower triglyceride levels. They also lower PAI-1 levels and raise HDL cholesterol.

One of them—nicotinic acid—has the added benefit of lowering LDL cholesterol. A common side effect of nicotinic acid is facial flushing.

Self-defense: To minimize flushing from nicotinic acid, increase the dose gradually.

Two other effective drugs are *gemfibrozil* (Lopid) and *fenofibrate* (Tricor). In rare cases, however, they can cause liver damage.

Self-defense: Talk to your doctor about testing liver function periodically.

- **Blood pressure medication.** Fifty percent of people with high blood pressure have syndrome X. But some blood pressure drugs can worsen the condition.

Talk to your doctor about the potential risks of high-dose diuretics and beta-blockers if you have syndrome X.

Because syndrome X is caused by insulin resistance, it's logical to ask whether *thiazolidinediones*—drugs that increase insulin sensitivity—might be helpful.

Such drugs are currently used to treat type-2 diabetes.

Ongoing research will determine if thiazolidinediones improve syndrome X. Until the studies are completed, these drugs should *not* be used to treat the condition.

About Defibrillators

People with implanted defibrillators are less likely to die suddenly from cardiac arrest than those who rely on anti-arrythmia drugs. In a study of more than 700 cardiac patients with dangerous heart arrythmias, those treated with drugs were four times as likely to die suddenly from cardiac arrest as those with a defibrillator. In fact, drug treatment produced no better results than doing nothing. Researchers suggest that a defibrillator be used for cardiac patients with arrythmias reproducible during electrophysiological testing.

Alfred E. Buxton, MD, professor of medicine, Brown University Medical School, Providence, RI.

New High-Tech Weapons To Help You Win the War On Heart Disease

Gary Francis, MD, director of the coronary intensive care unit at the Cleveland Clinic.

Regular exercise, low-fat eating, not smoking and other "low-tech" approaches remain the cornerstones of heart health. *But recently there have been several exciting "high-tech" advances...*

CHOLESTEROL-LOWERING DRUGS

A class of drugs known as "statins" have become the drugs of choice for people with elevated cholesterol.

These prescription medications can cut cholesterol levels up to 40% in a matter of weeks.

And—new research shows that statins can reduce the risk for heart attack even in individuals with so-called "normal" cholesterol levels.

In light of this new evidence, doctors have begun prescribing statins for most heart attack patients...as well as certain patients at high risk for heart attack. Because these drugs have side effects, be sure to discuss the pros and cons with your doctor.

BYPASS ALTERNATIVE

An experimental technique called *transmyocardial revascularization* (TMR) is a boon for people with severe coronary artery disease, who are unlikely to benefit from angioplasty or bypass surgery. It involves the use of a laser to "punch" a dozen or so small holes in the heart's muscular wall.

Some cardiologists had considered TMR a bogus, pseudoscientific procedure. But now there's compelling evidence that TMR can improve blood flow to the heart, reducing angina pain.

How does TMR work? Most cardiologists now believe that TMR works by promoting the growth of new "micro-blood vessels" in the heart muscle...or by causing death of small sensory nerve endings in the heart.

MEDICATED STENTS

Angioplasty has become one of the most common procedures for reducing the fatty deposits (plaques) that threaten to occlude coronary arteries. In this procedure, a tiny balloon is inflated inside a coronary artery, squashing the plaque deposits against the artery wall and thus opening the artery for resumed blood flow.

The problem with angioplasty is that the cleared artery often clogs up again—sometimes in a matter of months.

To prevent this phenomenon (restenosis), doctors often line the cleared arteries with metallic mesh tubes. Called stents, these tubes act as scaffolding to keep the artery from clogging again.

Unfortunately, there can be regrowth of artery-clogging tissue in the artery even after the stent has been inserted.

Doctors have found that this form of restenosis can be treated via an experimental technique in which a tiny radioactive pellet is inserted into the stent.

HEART FAILURE SURGERY

Congestive heart failure (CHF) occurs when a person's heart becomes enlarged and weak. The condition has long been treated with digitalis, diuretics and other drugs. No surgical fix was available.

In the mid-1980s, a Brazilian surgeon named Randas Batista, MD, surprised cardiologists in the US when he reported having had success treating CHF surgically.

In the Batista procedure, the heart is effectively made smaller by removing a triangular piece of the heart and then sewing the heart back together. The Batista procedure is sometimes effective at controlling breathlessness, fatigue and other symptoms of CHF. But it is now being supplanted by the Dor procedure, which may be more effective. The Dor procedure was developed by Vincent Dor, MD.

The Dor technique gets rid of scar tissue (the aftermath of a heart attack) that underlies many cases of CHF. Once this scar tissue is removed, the heart can pump efficiently again.

HEART PUMP

Another important new development for heart failure patients is left-ventricular assist devices. These fist-sized devices—implanted in the patient's chest or abdomen—take over some of the heart's pumping duties. They're typically used as a "bridge" treatment for people awaiting heart transplantation.

Most Common Times for Heart Attacks to Strike

Most heart attacks occur during the morning or late evening. In a poll of heart attack sufferers, 25% said they were awakened by heart attack symptoms in the early morning. Another 25% said their heart attacks occurred within four hours of waking...and 20% said their attacks came 11 to 12 hours later—often following a heavy supper.

Robert W. Peters, MD, chief of cardiology, Veterans Affairs Medical Center, Baltimore. His study of more than 3,000 heart attack patients was published in the *Journal of the American College of Cardiology,* 9111 Old Georgetown Rd., Bethesda, MD 20814.

Heart attack deaths peak during December and January, when there are 33% more deaths from heart attacks than in summer and early fall. *Possible reasons:* Increased food, alcohol and salt consumption...additional stress...respiratory infections...and reduced hours of daylight.

Robert Kloner, MD, PhD, professor of medicine, University of Southern California, Los Angeles, leader of a study of deaths from heart disease during a 12-year period in Los Angeles, quoted online at *www.medscape.com.*

When Chest Pain Means Heart Attack And When It Doesn't

Chest pain is psychosomatic almost half the time, according to a study.

Key: If the pain is sharp and stabbing, or it's on the left side of the chest, it's likely caused by psychological stress. But a heavy, gripping sensation in the central chest is a typical heart attack symptom, especially if it lasts five or more minutes. Consult your doctor in either case.

Dr. Christopher Bass, King's College Hospital, London.

Heart Attack Symptoms ...Gender Differences

What are considered the classic signs of a heart attack are actually the symptoms experienced by men. Unfortunately, heart attacks in women are often undiagnosed—and untreated—because the signs of heart trouble are different. It is important to know the symptoms for each gender.

FOR WOMEN

- **Chest, stomach or abdominal pain that does not necessarily feel acute or crushing.**
- **Nausea or dizziness.**
- **Shortness of breath.**
- **Heart palpitations.**
- **Fatigue.**
- **General feeling of weakness.**

FOR MEN

- **Uncomfortable pressure,** fullness, squeezing or pain in the center of the chest that lasts more than a few minutes or quickly fades in and out.
- **Pain radiating to shoulders, neck, arms or jaw.**
- **Any of the above symptoms** accompanied by lightheadedness, sweating, nausea or shortness of breath.

Important: Whether man or woman, if you are having any of the above symptoms, immediately chew a full-strength (325 mgs) aspirin and get to the hospital as soon as possible.

Lynn Smaha, MD, PhD, president, American Heart Association, Dallas.

Controlling Blood Pressure Without Medication

Sheldon G. Sheps, MD, emeritus professor of medicine at Mayo Medical School, Clinic and Foundation, Rochester, MN, and chairman of the working group that produced the NHLBI guidelines on managing high blood pressure. He is editor in chief of *Mayo Clinic on High Blood Pressure.* Mayo Foundation.

High blood pressure is a time bomb—but it's one that ticks very quietly. This "silent killer" causes no symptoms, but elevated pressure in the arteries can, over years, cause severe damage to several organs.*

This damage sets the stage for stroke, heart attack, kidney failure...and premature death.

Fifteen million Americans are unaware that they have high blood pressure (hypertension). Of the 35 million who know they have it, only two out of five are getting adequate treatment.

A generation ago, doctors tended to think of blood pressure as being "normal" or "high." Now the National Heart, Lung and Blood Institute (NHLBI) recognizes six levels of blood pressure. *Each succeeding level is associated with a higher degree of risk...*

- **Normal**...below 120/80.
- **Prehypertension**...120/80 to 139/89.
- **Stage 1 hypertension**...140/90 to 159/99.
- **Stage 2 hypertension**...160/100 and above.

If you don't know your blood pressure, have a doctor check it. *If your pressure is elevated, here's how to get it down...*

*Blood pressure readings are expressed as fractions—130/80, for example. The numerator (top number) represents systolic pressure—that existing in the arteries when the heart's main pumping chamber (left ventricle) contracts. The denominator (bottom number) represents diastolic pressure—that which exists between beats.

- **Follow the DASH diet.** In 1997, the Dietary Approaches to Stop Hypertension (DASH) study concluded that high-normal people and stage 1 hypertensives could achieve significant reductions in blood pressure simply by switching to a diet that stresses fruits, vegetables, grains and dairy products.

On average, study participants who followed the DASH diet lowered their blood pressure by 11 points systolic...and 5.5 points diastolic.

That was virtually the same level of reduction that is typically achieved with pressure-lowering medication—without the side effects associated with medication.

The daily DASH meal plan consists of...

- Seven or eight servings of grains, bread, cereal or pasta—preferably whole-grain varieties.
- Eight to 10 servings of fruits and vegetables.
- Two or three servings of nonfat/low-fat dairy products.
- Two or fewer servings of meat, poultry or fish.

The DASH diet also calls for four or five servings per week of beans, peas, nuts or seeds.

- **Eat less salt.** Only about 40% of people with high blood pressure are salt-sensitive, but it's hard to know who falls into this category. For this reason, everyone should limit sodium intake to 2,500 mg a day...

- Read food labels and tally the sodium content of all the foods you eat in a typical day.
- Cut out offending foods—such as fast food, cheese, bacon, pickles—as required.
- Avoid salt at the dining table...and in food preparation. Flavor foods instead with red pepper, cumin, onion, dill, lemon, etc. It can take up to six weeks for your taste buds to adapt to less salt—so be patient.

- **Cut back on caffeine—and nicotine.** The caffeine in coffee, tea and soft drinks causes blood vessels to narrow for several hours, causing a transient rise in blood pressure. People with hypertension should limit their daily caffeine intake to two cups of coffee, four cups of tea or four cans of caffeinated soda.

Like caffeine, nicotine causes a transient rise in blood pressure. Smoking just two cigarettes boosts systolic *and* diastolic pressure by up to

10 points. This increase persists for up to 90 minutes.

●**Limit your drinking.** Excessive drinking—more than two drinks a day for men or one for women—is clearly a major contributor to hypertension. If your drinking exceeds these levels, cut back. Do so gradually, over a few weeks. Going "cold turkey" can cause a rapid and potentially dangerous rise in blood pressure.

●**Lose weight.** The heavier you are, the larger the network of blood vessels your body must maintain. The larger this network, the more forcefully your heart must pump. This means higher blood pressure. If you're overweight, losing even 10 pounds is often enough to lower your blood pressure one full level on the six-part scale.

●**Alleviate psychological stress.** Stress causes the body to produce hormones that constrict blood vessels, thereby raising your blood pressure. Get organized…make lists of tasks…set priorities…clean out clutter…say "no" to additional responsibilities…delegate work…try meditation and other relaxation techniques.

●**Get more physical activity.** Walking, cycling, running and other forms of aerobic exercise boost your heart's pumping efficiency. The more efficient your heart, the wider the arteries open and the less forcefully the heart must contract.

Bonus: Regular exercise helps alleviate stress and promotes weight loss—thereby augmenting its pressure-lowering effect. Aim for five to seven 30-minute workout sessions weekly.

Silent Stroke Warning Sign

Sudden depression in someone over age 50 may signal a "silent stroke."

These silent strokes occur when small blood vessels in the brain become blocked or rupture, interfering with the brain's ability to produce the mood-regulating chemicals serotonin and norepinephrine.

Silent strokes don't result in classic symptoms (severe headache, dizziness, loss of motor skills), but are often the precursor to full stroke.

Older people who show signs of sudden depression, such as apathy or loss of interest in usual activities, should be closely monitored by their doctors.

David C. Steffens, MD, assistant professor of psychiatry, Duke University Medical Center, Durham, NC.

Seven Out of 10 Stroke Patients Suffer Disability or Death

Thomas G. Brott, MD, professor of neurology at the Mayo Clinic in Jacksonville, Florida. While serving as director of the Stroke Research Center at the University of Cincinnati Medical Center, Dr. Brott helped to develop one of the most successful citywide emergency stroke treatment programs in the US. He is coauthor of a review of stroke treatment published in The New England Journal of Medicine, *10 Shattuck St., Boston 02115.*

Every 53 seconds, an American suffers a stroke. Unfortunately, one in three people does not recognize the symptoms quickly enough to benefit fully from state-of-the-art diagnostic methods and treatments.

If you—or someone you know—suffers a stroke, your response time in seeking medical treatment can mean the difference between full recovery and permanent disability or death.

CAUSES OF STROKE

Think of stroke as a "brain attack." It occurs when the flow of blood—and the oxygen it carries—to the brain is interrupted.

Result: Body functions controlled by oxygen-deprived brain cells may be weakened or lost.

In an *ischemic* stroke, the more common type, a blood clot blocks a blood vessel, usually an artery. It is typically painless but causes weakness, paralysis or loss of sensation on one side of the body…loss of vision in one eye…sudden confusion, trouble speaking or understanding…and/or staggering or inability to walk.

In a *hemorrhagic* stroke, rarer and more dangerous, a blood vessel bursts, leaking blood into the brain or surrounding area. This usually causes a severe headache…difficulty breathing …nausea…and/or vomiting.

Good news: A clot-busting medication known as *tissue plasminogen activator*—or tPA (Activase)—is effective at preventing brain damage—but only in ischemic stroke victims and only if it is administered within three hours of the onset of symptoms.

EVERY MINUTE COUNTS

If you experience or witness even one stroke symptom, call 911 immediately. Stroke victims may be unable to speak to medical personnel, but a family member or friend can help ensure proper care. *Here's how…*

An up-to-date list of all medications the patient takes is crucial for appropriate stroke treatment. Make sure such a list is in his/her wallet and/or posted on the refrigerator. That's where emergency medical technicians (EMTs) routinely look for this information.

Next best: Put the patient's medications in a paper bag and take it to the hospital.

When the ambulance arrives, ask the EMTs to take the patient to the nearest hospital that uses tPA.

Remind the EMTs to alert the hospital's emergency room (ER) that a possible stroke patient is en route. This allows the ER staff to notify the hospital's stroke team or neurologist on duty…and ask the pharmacy to be ready to do immediate (stat) blood tests.

DIAGNOSIS

In the ER, a physician should take the patient's vital signs and request a computed tomography (CT) scan or magnetic resonance imaging (MRI) scan to identify the type of stroke that has occurred, its precise location in the brain and the extent of the damage.

CT scans are routinely used, but MRI scans provide more information. CT scans are preferable if the patient is agitated, however, because MRIs require him to remain still during the procedure.

When tPA is administered intravenously for about one hour or via a catheter directly into the brain, it dissolves 60% to 80% of stroke-related blood clots.

Danger: The drug can cause life-threatening brain hemorrhage if it is used beyond the three-hour cutoff…in patients who have suffered a hemorrhagic stroke…or in people who take the blood thinner warfarin (Coumadin).

In patients who are not candidates for tPA, treatment involves controlling the heart rhythm, stabilizing blood pressure and monitoring brain function.

For all stroke patients, the doctor should also order tests that examine blood flow to the brain to determine the cause of the stroke.

Common causes of stroke: Blockage of the blood vessels in the neck or brain from hardening of the arteries…blood clots in the aorta, the artery that leads to the heart…and blockage of the small blood vessels in the brain, often related to high blood pressure.

HOSPITALIZATION

Stroke patients who have suffered a hemorrhagic stroke…received tPA…or are in serious or unstable condition are typically transferred from the ER to the intensive-care unit (ICU). Other stroke patients are admitted to a general neurological unit. Doctors then watch for medical complications. Because a stroke can affect breathing, movement and swallowing, pneumonia can develop. A blood clot in a leg vein can move to the lungs, causing a life-threatening pulmonary blood clot (embolus).

REHABILITATION

Within two days of the stroke, rehabilitation typically begins in the hospital's rehab unit. Patients work with physical, speech and occupational therapists to relearn basic skills, such as eating, dressing and walking.

Depending on the severity of the stroke, patients continue their rehabilitation at home or at an inpatient rehabilitation facility. Although some patients require long-term care in a skilled nursing facility, up to two-thirds of stroke survivors regain their independence within one year.

Important: Notify a physician if the stroke patient develops a fever of 101°F or higher. This can be a sign of infection or another serious complication.

Up to 30% of stroke patients develop depression. Signs include persistent sadness…and/or changes in sleep habits or appetite. Such patients should consult a psychiatrist or other experienced psychotherapist.

PREVENTION

Of course, the best way to minimize damage from strokes is to prevent them in the first place. *Best:*

- **Eat a diet that is low in fat.**

- **Exercise regularly.**

- **Eliminate risk factors such as being overweight and smoking.**

- **See a doctor on a routine basis for blood-pressure checks.** Seek regular treatment if you have medical risk factors, such as diabetes or heart disease.

- **Don't take oral contraceptives if you smoke.** If you live with a smoker, consult your doctor to determine whether or not contraceptives are safe for you.

- **Avoid over-the-counter diet pills.** Most contain ingredients that increase the risk of stroke.

Finally, people who have aneurysms can elect to have surgical treatment that can prevent stroke.

What happens: Blood flow to the aneurysm is prevented with the placement of a permanent metal clip at the base of the aneurysm that allows blood to flow normally through the rest of the artery.

When Stroke Treatment Is Most Effective

Treatment for stroke is most effective when administered within six hours of the onset of symptoms. Seek help immediately if you experience unexplained weakness on one side of the body...loss of vision or double vision...difficulty speaking...numbness on either side of the body...severe dizziness or loss of balance.

David Sherman, MD, professor and chief, department of medicine/neurology, University of Texas Health Science Center, San Antonio.

Dangerous New Infectious Diseases

Mohammad N. Akhter, MD, MPH, executive director of the American Public Health Association and clinical professor of family and community medicine at Georgetown University Medical School, both in Washington, DC.

Nowadays, it's very easy for people to travel to and from places that used to be too remote to visit. When people travel, infectious diseases travel with them.

From West Nile virus and Ebola virus to Marburg virus and hantavirus infection, new diseases can crop up anytime, anywhere.

We're also threatened by Lyme disease and variants of "old" diseases, such as tuberculosis. Even influenza remains a major threat. Each flu epidemic kills 20,000 to 40,000 people in the US.

HANTAVIRUS INFECTION

This potentially lethal virus is contracted through contact with feces of infected rodents. It first appeared in the southwest US in 1993 and has shown up in a dozen states since.

The people most likely to contract hantavirus include workers who enter the crawl spaces under houses...and anyone who spends time in places where they could touch or inhale rodent droppings.

Many victims say they didn't even *see* rodents or droppings.

Symptoms: Fatigue, fever and muscle aches in the beginning. Later on, coughing and shortness of breath.

Treatment: None for the hantavirus itself. But people who seek emergency care have a better chance of surviving respiratory distress—the deadliest problem associated with this infection.

Prevention: Protect yourself against rodents. Keep your kitchen clean. Whenever possible, stay out of barns and sheds. Clear away brush that could provide nesting places. If rodents are a problem in your neighborhood, alert your local public health department at once.

INFLUENZA

New flu strains emerge every year. A flu shot provides some protection—but it's not foolproof.

Symptoms: Headache, runny nose, sore throat, fever and fatigue. Serious complications, such as pneumonia, can be fatal.

Treatment: Liquids, good nutrition, bed rest and aspirin help control symptoms. Ask your doctor about the antiviral drugs that are now available for influenza—*amantadine* (Symmetrel), *rimantadine* (Flumadine), *oseltamavir* (Tamiflu) and *zanamivir* (Relenza).

Prevention: Get an annual flu shot as soon as it becomes available (typically in October).

Especially if the vaccine is in short supply—wash your hands frequently...stay in good physical shape...get adequate sleep...and eat healthfully to support your immune system.

LYME DISEASE

This tick-borne viral illness is a growing problem in the Northeast, mid-Atlantic and upper Midwest.

Symptoms: A rash that resembles a bull's-eye and swollen lymph glands near the bite. As the illness progresses, joint pain, facial palsy and fever. In the worst cases, arthritis, personality changes and memory loss may also occur.

Treatment: Oral antibiotics can usually cure Lyme disease if it has been caught early. Once the infection has progressed, intravenous antibiotics are used—but may not always be effective.

Prevention: Before going into wooded areas, use insect repellent containing DEET. Wear closed-toe shoes, a long-sleeved shirt and long pants. Choose light-colored clothing, which makes it easier to spot ticks.

Walk in the center of trails to avoid brushing against vegetation that might harbor ticks. Avoid sitting on the ground. Once a day, do a full-body "tick check."

You might also consider getting the Lyme vaccine. Lymerix appears to prevent the illness, but there have been reports of severe reactions, including arthritis.

WEST NILE VIRUS

Over the past few years, this mosquito-borne illness has caused a potentially deadly brain inflammation known as West Nile encephalitis.

Symptoms: Flu-like illness, headache, rash, neck stiffness, muscle weakness, incoherence and paralysis.

Treatment: None for the illness itself. Anyone who exhibits suspicious symptoms should seek immediate medical help.

Prevention: During warm weather, protect yourself against mosquitoes when outdoors. Apply insect repellent containing DEET. Wear long pants and a long-sleeved shirt.

Remove any standing water, where mosquitoes like to breed. Stay inside at dawn and dusk, when mosquito populations are at their highest.

17

All About Hospitals, Surgery, Medical Procedures and Tests

How to Prepare for Common Diagnostic Tests And Surgical Procedures

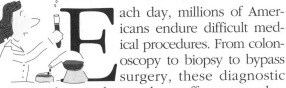Each day, millions of Americans endure difficult medical procedures. From colonoscopy to biopsy to bypass surgery, these diagnostic tests and surgical procedures affect us psychologically as well as physically.

Will the procedure hurt? Are there risks? Will it put me in an embarrassing position? Even worse, we fear the outcome. Do I have cancer? Will I need surgery? Will the treatment work? Could I die?

At the crux of these anxieties lies the fear of losing control. *Here's how to regain that sense of control...*

•**Make sure you know *why* you need the test or procedure.** People who lack a clear understanding of why they need a particular procedure require more pain medication and recover more slowly than do people who undergo the procedure with all their questions answered. *Ask the doctor...*

•Why do I need this test or treatment?

•What will happen if I don't have it? If it's a diagnostic test, how will the results affect my treatment?

•What risks and side effects are associated with this procedure? How common are they?

•Are alternative procedures less invasive and/or less costly?

•How likely is a successful outcome?

Do not shy away from asking any question that occurs to you. Worried that you'll be left with an unsightly scar? That your sex life will be affected? Discuss your concerns with the doctor.

•**Find out exactly what to expect.** Videotapes that detail what you'll experience may be available through your doctor's office, hospital or diagnostic treatment center.

Bernie Siegel, MD, author of several books, including *Love, Medicine & Miracles* (HarperPerennial), and creator of *Getting Ready* (Hay House), an audiocassette that helps patients prepare for medical tests and procedures.

247

If not, contact the practitioner slated to administer the test or procedure to ask if you can stop by for a quick preview of the equipment that will be used.

This can be especially helpful if you're unusually apprehensive about the procedure.

Example: If you are afraid that a magnetic resonance imaging (MRI) scan will make you feel claustrophobic, you may be relieved to discover that newer MRI scanners are "open"—that is, during the procedure you won't have to lie in a narrow tube.

Once you've gotten all the information you need to make the decision about whether to undergo the procedure, it's *your* decision to make. After all, you are in charge of your own life.

•**Mentally rehearse the experience.** I recommend *guided imagery,* a visualization technique often used by athletes.

What to do: Sit in a comfortable chair, close your eyes and breathe deeply for a minute or so. Picture yourself undergoing the procedure one step at a time. See yourself walking into the exam room...chatting calmly with the nurse...positioning yourself. Notice that you feel relaxed, pain free and "in control."

As you see yourself completing the procedure, imagine yourself feeling energized and happy that you took the steps necessary to get your health back on track.

Use this technique four times a day for the week leading up to the procedure, and you'll have "completed" 28 successful procedures before the actual event.

In addition to giving you more confidence, this "programs" your body to experience less pain and fewer side effects.

•**Seek help from family and friends ...and from other patients who have "been there, done that."** Share your concerns with those closest to you. If you'd like someone to accompany you on the day of the procedure, ask. Be sure to make it easy for the person to say "no" if he/she doesn't feel up to the task.

Many hospitals conduct support group and group therapy sessions for breast cancer patients, heart patients, etc. But if you just want to chat with someone who has had, say, a liver biopsy or thallium stress test, ask your doctor if he can put you in touch with someone.

Most people are happy to share their experiences.

•**During the test or procedure, "go" someplace else you'd rather be.** Close your eyes, breathe deeply and visualize yourself in an environment where you feel safe and relaxed.

Maybe it's lying on a beach, listening to the surf...hiking in a forest...or just sitting at home in your favorite easy chair.

Focus on *every* detail of the setting, including sights, sounds and odors. If you lose track of time, you'll forget about your fear—and may not even feel any pain.

If you have trouble being visual, consult a hypnotherapist. Ask him to help you prepare a visualization audiotape that you can listen to during the procedure.

To find a hypnotherapist in your area, contact the American Society of Clinical Hypnosis, 33 W. Grand Ave., Suite 402, Chicago 60610. 630-980-4740.

Another option: Many people find slow baroque music, such as Pachelbel's *Canon,* especially tranquilizing during a procedure. But any music you enjoy and associate with positive feelings can be beneficial.

Ask your surgeon or anesthesiologist if you may bring along your own tape player or CD player and headphones.

You might even ask about aromatherapy. Doctors at Memorial Sloan-Kettering Cancer Center in New York City reported recently that the percentage of patients who panicked during MRIs dropped dramatically once the exam room was scented with vanilla and music was played.

•**Keep smiling.** Rent a humorous videotape or buy a book of jokes to keep your spirits high in the days before and after the procedure. Laughter is a terrific antidote to tension. What's more, studies show that it alters brain chemistry, producing more of the body's natural painkillers.

How to Get VIP Treatment In a Hospital

The first thing an admitting clerk does when you're brought into a hospital is slip a plastic tag with an identity number onto your wrist. From that point on, like it or not, you are a number to most of the hospital staff.

Being a number instead of a name can be an awful shock. It means that you may be treated as if you have no identity—except for your symptoms, vital signs and medical treatment.

Fortunately, there are steps you can take to improve that treatment. And those steps, if successful, not only will make you feel more comfortable and human during your hospital visit, they could dramatically affect your state of health by the time you're ready to be discharged. In fact, it may be the issue that determines whether you leave alive or dead.

So how do you get the hospital to treat you like a person instead of a number?

In general, you've got to use the same techniques you use in other aspects of your personal and business life. The key word is assertiveness.

FINDING THE RIGHT DOCTOR

The first step in getting VIP treatment in a hospital should be taken long before you're admitted—and that's finding a doctor who can provide the leverage you'll need. You want someone with more than an MD after his name.

Every community has a clique of doctors who have "political" clout. Usually, these are physicians who serve on the local hospital's board of directors. Be aware, however, that a doctor with clout doesn't necessarily have the skills or any other attributes that make a physician a superior healer. Do you want such a person as your personal physician? Generally speaking, the answer is no, but there are exceptions. If you're satisfied that such a doctor can serve double-duty, so to speak, then you need go no further.

The drawbacks: Aside from the possibility that such a doctor may be more expert in a boardroom than an operating room, there are other potential problems.

The most serious: He may be more interested in keeping his professional calendar and the institution's beds filled than in your welfare.

If he wants to admit you to the hospital for treatment and there is any doubt in your mind about this decision, ask for a consultation with another doctor.

We've heard of many instances where doctors are annoyed when a patient wants a second opinion. If you ever face a less-than-cooperative response to such a request, seek out another doctor immediately. It's well within your rights to consult with as many physicians as you wish.

THE PERSONAL TOUCH

To guarantee better attention once you know that you're going to spend time in the hospital, make a date with the hospital administrator. Introduce yourself. Tell him that you're a little concerned about your hospital stay and that you'd appreciate it if he'd take a personal interest in your case.

He'll get the message, and in all likelihood, he'll make sure that you're well cared for. Now that you've made your presence known, he will probably, out of courtesy, call the head of nursing and the admitting office and tell them you're coming to the hospital and that they should be expecting you. It's just such words, without pressure, that may make all the difference in the way you're subsequently treated.

ONCE YOU'RE IN THE HOSPITAL

There are still things you can do to ensure good treatment, if not VIP treatment.

●**During the admission procedure, ask what rooms are available.** You may prefer a private room, or for the sake of company, you may want to share a room with someone else. If you do want to share, ask about your potential partner's medical status to be sure that you can deal with his illness.

●**After settling into your room, ask to see the dietitian.** Explain that you understand that the hospital is not a hotel, but within reasonable bounds, and limited by doctor's orders, there are foods that you do and do not like. Itemize them. If you present your request with tact, the dietitian will probably try to meet your reasonable requests.

●**Go out of your way to be polite to the nursing staff.** They are your lifeline—literally. If the nurses take a dislike to you, the recuperation period will not be smooth.

• **It's not tacky to provide small favors,** such as a box of candy, and even flowers, on each of the three nursing shifts: the 8 am to 4 pm, the 4 pm to midnight and midnight to 8 am. Don't offer a gratuity until you're ready to be discharged. Nurses are professionals, and most would resent the offer. But if you received extra special care from a nurse during your stay, a tasteful gift isn't inappropriate.

• **Make it clear that you'd like to know what medication or treatment is being given to you beforehand.** That will require a discussion with your doctor. Most doctors work on the premise that patients don't want to know too much, and so only provide information as it's necessary or if the patient specifically requests it.

Why you should want this information: Unfortunately, mistakes are made now and then, but if you ask the nurse, "What are these pills?" or, "What exactly will you be doing to me?", and she has orders from your doctor to provide that information on request, then it gives the staff the opportunity to double-check what they are doing and it gives you a chance to say, "Wait a minute!" if an obvious error is being committed.

How to complain: If you're not happy with your care, explain your complaint firmly and politely to the nurse. If that gets you no place, ask to speak to the head nurse. And if that fails, you may have to speak to either your doctor or the hospital administrator. Usually, when you reach that level, and you're not being unreasonable, steps will be taken to satisfy your complaint and resolve your problem.

Planning Pays: How to Get the Best Care in a Medical Emergency

Peter Canning, EMT-P (emergency medical technician-paramedic) in Hartford, Connecticut. He is author of Paramedic: On the Front Lines of Medicine. *Fawcett Columbine.*

If you or a loved one ever requires emergency care, here's how to get the fastest, most effective help possible...

• **Make sure your home is easy to spot.** Emergency Medical Service (EMS) personnel often waste precious time trying to locate the victim's home—especially at night, when house numbers are hard to identify.

Mark your house with large, reflective numbers and/or paint your house number on the curb with fluorescent paint. Trim any foliage that might obscure your address.

If an emergency occurs, turn on all the lights—including your porch light. If possible, ask someone to stand out front to wave down the ambulance.

• **Post your medical information in a prominent place.** EMS workers also waste time searching patients' homes for medicine bottles and other clues about their health status.

To save time: Write a brief medical history of yourself (and anyone else living in the house) on an index card. Tape the card to your refrigerator door. Be sure to include...

• Your doctor's name and telephone number.
• Medical conditions you have.
• Allergies you have.
• Names and dosages of all drugs you take.
• Name of your insurance carrier, plus your group and personal identification numbers.

• **Prepare your phones for emergency use.** If you have a chronic ailment, install a phone in every room of your house.

If your community lacks 911 service, program the phones with the local emergency number (typically the police or fire department).

• **When phoning for help,** be sure to give the right information. Be as specific as possible.

Sample script: "My husband is having chest pains and severe dizziness. He has a history of heart disease."

• **Don't delay calling for help.** People experiencing persistent chest pain or pressure sometimes tell themselves, "It's probably just indigestion. I'll wait to see if it goes away." Some wait so long that doctors cannot save them.

Especially if you're having a heart attack or stroke, the sooner you get medical attention, the better. Emergency personnel can administer lifesaving drugs before you get to the hospital...and alert the emergency room staff so that they can prepare to care for you without delay.

Reused Medical Device Warning

Single-use medical devices—such as syringes, cardiac catheters, obstetrical forceps, laser tips and intubation tubes—are increasingly being cleaned, sterilized and reused by doctors and hospital workers to cut costs, putting patients at greater risk for infection. *Self-defense:* At the time a procedure is to be performed, tell the doctor or nurse that you do not want a resterilized single-use product. Request that only new devices be used for your care.

Charles Inlander, president, People's Medical Society, 462 Walnut St., Allentown, PA 18102.

Tape Trap

Hospital tape—often used to secure intravenous lines to the body—is sterile when it comes out of the box. But in a recent study, 74% of opened rolls were found to harbor bacteria. And 92% of tape samples removed from patients were contaminated. This finding may help explain why one in 20 patients develops an infection while hospitalized. *Self-defense:* Ask hospital workers to use a new roll of tape—or to unravel it at least one full turn—before using it on you.

Don Redelmeier, MD, associate professor of medicine, University of Toronto Faculty of Medicine. His study of bacterial growth on hospital tape was published in the *Journal of General Internal Medicine,* University and Woodland Aves., Philadelphia 19104.

Medication Alert

Medication errors at hospitals would be cut in half if all hospitals used computerized drug-dispensing systems. *Reasons:* These systems eliminate handwriting problems…labels are scanned at the patient's bedside to confirm that the correct drugs have been dispensed. *Problem:* Currently, few US hospitals have these systems.

Charles Inlander, president, People's Medical Society, 462 Walnut St., Allentown, PA 18102.

Intravenous Fluid Danger

Emergency intravenous fluids may do more harm than good when given to patients with severe bleeding. For decades, bleeding has been treated with an intravenous solution of saline or Ringer's lactate—given immediately, in an attempt to elevate the patient's blood pressure and to prevent organ damage and shock.

Finding: Among patients given intravenous fluids immediately, 62% survived. The survival rate among patients given intravenous fluids after the bleeding had stopped was 70%. *Also:* Patients given fluids after the stoppage of bleeding left the hospital sooner and had fewer complications.

Theory: Fluids encourage bleeding both by keeping blood pressure high and by diluting coagulants in the blood.

William H. Bickell, MD, director of research, St. Francis Hospital, Tulsa. His 37-month study of 289 trauma patients treated at Houston's Ben Taub General Hospital was published in *The New England Journal of Medicine,* 10 Shattuck St., Boston 02115.

Better Hospital Recuperation

Patients whose rooms contained water-dominated nature photographs reported substantially less postoperative anxiety than those whose rooms contained photos of trees, abstract paintings…or a blank wall. Those exposed to the water photo also needed the least-strong pain medications.

Self-defense: Bring your own pictures for the hospital wall—ones that you like and find relaxing to look at.

Study of 160 Swedish cardiac patients, led by Roger Ulrich, PhD, professor, College of Architecture, Texas A&M University, College Station.

When You Need More Time In the Hospital

Timothy McCall, MD, an internist based in Boston, and author of *Examining Your Doctor: A Patient's Guide to Avoiding Harmful Medical Care*. Citadel Press.

In an effort to boost their bottom lines, HMOs and other managed-care plans have dramatically reduced the lengths of their patients' hospital stays. To remain competitive, many traditional insurers are adopting similar tactics.

For bypass surgery, stays of two weeks were common just a few years ago. Now it's down to four days. Women having hysterectomies sometimes get as few as two days in the hospital.

This isn't all bad. There's good scientific evidence that hospital stays were too long in the past. Under the old system, doctors and hospitals had a financial incentive to keep patients hospitalized as long as possible. Under managed care, doctors can be penalized—or even fired—if their patients stay longer than the HMO deems necessary.

Unfortunately, the logic used by HMOs seems to be, "If cutting a little was good, then cutting more is better."

Example: Childbirth is the leading cause of hospitalization. In 1970, women having normal deliveries stayed an average of four days. By 1992, it was two days. A few years later, however, some California plans were hustling mothers out of the hospital after only eight hours.

In response, laws were passed mandating that insurers pay for two-day stays for normal deliveries and four days for C-sections. Unfortunately, these laws don't help people who are hospitalized for other reasons.

PROTECT YOURSELF

How can you prevent your loved ones or yourself from being thrown out of the hospital too early? *Be assertive*. Keep in mind that in calculating when to send you home, managed-care plans rely on best-case scenarios. Be prepared to explain why your case may not fit that definition.

If your specified number of days is up but you don't feel well enough to go home, tell your doctor (or have a family member do so for you). Though they don't always tell their patients, doctors have the ability to challenge the discharge decisions of insurance companies and hospital "utilization reviewers." If necessary, make your case to the hospital ombudsman.

The major determinant of whether it's okay to go home early is your medical condition. Any fever should be resolved. You should be able to take food by mouth. You shouldn't be so confused or lightheaded that you risk falling when you walk to the bathroom. If you've had surgery, you should be able to urinate on your own, and your pain must be controllable with oral medications.

The other important determinant is the situation at home. Is the environment conducive to healing? Will someone be there to take care of you? Will your insurer arrange for visiting nurses or other home care? Is there adequate backup if a problem arises? If these conditions aren't met, alert your doctor and your insurance company.

Many people prefer to recover at home—if it's feasible. The surroundings are familiar, and there's more privacy. And given the risk of catching infections or developing other complications in the hospital, it makes sense to be discharged as soon as you can.

But the decision should be based on what makes sense medically—not on the HMO's bottom line.

Most Frequent Hospital Bill Mistake

Ninety-seven percent of hospital bills are wrong, and less than 2% of those errors are in the patient's favor. *Average error:* $1,400.

Frequent mistake: Billing for items or services never delivered (lab work, medication, thermometers, wheelchairs, etc.).

Self-defense: Insist on completely itemized bills...and review them carefully.

Harvey Rosenfield, head of the watchdog group Bills Project.

Secrets of Successful Anesthesia for Very Successful Surgery

Jeanette Liska, PhD, founder of Awareness with Anesthesia Research Education (AWARE), 1563 Summit Ave., Cardiff by the Sea, CA 92007.

In the 28 million surgical procedures performed each year, about 250,000 patients report being painfully and traumatically aware during the operation. Here's what to do to reduce the odds of that happening to you.

Questions to ask your anesthesiologist or nurse anesthetist—prior to your surgery…

●**Will I need a muscle relaxant?** Anesthesia is usually a combination of drugs. This mix typically includes a drug to knock you out…a hypnotic drug to help hinder memories…and a muscle relaxant to prevent movement during surgery. But if a muscle relaxant is used, it might be impossible for you to signal anyone if the anesthesia isn't working properly.

●For surgery under 30 minutes, a muscle relaxant might not be necessary. If a muscle relaxant isn't necessary, ask that it not be used. Without it, signaling the surgeon will be easy.

●For longer procedures—such as heart, spine or brain surgery—a muscle relaxant is a must.

●**What hypnotic drug will I be given?** Based on my study of 11,000 patients, the drug *Versed* led to the fewest awareness episodes, however, it appears to last for less time than *Propofol,* the common alternative.

Request a monitor that measures consciousness. These monitors have sensors that are attached to your head to track brain-wave activity.

Example: Aspect Medical (Natick, Massachusetts) makes a monitor now used in more than 175 hospitals nationwide.

If an awareness monitor is not available at the hospital your surgeon chooses for a procedure, consider asking to use a hospital that has one.

Blood Transfusion Self-Defense

James P. AuBuchon, MD, professor of pathology and medicine at Dartmouth–Hitchcock Medical Center in Lebanon, NH. He is coauthor of an article on transfusion medicine that appeared recently in *The New England Journal of Medicine,* 10 Shattuck St., Boston 02115.

Just when Americans were feeling reassured about the safety of the nation's blood supply, a new scare has emerged concerning mad-cow disease (bovine spongiform encephalopathy, or BSE). That's the deadly neurological disease that swept through cattle herds in England a few years ago.

James P. AuBuchon, MD, a distinguished specialist in transfusion medicine, answers some important questions.

●**Is it possible to get mad-cow disease from a blood transfusion?** In 1999, US blood banks began turning away potential donors who had spent more than six months in the United Kingdom between 1980 and 1996. The move was prompted by the fear that people who had eaten beef from cattle with BSE might themselves become infected…and pass on infectious blood.

There's *no* evidence that the disease can be transmitted through blood. We know that a related human disease—Creutzfeldt-Jakob disease—is not transmissible via blood.

●**How about getting AIDS from a transfusion?** The risk of contracting AIDS from donated blood plummeted in the 1980s. That's when blood banks started using screening tests that detected antibodies to the AIDS virus—a sure sign that the virus was present.

But some risk remained, because of the two-week "window" between the time of infection and the time that antibodies appear in the blood.

By 1995, when additional tests were added, the risk that a particular unit of blood was infected with the AIDS virus was one in 676,000. That's a very tiny number, but still worrisome.

Today, the risk of getting AIDS-infected blood from a transfusion is about one in a million. That's because blood banks have added *nucleic-acid testing* (NAT), in which the AIDS virus itself—and not antibodies to it—is detected.

●**How about other viral infections?** Several other viruses can be spread via transfusion. The most serious is hepatitis C, which can lead to cirrhosis and possibly liver failure or liver cancer.

The good news is that NAT ferrets out the hepatitis C virus as well as the AIDS virus, so the risk that a unit of blood contains hepatitis C is now one in 500,000.

NAT does not detect the hepatitis B virus, which typically causes muscle aches, fever and fatigue but which can also destroy the liver. Fortunately, other tests do detect it. The risk of getting a unit of blood that contains the hepatitis B virus is one in 63,000.

●**I've seen ads for "premium" blood that's guaranteed to be safe. Is that a good idea?** The ads, which have been appearing in newspapers, are for a product called *Plas+SD*.

Actually, this isn't "whole" blood. It's blood *plasma* that's been chemically treated to destroy the viruses that cause AIDS and hepatitis B and C.*

A one-pint unit of Plas+SD costs about $85, as compared with $45 or so for a unit of untreated plasma.

Since NAT effectively screens out AIDS and hepatitis C, the only meaningful advantage of Plas+SD is a reduced risk for hepatitis B.

In any case, most transfusions involve red cells—not plasma.

●**What about donating blood for myself?** You can set aside a pint or more of your own blood before surgery. Called *autologous donation,* this technique became popular when the AIDS virus threatened the nation's blood supply.

Now that blood is carefully screened, however, there's less advantage in going this route. Your blood is only a tiny bit safer than a stranger's blood. And, of course, autologous donation does nothing to prevent the possibility that a mix-up in the blood bank could cause you to receive the wrong—incompatible—blood.

Receiving incompatible blood kills two dozen Americans a year—and there's really nothing patients can do to eliminate this small risk.

*Plasma is a straw-colored liquid that's left over when blood has been stripped of its oxygen-carrying red cells. It's typically given in cases of massive blood loss.

Autologous donation should be considered only if you're facing orthopedic surgery or some other operation that's likely to cause significant blood loss.

Make the donation well in advance of the surgery to give your red cell count time to recover. Red cells can be stored for about six weeks.

●**What can I do to reduce the need for transfusion?** If you're anemic and/or facing major surgery, ask your doctor about taking the hormone *erythropoietin.* Administered a few weeks before surgery, it can crank up production of red cells.

During certain operations, special cell-washing devices can be used to collect and reinfuse red cells that come out of your body.

Some surgeons have begun doing so-called "bloodless" surgery, in which various techniques are used to minimize blood loss. These include reducing blood pressure, administering certain drugs and careful cutting and suturing.

These blood-saving techniques may be appropriate if you are undergoing surgery in which there is potential to lose a lot of blood, such as cardiovascular or orthopedic surgery. Discuss the matter with your doctor.

Good News for Hemorrhoid Sufferers

Painful hemorrhoid surgery may soon be a thing of the past. Patients who underwent *neodymium:YAG* laser surgery reported 65% less pain than did those who had traditional scalpel surgery. *More:* The laser surgery group experienced fewer complications…and returned to work faster.

Khalique Zahir, MD, plastic surgery fellow, Vanderbilt University School of Medicine, Nashville, TN. His study of 50 hemorrhoid sufferers was presented at a recent meeting of the American Society for Laser Medicine and Surgery.

Safer Gallstone Surgery

The *laparoscopic* technique reduces the likelihood of death by 80%, compared with the traditional "open" surgical technique. In laparoscopic surgery, stones are removed via a narrow "telescope" inserted through four small incisions in the abdomen. Conventional "open" gallbladder surgery necessitates a much larger incision.

Claudia A. Steiner, MD, MPH, senior fellow, Johns Hopkins University, Baltimore. Her review of discharge records at 54 Maryland hospitals was published in *The New England Journal of Medicine,* 10 Shattuck St., Boston 02115.

Hernia Operation

The "plug-and-patch" method is cheaper, safer and faster-healing than the standard surgical techniques. The plug, shaped like a badminton birdie, fills the hernia defect. A mesh patch covers the repair site. Plug-and-patch is done with local rather than general anesthesia. Patients can resume normal activity in three days, as opposed to weeks or months with standard techniques. The recurrence rate with plug-and-patch is virtually zero, in contrast to 10% to 15% for other methods. The technique is now widely available.

Keith W. Millikan, MD, associate professor of surgery, Rush–Presbyterian-St. Luke's Medical Center, Chicago.

No More Stitches

The surgical zipper is often a good alternative to sutures and staples as a means of closing incisions. The device consists of a polyester patch with a polyethylene zipper running lengthwise down the middle. An adhesive backing secures the patch to the skin. To close an incision, the surgeon places one edge of the zipper on each side, then pulls the zipper's tab to bring skin edges together. The zipper is quicker to apply than sutures and staples,

leaves a smaller scar and can be peeled off in the shower after about 10 days.

Mitchell Roslin, MD, director of bariatric surgery, Maimonides Medical Center, Brooklyn, NY.

Eight Questions That Could Save Your Life

Ervin Moss, MD, executive medical director of the New Jersey State Society of Anesthesiologists in Princeton Junction and clinical professor of anesthesiology at Robert Wood Johnson Medical Center in New Brunswick, NJ.

Surgery has moved outside the hospital surgical suite. Thirteen percent of all surgical procedures are now done in doctors' private offices. By 2005 that figure is expected to rise to 20%. That's almost 10 million operations a year. These include cataract surgery...biopsies...ear tube insertions...cosmetic and plastic surgery...and hernia repairs.

Office surgery costs less than similar procedures done in hospitals or outpatient surgical facilities. It can be more convenient and "patient friendly," too. But office surgery also poses potential risks.

Even the best-equipped doctor's office lacks the state-of-the-art surgical suites and extensive support staffs found in hospitals. Some in-office surgeons lack the training required of their hospital counterparts. And office surgery generally isn't regulated by state or national agencies.

That's not to say that surgical procedures can't be done safely in doctors' offices. But before bypassing the hospital, patients should ask the surgeon...

●**Do you have hospital privileges to perform this procedure?** Surgeons earn hospital privileges—the right to operate in the hospital—by undergoing intensive scrutiny. Only surgeons who provide exemplary care get the privileges.

Surgeons who work in office settings may not have those privileges. And if they have a high rate of poor outcomes, they normally aren't required to report it.

255

Also important: Ask your doctor if he/she is board-certified for the type of surgery to be done. Certification means that the surgeon has completed an accredited residency program and has passed a rigorous certification exam.

● **How many similar procedures have you performed?** Surgeons get better with practice. A surgeon who has done only a few dozen procedures is still learning. Patients should choose surgeons who have performed many operations similar to the one they will undergo.

● **Who will administer the anesthetic?** The person administering the anesthetic should be a board-certified anesthesiologist or a certified nurse-practitioner-anesthetist. That's a registered nurse (RN) who has had two years of specialized training in anesthesiology.

States have standards regarding the types of anesthetic that nurse-anesthetists can administer in the hospital and the circumstances under which they can do so. These standards vary among states. Ask your doctor which standards his hospital follows. His in-office surgical practice should follow the same standards.

● **Is your office prepared for emergencies?** Are resuscitation and life-support equipment and medicine on hand in case things go wrong during surgery?

At a minimum, this equipment should include a "crash cart" with a defibrillator and airway resuscitation equipment.

● **Do you have an ongoing relationship with an ambulance company?** The drivers should know exactly where the office is...the best routes to get there and from there to the hospital...and which entries and exits are large enough to accommodate a stretcher.

● **Who staffs your office?** The doctor's office should employ at least one RN who, like the surgeon and anesthesiologist, has training in advanced cardiac life support.

All nurses assisting during surgery should be RNs specializing in operating room procedures. And—all RNs caring for patients after surgery should be specialists in post-anesthesia recovery.

● **Has your facility been accredited?** Several agencies inspect physicians' offices, protocols and procedures to certify that they meet standards for quality in-office surgery.

The most demanding agency is the Joint Commission on Accreditation of Healthcare Organizations (JCAHO).

Facilities offering in-office surgery aren't required to be JCAHO-accredited, but some go through the procedure voluntarily. Ask to see the accreditation certificate. It assures you that the facility is well-run and up-to-date.

● **How long will my procedure take?** In-office surgery is safest when it does not exceed four hours. Any operation lasting longer should be done in a hospital.

Bypass Surgery: Who Really Needs It?

Thomas B. Graboys, MD, associate professor of medicine at Harvard Medical School and director of the Lown Cardiovascular Center at Brigham and Women's Hospital, both in Boston.

The number of heart bypass operations performed in the US is soaring. For individuals whose heart vessels are so blocked that they feel chest pain (angina) even while resting, bypass surgery can be a lifesaver. But estimates are that up to half of bypass operations may be unnecessary—exposing patients to needless expense and risk of death.

Self-defense: If a doctor recommends bypass surgery for you, *be sure to get a second opinion if...*

● **You feel no chest pain while resting.**

● **You feel slight chest pain *only* when you exert yourself**—when running to catch a bus or taking a hike up a hill, for instance.

In these instances, medications and lifestyle changes—quitting smoking, exercising more and eating less fat—are better.

Why? Because although generally safe, bypass surgery is not without risk. Two percent of patients younger than 70 who undergo bypass die from the surgery, and 3% to 4% of people older than 70 die.

And bypass surgery is only a quick fix. Heart vessels can clog up again—especially if lifestyle changes aren't made.

Don't get a second opinion from another doctor in your own doctor's practice or HMO. *Better:* A doctor who practices at a local hospital—especially one that's affiliated with the cardiology department of a university.

If bypass surgery is necessary, shop around. Surgeons and hospitals that do the most bypass surgery procedures have the best survival rates.

Helpful: *US News & World Report's* annual guide to the best hospitals in America, published in the magazine each July. Articles and rankings, segmented by specialty and region, are available at its Web site, *www.usnews.com.*

Death-from-Heart-Disease Predictor

The *ankle/arm blood pressure index (AAI)* is a fast, noninvasive test that compares blood pressure in the upper and lower extremities. A reading of 0.9 or lower suggests an increased risk of death—even in persons who seem healthy.

Finding: Women 65 and older with low AAI values were five times more likely to die of heart disease than women of the same age with higher values. A separate study yielded similar results for men.

Self-defense: Periodic measurement of AAI in a physician's office or screening center may be appropriate to identify older men and women at high risk of premature death.

Molly T. Vogt, PhD, assistant professor of epidemiology, Graduate School of Public Health, University of Pittsburgh. Her four-year study of almost 1,500 women was published in the *Journal of the American Medical Association,* 515 N. State St., Chicago 60610.

A Test That's a Must If You're Over 60

Have your protein status checked at your next physical exam if you are in your 60s or older or have surgery scheduled. A simple blood test for *albumin* can indicate whether your body has enough stored protein. Adequate protein is important for fighting off postsurgical complications—particularly infection. *Cost:* Generally less than $10.

Bruce Yaffe, MD, board-certified internist and a digestive disease subspecialist in private practice, New York.

To Detect Heart Disease

Experimental diagnostic test detects heart disease faster, more safely and at lower cost than X-ray angiography. *Three-dimensional coronary magnetic resonance angiography* (MRA) pinpoints the location of blocked coronary arteries using powerful magnets. MRA takes just 30 minutes, unlike traditional X-ray angiography, which can take up to six hours. It is noninvasive and involves no injected dye and no radiation exposure to the patient. *Bonus:* MRA costs only 30% as much as X-ray angiography.

René M. Botnar, PhD, clinical scientist, Cardiac MR Center, Beth Israel Deaconess Medical Center, Boston.

A Test That Predicts a Second Heart Attack

Blood flow imaging predicts second heart attacks better than an exercise stress test. A study found that when blood flow imaging (called myocardial perfusion imaging) was performed after giving patients a drug to increase blood flow to the heart, it could be given three to five days sooner after a heart attack—and was better at predicting repeat cardiac attacks—than the traditional exercise stress test. Blood flow imaging gives physicians an opportunity to act more quickly to prevent repeat heart attacks.

Kenneth A. Brown, MD, professor of medicine, University of Vermont, Burlington.

Unnecessary Chest X Rays

Half of all chest X rays performed prior to surgery are unnecessary. Doctors often order them anyway out of habit or because they fear being sued for failing to diagnose a problem that an X ray might have revealed.

Perry G. Pernicano, MD, assistant chief, radiology service, Veterans Affairs Medical Center, Ann Arbor, MI. His study of 108 pre-op chest X rays was presented at a meeting of the Radiological Society of North America, 2021 Spring Rd., Oak Brook, IL 60521.

Unnecessary Tests for Migraine Sufferers

Migraine sufferers do not benefit from routine MRIs and CAT scans—although many physicians continue to order these costly and potentially frightening tests for their migraine patients.

Exceptions: To rule out brain tumors, these scans may be appropriate for individuals whose headache patterns change...who have a history of seizures...or who are experiencing numbness, weakness, changes in vision, difficulty maintaining balance or other neurological problems.

B.M. Frishberg, MD, clinical assistant professor of neurology, Georgetown University School of Medicine, Washington, DC, and a neurologist in private practice in Bethesda, MD. His review of 17 studies involving 2,722 headache sufferers was published in the *American College of Physicians Journal Club,* Independence Mall West, Sixth Street at Race, Philadelphia 19106.

18

Medications and Vaccines

Wise Ways to Buy Prescription Drugs Online

Many people like the idea of purchasing drugs from online pharmacies. Some find it more convenient than standing in line at the local drugstore. Others hope to save money. Still others are too embarrassed to ask their doctors to prescribe drugs like the baldness remedy *finasteride* (Propecia) or the impotence drug *sildenafil* (Viagra).

I think online pharmacies are going to play an increasingly big role in coming years. They offer many advantages—especially to older people, individuals with disabilities and people living in remote areas. But many kinks in the system haven't been worked out yet. Before you buy drugs online, here's my advice.

•**Stick with reputable sites.** Look for sites certified by the National Association of Boards of Pharmacy (NABP). Its Verified Internet Pharmacy Practice Sites (VIPPS) program ensures that an online pharmacy complies with the licensing requirements of each state in which it sells drugs. Certification also ensures that the pharmacy protects patient privacy, verifies prescriptions and gives meaningful consultation to patients.

A seal on the online pharmacy's site identifies it as VIPPS-approved. Two popular online pharmacies, *www.planetrx.com* and *www.yourpharmacy.com*, display the seal. So does *www.cvs.com,* the online site of CVS drugstores. Approval is pending for several other sites. If you don't see the seal on the site, you can check to see if it's certified by going to the NABP Web site: *www.nabp.net.*

•**Don't assume that the Internet is always cheaper.** Thanks to increasing competition, significant discounts are often available online. Some chains price drugs on their Internet sites lower than in their own stores.

But watch out. A recent study in the *Annals of Internal Medicine* found that sildenafil and

---

Timothy McCall, MD, a Boston internist and author of *Examining Your Doctor: A Patient's Guide to Avoiding Harmful Medical Care.* Citadel Press.

finasteride cost more online than at Philadelphia pharmacies. To be sure of a bargain, compare prices at several Internet vendors with those at the drugstore or mail-order outfit you normally use.

• **Don't use Internet pharmacies for urgent prescriptions.** You could easily wait several days for drugs to arrive from an online vendor. That's fine for blood pressure medication if you've got enough to last awhile. It's not okay if the prescription is for an antibiotic to treat a sinus infection.

• **Think about confidentiality.** Reputable online pharmacies have safeguards in place to protect confidentiality, but even then there is no guarantee of complete privacy. If confidential medical information is intercepted—such as data about cancer or AIDS treatments—you could wind up harming your chances of getting insurance or a job in the future.

• **Steer clear of online prescribing.** Some sites employ doctors who dispense prescriptions online. As tempting as it may be to use this service to obtain, say, Viagra, I don't recommend it. You usually know nothing about the qualifications of an online doctor. Worse, he or she knows almost nothing about you. It's only by actually talking with and examining a patient that a doctor can determine if a drug is appropriate.

That brings up a final point. If you do get a prescription from an online physician, overcome your embarrassment and tell your regular doctor. He or she might otherwise fail to recognize side effects or prescribe another drug that causes dangerous interactions.

There's no room for fear or shame in doctor–patient communication. If you find it hard to be honest with your doctor, work together to pinpoint and correct difficulties in your relationship. If they seem insoluble, switch to a doctor with whom you feel more comfortable.

Reduce Medication Mix-Ups

Ask your doctor to spell aloud the name of any drug he/she prescribes for you. Ask

what the drug is for and what the pills look like. Jot this information down, and use it to double-check that the pharmacist has given you the right drug. *Also helpful:* A pill reference book, such as *Complete Drug Reference* (Consumer Reports Books). *Trap:* An estimated 1,100 pairs of drugs have similar brand names or generic names. Fosamax *(alendronate)* treats osteoporosis, while Flomax *(tamsulosin)* is for prostate enlargement. Nicoderm *(nicotine)* helps smokers quit, while Nitro-Derm *(nitroglycerin)* treats angina.

Bruce L. Lambert, PhD, associate professor of pharmacy administration, University of Illinois, Chicago.

Customized Medications

Medications can be customized with doctor's approval to meet patients' needs. *Example:* If you cannot tolerate an oral medication, such as ibuprofen, a compounding pharmacist sometimes can prepare suppositories or transdermal (skin) gels. *When compounding may help:* For a dosage that is not commercially available...more natural formulation, such as for hormone-replacement therapy...better-tasting version...one that has no dye, lactose, preservative, etc. *Drawback:* Few health insurers cover compounded medications. *To find a compounding pharmacist:* Ask your doctor...or contact International Academy of Compounding Pharmacists, 800-927-4227, or Professional Compounding Centers of America, 800-331-2498.

Robert GiaQuinto, RPh, pharmacist/owner, Rye Beach Pharmacy, Rye, NY.

Medication Wallet Card

A medication wallet card lists all the prescription and over-the-counter medications you take...drug allergies...emergency telephone numbers.

National Council on Patient Information and Education, 4915 St. Elmo Ave., Suite 505, Bethesda, MD 20814.

Best Times to Take Medicines

Time medicines for the most benefit. *Examples:* Many asthma attacks occur between 2 am and 4 am—so medication taken in late afternoon works better at preventing attacks than medication taken at other times of the day. Hay fever often flares overnight as the body's cortisol and adrenaline levels drop—so taking an antihistamine right before bedtime may help. *Caution:* Check with your doctor before changing any medication schedule.

Monica Kraft, MD, assistant professor of medicine, University of Colorado Health Sciences Center, Denver.

Painkiller Danger

Taken in high doses and for long periods of time, Advil, Nuprin, Motrin, Aleve, Naprosyn, Indocin and other nonsteroidal anti-inflammatory drugs (NSAIDs) may cause elevated blood pressure. Often used to treat arthritis, gout and other painful conditions, NSAIDs have long been known to cause small increases in blood pressure.

Now: A study has linked these drugs to an increased need for antihypertensive therapy, particularly among the elderly. Although the link was found with prescription NSAIDs, users of over-the-counter versions of these drugs often take more—sometimes much more—than the label recommends.

Self-defense: Take only as much of any NSAID as is prescribed or indicated on the label, or switch to Tylenol or another pain reliever containing acetaminophen. Aspirin in low doses has not been linked to increases in blood pressure.

Jerry H. Gurwitz, MD, assistant professor of medicine, Harvard Medical School, Boston. His study of NSAID use among 9,411 Medicaid patients was published in the *Journal of the American Medical Association,* 515 N. State St., Chicago 60610.

Dangerous Drug Mix

Anticoagulants such as *warfarin* (Coumadin), taken in combination with aspirin, ibuprofen or another nonsteroidal anti-inflammatory drug (NSAID) could cause problems. Those who combine both drugs have a 13-fold risk of developing a bleeding peptic ulcer, compared with those who use neither drug. Patients taking anticoagulants should ask their doctors about substituting a NSAID alternative, such as acetaminophen.

Ronald I. Shorr, MD, assistant professor of pharmacoepidemiology, Vanderbilt University School of Medicine, Nashville. His study of anticoagulant use was published in *Archives of Internal Medicine,* 515 N. State St., Chicago 60610.

Herb Alert

Drug–herb interactions can complicate surgery. Herbs such as St. John's wort can make narcotics and anesthetics last longer. Many herbs can interfere with blood clotting, causing potentially dangerous bleeding during surgery. Some herbs can cause rapid heartbeat or high blood pressure. *Self-defense:* Avoid all nonprescription natural medicines for two weeks before surgery…or consult an herbalist, licensed naturopathic physician or knowledgeable medical doctor.

Andrew L. Rubman, ND, adjunct professor of clinical medicine, Florida College of Integrative Medicine, Orlando, and medical director, Southbury Clinic for Traditional Medicines, CT.

Sexual Side Effects of Commonly Prescribed Drugs

M. Laurence Lieberman, a pharmacist in New York and author of *The Sexual Pharmacy.* New American Library. His book lists 226 drugs that are known to influence sexual performance or enjoyment.

In the past, doctors attributed most sexual disorders to psychological causes. But there is a growing awareness—fueled by a growing number of studies—that more than half these conditions are triggered by physical ailments or, more surprisingly, the drugs used to treat these ailments.

Many commonly prescribed drugs produce sexual side effects that most patients—no matter how frightened or delighted they are by the effects—are too embarrassed to discuss with their doctors. Knowing about these drugs ahead of time can help to alleviate the problems.

DRUGS THAT ENHANCE SEXUAL PERFORMANCE AND ENJOYMENT

We've all heard about Viagra (sildenafil) but many other drugs can enhance sexual performance and enjoyment.

●**Labetalol** is an antihypertensive drug. But unlike most drugs of its kind, which are notorious for causing impotence, this one may actually delay loss of erection after intercourse.

●**Levodopa,** used to treat patients with Parkinson's disease, increases the body's level of dopamine (a natural sexual stimulant) and causes patients to feel sexually aroused. As a result, the drug has been used to treat impotence in otherwise healthy subjects. *Success rate in one study:* 70%.

●**Nitroglycerin** is a vasodilator used to treat patients with angina. It may also increase blood flow to the genitals, thereby facilitating erections in men who have trouble achieving them.

●**Oral contraceptives** can work both positively and negatively. Many women experience a decreased sexual drive when taking the Pill, while others report an increased sex drive. Researchers are still unclear as to why these contradictory effects occur.

●**Papaverine** is another vasodilator which increases the flow of blood to the genitals and is often prescribed to treat impotence. The patient simply injects the drug at the base of his penis immediately prior to intercourse. An erection is almost instantaneous.

Caution: If an erection lasts more than four hours or becomes painful, contact your doctor immediately.

●**Phenoxybenzamine** and **phentolamine** are alpha-blockers that are most commonly used to lower blood pressure. But since they prevent the constriction of blood vessels, they are also being used to treat impotence.

●**Valium** and valium-like drugs inhibit sexual performance when taken in high doses. But when given in very low doses to patients with psychologically caused sexual problems, they enable these patients to relax and become sexually aroused. These drugs can also delay ejaculation and orgasm.

DRUGS THAT INHIBIT SEXUAL PERFORMANCE AND ENJOYMENT

●**Alcohol,** ingested alone or in liquid medications (cough medicine, etc.), can cause inhibited erection, decreased sexual desire, delayed ejaculation, male infertility and gynecomastia (painful breast growth in men).

●**Anabolic steroids** are analogs of testosterone that are prescribed to build muscle tissue in malnourished patients. While they are not widely prescribed, they are widely abused by athletes, especially bodybuilders. In males these drugs can cause reduced sex drive, impotence, decreased testicle size and sperm production, gynecomastia and priapism (prolonged, painful erections). In females, they can cause male-type hair growth and balding, deepening of the voice, reduction in breast size, clitoral enlargement, decreased uterine size, irregular menstruation and cessation of ovulation.

●**Digoxin** is prescribed to regulate heart beat. It very closely resembles the female hormone estrogen, and can cause decreased sex drive, impotence and gynecomastia.

●**Isotretinoin** (Accutane) is an extremely effective drug for severe cases of acne. It has received a lot of attention, however, because of the risk of birth defects in the children of women taking it. It can also cause impotence, decreased sex drive, menstrual irregularities, galactorrhea (discharge from the female breasts) and vaginal dryness.

●**Lithium,** prescribed for the treatment of manic depressive disorder, can cause decreased sex drive, inhibited erection, male infertility and the discharge of milk from female breasts.

• **Nicotine** is a vasoconstrictor that often blocks blood flow to the genitals. As a result, it can cause impotence, vaginal dryness and even early menopause.

• **Penicillin** and related antibiotics can accumulate in the semen, triggering allergic reactions in susceptible partners.

• **Thiazide diuretics,** which account for about 90% of diuretics, cause a loss of zinc through the urine. Since zinc is vital to male potency, men using this drug often become impotent.

• **Timolol,** a beta-blocker, is the only eyedrop that has been associated with impotence and decreased sex drive.

with your physician or pharmacist. *Common drugs that fall into this category include:*

• **Acetaminophen*** (Tylenol, etc.)
• **Enteric-coated aspirin**
• **Ampicillin**
• **Erythromycin**
• **Epsom salts**
• **Levodopa**
• **Mineral oil**
• **Magnesium hydroxide** (milk of magnesia)
• **Penicillin G and V**
• **Tetracycline**
• **Procainamide**

50+: The Graedon's People's Pharmacy for Older Adults by Joe and Teresa Graedon. Bantam Books.

*Generic names are given.

Anticoagulant Danger

Anticoagulants taken to reduce risk of cardiovascular disease can lead to severe internal bleeding—if doses are too high.

Self-defense: If you're on anticoagulants, ask your doctor about prescribing the lowest effective dose. Have periodic blood tests to check your anticoagulant levels. Avoid aspirin. Alert your doctor if there are any changes in your diet or use of alcohol.

C. Seth Landefeld, MD, senior research associate, department of medicine, Cleveland Veterans Affairs Medical Center, and associate professor of medicine, Case Western Reserve University, Cleveland. His review of risks from anticoagulant-related bleeding was published in the *American Journal of Medicine,* Box 7722, Riverton, NJ 08077.

New "Last Chance" Antibiotic

Many bacteria have become resistant to some or even all antibiotics. The trend is especially pronounced in hospitals. Without effective antibiotics, patients die of once-curable infections. *Now available:* A combination of *quinupristin* and *dalfopristin* called Synercid. This intravenous drug works against most resistant strains of *Enterococcus faecium,* a common hospital-acquired pathogen.

Alexander Rakowsky, MD, team leader, medical review team, anti-infective division, Center for Drug Evaluation and Research, Food and Drug Administration, Rockville, MD.

Drugs That Work Best When Taken on an Empty Stomach

Food slows the absorption of certain drugs, so they are best taken without food. If nausea or stomach upset results, discuss it

Dangerous Over-the-Foreign-Counter Drugs

Many drugs available by prescription in the US are sold over the counter in other countries. Don't buy them online or while traveling.

Reasons: They may be poorly regulated and it can be hard to verify if a drug is legitimate or dosage is correct.

Charles Inlander, president of People's Medical Society, America's largest nonprofit consumer health advocacy organization, 462 Walnut St., Allentown, PA 18102.

When You Need a Tetanus Shot

Get a tetanus shot at least once every decade. If you sustain a serious puncture wound five or more years after your last shot, ask your doctor about getting another booster.

Also: Be sure to thoroughly wash any cut, abrasion or puncture wound—no matter how minor—with soap and water. You may wish to apply an over-the-counter antibiotic ointment …and keep the wound clean and dry with a bandage. If redness surrounding the wound extends more than one-quarter inch, see a doctor right away. It may be infected.

James Brand, MD, assistant professor of medicine, University of Oklahoma Health Sciences Center, Oklahoma City.

19

Very, Very Personal

Jump-Start Your Sex Life...Naturally

Well before *sildenafil* (Viagra), people relied on aphrodisiacs to increase sexual desire...boost stamina...improve performance...and increase pleasure.

Many of these compounds owe their reputation to folklore, but several herbs and dietary supplements have proven sex-enhancing effects.

Good news: Products that improve sex naturally may be less likely to cause serious side effects than prescription drugs. Many strengthen the cardiovascular system and help regulate hormone production. That's as important for good sex as having an erection or being sufficiently lubricated.

Unlike sildenafil, sex-enhancing herbs and supplements aren't taken just an hour or so before sex. They're taken daily until there's a noticeable improvement in sexual performance.

At that point, some people take a pause to see if the herbs and supplements are no longer necessary. Others continue taking the preparations indefinitely.

Important: Use herbs and supplements only under medical supervision. That way you'll be sure to get the product and dosage that's right for you.

Caution: Fresh or dried herbs differ greatly in potency from batch to batch. Use capsules or tinctures, ideally ones that have been standardized to contain the proper amounts of active ingredients.

For better sex, try one of the following natural enhancers. Select the one that best suits your needs. Give each preparation a few months to work. If you see no effect, try another.

GINKGO BILOBA

Ginkgo contains a variety of compounds that relax blood vessels and increase circulation to the brain and pelvic area.

For women, increased blood flow improves vaginal lubrication and sexual responsiveness.

Chris D. Meletis, ND, dean of clinical affairs and chief medical officer of the National College of Naturopathic Medicine in Portland, OR. He is author of *Better Sex Naturally*. HarperResource.

For men, adequate blood flow is essential to achieve and sustain erections.

Typical dosage: *Capsules:* 40 mg to 60 mg of 24% standardized powdered extract three to four times daily. *Tincture:* 30 drops three to four times daily.

Side effects: Ginkgo may cause dizziness, headache or heart palpitations.

Caution: Ginkgo is a blood thinner and can increase the blood-thinning effects of aspirin and *warfarin* (Coumadin). Check with your physician before using ginkgo if you're taking either medication.

MUIRA PUAMA

Also known as "potency wood," this herb contains sterols and other compounds that boost levels of testosterone, a hormone that plays a critical role in sexual desire in women as well as men.

Muira puama also contains volatile oils that are thought to restore sex drive by stimulating the brain's pleasure center.

Typical dosage: 250 mg three times daily in capsule form.

Side effect: Muira puama may lower blood pressure by as much as 10%. Check with your doctor before using this herb if you have low blood pressure (hypotension).

GINSENG

This herb is an "adaptogen," meaning it helps the body compensate for extended periods of stress. Stress can cause sexual desire and performance to plummet.

Compounds in ginseng root lower levels of adrenaline and other stress hormones.

These compounds also improve blood flow to the penis, help tissues use oxygen more efficiently and boost production of testosterone in men and progesterone in women.

Typical dosage: *Capsules:* 10 mg to 50 mg one to three times daily. *Tincture:* 30 to 60 drops daily.

Side effect: Ginseng may cause diarrhea... high blood pressure...sleeplessness.

ASHWAGANDA

A member of the pepper family, this herb contains *withanolides,* substances that increase the activity of testosterone and progesterone.

Ashwaganda also relieves stress and anxiety.

Typical dosage: *Capsules:* 1,000 mg once or twice daily. *Tincture:* 60 to 90 drops two or three times daily.

Side effects: Because ashwaganda has anti-anxiety properties, it should not be used by anyone taking medications to treat anxiety and/or depression. The herb could intensify the drugs' actions as well as their side effects. Ashwaganda may also trigger miscarriages.

ARGININE

Taken in supplement form, this amino acid has been shown to relax smooth muscle contractions. This boosts arterial dilation, bringing more blood to the pelvic area.

The body uses arginine to produce nitric oxide, a chemical needed to achieve erections. (Sildenafil works in part by making nitric oxide more readily available in the body.)

Typical dosage: 1,000 mg to 2,000 mg twice daily in capsule form. Take capsules between meals, since many foods contain lysine, an amino acid that counteracts arginine's effects.

Side effect: Don't take this herb if you get cold sores caused by the herpes simplex virus. Arginine stimulates viral replication.

FOR WOMEN ONLY

The herb *dong quai* contains plant sterols that help correct estrogen deficiencies.

Studies suggest that dong quai can increase sexual desire as well as the intensity of orgasms.

Typical dosage: *Capsules:* 1,000 mg three to four times daily. *Tincture:* 45 to 60 drops two or three times daily.

Caution: Pregnant and lactating women should not use dong quai. The herb also increases sensitivity to sunlight.

Viagra Warning

Heart patients bothered by impotence should undergo a treadmill stress test before starting to take the impotence drug Viagra *(sildenafil).* A man who is capable of exercising up to at least five METs (metabolic equivalents of oxygen consumption) without chest pain, abnormal heartbeats or other problems is unlikely to suffer a heart attack during sexual intercourse. It's safe for him to use Viagra. Viagra should be off-limits to men who cannot exercise at this level without problems. They're at risk for a sex-triggered heart attack.

Sanjay Kaul, MD, assistant professor of medicine, University of California, Los Angeles, School of Medicine, and associate director of the coronary care unit, Cedars-Sinai Medical Center, Los Angeles.

Don't Take Viagra Before Surgery

Viagra dilates blood vessels so blood flows easily to the penis. But dilation affects the rest of the body, too—lowering blood pressure. This can be dangerous during surgery because some anesthetics have the same effect on blood pressure. Do not use Viagra within 24 hours of surgery—and tell your doctor and anesthesiologist when you last took it.

Patrick C. Walsh, MD, urologist-in-chief, Johns Hopkins Medical Institutions, Baltimore.

Sex Is Good for Your Health

Sex boosts the immune system—and can help prevent colds and headaches. People who averaged one to two sexual encounters per week had higher levels of *immunoglobulin A* —which protects against disease. And people who had sex two or three times a week reported fewer migraine headaches—because sex releases hormones that prevent migraines.

Alexander Mauskop, MD, director, New York Headache Center, New York.

For Women Only

Women's sexual desire may grow stronger following hysterectomy—that was the surprising conclusion of a study of 1,000 women by the University of Maryland School of Medicine. Researchers discovered that after surgery, 15% more of the women desired sex at least once a week, 12% more made love at least five times a month and 9% more experienced orgasms. Only 5% felt the quality of their sex life had deteriorated.

Kristen H. Kjerulff, PhD, associate professor of epidemiology, University of Maryland School of Medicine, Baltimore.

Older Men and Sex

It is a myth that older men are dissatisfied with the quality of their sex lives, according to the largest research study on impotence since the famous Kinsey report.

It is true that more than half of men between 40 and 70 experience some difficulty in obtaining and maintaining erections. But they expect a decline in performance to occur as they age, so their level of satisfaction with sex remains the same as when they were younger.

John McKinlay, PhD, an epidemiologist with the New England Research Institute, Nine Galen St., Watertown, MA 02472.

Older men who have trouble attaining erections at night can do better with morning sex. Testosterone levels are higher earlier in the day.

Medical Aspects of Human Sexuality.

Sex for Seniors

To improve your sex life as you grow older— *take your time*. Stick to easy positions, and try alternating occasions—each of you is touched one day and does the touching the next. *For men only:* Thinking about sex or looking at sexy pictures may no longer be enough to arouse you. But touching yourself—or having your partner touch you—usually works.

Ruth Westheimer, PhD, authority on human sexuality and intimacy, writing in *Are You Old Enough to Read This Book? Reflections on Midlife* (Reader's Digest Association), a collection of writings from prominent individuals over age 50.

disorder. A dose of 50 milligrams (mg) increased time before ejaculation from an average of 81 to 409 seconds. At 25 mg, ejaculation was delayed to an average of 202 seconds. *Side effects:* Dry mouth and constipation.

Stanley Althof, PhD, psychologist in sexual disorders, Case Western Reserve University, Cleveland. His study of 15 monogamous couples 21 to 65 years of age was presented at a meeting of the American Urological Association, 1120 N. Charles St., Baltimore 21201.

Treatment for Penis Curvature

Severe penis curvature *(Peyronie's disease)* can be minimized via injections of *verapamil,* a calcium channel blocker. Peyronie's is caused by scar tissue resulting from injury to the erectile bodies, the two long chambers within the penis that fill with blood to form an erection. If severe enough, this curvature can make intercourse impossible.

Now: Regular injections of verapamil into the scar resulted in better erectile function in 80% of the men who received treatment. Seventy percent of the men noted a reduction in the curvature. All the men reported a significant decrease in the narrowing of the penis, another common result of Peyronie's. If you have a curved penis, ask a urologist about verapamil.

Laurence Levine, MD, director of the male sexual function and fertility program, Rush-Presbyterian/St. Luke's Medical Center, Chicago. His study of 14 men with Peyronie's disease was published in the *Journal of Urology,* 1120 N. Charles St., Baltimore 21201.

Overcoming Premature Ejaculation

Premature ejaculation can be overcome with *clomipramine* (Anafranil)—a drug long used to treat depression and obsessive-compulsive

Love Handles—Impotence Connection

Love handles often go hand in hand with impotence. *Recent finding:* Men with a 42-inch waist were twice as likely to be impotent as were men with a 31-inch waist. *Theory:* In overweight men, inability to achieve or maintain erection is an early sign of heart disease—which is often associated with impotence. *Best advice:* Shape up. Inactive men are 40% more likely to experience impotence than those who exercise.

Eric Rimm, ScD, assistant professor of epidemiology and nutrition, Harvard School of Public Health, Boston. His survey of 1,981 men was presented at a meeting of the American Urological Association.

Impotence Predicts Heart Disease

Twenty-five percent of men who see doctors for impotence caused by vascular problems have a heart attack or stroke within five years of the start of impotence. *Reason:* Sexual impotence is often caused by the same problems that cause heart trouble, including diabetes, smoking, high blood pressure and high cholesterol levels.

Kenneth Goldberg, MD, director, Male Health Center, Lewisville, TX.

Genital Bites

Treatment of genital bites is often delayed because victims are embarrassed. Men bitten by dogs typically go to an emergency room within an hour. But men whose penises are bitten or scraped during oral sex often ignore the injury even after infection sets in—and may not seek help for 24 hours to six weeks.

Danger: Infected human bites can be more serious than dog bites. Bitten men need to be treated for infection and tested for sexually transmitted diseases.

J. Stuart Wolf, Jr., MD, associate professor of urology, University of Michigan Medical Center, Ann Arbor.

Prostate Cancer— How to Outsmart the #2 Cancer Killer of Men

Gerald W. Chodak, MD, professor of surgery at the University of Chicago Hospitals, and director of the prostate and urology center at the Louis A. Weiss Memorial Hospital in Chicago.

Prostate cancer is the second-leading cause of cancer death in men (after lung cancer). It kills an estimated 38,000 men a year.

Experts disagree on how to fight the disease. Should men take the blood test to detect prostate cancer? And how should they treat the cancer if it's detected? *We asked Gerald Chodak, MD, to clear up the confusion...*

Dr. Chodak, what causes prostate cancer?

We don't yet know the precise causes, but we have identified several factors that put men at increased risk...

- **Being African-American.**
- **Having a father, grandfather or uncle who had the disease.**
- **Eating a diet high in fat, especially animal fat.**
- **Possibly infrequent sexual activity.**

Exposure to sunlight seems to help prevent prostate cancer, although the reason for this protective effect is unknown. But it's possible to get prostate cancer even in the absence of these risk factors. Any man can get prostate cancer.

What's the best way to detect prostate cancer?

In the past few years, doctors have begun to rely on the prostate-specific antigen (PSA) test. This test measures the blood level of PSA, a protein released in microscopic amounts by the prostate gland. The digital rectal exam is also an important diagnostic tool.

But I've heard that the PSA test isn't always accurate.

That's true. A high PSA reading may be a sign of cancer. But high readings sometimes occur in men who are cancer-free—causing needless alarm and the expense of additional tests.

Even if prostate cancer is accurately detected, it may grow so slowly that the man dies of an unrelated ailment long before the cancer has a chance to harm him.

Prostate cancer experts still don't know whether aggressive treatment of these slow-growing tumors is beneficial—especially since surgery and radiation have severe side effects, including incontinence and impotence. Some doctors think it's better to do nothing—to try "watchful waiting" instead.

Even if surgery or radiation is performed, there's no guarantee that the cancer won't spread to other areas of the body. Men who take the PSA test might be setting themselves up for needless expense, worry and treatment-related complications, without gaining any survival benefit.

What's your view of the PSA test?

I tell my patients that if their desire to minimize their risk of prostate cancer outweighs their concern about being subjected to possibly unnecessary, possibly harmful medical care, then they should get tested. You can discuss the matter with your own doctor, but ultimately it's your decision.

What role does a man's age play in determining whether he should be tested?

For men younger than 50, there's not much to be gained by getting tested. *Reason:* Prostate cancer is very rare in men that young. If you have a family history of the disease or if you're

African-American, however, you might benefit from getting the test before age 50. That's something to discuss with your doctor.

If you are older than 70, or if other ailments have cut your life expectancy to 10 years or less, odds are you won't benefit much from the test, either. Even if you did have prostate cancer, you'd probably die of another cause. There would be no reason to treat the cancer.

Men between the ages of 50 and 70 are most likely to benefit from PSA testing. Men at the lower end of that age range are especially likely to benefit.

Have you had a PSA test?

I probably will get tested when I'm 50. I'd like to reach 80. I'd prefer to reach 90, and I don't want prostate cancer to get in the way.

How often should men get tested?

Men who are especially concerned about prostate cancer can get a PSA test once a year. Even once every six months is not too often. That way you'll know what's normal for you—and be able to see if the numbers shoot up, signaling cancer growth.

What do the test results mean?

The traditional view has been that any PSA level over 4.0 suggests trouble. But evidence suggests that numbers well below 4.0 might be risky for younger men...while higher numbers might be normal in elderly men.

For a 40-year-old man, a PSA above 2.5 is now considered abnormal. But among 60-year-olds, a reading as high as 6.5 might be normal.

What if my PSA reading is suspiciously high?

Your doctor should refer you to a urologist, who will perform an ultrasound exam to try to locate a tumor site. If a tumor is found, you'll have a biopsy to determine whether it is malignant. Don't worry—a biopsy does not spread the cancer.

What if cancer is found?

The decision about treatment is about trade-offs. The older the patient and the shorter his life expectancy, the smaller a chance of benefiting from aggressive treatment. But at any age, some of the treated men will probably benefit. The question is whether the benefit is worth the risk.

For younger men who are otherwise healthy, the benefits of treatment outweigh the risks. If the cancer were to remain untreated, your risk of dying of prostate cancer in the next 20 years would be about 60%.

What's the best treatment for prostate cancer?

Complete surgical removal of the prostate (a procedure called radical prostatectomy) offers the best chance for a cure. But surgery has drawbacks. Studies of Medicare patients have shown that up to 70% of men experience impotence following surgery. Of course, many older men are already impotent due to other diseases.

Good news: It's often possible to remove the prostate without injuring the nerves to the penis. Ask your surgeon if you're a candidate for nerve-sparing surgery.

About 18% of men will experience at least minor incontinence after surgery. But only 2% to 4% say that postsurgical incontinence is a serious problem.

What about radiation therapy?

Radiation is roughly comparable to surgery in terms of its ability to prolong life. And radiation controls the cancer while avoiding some of the complications of surgery.

Problem: For at least two years following the treatment, it's hard to tell whether radiation therapy has worked. In cases where radiation therapy does not work, it becomes very difficult to find a cure. And when incontinence and impotence occur following radiation, they're often harder to treat than the same problems caused by surgery.

Bottom line: Either surgery or radiation is a reasonable alternative, depending on your own preferences.

I read that it's possible to treat prostate cancer with radioactive "seeds." Is that effective?

While definitive evidence is not in, some experts believe that radioactive seed implants may be a viable alternative to radical prostate surgery and radiation therapy in the treatment of localized prostate cancer. Studies in coming years should help sort out the treatment options.

Prostate Cancer Trap

Prostate cancer is misdiagnosed more often than many men realize.

Most malignancies, including breast cancer and lung cancer, produce solid grape-like tumors. But prostate tumors are often diffuse, spreading finger-like throughout the gland. That makes them easy to be overlooked.

Self-defense: Get a second opinion for any prostate biopsy.

Jonathan I. Epstein, MD, professor of pathology, urology and oncology, Johns Hopkins University School of Medicine, Baltimore.

Seed Therapy Safety

Radiation used for prostate cancer poses no danger to a patient's family members. The dosage in the tiny radioactive seeds is too low to affect others.

Jeff Michalski, MD, radiation oncologist, Washington University School of Medicine, St. Louis.

Testicular Cancer Self-Defense

Self-exams for testicular cancer should be performed monthly. After a bath or shower, when the skin of the scrotum is relaxed, look for any swelling on the skin. Examine each testicle separately by rolling it between the index and middle fingers. Look and feel for any hard lumps or a change in the size or shape of testicles. It is normal for one to be slightly larger than the other. If you notice any changes from the previous month, see your doctor. This is especially important for men ages 20 to 40, who are at the highest risk.

Patrick C. Walsh, MD, urologist-in-chief, Johns Hopkins Medical Institutions, Baltimore.

Baldness/ Heart Trouble Link

Men who are losing the hair on the crowns of their heads have a 36% greater risk of heart problems than men who are not going bald…or who have mildly receding hairlines. Going bald at the crown is an inherited characteristic that may be linked to elevated male hormone levels. Anyone going bald in this way should carefully watch his blood pressure and cholesterol levels, and be especially careful to exercise regularly, not smoke and eat a heart-healthy diet.

JoAnn Manson, MD, DrPH, chief of preventive medicine, Brigham & Women's Hospital, Boston, and coauthor of a study of 22,000 male doctors, ages 40 to 84, reported in *Archives of Internal Medicine.*

Women Continue to Get Shockingly Substandard Medical Care

Leslie Laurence, coauthor of *Outrageous Practices: The Alarming Truth About How Medicine Mistreats Women.* Fawcett Columbine.

For the past several decades, American women have been systematically excluded from most research on new drugs, medical treatments and surgical techniques. As a result of this neglect, women are often denied the life-saving and life-extending treatments routinely offered to men.

Example I: Women are less likely than men to be referred for angioplasty, a surgical technique proven to clear blocked coronary arteries.

Example II: Among sufferers of kidney failure, women are 30% less likely than men to receive kidney transplants.

This sex bias pervades medicine, directly undermining the treatment women receive in clinics, hospitals and doctors' offices across the country.

Common problems women face when seeking medical care...

• **Having your symptoms dismissed as being "all in your head."** Medical mythology has it that women are "complainers" whose symptoms often stem from emotional stress. This insidious attitude among doctors keeps women from getting the diagnostic tests they need.

In one study, only 4% of women with abnormal stress tests received follow-up tests necessary for pinpointing arterial blockages. But these important tests were ordered for 40% of men with abnormal stress tests.

Similarly, because women's physical complaints are often viewed as evidence of psychological problems, women are more likely than men to receive prescriptions for psychiatric drugs.

Women make up 66% of those diagnosed with depression, yet they receive 73% of prescriptions for psychiatric medication—and 90% when the prescribing doctor is not a psychiatrist.

Self-defense: Communicate your problem to your doctor as clearly and concisely as possible.

Before your office visit, make a list of the questions you want to ask—in order of importance. If you get interrupted before you're through, at least you'll have covered the most crucial information.

If you feel your doctor is being dismissive, say so. If he/she still refuses to take your problem seriously, find another doctor.

• **Having your symptoms of heart disease go unrecognized.** Unlike men, women experiencing a heart attack often do not experience the classic symptoms—pain radiating down the arm or the elephant-sitting-on-your-chest type of pain.

Self-defense: Women should realize that vague abdominal discomfort, nausea, vomiting and shortness of breath can all be signs of heart attack. Take these symptoms very seriously. Make sure your doctor does, too.

• **Not being told to have routine mammograms and Pap smears.** Women over 65 account for almost half of the deaths from cervical cancer and are at greater risk of breast cancer than women of other age groups. But these older women are less likely than younger women to get the appropriate screening tests, often because their doctors fail to refer them for testing.

Self-defense: Annual mammograms, clinical breast exams and pelvic exams are recommended for all women 50 to 64 years of age.

The National Cancer Society recommends mammograms every one to two years for women 40 to 49 years of age.

A panel convened by the National Cancer Institute and the National Institute on Aging urges women 65 to 74 to have a clinical breast exam annually and a mammogram every two years, and women 75 and older to have both tests every two years. After three consecutive Pap smears with normal results, older women should have a Pap at least every three years. Younger women also need routine Pap smears.

• **Not being told that lumpectomy is a safe alternative to mastectomy.** Ninety percent of women with breast cancer are eligible for lumpectomy (removal of the tumor and a small margin of tissue), yet many undergo mastectomy (removal of the entire breast). The type of surgery a woman receives depends on such nonmedical factors as where she lives, her age, income and race.

Most likely to have a mastectomy: Black women, Medicare recipients, older women and women who live in the Midwest or South.

Self-defense: If your doctor says you need a mastectomy, get a second opinion—from a surgeon unaffiliated with your doctor's institution. Ask your doctor if he/she is aware of studies showing that lumpectomy followed by radiation is just as effective as mastectomy in treating early-stage breast tumors.

For more information on lumpectomy, call the National Cancer Institute at 800-4-CANCER.

• **Not having your early warning signs of AIDS recognized in time for effective treatment.** AIDS is now the fifth-leading killer of reproductive-age women. Not all doctors recognize female-specific symptoms of AIDS.

Self-defense: If you're involved in a new sexual relationship or if you're in a relationship with a man who may be unfaithful, insist that he wear a condom.

If you have recurrent vaginal yeast infections, genital herpes or cervical dysplasia, get tested for the AIDS virus. These conditions may be an early sign of infection.

•Being subjected to a needless hysterectomy. Many of the hysterectomies performed annually in the US are medically unjustified.

Self-defense: Women should know about the proven alternatives to hysterectomy. *Example:* Uterine fibroid tumors, which are usually benign, can often be shrunk with medication, then removed in a comparatively minor surgical procedure called myomectomy.

Women should also ask about subtotal hysterectomy—a procedure in which only the top of the uterus is removed and the cervix is left intact. This method, which is common in Europe, helps women maintain sexual responsiveness.

•Being prescribed drugs that were never properly tested in women. Women may suffer more or different side effects than men who take the same medication. *Example:* Doctors are often unaware that some drugs cause adverse reactions when combined with estrogen-replacement therapy or oral contraceptives.

Self-defense: If you're experiencing troublesome side effects, ask your doctor if you can switch to another medication. Realize that anti-anxiety drugs and postmenopausal estrogen taken together increase the risk of seizures and reduce the effectiveness of estrogen in treating hot flashes and other symptoms of menopause.

Hormone-replacement therapy (HRT) and oral contraceptives decrease the liver's metabolism of tricyclic antidepressants, leading to a greater risk of toxicity in women. For some women, doses of antidepressants may also need to be increased premenstrually.

•Being urged to go on hormone-replacement therapy despite the continuing debate over its long-term safety. Estrogen must be used continuously to maintain its benefit on bones. But most women—fearful of the risks of HRT—take it for a few years to relieve hot flashes and other menopausal symptoms and then stop.

Self-defense: Women may get almost as much protection if they take HRT to relieve short-term symptoms, discontinue it and start up again in their 70s. It's something to discuss with your doctor.

•Being overmedicated. Many common medical complaints of older women—including confusion and incontinence—may be caused by overmedication. Older women take drugs at twice the rate of older men, and are more apt to take multiple medications, increasing their risk of toxic side effects.

Self-defense: Older women should be aware that they metabolize many drugs differently than men. In women older than 65, for example, psychotropic drugs have a longer half-life, meaning that they remain in the body longer. To reduce the risk of side effects, physicians may need to reduce the doses of these drugs by one-third.

Elderly women also need to know that high doses of antipsychotic medication may increase their risk for chronic side effects such as tardive dyskinesia, a neurological disorder that results in abnormal movement of the mouth and tongue.

•Receiving medical care that is haphazard or fragmented. While men may see one doctor for all their health-care needs, women may see a gynecologist for a Pap smear and pelvic exam, an internist for a general physical exam and a radiologist for a mammogram.

Typically, one doctor doesn't know what the other is doing. Services often overlap, wasting time and money—and leading to inadequate care.

Self-defense: Find an internist with training in gynecology, qualifying him/her to perform pelvic exams and Pap smears. Find out whether there's a comprehensive women's health center in your community. These centers, generally affiliated with a major teaching hospital, offer one-stop medical care. Practitioners with training in gynecology, general medicine, cardiology, menopause care, oncology, infectious diseases, endocrinology and bone metabolism make themselves available to you during a single appointment.

With this trend toward women-centered care, women may finally be seen by the medical establishment not as a collection of reproductive organs but as human beings with hearts and lungs and colons and kidneys—just like men.

Mammography Report

Doctors should tell their patients of abnormal results, but they don't always do so.

Good news: The FDA now requires mammography testing facilities to send results directly to women within 30 days. Women who fail to get a report should call the testing facility.

Sharon Snider, press officer, Food and Drug Administration, Rockville, MD.

Mammogram Advice

Annual mammograms are a good idea for all women 40 or older. Annual screening permits detection of tumors at the earliest possible time. Early detection means better chances for survival, more treatment options and less disruption of daily life.

Christine E. Williamson, MD, director of breast imaging, Providence Medical Center, Seattle, and a member of the American Cancer Society's breast cancer task force.

HRT & Mammograms

Hormone replacement therapy (HRT) can raise the risk for falsely negative mammogram readings.

Recent finding: Mammograms detected only 64% of breast cancers in women 50 to 69 years of age who were on HRT. The test detected 80% of cancers in women of that age who were not on HRT.

Theory: HRT increases the density of breast tissue, making it more difficult to detect signs of cancer.

Important: Despite these findings, mammograms remain the most effective way to screen for breast cancer.

Anne M. Kavanagh, PhD, senior research fellow, Australian Research Centre for Sex, Health and Society, La Trobe University, Melbourne. Her two-year study of 103,770 women was published in *The Lancet,* 84 Theobald's Rd., London WC1X 8RR.

Benign Breast Lumps

Benign breast lumps occur in more than half of all women at some point in their lives. For 97% of these women, such lumps represent no significant increase in their risk of developing breast cancer. But any woman who notices a lump, particularly one that doesn't come and go with her menstrual cycle, should see her doctor right away.

James R. Dolan, MD, assistant professor of obstetrics, gynecology and gynecologic oncology, and codirector of the Breast Care Center, Loyola University Medical Center, Maywood, IL.

Breast Cancer Scandal

Women who've had a lumpectomy (removal of the breast tumor alone) should not be alarmed by reports of falsified data in breast cancer studies. Thousands of breast cancer patients opted for lumpectomy after several studies concluded that this procedure was just as safe and effective as mastectomy (removal of the entire breast). The fact that one of these studies has been questioned does not affect the validity of the others. Lumpectomy is still a valid option.

Harmon Eyre, MD, chief medical officer, American Cancer Society, 1599 Clifton Rd. NE, Atlanta 30329.

Lumpectomy Myth

Lumpectomies alone do *not* cure breast cancer. Standard treatment guidelines call for radiation and lymph node biopsies. *Troubling:* One-third of American women who had breast-conserving operations from 1990 to 1995 did not receive other needed treatment. *Self-defense:* Get second opinions…be treated by a team that includes surgeons, chemotherapists and radiation specialists.

Ann Butler Nattinger, MD, MPH, professor of medicine, Medical College of Wisconsin, Milwaukee, and leader of a study of nearly 145,000 women treated from 1983 to 1995, reported in *The Lancet,* 84 Theobald's Rd., London WC1X 8RR.

Pelvic Exams and Aging

Continue periodic pelvic exams even after menopause. Some cancers are more common in older women, including cancers of the vulva, vagina, cervix, uterus and ovaries. These cancers may have no obvious symptoms—but could be discovered by a doctor during a pelvic exam. This regular appointment also allows for discussion of health issues, sexuality and screening and prevention of major diseases that affect women as they age. *But:* After three consecutive normal tests, a postmenopausal woman at low risk for cancer may not need Pap tests every year. Ask your doctor.

Vicki Mendiratta, MD, clinical physician, obstetrics and gynecology, University of Washington Medical Center, Seattle.

Frequently Misdiagnosed: Vaginal Infections

Most women being treated for chronic yeast infections—either by their internists or by themselves with over-the-counter preparations —actually have a different condition.

Other causes of symptoms: Bacterial vaginosis or herpes infections, which require different treatments than that for yeast infections.

Caution: Never diagnose yourself. Over-the-counter treatments could make your symptoms worse. If you think you have a vaginal infection, ask your doctor to perform a complete physical examination and comprehensive medical history.

Karen Carroll, MD, departments of pathology and infectious diseases, and Paul Summers, MD, department of obstetrics and gynecology, both at the University of Utah Medical Center in Salt Lake City.

Cancer Warning

Vaginal bleeding or "spotting" following menopause can signal cancer of the cervix, uterus or vulva. Postmenopausal women too often disregard such bleeding, but a doctor's exam is important to rule out these serious ailments. Cervical, uterine and vulvar cancer kill nearly 12,000 American women a year.

Katherine O'Hanlan, MD, associate director of the gynecologic cancer service, Stanford University Medical Center, Palo Alto, CA.

Surgery Preventive For Women

Precancerous lesions of the cervix may not always require treatment with surgery or lasers. Repeated topical application of the acne drug *retinoic acid* (Retin-A) reversed early (stage 2) lesions. However, retinoic acid was ineffective against stage 3 lesions. *Side effect:* Mild vaginal inflammation.

Frank L. Meyskens, Jr., MD, director, Clinical Cancer Center, University of California, Irvine. His five-year study of more than 300 women with cervical lesions was reported in *The Medical Post*, 777 Bay St., Toronto, Ontario, M5W 1A7, Canada.

Pelvic Pain Trap

Pain caused by varicose veins around the ovaries and uterus often goes undiagnosed. *Reason:* Few doctors are familiar with the condition, known as *pelvic congestion syndrome*. When doctors do diagnose the ailment, they often recommend hysterectomy. That rarely solves the problem. *Better:* A new nonsurgical procedure that uses a catheter to plug the varicose veins with either coiled springs or a liquid agent that causes the veins to clot. These plugs prevent the pooling of blood that causes the pain.

Anthony C. Venbrux, MD, director, interventional radiology, Johns Hopkins Hospital, Baltimore.

Estrogen Trap

Estrogen replacement therapy (ERT) may contribute to asthma. *Recent finding:* Menopausal women on ERT have an 80% higher risk of developing asthma than women not taking hormones. *Theory:* Estrogen affects cells involved in the body's allergic or inflammatory response. *Important:* Women considering estrogen therapy should discuss all of the risks with their physicians.

Graham Barr, MD, fellow, Channing Laboratory, Brigham and Women's Hospital, Boston.

Treatment for Hot Flashes

It's no surprise that many postmenopausal women experience hot flashes. But hot flashes also afflict some men being treated for prostate cancer. In a study, the drug *megestrol acetate* (Megace) cut symptoms by 80%. Some women experienced menstrual bleeding one to three weeks after the medication had been discontinued...but that was the only side effect.

Charles L. Loprinzi, MD, associate professor of medical oncology, Mayo Clinic, Rochester, MN.

Better Sex After Serious Illness

leslie R. Schover, PhD, associate professor of behavioral science at the University of Texas M.D. Anderson Cancer Center in Houston. She is the author of *Sexuality and Fertility After Cancer* (Wiley) and *Sexuality and Chronic Illness* (Guilford Press).

Poor health does not eliminate the need for sexual intimacy. But the physical and psychological impact of heart disease, stroke, cancer or other serious illness—as well as the effects of many medical treatments—can impair your ability to enjoy sex.

Here are some additional steps you can take on your own to get your sex life back on track...

●**Ask your doctor about medication.** For men, prostate, bladder or colorectal cancer surgery may damage nerves, causing impotence. Women receiving chemotherapy may experience sudden menopause as a result of a drop in hormone levels. Many medications, such as the anti-depressant *fluoxetine* (Prozac) and some painkillers, can inhibit sexual desire and performance.

Hormone replacement and drugs like *sildenafil* (Viagra) may help restore desire and the ability to function.

Caution: Breast and prostate cancer survivors should *not* use hormone replacement. It can promote cancer growth.

●**Do not underestimate yourself.** After a heart attack, many people (and their partners) are fearful about sex. But for most people, the risk is small—heart rate is often lower during sexual activity than during a mildly stressful event at work.

Find out from your doctor whether it's safe for you to resume sexual relations...and how to minimize risk.

●**Strive for physical vitality.** The more you restore your sense of fitness—with rehabilitation, exercise and diet—the better you'll feel about yourself.

●**Practice the art of fantasy.** To keep anxiety and doubts about your attractiveness from intruding when you make love, focus on positive, arousing images.

●**Heighten your awareness.** It's important to experience the pleasures of contact—without having the pressure to "respond" or "perform."

What to do: For 15 minutes, lie passively while your partner caresses your body—but not the erogenous areas.

Focus on the physical sensations. Then reverse roles. While you're the "giver," focus on the pleasurable sensations of touching.

In later sessions, you can include breasts and genitals, but keep your focus on sensation. The goal is physical pleasure—not orgasm.

●**Talk about sex.** Tell (or show) your partner what helps you to respond sexually—and what feels good—rather than complaining about what doesn't. "It helps me get aroused when you start lovemaking slowly, spend more time and use a delicate touch" is much better than "Don't be so rough."

●**Schedule time for sex.** After serious illness, you may not feel in the mood at the time when you're used to lovemaking.

Timing can make a big difference. Sex may be more feasible at certain times of day (when pain medication is working but isn't making you drowsy, for example).

●**Take the pressure off.** Resuming sex after a period of weeks or months—after surgery or when severe illness has made it impossible, for example—can be anxiety-provoking. You wonder: *Will it work? How will I feel?*

Estrogen Update

Women who take estrogen after menopause tend to do better on memory tests than those who do not take the hormone. Estrogen may even reduce the risk of Alzheimer's disease. But hormone-replacement therapy can have side effects of its own—be sure to discuss it in detail with your doctor.

Sanjay Asthana, MD, Puget Sound Health Care System, American Lake Division, Tacoma, WA.

Pacemaker Surgery For Women

One type of pacemaker surgery for women allows the device to be implanted beneath the breast tissue. The technique leaves only small scars near the shoulder and under the breast, hidden from view.

Result: Patients can wear low-cut dresses or bikinis without the stigma of having a long scar along the neckline. Surgery takes about two hours and is performed under local anesthesia. Recovery takes less than a week.

Marc Roelke, MD, attending physician in cardiac pacing and electrophysiology, Beth Israel Hospital, Newark, NJ.

Conquering Incontinence

Mary Dierich, RN, a nurse-practitioner at the Center for Bladder and Pelvic Dysfunction at the University of Minnesota in Minneapolis. She is coauthor of *Overcoming Incontinence: A Straightforward Guide to Your Options.* John Wiley & Sons.

Urinary incontinence—leakage of urine—is a mainstay of TV and magazine ads. But the condition is rarely discussed where it ought to be—in doctors' offices.

At least 30% of the estimated 17 million Americans who have incontinence—two-thirds of whom are women—fail to bring it up with their physicians.

Many are silent because they believe incontinence is an inevitable part of aging...and that it's incurable.

They're wrong on both counts.

Incontinence has many causes besides aging. These include vaginal and urinary tract infections...constipation...medication side effects...childbirth...prostate disease...and neurological conditions.

Good news: Regardless of the cause, incontinence can usually be ameliorated.

TYPES OF INCONTINENCE

There are three different types of urinary incontinence...

●**Stress incontinence**—leakage that occurs with activity.

This is most commonly caused by weakness of the pelvic floor muscles that support the bladder and control the urinary sphincter. That's the muscle at the base of the bladder that controls urine flow.

●**Urge incontinence**—a sudden and uncontrollable need to urinate. Common causes of urge incontinence include bladder infection, medication and neurological disease.

●**Overflow incontinence**—leakage from an overly full bladder. It is common in men with enlarged prostates.

Other causes include blockage of the urethra or inability of the bladder to contract efficiently.

HELPFUL MEDICATIONS

Many incontinence medications are now available. *These include medications that...*

●**Reduce bladder contraction.**

- **Increase muscle tone of the urinary sphincter.**

- **Alleviate blockage of the urethra.**

Medications are often recommended as the first line of defense against incontinence. Drug therapy can be effective for the condition and is relatively inexpensive.

Trap: The medications can cause side effects, including heart palpitations, high blood pressure, dizziness, dry mouth and constipation. And using medications doesn't usually correct the *cause* of the problem—such as pelvic floor muscle weakness.

By contrast, individuals who are willing to go a nonmedical route can usually correct the problem's cause, not merely treat its symptoms.

SELF-HELP STRATEGIES

Nonmedical approaches do require commitment and follow-through—sometimes for a lifetime. *Eight self-help strategies can be remarkably effective...*

- **Avoid irritants that trigger bladder contraction.** These include caffeine, aspartame (NutraSweet) and alcohol.

- **Drink plenty of water.** Consume at least six eight-ounce glasses daily. This dilutes urine so it won't irritate the bladder.

- **Boost consumption of fruits and vegetables.** Five servings daily help prevent constipation, a potential trigger of stress and urge incontinence.

- **Avoid sleep medications.** Even over-the-counter sleeping aids induce sleep so deep that the signal to get up and urinate can be missed.

- **Do Kegel exercises.** These exercises work for stress and urge incontinence. Effective for men and women, they strengthen the pelvic floor muscles.

What to do: Two to three times daily, contract the muscles used to hold back intestinal gas and urine flow. To begin, do five contractions at a time while lying down. Hold each contraction for five seconds. Relax for 20 seconds after each contraction. Gradually work up to a total of 40 contractions daily, holding each for 10 seconds.

Once perfected, Kegels can be performed standing or sitting.

Some people have trouble doing Kegels. *If you do, ask your doctor about trying...*

- *Biofeedback.* A sensor placed in the vagina or rectum monitors pelvic floor muscle contractions. A computer analyzes the contractions and points out problems. Biofeedback typically requires about five sessions—at home or at an incontinence specialist's office—to learn how to correct the errors and do Kegels reliably.

- *Pelvic muscle stimulation.* Pelvic muscles are stimulated by a device briefly inserted into the vagina or rectum. Equipment is used in medical offices or at home. Treatment typically takes at least three months. After it's completed, the muscles are strong enough to do Kegels effectively.

- Pulsed magnetic therapy. In this newest method, a mild magnetic current flows through the seat of a special chair called the "NeoControl" chair. The current stimulates contraction of pelvic floor muscles. No device is inserted into the body. Individuals remain clothed during treatment.

Therapy usually involves two 20-minute sessions each week for eight weeks. After treatment, muscles are strengthened and Kegels are done more effectively. The chairs are not yet widely available. To locate a practice that uses the NeoControl chair in your area, call the manufacturer at 877-636-2668.

- **Try bladder retraining.** People who get the hang of Kegels can use them to "retrain" their bladders to empty less frequently. This approach—which helps with urge incontinence—trains people not to respond to every signal the bladder sends.

Begin by permitting yourself to respond to the signal to urinate only every 90 to 120 minutes. Increase the time between voiding by 15 minutes each week for six weeks. Use Kegels to prevent urination outside these times.

AND FOR WOMEN ONLY

- **Use a vaginal cone.** This tampon-like weight—available by prescription—takes advantage of Kegel contractions to strengthen pelvic floor muscles.

As the device works its way down the vagina, the muscles automatically contract.

- **Try pessaries, continence rings and bladder prostheses.** Inserted into the vagina, these devices support a fallen bladder (pessary)...

press the bladder neck closed (ring)…or lift the urethra to position it correctly (prosthesis). They need not be removed before urination.

GETTING COVERAGE

Some health insurers cover biofeedback, pelvic muscle stimulation and the NeoControl chair. *If yours doesn't…*

● **Contact your insurer's customer service department.** Most companies will provide coverage if you can show that self-help methods are more economical than other approaches, such as surgery.

● **Get permission to try self-help strategies for two months.** At that point, your health-care provider must send a letter documenting your progress.

● **Choose an incontinence specialist experienced in working with insurers.***

WHEN SURGERY IS NECESSARY

Surgery is an option if self-help strategies and drug therapy fail. Surgical procedures include adding bulk to the urethra to increase its resistance to urine flow…repositioning the base of the bladder and the urethra…and inserting a "cuff" around the urethra to keep it closed until urination is desired.

Incontinence Update

The incontinence drug *tolterodine* (Detrol) works just as well as older drugs—and is less likely to cause dry mouth and other troublesome side effects. The first new drug for overactive bladder in 20 years, Detrol may be effective in curbing symptoms of urinary frequency and urgency.

Harold P. Drutz, MD, professor and head of urogynecology, University of Toronto Faculty of Medicine.

*To find a qualified incontinence specialist, contact the National Association for Continence (800-252-3337).

Natural Relief

To relieve constipation, mix one-half cup of unprocessed bran, one-half cup of applesauce and one-third cup of prune juice. Refrigerate the mixture. Take two tablespoons after dinner, followed by a glass of water. If this does not relieve constipation, increase the dose to three or four tablespoons. *Diet hints:* Eat plenty of fresh fruit, vegetables and fiber. If the extra fiber causes excess gas, try the herbal remedy *epazote. Note:* For people with restricted mobility, more fiber can aggravate constipation.

Craig Rubin, MD, professor of internal medicine and chief of geriatrics, University of Texas southwestern Medical Center, Dallas.

Easy Steps to Avoid Irregularity and Constipation

St. Luke's Episcopal Hospital, Houston, TX, a member of the Texas Medical Center.

Irregularity and constipation are common in children and in older adults and, although there may be many causes, including diet, stress and even medications, there are some easy ways to deal with these problems.

What they are: The experts at St Luke's Episcopal Hospital, Houston, Texas, explain that irregularity means bowel movements that do not occur regularly, while constipation means infrequent or difficult bowel movements, or hard, dry stools. Because there is no normal pattern for bowel movements, and frequency ranges from as many as three a day to as few as three or four a week, frequency alone is not necessarily an indicator of irregularity and constipation. But a change in normal pattern and difficult bowel movements may suggest that they are present.

Whatever the diagnosis, the common symptoms of irregularity and constipation include a bloated, full feeling, sluggishness, headache, loss of appetite, straining to move the bowels, a general sense of feeling out of sorts and occasionally nausea.

How to avoid problems: Six simple changes in your habits can go a long way to freeing you of suffering from these maladies:

- **Set aside a time for regular bowel movements,** and do not delay when you feel the urge to have a bowel movement.

- **Avoid straining when going to the bathroom.**

- **Drink lots of liquids**—six to eight 8-ounce glasses a day—unless otherwise instructed by your doctor.

- **Increase the soluble fiber in your diet gradually** by eating more cereals, breads and whole grains (such as bran, whole wheat, oatmeal and brown rice), and fresh fruits and vegetables (such as celery, beans, prunes and leafy vegetables). Your physician may recommend soluble fiber supplements.

- **Eat regular meals,** and chew food thoroughly and slowly.

- **Exercise daily.**

Men and Menopause

Barbara Sherwin, PhD, co-director of the McGill University Menopause Clinic in Montreal and associate professor of psychology and obstetrics and gynecology at McGill University.

Not enough men understand what menopause is. As a result, even the most sympathetic man may be thrown completely off balance when the woman in his life begins to exhibit the physiological and emotional symptoms of menopause. Sadly, his ignorance will prevent him from helping the woman he loves …and may even cause him to inadvertently do and say things that make matters worse.

Thanks to books like Gail Sheehy's *The Silent Passage* and Germaine Greer's *The Change,* magazine articles and TV talk shows, the whole subject of menopause has come out of the closet. But plenty of myths and misconceptions remain…and they often lead to problems between men—who see in menopause their own mortality—and their menopausal wives. *Answers to basic questions:*

What is menopause? Menopause occurs when the ovaries stop producing the female hormone estrogen and menstruation ceases.

When does menopause typically occur? Menopause is actually a prolonged series of events that occur over years. On average, it starts at around age 51, but the symptoms are the most intense during perimenopause—about two years before and two years after.

What's causing my wife's physical and emotional changes? The hot flashes, the thinning of the vaginal tissues, the decreased vaginal lubrication, the mood swings are all the result of the ovaries producing little or no estrogen now. Any or all of these changes are perfectly normal and to be expected.

Why is my wife less interested in sex now? *A couple of reasons:* The changes in the reproductive tract may make intercourse painful. And hormonal changes may cause a decrease in her sexual desire.

Is there any good news? Definitely! Most of the worst symptoms of menopause can be alleviated with hormone-replacement therapy. Even if she doesn't take hormones, some of the troublesome symptoms may naturally wane in time. She should discuss her course of action with her gynecologist. *Advantages of hormone therapy:* Control of hot flashes…restoration of integrity of genital tissues…women generally feel better. *Long-term bonus:* Hormonal therapy helps protect against osteoporosis and possibly Alzheimer's disease. *Disadvantages:* Women with an intact uterus also receive progestin to prevent endometrial cancer, and this can cause resumption of menstruation. *Long-term risk:* Estrogen therapy for more than 15 years can cause a slightly increased risk of breast cancer.

How can I be more supportive of my wife now? Visit the gynecologist with her, so that you can show your support and get your own questions about menopause answered—just as more and more husbands are going to prenatal classes to learn about pregnancy and labor and to be there for their wives.

Give your wife a break. If she's more tired than usual these days, tell her you won't mind if she isn't up to attending the theater or going out after work. *Better:* Make dinner for the two of you, order in…or take her out to eat more often. Don't gripe when she wants to fling open the windows in mid-December—just get yourself another blanket. Offer to rub her feet or bring her a cup of tea. You get the idea.

Anything else? Avoid such inflammatory comments as:

"It's all in your mind!"…"There's nothing wrong with you!"

We have to be careful not to make menopause sound like an illness. Without the fear of pregnancy now…with the children perhaps grown and out of the house…with greater time for recreation and for each other, many couples report that this is the happiest time in their life…and that sex is better than ever. Menopause can actually be the start of a wonderful new phase for you both.

Tips for Denture Wearers

Removing dentures at night can lead to aching jaws, headaches and insomnia.

Reason: Jaws adapt to closing over teeth. If you sleep without your dentures, you may "overclose"—which strains the jaw joint and muscles.

Recommended: If you have morning-after pain, try leaving dentures in at night (but remove them for four hours during the day).

An Army study of 200 denture wearers, cited in *American Health,* 28 W. 23 St., New York 10010.

Music vs. Rectal Exam Pain

Colorectal cancer is the second-leading cause of death by cancer in the US, but many patients are reluctant to undergo a sigmoidoscopy because the exam can be embarrassing and uncomfortable.

Good news: 88% of patients who listened to music during a sigmoidoscopy reported reduced

levels of anxiety and pain. Their blood pressure and heart rates were also lower than those of people who didn't listen to music.

Brian Sweeney, MD, assistant professor of surgery, University of Massachusetts Medical Center, Worcester. His study of 50 men and women 20 to 76 years of age was presented at a meeting of the American Society of Colon and Rectal Surgeons, 85 W. Algonquin Rd., Arlington Heights, IL 60005.

Try Plato, Not Prozac!

Lou Marinoff, PhD, associate professor of philosophy at City College of New York, New York. He is founding president of the American Philosophical Practitioners Association and author of *Plato, Not Prozac! Applying Eternal Wisdom to Everyday Problems.* HarperCollins.

Life isn't always to our liking. Marriages can be filled with strife. We fall ill. We lose those we love. We retire…and find leisure empty.

Faced with problems, worry and confusion, more and more people today seek help by talking through their painful emotions with a psychotherapist, or taking potent medications. Sometimes, these are absolutely necessary. But in many cases, they're not.

Often, suffering isn't a matter of emotional maladjustment or brain chemistry, but understanding. What we need to examine are our lives and our beliefs…what we need to change is how we see things. What we need isn't therapy, but philosophy.

WHY PHILOSOPHY?

What are you? On the one hand, you're a biological creation—flesh, blood and chemical reactions. Something goes awry in your metabolism, and you get diabetes. Or a disorder in brain cells with which you think and feel can cause misery or anxiety and require medication.

On the other hand, you're a psychological creature, shaped by decades of experience. If you were abused as a child or grew up in a family where anger must be buried at all costs, you may have emotional difficulties that require the help of a psychotherapist.

But human beings are also thinking beings governed by beliefs, not biology or emotion. How you explain the world to yourself, what you see as truly important, why you're here and where you're going...these can create and dispel turmoil. That's where philosophy comes in.

Philosophy has much to offer. All you need is a willingness to lead an examined life, to take a step back, look inside the things that bother you, consider what you truly believe and explore what you can do about it.

LOOKING AT LIFE PHILOSOPHICALLY

A "philosophy of life" may sound like something for gurus, but actually everyone has one—although most of us don't put it into words.

Everyone, that is, has beliefs about how the world works, what counts and what doesn't, what's right and what's wrong.

An important step in resolving problems is becoming aware of what you already believe: To look at what's troubling you in an analytical way...to see—and understand—what turns a "situation" into a "problem." And to understand how your philosophy of life can help you make the most of it.

Many people have found help in this process from a new breed of counselors, "philosophical practitioners" who have studied philosophy intensively and are experienced in applying ideas to life problems. But you may be able to do it on your own. *Here's how...*

"PEACE" IS THE WAY

It's best to work systematically using the "PEACE" process...

- **Identify the *problem.***
- **Take stock of the *emotions* that it evokes.**
- ***Analyze* your options.**
- ***Contemplate* the entire situation.**
- **Reach an *equilibrium* through understanding and effective action.**

Although we usually think we know what's bothering us, sometimes introspection takes us deeper. What seems like just bad luck or ill treatment may turn out, on closer inspection, to be more complex.

Example: The company where you've worked for 30 years has downsized, forcing you to retire sooner than you wanted. The "problem" seems obvious—you've lost your job and suddenly have less money than you're used to. But closer thought makes you recognize that you can get by quite easily. Then why do you feel so anxious and unhappy? Your *reaction* is the real problem.

Looking analytically at your emotions, you see that underneath the dismay and worry lies anger...you feel you've been treated unfairly by those you gave much of your life to. You're also feeling insecure and disoriented by the sudden change in circumstances.

What are your options? Your job is gone. You can nurse a grudge or spend hours fuming and fantasizing revenge. Or, you can put it behind you and seek other employment. Or make a virtue of necessity, planning how to make your retirement full and rewarding.

Contemplating the situation means thoughtfully pondering these alternatives, weighing their consequences and trying to develop the philosophical outlook that works best for you. The first two options, you realize quickly, are unlikely to bring you happiness or lasting pleasure.

You know it would be best to go beyond the setback and enjoy the rest of your life, but you hurt!

Making peace with the situation takes time... it may take weeks, even months, of thoughtful contemplation to put the problem in perspective. You may need to ponder just why you're angry—perhaps at the "unfairness" of it all—and resolve this with the realization that the cost-cutting move wasn't directed at you personally. You're upset by the change, but come to the recognition that change is simply an inexorable fact of life.

Contemplation may involve searching exploration of yourself—who are you? What's most important to you? Which of your feelings come from deep inside you...and which did you simply learn from others? If being independent emerges as a powerful value, then you can see this situation as an opportunity to develop that trait.

Finally, you put the fruits of your contemplation into action. The "problem" is no longer a problem, but a fact of life, and the understanding you've attained tells you where to go from there. You've achieved a new equilibrium that allows you to go on with your life.

20

Self-Defense

The Ultimate Guide to Avoiding Violent Crime

The first rule of avoiding violent crime on the street or in the home is to understand this—*it can happen to you*. No neighborhood is immune.

You can improve your odds that the bad guy won't pick you. How? Make yourself a tough target.

Just as the lion chooses the weakest antelope to pick off from the pack, the bad guy chooses the easiest victim—the weak one, the one who isn't paying attention, the one least likely to resist.

But there's a trick to this game. It's not how tough you really are—it's how tough you *look*.

Psychologists use the term, "displaying the weapons of aggression." Dogs bare their teeth, cats show their claws and you should show the bad guys you have something to fight back with, too.

Example: A woman who jogs with a dog might be no tougher than one without a dog, but she looks tougher. The dog is an unknown quantity to any would-be muggers—and muggers don't like to take unnecessary chances.

PEPPER SPRAYS AND PERSONAL ALARMS

Another weapon of aggression you should consider is pepper spray. It's easy to use. Pressing the button sprays a stream of oleoresin capsicum more than 1,000 times more powerful than Tabasco sauce. Unlike tear gas, pepper spray deters even crazed drug users and vicious animals. That's why mail carriers use it.

If you're afraid you wouldn't be able to use pepper spray on someone, consider a personal alarm. Pull out the pin, and it emits a piercing alarm until you reinsert the pin. They're better than whistles, because whistles stop making noise the moment you stop blowing.

Important: To scare off potential attackers, keep the spray in your hand, ready for fire. Keep

J.J. Bittenbinder, a retired detective with the Chicago Police and a frequent lecturer on personal safety.

283

the alarm attached to your waistband or in a jacket pocket.

Personal alarms and pepper sprays are available in hardware stores and gun shops. If you have trouble finding them, call your local police department and ask where they get theirs.

People often ask me whether it's a good idea to own a gun. It's always a personal choice, but I don't recommend it. A gun in the home is far more likely to be fired by accident, during a domestic dispute or in a suicide, than used to protect the family from an intruder. Any situation that reaches the point where you need to use a gun has already gone too far. Prevention is much better.

AVOIDING SEXUAL ASSAULT

To keep a date from turning into date rape, a woman should resist unwanted sexual advances strongly and clearly, or she runs the risk of being misunderstood.

If a man kisses you against your will, bite down on his lower lip...or grab his scrotum and wring it like a towel.

Teach your children that it's okay to say no to adults—especially in the area of forced affection. Never insist that a child allow Grandpa to kiss her—give her the choice. Otherwise, you'll be giving her the message that it's okay for adults to force themselves on her.

When kids go somewhere together, remind them never to leave one another behind. If they have to run, the faster one should always wait for the slower one.

BANK MACHINE SELF-DEFENSE

Automatic teller machines (ATMs) are certainly convenient, but they can leave you exposed to muggers.

To minimize risk: Use a drive-through ATM whenever possible. If anyone approaches, drive away. Failing that, stick to an ATM in an enclosed kiosk—one that requires a magnetic card for entry and which is equipped with a security camera. ATM kiosks inside a building or store are safer than stand-alone kiosks.

Avoid ATMs located directly on the street—especially if it's a deserted street at night. If the ATM is next to an alley, where someone can pop out with no warning, that's even worse.

If you must use a street ATM, do so during the day or with a friend—in an area with people around.

Special problem: ATMs with vertical keypads. They allow a robber to watch as you punch in your personal identification number—increasing the odds that he'll try to steal your card. Try to use an ATM with a horizontal keypad—one that's parallel with the ground.

ON THE STREET

Don't make things easy on muggers by wearing headphones and listening to loud music. Headphones prevent you from hearing someone coming up behind you—making you an easy target.

Don't flash jewelry on the street, subway or bus either—even if it's fake.

Women: Carry your purse in front of you, not bouncing on your hip.

Men: Keep your wallet in your front pants pocket or in the vest pocket inside your coat. Using the back pants pocket only invites pickpockets.

If you're approached by a suspicious-looking character, cross the street or walk in the middle of the street to maintain your distance. Don't worry about appearing overly cautious.

Helpful: Wrap two $1 bills inside a $5 bill and put them in a money clip. If a robber demands your money, toss the clip in one direction, say, "That's all I've got," and run as fast as you can in the other direction.

IN YOUR HOME

There's no doubt about it—good locks and bright lighting are your best bet against a break-in. Keep shrubs pruned so that they don't hide your windows from neighbors' view.

The best alarm systems are those monitored by the company that sells them. Typically, these alarm systems call the police or fire department when a signal goes off.

You're provided with code numbers to use in case you set it off accidentally...and a "hostage code" to secretly alert police that you're being held.

At the first sound of an intruder, dial 911. If you own a cellular phone, keep the recharger near your bed. That way, if an intruder cuts your phone lines, you can still call 911.

THWARTING CARJACKERS

A car phone is a great investment in safety. You can use it to dial 911 in any emergency. And just the sight of it is often enough to deter would-be attackers.

Some motorists are now equipping their cars with electronic homing devices that automatically alert the police if their car is stolen—and lead them to it. These devices are effective—but expensive for many people.

Every car is already equipped with the best possible anti-carjacking device—the door locks. Use them even when you're inside the car. It's hard for a carjacker to be successful if he cannot get inside your car.

If someone does get in—get out. No car is worth dying for.

If someone orders you into a car—his or yours—don't do it. Odds are you'll never come back. *Instead:* Run for it. Statistics show that 95% of people who run from an armed kidnapper survive. Most kidnappers won't shoot. The few who do usually miss.

Protecting Yourself Against Muggers

Ken Glickman, coordinator of Educational Services, Greenwich Institute for American Education, Stamford, CT 06901.

The best defense against becoming a crime victim is to avoid a setup. Muggers, like most people, don't take more risks or work harder than they have to. *Point:* They choose victims who seem easy to handle. And they create situations that make the attack simpler.

Chief defense: Don't allow yourself to be distracted, isolated or simply stopped on the street by a stranger. Muggers prefer victims who have stopped moving. They use every technique to accomplish that—asking for directions, a match or a handout.

First and most important rule: When spoken to by a suspicious stranger, don't stop. Move away quickly. Don't slow down to watch an argument or any other commotion on the street. Fake street fights are a favorite way to set up a robbery.

DEFENSIVE TACTICS

Walk down the middle of the sidewalk near the street. Be wary of corners and doorways. Reduce the possibility of being grabbed from the shadows. Hugging the curb permits you to see around the corner while at a distance. Be alert to someone hiding between or behind parked cars.

Walk a couple of extra blocks to take a safe route, especially late at night. Keep to known neighborhoods. Identify in advance where the places of refuge are, in the event of trouble.

Look ahead, up the street (not down) to see what's happening. Be alert, especially to people loitering or moving suspiciously. *Example:* Two men up ahead who suddenly separate and begin walking apart. They could be preparing to set you up.

However foolish or rude it may seem, don't get on any self-service elevator if there's somebody at all suspicious on it. Never let an elevator you are on go to the basement. *How to avoid it:* When entering an open elevator, keep a foot in the door while pressing the floor number. Keep your eyes on the elevator indicator. If the arrow is pointing down, don't get in.

Don't get into a self-service elevator late at night without making sure nobody is waiting on an upper floor to intercept you. *How to do it:* Push the top floor elevator button, but don't get in. If the elevator does not stop on any floor on the way up or down, it's safe.

Avoid places where gangs of juveniles congregate. They can be more dangerous than professional muggers because they will often hurt a victim rather than take the money and run.

Get into the habit of automatically saying *excuse me* when you bump into someone on the street. Say it no matter whose fault it is.

Never show money in public, whether at a newsstand, market, bank or getting out of a cab. Muggers are watching.

If you are mugged: Cooperate. Above all, communicate the willingness to cooperate. Keep calm. It can help relax the mugger, too, which is crucial. *Reason:* If a mugger is pointing a cocked revolver, nervousness on his part could be fatal to you. *Ways to calm the situation:* Say something reassuring, or ask a distracting question that establishes the mugging as a businesslike transaction. *Example:* "You can have anything you want. Do you mind if I just keep my driver's license?"

Never move suddenly. *Tell the mugger where your wallet is and ask:* "Do you want me to get it or do you want to get it?"

A woman mugger with a knife or gun can kill just as easily as a man. Letting macho feelings interfere with cooperating is suicidal.

Don't show the slightest condescension or hostility. Be careful of your tone of voice. Cooperating with disdain can set off violence. *Best attitude to project:* You've got to earn a living, too. *Or:* I don't hold this against you at all; times are tough.

Don't make jokes. They are too risky, and the chance for misinterpretation is too great.

Avoid direct or steady eye contact.

If a mugger is particularly hostile, be supercooperative. Offer money or possessions he has overlooked.

Bottom line: Always carry mugger money. Keep $25 to $100 in your pocket as insurance. A happy mugger is much less likely to do harm than one who comes away empty-handed.

What You Can Do To Avoid Terrorism

Rebecca Shannonhouse, editor, *Bottom Line/Health,* 281 Tresser Blvd., Stamford, CT 06901.

The enormity of recent terrorist attacks have made us all vigilant. But what specific steps are necessary to avoid being hurt in the midst of an attack?

We spoke with Michael Zanker, MD, assistant professor of clinical emergency medicine at the University of Connecticut in Hartford and a well-known expert on terrorism. He offered several pointers on how to avoid being hurt in a terrorist attack…

● **If you see several people vomiting or having seizures,** do not rush over to help. These symptoms can be caused by chemical agents such as the nerve gas released in the Tokyo subway in 1995. Good Samaritans who offer assistance could wind up being exposed to the same agent.

It's probably okay to give aid if only one person is ill. But stay away and alert the authorities if two or more people exhibit the same odd symptoms.

● **In case of a bomb blast while you're indoors,** crouch under a heavy desk or table or a door frame. If outside, run for it. Do not stick around. Terrorists often set a second bomb to go off minutes after a first.

● **And…if you see an unattended suitcase or parcel in a public place**—airport, train station, etc.—alert the authorities at once. It could harbor a bomb or a biological or chemical weapon.

If you're headed overseas, you can get details on recent terrorist activity at your destination from the US State Department. Go to *www.state.gov,* and click on "travel and living abroad."

Police-Impersonator Self-Defense

The color of the flashing lights atop police cars are not standardized across the United States. While red flashers are common, many police forces use combinations on their vehicles, such as blue-and-red and blue-and-white. Other police forces use just blue lights.

Self-defense: To protect yourself from criminals impersonating highway police—without violating the law—turn on emergency flashers when an unmarked vehicle signals you from behind …stay on the road…slow down…then stop at the first well-lighted, populated area, such as a gas station.

Phil Lynn, manager, National Law Enforcement Policy Center, International Association of Chiefs of Police, Alexandria, VA.

How Not to Be Swindled

J.L. Simmons, PhD, author of *67 Ways to Protect Seniors From Crime.* Henry Holt and Co. Inc.

Here's some very good advice to help you steer clear of swindlers and avoid being an easy mark...

●**If any offer sounds too good to be true,** you can be virtually certain that it is.

●**Never rush or impulse buy.** Swindlers don't want to give you any time to think the deal over because your common sense might prevail.

●**Responses to help separate the good guys from the bad guys:** "Well, let me talk this over with my attorney."..."I'll check this out with the Better Business Bureau and get back to you."

●**If an offer is in person or by phone,** insist on getting details in writing before making a decision.

●**Check out any offer or recommendation thoroughly.** Call your local Area Agency on Aging or Better Business Bureau.

●**Investigate and comparison shop as you would with any major purchase.** Check it out with knowledgeable people.

●**Don't sign anything until you've done your investigation.**

●**Use credit cards, or at least checks—** never cash. With credit cards and checks there is a legal record of your payment.

●**Never give out your credit card,** Medicare, Social Security, telephone calling card or bank account numbers to solicitors.

●**The fact that an offer appears on network TV** or in a respected magazine or major newspaper means nothing. Acceptance standards for ads are notoriously lax and virtually anyone can buy advertising.

●**Beware of anyone touting "little or no risk."**

●**If you get taken, don't be too embarrassed to report it to the police,** your local attorney general, the Better Business Bureau and any relevant professional association. You might help save others from being hurt.

Before You Give To Charity...

Check on how a charity spends its money before you donate. Send the name of the charity and a self-addressed, stamped envelope to the BBB Wise Giving Alliance, *www.give.org,* 4200 Wilson Blvd., Ste. 800, Arlington, VA 22203. By sending a donation, you can also request a copy of the BBB's *Wise Giving Guide,* which evaluates 300 charitable organizations.

Nancy Dunnan, editor and publisher, *TravelSmart,* Box 397, Dobbs Ferry, NY 10522.

High-Tech Scams

Beware: Criminals are using new technology to perpetuate old scams. *Examples:* Work-at-home schemes still promise untold riches—but solicitations now arrive by e-mail and tout medical-billing software instead of envelope-stuffing kits...official-looking notices of travel "bargains" are faxed to companies to trick employees into booking scam vacations with their credit cards. *Increasingly important:* Check out a company by calling your local Better Business Bureau or visiting *www.bbb.org. Caution:* Burgeoning area codes make it hard to tell whether a phone number is domestic or international. *To identify* unfamiliar area codes: *www.555-1212.com*. If your money leaves the country, it is nearly impossible to get it back.

Holly Cherico, vice president of communications, Council of Better Business Bureaus, Inc., Arlington, VA.

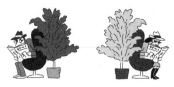

How to Keep *Them* From Knowing Too Much About *You*

Robert Ellis Smith, publisher of *Privacy Journal*, Box 28577, Providence, RI 02908. He is author of *Ben Franklin's Web Site: Privacy and Curiosity from Plymouth Rock to the Internet*. Privacy Journal.

New technology allows more scrutiny than ever of your public and private actions—your data are available to everyone from con artists and telemarketers to your bank, employer, insurance companies and more.

You can't prevent disclosure of *some* of your private information. But you can do a personal risk assessment. Often, a small amount of caution can neutralize large risks to your privacy.

ONLINE ACTIVITY

Every Web site you visit collects information about your surfing habits.

Result: Your e-mailbox is flooded with unwanted solicitations.

With just your e-mail address, anyone can find out your spouse's name, where you live, how much you paid for your house, etc. *Self-defense...*

●**Use a special e-mail address for surfing the Internet**—especially if you visit chat rooms, newsgroups or register on Web sites. That's where junk mailers harvest information. This way, you can more easily sift through undesirable e-mail.

If you want to use your regular e-mail address in newsgroups, insert "no-spam-"* when you are asked to give your e-mail address.

*Spam is unsolicited e-mail.

Example: *no-spam-john-doe@isp.com*. If junk mailers try to reach you at this e-mail address, their mail will be returned.

Individuals who really want to reach you can simply strip off the "no-spam" portion of the address when they reply.

●**Don't reply to spam or junk e-mail,** even if it's to ask the sender to remove you from its list.

Reason: Responding confirms your e-mail address and invites more spam.

Better: Send a complaint e-mail to your Internet Service Provider (ISP). It should contact the spammer's ISP.

You can also use antispam software. It works in conjunction with your e-mail software to filter out junk e-mail.

Popular: SpamScan97 (*www.webster-image.com/SpamScan97*)...and Spam Buster (*www.contactplus.com*).

●**Alter your browser to reveal less information about you** when you download files from Web sites. If you use Netscape, choose Communicator from the system menu and select *Messenger*.

●Under *Edit* menu, select *Preferences*.

●Scroll down and click *Advanced*.

●Remove the checkmark in the *Send e-mail as anonymous FTP password* box.

●Click on *OK*.

If you use Microsoft Internet Explorer 5, go to Tools–Internet Options.

●Click the *Security tab*. Highlight the *Internet* icon.

●Click the *Custom Level* tab.

●Scroll down to *User Authentications/ Logon*.

●Click *Anonymous Logon*.

Warning: Don't disable your cookies. Cookies are data strings in your Internet browser that identify you when you visit a Web page. If you turn off this function to remain invisible, most sites will not allow you to enter.

●**Examine the "privacy policy"** before you use a Web site regularly. Some sites enable you to check an "opt-out" box if you don't want to receive e-mail from marketers.

●**Investigate yourself online**—to see how much about you is available to the public. Type your name into search engines, such as *www.lycos.com* and *www.excite.com.* To check your postings in Internet newsgroups, search *http://groups.google.com* Ask directories that list e-mail addresses, home addresses, phone numbers, etc. to remove yours. *Big ones include…*

- *www.anywho.com*
- *www.bigfoot.com*
- *http://people.yahoo.com*
- *www.infospace.com*
- *www.switchboard.com*
- *www.whowhere.lycos.com*

Use a specific credit card only for online purchases. That way you can conveniently cancel the card if it is stolen or misused.

Warning: Purchases made through conventional retail stores may also be monitored if you pay by credit card or check—or if you are a member of the store's "customer club." To keep your purchases anonymous, pay by cash and don't give any personal data—not even a phone number.

YOUR MEDICAL RECORDS

More and more nonmedical employees in the health industry have access to your confidential information. *Self-defense…*

Check your medical records the same way you would your credit reports. Look over HMO, Medicare and Medicaid files twice a year. Check for incorrect, embarrassing or outdated entries.

Example: If you haven't had high blood pressure for five years, ask your health-care provider to remove—or at least segregate—the item.

Helpful resource: The Medical Information Bureau (MIB), a central database of personal medical information on millions of Americans. It is used by many insurance companies.

Get a copy of your file by writing to: MIB, Box 105, Essex Station, Boston 02112…or call 617-426-3660. *Cost:* $8.50, or free if you receive a letter from an insurance company stating that it used MIB information to make a decision about you.

●**Talk with your physician and his/her staff.** Request in writing that the office physician give out the minimum amount of medical information from your file that is required. Many doctors hand over a patient's entire file without thinking about the potential consequences.

Example: If you have an auto accident, the insurance company should get the information that it needs to settle the claim. But it doesn't need to know that you once took antidepressants or that you are diabetic.

In court: If your medical records are ever subpoenaed, they become public record. Ask the court to allow only the relevant portions of your medical record as evidence. A judge will decide what parts should be kept private. After the case is over, ask the judge to "seal" the court records containing your medical information.

●**Never sign a standard "blanket waiver."** It authorizes the release of all information regarding your medical history, symptoms, treatment, exam results or diagnosis.

Better: Edit the waiver. Write in your own specific terms to limit what's released…

I authorize information from my records to be released from hospital X as relates to my condition Y.

Be sure to add an expiration date to the release.

FINANCIAL INFORMATION

Large banks and credit card companies routinely sell your financial data—from account balances to payment histories—to marketers. This leads to a deluge of promotional mail and phone calls. *Self-defense…*

Find out about the "opt-out" provisions before you use a financial service.

Example: American Express never gives detailed account information to outside merchants. It also sends customers a notice asking if they want to receive product offers from American Express or other marketers.

●**Diminish mail and dinner-time phone calls from direct marketers.**

●Add your name to the "Telephone Preference Service" and "Mail Preference Service" lists maintained by the Direct Marketing Association, Box 9008, Farmingdale, NY 11735.

• List your telephone number but not your street address in the telephone book. This will foil compilers of many marketing lists.

• Ask each of the four major credit bureaus not to disclose your credit information to marketers. Call 888-5OPTOUT—this number reaches the four credit bureaus.

Send a check to yourself if you do electronic banking. This is an excellent way to test your bank's privacy loopholes. See if the bank sends you as the payee any unnecessary data.

SOCIAL SECURITY NUMBER

Social Security Numbers (SSNs) are commonly used in computer recordkeeping.

Your SSN gives a thief access to your entire identity—and all information that is associated with it financially. *Self-defense...*

• **Only disclose your Social Security Number to private companies** when there are tax consequences, such as opening an interest-bearing account at a bank. Most insurance companies and some credit card companies will back off if you refuse to give your SSN. As a fallback position, offer to provide the last four digits.

• **Review your Social Security statement,** which the government now automatically mails annually to every worker over age 25 (about three months before his/her birthday). *If needed sooner: www.ssa.gov.*

• **Never put your Social Security Number on your checks** or any identifying information.

If your state's Department of Motor Vehicles uses the SSN as the driver's license number, ask for an alternative number. Most states will grant one.

If a private business requests your SSN on an application, simply leave the space blank or write "refused." Most companies will not question this—or will back off when you ask to see a written policy requiring your SSN.

Web Site Trap

Medical Web sites do not protect visitors' privacy—even if they claim they do. Georgetown University's recent study found that most leading health sites share the information they collect with other companies—from health-care providers and direct marketers to manufacturers of drugs or health-care products. The study also found that visitors to health Web sites are not anonymous, even if they think they are. *Trap:* Many medical organizations require online registration to access their Web sites. *Self-defense:* Give as little personal information as possible ...do not complete surveys.

John Featherman, president, featherman.com, consumer privacy consultants, P.O. Box 22452, Philadelphia, PA 19110.

Choose Your Passwords Carefully

A recent security test at Stanford University found that a simple password-cracking program could deduce one-fifth of all university account passwords. *Helpful:* Choose longer passwords...mix letters, numbers and special characters...use different passwords for different applications...change passwords at least every six months. *Avoid:* Your name...mother's maiden name...birthday...Social Security number. *Critical:* If you suspect someone is trying to determine your password, report it to relevant authorities.

John Featherman, president, featherman.com, consumer privacy consultants, P.O. Box 22452, Philadelphia, PA 19110.

New Privacy Danger

A federal court decision allows phone companies to sell data about customers to third parties—without customers' permission. Phone companies successfully argued their right of free commercial speech lets them use data they collect any way they wish. *Troubling trend:* Many Web sites collect browsing preferences...banks sell account information...and even medical files are not fully protected. The court decision on phone data is being appealed. If it stands, contact your local and long-distance companies and opt out of all data-transfer arrangements.

John Featherman, president, featherman.com, consumer privacy consultants, P.O. Box 22452, Philadelphia, PA 19110.

Phone Bill Alert

Check your long-distance phone plan quarterly to find out if it is still best for you. Rates and calling plans change continuously. If your monthly long-distance bills exceed $50, inquire *monthly*. Ask your carrier to check your calls to see if it has a cheaper plan. To save money on your long distance bill, visit *www.trac.org*. They will give you four steps that will help you save money on your long distance bill.

Samuel Simon, founder of TRAC—Telecommunications Research & Action Center, Box 27279, Washington, DC 20005.

Slamming Self-Defense

Slamming—the unauthorized switching of long-distance telephone service—is still common. *Helpful:* Call your local phone company, and ask for a Primary Interexchange Carrier (PIC) freeze. This locks you into your current long-distance carrier so your service cannot be switched unless you call the local phone company.

Holly Anderson, director of communications, National Consumers League, 1701 K St. NW, Suite 1200, Washington, DC 20006.

Dangers Where You Least Expect Them

Melinda Muse, a health journalist and author of *I'm Afraid, You're Afraid: 448 Things to Fear and Why*. Hyperion.

As a health journalist, I read and write a lot about medical advances. One big lesson I've learned is that life today is no longer survival of the fittest—but of the wariest.

Here are some surprisingly dangerous places, things and situations…

●**Personal computers and the Internet.** The Web is a virtual downer. People who spend even just a few hours a week online are more depressed and feel more isolated than those who log on less frequently.

Hunching over your computer for hours isn't good for your physical health, either. After observing elementary school students slumped at computer workstations, Cornell University researchers concluded that at least 40% were at risk for serious repetitive stress injuries.

●**Frequent flying.** Hazards of flying include luggage carts, which have those elastic tethers with metal hooks on each end. They have snapped back into eyes, causing dislocated lenses, internal bleeding, retinal detachment and temporary loss of sight.

Think twice before grabbing that aisle seat. Every year, some 4,500 passengers are hit by items falling from overstuffed luggage bins. Briefcases are the most common missiles in the carry-on arsenal, but it also includes laptops, golf clubs and heavy backpacks.

●**Long flights.** An estimated 350 passengers die in-flight in the US every year, with heart attacks the leading cause. Sitting for four hours or more in arid cabins risks dehydration and reduces circulation in the legs by half, which could cause blood clots. If a piece of the clot breaks off and makes its way to the lungs, it can be deadly.

What to do: During long flights, walk the aisles often…and drink plenty of bottled water (unbottled airline water can carry additional health risks).

●**Hotel rooms.** Check out your room before you check in. Blood, semen and other bodily fluids have been found on purportedly "clean" sheets, blankets and bedspreads.

According to Johns Hopkins School of Public Health, it is possible to contract hepatitis from soiled bed linens, as well as to pick up body lice, which burrow in mattresses and covers.

What to do: Never lie on a hotel bedspread —strip it off. Check sheets for freshness. And don't pad around barefoot, since bathroom floors may host athlete's foot fungi.

●**Yard work.** Need good reasons not to spend hours grooming your lawn?

Americans scatter 70 million pounds of pesticides on their yards every year. Your hands are most likely to be exposed, but your forehead, abdomen and crotch absorb pesticides faster than other body parts.

Research at Memorial Sloan-Kettering Cancer Center in New York suggests that sunscreen, while preventing sunburn, gives people a false sense of security, making them feel they can indulge in more sun time. One million Americans are diagnosed with skin cancer every year. Protect yourself by covering up.

●**Garage sales.** These hagglers' havens are notorious for unloading unsafe products, including bunk beds that can strangle…cribs that can suffocate…dangerous baby carriages …collapsing playpens…beanbag chairs stuffed with foam pellets that have choked children.

●**Money.** Coins and greenbacks are cruddy with germ colonies, including fecal bacteria… Staphylococcus, which causes food poisoning …and acne-causing Propionibacterium. It seems the smaller the denomination, the more dangerous.

A test of $20 bills uncovered money's other dirty secret—cash is contaminated by cocaine. The *Journal of Forensic Sciences* says, "…most Americans handle small amounts of cocaine every day…on dollar bills." Follow Mom's advice about keeping your hands out of your mouth.

●**Gemstones.** Radiation is sometimes used to deepen the color of gemstones, which greatly enhances their value. Although "nuked" gems should be kept in lead casings for several years while their radiation levels taper off, unscrupulous traders have released to the market "hot" cat's-eye gemstones, some registering 51 times the US radiation limits. Experts estimate that thousands of radioactive stones are in circulation in the US, Europe and Asia.

●**Mondays…Fridays…and Saturdays.**

●Mondays produce more suicides than any other day, says the American Association of Suicidology. It is also the day when the most heart attacks occur.

●Fridays produce more car accidents than any other day of the week.

●Saturdays produce the greatest number of fatal motor vehicle crashes. Most occur between 4 pm and 4 am.

●**Casinos.** The odds are lousy. Only 150 of 736 high rollers who suffered a heart attack in Las Vegas casinos lived to place another wager, according to a recent study. Paramedics must maneuver through throngs in the mammoth gaming halls, wasting valuable life-saving time. Hedging their bets, many casinos have installed defibrillators.

●**Kissing your dog.** Each year, more than one million Americans get parasites, such as roundworms, hookworms and pinworms, from kissing their canine pals. Since parasitic infections are difficult to diagnose in humans, people often never discover the causes of their headaches, liver ailments or sinus infections. Teach Rover to shake.

Although in my book I chronicled 448 things to fear, I urge people to not let their fears overwhelm them. After all, optimism is a tonic for a longer, healthier and—dare we hope—safer life.

Health Scams

Stephen Barrett, MD, a retired psychiatrist, consumer advocate and board member of the National Council Against Health Fraud, Box 1276, Loma Linda, CA 92354. He is coauthor of *The Health Robbers: A Close Look at Quackery in America.* Prometheus Books.

If you think quacks are sleazy-looking characters whom you can spot a mile away— think again.

Many of today's medical hucksters have so much medical knowledge and are so familiar with medical jargon that they're capable of fooling doctors. In fact, some quacks are themselves doctors who believe in the ill-conceived treatments they offer. *The trendiest and most dangerous health scams now...*

●**False memory syndrome (FMS).** The darling topic of afternoon talk shows, FMS involves adults undergoing psychotherapy who suddenly recall long-repressed cases of physical and/or emotional abuse. As a result, many FMS "victims" falsely accuse, disown or sue onceloved relatives.

Recovered memories may be legitimate in rare cases. But I'm convinced that many of these people—with the help of misguided or incompetent psychotherapists—are "recalling" past events that never occurred.

These therapists—some of whom call themselves "traumatists"—often misuse hypnosis, meditation or guided imagery to help patients regress to their childhood or even to "past lives." Or the patient may be inspired by FMS books or talk show guests, and the therapist fails to help the patient distinguish fact from fantasy.

As someone who practiced psychiatry for more than 35 years, I find it very hard to believe that a person could forget such abuse. Indeed, it's much more common for victims of abuse to have trouble putting memories of abuse out of their minds.

●**Diet hocus-pocus.** Beware of any weightloss product or program that purports to melt off pounds by suppressing appetite through hormonal manipulation or by blocking the absorption of fats, carbohydrates, sugar or calories. Such products are always phony.

And while very-low-calorie diets can help obese people under medical supervision, do-ityourself starvation plans are dangerous. They force the body to burn lean body mass for fuel. These plans can also cause anemia, liver damage, kidney stones and mineral imbalances. In some cases they are fatal.

Some diets—including many of those spelled out in popular diet books—are pure nonsense. Authors of these hugely profitable books, who often have no training in nutrition, claim they've discovered weight-control secrets.

For example, one popular book says that when certain foods are combined in the body, they rot, poison the system and make a person fat. To avoid this, dieters are urged to eat fats, carbohydrates and protein at separate meals, concentrating on fruits in the morning and vegetables in the afternoon. The premise is utter nonsense.

Commercial weight-loss programs and diets are very popular. While these programs may help people lose weight, they don't teach dieters how to maintain their weight loss with proper eating and exercise. *Result:* The weight comes right back on.

The only sensible way to lose weight is to exercise more and eat less. Bringing about these changes may require help from a registered dietitian or another professional.

●**Chelation therapy.** This treatment involves intravenous injections of EDTA, a synthetic amino acid.

While chelation therapy is a legitimate treatment for lead poisoning, some advocates maintain that it can prevent or even reverse the accumulation of fatty deposits along artery walls (a process known as atherosclerosis).

Duped by this claim, some patients with badly blocked coronary arteries are forgoing the bypass surgery that they so desperately need, opting instead for worthless chelation injections. At least one person suffered a heart attack while on chelation therapy. Others undergoing the treatments have died of kidney failure (EDTA can be very toxic to kidneys if not properly administered).

Some proponents of chelation therapy also claim that it is effective against arthritis, Parkinson's disease, emphysema, multiple sclerosis, gangrene and psoriasis. But there's absolutely no scientific evidence to back up these contentions.

●**"Environmental illness."** Certain practitioners called clinical ecologists say the immune system can become overloaded by constant exposure to toxins in the environment.

As a result of being exposed to these toxins, these practitioners claim, certain people develop a host of ailments ranging from depression, irritability, inability to concentrate and poor memory to fatigue, respiratory problems, rashes, headache and muscle and joint pain.

Clinical ecologists "diagnose" their patients by injecting them with suspected chemical culprits and then observing their reactions—even though careful research has invalidated this provocation and neutralization test. And scientific panels have deemed the entire field of clinical ecology speculative and unproven.

Still, desperate patients agree to treatment. Some go so far as to move to the desert or rip apart their houses to get rid of synthetic chemicals...or even avoid contact with certain people suspected of giving off irritating odors.

Some patients ultimately become hermits in their own homes—afraid to venture out into a toxin-tainted world.

In fact, the symptoms these people suffer are real. But the origin of these symptoms is usually psychological, not chemical. Once patients understand this, psychotherapy may help them.

SPOTTING A QUACK

While it's essential to maintain a healthy level of skepticism when discussing medical treatments, skepticism alone is not enough to protect yourself against quacks. *I also recommend avoiding any doctor who...*

•**Claims that everyone needs to take vitamin supplements.** There's simply no evidence for this.

•**Recommends vitamins for a large number of ailments.** In fact, vitamin supplements are useful only against a very limited number of conditions.

•**Uses anecdotes and testimonials to support his/her claims.** Look instead for carefully controlled clinical studies.

•**Says that most diseases are caused by hidden allergies.** This is untrue.

•**Claims that large numbers of Americans suffer from low blood sugar** (hypoglycemia) or hidden yeast infections. Again, not true.

Beware of Nutritionists Who Advertise

Fewer than half of the so-called professionals listed in the *Yellow Pages* in 32 states were reliable sources of sound, scientifically based nutrition information. Seventy percent of those who claimed to be PhDs had phony degrees or delivered fraudulent information. Others boasted nonexistent degrees—certified nutritionist (CN), doctor of nutrimedicine (NMD) and nutrition counselor (NC). Still others had "degrees" from nonaccredited schools.

Bottom line: Don't trust nutritionists who cannot show their credentials from an accredited college or university. For a directory of accredited schools, see the *Accredited Institutions of Postsecondary Education* in your local library.

Survey by the National Council Against Health Fraud, reported in *Tufts University Diet & Nutrition Letter,* 10 High Street, Suite 706, Boston 02110.

Pacemakers and Store Security Scanners

In-store security scanners pose little threat to people with an implanted cardiac defibrillator (ICD) or pacemaker. Cases have been reported in which ICDs or pacemakers went off inappropriately when exposed to the electromagnetic beams used by the scanners, which are positioned at store exits. But in each case, the individual with the ICD lingered near the machines instead of passing through quickly. *Also:* ICD and pacemaker patients should ask airport security agents to pass security wands over the devices quickly.

Douglas P. Zipes, MD, distinguished professor of medicine and pharmacology, Indiana University School of Medicine, Indianapolis.

Self-Defense for Older Drivers

Older drivers need to take precautions to compensate for the physical and perceptual changes associated with aging.

Self-defense: Plan your trips—and drive your plan. Knowing your route lets you concentrate on driving, not navigating…choose less demanding routes, such as intersections with safer left-turn arrows…drive with a large "anticipation zone," giving yourself room to react.

For a copy of the American Association of Retired Persons' handbook, *Older Driver Public Policy Institute Fact Sheet* (Item #AC 1613) contact AARP at 800-424-3410.

How to Drive Safely Through Bad Winter Weather

Dave Phillips, tactical driving instructor at International Training Inc., the country's leading defensive driving school for businessmen, bodyguards and chauffeurs, Box 709, West Point, VA 23181. He is an ex-police chief and former special agent for the Office of Special Investigations in the US Air Force.

Winter rain, snow and ice can cause even good drivers to make dumb mistakes. Even the most cautious drivers panic when their vehicles slide out of control.

I've taught hundreds of good drivers how to be great drivers in the worst road and weather conditions. *Best self-defense techniques…*

BETTER BRAKING

•**Use heel-to-toe pivot.** This is the most efficient way to move your foot between the brake and gas.

How it works: Keep your right heel on the floor…swivel it as you switch the top half of your foot between pedals. You can move your foot twice as fast this way as you can by lifting your leg and foot each time you change pedals.

If you wear boots while driving in the winter, be sure the heel is no higher than on regular shoes. Or remove boots in the car, and slip on flat shoes or sneakers.

•**Learn your car's brake threshold.** This is the point at which you can apply brakes hardest before they lock up. When brakes lock up, wheels lose traction and the car skids.

If you don't have antilock brakes: Drive to an empty parking lot. Accelerate to 40 miles per hour. Engage the brakes with varying pressure to see how well you can control the car. Repeat at different speeds and on different surfaces.

Avoid jamming down the brake and releasing it completely when you feel the wheels lock up—commonly known as *pump braking*. You'll only be using half of your car's braking potential. Pump braking pulls the car's weight away from front tires—causing loss of traction for steering.

Better: Apply more constant pressure to the brakes. Press the brakes until the car starts to skid. Then ease up slightly. This will keep the front tires in contact with the road.

If you have antilock brakes: Push the pedal down firmly with your foot until it stops, and hold it there. The antilock mechanism applies constant pressure-and-release automatically and in a fast, efficient way.

Antilock brakes need a longer braking distance to stop. They are designed to keep the front wheels rolling so that you can continue to steer.

CAREFUL CORNERING

•**Decelerate and brake before a turn.** Braking hard while your wheels are on a curve greatly increases your chance of a spinout. Let the momentum of the car carry you through the turn. Lightly squeeze the brake pedal. Take the widest possible turn in the road if there aren't any other cars next to you.

Example: On a bend that hooks to the right, enter the turn on the far left of your lane. Then move across the middle to the far right of your lane as the curve straightens out. This angle will reduce the weight shift of the vehicle.

Don't accelerate until the car's front tires are pointed straight again in the direction you want to go.

•**"Shuffle" your hands along the steering wheel as you turn**—rather than using the hand-over-hand method. Taking your hands off the wheel crosses up your arms and makes it easier to lose your grip. Shuffle steering is performed with both hands on the wheel. Your physical size will determine your hand placement at positions of 10:00 and 2:00...9:00 and 3:00...or 6:00 and 4:00.

These hand positions on the wheel also are safer should your airbag go off. Your hands are less likely to be thrown directly into your face.

●**Inflate tires four pounds above your carmaker's recommended level.** Your car manufacturer's recommended tire pressure will give you a smooth, comfortable ride—but slightly overinflated tires in winter will stiffen up the sidewalls, maximizing the amount of tread on the road and providing much better control in turns.

Your vehicle's tire pressure information is in your owner's manual...on the sticker inside the glove-compartment door...or on the portion of the chassis that holds the driver's side door.

●**Look beyond the car in front of you.** When driving, it's natural to focus on the rear bumper of the car ahead of you. But if there's a problem on the road ahead of that driver, you won't react until the driver in front of you does.

By training yourself to constantly scan as far ahead as possible, you can anticipate obstacles and other drivers' reactions.

USING YOUR EYES

●**Position the rearview mirror so it reflects the entire rear window.** Now turn your head and look at the left sideview mirror. Maneuver it until you can no longer see the side of your car. Repeat for the right sideview mirror.

This shrinks the blind spot so you should only have to turn your head as far as your shoulders to see a car passing on either side.

●**Swing your gaze left and right to find safer options** if you are skidding toward an object. Many people get into accidents because their natural reaction is to look at the object they are about to hit.

To avoid or get out of a skid: Lift off the brake slightly to allow the front wheels to roll, which will enable you to steer the vehicle where you are looking.

BAD-WEATHER MOVES

●**If you hit an area of the road that has collected water and ice** and you feel your car's wheels losing contact with the road, remove your foot from the gas to slow down the car. Keep the wheels pointed straight, and resist the urge to brake hard. If you turn your wheels, you risk losing even more traction.

●**At lights, stop while you can still see the rear tire of the car in front of you.** Most people stop when the car's bumper in front of them disappears from view. But if you're hit from behind on a wet or icy surface, you could hit the car in front of you.

Air Bag Warning

Measure precisely how far you sit from your car's air bag. Check the distance between the center of your chest and the hub of the steering wheel. Anything less than 10 inches may subject you to serious injury if the bag inflates.

Maria Segui-Gomez, MD, ScD, assistant professor of health policy and management, Johns Hopkins University School of Public Health, Baltimore.

Lemon Law vs. Manufacturer's Responsibility

If your new car is a lemon, first give the dealer a chance to fix it and keep copies of all the repair orders. After the second unsuccessful repair attempt—or after the car has been out of service for 15 days—contact the manufacturer's regional office and ask for assistance in getting the car repaired. After three repair attempts—or after the car has been out of service for 20 days—write to the manufacturer's headquarters and explain that you will invoke your lemon law right to a refund or replacement unless repairs are successful. After four repair attempts or 30 days out of service, demand a refund or replacement. If the manufacturer refuses, go to court or arbitration—attorney fees can be redeemed under federal or state lemon laws.

Clarence Ditlow, executive director of the Center for Auto Safety. For a lemon-lawyer referral, write to Center for Auto Safety, 2001 S St. NW, Washington, DC 20009. Include a self-addressed, stamped, business-sized envelope.

Snow-Shoveling Self-Defense

Do not hold your breath and strain when lifting a shovelful—this slows blood flow to the heart. When breath is released, blood pressure suddenly rebounds and becomes significantly elevated—which can create a dangerous heart overload.

Correct way to shovel: Breathe out as you lift the shovel and toss the snow off to the side.

Cardiac Alert, 7811 Montrose Rd., Potomac, MD 20854.

New Drinking Water Threat: Cryptosporidium

The threat posed by this microbe is smaller than media reports suggested. There's no need to boil tap water or drink bottled water unless your water utility issues an alert. Utilities are usually extremely vigilant. If there is an alert, boil *all* the water you ingest—that used for brushing your teeth, washing produce, etc., as well as for drinking. If you were to ingest crypto, you'd experience diarrhea and nausea lasting one to two weeks.

Exception: Crypto may be fatal to AIDS patients and others with weakened immune systems. Several experts now urge these individuals to boil their water even in the absence of a crypto

alert, although there's really not enough evidence to say that this precaution is necessary.

Rosemary Soave, MD, associate professor of medicine and public health, New York Hospital-Cornell Medical Center, New York.

The Importance of Washing Your Hands

Inadequate hand-washing is responsible for most cases of diarrhea and vomiting.

Self-defense: Always wash your hands before eating or handling food. Always wash after handling uncooked food—especially meat...after handling money or garbage...after using a bathroom or changing a diaper...after blowing your nose, sneezing or coughing into your hand...after playing with a pet.

Most effective: Apply soap to hands, rub vigorously for at least 10 seconds in warm water, then rinse thoroughly. Be sure not to miss your cuticles and underneath your fingernails.

Mayo Clinic Health Letter, Mayo Foundation for Medical Education and Research, 200 First St. SW, Rochester, MN 55905.

Lighting and Your Health

An 85-year-old needs more light than a 15-year-old to see the same thing. Make sure lights are bright wherever possible. *Also:* Use contrasting colors. It is easier for older people to see furniture, toilet seats and counters if they are a different color from the floor.

Maria Meyer, cofounder of CareTrust, Inc., a firm that helps develop affordable housing and assisted living for the elderly, Portland, OR, and coauthor of *The Comfort of Home: An Illustrated Step-by-Step Guide for Caregivers.* CareTrust Publications.

Skin cancer risk is boosted by exposure to fluorescent lighting—but only slightly. Eight hours under an unshielded fluorescent light is equal to 1.2 minutes of July sunlight in Washington, DC. To eliminate this slight risk, cover lights with *acrylic transmission diffusers—* plastic covers.

W. Howard Cyr, PhD, senior biophysicist, office of science and technology, Center for Devices and Radiological Health, Food and Drug Administration, Rockville, MD.

Diagnosing Difficulty

Hypothyroidism, or an underactive thyroid, is often underdiagnosed because symptoms are subtle. See your doctor if you have two or more of the following symptoms for two weeks or more: Fatigue...sluggish thinking...dry skin...and cold sensitivity. Anemia and high total cholesterol (above 220) are also warnings.

Paul W. Ladenson, MD, director, division of endocrinology and metabolism, John Hopkins University Medical School, Baltimore.

Thyroid Treatment Trap

Treatment for thyroid cancer and hyperthyroidism may involve swallowing a solution containing radioactive iodine. But an individual treated this way emits radiation for up to one week afterward. This can pose a threat to those who spend a lot of time in close proximity. *Helpful:* For at least one week following treatment, patients should sleep at least 18 inches from their partners and stay away from children younger than one year old. Talk to your doctor about other precautions that may be necessary.

Kichiro Koshida, PhD, associate professor of health sciences, Kanazawa University, Kanazawa, Japan. His study was published in *Radiation Protection Dosimetry,* Box 7, Ashford, Kent TN23 1YW, England.

21

Keeping Up in a High-Tech World

New Technologies to Improve Your Life

There is a lot of speculation about how cutting-edge technologies will change the planet. To find out what is theory—and hype—and what is possible, we spoke to noted futurist Arnold Brown.

WITHIN TWO YEARS

Smart cars: The transformation of the car into a global communications center. Drivers will interact with a voice-activated computer that is continuously linked to the Internet. *Benefits...*

- **Instantaneous suggestions for local restaurants.**
- **Gas price comparisons in the area.**
- **Centralized monitoring of driving performance by automakers**—as well as engine maintenance and upgrades.

Available: General Motors' OnStar Virtual Advisor gives drivers voice access to Web-based information.

Biometrics: Applications for biological data, such as using scans of body parts (eyes, fingerprints) for identification.

- **As more personal information about you goes online,** the need for foolproof security will become vital.
- **Today's technology enables anyone to intercept private information**—medical information...credit card and Social Security numbers...etc.
- **Biometrics will be more convenient than plastic cards,** metal keys and personal identity numbers.

Example: Veincheck, now being tested, scans the vein patterns on the backs of hands to allow students entry into dormitories.

Interactive entertainment: The convergence of television, radio, computers and the Web into a single appliance. Expect to see it soon now

Arnold Brown, chairman of Weiner, Edrich, Brown, Inc., consultants in strategic planning and management of change for businesses and nonprofit organizations, 200 E. 33 St., Suite 91, New York 10016. He is coauthor of *Office Biology*. MasterMedia.

299

that most of the US cable infrastructure can receive digital and video data. *Benefits...*

●**Free digitized books and music will be disseminated easily.**

●**Authors will make money by adding value to their products,** such as lecturing, rather than just from book sales.

●**"T-commerce" ("T" for television)**—the integration of entertainment and consumerism —will become hot.

Examples: While watching your favorite sitcom, you might see a chest of drawers you like. A click on your remote control takes you to a shopping channel that gives information on the make, model, price and where you can buy it.

●**Your TV set will alert you to upcoming films or sports shows you may like based on your past viewing patterns.**

●**Your stock portfolio will scroll across the bottom of the screen while you watch the evening news.**

●**An interactive Judge Judy will let you select particular cases to watch.**

WITHIN FIVE YEARS

Wearable computers: Built into clothing, these will enable fabrics to receive and transmit data. *Examples...*

●**Apparel with global positioning technology will allow you to track kids at all times.**

●**Clothing will adjust to temperature** —if it is cold, the insulation will warm you...if it is hot, the weave will loosen to cool you.

Virtual spaces: Advanced video-communications to alter the environments in which we live, work and learn. *Examples...*

●**Virtual reality guru Jaron Lanier is heading an effort to create electronically linked work spaces.** Instead of walls, you'll have screens that let you see and interact with distant colleagues.

●**Distance learning in schools will solve educational problems,** such as the lack of good teachers and funding. The lectures by the best instructors will be broadcast to thousands of schools. On-site teachers will function more like teaching assistants.

Sense augmentation: Medical devices—implants, surgical tools and diagnostic machines—that make up for physical shortcomings. *Examples...*

●**Battery-powered exoskeletal muscle suits will give you more "lift power"** and help avoid hernias and lower-back problems.

●**Eyeglasses will self-adjust to fit almost any prescription**—the fluid-filled lenses will be altered with a small pump.

●**For the more seriously visually impaired,** Johns Hopkins University researchers are creating a retinal implant. It restores partial vision by sending wireless images from a camera in a prosthetic eye to electrodes implanted in the retina.

Smart appliances: Semiconductor chips imbedded in even the most common household tools. *Examples...*

●**You'll be able to use your voice mail to control your appliances.**

●**Dial up your kitchen on the way home from work,** and tell your stove to heat up a casserole.

●**Ask your VCR to record a favorite television show.**

●**Your refrigerator will have a flat-panel computer screen** connected to a bar-code scanner to order groceries from the Web when you run low.

●**A Web-enabled dishwasher will transmit diagnostic problems directly to the manufacturer.**

Special example: Japanese electronics giant Matsushita has developed a toilet with sensors that monitor body fluids for irregularities. For instance, it checks levels of sugar and protein in urine of diabetes patients and sends the data to their doctors. This product is now available in Japan.

IN 10 YEARS OR MORE

Brain chips: Small computer chips embedded in the brain. *Benefits...*

●**You'll trigger electronic devices by looking at them or just thinking about them.**

●**Advanced contact lenses will project images,** allowing you to read e-mail and scan documents sent wirelessly from a computer.

●**Your brain will be able to scan databases** all over the world for information.

Potential problem: The two-way nature of such communication. If your thoughts can influence a computer, will commands from that computer be able to influence your thoughts?

Nanotechnology: Robots too small for the eye to see. *Benefits...*

- **So-called "nanobots" will move through your bloodstream,** delivering accurate drug doses to select tissue or killing diseased or dangerous cells.

- **Nanobots will also revolutionize preventive medicine.** They'll be programmed to live inside your body as early warning sensors providing, for example, your doctor with X rays to detect diseases like lung cancer.

The Brave New World of Genius Computers

Raymond Kurzweil, PhD, founder and chairman of Kurzweil Technologies Inc., pioneer in the application of artificial intelligence, 15 Walnut St., Wellesley Hills, MA 02481. He is author of three books, including *The Age of Spiritual Machines.* Viking. He was named Inventor of the Year by Massachusetts Institute of Technology.

Advances in computing speed and capacity won't merely continue at today's pace into the next century. They will accelerate as technology moves beyond today's two-dimensional silicon microchips to three-dimensional circuits created from microscopic particles.

In fact, there will be incredible technological change in the next 20 years...

- **By the year 2004,** cell phones will have enough computing power to automatically translate your words into the language of the person to whom you are speaking.

- **By 2009,** a $1,000 personal computer will operate 1,000 times faster than current models.

- **By 2019,** a $1,000 personal computer will match the computational ability of the human brain—20 million billion calculations per second.

Instead of being housed in large plastic boxes, tiny but enormously powerful computers will be embedded everywhere—in walls, furniture, jewelry, even human bodies.

Far from being something to fear, this age of genius machines will bring advances to human life that were never before possible. You will lead a more prosperous life—in better health, with more career choices and personal challenges open to you.

Here's how to make the most of the opportunities this age of genius machines will provide...

- **Prepare for unparalleled prosperity.** Innovation creates new wealth, which is why the economy grew much faster in the 1990s than economists of the 1980s thought possible. Silicon Valley alone has created $1 trillion in new stock market capitalization over the past 10 years. The creation of wealth through innovation will only accelerate in the next century.

Advances in technology will change the economic landscape beyond recognition. Everyone must learn to be entrepreneurial in the coming age of genius machines.

The barriers to launching a new business will become lower than ever. All that will be needed to achieve great economic success in the next century will be a $1,000 computer and the idea for a more intelligent product.

Genius machines hold out the promise of new enterprises involving very small groups of people creating substantial wealth.

- **Expect to succeed even if you don't have technological skills.** Those with engineering skills will build tomorrow's genius computers. But those with the ability to create knowledge of any kind will be the ones who are best able to extract great value from them.

The way to create value in the age of genius machines will be to compile and disseminate knowledge that other people will find useful—from medicine to golf to Florentine painting.

The more specialized the knowledge on a Web site, the greater its value to users.

Find your passion, and then find a way to express that passion online. In tomorrow's world of machine intelligence, interactive computers and virtual reality, you can make that passion come alive in ways that will captivate your audience.

- **Become a lifelong student.** Learn everything you can about as much as you can.

You must keep up with the advances in technology because each one will create more opportunities for your success.

But you must expand your studies far beyond technology. It is impossible to know today all the skills that might make you successful in the age of genius machines.

When you discover your passion, pursue it because that is where you can make your real contribution in the age of genius machines.

Learning must last your whole life. Even now, the model in which you had a specific skill that would carry you for a whole career is dying.

You will not have to attend school in order to gain these new skills. Instead, genius machines will deliver the interactive learning courseware to you, wherever and whenever you want it. All you must have is the desire to keep learning.

●**Assume that no ailment or handicap will limit you.** The age of genius machines will remove all physical and mental limitations from what humans can accomplish.

Examples: Soon bioengineering treatments for cancer and heart disease will greatly reduce the mortality from these diseases. Such technological answers to medical problems will become commonplace as computers become vastly more powerful and far smaller.

In less than 20 years, blind people will use "seeing" machines to explore and understand their visual environment.

The deaf will "hear" what other people are saying through computers mounted in eyeglasses. A combination of computer-controlled nerve stimulation and robotic devices will help quadriplegics walk and climb stairs.

Potential medical problems will be diagnosed by doctors using telemedicine—and resolved before they become limitations on your life.

Your brain: Within 30 years, implants of microcomputing devices directly into the brain will enhance human intelligence and learning. People will be able to acquire and transfer knowledge as never before.

Prevent Computer Screen Eyestrain

Adjusting room lighting conditions can help prevent the eyestrain problems often caused by spending hours staring at a computer screen. *Some suggestions...*

●**Adjust window coverings to reduce reflection of sunlight by the screen.**

●**Set up the computer screen to show black letters on a white background and adjust the brightness so the screen,** the room lighting, the keyboard and any reading matter you are using all appear equally bright.

●**Wear dark clothes to minimize reflections in the screen.**

●**Adjust sitting position so your eyes are equidistant from the screen,** keyboard and anything else you are reading as you work.

Sylvan R. Shemitz, FIES, CEO of Sylvan R. Shemitz Associates, lighting consultants in West Haven, CT.

Computer Virus Rx

If you think your computer has a virus, stop using the computer immediately. Quit all programs, and run a virus-checking program. *Better:* Run two separate ones, since different programs may identify different viruses. Do not use any floppy disks—they may be infected or may pick up a virus and spread it. Use the antivirus software to scan all floppies—before you work from them—and destroy any viruses found on them.

John Edwards, high-tech consultant and writer, Gilbert, AZ.

How to Get Started On the Internet

John R. Levine, coauthor of *The Internet for Dummies,* Sixth Edition (IDG Books WorldWide), and an Internet Web host, consultant and lecturer.

Ten years ago, few people had even heard of the Internet. Today, it is an integral part of the lives of millions, young and old, at home and at work.

Recent estimates put the number of Internet users worldwide at more than 200 million, and project nearly half a billion will be online within five years.

If you're not already among them, you're missing one of the most significant communications revolutions ever to shake the planet.

The Internet literally places all the information resources of the *world* at your fingertips. *Bonus:* You can use the Internet to find and communicate with people who share your interests.

Until you explore the Internet, you can't begin to comprehend the breadth or depth of all it offers. There's really not much required. All you need is a system, a connection…and curiosity.

THE BASICS

For most users, the *system* is synonymous with *computer*. Any new computer you buy today is Internet-ready. *Included in the computer package are…*

- **Internet browser**—such as *Netscape Navigator* or *Microsoft Internet Explorer*.
- **Modem for connecting to the Internet over a phone line.**
- **E-mail program.**

Expect to pay around $800 for a new Internet-ready computer.

Minimum requirements in a Microsoft Windows system…

- **Pentium IV processor.**
- **128MB RAM.**
- **CD-ROM drive.**
- **56K modem.**

All of Apple's iMac models are Internet-ready.

Alternative: If you have no real need for a computer but still want access to the Internet, look into MSN® TV. *Cost:* Around $100 to $350.

The system/service includes a box you connect to your TV, a remote and optional keyboard. It empowers your TV to bring the World Wide Web to your living room.

NO-RISK INTRODUCTION

Most public, college and university libraries have one or more computers connected to the Internet. You can use these to sample how the Internet might benefit you before making any investment.

Before any system can connect with the Internet, it must first connect with a server, which is owned and maintained by an Internet provider.

YOUR CONNECTION

Servers are your gateway to the Internet, and charge a monthly fee for the privilege. You have a couple of choices, but the basic package you get from any Internet service provider (ISP) is about the same. *You get…*

- **User name and password.**
- **CD-ROM loaded with the required software tools for getting you on the Internet.**
- **E-mail account.**
- **Access to the Internet.**

Most providers offer unlimited access, but some impose a surcharge after you've exceeded a set number of hours.

Average cost: Around $20 a month (depending on provider and services).

America Online (AOL) is the best known of the commercial online services. Others include CompuServe and the Microsoft Network.

Well organized, they offer subscribers the company's unique content, events and services along with the Internet connection.

INTERNET SERVICE PROVIDERS

If all you want is access to the Internet and none of the many other options that services such as AOL provide, an Internet service provider may be a better bet than a commercial online server. As the name implies, its only service is connecting you with the Internet and providing technical help over the telephone when you have problems.

You're probably best served by a local ISP familiar with the local operating environment. Check the *Yellow Pages* under *Internet service providers*.

Other choices: MSN® TV (mentioned earlier) or your local cable company, which may now be an Internet provider.

The cable modem access ISPs provide is considerably faster than basic telephone connections, but costs about twice as much.

The quality of service from ISPs can vary greatly, so carefully consider these points for comparison…

- **Make sure you can connect by a local call.**
- **Find out how many hours of Internet access the monthly fees allow you.**

●**Ask if there are surcharges in addition to the monthly fee.**

●**Ask about the speed and types of connections the provider's system supports.**

●**Find out the number of users the ISP can handle at any given time.**

Put these questions to the Internet service provider's customer/tech support line. Polite, informative answers are a good sign.

Caution: Be wary of any ISP whose tech support line is always busy or doesn't answer calls.

Get recommendations: Your best insight into the provider will come from other users. Ask around and find out how satisfied they are with the service, and what, if any, problems they may have had.

JOINING THE REVOLUTION

Before you can connect to the Internet, you must create an account. The software supplied by your ISP reduces account creation to simply filling in the blanks with basic information about you and your system configuration.

You'll need to give a "user name," a password of your choice, the name and possibly a number address of your Internet provider and the addresses of its e-mail and news servers.

This takes only a couple of minutes to complete. If you have any trouble, the provider's tech support will guide you through the process.

Once your account is established, making the connection to the Internet is as simple as launching your Internet browser or e-mail program—just click on the provider's icon.

Once the Internet connection is established, your browser fills the screen with a "home page." You can change it later, but first time out it's usually the home page of your ISP or the supplier of your computer or browser.

Helpful: Every location, or site, you'll find on the World Wide Web has a name: *www.what youwant.com*. If you know a Web site address you want to visit, just type it on the address bar of your browser and hit "enter" on your keyboard.

The best way to understand the way the Web works is simple—just start exploring.

Learn to use search engines. They can locate whatever you want online. (Try *www.yahoo.*

com or, better still, *www.google.com* or *www. excite.com.*)

Experiment with a few research projects. Track down information on a medical condition a relative is concerned about or a recipe that you have always wanted to try.

Best Ways to Use the Web For Better Health

Tom Ferguson, MD, adjunct associate professor of health informatics at the University of Texas Health Science Center in Houston and editor of *The Ferguson Report* (*www.fergusonreport.com*), a free online newsletter covering the online health industry. He is author of *Health Online: How to Find Health Information, Support Groups, and Self-Help Communities in Cyberspace.* Addison-Wesley.

It's no secret that the Internet is a terrific source of medical news and information. But getting the latest on specific diseases and treatments is just the most obvious of what health-minded people can do online.

Here are six other ways to use the Internet for better health—with a choice of the best sites...

CONSULT A PHYSICIAN

There's no substitute for a face-to-face meeting with a doctor. But you can get basic medical questions answered via online medical consultation services. *How it works:* A doctor answers queries that you type in while logged on.

●**AmericasDoctor.com** (*www.americas doctor.com*) offers free, real-time consultations with board-certified or board-eligible physicians 24 hours a day. All communications are private and one on one.

The physicians answer your questions and suggest reliable sources of information. They do not diagnose any condition or recommend treatment.

FIND A DOCTOR

Selecting a family doctor or specialist can be difficult. Online referrals are a useful adjunct to referrals from family members, friends and other physicians.

●**Physician Select** (*www.ama-assn.org*), operated by the American Medical Association

(AMA), provides detailed information about virtually every physician licensed to practice in the US.

Listings include the physician's medical school and year of graduation, residency training and primary practice specialty. You can search by name, location, specialty, etc. To get to Physician Select, click on "Doctor Finder" on the AMA home page.

GET SUPPORT

Nowadays there's an online support group for virtually every ailment. These can be of great help to patients and their families alike.

●**Self-Help Sourcebook Online** *(www. mentalhelp.net/selfhelp)* offers links to more than 800 national and international self-help support groups. You can search by ailment or by keyword—cancer, depression, heart disease, etc. There's also guidance on starting your own group or linking up with a traditional off-line support group in your area.

MAINTAIN MEDICAL RECORDS

Having all your medical records in one place isn't just convenient. In an emergency, it can be a lifesaver. Some sites require you to do the work yourself. Others work with your doctor to keep records up to date.

●**PersonalMD.com** *(www.personalmd. com)* is a free service that acts as an electronic repository of your medical records, including details about your blood type, allergies, etc. These records can quickly be accessed from anywhere in the world via the Internet or fax. You are responsible for entering and maintaining data and can decide who gets access (through the appropriate password and personal identification number).

Electrocardiograms and other graphical documents can be faxed to the service to be scanned into your personal records.

FIND A CLINICAL TRIAL

Patients who have exhausted all standard treatment options or are interested in being on medicine's cutting edge may be able to enroll in clinical trials—studies of promising experimental treatments. Online services help steer patients to these studies.

●**Drug Study Central** *(www.drugstudy central.com)* lets you search for trials by dis-

ease name, medical condition or geographic location. The site provides details of each study and sends e-mail alerts about new ones.

BUY HEALTH INSURANCE

Online health insurance is no cheaper than health insurance obtained through traditional channels. But it's easier to compare policies online—and you don't have to deal with high-pressure salespeople.

●**Healthaxis.com** *(www.healthaxis.com)* sells health and prescription medicine coverage. It also provides instant quotes and insurance-buying advice.

Important: Not all policies are available in all states.

E-Mail Your Doctor

Use e-mail for simple queries if your doctor or pharmacist is equipped for it. A two-minute e-mail exchange may eliminate the need for a time-consuming office visit. Managed-care doctors who are paid a set amount per patient are especially likely to use e-mail. Doctors who are reimbursed based on office visits may discourage it.

Consensus of doctors—some who use e-mail and some who do not—reported in *The Wall Street Journal.*

Better Online Bill Paying

Use an Internet-based bill-payment service, not a bank. Internet services make a contractual commitment to protect users' privacy. Not all banks do this—most banks want to cross-market products or sell customers' names. *Also:* Internet-based services are usually more comprehensive. *Example:* They let you arrange to have all your bills sent to them…then notify you by e-mail when bills arrive. Check offers at *http://pmb.paytrust.com...*and *www.statusfactory.com.*

Susan Wyland, managing editor, *Real Simple*, Time-Life Building, Rockefeller Center, New York 10020.

How to Use the Internet To Cut Your Taxes

James Glass, Esq., a New York–based tax attorney.

Now you can obtain free tax information that formerly you could get only by paying a tax professional—if you could get it at all.

FREE FROM THE GOVERNMENT

•**IRS Web site, *www.irs.gov,*** is the most important tax Web site of all. *It offers a huge array of resources...*

•Forms and publications. No more trips to the IRS office or waiting for tax forms to arrive by mail.

•Local resources. Get help from your local IRS office that you may not know is available.

Examples: Free tax counseling for seniors ...schedules of problem-solving days...small-business workshops...citizen advocacy groups...and much more.

•Latest news. The IRS's e-mail letter provides national tax news and news of your local IRS district.

•Tax research. Official IRS regulations, rulings, procedures and announcements, along with the IRS manual and many other official documents.

•Questions answered. Submit questions to the IRS through its Web site. Receive responses via e-mail.

This is just a sampling. The IRS site is well worth examining in detail.

•**US Tax Court, *www.ustaxcourt.gov.*** Learn how to use the Court's "small case division" to contest a tax bill involving up to $50,000 (excluding penalties and interest) per year—without a lawyer...and under simplified rules. This site also lists all Tax Court decisions issued since the beginning of 1999.

•**State and local tax agencies.** A great many of these agencies are now on the Internet. You can find a comprehensive listing at *www.taxsites.com/state.html*. This site, maintained by Professor Dennis Schmidt, PhD, CPA, of the University of Northern Iowa, Cedar Falls, also lists many local taxpayer advocacy groups, which can assist individuals and local businesses.

ANSWERS FROM PROFESSIONALS

One of the best features about the Internet is that you can use it to get your questions answered by tax professionals—*for free*. These groups are a great starting point for tax research, but you should still contact a tax professional.

•**Tax newsgroups.** These are open, ongoing discussion groups that anyone can join. *The two major newsgroups for US taxes are...*

•*misc.taxes.moderated*. This has a number of tax professionals as "regulars" who answer questions from anyone. A tax professor moderates the group, screening questions so discussion is polite and focused on practical tax issues.

•*misc.taxes*. This group is not moderated, so "anything goes."

Newsgroups are *not* part of the World Wide Web. To reach them, use your Web browser's "News and Message" function—Internet Explorer's *Outlook Express* or Netscape Communicator's *Collabra* message center.

A complete, searchable archive of all the messages that have appeared in these groups is also available on the Web at DejaNews, *http://groups.google.com*. And—visit the Usenet Info Center Launch Pad, *www.ibiblio.org/usenet-i/home.html*.

•**E-mail discussion groups.** If you want to focus on a specific tax issue, you can join one of many specialized Internet discussion groups that are hosted by professional groups and universities. Questions and comments are submitted via e-mail to a moderator, who compiles them in a document that is e-mailed to all group members.

To find a discussion group on a particular topic: Use the University of Chicago's Law Lists search engine, *www.lib.uchicago.edu/cgi-bin/law-lists*. Type in "tax" for a list of tax groups.

TAX-FILING HELP

You don't have to buy software every year to prepare your tax return and keep records. Some Web sites do it for you. *The best...*

●**TurboTax for the Web, *www.turbotax. com,*** is the online version of the popular Turbo Tax return-preparation software. *Cost:* $29.95-$79.95 per federal and $29.95 per state return.

●**H&R Block TaxCut OnLine, *www.tax cut.com,*** offers free services to help you prepare and file your federal and state tax forms electronically. Ideal for students and those with simple tax returns.

MORE RESOURCES

Still more useful sources of free tax information on the Web...

●**Nolo Legal Encyclopedia, *www.nolo. com/lawcenter/ency/index.cfm.***

●**Fairmark Press Tax Guide for Investors, *www.fairmark.com.*** Includes one of the most extensive explanations of Roth IRAs, as well as tax news and discussion boards on investment tax subjects.

●**irs.com, *www.irs.com.*** Includes lists of frequently asked questions as well as perhaps the broadest collection of links to tax discussion groups, taxpayer organizations and other tax resources.

Cyber-Directories Save Time—Big Time

Business directories available online can quickly locate firms and their phone numbers for free. *Useful...*

●**Anywho, *www.anywho.com,*** provides the AT&T directory of business and personal phone numbers.

●**Bigfoot, *www.bigfoot.com,*** is a leading directory of phone numbers and e-mail addresses for individuals.

●**Global Yellow Pages, *www.globalyp. com,*** gives links to the *Yellow Pages* for more than 40 countries.

●**Verizon Super Pages, *www.superpages. com,*** provides more than 16 million business listings in the US and links to the Web pages of many.

Nancy Tanker, managing editor, *Specialty Retail Report,* 293 Washington St., Norwell, MA 02061.

Thinking About a New Cell Phone?

Here is what to do if you're in the market for a cell phone or service provider...

●**Pick a service plan before you pick a phone.** New cell phone designs are so seductive that many people sign up with providers only if they carry the phones they want. That can leave you with excessive calling charges.

Consider before signing up...

●The number of minutes you'll likely be on the phone each billing cycle.

●How often you'll use your phone outside your local region. Long-distance "roaming" charges are expensive.

●Phone size and options you prefer.

Also, most people are unaware that if they decide to switch service providers, they will have to buy new phones.

Reason: While service providers sell identical-looking phones built by the same manufacturers, each phone is designed to access the network of one carrier—and one carrier only.

●**Don't sign a service contract that lasts longer than one year.** Some firms offer two- and three-year deals with what appear to be attractive rates. But considering how far prices have fallen and how much cell phone technology has improved in the past three years, any contract today will be a terrible deal three years from now. Also, any phone will be obsolete in three years.

Mike Feazel, managing editor, *Communications Daily,* a magazine for the telecommunications industry.

Guarding Against Potential Cell Phone Dangers

Timothy McCall, MD, a Boston internist and author of *Examining Your Doctor: A Patient's Guide to Avoiding Harmful Medical Care*. Citadel Press.

Recently, I became one of the 100 million Americans who carry a cell phone. I had resisted for a long time—primarily because I don't like to be accessible at all times. But I finally gave in.

Like many of you, I've been following the ongoing debate about cell phone safety. Some scientists argue that the phones can cause everything from memory problems to brain cancer—and some preliminary findings do seem to support this view. Other scientists say there is no danger.

The central issue is whether microwave radiation given off by the phones affects the brain. Studies involving rats suggest that long-term memory can be affected by cell phone use. And a new study from Sweden found that—among brain tumor patients who used a cell phone—tumors tended to develop near where the cell phone was habitually held.

Since cell phones have only recently come into widespread use—and since cancer can take decades to turn up—it will be years till we can sort out this controversy. In the meantime, here's what I suggest to stay on the safe side:

●**Use cell phones sparingly.** Cell phones can be lifesavers in an emergency, and they're a great convenience when no conventional telephone is handy. It's prudent to use a land line whenever possible—especially for conversations that last more than a few minutes. Of course, conventional phones usually cost less to use and offer better sound quality.

●**Choose the model carefully.** Studies suggest that digital phones give off less radiation than do older analog models.

Another important feature to look for is a built-in speakerphone. That lets you put more distance between your head and the cell phone antenna—the source of the radiation. The greater this distance, the lower the potential risk.

I often switch my cell phone to the speakerphone and put it on the desk in front of me—especially when the other person is doing most of the talking.

●**Forget about "radiation blockers."** Several devices now on the market are said to reduce radiation from cell phones. But recent tests cast doubt on their effectiveness. Some recent research suggests that headsets—sometimes touted as a way to reduce radiation exposure—can act as antennas, actually increasing the dose to your brain. But other studies have found they could decrease the radiation.

●**If you have a pacemaker, watch out.** Cell phone radiation can interfere with pacemaker signals, so it's best to keep the cell phone as far as possible from the pacemaker. Use the phone on the opposite side of the body from the pacemaker, and don't keep the phone in a breast pocket.

●**Take extra care with children.** If cell phones do turn out to affect brain tissue, kids could pay the highest price. Their skulls are thinner, their neurological systems are still developing and they are more sensitive to the effects of radiation. I believe it's prudent to limit kids' use to emergency situations.

●**Limit cell phone use in cars.** Unless the phone is connected to a roof-mounted antenna, using a cell phone inside a car exposes your brain to more radiation.

But the biggest risk faced by motorists who use cell phones is distraction. Talking on a phone while driving is just as dangerous as driving drunk, according to a *New England Journal of Medicine* study. If you must use your phone while driving, dial only when you're stopped—or have a passenger dial for you.

The New World of Digital Imaging

Bill Schiffner, editor in chief of the imaging industry publication *Photographic Processing* and a contributor to *Digital Photographer* magazine and *JetPrintPhoto.com*. Mr. Schiffner has been covering the photo industry for more than 15 years.

Digital imaging now offers a practical, affordable complement to film photography.

With a digital camera you can take a picture, view it immediately, share it on the Web—or make a print. A scanner lets you convert favorite photos into image files that you can retouch and restore on your computer and distribute online…or as prints.

Most photo centers can now upload pictures captured on film to the Internet, as well.

While film still offers the most economical solution for quality prints, digital imaging's advantage and appeal is as an extension of your computer system for visual communications.

HOW IT WORKS

A digital image begins as a file of information. That file is the digital equivalent of a negative, but you can work with it in ways never practical with film: Revise it, enhance it, archive it to disk or transmit it over the Internet. *Some basics…*

●**Resolution.** The quality of a digital image is defined by its *resolution,* expressed in pixels—the more pixels the better.

Most digital cameras offer several resolution modes, from standard to super fine. Typically, the higher the resolution, the higher the quality of the image. Resolution determines the size of the image file.

●**Image capture.** This is accomplished with a CCD (Charged Coupled Device) or CMOS (Complementary Metal Oxide Semiconductor) image chip. CMOS is better for dim lighting situations, but CCD is said to deliver cleaner images generally.

Pictures are stored in microchips or PC cards as a kind of "digital film." These are removable memory cards, such as CompactFlash, Miniature Card or SmartMedia. With removable storage cards you can take unlimited pictures by just replacing the storage cards.

●**Printing.** Producing a quality print from a digital image at home requires buying inks and paper. Even then, the results may not be what you'd expect from film. However, you can also have them printed at a photo lab, as well as share them online.

WHAT YOU'LL NEED

●**Imaging system.** The computer is the core of any digital-imaging system. Know your system specs when you shop for a camera. Suppliers publish the minimum requirements in computer RAM, processor speed and hard drive needed to support their cameras or scanners.

●**Cameras.** Digital cameras start in the $200 range and climb to more than $1,000. Available from traditional suppliers of photographic, computer and electronics equipment, they are best purchased in stores specializing in these products where experts are available to advise you.

If you merely want to share photos online, an entry-level camera will prove adequate. These are the digital equivalent of a point-and-shoot 35mm camera and offer basic features.

●**Scanners.** A scanner offers a less-expensive entry into digital imaging. Basic flatbed scanners, adequate for home users, sell for $100 or less. These "read" your photos, reflective art or text documents and convert them into a digital file within seconds.

Many people find the scanner the ideal way to copy treasured family photos, preserve them on disk and share them with family and friends. With the right paper, some photo realistic printers can give the images from your digital camera or your scanner the look and feel of prints from regular 35mm film.

●**Digital services.** Want to experiment with digital imaging without buying new equipment? Inquire at local photofinishing centers about what digital services they offer. Most now "digitize" film as part of basic services.

Along with prints, you can copy photos to CD-ROM or upload to the Internet to a photo-sharing site such as *www.ofoto.com*—where they can be shared by family and friends.

You'll also find more of these centers equipped with digital minilabs and self-serve kiosks. These minilabs combine traditional print and digital services, regardless of what camera you use. With the kiosks, you step up, insert your digital "film," place your order and it's ready in minutes.

TAKING IMAGES ONLINE

There are two ways to share images online...

•**E-mail.** Compose a message, attach an image file and send. All the recipient needs to do is click on the message and view the image. Or, you can upload images to your Web page or a commercial Internet site for viewing.

•**Upload to the Internet.** You can also have your photofinisher digitize and upload your pictures to the Internet. Once there, the images are assigned a URL, which you and others can use to view the pictures.

Buying a DVD Player

If you've been waiting to buy a DVD player, now is the time. A wide range of movies is available on digital videodiscs—for $15 to $30 each...renting costs the same as renting video-cassette tapes. You can buy a low-end player for as little as $169. Brand names—Panasonic, Sony or Toshiba—start at $249. If you own a Dolby Digital audio/video (A/V) receiver, hooking it up to a DVD player will give you top-quality digital sound suitable for a home theater. *Cost:* $250 and up. If your audio requirements are less ambitious, don't spend more for a DVD player with a built-in Dolby digital receiver. *Better:* A DVD/CD changer that handles five discs—$350 to $450.

David Elrich, an independent reviewer of electronic devices and a freelance writer for a number of consumer and trade publications.

Global Positioning On Your Wrist

Casio's *GPS Satellite NAVI* pinpoints your location anywhere, using the global satellite system. Latitude and longitude coordinates help you plot your location on a map. Good for hikers, bikers, boaters, balloonists, drivers or anyone traveling in unfamiliar territory. Strap-on unit, about the size of a wristwatch. Also tells time. *Cost:* $500. *More information:* 800-962-2746...*www.casio.com*.

22

Travel Tips and Traps

Handling Money When You Travel

Before you leave on a trip, accommodations must be made to cover financial matters while you're away from home, especially if you plan to be gone for an extended period of time. *Here are a few areas to consider...*

•**Consolidate and simplify.** Arrange to have as few bills coming in as possible while you're away. *Helpful:* Limit the number of credit cards you carry.

Example: Instead of carrying five gasoline credit cards in your wallet, pay for fuel using a single Visa or MasterCard or carry the one gasoline card you use most—eg. Mobil, etc.

Contact creditors about setting up automatic payment plans to pay regular monthly bills directly from your checking account. *Including:* Mortgage payments...utility bills...insurance premiums. Arrange for direct deposit of regularly arriving checks. *Including:* Social Security...dividends...pension payments. You can also pay bills via the Internet while away from home or office.

•**Have a trusted friend or family member pick up your mail.** Leave a supply of pre-signed checks so they can pay any unexpected bills that arrive. *Also:* Have them review your mail to make sure nothing important—such as a notice from the IRS—goes unanswered.

Alternative: If you're going to be traveling on a schedule or will be in only one location, have your mail forwarded directly to you.

How: If you will be in only one location, have your local post office forward your mail. If you'll be moving around, contact a mail forwarding service—listed in the *Yellow Pages* (look under "Mail Receiving Services"). These services will receive your mail from the post office, bundle it up and forward it to you anywhere in the world. *Including:* To a private mailing address ...a hotel...RV campsite office...post office general delivery.

Bob Howells, correspondent for *Outside Magazine* and writer for *National Geographic Adventure*. He is author of *The RVer's Money Book*. Trailer Life Books.

311

●**Get an Automated Teller Machine (ATM) directory.** Contact your bank or ATM card network for a directory of locations. In the US, machines are easy to find, but in some countries, machines are tied into only one network.

ON THE ROAD

Gaining access to your money when you're on the road can be a problem. *There are several useful options...*

●**Traveler's checks.** The old standby for travelers, traveler's checks are readily negotiable in an emergency—or when you are temporarily unable to find an ATM for some reason.

Carry—at most—only several hundred dollars in traveler's checks. *Reason:* You usually have to pay a 1% service charge, plus you'll tie up money that could otherwise be earning interest.

●**ATMs.** ATMs give you instant access to your money, and with so many available in the US and Canada, one is always nearby. Plus, more and more businesses are accepting ATM cards for purchases.

Strategy: Keep most of your funds in an interest-bearing checking or savings account linked to your ATM card so you'll continue to earn interest on your money until the day you withdraw it.

Important: ATMs often charge transaction fees of $1 to $2 for network withdrawals, so compare charges when selecting a bank.*

●**Credit cards.** A great convenience for travelers, credit cards eliminate the need to carry a lot of cash and allow you to "float" your money for as long as 60 days—the time from when you make a purchase to when you have to pay for it.

You may need to carry two credit cards. One for making purchases and the second for checking into hotels or renting cars.

Background: When a hotel or car rental company makes an imprint of your card, a portion of your credit line is tied up as a security measure to cover damage to the room or car. It may be two to three weeks before that amount is released—usually only when payment is received from the card company.

Problem: If you rent a few cars or stay in several hotel rooms, your credit limit can easily be exhausted, making the credit card worthless.

Self-defense: Carry another emergency card or a charge card—such as American Express or

*Average fee is $1.49; range is 50¢ to $2.50.

Diner's Club—which has no credit limit. In an emergency, most credit cards can be used to withdraw cash from ATMs.

Note: These withdrawals—via credit card—are considered cash advances and begin accruing interest from the moment the money is withdrawn.

Cash-advance fees: Most cards charge cash-advance withdrawal fees of up to 3% of the total amount withdrawn.

●**Carry a telephone calling card.** Available from AT&T, MCI, Sprint and other long-distance providers, they let you bill telephone calls to a personal account, use the provider of your choice and avoid the exorbitant rates charged by no-name long-distance companies.

Precaution Before a Trip

Before taking a trip, put valuables that you usually keep at home in a safe-deposit box or leave them with a friend or relative. Pay bills before you leave so they are not overdue when you return. Have your burglar and fire alarms checked to be sure they are working properly. Leave an itinerary with a friend, colleague, neighbor or relative so you can be reached in case of emergency.

Ira Lipman, president, Guardsmark, Inc., one of the world's largest security services companies, Memphis.

How to Save Big Money And Prevent Big Travel Hassles

Deborah Burns, acquisitions editor with Storey Books, Williamstown, MA, and author of Tips for the Savvy Traveler. *Storey Books. She has visited 42 countries—traveled from Hong Kong to Cochabamba, Bolivia, trekked in the Himalayas, ridden cargo boats down the Amazon, cruised through the Caribbean—and has visited every state in the US.*

Travel provides an education—about yourself and about the places and people you encounter. But there are some things travelers really don't want to learn.

I learned the hard way that not every doctor in the world speaks English. I also learned that after a long airplane flight, it is dangerous to drive a car in a country where they drive on the left.

MONEY LESSONS

•**Plan for the worst.** Currency rates can change suddenly, sometimes just before or even during a foreign trip. That can turn a budget holiday into an unexpectedly expensive splurge.

Always budget for 20% more than current prices. If exchange rates change in your favor, you'll have an extra cushion.

•**Choose your indulgences in advance.** On some trips, I make eating well a priority—and skimp on hotel rooms. Of course, in developing countries, paying more for food is not an extravagance—but a necessity.

If you're going to a beach resort, lodging near the surf might be the place to spend money. In cultural capitals, such as London or New York, the theater might be your priority.

•**Learn the local currency.** Knowing the value of foreign coins and bills will facilitate quick conversions.

Helpful: Know the dollar value of 10 units of foreign currency or the euro *Example:* 10 UK pounds is worth about $15 or 14 euros.

A currency converter is helpful, but most savvy travelers prefer doing quick, rough calculations so they don't feel so obviously foreign—and at a bargaining disadvantage.

•**Monitor your spending.** Keep track of the traveler's check serial numbers—in case any checks are lost or stolen.

Keep an eye on how much credit you're charging...and the fact that ATMs are giving you local currency.

Best exchange rates: Banks, ATMs or American Express. Many hotels and shops tack on stiff surcharges.

Reminder: Convert $100 before departing on your trip. Keep $100 in US dollars for your return home...and for emergencies.

HEALTH LESSONS

•**Know your prescriptions.** Have your physician write out the chemical name for any prescription you might need refilled while traveling. Foreign pharmacists can be confused by US brand names.

•**Keep all essential drugs with you.** Do not pack them in your checked luggage. Older travelers should bring along a medical history that lists blood type and other important health information.

•**Plan for medical emergencies.** Join the *International Association for Medical Assistance to Travelers.* Subscribe to this free service and you'll get a list of English-speaking doctors around the world. *Information:* 519-836-0102. *www.iamat.org.*

Another group worth knowing about is HotelDocs. This service will send a doctor to a hotel room within 40 minutes of a call. *Cost:* $150 for doctor's visit, plus medications. *Information:* 877-244-7362...or *www.hoteldocs.com.*

PACKING LESSONS

•**Take half the clothes you planned to pack.** "Just in case" items probably will never leave the suitcase—but you'll feel them every time you pick it up.

If you need something once you reach your destination, buy it there. You'll have a better feel for the weather and local style. You might also find regional bargains—silk in Asia, woolens in Europe—that become treasured souvenirs as well.

Exception: Business travelers should always pack an extra outfit—in case your first set of business clothes become soiled or are lost.

•**Bring an inexpensive or disposable camera.** Taking pictures will be more enjoyable if you're not worried that your expensive camera might be stolen. And pack extra film and camera batteries, which may cost much more abroad.

TRANSPORTATION LESSONS

•**The Internet has made a huge difference in airfares,** and I don't mean just the auctions and lowest-fare searches. The Internet has empowered travelers.

Often the local travel agent will quote a price that is twice the fare available online—and if you tell the agent of the lower price you found, he/she will often match or beat the lower fare. Always do fare searches both through the Internet and with a travel agent.

● **Bring your own snacks when flying.** Surrounding passengers will look enviously at you munching on fresh apples, crackers and Brie while they nibble on airline peanuts.

● **Rent a bicycle.** Bicycling is often the best way to see the land. If you want to bring your own, most airlines accept bikes as luggage. Get a shipping box from a local bike shop.

FOOD LESSONS

● **Read up on the cuisine before departing.** Travelers in France, for example, should learn the words for different animal body parts—unless you don't mind ordering feet, blood sausage, brains or other organs that are considered delicacies in that country.

● **Photocopy the food section in your favorite guidebook**—so you have a reference to pull out at the table.

SHOPPING SMARTS

● **Never buy anything on your first day in a new city.** You'll usually find something cheaper...or something you like better.

Best times to bargain: Early morning and late afternoon. Early in the morning, vendors are eager to start selling. Late in the day, they are more anxious to clear out their stalls.

Caution: Duty-free doesn't necessarily mean cheaper. Know the approximate prices of liquor and other goods you might be tempted to buy in a duty-free store. Make sure they are a better deal than what you can get at home.

Health Tips

Prevent traveler's stomach trouble by taking an acidophilus supplement. Start a few days before your trip, and continue following the package instructions until you return home. Acidophilus, which is a healthful bacteria, helps maintain your intestinal environment—making you less susceptible to traveler's diarrhea and similar problems.

Allison Clough, MD, MPH, Travel and Geographic Medicine Clinic, Tucson, AZ.

Antibiotics can be taken to prevent traveler's diarrhea. But the best approach in many cases is to take chewable bismuth tablets. Bismuth is the active ingredient in over-the-counter remedies such as Pepto-Bismol. Chewing two tablets four times daily throughout the trip should keep traveler's diarrhea at bay. *Still important:* When traveling in developing countries, don't drink tap water...avoid salads, ice cubes, ice cream ...and eat only well-cooked foods served hot.

Bruce Yaffe, MD, a gastroenterologist and internist in private practice in New York City.

You Don't Have to Travel Alone

Travel-companion matching helps single people find someone to travel with. Most clients are over age 45. More than 70% either request a companion of the opposite sex or are willing to accept one. Profiles of all members are required, and clients are urged to meet and spend time together before any trip. *More information:* Travel Companion Exchange, 800-392-1256 or *www.whytravelalone.com.*

Smarter Trip Planning

Save big on airfares by studying a map before you purchase tickets. Make a list of cities within driving distance of your destination and ask about the fares to those cities.

Example: A round-trip fare from Chicago to Cincinnati for a family of four was $1,028. By flying to Louisville, a route with a "friends fly free" program to a city that is one hour's drive from Cincinnati, the round-trip fare was $196.

Tom Parsons, editor of *Bestfares.com.*

Airline-Ticket Buying Savvy

When ordering airline tickets, pay for them with credit cards. People who pay cash are in danger of losing their money if a carrier goes under or there are any other unforeseen circumstances. Credit card customers usually can get a refund.

How to Fly Free

Linda Bowman, author of *Freebies (and More) for Folks Over 50*. COM-OP Publishing.

Big bargains on air travel are available and are easy to get. The hard part is getting someone to tell you what these deals are and how you can take advantage of them. *Examples...*

● **If you fly to a nearby "secondary" airport,** you may be able to save 10% to 34% on your ticket, and avoid many of the hassles associated with overcrowded primary airports.

● **If you fly on Thanksgiving, Christmas or New Year's day,** you can save up to 70% on your ticket—and still arrive in plenty of time for dinner.

RESEARCH PAYS

If you take the time to do the research and analyze your options, you will be able to take advantage of special fares and money-saving situations. Examples...

● **Hidden city flights.** The trick here is to get off or on in the connecting city, rather than take the plane to its final destination.

Example: A one-way fare for the nonstop, direct flight from Dallas/Ft. Worth to Phoenix might cost $393, but if you booked a nondirect flight from Houston to Phoenix where you changed planes in Ft. Worth, you might pay as little as $207 and beat the higher fare. You would get on the plane in Ft. Worth and only use that part of your ticket.

● **Split ticketing.** Beat the mandatory Saturday night stay on excursion fares to cities you'll visit more than once by buying two round-trip discount tickets.

Here's how to do it...

● Ticket A from your home town to your destination and back again.

● Ticket B from your destination to your home, and back to your destination.

You use the outbound part of your ticket A to get you to your destination, but use the outbound ticket from ticket B to get home. The airline will not realize that you didn't stay over on a Saturday. Use the remaining portions of your two round-trip tickets for your next trip.

● **Special member discounts.** Members of the clergy, Red Cross workers, military personnel, medical students, children, job corps trainees and seamen all can qualify for as much as a 50% discount on air travel.

● **Consolidator fares.** Independent discount travel brokers buy blocks of surplus seats on international flights and sell these seats at fares far less than those a retail travel agent or the airline can offer you directly.

Check the travel sections of major metropolitan newspapers or ask your travel agent if he/she uses consolidators or wholesalers.

● **Bumping from an overbooked flight.** Some people hope to be bumped from flights so that they can receive a free flight voucher as compensation. To help make this happen, book your flight during a time when there is a great likelihood that there will be bumping. Take only carry-on luggage. Seat yourself very near the check-in clerk so that you can be the first to volunteer when volunteers are called for.

You'll have lost a few hours in travel time, but gained a free ticket for your next adventure.

THE FLEXIBLE TRAVELER

If you've always got your bags packed, and you are ready to go, but are interested in the best deals to the best places, subscribe to *Best Fares* (800-880-1234), *Travel Smart* (800-FARE-OFF).

These are very thorough monthly publications specializing in the latest information about travel promotions and discounts being offered by cruise lines, airlines, hotel chains, car rental agencies and frequent flyer programs.

TRAVELING ABSOLUTELY FREE

•**Group leader.** Organize your entire extended family for a trip, or get together a group of friends with similar interests.

If you can put together a big enough tour group—sometimes six is big enough—you can go free.

If you can recruit 12 fellow travelers, you may be able to bring a friend free, too.

Work with your travel agent or directly with an airline group travel representative to set it up.

•**Tour escort.** If you are fluent in a foreign language, you can become a tour escort. Check with large travel agencies or tour operators.

•**Courier.** Volunteer your services as an air courier and escort freight (usually documents) to a distant client. Air couriers fly free to exotic spots all over the world. Check the *Yellow Pages* or metropolitan papers for advertisements.

KNOW IT ALL

The key to traveling inexpensively is to do the research yourself by creating a file of cheap flight advertisements, subscribing to travel publications, scouring the travel sections of the Sunday newspapers and comparing all your options before you pick up the phone to book your trip.

Bottom line: Always use a charge card to pay for your trip so you'll have some recourse if your trip doesn't go as planned.

And if you're hoping to sleep en route, bring along a U-shaped, blow-up pillow—they're great.

Information Source

Weather conditions and airport delay information for 150 US airports always are available free on the Web site of the Weather Channel, *www.weather.com*. The site also provides driving conditions around the country, a database of hotels and restaurants and other resources for business travelers.

Airport Scams Are Multiplying...Self-Defense Made Simple

Alvy Dodson, director of public safety at Dallas–Fort Worth Airport, where he oversees more than 300 officers who patrol an area the size of Manhattan. He has been with DFW Airport for 22 years.

Airport thieves have devised very clever schemes to separate you from your valuables...

Scam: **Stealing your luggage left with strangers.** It is not a good idea to entrust your property to strangers...*ever*.

Scam: **Stealing luggage in men's rooms.** A popular area for theft in airports is at the small, crowded entrance to the urinal area. Thieves wait for travelers to pile up their bags and turn their backs for a moment.

Also popular—the shelf above sinks, where travelers place rings, watches or cell phones while washing their hands.

Self-defense: If possible, wait until an end urinal or stall is available, so luggage can be placed against the wall. At the sink, place valuables in your front pockets while you wash. Put your luggage on the floor between your feet.

Scam: **Looting your luggage cart at the airport.** Thieves look for a cart loaded with bags and follow it until you stop to hail a cab or buy a magazine. Then one or two of them create a diversion while a third slips one of your bags out from the bottom.

Self-defense: Always push luggage carts —never pull them behind you.

Also, run twine through the handles of your luggage, especially smaller ones. That way a thief trying to grab a bag will make a commotion as he/she pulls the others along with it. If you must stop with your cart, do so in an area away from the flow of the crowd or against a wall where no one can get behind you.

Scam: **Cutting your fanny pack.** These are the wraparound pouches people wear on their waists.

Thieves follow you up an escalator. One gets on in front of you...the other behind you. The lead person stumbles as he gets off the escalator, causing you to nearly fall over him. The second person sandwiches you and uses a knife or razor to slice the pack's waistband.

Self-defense: If you wear a fanny pack, wear it with the pouch in front and keep it under a jacket or sweater.

Scam: **Stealing luggage off the carousel.** Thieves take the black, pull-along suitcases that are so common now. If challenged after they grab yours, they claim it was an honest mistake.

Self-defense: If you must use a black pull-along, make it distinctive. Put your initials in reflective tape on the side. Arrive at the baggage claim area as quickly as possible so you can retrieve your luggage as soon as it is delivered.

Scam: **The baggage-handler rip-off.** Some dishonest airport employees who load and unload bags from planes run their hands through bags looking for valuables. This is hard to prevent—even if you use small locks on your bags. Small locks are easily broken...although they are better than nothing.

Self-defense: If you must carry valuables, keep them in your carry-on bag. If you must pack them, roll valuables in your clothing and place those garments in the middle of the bag. Thieves will open a zippered compartment or rummage through the top of the contents of your luggage.

Also, make your bags "tamper-obvious." Thieves avoid luggage that will show obvious signs of pilfering.

Helpful: Many airports have kiosks that will wrap checked luggage in a thick layer of transparent plastic. *Cost:* About $6/bag.

Scam: **Picking the pockets of victims at food kiosks.** Thieves move in close to see in which trouser pocket or zippered luggage compartment you keep your wallet. They also want to see your money and credit cards.

Self-defense: Remove the money and credit cards you need *before* entering the airport terminal. Keep them in a clip in your front pocket. Women should avoid carrying their wallets in their purses. Instead, conceal them in a coat or sweater pocket where they do not show.

Scam: **Stealing at checkpoints.** A favorite place for distraction is screening checkpoints. When you are presenting your carry-on articles for X-ray inspection, be ready to proceed *immediately* through the magnetometer. This can be accomplished by removing all metal objects—coins, jewelry, keys, etc.—*before* you approach the checkpoint.

The Best Airline Seating

To get the best airline seating, make a reservation as early as possible—and ask immediately about seat assignment. If your travel agent or airline says that seat assignments open at a later date, mark your calendar and call then—or make sure the travel agent does. If boarding passes become available at still another time before the flight, be sure to call again for them.

Bottom line: Seat-assignment policies vary by airline. Most reserve some of the best seats for their most-frequent travelers and people paying the full fare. This leaves fewer good seats available for others.

Consensus of airline officials reported in *The New York Times.*

Visit National Parks Off-Season

Jim Yenckel, former chief travel writer for *The Washington Post* and a freelance travel writer based in Washington, DC.

Hate camping but want to see beautiful parks? Here are affordable places to stay at five of our national treasures. These sites are breathtaking year-round—but contact the lodge to find out when peak season is so you can avoid the rush.

DEATH VALLEY (CALIFORNIA)

●**Stovepipe Wells Village.** In the summer, this is one of the hottest places on earth. But in winter, it's a perfect spot for hiking, biking and four-wheel driving. Stay in the heart of the park, near breathtaking Mosaic Canyon, the Sand Dunes and an abandoned mining town, among other unique attractions. The village has 83 rooms, starting at $75 a night.

760-786-2387...*www.stovepipewells.com.*

YOSEMITE (CALIFORNIA)

●**Curry Village** is a small city of tent cabins. The spartan accommodations—a bed... canvas "walls"...and shared bathrooms—start at only $59 per night. The setting, however, is spectacular—woods and boulders near the famous Half Dome. In summer, there's a pool. In winter, an outdoor ice-skating rink. There are also more expensive wooden cabins ($92 per night).

Even in the summer, you can sometimes find a vacancy without a reservation. Bring a flashlight to find your way around at night.

559-252-4848...*www.yosemitepark.com.*

GRAND CANYON (ARIZONA)

●**Maswik Lodge** is about one mile from the canyon's South Rim in a spectacular pine forest. It is a quiet place, located away from the crowds. Cabins with bath and TV cost $63 a night in the summer. Motel-style rooms start at $76.

Reservations are necessary during the summer peak, but rates are cheaper and crowds sparse during the winter, when the weather may still be lovely.

Just a few feet from the rim, the **Bright Angel Lodge and Cabins** has rooms that start at $56 for a shared bath and no TV. The lodge is located in the historic section of Grand Canyon Village.

303-297-2757...*www.grandcanyonlodges.com.*

YELLOWSTONE (WYOMING)

This vast park has nine separate lodges. Most have budget cabins that start around $58 per night with shared bath. Booking early is essential.

Alternative: Stay in West Yellowstone, just outside the park entrance in Montana. The town is packed with motels. It's a beautiful, 30-mile drive to Old Faithful, and you can plan different loop drives through Yellowstone for different days. If you need a reservation quickly, this is the place.

Yellowstone Park: 307-344-7311...*www.travel yellowstone.com.* ***West Yellowstone Chamber of Commerce:*** 406-646-7701...*www.westyellowstonechamber. com.*

MAMMOTH CAVE (KENTUCKY)

●**The Mammoth Cave Hotel,** located near the entrance to the caves—the world's biggest cave system—offers cottages from spring through fall. They start at $36 a night for a single. Rooms in the hotel and lodge cost more but are available year-round.

If descending hundreds of feet into the earth doesn't thrill you, the park is loaded with aboveground activities, such as hiking, fishing and boating.

270-758-2225...*www.mammothcavehotel.com.*

How to Stay Healthy While Traveling By Air

Thomas N. Bettes, MD, MPH, southwest area medical director for American Airlines in Fort Worth, TX. He wrote about medical advice for commercial air travelers in a recent issue of *American Family Physician,* 11400 Tomahawk Creek Pkwy., Leawood, KS 66211. 800-274-2237...*www.aafp.org.*

The time you spend on airplanes can leave you tired, stiff and dehydrated... and, if you have a chronic health condition, raise your risk of serious complications.

Here are the leading threats to airline passengers' health—and how to counter each...

●**Dehydration.** During flight, cold, dry air inside the cabin can dry the skin, throat, eyes and nostrils.

To protect yourself, drink noncaffeinated beverages—six to eight ounces per hour while aloft. Pass up caffeine and alcohol. They're diuretics. Use moisturizer to keep your skin from drying out. Over-the-counter saline eye drops can help prevent dry eyes.

If you're flying overseas: Ask to be booked on a nonsmoking flight. If no such flights are available, ask to be seated well away from the smoking section.

All domestic airlines are now smoke-free.

●**Altitude sickness.** Airliner cabins are typically kept at a pressure equivalent to that found at 8,000 feet above sea level. This reduced pressure can cause mild *altitude sickness—* headache, fatigue and trouble concentrating.

There's no way to prevent altitude sickness, but being aware of it can ease any anxiety you might feel as a result of the symptoms.

If altitude sickness doesn't cause you to have headaches, engine noise might.

Self-defense: Ask for a seat far away from the engines. Bring along earplugs and *acetaminophen* (Tylenol) or another nonprescription pain medication.

●**Blood clots.** Stiffness isn't the only problem that can result from spending long hours in a cramped airplane seat. If blood pools in the legs, dangerous blood clots can form.

If your flight is longer than three hours, try to get up once an hour to stretch and walk around. While seated, periodically extend and flex your feet.

Caution: If you're already at risk for blood clots—because of smoking, obesity, oral contraceptive use or a history of deep venous thrombosis—ask your doctor about taking aspirin and wearing support stockings during the flight.

If possible, get a bulkhead seat. It will provide more legroom.

Prolonged sitting can also cause swelling of the feet and ankles, especially in pregnant women and people with kidney trouble or heart failure.

To minimize swelling: Elevate your legs …walk around the cabin…and avoid nuts, pretzels and other salty foods.

AVOIDING COMPLICATIONS

If you've had recent surgery or have a chronic health problem, ask your doctor if you're stable enough to fly…

●**Recent surgery.** Postpone flying at least one week after major surgery—two weeks after coronary bypass surgery.

The danger is that air that might have been trapped inside the body during surgery could expand under reduced air pressure. This could cause torn sutures and other problems.

●**Special oxygen needs.** If your doctor recommends that you have supplemental oxygen during the flight, you'll need to call the airline to order it at least 48 hours in advance.

You'll also need to provide the airline with a medical certificate that spells out the proper flow rate and other important points.

●**Heart disease.** Anyone who has had a heart attack should wait at least two weeks before flying. Wait at least six weeks if there were complicating factors, such as arrhythmia or left ventricle dysfunction.

If there's any doubt as to your ability to fly safely following a heart attack, your doctor should give you a treadmill stress test.

If you take an antihypertensive drug or another heart medication, be sure to bring enough to last the entire trip. Keep it in your carry-on luggage.

It's also a good idea to bring along a copy of your most recent electrocardiogram.

Caution: Flying is off limits to individuals with unstable angina, severe heart failure, uncontrolled hypertension and certain heart arrhythmias.

●**Diabetes.** Be vigilant about monitoring your blood glucose levels while flying…and about scheduling meals and medication dosing—especially if you'll be traveling across time zones.

Pack *twice* as much medication and supplies as you think you'll need. Bring half the supply on board with you in your carry-on luggage. Bring *all* of your insulin on board with you to avoid exposure to freezing temperatures in the cargo hold.

Important: Bring a "diabetes alert card" and a doctor's note specifying your dosages and explaining why you're carrying syringes. To obtain a free card, contact the American Diabetes Association at 800-342-2383, *www. diabetes.org.*

IN-FLIGHT EMERGENCIES

Domestic airlines are required to carry basic medical equipment, and crew members are trained in basic first aid.

Unfortunately, the first-aid kit can be used only by a physician or another trained medical professional, such as a nurse or paramedic. Whether there'll be one on your flight is a matter of luck.

Good news: Many airlines recently upgraded their medical kits. A wider range of medical problems can now be treated on board, including heart attacks, asthma attacks and seizures.

These days some airliners are equipped with automatic defibrillators, which can shock an erratically beating heart back into a normal rhythm. These devices can be operated by flight attendants.

AVOIDING JET LAG

Many travelers rely on over-the-counter supplements, such as melatonin. But recent studies have had conflicting results. And since melatonin is not regulated by the FDA, its purity and long-term safety are uncertain.

To minimize fatigue and disorientation after your arrival, remain active during daylight hours...adopt local mealtimes and bedtimes...eat small, well-balanced meals...avoid alcohol...and get moderate exercise.

Second Passports: The State Department's Best-Kept Secret

Information from our insiders at the US State Department.

Some countries won't permit entry to travelers whose passports show that they've previously visited certain other countries. Most Arab countries, for example, won't allow entry to people whose passports have a stamp showing that they've visited Israel. A similar situation confronts people traveling among some African countries. Traveling freely among these countries is a matter of carrying two passports and knowing when to use them.

You can get a second passport that looks just like a regular US passport and is only valid for a limited period of time, usually two years.

Apply for one at your regional passport office, but be prepared to document your legitimate need...itinerary, assignment from your employer specifying that you need to do business in a particular country, etc. Take two passport-sized photos.

To find out if you'll need a second passport, check the "Visa Information Sheet" available from any passport office. That document will help you to determine if there are visa or passport conflicts among the countries on your itinerary. *Extra protection:* Check with the consulate or embassy of each country you plan to visit.

Reason: Customs regulations of foreign governments change so quickly that even the State Department is unable to keep its information on these regulations absolutely up-to-date.

Avoid relying on information from travel agencies. They use the Travel Information Manual put out by an airline organization. Because the compiling, distribution, etc., can take a long time, the manual can be out-of-date as soon as it's issued.

While traveling, be sure to stay on top of possible entry-rule changes at borders you plan to cross. If entrance to a country depends on the second passport, show only that document. Put away your regular passport. Using two passports is officially frowned upon by most governments, so there could be repercussions.

If you use the wrong passport on arrival, you'll probably be refused entry. If you're caught with the wrong document when leaving, on the other hand, chances are the border guards will let you depart.

Combating Air-Travel Fatigue

Warren Levin, MD, and Howard Bezow, MD, World Health Group, New York.

Before takeoff: Eat and drink lightly for 24 hours before a flight. *Recommended:* Salads, fish, chicken. *Avoid:* Liquor, bon voyage parties.

Forty-eight hours before departure: Ask the airline for a special severe hypoglycemia (low blood sugar) in-flight meal. You will probably get a nice seafood salad from the first-class galley, even if you have an economy ticket. On boarding, remind the chief flight attendant about the special meal you ordered.

Clothes: Wear loose-fitting clothing. Bring slip-on shoes. *Reason:* Long hours of sitting can cause swelling of the legs and, especially, of the ankles.

Women: If possible, plan to fly within seven to 10 days after the onset of the menstrual cycle.

Medication: Take an adequate supply and a copy of your prescriptions. A note from your doctor can often avoid hassles with overzealous customs officials.

•In the air. Avoid consuming all the food and drink offered. Alcohol, soft drinks and other foods that have empty calories can cause a swing from high to low blood sugar. You go from feeling great to feeling tired, cramped and headachy.

Don't do important business work while flying. *Reason:* Decision-making and complicated paperwork add to an already increased stress level. *Better:* Accomplish as much as you can before departure. *Aboard:* Read nondemanding work-related material. *Preferred:* Relax by reading an absorbing book or watching the movie.

•At your destination. Changes of time, space and place can cause a feeling of dislocation. Continue following the airborne guidelines of moderation suggested. Realize that your tolerance level for everything from decision-making to dining are below average while on a short trip abroad.

Foreign Airport Danger

Airport thieves target tourists *traveling* to their destinations, not returning from them. That's because tourists carry more money early in a trip.

This means that if you travel abroad, you will be more at risk when you arrive in a foreign airport than later when you depart from it.

Also, when you first arrive in a foreign land, you are least familiar with your surroundings —which increases your vulnerability to thieves.

More risk: Travelers are at special risk after changing money at an airport bank or ATM. Thieves watch these areas to see how much money travelers are carrying and where they are keeping it.

Jens Jurgen, president of Travel Companion Exchange and editor of *Travel Companions,* Box 833, Amityville, NY 11701, *www.travelcompanions.com.*

Better Car-Rental Rates

Quote the advertised discount directly from the company's ad when calling the reservation number. *Problem:* Reservation agents often will not volunteer the best available price up front.

Helpful: Mention the promotion's discount code, usually listed in small print beneath the boldly displayed rate, or in the description of the terms and conditions of the rental.

Money Savers

Don't prepay for gasoline when you rent a car at an airport. Rental-car employees often urge travelers to prepay for a tank of gas when renting a car.

Reality: Most off-airport gas stations charge less than rental car firms do. And people who prepay get no refund for gas left in the cars when they return them.

Better: Fill up the gas tank on your own just before returning the car.

Survey of 58 rental car employees at 12 airports, reported in *USA Today*, 1000 Wilson Blvd., Arlington, VA 22229.

Renting a car in Europe costs much more if you want an automatic transmission. Most Europeans drive stick shifts, and European car rental companies have a difficult time selling cars with automatic transmissions, so they get their profits by charging more for renting them.

Result: You may save a lot by renting a car with a manual transmission in Europe.

Brent Rolfe, vice president of operations, Auto Europe, quoted in *Travel Holiday*, 1633 Broadway, New York 10019, *www.travelholiday.com*.

Great Ways to Cut Hotel Costs

Christopher J. McGinnis, director of Travel Skills Group, a communications and consulting firm specializing in the business travel industry, Box 52927, Atlanta 30355. He is author of *The Unofficial Business Travelers Pocket Guide*. McGraw-Hill.

Why not get a great hotel room for the same money, or less, than you'd pay for a standard room? *Try these strategies I recommend to my business-traveler clients...*

●**Consolidators.** National consolidators provide deep discounts. Try Quikbook (800-789-9887 or *www.quikbook.com*)...Hotels.com (800-964-6835)...or Priceline *(www.price line.com)*.

Example: The Beverly Plaza in Los Angeles charges $139 to $151 for a room...Quikbook's rate is $129.

Downside: Some consolidators require advance payment.

Beware: Hotels that are "frayed around the edges" often unload rooms with consolidators. But some desirable properties—such as Chicago's Drake and Palmer House hotels—do work with consolidators. Know your hotels before you book.

●**Travel consortia.** Many travel agencies belong to networks that can provide discounts and upgrades. Leaders include Hickory Travel Systems* (800-448-0349).

●**Be specific when you book a room.**

Example: Nonsmoking, lake view, between floors three and 10, away from the pool, etc. This way, if the hotel can't meet your specifications, it might give you an upgrade.

●**Get out of the mainstream.** Check out lesser-known boutique hotels, such as those of...

●The Kimpton Hotel Group (800-KIMPTON or *www.kimptongroup.com*) on the West Coast.

●Manhattan East Suite Hotels (800-637-8483 or *www.mesuite.com*).

●Boutique Hotels (877-847-4444...call hotels individually, listed at *www.boutiquehg. com*) in New York and Manhattan Seaport Suites.

●**Use clout on the right people.** A couple of weeks before you leave, send a note to the manager of guest relations or the front-desk manager. Introduce yourself...suggest that you might be staying often...and that you might refer business.

When you get to the hotel, say hello to these people. You may get a better room or free breakfast. If you do, write a thank-you note.

●**Work the wiggle room.** Rates are not set in stone. Smoke out the lowest price in town, and ask the manager you've met to match it. Also, ask for the corporate rate of the company that you are visiting. Often the hotel has a local rate that only in-house reservationists are aware of. If you can't get a break on the room, ask for free upgrades—breakfast, valet services, transportation.

●**Call right after 6 pm.** This is when hotels wipe out all reservations unsecured by

*Hickory is a consortium of corporate travel agencies, serving only corporate clients

a credit card...and may offer rooms at a bargain rate. In high-occupancy cities—New York or San Francisco—many hotels have a 4 pm deadline.

•**Join the club**...a frequent-guest program will get you a few extras—and it costs nothing to join.

Example: Starwood Preferred Guest Program offers Gold Preferred Guest Benefits... upgrade, late checkout and free weekend night with 2,000 points; convert points to airline miles. For more information, call 888-625-4988, *www. starwood.com.*

Credit Card Calling

When you have more than one phone call to make from a hotel or pay phone, don't hang up after each call. Push the # button between calls. This will allow you to stay connected with your chosen long-distance carrier.

Added benefit: Most hotel computers will register several calls made this way as a single local call, saving you surcharges.

Travel and Leisure, 1120 Avenue of the Americas, New York 10036.

Best Places to Eat

To save money while traveling abroad, don't eat in a hotel unless breakfast is included in your room rate. Coffee shops across America have large, inexpensive breakfasts. Look for tasty ethnic restaurants— they're real bargains in cities such as London, where traditional fare can be very expensive. Plan to eat only two big meals a day and snack the rest of the time. You can almost always buy fresh fruit or wrapped sandwiches at take-out groceries.

Family money-saver: Ask at museums and historic spots for a family pass. They are often available—and provide significant savings over the price of individual admissions.

Alex Kennedy, editor, *Family Fun,* 114 Fifth Ave., New York 10011.

Bed & Breakfast Club For Seniors

Bed & breakfast club for persons 50-plus has hosts in more than 2,000 cities in North America. You may stay in a private home, condo or farm for $15/day for two, breakfast included. To be a member, you must be willing to be a host. There are more than 3,500 members and growing. Contact the *Evergreen Bed & Breakfast Club, www.evergreenclub.com* or 800-962-2392. *Dues:* $75/year for two people, $60 for a single membership.

Nancy Dunnan, publisher, *TravelSmart,* Box 397, Dobbs Ferry, NY 10522. 800-FARE-OFF, *www.travel smartnewsletter.com.*

Grandchild Trap

Travel with grandchildren may require special documentation. Many countries require specific forms for minors traveling alone, with only one parent or with an adult who is not a parent. Check the rules before you go.

Christopher Lamora, press officer, Bureau of Consular Affairs, US Department of State, Washington, DC.

How to Get Paid To Take a Vacation

Cruise lines hire many retirees, semiretirees and students to work on their luxury cruise ships. And with many new ships entering service, hiring is increasing.

Trade-off: Cruise ship employees receive spartan accommodations compared with those provided to passengers, and are required to work to high standards. But they are paid for traveling the high seas and great rivers and lakes of the world, and for visiting exotic ports of call.

Jobs of all kinds are available on ships that often now resemble floating cities.

Examples: Purser, photographer, beautician, casino staff, counselor, host, clerk, doctor, nurse, youth counselor, sports trainer and many more. Persons with special skills may be hired as lecturers on subjects such as investing and the arts.

Pay range: From $1,700/month (bartender) to as much as $8,000/month (cruise director).

For more information...

•***How to Get a Job with a Cruise Line,*** by Mary Miller (Ticket to Adventure Press), 800-929-7447.

•**New World Cruise Ship Employment Agency.** Read the "Frequently Asked Questions" list at *www.cruiseshipjob.com.*

•**Cruise Lines Employment Guide 2003,** *www.cruiselinejob.com.* Provides job descriptions, profiles cruise lines and gives contact numbers, employment contracts and other information for different cruise lines.

•**Small Ship Cruises,** 800-290-0077, *www.smallshipcruises. com,* provides a directory of small ships, windjammers and river barges that visit ports of call ocean liners never reach—for persons seeking special ventures.

When you find a cruise line that visits ports attractive to you, contact it directly or visit its Web site for job openings.

Nancy Dunnan, publisher, *TravelSmart*, Box 397, Dobbs Ferry, NY 10522. 800-FARE-OFF, *www.travel smartnewsletter.com.*

23

Doing Your Own Thing

High-Quality, Affordable, Educational Adventures For Anyone Over 55

Go behind the scenes at an archeological dig. Take part in reef research in Hawaii. Study American Indian, Scottish, Irish or Afro-American culture at historic sites. Take field trips to rarely visited birding sites with an expert ornithologist. Learn the art of woodcarving. Attend a guided tour of American music from the colonial times to the end of the 20th Century. Explore Canada by train, guided by historians and naturalists.

All this and much more is available through the Elderhostel program, founded in 1975 as a not-for-profit organization. They offer stimulating adventures in lifelong learning across the 50 US states, Canadian provinces and territories and in 85 countries. Elderhostel also sponsors exciting educational programs that explore the world from the unique vantage point of a floating classroom.

In addition to travel-based education/adventure programs you can take part in community-based educational opportunities or volunteer as an aid in doing meaningful research.

What does an Elderhostel program cost and what's included? Participants are responsible for getting themselves to and from the program, but once you start, the cost of registration, accommodations, all of your meals, classes and field trips noted in the program description are covered and cultural excursions & social functions. All Elderhostel program costs also include limited accident insurance. The cost of a six-night program in the US averages $690 while for a five-night program it is $575, with programs in Hawaii and Alaska slightly more.

What's the catch? There really is no catch. Elderhostel is committed to providing high-quality, educational opportunities to older

Elderhostel, Inc., 11 Avenue de Lafayette, Boston 02110.

adults at very affordable prices. The many colleges, museums, national parks and learning institutions that make up their 'campus' share this commitment.

Who's eligible? Anyone 55 or over. (Younger adults are welcome if accompanying a senior.) Singles are welcome. On a typical Elderhostel program, there is always a mix of couples and singles and the atmosphere is very friendly and social. Accommodations can be made for special diets and disabilities.

Do you have to participate in every activity? The sponsors believe that a complete Elderhostel experience means full attendance in every aspect of the program! If you feel, however, that a particular excursion or field trip may be too strenuous for you, or you would like to take the afternoon to explore on your own, you may forgo a lecture or activity.

To learn more: Call toll-free at 877-426-8056, Monday through Friday, 8 am–9 pm (Eastern Time). *TTY line:* (toll-free) 877-426-2167. *Callers outside the U.S. and Canada dial:* 978-323-4141. Elderhostel's online catalog is a fast way to quickly search out a program by season, subject and location. You can also check program availability and even register online at *www.elder hostel.org.*

Golf Smarts

To improve your golf game: While waiting your turn at the tee, take some practice swings from the opposite side—if you are right-handed, take swings left-handed. Start slowly, and do not go more than 70% of your normal swing speed. Do the swings a few times on the first three or four holes of every round. Also do a few opposite-side swings at the driving range. They will help strengthen and balance your muscles, making it easier to hit longer drives.

Gregory Florez, golf trainer, Salt Lake City, quoted in Men's Health, 33 E. Minor St., Emmaus, PA 18098.

Golfextras.com Web site offers an extensive selection of golf accessories and instructional items. You can also find collectibles, gifts and awards and "Hot Deals." *www.golfextras.com.*

Improved Backswings For Older Golfers

Backswings get shorter as golfers get older. When the swing gets too short, you'll lose distance, accuracy and consistency.

Remedies: Hold the club lightly. *Reason:* Too tight a grip tenses the arm and shoulder muscles and restricts the backswing.

Put more weight on your right foot, especially on full swings with woods and longer irons. *Result:* A head start on your swing and less weight to shift.

Turn your chin to the right (or to the left, if you're a southpaw) as you start your backswing. If it throws your timing off, cock your chin in the direction of the backswing before you swing.

Appropriate Tips for Helpful People

●**Golf caddie.** If you are a guest at an upscale course, offer to pay the customary $25/bag club fee for the caddie. If your host declines the offer, discreetly give the caddie a tip of $5 (stingy) to $15 (generous).

●**Tennis pro.** $5 to $10, unless you are at a private club, where no tipping is required.

●**Crew members on a yacht or a powerboat.** For first-class service, tip the captain $50 and crew members $25 each. If they were surly and unhelpful—not too likely, of course—reduce these amounts to $10 and $5.

●**Captain or mâître d' at a club.** In addition to the club's service fee and the annual collection for a holiday gift...if you give a party at the club, tip between $15 and $50 (no one should see you do it).

Letitia Baldrige, leading authority on practical etiquette and author of *In the Kennedy Style*. Doubleday.

Fishing a New Lake

If you know where to start looking, you can fish any lake successfully.

WHERE BASS CONGREGATE

•**Near trees that have recently fallen into the water.**

•**In hot weather.** Under lily pads, especially in the only shallow spots around.

•**In consistently mild weather.** In backwater ponds and coves off the main lake. *Best:* Good weed or brush cover, with a creek running in.

•**Any time at all.** In sunken moss beds near the shore.

Outdoor Life, Two Park Ave., New York 10016, 800-365-1580...*www.outdoorlife.com.*

Surf Casting—a Different Kind of Fishing

For more than just a day at the beach, try surf fishing. It is easy to learn, and basic gear is inexpensive—rod-and-reel combinations can cost $50 or less. Talk to tackle-shop personnel about fishing. Ask which bait to buy and how to thread it onto the hooks. Find out if casting lessons are available. If you decide to buy a rod and reel, the lessons may come free.

T. Edward Nickens, freelance writer, *Cooking Light,* PO Box 62376, Tampa, FL 33662. *www.cooking light.com.*

Best Guides for Bird-Watchers

Sheila Buff, author of many books about birding and the outdoors, including *The Complete Idiot's Guide to Bird Watching.* Macmillan.

Birders now have a number of excellent guides from which to choose. *Following is a short list to get you started...*

•*The Sibley Guide to Birds,* written and illustrated by David Sibley (Knopf).

This comprehensive new book is on bestseller lists across the country for good reason. Its 6,600 detailed illustrations show the birds in realistic positions and include field identification marks, how the birds look in flight and more.

The book also contains detailed identification tips and up-to-date range maps.

Every birder needs this book. *One drawback:* At 544 pages, 6" x 9" and about 2.5 pounds, it's too large and heavy to use easily in the field.

•*Birds of North America,* by Kenn Kaufman (Houghton Mifflin).

This new field guide by a legendary birder uses more than 2,000 digitally enhanced photographs to illustrate the birds and emphasize their field marks. The organization by related bird families is especially helpful for beginning birders.

•*Peterson Field Guides: Eastern Birds/ Western Birds,* by Roger Tory Peterson (Houghton Mifflin).

The classic and in some ways still the best, particularly for new birders. Peterson's lifelike illustrations feature arrows indicating important field identification marks. The crisp text describes birds and their songs in terms so memorable that many experienced birders can quote the descriptions by heart.

The dividing line for the Eastern edition and the Western edition is the 100th meridian, or roughly the Rocky Mountains.

•*National Geographic Field Guide to the Birds of North America,* by Jon L. Dunn (National Geographic Society).

This volume—a favorite among experienced birders—features excellent illustrations, range maps and good text. The pages are larger than the pages of most field guides. They have some white space, which is handy for making notes.

•*Birds of North America: A Guide to Field Identification (Golden Field Guide),* by Bertel Bruun, Chandler S. Robbins and Herbert S. Zim (St. Martin's).

More than eight million copies have been sold. Outstanding illustrations, informative text, range maps and sonograms (visual depictions of bird songs).

•**The Birder's Handbook,** by Paul R. Ehrlich, David S. Dobkin and Darryl Wheye (Simon & Schuster).

This book takes up where field guides leave off. It provides detailed, condensed information (but no pictures) about each species, along with highly readable and informative essays about birds and bird ecology, behavior and evolution.

How to Turn Your Yard Into a Haven for Wildlife

Sheila Buff, author of many books about birding and the outdoors, including *The Complete Idiot's Guide to Bird Watching.* Macmillan.

Gardens designed to attract birds and other wildlife are both beautiful and good to the earth. And as a bonus, they're easier to plant and maintain than conventional ornamental gardens.

TO ATTRACT MORE WILDLIFE, YOU NEED...

•**Plants that provide food.** Any plant that produces nectar-filled flowers, seeds, berries or nuts will attract butterflies, birds and small animals. The more variety, the better.

•**Plants that provide shelter.** Just as important to wildlife as the right food is the right kind of shelter. Birds need places to perch safely and to build their nests. Other wildlife such as squir-

rels, chipmunks and rabbits need shelter to rest safely from predators and raise their families.

•**Watering holes.** Especially in developed urban areas, fresh water for wildlife can be scarce. In addition to attracting wildlife, a bit of fresh water adds interest and beauty to any garden. You'll find that a birdbath, a fountain or a small pond (artificial or natural) will attract animals and birds you've never seen in your garden.

GETTING STARTED

1. *Use only organic methods.* Commercial pesticides, fungicides, fertilizers and other yard chemicals harm the very insects, birds and animals you're trying to attract. *Key organic gardening methods...*

•Use compost instead of chemical fertilizer.

•Use insecticidal soap rather than commercial pesticides.

•Mulch heavily instead of using chemical sprays to cut down on weeds and fungus infections.

•Let nature control the insect population. Some easily attracted animals can noticeably reduce the number of annoying insects in your garden.

Examples: A single tree swallow will eat hundreds of mosquitoes in a day. A bat can do the same in a single night.

2. *Look for good garden areas* that could be made more attractive to wildlife. *Possibilities...*

•A corner of the yard you don't use much. Turn it into an easy-to-care-for mini-meadow of wildflowers and grasses, or plant some food shrubs such as cotoneaster or serviceberry there.

•A fence around the yard. Make it more attractive to wildlife by planting climbing vines—such as trumpet vine, Virginia creeper or euonymus (wintercreeper)—to run along it. The fruits and flowers of these vines will attract birds. The foliage provides shelter.

Even better: Replace the fence with a hedge of boxwood or American holly.

•An open area near shrubbery. That's a good spot for a birdbath, garden fountain or small pond.

• Against the foundation of your house. For attractive covering, consider planting barberry and pyracantha (firethorn) for food and ornamental evergreens, such as creeping juniper, for shelter.

3. *Add a variety of levels to your garden.* A greater range of levels will increase the amount of bird and animal life in your garden. *To add levels...*

• Plant vines that climb up walls, tree trunks and fences.

• Build stone walls, rock gardens and raised beds.

• Plant shrubs and small trees.

CHOOSING THE RIGHT PLANTS

Many ornamental plants—azaleas, for instance—are very attractive to human eyes, but they don't do much for butterflies, birds and other animals.

Your goal: Add plants that are attractive to both you and wildlife. And if the plants are easy to care for, so much the better.

• **Plants that attract butterflies.** Any flowering perennial or annual with flat-topped, sweetly scented blossoms will do the trick.

Good perennial choices are aster, butterfly bush, coreopsis, hollyhock, lilac, Shasta daisy and wallflower.

Good butterfly-friendly annuals include ageratum, cosmos, heliotrope, Johnny-jump-up (viola), marigold, Mexican sunflower, sweet alyssum, sweet william, verbena and zinnia. Herbs such as thyme and basil, if left to flower, are also good choices.

• **Shrubs that attract birds.** Shrubs provide both food and shelter. *Best:* Shrubs that produce berries and/or bushy foliage.

Good choices include arrowwood (viburnum), bayberry, blackberry, cotoneaster, dogwood, elderberry, juniper, holly, Oregon grape, serviceberry and sumac.

• **Plants that attract birds.** The seeds of flowering plants—perennials and/or annuals—attract birds.

Sunflowers, for example, work magic on wildlife. And because they're very easy to grow, they're a great way to introduce kids to gardening.

Other useful easy-to-grow annuals and perennials include ageratum, blazing star, candytuft, cornflower, cosmos, Indian paintbrush, phlox, purple coneflower, sage, sweet rocket, valerian and zinnia.

Caution: Don't "deadhead" these flowers—that is, remove the seed heads after the blossoms fade. Deadheading will get you more flowers, but few seeds.

• **To attract hummingbirds.** Any flowering plant or shrub with red or orange tubular blossoms will attract hummingbirds. Bee balm (monarda) is highly attractive and very easy to grow. Other good choices include columbine, fire pink, flowering tobacco, honeysuckle, jewelweed (wild impatiens), penstemon, phlox and trumpet vine.

• **Trees for birds and small animals.** Smaller fruit-bearing trees will attract both birds and small animals such as chipmunks, squirrels and rabbits. Autumn olive, cherry, crabapple and mulberry are all good choices for backyards.

Bigger trees: Bats roost in the natural cavities found in larger trees. Other small animals—such as foxes, raccoons and squirrels—use tree cavities or dig dens under the roots of large trees for sleeping areas and to raise their young.

Don't cut down dead trees: Dead trees are just as useful as live trees for attracting wildlife. Woodpeckers and other birds—such as chickadees and nuthatches—dig nesting holes in the soft wood, for example, and bats roost in hollow trees.

Unless a dead tree is truly unsightly or threatens to fall over, consider leaving it in place and letting it be gradually covered by food-bearing vines such as wild grape and Virginia creeper.

Senior Softball World Series

For people over 50, series includes teams for age groups up to 80-plus. Women and men play on separate teams. Last year's playoffs involved 139 teams from 40 states.

More information: National Association of Senior Citizens Softball (NASCS), 810-792-2110.

Ken Maas, president and founder, NASCS, Box 1085, Mt. Clemens, MI 48046.

Small Towns with Great Antiques

Glendale, Arizona, 40 minutes northwest of Phoenix, has more than 40 antique shops downtown. 877-800-2601, *www.visit glendale.com.*

•**Essex,** Massachusetts, 25 miles north of Boston, has more than 35 shops. 978-283-1601, *www.capeannvacations.com.*

•**Abingdon,** Virginia, 135 miles southwest of Roanoke, near the Tennessee border, has a 20-block historic district with a dozen antique shops. 800-435-3440, *www.abington.com/ tourism.*

•**Waynesville,** Ohio, 40 miles northeast of Cincinnati, has more than 20 antique shops. 513-897-8855. *www.waynesvilleohio.com/ antiques.htm.*

Malcolm Katt, an antiques dealer and owner of Mill-wood Gallery, which specializes in Nippon and Pickard porcelain, Box 552, Millwood, NY 10546.

How to Outsmart Casinos at Their Very, Very Dirty Tricks

John Alcamo, a gaming expert who spent several years interviewing Atlantic City card counters. He is author of *Casino Gambling Behind the Tables.* Gollehon Books.

No matter how much we hope for big wins, casino odds are stacked against gamblers.

You can still have fun gambling—and dramatically improve your odds and limit your losses—*by knowing the strategies that casinos use to get gamblers to lose...and lose...*

•**Casinos want you to forget you're gambling.** The carefree, party atmosphere in a casino helps soften the blow when a player loses. The last thing a casino wants a player to do is dwell on how much he/she has lost.

•**Greed is good—for the casino.** It's hard for gamblers to stop while they're winning. That's why casinos have pictures of big winners displayed when you enter. They want you to think, "Hey, I could win a pile, too." That way, if you win a few hundred dollars—even $1,000—you'll feel unsatisfied and try to parlay it into a huge win.

•**Casinos hate players with a plan.** A casino's nightmare is a bettor who refuses to lose more than a certain amount, no matter what. Luckily for the casino, few players have such discipline. The majority of players violate the mental limits they set. After losing the allotted bundle, a player thinks he can break even by risking just a little more. So the losses add up. The more the player loses, the more desperate—and foolish—his bets become.

•**Cashing out is purposely difficult.** By design, gamblers who want to cash out have to get past a gauntlet of table games and slot machines before they get to the cashier's window. *Don't be tempted to bet more.*

You'll also often find a line of customers at the cashing-out windows. The casino wants you to become impatient and resume play. Don't give in.

•**Every comp is strategic.** Casinos give out complimentary tickets—freebies—to customers because they want them to keep playing and eventually visit again.

Casinos roll out the red carpet for big winners because they don't want them to leave. The longer a player stays in a casino, the more likely he is to lose money.

Strategy: Accept comps...but don't be swayed by them.

GAME TRICKS

•**Blackjack.** Card counting doesn't work. Skilled counters can *theoretically* get a mathematical edge in blackjack. But casino employees are adept at spotting card counters. When they do, the pit boss can order the cards to be shuffled, negating the counter's hard work.

●**Keno.** Worse than a lottery—because there is no guaranteed winner.

●**Roulette.** Tracking numbers is a sucker's game. It gives you no mathematical edge. But casinos will gladly give you a scorecard because they know that people who keep "score" play longer—and lose more money.

●**Slot machines.** Credits are diabolical. Years ago, slot machines dispensed actual coins if you won. Today's slot machines register "credits." Casinos changed their methods because gamblers are more likely to fritter away credits since "they're not real money."

Remember: Credits are real money—with or without a dollar sign.

●**Video poker.** Can be misleading. If you're playing Jacks-or-Better and you end up with a pair of jacks, the machine will tell you that you won. If you bet five coins, five coins will be returned to you.

But you didn't win. You tied and got back only what you wagered. In blackjack, this would be called by its right name—a *push.* Video poker machines call it a win so you'll feel better and keep playing…and lose more money.

The Best Slot Machines

Las Vegas rules are most chaotic for slot machines. In Atlantic City, all machines must return at least 83% of the amount wagered…and a few return even more than 83%. But in Nevada, one machine might pay back 99%, while the one right next to it pays back only 60%. The bettor's problem is that it's impossible to identify the hot machines. Their placement is the casino's closely guarded secret.

The best-paying machines are usually found third or fourth from the end of a busy aisle, where the most people will see and hear the payoffs.

Worst payoffs: Any machine near the door of a casino showroom.

Among Atlantic City's casinos, the variations are narrower than in Vegas, but they can still be worked for or against you.

Lee Pantano, Box 47, Atlantic Highlands, NJ 07716.

Vacation Traps…and Wonderful Alternatives

It's a shame to waste money on a vacation that fails to meet your expectations. *Overrated destinations…*

Trap: **Hawaiian "fantasy" resorts.** In both architecture and amenities, these multimillion dollar resorts completely lack any feel for the culture of Hawaii. Guest activities include Clydesdale horse riding and gondola sailing on man-made lakes. If fantasy is what you're looking for, go to Disney World instead.

Better: The island of Lanai, once home to pineapple plantations. Though the island has seen the opening of several major resorts, it still retains the atmosphere of early Hawaii.

Trap: **Bermuda in winter.** Many vacationers don't realize that this island is located in the Atlantic Ocean, not the Caribbean—at about the same latitude as North Carolina. Winter weather is often rainy and chilly.

Better: Cancun or Cozumel on the Mexican Caribbean. Both offer good winter rates.

Trap: **Venice in the summer.** Poor sanitation, hordes of tourists, and heat and humidity combine to make Venice smelly and unpleasant in the summer. Visit at another time of year.

Better: If you want both art and canals, try Amsterdam.

Trap: **Miami Beach.** The city lost its luster long ago. Hotel Row has become crowded and expensive.

Better: Fort Morgan Island on the Alabama Gulf Coast. This 25-mile breaker island is quiet and offers a pleasing southern atmosphere. *Drawback:* Winter weather isn't as mild as in South Florida.

Trap: **The overbuilt Caribbean islands.** These include Nassau/Paradise Islands in the Bahamas, the Montego Bay area in Jamaica and the Dutch side of St. Maarten.

Better: The quieter Bahamian islands of Eleuthera and Exuma. If you want quiet and excitement, Anguilla is only a 20-minute ferry ride from the shopping and casinos of St. Maarten.

Summer Camps For Adults

These summer camps offer grown-up versions of the fun kids have at camp, *plus a chance to follow specific interests…*

•**The Clearing in Ellison Bay,** Wisconsin, 877-854-3225—one-day to week-long classes in such fields as music, painting, photography, writing and bird identification. $300–$900 including tuition, room and meals.

•**Camp Mom & Camp Getaway.** In Oceanside, CA, near Big Bear in Southern California. 760-806-4582. For women. Don't have to be a mother. Traditional camp activities, such as hiking, arts and crafts, archery, karaoke plus facials, massage, manicures and line dancing. Cost: $275 and includes meals, lodging, activities and "feminars." *www.camp getaway.com.*

•**Camp Cheerio.** In Roaring Gap, North Carolina, 19 miles north of Elkin. 800-226-7496, For people over age 50. Swimming, tennis, arts and crafts, guided walks, bingo. *Cost:* $180-$220 for 5 days. Includes room and board and all activities. *www.campcheerio.org.*

Alycia Borer, travel writer, quoted in Good Housekeeping, 959 Eighth Ave., New York 10019.

Bike Tours for People Over Age 50

Cycle along flat or gently rolling terrain. Tours usually start with easy mileage—defined as 15 to 50 miles per day.

•**Canadian Trails Adventure Tours,** 800-668-2453 or *www.canadiantrails.com,* run three to eight days—prices start around $1,300 (CAN).

•**Cape Cod Bicycle Adventures,** 888-644-4566 or *www.capecodbybike.com,* offers six-day tours for $1,895.

•**Elderhostel,** 877-426-8056 or *www.elder hostel.org,* has 14-day European bike tours starting around $2,600—including airfare. It also has five- to nine-night North American tours—prices start at about $500.

Nancy Dunnan, publisher, *TravelSmart,* Box 397, Dobbs Ferry, NY 10522. 800-FARE-OFF, *www.travel smartnewsletter.com.*

America's Very Special And Very Different Little Museums

Lynne Arany and Archie Hobson, coauthors of *Little Museums: Over 1,000 Small and Not-So-Small American Showplaces.* Henry Holt.

CALIFORNIA

•**Musee Mécanique** (San Francisco). Arcade games ranging from Victorian-era carnival fortune-tellers to computer games are all playable. *Admission:* Free.

Pier 45, Shed A, Fisherman's Wharf, 415-386-1170… *www.museemechanique.citysearch.com.*

DELAWARE

•**Treasures of the Sea** (Georgetown). Gold bars, silver jewelry and treasures from a royal Spanish vessel that sank off Florida's coast 300 years ago. *Admission:* $2.50 for adults…$1.50 for children and seniors. Half price, October–May.

Delaware Technical and Community College, Rte. 18, 302-856-5700…*www.treasuresofthesea.org.*

ILLINOIS

•**The Cookie Jar Museum** (Lemont). A half-hour south of Chicago, this museum displays 2,000 rare cookie jars. *Admission:* $2 for adults…$0.50 for children.

111 Stephen St., 630-257-5012.

MICHIGAN

●**American Museum of Magic** (Marshall). Magicians' secrets of the past 200 years, including many of Houdini's props. *Admission:* Free.

107 E. Michigan Ave., 269-781-7674 or 269-781-7666... *www.marshallmi.org.*

VIRGINIA

●**Money Museum** (Richmond). Located in a Federal Reserve Bank, exhibit shows the history of money over the past 3,000 years. *Must see:* Uncut sheets of $100,000 gold certificates. *Admission:* Free.

701 E. Byrd St., 804-697-8108... *www.rich.frb.org.*

WASHINGTON

●**World Kite Museum** (Long Beach). Hundreds of exotic kites. *Activities:* 28 miles of open beaches and brisk winds provide the best kite-flying conditions in the country. *Admission:* $3 for adults...$2 for children and seniors.

112 3rd St. NW, 360-642-4020... *www.worldkite museum.com.*

Search for Volunteer Opportunities Online

Visit the Web sites of well-known organizations that depend on volunteer help.

Examples: Peace Corps, *www.peacecorps. gov.*...Red Cross, *www.redcross.org.*...Volunteers of America, *www.voa.org.* Or look for positions near your home by checking the databases at Volunteer Match, *www.volunteermatch.org.*...SERVEnet, *www. servenet.org.*

Carey Millsap-Spears, writer, *Consumers Digest,* 8001 N. Lincoln Ave., Skokie, IL 60077.

Volunteer Vacations

Mix work and pleasure—and maybe get a tax deduction. In *Hawaii,* 10-day Sierra Club trips monitor humpback whales. $1,575 plus airfare. 415-977-5522 or *www.sierraclub. org/outings.* In *Georgia,* the Caretta Research Project helps protect endangered loggerhead sea turtles. $550/week. 912-447-8655 or *http:// members.aol.com/wassawcrp.* Cross-Cultural Solutions in *India* uses volunteers for teaching and community-planning in New Delhi. $2,315 for three weeks, plus airfare. 800-380-4777 or *www.crossculturalsolutions.org.*

Travel Holiday, 1633 Broadway, New York 10019.

Millennium Trails develops new cycling and hiking trails and restores historic routes. *www. millenniumtrails.org.* Millennium Service Project works with local people on community projects—and needs volunteers who can contribute at least a week of their time. There is a tax-deductible service project fee of $450. *www.globalvolunteers.org* or 800-487-1074. Earth Day Network goes beyond the official April 22 Earth Day to plan year-round activities about health, wildlife, land use and more. *www.earthday.net* or 202-518-0044.

Cooking Light, Box 1748, Birmingham, AL 35201.

Here's How to Make Working at Home Work For You!

Barbara Weltman, an attorney practicing in Millwood, NY, *www.bwideas.com.* She is author of *The Complete Idiot's Guide to Starting a Home Based Business.* Alpha Books.

More than 45 million Americans now work from home either full-time or part-time (43% of all U.S. households). Many millions more are expected to join these ranks as our economy changes.

HOW TO MAKE THIS WORKING ARRANGEMENT SUCCESSFUL

Problem: Separating business from personal time and space. Many people work from home because they want to balance work with family obligations—caring for a child, grandchild or parent. Or they want the time to do other things—exercise, volunteer, write or simply kick back and relax. They expect that an at-home work arrangement will afford them the flexibility to plan out their day so they can do it all.

Reality: People who work from home usually work longer hours than they did in an office. This can make it harder to balance business and personal concerns.

If they're starting a business from home, then general start-up issues—organizing the business, making connections, getting the ball rolling—eat up time. And whether they're running their own business or telecommuting, the plain fact is that the business is always there.

Discipline: To maintain the balance you want to achieve, you need to use discipline. *Set boundaries for both space and time...*

●**Fix your business hours.** While you may not always stick to your schedule, at least you'll have a guideline for your time.

●**Separate your business from your personal life**—use separate phone lines for each.

Bonus: You'll earn a tax deduction. The first line to a home is not deductible even if used for business...the second line is.

●**Answer your business phone only during business hours.**

●**Advise clients and customers of your business hours.** Tell them you don't work weekends or after a certain hour during the week.

SETTING UP YOUR WORK SPACE

You're going to be spending considerable time in your home office, so set it up right. *Two things to make your home office function properly...*

●**Sufficient space.** You need to find room for the office furniture and equipment you'll use in your business. List the equipment you'll need to fit into your office space—a computer, an easel or anything else required for you to function properly. Then map out where everything will go. You may also need space for samples or inventory.

●**Separate space.** You need office space apart from your personal living space. It's difficult to make a kitchen table function as an office if you also use it for family meals.

Note: Setting up separate space for a home office is necessary if you want to claim a home-office deduction.

The tax law requires that your space be used regularly and exclusively for business. This means you can't use your den as an office by day and a family room by night. You don't necessarily need an entire room for business or even a partitioned space within a room. All you need is a clearly defined area devoted solely to business.

MAINTAINING A PROFESSIONAL IMAGE

Working from home may allow you to go to the office in a robe and slippers. But you need to present a professional image to the outside world. *This means infusing quality into everything you do...*

●**Consistently use your business identity.** Answer the phone with the name of your business.

●**Be prompt in returning calls and correspondence**—snail mail or e-mail.

●**Keep your office space neat**...and free from personal effects. This is especially important if clients or customers come to call.

Office address? It may be helpful to use a post office box—or other box number—as your official mailing address. Doing this will maintain your privacy. (Customers and other business associates won't know your home address.)

A mailbox can also afford you a prestigious address if you think it will help your business image.

Example: You live down a dirt road outside a small town that nobody knows. Consider renting a commercial box from a service, such as Mail Boxes, Etc. This will give you a known address, probably one on the main street of your home town. *Other benefits of a box...*

• Deliveries can be made to the box, even if you're away from home.

• Neighbors won't know about your business.

MORE ABOUT HANDLING PERSONAL ISSUES

Working from home presents a range of issues you won't have at a downtown office. *List the issues that trouble you and devise ways to minimize or avoid problems...*

• **Distractions.** Working at home means that the demands of running a home are always at hand. Laundry, cleaning and home repairs are never out of sight.

Solution: Set business hours and stick to them. Do household chores only after business hours.

For some, a big distraction in working at home is the refrigerator. While about half of those who start working from home don't have any weight change, about one-third do gain weight. To maintain your weight, stay away from the refrigerator during business hours.

• **Interruptions.** An at-home spouse...a needy neighbor...calls from friends.

These and other interruptions eat into your concentration and detract from your business performance.

Solutions: Set limits. Put a "do not disturb" sign on the door. Give strict instructions that you don't want to be interrupted during business hours.

• **Isolation.** Working at home means no more juicy conversations at the office watercooler. While some people thrive on being alone during work hours and are more productive because of it, others suffer from feelings of isolation.

Solutions: Working from home doesn't mean you're locked in. Just the opposite. It means you're free. *You can...*

• Schedule outside appointments. Instead of having clients or customers come to you, visit them at their place of business.

• Join business and professional groups. This will give you the opportunity to network and make important business connections. It will also give you an incentive to get out of the house.

• Make breakfast and lunch dates. Meet friends or business associates for a meal, at least once a week.

Earn Money in Your Free Time The Way You Want

The new Freetimejobs.com service matches people looking for freelance work of all kinds with those looking to hire them, nationwide. Jobs range from high-tech to basic.

Examples: Jobs recently were posted for computer network specialists, baby-sitters, financial consultants, translators, advertising copywriters, bartenders, bookkeepers and persons willing to make wake-up calls. Categories of jobs include law, sales, marketing, education, household, writing and many others. The service is free to those looking for jobs. Those looking to hire someone can post one job at a time free, or an unlimited number for $50 per month. On the Web at *www.freejob.com.*

Cristina Gair, writer, *Home Office Computing,* 156 W. 56 St., New York 10019.

How to Make Money As a Consultant

Charles Moldenhauer, VP, Lefkowith, Inc., marketing and corporate communications consultants, New York.

At one time or another, most executives consider selling their expertise on their own, as consultants. The majority are at least moderately successful, but many fail. Most commonly, they overestimate the salability of their services and underestimate the effort needed to sell them.

PITFALLS FOR NEW CONSULTANTS

• **Not realizing that consultants,** especially new ones, spend more time selling their services than performing them.

• **Wasting time on unproductive prospects.**

• **Choosing too broad a field in which to consult.**

• **Not learning to talk the client's language.** This is essential because many consultants sell a highly specialized service with its own vocabulary to an equally specialized customer who uses a completely different language. *Example:* A computer expert who is hired to automate market research for a diaper manufacturer.

To sell their services, successful consultants...

• **Maintain pressure by keeping in touch with clients and prospects.**

• **Master sales and marketing tools,** such as writing effective letters, making convincing phone calls and developing presentations.

• **Start at the top,** contacting the chief executives of the Fortune 1,000 companies.

How to Put Together an Inspiring Reading Group

David Laskin, author of numerous books, including, with Holly Hughes, *The Reading Group Book: The Complete Guide to Starting and Sustaining a Reading Group, with Annotated Lists of 250 Titles for Provocative Discussion.* Plume.

Reading groups are blooming and booming across the country. These groups provide intellectual stimulation and are a great way to socialize with friends and make new ones.

CHOOSING MEMBERS

Reading groups typically start with a small cluster of friends who decide to get together. Find, create or expand yours by word of mouth, notices posted on bulletin boards at the library, "Y" or bookstore, ads in a college magazine or the newsletter of a local chapter of a national organization such as the American Association of University Women.

Hook up with fellow book lovers when a novelist or poet comes to town for a book signing.

Mixed-gender groups tend to be livelier and more challenging than single-sex groups. For me, the most rewarding combination is 10 to 12 men and women of assorted backgrounds and ages who are able to discuss books passionately.

Not everyone must be a lifelong bookworm. People grow with the group. One member of my former book group in Seattle had read mostly detective fiction, but was eager to widen his literary horizons.

WHERE TO MEET, WHAT TO EAT

Rotating among members' homes is the most common method. Other groups meet at libraries, alumni clubs, bookstores, schools and restaurants.

Meals run the gamut from brown-bag lunches to elaborate dinners designed around the book's theme or setting. See what your group wants and try it. Many groups find that limiting food to snacks or dessert helps focus conversation on the book.

WHO LEADS?

Start the meeting with a presentation by a pre-arranged leader other than the busy host. A member with special knowledge or experience in the topic at hand may wish to lead that session.

Hiring a professional book group leader can solve common problems, such as not knowing how to get started...falling into the "I loved it"/ "I hated it" trap...getting bogged down by the repeated recitation of personal anecdotes or agendas.

SETTING GROUND RULES

• **Socialize selectively.** As members become friends, they'll want to discuss matters besides books. Set aside a time at the beginning or end of the meeting for this.

• **Finish reading every book.** Insist that all members read to the end. If not, they should attend anyway, but meetings will not be disrupted by plot summaries, nor will the ending be kept secret.

• **Limit the length of meetings.** Participants should go home refreshed, not exhausted. Three hours is a good maximum.

• **Ban filibusters.** Limit the amount of time an individual can talk before someone else has a say. Ten minutes is plenty.

●**Participate.** Everybody must say something or at least ask a searching question at every meeting. Prolonged silence from one corner creates a black hole that sucks energy from the group.

●**Welcome guests.** Inviting new faces can refresh the group.

●**Communicate.** Agree to air problems as they arise.

●**Have fun.**

KINDS OF BOOKS TO READ

While your group can focus on a single genre, period or author, limitations lead to boredom. Discussions soon feel like classes, not open-ended and freewheeling.

Variety is the spice of book groups. The best ones allow themselves the freedom to choose different things and surprise themselves. One of the greatest joys of reading groups is discovering a wonderful book or author. Delve beyond novels into short stories, nature essays, poetry, biographies, travel writing and plays.

SELECTING BOOKS TO READ

Choosing books is one of a group's most intensive experiences. Some groups use the last 15 minutes of each meeting to select the book for the next meeting.

Disadvantages: This method steals time from the discussion and invariably involves someone saying, "You decide. Gotta go."

Try setting aside one meeting per year to determine the entire next year's schedule. All participants must come prepared to suggest (and fight for) books they have read.

Your picks shouldn't merely have pleased or inspired you. They should be controversial, packed with discussable issues and likely to elicit strong opinions.

SOURCES OF BOOK IDEAS

Some independent bookstores maintain shelves of books that have worked well for book groups. A knowledgeable staff member might agree to give your group a presentation. *Other sources of good ideas…*

●**Subscribe to *The New York Review of Books* or *The New York Times Book Review*** (you can get it without the rest of the paper).

●**Read the book sections** of the *Los Angeles Times, Chicago Tribune* or *The Washington Post.*

●**At your library, look for the March 15 issue of the ALA** (American Library Association) magazine *Booklist,* which summarizes the previous year's best books. Also check out *Publishers Weekly* and *Kirkus Reviews.*

●**Scan lists of winners of The Pulitzer Prize,** National Book Award, PEN/Faulkner Fiction Prize, Booker Prize and Whitbread Book Awards (both in England), Goncourt Prize (France) and Nobel Prize in Literature, awarded for the complete work of a writer of international stature.

In our New York group, we set aside 15 minutes at our "anniversary" meeting each year to discuss what we read the previous year. This sparks new ideas and reminds us of a favorite author to try again.

●**Troll the Internet.** Many publishers post reading group suggestions and guides or offer free pamphlets listing topics for discussion about specific books.

My book with Holly Hughes, *The Reading Group Book,* includes more than 60 pages of annotated group-friendly book lists in dozens of categories.

"DOING" THE BOOK

Discussion topics that cover the book thoroughly…

●**Context and background.**
●**Meaning of the text.**
●**Content.**
●**Technique.**
●**Appreciation.**

Write Your Lifestory

Denis Ledoux, director, Soleil Life-story Network of Lifewriting Seminar Leaders. He is author of several books, including *Turning Memories into Memoirs: A Handbook for Writing Lifestories.* Soleil Press.

There are good reasons why you should go to the trouble of writing your lifestory and all the family stories you can remember…

●**Preserve the past.**

- **Through your stories, show children, grandchildren and future generations** how the family was shaped and how they all fit in.

- **Record and celebrate personal as well as professional accomplishments.**

Key to lifewriting: Simply getting started. Don't waste time thinking about it, talking about it or wishing you could do it. Sit down right now and get started. *Helpful...*

- **Make a lifelist of the relationships and experiences** that have formed you and determined your path in life.

Your lifelist is likely to be long and may take several weeks—or months—to create. Add to it freely as significant people or events occur to you. *Examples...*

- Incidents of serious illness, death and divorce in the family.

- Facts about the ethnic or religious group you grew up in.

- Key events and relationships.

- A decision to go to college or not, marry or not, have children or not, etc.

- Falling in love.

- Natural disasters.

- **Create a core lifelist.** From your lifelist, choose the 10 most crucial events or relationships—those which, had they not happened, would have made you become a different person.

On a separate sheet of paper, briefly describe the 10 events or relationships and explain how each influenced you. *Examples...*

- My parents' divorce in 1940 surprised me and made me feel uncertain of the world and my place in it.

- The flood that destroyed my father's print shop in 1950 forced me to reconsider plans for college and my career as a doctor.

- Deciding not to marry Larry Smith because of his drinking led to my renting an apartment and learning to be self-sufficient.

- **Pick a memory—write a story.** Select one item from your core lifelist and write three to five pages about it. Repeat this process until you've tackled all 10. *Helpful...*

- Write vignettes, scenes or dialogues without worrying about chronology or how they'll fit together.

- Concentrate on writing many short stories instead of one long one.

- *Use an active voice, writing from your own point of view:* "I remember Grandpa wheeling himself over to the oak cabinet, looking around to make sure Grandma wasn't in sight, and sneaking a piece of chocolate from the hidden panel."

- Writing down your stories will prime the pump of your memory. If it doesn't, try jogging your memory with photographs, conversations with family members, old journals, yearbooks, period-specific songs or newspaper clippings.

- If you have trouble getting started, write down a well-loved family story. It will help get your story-telling juices flowing.

- Don't worry about spelling, grammar, sentence structure, etc. You'll take care of all that in the editing process. It's best to use a computer or typewriter. Double-space. Type only 6" to 6½" wide.

- **Write down all the facts.** Precise dates and descriptions are helpful for preserving your family's history. To make your writing as factual as possible, check dates and details with others who've shared your experiences, or spend time in the library researching a particular time period.

EDIT YOUR WORK

After you've finished a story, put it away and don't look at it for two to four weeks. Time will give you the emotional distance you need to look at the story with a fresh eye and consider how you might improve it. *Other editing ideas...*

- **Give the story to a friend or family member who can read it objectively.** It helps to send written questions along with the story. Ask the reader if the story is easy to understand, what he/she liked about it, what he didn't like about it, what he would change about it, etc.

- **Read the story aloud to yourself.** Hearing the story read aloud will alert you to awkward sentences, false-sounding dialogue and more.

- **Turn your lifestory into a real book.** When you've finished your lifestory, add photographs, poems, old family letters and other items that illustrate your stories. Then, have 10 or fewer copies of your book bound by a local copy shop at a cost of around $8 to $15 per book.

Inscribe them. Donate a copy to your local public library or historical society. Your lifestory will be a gift your children and grandchildren and your community will treasure forever.

Index

Fat
  eliminating dietary, from diet, 152
  problems with removal, 144
Fatigue, combating air-travel, 321
Fiber content, 171
Financial adviser, hiring, 33
Financing, retirement home, 126
First-aid kit, essential supplies in, 189
Fish and seafood
  ciguatera fish poisoning and, 169–70
  in diet, 154, 169
Fishing, 327
Flea markets, saving money at, 90–91
Food allergies, gene-swapping and, 161
Foods. *See also* Diet
  fiber content of, 171
  genetically engineered, 160–61
  special-order, 172
Food safety
  additives and, 170–71
  ciguatera fish poisoning and, 169–70
  cookware and, 171
  cryptosporidium, 297
  garlic and, 160
  travel and, 314
  washing hands and, 297
Foot pain, relief from, 214
Foreign airports, dangers in, 321–22
Foreign travel, second passports in, 320–21
Formaldehyde, in house, 135
Foundation, setting up private, 28
401(K), 11–13, 48
Fractures
  drugs for, 215
  hip, 215
Fraud, in weight-loss programs, 154
Freebies, 81–82
Free radicals, 162, 163–64
Friends, making new, 120
Frugality, secrets for, 81–82
Fruits, in diet, 106
Full-service broker, need for, 33
Funeral, planning, 118
Furniture, cleaning, 137

G

Gallstones, managing, 219–20, 255
Gambling, 330–31
Garage sale, holding, before selling house, 132–33
Garden, attracting wildlife to, 328–30
Garlic, botulism and, 160
Gastroesophageal reflux disease, yellowed teeth and, 148
Gender differences in heart attack symptoms, 241–42
Generation-skipping tax, 20, 25–26
Gene-swapping, food allergies and, 161
Genetically engineered foods, 160–61
Genital bites, treatment of, 269
Gifts
  versus bequests, 24
  in cutting estate taxes, 20
  to grandchildren, 22–24, 112–14
Gift taxes, state treatment of, 20
Ginkgo biloba
  for allergies, 209–11
  sexual effects of, 265–66
Ginseng, sexual effects of, 266
Glaucoma, preventing and treating, 221–22
Global Positioning System Pathfinder, 310
Gluten, intolerance to, 219

Goals, setting, for retirement, 3
Golf game, improving, 326
Government aid, getting, for health care, 204–6
Grains, for longevity, 107
Grandchildren
  enjoying birth of, 109–10
  giving gifts to, 22–24
  tax-wise ways to help, 112–14
  travel with, 324
Grandparent, being better, 110–12
Green tea, in fighting disease, 159
Grief, stages of, 118–20
Gum disease, protecting yourself from, 224–25

H

Habits, self-hypnosis in overcoming bad, 184–85
Hair, dangers from blow-drying, 147
Hair dye, cancer and, 147
Hair-transplants for men, 147
Hands
  managing trembling, 212–13
  washing, 297–98
Head injuries, home management of, 187–88
Healing
  with life force, 182–83
  mind/body connection and, 173–75
  music and, 183
  plants in, 183–84
  prayer in, 184
Health
  imagination and, 175–76
  travel and, 314, 319–20
Health care
  for allergies, 209–10
  for arthritis, 214, 215–17
  for asthma, 207–8
  at-home nursing care, 196–98
  being better patient, 195–96
  for bug bites, 213
  for carpal tunnel syndrome, 219
  for celiac disease, 219
  for chronic coughs, 210
  for common cold, 210
  for dental problems, 225
  for dizziness, 211–12
  doctors in, 192–95
  for epilepsy, 219
  for foot pain, 214
  for fractures, 215
  for gallstones, 219
  getting government aid for, 204–6
  for glaucoma, 221–22
  for gum disease, 223–25
  for hearing loss, 222–23
  for heartburn, 211
  for incontinence, 277–79
  Internet resources for, 304–5
  for irregularity and constipation, 279
  for kidney stones, 220
  for knee pain, 214
  for leg cramps, 214
  for Lyme disease, 213
  for macular degeneration, 220
  medical directives in, 198, 199, 200
  for migraines, 218
  for osteoporosis, 214–15
  pain management in, 217–18
  saving money on, 87, 93–94
  secrets of recuperation, 200–1
  for shingles, 213
  for sinus congestion, 210
  for stomach problems, 218–19

  for terminal illness, 201–3
  for tinnitus, 223
  traveling and, 312
  for trembling hands, 212–13
  for vision problems, 220–23
  for West Nile virus, 214
  for women, 271–74
Health care agent, picking, 198, 199
Health insurance, choosing best, 61–63
Health maintenance organizations, 61–62
Hearing, 222–23
Heart, diet in protecting, 155–57
Heart attacks
  chest pain in, 241
  defibrillators and, 240
  gender differences in symptoms, 241–42
  healing from spouse's, 115–16
  home management of, 188
  pacemaker surgery for women and, 276–77
  syndrome X and, 238–39
  test for predicting second, 257–58
  timing of, 241
Heartburn, managing, 211
Heart disease
  aspirin and, 164
  baldness and, 271
  detecting, 257
  high-tech weapons for, 240–41
Heating, saving money on, 82, 87
Hemorrhoids, surgery for, 254
Hepatis, 237–38
Herbs
  for allergies, 209–10
  benefits from, 166–67
  for sinus congestion, 210
Hernia, surgery for, 255
Hip fractures, tranquilizers for, 215
Home, working at, 333–35
Home appraisals, 77
Home-equity loan, 77
Home insurance
  mistakes when filing claims, 70
  saving money on, 82–83
Home management of medical emergencies, 187–89
Homeopathy, 191–92
Hormone-replacement therapy (HRT)
  estrogen in, 276
  mammograms and, 274
  osteoporosis and, 215
Hospitals. *See also* Surgery
  anesthesia at, 253
  better recuperation at, 251–52
  blood transfusions at, 253–54
  fighting premature discharge, 252
  getting fast emergency care in, 250–51
  getting VIP treatment in, 249–50
  intravenous fluids at, 251
  medication errors at, 251
  mistakes on bills, 252
  single-use medical devices at, 251
  tape use at, 251
Hotel, cutting costs in, 322–23
Hot flashes, treating, 276
House
  bug zappers for, 136
  dangerous chemicals in, 135–36
  environmentally safe, 134
  fix-ups in attracting buyer for, 132
  methods of cleaning, 136–38
  misrepresentation of problems in, 131
  selling, 131–33
  smoke detector for, 136

IMPORTANT

HERE IS YOUR REGISTRATION CODE TO ACCESS MCGRAW-HILL
PREMIUM CONTENT AND MCGRAW-HILL ONLINE RESOURCES

For key premium online resources you need THIS CODE to
gain access. Once the code is entered, you will be able to
use the web resources for the length of your course.

Access is provided only if you have purchased a new book.

If the registration code is missing from this book, the registration screen on our
website, and within your WebCT or Blackboard course will tell you how to obtain
your new code. Your registration code can be used only once to establish access.
It is not transferable

To gain access to these online resources

1. **USE** your web browser to go to: **www.mhhe.com/bearden07**

2. **CLICK** on "First Time User"

3. **ENTER** the Registration Code printed on the tear-off bookmark on the right

4. After you have entered your registration code, click on "Register"

5. **FOLLOW** the instructions to setup your personal UserID and Password

6. **WRITE** your UserID and Password down for future reference. Keep it in a safe place.

If your course is using WebCT or Blackboard, you'll be able to use this code to
access the McGraw-Hill content within your instructor's online course.

To gain access to the McGraw-Hill content in your instructor's WebCT or
Blackboard course simply log into the course with the user ID and Password provided by your instructor. Enter the registration code exactly as it appears to the
right when prompted by the system. You will only need to use this code the first
time you click on McGraw-Hill content.

These instructions are specifically for student access. Instructors are not required
to register via the above instructions.

The McGraw-Hill Companies

McGraw-Hill
Irwin

Thank you, and welcome to your
McGraw-Hill/Irwin Online Resources.

Bearden, Ingram, LaForge
Marketing: Principles and Perspectives, 5/e
ISBN-10: 0-07-322284-4
ISBN-13: 978-0-07-322284-4

SO-BCK-918

QF6J–CPBM–NXF9–RDFM–HM

REGISTRATION CODE
REGISTRATION CODE

McGraw-Hill
Irwin

The McGraw-Hill Companies

Mc
Graw
Hill

MARKETING

Principles and Perspectives
Fifth Edition

William O. Bearden
University of South Carolina

Thomas N. Ingram
Colorado State University

Raymond W. LaForge
University of Louisville

Boston   Burr Ridge, IL   Dubuque, IA   Madison, WI   New York   San Francisco   St. Louis
Bangkok   Bogotá   Caracas   Kuala Lumpur   Lisbon   London   Madrid   Mexico City
Milan   Montreal   New Delhi   Santiago   Seoul   Singapore   Sydney   Taipei   Toronto

ISBN-13: 978-0-07-310120-0
ISBN-10: 0-07-310120-6

Editorial director: *John E. Biernat*
Publisher: *Andy Winston*
Sponsoring editor: *Barrett Koger*
Developmental editor I: *Anna M. Chan*
Executive marketing manager: *Dan Silverburg*
Producer, Media technology: *Damian Moshak*
Project manager: *Bruce Gin*
Lead production supervisor: *Michael R. McCormick*
Lead designer: *Matthew Baldwin*
Senior photo research coordinator: *Jeremy Cheshareck*
Photo researcher: *Mike Hruby*
Lead media project manager: *Brian Nacik*
Cover design: *Joanne Schopler*
Interior design: *Matthew Baldwin*
Typeface: *10.5/12 Sabon*
Compositor: *Carlisle Communications, Ltd.*
Printer: *Quebecor World Dubuque, Inc.*

Library of Congress Cataloging-in-Publication Data
Bearden, William O., 1945–
    Marketing : principles and perspectives/William O. Bearden, Thomas N. Ingram,
Raymond W. LaForge.—5th ed.
        p. cm.
    Includes indexes.
    ISBN-13: 978-07-310120-0 (alk. paper)
    ISBN-10: 0-07-310120-6 (alk. paper)
    1. Marketing—United States. I. Ingram, Thomas N. II. LaForge, Raymond W. III. Title.
HF5415.1.B4155 2007
    658.8—dc22   2005053358

To Patti, Anna, Wallace, and their families, and in honor of my parents.

Bill Bearden

To Jacque and Rocky.

Tom Ingram

To Susan, Alexandra, and Kelly, and in memory of my mom and dad.

Buddy LaForge

Meet the Authors

William O. Bearden

(Ph.D., University of South Carolina)
University of South Carolina

Bill Bearden is the Bank of America Professor of Business Administration at the University of South Carolina. He has focused his teaching and research interests in consumer behavior and marketing research. In addition, Bill teaches principles of marketing and marketing management. His teaching awards include Outstanding MBA Teacher, the College of Business Administration Alfred G. Smith Excellence in Teaching Award, and the University of South Carolina AMOCO Award for Excellence in Undergraduate Teaching.

He is currently a member of the editorial review boards for the *Journal of Consumer Research,* the *Journal of Consumer Psychology,* the *Journal of Marketing,* the *Journal of Retailing,* and *Marketing Education Review.* His professional experience includes past president of the Southern Marketing Association and the Education Division of the American Marketing Association, and member of the American Marketing Association Board of Directors. Previously he served as codirector of the USC Lilly Endowment Teaching Fellows Program and as an associate editor for the *Journal of Consumer Research,* and currently he coordinates the Ph.D. Program in Marketing at USC.

Bill lives in Columbia, South Carolina, with his wife Patti, while his two daughters, Anna and Wallace, live in Washington, D.C., and Charlotte, NC, respectively. Bill and Patti have two grandchildren, Maggie and Tommy.

Thomas N. Ingram

(Ph.D., Georgia State) Colorado State University

Tom Ingram is FirstBank Professor of Business Administration and Chair of the Marketing Department at Colorado State University, where he teaches principles of marketing, marketing management, and sales management courses. Before commencing his academic career, Tom worked in sales, product management, and sales management with ExxonMobil.

Tom has received numerous teaching and research awards, including being named the Marketing Educator of the Year by Sales and Marketing Executives International (SMEI). He is a recipient of the Mu Kappa Tau National Marketing Honor Society Recognition Award for Outstanding Scholarly Contributions to the Sales Discipline. Tom has served as the editor of *Journal of Personal Selling and Sales Management,* chairman of the SMEI Accreditation Institute, a member of the SMEI board of directors, and editor of the *Journal of Marketing Theory and Practice.*

Tom has published extensively in professional journals, including the *Journal of Marketing,* the *Journal of Marketing Research,* the *Journal of the Academy of Marketing Science,* and the *Journal of Personal Selling and Sales Management.* He is coauthor of *Sales Management: Analysis and Decision Making,* 6th ed., and *Professional Selling: A Trust-Based Approach,* 3rd ed. He and his wife Jacque enjoy skiing, golf, and exploring the mountains of Colorado.

Raymond W. (Buddy) LaForge

(DBA, University of Tennessee) University of Louisville

Buddy LaForge is the Brown-Forman Professor of Marketing at the University of Louisville. He founded the *Marketing Education Review,* served as editor for eight years, and is currently executive editor. Buddy has coauthored *Strategic Sales Leadership, Sales Management: Analysis and Decision Making, Professional Selling: A Trust-Based Approach,* and *The Professional Selling Skills Workbook,* and has co-edited *Emerging Trends in Sales Thought and Practice.* His research is published in many journals including the *Journal of Marketing,* the *Journal of Marketing Research,* the *Journal of the Academy of Marketing Science,* and the *Journal of Personal Selling and Sales Management.* Buddy has served on the Direct Selling Education Foundation board of directors and executive committee, Du Pont Corporate Marketing Faculty Advisory Team for the Sales Enhancement Process, and the Family Business Center Advisory Board; as Vice President of Conferences and Research for the American Marketing Association Academic Council; and as Vice President/Marketing for the Academy of Business Education. He is developing The Sales Program at the University of Louisville.

Buddy and his wife, Susan, and daughters, Alexandra and Kelly, enjoy golf and thoroughbred racing in Louisville, Kentucky.

Preface

The marketing world is changing rapidly. Global economic conditions, political situations, and competitive landscapes are in constant flux. Marketing approaches that worked yesterday may not work tomorrow. Increasingly, marketing success requires doing things differently. Students will face a marketing environment different from the one discussed in our classes today. Learning what was done in the past will not prepare them entirely for what they need to do tomorrow. Consequently, in the fifth edition of *Marketing: Principles and Perspectives,* we have presented the topics that remain relevant and important, while simultaneously emphasizing new thinking and approaches to marketing practice. Because students need to be prepared to operate in the complex and dynamic marketing world of the future, they need to develop the capacity to think and act like marketers in a difficult and uncertain environment. This requires the ability to assess complex and changing marketing situations, to determine the best marketing strategies for these situations, and to execute the strategies effectively.

Every idea presented in the text and expanded on in the accompanying teaching resources is intended to help students develop the understanding and skills to become successful marketers. The text is designed to facilitate student learning from individual reading and study. The teaching resources provide useful tools for instructors to go beyond what is covered in the text. Together, the text and teaching resources represent an integrated package for preparing students for marketing in the future.

We have received many positive comments about the text from students over the years. Students find the text easy to read and understand. The many examples and comments from practicing marketers engage the students and help them see the relevance of what is being discussed. These favorable comments are appreciated greatly because the text is written for the students. We are delighted that it is effective and is having an important impact in marketing education.

Key Features and Changes

In preparing the fifth edition of *Marketing: Principles and Perspectives,* we have kept what works well but have added new coverage and updated the text throughout. The basic table of contents and chapter format have been very successful and are maintained. Here are some of the key changes integrated into this edition:

- The new American Marketing Association definition of marketing is presented in Chapter 1, compared to the previous definition, and referred to throughout the text. "Creating Customer Value" boxed inserts and the relationship perspective are integrated in the text to support the new marketing definition.

- The new American Marketing Association Code of Ethics is also presented in Chapter 1, and "Acting Ethically" boxed inserts are dispersed throughout the text to emphasize the importance of ethical and socially responsible behavior by marketers.

- A marketing philosophy, the marketing concept, a market orientation, customer relationship management (CRM), and customer equity are presented and discussed in an integrated framework.

- The global marketing environment discussion has been updated completely with the latest trends and statistics.

- More discussion and examples of multicultural marketing are presented.

- Discussion of shifts in consumption patterns and the implications of consumer preferences for segmentation strategy have been added.

- More emphasis is given to marketing research approaches, such as field experiments and studies, online research, observational research, and cross-cultural research.

- The new dominant logic of marketing with an emphasis on a services orientation and cocreation of value with customers is discussed.

- A revised framework for building brands is presented with more discussion and examples of each stage in the process.
- The critical role of salespeople in creating customer value and building relationships is highlighted.
- New discussion of emerging forms of marketing communications, including blogs, interactive cell phone communications, online video ads, and consumer contests, is added.
- New coverage of the National Do Not Call List and its impact on the Telemarketing Sales Rule is presented.
- New sections on price bundling effects and the need for two-tiered prices and brands in emerging markets like China and India are added.
- New coverage of the 2003 CAN-SPAM Act is presented.
- New sections are added on the use of social responsibility as a marketing strategy, persuasion principles and consumer behavior, data mining and the importance of analyzing individual-level data, new product pricing, varying price elasticities, and the product life cycle.
- New "Acting Ethically" boxes are Tom's of Maine, the Federal Trade Commission, CompUSA and its suppliers, Blockbuster, data privacy issues, reducing package content versus increasing prices, and social responsibility at Aveda.
- New "Creating Customer Value" boxes highlight Dell Computer, SAP, Wegman's VF Corporation, Big Idea, Applebee's, Tyson Foods, FedEx, Buzzmetrics, ING Direct, Best Buy, and convenience stores.
- New "Using Technology" boxes feature TexYard, IBM, Springboard Retail Networks, RFID (radio frequency identification), Web-based television, small business use of eBay, Ralph Lauren, Nike, M&M, Kidrobot, InnerSell.com, Jigsaw Data, and www.shopzilla.com.
- New "Being Entrepreneurial" boxes are Hawthorne Direct, W.L. Gore & Associates, and Hindustan Unilever.
- New chapter openers include IMS Health, Acxiom, Wal-Mart, Office Depot, Timbuk2, Best Buy, FedEx, McDonald's, and Skechers USA.
- New "Speaking from Experience" executives are a communications manager from Michelin, a CEO from a marketing research firm, a merchandising manager from Hanes, an executive from IBM, and a director of strategic initiatives from an identity theft protection company.
- New end-of-chapter cases include Red Bull, Adidas, Hummer, Saturn, Google, PaperPro, and Kraft.

An Emphasis on Student Learning

We see important trends emerging in marketing education. For one thing, teaching is receiving more emphasis at most colleges and universities—but not teaching as traditionally viewed and practiced. It really does not matter what we teach, if students do not learn. And student learning is viewed differently, too. Learning is not just the recall of facts by passive students, but the understanding of concepts and the ability to apply them appropriately. Such learning requires the active participation of students.

The complete package for *Marketing: Principles and Perspectives,* fifth edition, is oriented toward student learning, and the text and the teaching resource materials are designed to complement each other toward that end. In keeping with our philosophy that students should be able to understand the text largely from their own reading and study, we write in a lively, interesting, informal manner to capture their attention and interest. Major concepts are presented clearly and simply in a way that students can understand. Encouraged by our reviewing panels, we did not include everything we know about every topic, but only what we believe students at this level need to know. We streamlined the discussion of concepts and then reinforced them with interesting examples and exciting visuals, and incorporated a number of learning tools to facilitate the learning process. The pedagogical features emphasize our student-focused learning approach:

COMPANY CHAPTER OPENERS   Every chapter opens with discussion of a real company or organization. Companies represented include eBay, Pfizer, Disney, British Airways, and Dell Computer Corporation, to name a few. The book's home page will include links to the Web sites of these firms.

THINKING CRITICALLY   Critical thinking questions are included within each chapter to help emphasize the importance of effective decision making. Each question relates to one of the concepts within the chapter and is constructed to encourage the student to think critically about a complex issue. The decision-making scenarios presented here are drawn from both real and theoretical companies.

SPEAKING FROM EXPERIENCE   This edition also includes comments about marketing from business professionals. We highlight one such person in each chapter and include his or her comments on key issues discussed in that chapter. These "Speaking from Experience" remarks help bring to life the text material and add additional depth of explanation. The marketers included represent a range of large and small companies from a variety of industries. Example companies include Bank of America, ConsumerMetrics, The Pampered Chef, Brown-Forman, Hewlett-Packard, and Du Pont. Interestingly, the positions represented by these marketers include both senior individuals and young professionals in the early years of their careers. Consequently, students should be better able to identify and understand the varied opportunities available in marketing and how important marketing can be to professionals in other functional areas of business.

USING THE WWW IN MARKETING   Internet exercises are found at the end of each chapter. These questions require the student to consider how the Internet can be used to address marketing concepts or decisions. In addition, you can visit our home page, where additional marketing examples and up-to-the-minute information will be posted.

Other Student Features   All chapters in the fifth edition have been formatted so that each pedagogical feature contributes to student learning by supporting the text material, including the principles and concepts covered in the chapter.

STUDENT LEARNING OBJECTIVES   Every chapter begins with several learning guides to help students focus attention on major concepts in reading and studying the chapter. At the end of each chapter, the summary is organized around these introductory learning objectives.

BOXED INSERTS   Each chapter contains boxed inserts designed to provide current examples of four important topics: Creating Customer Value, Being Entrepreneurial, Using Technology, and Acting Ethically.

EXHIBITS AND PHOTOS   The visual aspects of each chapter are designed to increase student learning. The exhibits, photos, and ads visually enhance and expand on the chapter discussion.

UNDERSTANDING MARKETING TERMS AND CONCEPTS   The most important terms and concepts are in boldface and defined when first introduced. Each boldface term is listed at the end of each chapter with the page number where it is defined. A glossary of terms and definitions is also included at the back of the text.

THINKING ABOUT MARKETING   Many review and discussion questions also are included at the end of each chapter. These questions reinforce the decision-making aspects of the text by including both critical thinking questions and recall of the most important material covered in the chapter.

APPLYING MARKETING SKILLS   Every chapter includes three application exercises that can be used as either homework assignments or in-class discussion topics. The exercises provide varied and interesting ways for students to apply what they have read or are covering in class.

MAKING MARKETING DECISIONS   All chapters conclude with two cases representing well-known companies and current situations. At least one of each pair is global in orientation. Questions are included to encourage students to make decisions regarding the current activities of each company. A mix of both consumer and business-to-business cases, cases involving both multinational firms and small businesses, and cases reflecting both service and retail situations reflects the current diversity of the business world.

Organization

Marketing Principles and Perspectives, 5th Edition, is divided into seven parts. *Part One, Marketing in a Dynamic Environment,* defines and examines the scope of marketing. The first chapter, *An Overview of Contemporary Marketing,* presents an overview of marketing and the different philosophies that have guided marketing. An explanation of the marketing concept and the importance of satisfying customer needs, developing long-term profitable relationships with customers, and building customer equity are also discussed. Chapter 1 also describes the seven key marketing perspectives—global, relationship, ethics, productivity, customer value, technology, and entrepreneurship—that are integrated within the text and the many reasons why their consideration is needed for effective marketing practice. *Chapter 2, The Global Marketing Environment,* emphasizes the global marketplace and the external environments (social, economic, political, and competitive) that influence marketer decision making. *Chapter 3, Marketing's Strategic Role in the Organization,* describes the role of marketing at different levels within the organization and the importance of effective marketing strategy.

Part Two, Buying Behavior, contains two chapters that describe, first, the concepts and influences in consumer buying behavior and decision making, and second, business-to-business markets and organizational buying behavior. *Part Three, Marketing Research and Market Segmentation,* contains two chapters as well. In *Chapter 6, Marketing Research and Decision Support Systems,* an overview of the marketing research process and information systems is presented. *Chapter 7, Market Segmentation and Targeting,* includes the concepts of segmentation, targeting, positioning, and product differentiation.

The remaining four parts cover the marketing mix elements—product, price, distribution, and promotion or integrated marketing communications. In *Part Four, Product and Service Concepts and Strategies,* three chapters present basic product and service concepts (Chapter 8), new product development (Chapter 9), and product and service strategies (Chapter 10). Marketing services are emphasized throughout this section of the book.

The next part of the text, *Part Five, Pricing Concepts and Strategies,* covers fundamental pricing concepts and customer evaluations of prices (Chapter 11) and price determination and the managerial strategies used to guide pricing decisions (Chapter 12).

The distribution aspects of the marketing mix are covered in *Part Six, Marketing Channels and Logistics.* In *Chapter 13, Marketing Channels,* the different types of direct and indirect channels are discussed. Retailing is covered in a separate chapter (Chapter 14), which includes the many new advances in retailing technology and methods. The place or distribution component of the text concludes with a chapter on wholesaling and logistics management (Chapter 15).

Part Seven, Integrated Marketing Communications, contains five chapters. First, an overview of promotion and integrated communications is presented in Chapter 16. This chapter describes the communications process and marketing communications planning. The major components of the promotions mix are then discussed in the remaining four chapters. Up-to-date coverage of advertising and public relations is offered in Chapter 17. The objectives and methods of both consumer and trade sales promotions are described in Chapter 18. Personal selling and sales management, with particular emphasis given to relationship selling, are the focus of Chapter 19. A separate chapter on direct marketing is included in Part Seven; specifically, the newest direct marketing techniques are covered in Chapter 20, as well as the interactive aspects of marketing communications.

Appendix A presents an expanded marketing plan and a discussion of how to develop one. *Appendix B* describes many of the frequently used mathematical and financial tools used to make marketing decisions. A detailed glossary of terms and three indexes conclude the text. These indexes enumerate authors cited, companies and brands used as examples, and the subjects covered within the text.

Teaching Resources

INSTRUCTOR'S MANUAL   The instructor's manual comprises chapter outlines, lecture notes with supplemental lecture materials, answers to end-of-chapter questions, and ideas for individual and group student learning activities.

TEST BANK AND COMPUTEST   The test bank comprises more than 3,000 questions, including multiple choice, short answer, fill-in-the-blank, and critical thinking essay questions.

VIDEO LIBRARY   The current, dynamic video library includes video segments, one for each chapter plus the prologue. The video segments, which run between 6 and 15 minutes, demonstrate the marketing concepts from the text and are tied to specific chapter concepts.

INSTRUCTOR CD-ROM   The exciting presentation CD-ROM allows the professor to customize a multimedia lecture with original material and material from our supplements package. It includes video clips, all of the electronic slides, art from the text, the computerized test bank, and the print supplements.

ELECTRONIC SLIDES   PowerPoint slides are rapidly becoming a staple in the presentation tools that instructors use. Three hundred slides, approximately 15 per chapter, are available to adopters of the text.

HOME PAGE   The book's home page can be found at *www.mhhe.com/bearden07*. It contains Web Exploration Links (links to other Web sites) and Keeping Current (abstracts of issues in the news, referenced to a chapter in the book and accompanied by a list of discussion questions). For instructors, it will also offer updates of the examples and cases in the text, additional sources of marketing information, and downloads of key supplements.

Student Resources

The book's home page can be found at *www.mhhe.com/bearden07*. It contains self-quizzes for every chapter, interactive study tools such as flash cards to reinforce key concepts, and a link to PowerWeb for updates on what is going on in the world of marketing.

Acknowledgments

Writing a text requires a team effort, and we have enjoyed a collaboration with the best teammates imaginable. Cooperative, knowledgeable, creative, candid, and always encouraging—these are but a few of the positive things we found in our teammates. We are especially appreciative of the countless number of people involved in this project who time after time put forth the extra effort necessary to accomplish our mutual goals.

- The professionals at McGraw-Hill/Irwin led the way on what we feel is a terrific revision. Thanks to many, many people at McGraw-Hill/Irwin, including Barrett Koger (sponsoring editor), Dan Silverburg (marketing), Bruce Gin (production), Matt Baldwin (design), Jeremy Cheshareck and Mike Hruby (photo research), Teri Hampton (permissions), and Anna Chan (development editor).

- We would also like to thank several people who have been with us since the early days of this project. Eleanore Snow was our developmental editor on the first edition, and her early direction still serves as an inspiration to us. Rob Zwettler signed us to our first book contract years ago, and we truly appreciate his continuing support. Nina McGuffin and Lynn Mooney worked with us on previous editions—and sweated the deadlines as much as we did. Steve Patterson and Greg Patterson were instrumental in our decision to work with McGraw-Hill/Irwin on this book.

- We would also like to thank several individuals who have contributed significantly to the supplementary materials accompanying the text. Craig Hollingshead and Barbara R. Oates, both of Texas A&M, Kingsville, put together the comprehensive *Instructor's Manual*. An extensive set of objective test questions was developed by Tom and Betty Pritchett of Kennesaw State University. The PowerPoint slides were developed by John Girard of Minot State University. Appreciation is also expressed to USC doctoral students Kelly Haws and Courtney Droms for their help with examples and literature research.

- Our book has been improved by a long list of reviewers—both national and international—of three drafts of the manuscript. We were stimulated and encouraged by their comments and suggestions, and we incorporated many of their ideas into the text. Our thanks to our marketing colleagues listed here and to additional reviewers who prefer to remain anonymous. Because of length considerations we were not able to incorporate every good suggestion, but we considered all of them carefully and appreciate the reasoning behind them. We believe *Marketing: Principles and Perspectives* comes much closer to meeting your teaching needs and the learning needs of your students because of your efforts.

We would like to thank the following survey participants and reviewers of the fifth edition:

Arni Arnthorsson
University of St. Francis

Monty Bohrer
University of Sioux Falls

Harry Bronstein
Oakland Community College

David Faulds
University of Louisville

Karen Halpern
South Puget Sound Community College

Kathryn Carlson Heler
Manchester College

Dawn J. Johnson
Waldorf College

Patrick A. Mellon
New Mexico Junior College

Craig Brian Miller
Alverno College

Debi Mishra
Binghamton University

Susan D. Peters
California State Polytechnic University

Carol Vollmer Pope
Alverno College

Bob Reese
Illinois Valley Community College

Nick Sarantakes
Austin Community College

Bernard Schmit
Florida Metropolitan University

Patrick Simmons
Okefenokee Technical College

John A. Sondey
South Dakota State University

Frank Titlow
St. Petersburg College

Bill Bearden
Tom Ingram
Buddy LaForge

Guided Tour

The Cutting Edge of Marketing Education

The Fifth Edition of **Marketing: Principles and Perspectives** is your introduction to cutting-edge coverage of marketing. Among other advantages, the new edition gives students a penetrating look at key issues and decisions facing marketers in a dynamic business environment. Featured topics include integrated marketing communications, sales promotion, direct marketing, customer relationship management, and supply chain management.

Marketing introduces basic topics such as marketing strategy, segmentation, and consumer behavior in such a way that not only will you learn about the important perspectives needed for effective marketing, but you will also benefit from this edition's interactive exercises and supplements.

Introductory Prologue

Yum! Brands is a restaurant company that features five brands and over 33,000 restaurants in over 100 countries. In the text's Prologue you will be introduced to Yum! and learn how that company utilizes all seven perspectives of marketing to initiate successful marketing in the United States and abroad.

Prologue: Yum! Brands

Yum! Brands consists of Kentucky Fried Chicken (KFC), Taco Bell, Pizza Hut, Long John Silver's, and A&W All-American Food.

How many times in the last month have you eaten the following?

· Chicken at Kentucky Fried Chicken (KFC).
· Mexican food at Taco Bell.
· Pizza at Pizza Hut.
· Seafood at Long John Silver's.
· Hamburgers, hotdogs, or root beer floats at A&W All-American Food.

Yum! Brands hopes you eat at these restaurants often because it owns all of them! KFC, Taco Bell, and Pizza Hut were part of PepsiCo., Inc. In 1997 PepsiCo., Inc., decided to spin off its restaurants so it could focus more attention on its core beverage business. The new restaurant company was named Tricon Global Restaurants, Inc., to reflect the three restaurant icons or brands. Then in May 2002 Tricon purchased Long John Silver's and A&W All-American Food from Yorkshire Global Restaurants. Because the company now consisted of five brands, its name was changed to Yum! Brands (www.yum.com).

According to Chairman and Chief Executive David Novak, the passion and mission of Yum! Brands "is to put a yum on our customers' faces all around the world." Many things are done to reinforce the "yum" focus. For example, company meetings often start with a YUM cheer, such as "Give me a Y, give me a U, give me an M." Stock options are called YUMBUCKS, and the company newsletter is the *Yum! Buzz.*[1] Yum! Brands is the world's largest restaurant company with over 33,000 restaurants in more than 100 countries and territories generating sales in excess of 9 billion and employing around 840,000 associates worldwide.[2]

Chairman and CEO David Novak is a "Yum!" Cheer leader.

Why has Yum! been so successful? There are many reasons. One is certainly the leadership provided by Chairman and Chief Executive David Novak. Effective marketing is another. We have studied leading marketing companies, such as Yum! Brands, and identified seven key perspectives that help these companies better identify and respond to market opportunities. Our objective is to discuss each perspective and to illustrate the importance of each to the success of Yum! Brands.

xxix

Chapter Openers

Each chapter begins with *chapter objectives* that identify the major points covered in the chapter and provide a helpful guide for students in their comprehension. Each chapter opener continues with a *vignette* demonstrating effective use of marketing by a company that is dealing with an interesting issue that is relevant to the chapter. Featured companies include eBay, Dell, Wal-Mart, TimBuk2, and Frito-Lay.

Chapter One

AN OVERVIEW OF CONTEMPORARY MARKETING

After studying this chapter, you should be able to

1 Discuss what marketing is and why it is important to organizations and individuals.

2 Distinguish between marketing as an organizational philosophy and a societal process.

3 Understand the components of a marketing strategy and the different activities involved in marketing products and services.

4 Be aware of the various types of marketing institutions and the different marketing positions available in these institutions.

5 Understand the basic elements and relationships in the contemporary marketing framework.

Amazon

Amazon.com represents an interesting entrepreneurial story. Jeff Bezos started Amazon.com as a book retailer in 1995. The company's mission was to use the Internet to transform book buying into the fastest, easiest, and most enjoyable shopping experience available. Because Amazon.com did not have an inventory of books in a retail location, it could offer customers an enormous selection of books over its Web site. Customers could also shop and place orders 24 hours a day and seven days a week. The shopping experience was easy and fun, and various services were added to create value. This was the beginning, and growth has been phenomenal.

Sales have increased from about $150 million in 1997 to over $7 billion today. The company generated its first operating profit of $5.8 million in the fourth quarter of 2001. Profits last year were $588 million. Amazon.com is doing several things to keep sales growing and to be consistently profitable.

First, the company offers many different products and services on *www.amazon.com*. These include music CDs, videos, electronics, kitchen and houseware products, an auction service, a wedding gift registry, and many others.

Second, international sales have been increasing through international sites for the United Kingdom, Germany, Japan, France, Canada, and China.

Third, more than 925,000 merchants sell through Amazon.com. These merchants range from large retailers, such as Nordstrom and Target, to smaller retailers like Something Silver and eBags. The company generates about 25 percent of unit sales and around 5 percent of sales revenue from these independent merchants.

Fourth, Amazon.com is continuously looking for new opportunities that leverage its strengths. For example, it recently purchased BookSurge and is expected to move into exclusive publishing in the future. There is also speculation that Amazon.com might try to capitalize on the growth in Internet advertising.

One of the major reasons for the success of Amazon.com is its growing number of satisfied and loyal customers. Amazon.com continues to add new customers and expand relationships with existing customers by offering a wide selection of products and by giving customers a personalized, satisfying shopping experience.

Chapter Pedagogy

Thematic Boxes

These boxed inserts are featured throughout the chapters, focusing on key areas important to marketers today. The fifth edition introduces a new box highlighting the increasing importance of ethical behavior by companies. The topic areas now covered are *Creating Customer Value, Being Entrepreneurial, Using Technology,* and *Acting Ethically.*

CREATING CUSTOMER VALUE

FedEx: Customer relationships delivering success

As the market for delivery services flattens, FedEx strives to improve its position by enhancing customer value. As part of its efforts, FedEx has embraced customer relationship management. Billing, claims, and product tracing areas now share information in an integrated approach. Customer satisfaction and the productivity of FedEx's 4,000 plus agents have im- customer. The merger with Kinko's chain also enables customers to print directly from Windows desktops to copy centers. In addition, the company is rolling out an online loyalty program that encourages closer relationships with small and medium-sized customers. FedEx also is developing strengths internationally with revenues growing dramatically in China. In

---

BEING ENTREPRENEURIAL

Abercrombie & Fitch: "Tween" the segments

Abercrombie and Fitch realizes that Joe College does not want to hang out with Joey Junior High. As such, A&F has made efforts to remain focused on its primary segment while expanding its appeal to younger market segments. That is, A&F wants to remain cool with college-age and young adults and not become diluted in its A&F positioning from attracting younger patrons. In efforts to appeal to multiple segments, A&F has begun a rollout of a lower-priced chain, Hollister, catering to 14- to 18-year-olds. This line of stores may also compete effectively with the value-oriented American Eagle. A third chain—Aber- crombie with a little "a"—is aimed at 7- to 14-year-old customers and has 100-plus stores. These entrepreneurial efforts will require creative strategy in efforts to effectively manage and coordinate different but complementary product lines and market mix configurations.

More recently, A&F has considered ways to grow internationally. As part of that effort, a new brand, Ruehl, is being established. The concept is seen as pitching slightly older customers than A&F and is designed to compete with J. Crew and Banana Republic pricewise, but with more modern styles.

USING TECHNOLOGY

TexYard.com makes apparel industry exchange work

TexYard.com is an online exchange in the European apparel industry, using computer technology and the Internet to bring buyers and sellers together in a neutral buying environment. This B2B exchange enables buyers to find suppliers more easily, complete transactions more efficiently, lower their administrative costs, obtain competitive pricing, and shorten their time-to-market cycle. TexYard uses auctions that allow buyers to define their needs in detail, from manufacturing specifications to delivery and quality requirements. A key to TexYard's success is that its exchange system greatly reduces the time spent in communicating requests, comparing price quotes from suppliers, and negotiating final prices.

ACTING ETHICALLY

Segmentation and data privacy

Data mining and data-based market segmentation practices are employed by many companies. Even pursuit of the principles associated with customer relationship management requires the extensive analysis and use of information collected at the individual customer level. In many instances, the information obtained is for individual consumers. Although these practices benefit firms in their ability to provide more effective product offerings, issues related to privacy are being raised by lawmakers who seek greater data protection. Identity theft and improper use of private information are increasing pressures to control how personal information is made available and used. The safety of personal financial data is a top priority following recent incidents in which data brokers misused or lost personal records.

In addition to many four-color ads and exhibits featured throughout the text, each chapter contains *Speaking from Experience* boxes featuring real business professionals discussing how real marketing is practiced. Further comments from these practitioners are woven through the chapter to add depth of explanation. The *Thinking Critically* feature in each chapter relates a critical concept to a decision-making scenario. These questions emphasize the importance of effective decision making on complex marketing issues.

Speaking from Experience

"Satisfying the needs of customers is the key to our success. The philosophy of direct selling is based on one-on-one interaction with customers. Through this direct interaction, customers provide feedback directly to the company regarding product quality, design, and service. At the Pampered Chef we believe that our products should earn the right to be in your kitchen. We say 'This is a good product, now how can we make it better?' We've made our mark by listening to our customers, improving our products, and offering them at competitive prices."

Doris K. Christopher
Founder
The Pampered Chef

Doris started The Pampered Chef as a direct seller of high-quality kitchen tools in her suburban-Chicago basement in 1980. She grew the company to over $700 million in annual sales and sold it to Berkshire Hathaway. Doris has served as the chairperson of the Direct Selling Association, was named a regional winner of Ernst & Young's National Entrepreneur of the Year Award, and wrote Come to the Table: A Celebration of Family Life. She earned a B.S. in Home Economics from the University of Illinois at Urbana-Champaign.

Thinking Critically

You have decided to open a pizza restaurant that would provide customers with the highest-quality pizzas.

- What are the characteristics of a quality pizza as defined by most customers?

- How do you evaluate the quality of the pizzas offered by the existing pizza restaurants (Pizza Hut, Godfather's, Papa John's, etc.)?

- What do you plan to do to make your pizzas higher quality than what competitors offer?

- Nissan experienced losses in the late 1990s. The company decided to turn things around by introducing many new models. This strategy was successful as the company generated thousands of new customers for the 13 new vehicles it introduced since 1999. The company also returned to profitability. However, it fell from sixth to eleventh on the Initial Quality Survey with more customer complaints than the industry average. The company is trying to improve its product quality to keep its new customers and to reduce warranty costs.[7]

- When the Korean carmaker Hyundai entered the U.S. market, its cars were of low quality. The company decided to try to improve quality to "Toyota levels." Among other things, it increased the quality team from 100 to 865 workers and held twice-monthly quality meetings. This approach is apparently paying off. Five years later, Hyundai came within one complaint of Toyota in the Initial Quality Survey. It still lags behind many brands in the Vehicle Dependability Study, but it is working to improve this score. With a 10-year drive train warranty and 5 years on everything else, and improving quality, Hyundai has seen sales and profits increase significantly.[8]

- Mercedes's situation was almost the opposite of Hyundai's. Mercedes was a quality leader for many years. However, when Toyota and Nissan introduced lower-cost luxury cars, Mercedes changed its engineering approach to respond quickly to this competition. Unfortunately, the new cars generated many consumer complaints, and Mercedes dropped to number 26 in the 2003 Vehicle Dependability Study. Before it lost customers, the company moved quickly to solve the quality problems and moved back to a top five position in 2005. The newest models are receiving rave reviews from consumers and high scores from J.D. Power.[9]

End-of-Chapter Resources

Each chapter concludes with a summary of the important concepts that also serves as a quick review. To further enforce the chapter's topics, *Thinking about Marketing, Applying Marketing Skills,* and *Using the www in Marketing* exercises put students in the mindset of the marketer by applying learned concepts to real business situations. *Making Marketing Decisions* cases feature well-known companies in current marketing situations. Featured companies range from multinational firms to small businesses in both service and retail sectors.

NEW Comprehensive Marketing Plan

A real marketing plan for Willamette Furniture is featured in Appendix A. Willamette Furniture is a manufacturer of high-quality office furniture, focusing on a niche target market. Willamette Furniture provides a good example of the use of research and market segmentation (Chapters 6 and 7), and development of an Internet catalog as a channel (Chapter 13) contributes to its overall marketing strategy.

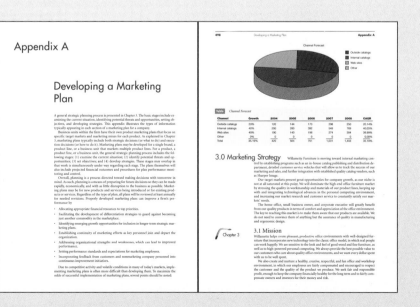

Online Learning Center

www.mhhe.com/
bearden07

For Instructors

The resources available online for instructors include downloadable versions of the Instructor's Manual, PowerPoint presentations, video clips, instructor newsletter, and message board.

For Students

Students will find a wealth of helpful study tools to reinforce what they learn from the text. These tools include self-assessment quizzes, video clips, and marketing. New to the site is an Interactive Marketing Plan template that will walk students through the development of their own marketing plan. Online resources are listed with each section to further guide students through creating their plan.

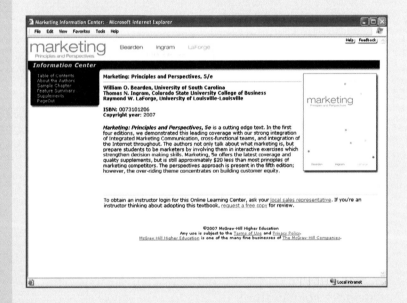

Contents in Brief

Contents

Part Three
Marketing Research and Market Segmentation

Chapter Six

Part Seven
Integrated Marketing Communications

Appendix A
**Developing a Marketing
Plan**

Appendix B
**Applications of Mathematical
and Financial Tools to
Marketing Decisions**

Where to Find . . .

Chapter Openers

Speaking from Experience

Prologue: Yum! Brands

Yum! Brands consists of Kentucky Fried Chicken (KFC), Taco Bell, Pizza Hut, Long John Silver's, and A&W All-American Food.

How many times in the last month have you eaten the following?

- Chicken at Kentucky Fried Chicken (KFC).
- Mexican food at Taco Bell.
- Pizza at Pizza Hut.
- Seafood at Long John Silver's.
- Hamburgers, hotdogs, or root beer floats at A&W All-American Food.

Yum! Brands hopes you eat at these restaurants often because it owns all of them! KFC, Taco Bell, and Pizza Hut were part of PepsiCo., Inc. In 1997 PepsiCo, Inc., decided to spin off its restaurants so it could focus more attention on its core beverage business. The new restaurant company was named Tricon Global Restaurants, Inc., to reflect the three restaurant icons or brands. Then in May 2002 Tricon purchased Long John Silver's and A&W All-American Food from Yorkshire Global Restaurants. Because the company now consisted of five brands, its name was changed to Yum! Brands (*www.yum.com*).

According to Chairman and Chief Executive David Novak, the passion and mission of Yum! Brands "is to put a yum on our customers' faces all around the world." Many things are done to reinforce the "yum" focus. For example, company meetings often start with a YUM cheer, such as "Give me a Y, give me a U, give me an M." Stock options are called YUMBUCKS, and the company newsletter is the *Yum! Buzz.*[1] Yum! Brands is the world's largest restaurant company with over 33,000 restaurants in more than 100 countries and territories generating sales in excess of $9 billion and employing around 840,000 associates worldwide.[2]

Why has Yum! been so successful? There are many reasons. One is certainly the leadership provided by Chairman and Chief Executive David Novak. Effective marketing is another. We have studied leading marketing companies, such as Yum! Brands, and identified seven key perspectives that help these companies better identify and respond to market opportunities. Our objective is to discuss each perspective and to illustrate the importance of each to the success of Yum! Brands.

Chairman and CEO David Novak is a "Yum!" cheerleader.

A Global Perspective

A **global perspective** means that marketers should consider the world as their potential marketplace. Customers, suppliers, competitors, partners, and employees can come from anywhere, no matter where a firm is located or where its product is marketed. Astute marketers take a global perspective in identifying growth opportunities and when developing and executing marketing strategies to capitalize on these opportunities.

Identifying Growth Opportunities

Many firms operate in mature domestic markets that provide only limited opportunities for future growth. These companies often cannot meet desired growth objectives unless attractive growth opportunities in international markets are identified.

Yum! Brands operates in the quick-serve restaurant (QSR) segment of the food service industry and competes against companies such as McDonald's, Subway, Burger King, Wendy's, Domino's Pizza, Dairy Queen, and many others. QSR growth in the United States is limited, and competition is fierce. Because of this, one major growth strategy is to expand internationally, especially in China. Yum! expects about 70 percent of its growth to be outside the United States. The company is opening over 1,000 international restaurants a year, about 350 of which are in China. Over 40 percent of Yum! restaurants are located in international markets.[3]

An example of the international growth opportunities is KFC and China. KFC sales growth in the United States has been flat. KFC sales and profits in China are booming. There are more than 1,200 KFC restaurants in China with over 100 outlets in both Beijing and Shanghai. KFC operated in only 20 Chinese cities in 2000. Now there are KFC restaurants in 280 Chinese cities and every province and region except Tibet. Yum! is also opening Pizza Hut and Taco Bell restaurants in China. Sales in China have increased from $261 million in 1998 to over $1 billion in 2004, and profits were up 20 percent last year to more than $200 million. With more than 500 million urban consumers, Yum! expects continued growth in China and other international markets.[4]

KFC has over 1,200 restaurants in China and has been rated the number one consumer brand in all of China.

Yum! Brands operates in over 100 countries around the world.

Successful Marketing Strategies

A global perspective is needed not only to identify potential market opportunities but also to help firms develop and implement marketing strategies to take advantage of these opportunities. Understanding the culture, language, customs, and other unique aspects of an international market is critical for marketing success.

Although Yum! looks for global opportunities, it develops marketing strategies to meet the needs of local markets. While its core products have universal appeal, the company also develops products with local appeal. KFC, for example, offers tempura crispy strips in Japan, gravy and potatoes in England, fresh rice with soy or sweet chili sauce in Thailand, potato-and-onion croquettes in Holland, and pastries in France. KFC has tailored many dishes to meet Chinese tastes. For example, it has introduced a twister sandwich that is similar to the way Peking duck is served, has replaced coleslaw with seasonal vegetables such as bamboo shoots and lotus roots, and offers a breakfast menu that is not available in the United States.[5] These examples illustrate how Yum! adapts its marketing strategies to reflect important differences in international markets.

A Relationship Perspective

The increasingly complex business environment drives companies and marketers to work together for mutual benefit. No longer can one individual or company have all of the knowledge, skills, or resources necessary for marketing success. Instead, networks of various relationships are necessary. A **relationship perspective** consists of building partnerships with organizations outside the company and encouraging teamwork among different functions within the firm to develop long-term customer relationships.

Customer Relationships

Marketing has traditionally been viewed as the sales-generating business function. Its importance is reflected in the adage "nothing happens until a sale is made." This sales orientation sometimes leads firms to focus too much on generating sales in the short run, with little consideration for customer retention or profitability over the long term. Fortunately, the short-term sales orientation is being replaced by more emphasis on developing, maintaining, and expanding long-term, profitable relationships with targeted customers.

100% CHAMPS with a YES! Attitude

C	Cleanliness
H	Hospitality
A	Accuracy
M	Maintenance (equipment and facilities)
P	Product quality
S	Speed with service

The 100% CHAMPS with a Yes! Attitude is the driving force behind the Customer Mania culture.

Yum! depends on effective partnerships with franchisees and joint venture partners.

Teamwork among employees at each restaurant is critical for Yum!'s success.

The Supplier Code of Conduct helps build organizational partnerships with suppliers.

The importance of customer relationships is evident at Yum! Brands. The company is driven by a passion for satisfying customers every time they eat at a Yum! restaurant and doing it better than any other competitor. This is accomplished by offering customers food they crave and a unique eating experience that will make them smile and inspire their loyalty for life.

Yum! conducted marketing research to determine what customers wanted in a restaurant experience. The results were translated into a Customer Mania culture driven by 100% CHAMPS with a Yes! Attitude. All Yum! restaurants around the world try to provide customers with a restaurant experience characterized by cleanliness, hospitality, accuracy, maintenance, product quality, and speed with service. The 100% CHAMPS with a Yes! Attitude program is the key to Yum!'s success in developing long-term, profitable relationships with customers.[6]

Organizational Partnerships

Few firms can themselves perform all of the necessary marketing activities productively and profitably; therefore, it is necessary to work with different organizations in various ways. Examples include relationships with marketing research firms to conduct marketing studies, advertising agencies to develop and execute integrated marketing communications programs, and wholesalers and retailers to distribute a firm's products. A company's success in establishing long-term customer relationships typically requires close working relationships with many different organizations.

Yum!'s most direct and enduring partnerships are with franchisees and joint venture partners. Over 22,000 of Yum!'s restaurants are owned and operated by franchise and license partners. This approach reduces Yum!'s capital requirements for restaurant expansion, but requires effective working partnerships to be successful. Yum! helps these partners in various ways and generates revenues from these arrangements. These and other organizational partnerships are critical for Yum! to achieve its growth objectives.

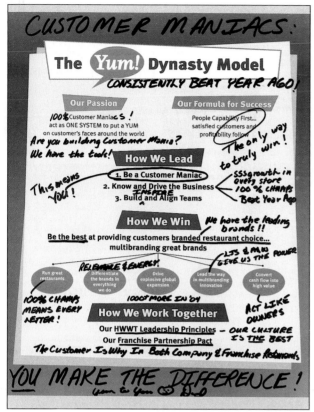

The "How We Work Together Principles" promote teamwork at Yum! Brands.

Teamwork Relationships

The days when marketers operated in isolation from other business functions are over. Success in the contemporary business environment requires that all company members work as a team toward achieving common objectives. No single individual or function performs effectively as an independent entity. Cooperation and teamwork are critical to succeed in an increasingly complex and rapidly changing global business environment.

Yum! Brands is a people-oriented company and does many things to encourage employees to work together. Chairman and Chief Executive David Novak believes that it is important to focus on making employees happy and energizing them to work together as "customer maniacs" who make customers happy. This teamwork orientation is expressed formally in the "How We Work Together (HWWT) Principles." These HWWT principles express the key Yum! values in terms of how employees are expected to be treated by the company and each other, and how they need to work together to satisfy customer needs and develop customer relationships.[7]

An Ethics Perspective

Because marketers work at the interface between the company and its customers, partners, and other groups, ethical considerations are important and complex. An **ethics perspective** involves proactively addressing the morality of marketing decisions and practicing social responsibility to include ecological considerations.

Marketing Ethics

A company must project a high level of morality to establish trust between itself and its customers and other stakeholders. Trust provides the foundation for long-term customer relationships and organizational partnerships.

Yum! Brands is dedicated to meeting the needs of its customers, providing a safe and healthful work environment for employees, and being a responsible corporate citizen wherever it operates. Ensuring that everyone in such a large and diverse company understands and practices basic company values is difficult. Yum! has developed a worldwide code of conduct to communicate its core principles to employees and stakeholders. This code presents guidelines for specific operations and activities of the company's employees and units.

Ecological Orientation

Yum! practices an ecological orientation by using delivery boxes that are 100 percent recyclable.

Marketers practicing an ecological orientation consider the environmental impact of marketing decisions. This can result in making changes, such as using recyclable materials, to reduce the negative ecological effect of marketing activities. In addition, astute marketers are finding many profitable opportunities to appeal to the growing number of environmentally concerned consumers.

Yum! Brands's worldwide code of conduct addresses many areas of ecological responsibility. The company recycles packaging wherever possible. One success is that all Pizza Hut take-out/home delivery boxes are 100 percent recyclable. Energy has received considerable

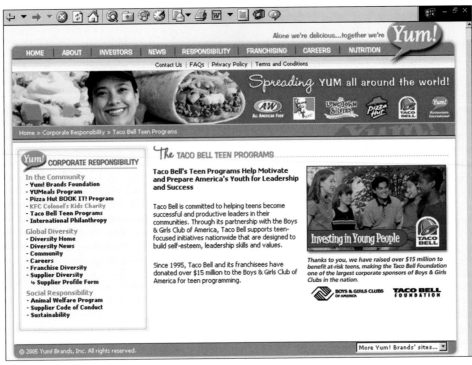

Yum! exhibits social responsibility by being involved in many community activities.

attention at Yum! with programs designed to reduce both ecological pollutants and energy usage. These and other efforts at Yum! make good business sense and have a positive impact on the environment.

Social Responsibility

Social responsibility refers to ensuring that marketing actions have a positive impact on society. This includes minimizing social costs, such as environmental damage, and taking specific actions that benefit society. Businesses are social institutions with a responsibility to contribute to societal welfare.

Yum! Brands prides itself on the many positive things it does in various communities. Several examples illustrate this social responsibility commitment. The Pizza Hut Book It!® Program motivates children in kindergarten through the sixth grade to read by rewarding them for their reading accomplishments. The Taco Bell TEEN Supreme® Program is a strategic partnership with Boys & Girls Clubs of America. This partnership establishes centers for teen-oriented programs, a training academy for Boys & Girls Club professionals, and a special club to promote citizenship and leadership development for teens. KFC's Colonel's kids program helps provide extended-hour day care in a partnership with YMCAs. Yum! Brands is also the world's largest provider of prepared food to those in need. The company is fighting hunger by feeding families. These and many other programs and donations help Yum! contribute to communities around the world.

A Customer Value Perspective

Business buyers and consumers are continually trying to get more for less. Both groups assess what they get for what they have to give. "What they get" includes not only the basic features of the product but also other important factors related to the purchase, use, and disposal of the product. These might include the convenience of the purchase, training in product use, dependability of delivery, after-sale service, ease of disposing of the product, and other factors. "What they give" includes the monetary price of the product, but also time and effort to purchase the product, costs associated with using the product, and other factors. A **customer value perspective** means constantly looking for ways to give customers more for less.

Yum! Brands provides customer value in two fundamental ways. First, the company is a leader in multibranding by offering two or more brands at one restaurant location. Typically, these are combinations of KFC, Pizza Hut, Taco Bell, Long John Silver's, and A&W All American Food. Customers can choose from a large variety of food options by traveling to only one location. Families with different food preferences find these multi-branded restaurants especially valuable. Then, within each restaurant Yum! offers high-quality/value price options. Value meals also give customers a lower price for various combinations of menu items and drinks. Continuously providing customers with value is an important element of Yum!'s success.

A Productivity Perspective

The multibranding strategy is one of the keys to Yum!'s success.

A **productivity perspective** is trying to get the most output for each marketing dollar spent. *Productivity* is typically defined in terms of output per unit input ratios. For marketers example outputs might be sales or market share. Inputs include the dollars spent on advertising, number of salespeople, or other marketing activity. Therefore, sales per advertising dollar or sales per salesperson are important productivity measures for marketers.

The multibranding strategy emphasized by Yum! Brands not only provides value to customers but also is a very productive use of marketing resources. The multibranded restaurants are more productive and profitable because it costs less to build and operate one multibranded unit than two separate restaurants, and sales are much higher than for single-brand locations. The company has also reduced purchasing costs by creating the world's largest purchasing co-op and lowered advertising costs by consolidating its media buying across brands. In addition, Yum! is always looking for ways to be more productive by sharing best practices across the company.[8]

A Technology Perspective

Technology is advancing at a tremendous pace. New developments in artificial intelligence, biotechnology, optoelectronics, and many other areas are reported daily. The dizzying pace of technological change challenges marketers to embrace a **technological perspective** so they can translate new and emerging technologies into successful products and services, and use technology to improve marketing practice.

Yum! Brands uses new technology products to help market its brands. One example is when Taco Bell used Amazon.com CEO Jeff Bezos to hold its new chicken quesadilla product as if it were a handheld computer. Then the chicken quesadilla was described in terms of its "gooey interface" and "ergonomic design for easy downloading" with the tag line "Think outside the bun."[9] Another example was the partnership with Microsoft to introduce its new video-game system, Xbox. Taco Bell supported the introduction with TV ads, in-store materials, window displays, tray liners, bags, and print ads. Taco Bell got product placements in some of the video games plus an association with a high-technology product.[10] Taco Bell and other Yum! brands all use Yum!'s Web site (*www.yum.com*) to market effectively to customers, franchisees, investors, employees, and other publics.

An Entrepreneurial Perspective

A dynamic business environment creates a need for firms to be flexible and responsive to marketplace demands. Slow and rigid bureaucracies need to be replaced by streamlined organizational structures and processes. Success often depends on being able to do some things differently from, sooner than, or better than

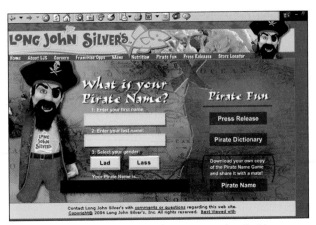

Long John Silver's is entrepreneurial in its approach to building customer relationships.

competitors. This requires that marketers bring an entrepreneurial perspective to their work. An **entrepreneurial perspective** has three basic dimensions: innovation, risk taking, and proactiveness. Marketers adopting an entrepreneurial perspective attempt to do things in new and unique ways, to make decisions in the face of uncertainty, and to be the first to try something different.

Yum! takes an entrepreneurial perspective toward developing new brands, expanding the multibranding concept, and introducing new products and promotions within existing brands. For example, it has introduced a new casual dining restaurant in Shanghai under the East Dawning brand. Although the KFC/Taco Bell combination has been a popular multibranding concept, the company is investigating different combinations among its five brands. Finally, new products and promotions are critical to the success of each brand. The Satay Twister in Australia and Dippin' Strips pizza-style breadsticks in the United States are examples of successful new products. The "Chicken Capital USA" represents an effective promotional campaign to increase KFC sales in the United States. Being proactive and innovative with informed risk taking are critical to the continued success of Yum! Brands.[11]

Integrating the Perspectives

Although we have discussed each perspective separately, the perspectives are highly interrelated. For example, continuing developments in information and communication technologies make it easier for firms to productively engage in business globally and to develop relationships with customers, partnerships with other organizations, and teamwork within firms, even when employees are located in different areas. These new technologies also introduce ethical issues that must be addressed if companies are going to earn the trust necessary for successful relationships of all types. The rapid and continuous changes in the environment require firms to be entrepreneurial, especially in trying to provide customers with more value.

Many of these interrelationships are critical to the future success of Yum! Brands. Yum! must continue to be entrepreneurial if it is to keep ahead of competitors in creating value for and developing relationships with customers. The company must keep expanding globally through various types of partnerships based on an ethical foundation. Efforts must also be made to increase productivity, often through the use of new technologies. Yum! is employing these marketing perspectives now, and its future looks bright.

Chapter One

An Overview of Contemporary Marketing

1

After studying this chapter, you should be able to

1 Discuss what marketing is and why it is important to organizations and individuals.

2 Distinguish between marketing as an organizational philosophy and a societal process.

3 Understand the components of a marketing strategy and the different activities involved in marketing products and services.

4 Be aware of the various types of marketing institutions and the different marketing positions available in these institutions.

5 Understand the basic elements and relationships in the contemporary marketing framework.

Amazon

Amazon.com represents an interesting entrepreneurial story. Jeff Bezos started Amazon.com as a book retailer in 1995. The company's mission was to use the Internet to transform book buying into the fastest, easiest, and most enjoyable shopping experience available. Because Amazon.com did not have an inventory of books in a retail location, it could offer customers an enormous selection of books over its Web site. Customers could also shop and place orders 24 hours a day and seven days a week. The shopping experience was easy and fun, and various services were added to create value. This was the beginning, and growth has been phenomenal.

Sales have increased from about $150 million in 1997 to over $7 billion today. The company generated its first operating profit of $5.8 million in the fourth quarter of 2001. Profits last year were $588 million. Amazon.com is doing several things to keep sales growing and to be consistently profitable.

First, the company offers many different products and services on *www.amazon.com*. These include music CDs, videos, electronics, kitchen and houseware products, an auction service, a wedding gift registry, and many others.

Second, international sales have been increasing through international sites for the United Kingdom, Germany, Japan, France, Canada, and China.

Third, more than 925,000 merchants sell through Amazon.com. These merchants range from large retailers, such as Nordstrom and Target, to smaller retailers like Something Silver and eBags. The company generates about 25 percent of unit sales and around 5 percent of sales revenue from these independent merchants.

Fourth, Amazon.com is continuously looking for new opportunities that leverage its strengths. For example, it recently purchased BookSurge and is expected to move into exclusive publishing in the future. There is also speculation that Amazon.com might try to capitalize on the growth in Internet advertising.

One of the major reasons for the success of Amazon.com is its growing number of satisfied and loyal customers. Amazon.com continues to add new customers and expand relationships with existing customers by offering a wide selection of products and by giving customers a personalized, satisfying shopping experience.

The Amazon.com story illustrates a basic principle of successful marketing: Identify market opportunities and respond by developing and executing marketing strategies to take advantage of the opportunities better than competitors do. Jeff Bezos realized that the Internet had the potential to offer customers new, exciting shopping experiences. He started in book retailing because Amazon.com could provide a better book selection, customized services, and lower prices than could typical book retailers. Finally, and most important, Amazon.com focuses on the customer; the company's key advantage is its large, growing base of loyal customers.

In a dynamic and turbulent business environment, marketers must continually revise their strategies to meet growth objectives. Amazon.com has done this by adding new product categories and new services. The firm now faces Internet competitors as well as traditional retail rivals. So it must continually look for ways to improve its existing operations, increase the value provided to customers, and manage customer relationships.

Amazon.com is actively involved in marketing. The most accepted definition of marketing is that presented by the American Marketing Association (AMA). For almost 20 years the AMA defined marketing as "the process of planning and executing the conception, pricing, promotion, and distribution of ideas, goods, and services to create exchanges that satisfy individual and organizational goals."[1] Although this definition includes key aspects of marketing, it does not capture the essence of contemporary marketing. Therefore, the AMA recently adopted the following definition:

Marketing is an organizational function and a set of processes for creating, communicating, and delivering value to customers and for managing customer relationships in ways that benefit the organization and its stakeholders.[2]

This new definition changes the emphasis from exchanges in the short term to creating value for and managing relationships with customers over the long run. Marketing at Amazon.com certainly fits this new definition. The company focuses on creating customer value by continually adding products and services, and it manages customer relationships by improving and personalizing the shopping experience for customers. We will now demonstrate the importance of marketing, examine different views of marketing, and discuss marketing as an organizational function and set of processes.

The Importance of Marketing

Marketing is usually associated with large business organizations. Most people are probably familiar with the marketing activities of consumer product firms such as Procter & Gamble, Sony, Nike, McDonald's, General Motors, and Sears. They also may be aware of marketing efforts by firms—such as Xerox, Monsanto, Caterpillar, Boeing, and DuPont—that market to other organizations.

Marketing also plays an important role for many different types of organizations, and the skills and knowledge possessed by effective marketers are valuable in many situations. Consider the following examples of the importance of marketing:

Marketing is important to many nonprofit organizations. The Humane Society uses advertising to promote animal protection.

- Victoria Hale is a social entrepreneur who created OneWorld Health as a nonprofit organization that markets drugs to the developing world. She tries to find promising drugs that have been abandoned by pharmaceutical companies because of limited profit potential. After five years her first drug is completing trials. If successful, the antibiotic for patients who contract deadly black fever from sandfly bites will be made available at an affordable price to the nearly 1.5 million of the world's poor with the disease. OneWorld has three promising drugs in the pipeline, including a malaria drug that will sell for less than a dollar a dose. The company has received funding from the Bill and Melinda Gates Foundation, but hopes to be paying its way and fighting disease in the developing world soon.[3]

- Farmers and ranchers operate in a volatile and risky environment. To better manage the risks and increase profits, many have joined marketing clubs. Although the clubs vary, many have speakers and provide opportunities for farmers to share marketing strategies. Some help members develop marketing plans for their farms or ranches. The clubs seem to be making a difference. For example, one study found that wheat farmers reported receiving as much as 12 cents a bushel more for their wheat after attending marketing club meetings and implementing new marketing ideas.[4]

- Washington's Arena Stage Theatre was America's first nonprofit theater. It had been very successful since being founded in 1950; but ticket sales and donations declined in the late 1990s, and the theater was in financial trouble. The board of trustees developed a long-term marketing program to rebrand the theater and increase attendance and donations. Marketing research provided valuable information, which led to various marketing activities to include a new logo, direct mail, a new Web site, a newsletter for season ticket holders, redesigned brochures, and print ads. The marketing program increased ticket sales and donations.[5]

- There is a trend toward consolidation in many industries, resulting in fewer but much larger firms. Mergers and acquisitions in the banking industry are an example. Interestingly, small community banks are using marketing to compete effectively against their large, national competitors. These banks are targeting markets that are ignored by the large banks, such as small businesses, minorities, and rural areas, and providing superior customer service to these customers. Extended business hours, personal attention, free investment advice, and free coffee and babysitting services are examples. These marketing strategies have been very effective as small bank profits have increased in recent years.[6]

- There are many attractive jobs and career paths within the marketing profession. These are discussed later in this chapter and throughout the book. However, those with marketing backgrounds are prepared to be successful in many endeavors. Some of these opportunities are within the same company. For example, companies are selecting more CEOs from the marketing ranks because these individuals have a strong customer focus and good communication skills. An example is GE, which replaced the legendary Jack Welch with Jeffrey Immelt, who held various marketing positions at GE for 20 years.[7] Other opportunities in marketing are to do new things. Examples include Ellen Shapiro moving from marketing video games to girls at Walt Disney to starting a toy invention company called Trixie Toys and George Gunn Jr. building on 30 years' experience in the advertising business to become CEO of a nonprofit organization.[8]

These examples illustrate the value of marketing to different types of organizations (social entrepreneurs, farmers, nonprofit organizations, and small firms) and to individuals (opportunities to advance within an organization or for different career options). Today more organizations and individuals realize that marketing is critical for success.

Views of Marketing

Most of the emphasis in this book is on marketing as defined at the beginning of the chapter. Nevertheless, marketing can also be viewed as an organizational philosophy and as a societal process.

Marketing as an Organizational Philosophy

An organization typically has some type of philosophy that directs the efforts of everyone in it. The philosophy might be stated formally, as in a mission statement, or it might become established informally through the communications and actions of top management. An organizational philosophy indicates the types of activities the organization values. Three different philosophies deserve mention.

A **production philosophy** exists when an organization emphasizes the production function. An organization following such a philosophy values activities related to improving production efficiency or producing sophisticated products and services. Production drives the organization. Marketing plays a secondary role because the organization thinks the best-produced products can be easily marketed. High-technology companies often follow a production philosophy.

A **selling philosophy** predominates where the selling function is most valued. The assumption is that any product can be sold if enough selling effort is given to it. Marketing's job is to sell whatever the organization decides to produce. Although selling is one component of marketing, organizations driven by a selling philosophy emphasize selling efforts to the exclusion of other marketing activities.

A **marketing philosophy** suggests that the organization focuses on satisfying the needs of customers. This focus applies to people in the marketing function as well as to those in production, personnel, accounting, finance, and other functions. Production and selling are still important, but the organization is driven by satisfying customer needs. Applied Materials reinforces the importance of a marketing philosophy every payday. "Your payroll dollars are provided by Applied Materials customers" appears on the front of every employee's paycheck.[9] Firms have implemented a marketing philosophy by practicing the marketing concept since the 1950s.[10] In recent years, many companies have pushed beyond the marketing concept to focus efforts on developing a market orientation, implementing customer relationship management (CRM), and building customer equity.

PRACTICING THE MARKETING CONCEPT   Marketing as an organizational philosophy has been based on the **marketing concept.** This concept consists of three interrelated principles:

1. An organization's basic purpose is to satisfy customer needs.

2. Satisfying customer needs requires integrated, coordinated efforts throughout the organization.

3. Organizations should focus on long-term success.

Firms practicing the marketing concept focus organizational efforts on satisfying customer needs and emphasize long-term success, typically in terms of profitability. However, evidence suggests that just satisfying customers may not be enough in today's competitive business environment.

Merely satisfied customers often leave and purchase from competitors. For example, Xerox polls 480,000 customers per year regarding their level of satisfaction using a five-point scale from 5 (high) to 1 (low). Analysis of these data indicated that customers giving 5s were six times more likely to repurchase Xerox equipment than those giving 4s. Now Xerox's objective is to have 100 percent of its customers being totally satisfied with Xerox products and services.[11] Xerox and other successful marketers are extending the focus beyond mere customer satisfaction to complete customer satisfaction.

DEVELOPING A MARKET ORIENTATION   In recent years firms have implemented a marketing philosophy by developing a market orientation. A **market orientation** consists of creating norms and values that encourage customer-oriented behavior throughout the organization. This typically includes generating customer and competitive market intelligence, disseminating it throughout the organization, and responding effectively to it. Research results indicate that developing a market orientation requires an emphasis from top management, interdepartmental connectedness, and systems that reward employees for customer-oriented behaviors. This research also suggests that a market orientation has a positive impact on profits, product quality, innovativeness, and customer loyalty. Developing a market orientation is difficult, but can be an effective way to implement a marketing philosophy and improve firm performance.[12]

IMPLEMENTING CUSTOMER RELATIONSHIP MANAGEMENT (CRM)   Although defined in a variety of ways, **customer relationship management (CRM)** is essentially an organizational strategy to select and manage the most valuable customer relationships. It means treating different customers differently and balancing customer needs with the cost of satisfying those needs.[13] New technological developments make it possible for companies to track all customer interactions with a firm. These databases are used to identify the preferences of individual customers or groups of similar customers, and to develop specific strategies to satisfy the needs of and manage relationships with these customers and customer groups. The key to successful CRM is the development and execution of effective, profitable strategies. Technology is merely a tool in this process. Successful CRM implementations are typically strategy-driven, and unsuccessful ones tend to be technology-driven.

Royal Bank of Canada (RBC), the largest financial institution in Canada, provides a successful CRM implementation example. RBC's marketing strategy was to make banking as convenient as possible. However, a marketing research study found that convenience was important, but that customers chose a bank based on how much a bank cared about them, valued their business, and recognized them as individuals no matter what part of the bank they did business with. RBC decided to implement a CRM strategy to meet the needs of its customers, especially its most valuable ones. It used technology to keep track of every contact with each customer. The data were used to customize product offerings and target the best customers. The results of the CRM implementation have been exceptional. RBC has had a 20 percent increase in high-value customers, a 13 percent increase in customer profitability, and an increase in the success rate on sales leads from the typical 2–5 percent to around 45 percent.[14]

BUILDING CUSTOMER EQUITY   Companies typically face choices: focusing on short-term versus long-term sales and profit growth and emphasizing new customers versus existing customers. Too often, short-term considerations and new customer acquisitions take precedence over long-term performance and current customers. The concept of customer equity can help firms implement a marketing philosophy and achieve a better balance in these areas.

Customer equity is the financial value of a firm's customer relationships. It consists of profits from first-time customers plus expected profits from future sales to these and other customers. Customer equity can be increased in several ways.[15]

- Acquire more profitable customers at a lower cost.
- Retain profitable customers longer.
- Win back profitable customers.
- Eliminate unprofitable customers.
- Sell more to profitable customers.
- Reduce service and operational costs.

Customer equity integrates short-term and long-term orientations and addresses both new and existing customers. Short-term sales and profit growth come from acquiring profitable new customers and expanding relationships with current customers. Long-term sales and profit growth are addressed by retaining new and existing customers longer and selling more profitable products at lower marketing expense to both groups.[16] Notice the emphasis on *profitable* customers. Customer equity is increased by acquiring and retaining profitable customers and eliminating unprofitable ones. This is an important consideration and one overlooked by many companies. Focusing on customer equity is a relatively new and promising approach for implementing a marketing philosophy.[17]

The process for building customer equity is illustrated in Exhibit 1–1. It is based on three key relationships:

1. Earning high levels of customer loyalty leads to increased sales growth, higher profitability, and higher customer equity.

2. Completely satisfying and delighting customers is the best route for earning customer loyalty.

3. Providing exceptional value is needed to delight and completely satisfy customers.

Research results suggest that the relationships depicted in Exhibit 1–1 are most relevant for customers that are or can become loyal purchasers and have a positive attitude toward the

Exhibit 1–1   *Customer equity relationships*

Marketing concept, market orientation, CRM → Providing exceptional customer value → Achieving completely satisfied customers → Earning high customer loyalty → Increasing sales growth and profits → Building customer equity

Exhibit 1–2   *Customer loyalty, sales, profits, and customer equity*

1. Keeping loyal customers requires no acquisition costs. Getting new customers often requires high acquisition costs.
2. The longer a firm keeps a customer, the more base profit earned from continuing purchases over time.
3. Loyal customers tend to buy more from a firm over time.
4. It usually costs less to deal with loyal customers than with new customers.
5. Loyal customers are typically an excellent source of referrals for new business.
6. Loyal customers are often willing to pay a price premium to receive desired value.

firm and its products. These are typically a company's best customers. Some customers are loyal purchasers but do not have attitudinal loyalty, and other customers will not be loyal customers. Different marketing strategies should be used for these customer groups.[18]

The basic reasons for the close relationship between customer loyalty and sales, profits, and customer equity are presented in Exhibit 1–2. Loyal customers contribute to increased sales growth because they tend to buy more over time and are an excellent source of new business referrals. Getting new customers from referrals usually lowers customer acquisition costs significantly. Some companies calculate the **lifetime value of a loyal customer** as the expected revenue or profit stream from repeat purchases and referrals.[19]

Typically, loyal customers involve limited acquisition costs, low operating costs, and higher profit margins. The conventional wisdom is that it costs at least five times as much to serve a new customer as an existing one. Sometimes the efforts to get new customers may not even be profitable. For example, MBNA was spending 98 percent of its marketing dollars on getting new customers. It found that it cost about $50 to get a new credit card customer; these customers were not profitable until the second year; and many left before the second year. The company changed its strategy and focused on keeping existing customers. It increased the customer retention rate to 50 percent and became one of the most profitable banks in the country.[20]

The link between customer satisfaction and customer loyalty is especially interesting. One study of this link in the automobile, business personal computer, hospital, airlines, and local telephone service markets concluded that completely satisfied customers are much more loyal than merely satisfied customers. Another study in the banking industry found that completely satisfied customers were 42 percent more likely to be loyal than merely satisfied customers.[21] These results are consistent with the Xerox example presented earlier.

How can organizations completely satisfy their customers? The simple answer is by continuously developing and implementing marketing strategies that provide customers with exceptional value. **Customer value** is defined as what a customer *gets* (benefits from product use, related services) for what a customer *gives* (price paid, costs to acquire and use the product). Value is determined by the customer. For example, Southwest Airlines is the only major airline to be profitable for over 25 years. One reason for this success is that Southwest's customers value frequent departures, on-time service, friendly employees, and low fares. Southwest consistently provides customers exceptional value that translates into complete satisfaction, loyal customers, increased sales and profits, and higher customer equity. Southwest does not assign seats, offer meals, or provide tickets as most other airlines do. Its customers do not value these services, so they are not offered.[22]

Organizations face a difficult challenge in continually providing exceptional customer value, completely satisfying needs, and earning customer loyalty. Those successful in these endeavors are likely to achieve higher levels of sales growth and profitability and more customer equity than those that do not. Organizations increasingly have to be market-driven and customer-focused to compete effectively in the future. Some guidelines for executing a

One way to promote customer loyalty is to reward customers for their loyalty. Friday's awards points to customers based on the amount spent. These points can be redeemed for free food at subsequent visits or other rewards.

Exhibit 1–3

Executing a marketing philosophy

1. Create customer focus throughout the business.
2. Listen to the customer.
3. Define and nurture your distinctive competence.
4. Define marketing as market intelligence.
5. Target customers precisely.
6. Manage for profitability, not sales volume.
7. Make customer value the guiding star.
8. Let the customer define quality.
9. Measure and manage customer expectations.
10. Build customer relationships and loyalty.
11. Define the business as a service business.
12. Commit to continuous improvement and innovation.
13. Manage culture along with strategy and structure.
14. Grow with partners and alliances.
15. Destroy marketing bureaucracy.

marketing philosophy that incorporates the marketing concept, a market orientation focused on building customer equity, and CRM are presented in Exhibit 1–3. These guidelines are relevant for those in marketing and nonmarketing functions within an organization.

Marketing as a Societal Process

Marketing as a societal process can be defined as a process that facilitates the flow of goods and services from producers to consumers in a society. At this level the emphasis is on issues such as these:

- What institutions are involved in the societal marketing system?
- What activities do these institutions perform?
- How effective is the marketing system in satisfying consumer needs?
- How efficient is the marketing system in providing consumers with desired goods and services?

Speaking from Experience

David Power
President
Power Creative Inc.

"Power Creative was regarded as just a supplier of advertising and marketing materials for many years. But in today's business world, with tight budgets and pressure to deliver higher margins, our customers view us as true business partners. Our objective is to improve the client's bottom line. Consistently delivering on this commitment has two major benefits. First, completely satisfied customers remain loyal. For example, we have worked with General Electric Appliances for many years. Second, loyal customers help us get new business. A recent example illustrates this. An individual we worked with at General Electric Appliances took a job as vice president and general manager of sales, marketing, and distribution for Lennox. He contacted us to develop programs to promote Lennox furnaces and air conditioners to housing contractors. We would never have been considered for this business without our previous successful relationship."

Power Creative provides integrated marketing communications services for the domestic and international operations of large blue-chip corporations. David received a BS in marketing from the University of Louisville in 1993 and joined Power Creative as an account executive, handling the RCA brand for Thomson Electronics. He has since been promoted to senior account executive, vice president, and president of the company.

- Identify the most important benefits of the societal marketing system in the United States. What changes would you recommend for this system to be more beneficial to U.S. society?

- Identify the most negative effects of the societal marketing system in the United States. What changes would you recommend to reduce these negative effects?

A society's marketing system is closely related to its political and economic systems. These close relationships are vividly illustrated by the tremendous changes that continue in Eastern Europe. Countries that operated under a communist political system with centrally planned economies did have some sort of marketing system: products and services were provided to consumers. The marketing systems, however, were woefully ineffective and inefficient, largely because most "marketing" decisions were made centrally by government bureaucrats. With little consideration of customer needs, these officials decided what to produce, in what quantities, how products were to be made available to consumers, and at what prices.

Ineffective marketing systems contributed to the overthrow of the communist regimes in Eastern Europe, and these countries continue to struggle with market-based economies. Take the situation in Poland as an example. The country has moved from a communist state with a centrally planned economy to a democracy with a free-market economy, and membership in the European Union, in 15 years. But there are two Polands. One is an entrepreneurial group that has created more than 1.5 million new companies. Some, such as Kross Bicycles, Delphia Yachts, and ComArch, have grown rapidly and achieved strong market positions. The other Poland consists of those who hold on to the remnants of the communist-era welfare state with its graft and slow-moving bureaucracy. This situation limits the growth of Poland's free-market economy and marketing system.[23]

A market-based economy requires an effective, efficient marketing system that can identify and satisfy consumer needs for products and services. As evident in the Poland situation, it can take a long time to develop the needed societal marketing system. China illustrates some of the successes and problems. Although China operates under a communist political system, it has moved toward a free-market economy and marketing system. It has achieved strong economic growth. This growth is producing more upscale and middle-class consumers, especially in the larger cities and coastal areas. However, the prosperity is uneven—incomes remain low in smaller towns and rural areas. Companies are responding to this situation by focusing on different markets. For example, Kodak markets specially designed digital cameras to the Chinese upscale market, cheaper digital cameras to the middle-class market, and cameras with traditional film in the low-income markets. The societal marketing system in China largely reflects differences in economic development and growth throughout the country.[24]

The move to free-market economies and more open marketing systems offers tremendous opportunities for many firms. Many companies are marketing grocery products to consumers in Shanghai.

The Poland and China situations illustrate typical results from the move to a market economy and new marketing system. Over time, more people are likely to benefit from these changes, but market economies and marketing systems are not perfect. For example, a recent study of the contributions of the aggregate marketing system to U.S. society found both benefits and criticisms. Benefits included economic well-being, quality of life, and social/psychological benefits to individual workers and consumers. Criticisms included negative effects on societal values, unethical marketing practices, and ecological problems. This analysis did, however, conclude that the contributions from the U.S. aggregate marketing system outweighed the negative impacts.[25]

Important relationships exist between marketing at the organizational and societal levels. People moving from a planned to a market-based economic system must learn and implement basic marketing practices. The success of a society's marketing system depends on the ability of individuals in organizations to identify and respond to consumer needs effectively and efficiently.

Marketing as a Set of Processes

Marketing as an organizational philosophy and a societal process is related to the way marketing is performed by organizations and individuals. We are now ready to discuss the major aspects of marketing as an organizational function and a set of processes.

Marketing Exchanges

Exchange has generally been viewed as the core element of marketing.[26] **Exchange** is defined as the "transfer of something tangible or intangible, actual or symbolic, between two or more social actors."[27] Thus the basic purpose of marketing is to get individuals or organizations to transfer something of value (tangible or intangible, actual or symbolic) to each other. The most familiar type of exchange occurs when a customer exchanges money with a retail store for a product. Every time a customer pays a Papa John's pizza delivery person and receives a pizza, a marketing exchange takes place.

Marketing exchanges are not confined to transactions of money for products, as shown in Exhibit 1–4. Businesses engage in barter where they exchange their goods and

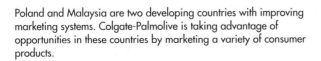

Poland and Malaysia are two developing countries with improving marketing systems. Colgate-Palmolive is taking advantage of opportunities in these countries by marketing a variety of consumer products.

Exhibit 1-4   *Marketing exchanges*

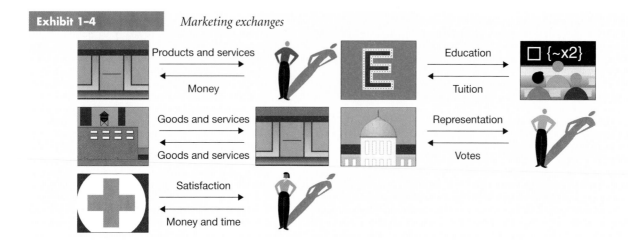

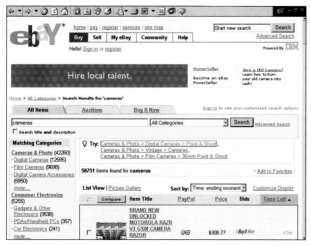

A basic purpose of marketing is to facilitate exchanges. eBay facilitates exchanges through auctions on the Internet.

services for the goods and services of another firm. Non-profit organizations, colleges and universities, politicians, and many other "social actors" are also involved in exchanges. Volunteers and contributors to nonprofit organizations, for example, exchange their time and money for the satisfaction derived from helping a good cause. Or consider the tuition that students pay a university or college in exchange for the education they receive. Even politics involves exchanges, with people trading their votes for the promise of representation from a political candidate.

The major objective of marketing exchanges is to satisfy the needs of the individuals and organizations involved. For an exchange to take place, each party must be willing to give up something to get something. What each party gets must be more valuable than what it gives up. If someone decides to buy a delivered pizza from Papa John's, the pizza must be valued more than the money exchanged to get it. Similarly, Papa John's must value the amount of money it receives from the customer as sufficient to cover the costs of the delivered pizza it exchanges.

As indicated in the new definition of marketing, facilitating exchanges by creating customer value is only one basic part of marketing. The second major element of marketing is managing customer relationships. This changes the emphasis from merely a short-term exchange with any customer to various types of long-term relationships with selected customers. Facilitating exchanges and managing customer relationships require that marketing strategies be developed and marketing activities performed. These processes involve people in various marketing positions. Some of these people are employed by the firm marketing the product, but others are part of organizations that specialize in specific marketing activities.

Marketing Strategies

Marketing strategies consist of selecting a target market and developing a marketing mix to satisfy that market's needs. A **target market** is a defined group of consumers or organizations with which a firm wants to create marketing exchanges and relationships. A **marketing mix** is the overall marketing offer to appeal to the target market. It consists of decisions in four basic areas: product (development of a product, service, or idea), pricing (what to charge), integrated marketing communications (how to communicate with the target market), and distribution (how to get the product, service, or idea to the target

Exhibit 1–5   *Marketing mix decisions*

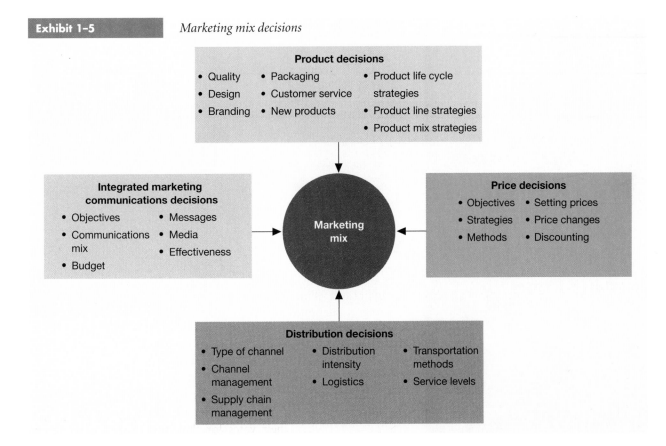

market). As is evident from Exhibit 1–5, many marketing decisions must be made within the product, pricing, communications, and distribution areas.

The cosmetics industry is a good place to look for examples of different marketing strategies. Note in Exhibit 1–6 that Maybelline, Mary Kay, and Clinique all market a variety of cosmetic products to defined target markets. Brands differ, as do the prices charged, the methods of distribution, and the types of marketing communications. Each company effectively blends product, price, distribution, and integrated marketing communications decisions into a different marketing mix designed to serve its target market.

Marketing Activities

Regardless of an organization's specific marketing strategy, a number of different marketing activities must be performed to move products from producers to end users. Exhibit 1–7 illustrates these important activities schematically.

Exhibit 1–6   *Marketing strategies*

	Maybelline	**Mary Kay**	**Clinique**
Target market	Low end	Middle	High end
Product	Cosmetics	Cosmetics	Cosmetics
Price	Low	Moderate	High
Distribution	Mass merchandisers	Direct to consumers	Upscale department stores
Marketing communications	Advertising through mass media	Personal selling to consumers in home	Targeted advertising and personal selling to consumers in stores

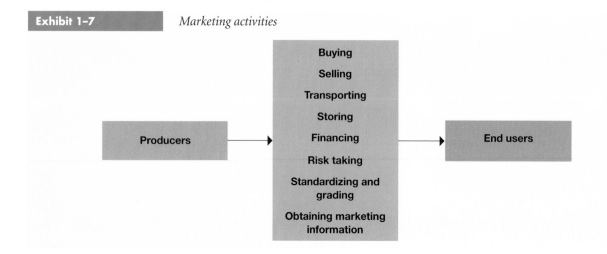

Exhibit 1–7   *Marketing activities*

Producers → Buying / Selling / Transporting / Storing / Financing / Risk taking / Standardizing and grading / Obtaining marketing information → End users

Retailers perform many of the activities required to get products from producers to customers.

Buying and selling activities are required to finalize an exchange and maintain a relationship. The product assortments desired by buyers must be transported to appropriate locations and stored in inventory. The inventories must be financed and the risk associated with holding the inventory assortment assumed. Quality and quantity of product assortments must be standardized and graded. Finally, marketing information about buyers and competitors is needed to make marketing decisions.

Say you want to buy a DVD player. A number of producers of DVD players—Toshiba, Sharp, Panasonic, Sony—would like to sell you their brand. But it would be inefficient if you had to visit each producer to examine its product and then purchase directly from the factory. To facilitate the exchange process, the producers market their DVD players through various types of retailers, such as Best Buy.

So now you can go to Best Buy, try out different DVD player brands, and easily purchase the one best suited to your needs. Best Buy has performed many of the marketing activities shown in Exhibit 1–7 that are required to complete an exchange between you and the producer of DVD players. Best Buy buys an assortment of DVD player brands, transports them to its retail outlets, and stores them there in inventory. It assumes the expense and risk of holding this inventory. It standardizes and grades the product quality and quantity. Because it wants to move the DVD players from inventory to end users, it advertises and promotes the brands it carries and the price at which it is willing to exchange each brand. Buyers come to the stores, talk with salespeople, and purchase desired brands. When you purchase the DVD player, an exchange has taken place. However, both the DVD producer and Best Buy would like you to purchase additional DVD players or other products from them in the future. Therefore, the shopping experience at Best Buy and after-the-sale service activities are important if this exchange is to evolve into a long-term relationship.

This would be the typical approach for getting DVD players from producers to consumers. However, with the tremendous growth of the Internet, other options are available. You might go to the Web site of one of the DVD producers and obtain information about DVD players, locate dealers for its brand, and possibly make a purchase. Or you could go to a shopping site, such as Amazon.com, and compare various DVD brands and purchase the one that best meets your needs.

One way or another, certain marketing activities must be performed for exchanges to occur between producers and end users. In some cases, marketing institutions, such as retailers like Best Buy, perform many marketing activities for producers. In others, most activities are performed by individuals within the producing firm. Sometimes consumers perform some of the required marketing activities.

Marketing Positions

There are a variety of marketing positions within most organizations. Examples are shown in Exhibit 1–8. Some of these positions, such as advertising manager, supply chain manager, or sales manager, indicate specialization in one area of marketing. Others suggest working across marketing areas (marketing manager, product manager, marketing research manager). The reality is that most marketing positions require close working relationships among different marketing and business functions. For example, advertising, sales, product, marketing, production, and accounting managers typically work together to develop and execute marketing plans for specific products.

Marketing positions are most prevalent in business firms, although similar positions exist in nonprofit organizations, hospitals, government agencies, museums, accounting firms, and other organizations. For organizations that follow a marketing philosophy, many employees are involved in marketing activities even though they may not hold formal marketing positions.

David Power, President, Power Creative, talks about being involved in marketing throughout his career: "Successful organizations are becoming increasingly customer-focused and are investing in ways to develop one-to-one relationships. These companies rely on everyone in the enterprise, from CEO to product development engineer to receptionist, to contribute to customer relationships. This means that everyone in the organization is involved in some marketing activities. And different positions perform different marketing activities. For example, as an account manager most of my job was to maintain and expand our relationship with one large account. Now, as president, I am involved in more strategic issues that span all of our customers. I still, however, call on prospects to get new business and on existing customers to keep their business."

Marketing Institutions

Some organizations specialize in specific marketing activities and become experts in performing them. Thus a firm may work with several of these organizations to handle the required marketing activities.

Exhibit 1–8	*Marketing positions*

Position/Alternative Titles	Duties
Marketing manager Vice president of marketing, director of marketing	Directs all company's marketing activities, including planning, organizing, staffing, directing, controlling, evaluating performance
Product manager Brand manager	Develops goals, objectives, plans, strategies, marketing mixes for product line or brand
Advertising manager Advertising director, director of communications, media manager	Devises advertising policy and strategy, selects advertising agencies, develops promotional campaigns, selects media, allocates advertising expenditures
Supply chain manager Logistics manager, traffic manager, transportation manager	Manages distribution system, including storage and transportation for all products and services
Purchasing manager Director of purchasing, director of procurement	Manages all purchasing activities, including buying product ingredients or components, supplies, equipment, needed materials
Marketing research manager Director of commercial research, director of market research	Develops research designs for specific problems; collects, analyzes, interprets data; presents results to top management
Public relations manager Director of public relations, director of communications, public affairs officer	Manages all communications with media and company stakeholders to present favorable public image
Customer service manager Director of customer relations	Provides customer service, handles customer complaints
Sales manager Vice president of sales; director of sales; national sales manager; regional, district, or branch sales manager	Organizes, develops, directs, controls, evaluates sales force

The competitor who is first to spot an opportunity is usually in the best position to capture it. By working to sharpen your vision, Accenture can help your business become a high-performance business. See how at accenture.com

Do you see opportunities when others don't?

Go on. Be a Tiger.

• Consulting • Technology • Outsourcing

accenture
High performance. Delivered.

Successful marketers identify and capitalize on opportunities better than competitors.

We have already discussed the important role that retailers, such as Best Buy, play in making a variety of different products and brands available to consumers. Sometimes wholesalers also undertake specific marketing activities for producers and retailers. Wholesalers engage in exchanges with producers and subsequently exchange products from their inventory to meet the needs of retailers. They might also perform specialized services for producers and retailers. Some of the leading wholesalers are McKesson Corporation (health care products), Fleming Co. (food), Produce Specialties (exotic fruits and vegetables), and United Stationers (office supplies).

Marketing research firms and advertising agencies also provide specialized services for client firms. Some firms emphasize specific types of marketing research, but the largest firms offer a full array of research services, including focus groups, concept tests, customer interviews, mail surveys, experiments, or other types of marketing research. The largest marketing research firms include ACNielsen, IMS International, Information Resources, Inc., and the Arbitron Co.

Advertising agencies also provide various services to help firms develop and implement marketing communications campaigns. Again, some of these firms specialize in specific areas; others provide full services, often including marketing research. The leading advertising agencies include Young & Rubicam, Saatchi and Saatchi, BBDO Worldwide, DDB Needham Worldwide, and Ogilvy & Mather Worldwide.

A Contemporary Marketing Framework

The contemporary marketing framework that underlies the focus for this book is presented in Exhibit 1–9. The framework has three major elements: the marketing environment, key marketing perspectives, and marketing.

A contemporary marketing framework

Marketing environment

Entrepreneurship

Global

Ethics

Productivity

Marketing

Customer value

Relationship

Technology

Marketing environment

Marketing Environment

The larger circle represents the uncontrollable environment within which marketers must operate. The marketing environment is categorized further into social, economic, competitive, technological, legal/political, and institutional environments. Each of these categories is examined in detail in Chapter 2 ("The Global Marketing Environment").

Marketing is largely concerned with identifying market opportunities and responding to these opportunities by developing and executing effective marketing strategies. Market opportunities are typically the result of conditions or changes in the marketing environment.

Thus successful marketing requires constant assessment of the marketing environment to identify opportunities and to determine the best way to capitalize on them. The difficulty is that the marketing environment is complex, turbulent, and uncertain.

Exhibit 1–10	*Key marketing perspectives*	
	Marketing Perspective	**Definition**
	Global	Viewing the world as the potential marketplace to include identifying and responding both to market opportunities around the world and to different cultural groups within each market.
	Relationship	Building partnerships with firms outside the organization and encouraging teamwork among different functions within the organization to develop long-term customer relationships.
	Ethics	Addressing the morality of marketing decisions and practicing social responsibility to include ecological considerations.
	Customer value	Constantly looking for ways to give customers more for less.
	Productivity	Trying to get the best return for each marketing dollar spent.
	Technology	Translating new and emerging technologies into successful products and services, and using technology to improve marketing practice.
	Entrepreneurship	Focusing on innovation, on risk taking, and on being proactive in marketing efforts.

Key Marketing Perspectives

We have identified seven key marketing perspectives to guide marketers in responding effectively to opportunities offered by the marketing environment (see Exhibit 1–9). These perspectives provide links between marketing and the marketing environment. The seven key marketing perspectives are presented in Exhibit 1–10, were discussed in the Prologue about Yum! Brands, and will be addressed in various ways throughout the remainder of the book. The Acting Ethically, Being Entrepreneurial, Creating Customer Value, and Using Technology boxes in subsequent chapters present specific examples for these important topics.

Although each of these perspectives is important and interrelated, we think it is appropriate to emphasize an ethical perspective. Most marketers operate in an ethical manner. However, the business press reports unethical marketing practices on a regular basis. The American Marketing Association has responded to this situation by introducing a new code of ethics to promote ethical behavior within the marketing profession (see Exhibit 1–11). Many firms are following suit by focusing on the development and enforcement of ethical codes. Because marketers interface with customers, competitors, and other stakeholders, the likelihood of facing complex ethical situations is high. It is important to assess the ethical implications of all marketing decisions and actions. The American Marketing Association Code of Ethics and those of individual firms can help marketers determine the most ethical practices.

David Power, President, Power Creative, comments on the importance of these key marketing perspectives: "These key marketing perspectives are extremely important in my business. Our clients operate globally, so we must have a global perspective to meet their needs. Relationships with customers and teamwork within our company are critical to our success. We must continuously look for ways to create value for our customers and to ensure we do business ethically. Increasing our productivity and the productivity of our clients is a constant concern. Often this requires being entrepreneurial, especially in using new technologies. We must be at the 'cutting edge' in applying new technologies in innovative ways. This will continue to be a challenge as the use of the Internet in marketing and e-commerce grows."

Marketing

The inner circle represents marketing as an organizational philosophy and a set of processes. Most of this book expands on topics that fit within this circle: the marketing concept, market orientation, CRM, and customer equity; and marketing exchanges, relationships, strategies, activities, positions, and institutions. Special attention is given to the process of selecting target markets and creating marketing mixes for the development of effective marketing strategies.

Exhibit 1–11 *Ethical norms and values for marketers*

Preamble

The American Marketing Association commits itself to promoting the highest standard of professional ethical norms and values for its members. Norms are established standards of conduct that are expected and maintained by society and/or professional organizations. Values represent the collective conception of what people find desirable, important, and morally proper. Values serve as the criteria for evaluating the actions of others. Marketing practitioners must recognize that they not only serve their enterprises but also act as stewards of society in creating, facilitating, and executing the efficient and effective transactions that are part of the greater economy. In this role, marketers should embrace the highest ethical norms of practicing professionals and the ethical values implied by their responsibility toward stakeholders (e.g., customers, employees, investors, channel members, regulators, and the host community).

General Norms

1. Marketers must do no harm. This means doing work for which they are appropriately trained or experienced so they can actively add value to their organizations and customers. It also means adhering to all applicable laws and regulations and embodying high ethical standards in the choices they make.

2. Marketers must foster trust in the marketing system. This means that products are appropriate for their intended and promoted uses. It requires that marketing communications about goods and services are not intentionally deceptive or misleading. It suggests building relationships that provide for the equitable adjustment and/or redress of customer grievances. It implies striving for good faith and fair dealing to contribute toward the efficacy of the exchange process.

3. Marketers must embrace, communicate, and practice the fundamental ethical values that will improve consumer confidence in the integrity of the marketing exchange system. These basic values are intentionally aspirational and include honesty, responsibility, fairness, respect, openness, and citizenship.

Ethical Values

Honesty: to be truthful and forthright in our dealings with customers and stakeholders.

- We will tell the truth in all situations and at all times.
- We will offer products of value that do what we claim in our communications.
- We will stand behind our products if they fail to deliver their claimed benefits.
- We will honor our explicit and implicit commitments and promises.

Responsibility: to accept the consequences of our marketing decisions and strategies.

- We will make strenuous efforts to serve the needs of our customers.
- We will avoid using coercion with all stakeholders.
- We will acknowledge the social obligations to stakeholders that come with increased marketing and economic power.
- We will recognize our special commitments to economically vulnerable segments of the market such as children, the elderly, and others who may be substantially disadvantaged.

Fairness: to try to balance justly the needs of the buyer with the interests of the seller.

- We will represent our products in a clear way in selling, advertising, and other forms of communication; this includes the avoidance of false, misleading, and deceptive promotion.
- We will reject manipulations and sales tactics that harm customer trust.
- We will not engage in price fixing, predatory pricing, price gouging, or "bait-and-switch" tactics.
- We will not knowingly participate in material conflicts of interest.

Respect: to acknowledge the basic human dignity of all stakeholders.

- We will value individual differences even as we avoid stereotyping customers or depicting demographic groups (e.g., gender, race, sexual orientation) in a negative or dehumanizing way in our promotions.
- We will listen to the needs of our customers and make all reasonable efforts to monitor and improve their satisfaction on an ongoing basis.
- We will make a special effort to understand suppliers, intermediaries, and distributors from other cultures.
- We will appropriately acknowledge the contributions of others, such as consultants, employees, and coworkers, to our marketing endeavors.

Openness: to create transparency in our marketing operations.

- We will strive to communicate clearly with all our constituencies.
- We will accept constructive criticism from our customers and other stakeholders.
- We will explain significant product or service risks, component substitutions, or other foreseeable eventualities that could affect customers or their perception of the purchase decision.
- We will fully disclose list prices and terms of financing as well as available price deals and adjustments.

Citizenship: to fulfill the economic, legal, philanthropic, and societal responsibilities that serve stakeholders in a strategic manner.

- We will strive to protect the natural environment in the execution of marketing campaigns.
- We will give back to the community through volunteerism and charitable donations.
- We will work to contribute to the overall betterment of marketing and its reputation.
- We will encourage supply chain members to ensure that trade is fair for all participants, including producers in developing countries.

Implementation

Finally, we recognize that every industry sector and marketing subdiscipline (e.g., marketing research, e-commerce, direct selling, direct marketing, advertising) has its own specific ethical issues that require policies and commentary. An array of such codes can be accessed through links on the AMA Web site. We encourage all such groups to develop and/or refine their industry and discipline-specific codes of ethics to supplement these general norms and values.

After examining key aspects of the marketing environment in Chapter 2 ("The Global Marketing Environment"), we discuss the important strategic roles of marketing within an organization in Chapter 3 ("Marketing's Strategic Role in the Organization").

Selecting target markets requires understanding buyer behavior. Chapter 4 ("Consumer Buying Behavior and Decision Making") and Chapter 5 ("Business-to-Business Markets and Buying Behavior") present buying behavior from the perspective of consumers and organizations. The process for obtaining information about buying behavior and other important information is covered in Chapter 6 ("Marketing Research and Decision Support Systems"). Chapter 7 ("Market Segmentation and Targeting") shows how to use this information to segment markets and then target specific markets for the development of marketing mixes.

Each element of the marketing mix is then covered in detail. Chapter 8 ("Product and Service Concepts"), Chapter 9 ("Developing New Products and Services"), and Chapter 10 ("Product and Service Strategies") address the important product strategy decisions to include developing new products and services and managing multiple products and services throughout their life cycles. Pricing decisions are discussed in Chapter 11 ("Pricing Concepts") and Chapter 12 ("Price Determination and Pricing Strategies"). Important aspects of distributing products to customers are covered in Chapter 13 ("Marketing Channels"), Chapter 14 ("Retailing"), and Chapter 15 ("Wholesaling and Logistics Management"). Developing an effective integrated marketing communications strategy to achieve specific objectives is discussed in Chapter 16 ("An Overview of Marketing Communications"), Chapter 17 ("Advertising and Public Relations"), Chapter 18 ("Consumer and Trade Sales Promotion"), Chapter 19 ("Personal Selling and Sales Management"), and Chapter 20 ("Direct Marketing Communications"). An example that illustrates how all of these areas are interrelated and must be addressed to develop effective marketing strategies is presented in Appendix A ("Developing a Marketing Plan").

Summary

1. **Discuss what marketing is and why it is important to organizations and individuals.** Marketing "is an organizational function and a set of processes for creating, communicating, and delivering value to customers and for managing customer relationships in ways that benefit the organization and its stakeholders." Marketing is important to all types of organizations because it focuses on satisfying the needs of customers. Individuals, such as politicians, also engage in marketing during campaigns for election and when developing and implementing policies. Marketing activities are performed by people in various positions at different organizations. Interacting with people is a major component of most marketing positions.

2. **Distinguish between marketing as an organizational philosophy and a societal process.** Marketing can be defined in different ways. As an organizational philosophy, marketing is an orientation where everyone in the organization is driven by the marketing concept to satisfy customer needs. At the societal level, marketing is the process that determines the flow of goods and services from producers to consumers in a society.

3. **Understand the components of a marketing strategy and the different activities involved in marketing products and services.** A marketing strategy consists of the selection of a target market and the development of a marketing mix to appeal to that target market. The marketing mix is an integration of product, price, communications, and distribution decisions to serve a target market better than competitors.

   Implementing marketing strategies to facilitate exchanges and manage relationships requires many activities, including buying, selling, transporting, storing, financing, risk taking, standardizing and grading, and obtaining marketing information.

4. **Be aware of the various types of marketing institutions and the different marketing positions available in these institutions.** The necessary marketing activities are performed by different institutions and various positions within these institutions. Although some producers can perform all required marketing activities, organizations specializing in specific marketing activities are often used. Typical marketing institutions are wholesalers, retailers, distributors, marketing research firms, and advertising agencies.

   Important marketing positions include marketing managers, product managers, advertising managers, purchasing managers, sales managers, marketing research managers, and individuals who report to these managers. Marketing activities are also performed by people in nonmarketing positions.

5. **Understand the basic elements and relationships in the contemporary marketing framework.** The contemporary marketing framework depicts the important relationship between marketing and the marketing environment. Seven key marketing perspectives are presented as orientations that drive marketing's interactions with the external environment.

Understanding Marketing Terms and Concepts

Thinking about Marketing

1. How can top management in an organization ensure that all employees are driven by a marketing philosophy?

2. What is an example of barter as a marketing exchange?

3. How would you describe the major target market and marketing mix for your college or university?

4. What are the marketing activities required to get toothpaste from a producer, such as Colgate-Palmolive, to a consumer, such as yourself?

5. What marketing activities do Internet auctions like *eBay.com* perform?

6. What are the relationships between marketing as a societal process and the economic and political systems in a country?

7. What do you think is the most innovative development in marketing practice during the past few years? Why?

8. What types of marketing positions interest you? Why?

9. Why is building customer equity important?

10. How can developing marketing knowledge and skills help you in your career?

Applying Marketing Skills

1. Pick a retail store at which you frequently shop. Identify and discuss the store's target market and the specific product, price, integrated marketing communications, and distribution decisions the management has made to develop a marketing mix.

2. Interview someone in a marketing position. Ask him or her about the activities involved in the position, about any expected future changes in the position, and about career opportunities.

3. Identify a nonprofit organization in your community. Determine the role of marketing in this organization by reading promotional materials and talking with someone in the organization.

Using the www in Marketing

Activity One Go to Amazon.com's home page (*http://www.amazon.com*).

1. What are the latest products and services offered by Amazon.com?

2. What services does Amazon.com offer to help you select a DVD player that will best meet your needs?

3. Evaluate the selection and services offered by Amazon.com to help customers in purchasing books.

Activity Two Go to the Barnes & Noble home page (*http://www.barnesandnoble.com*).

1. Compare and contrast the home pages of Amazon.com and Barnes & Noble.

2. Evaluate the selection and services offered by Barnes & Noble to help customers in purchasing books and compare these with what Amazon.com offers.

3. What would you recommend Barnes & Noble do to provide more value to its book customers?

Making Marketing Decisions

Case 1–1 *Coca-Cola: Reviving a Marketing Giant*

Coca-Cola has been one of the world's great marketers. Under the tutelage of Roberto C. Goizueta, Coke built a strong market position around the world and achieved strong sales and earnings growth for 16 straight years. Its stock increased a whopping 3,500 percent during this period. Unfortunately, Goizueta died of cancer in 1997. M. Douglas Ivester, chief financial officer at the time, took over as CEO.

Ivester faced a number of challenges during his tenure. Coke's international growth slowed considerably. The situation in the United States was also difficult. American consumers drink more soft drinks than in any country in the world, except Mexico, but growth is slow. Therefore, domestic sales growth has to come from increases in market share.

Although Coke's problems were not all Ivester's fault, the company's lackluster performance had reduced its stock price substantially and put Ivester under enormous pressure. On December 6, 1999, he stunned everyone by announcing his pending retirement in April 2000 and the appointment of Douglas N. Daft as the new CEO.

Daft faced the same problems as Ivester. He tried to instill a more marketing-oriented philosophy throughout the company, increased marketing expenditures, and tried to improve relationships with bottlers. These efforts did not turn around Coke's situation.

New CEO E. Neville Isdell took over in 2004. Coke has about 44 percent of the U.S. soft drink market, compared to Pepsi's 32 percent. However, the U.S. soft drink market is growing only about 1 percent annually. The situation in the noncarbonated beverage category is just the opposite. Sales of bottled water, juice, tea, and sports drinks are growing about 8 percent per year in the United States, but Pepsi has a 24–16 percent market share advantage. The situation is a little better for Coke internationally with soft drink sales increasing rapidly in China, and Dasani bottled water and Powerade sports drinks sales strong globally. But sales in India, Germany, and the Philippines have been erratic.

Isdell's marketing strategy is to improve and increase advertising for Coke's core brands in the United States and emerging markets overseas. He also wants to accelerate the development of new products, especially more healthful drinks. Because of lower margins, Coke has been slow to enter non–soft drink markets. However, Isdell's success will likely be determined by how well he can develop the right strategies for the soft drink and noncarbonated beverage markets both domestically and internationally.

Questions

1. Do you think Coke should focus on the U.S. or international soft drink or noncarbonated drink market? Why?

2. What should Isdell do to increase market share in the noncarbonated beverage market?

3. What would you recommend Isdell do to increase Coke's soft drink sales in the United States?

4. What would you recommend Isdell do to increase Coke's soft drink sales internationally?

Case 1–2 Jollibee: Beating McDonald's in Burgers

 McDonald's is clearly the most successful fast-food brand in the world. It dominates most markets by providing customers with consistent product quality and service—but not in the Philippines.

Jollibee Foods Corp. is a family-owned chain that has captured about 52 percent of the Philippines market (compared with 16 percent for McDonald's). The company has twice as many stores in the Philippines as McDonald's does. How has Jollibee's been able to beat McDonald's in this market?

The major key to success is understanding and meeting the needs of the local market. Jollibee offers spicy burgers, fried chicken, and spaghetti and serves rice with all entrees. The food is similar to what "a Filipino mother would cook at home" and is designed "to suit the Filipino palate." And Jollibee charges prices from 5 to 10 percent lower than McDonald's. This combination of the right food at a lower price gives customers real value.

Jollibee also uses some marketing approaches that have been borrowed from McDonald's. It works hard to attract kids by targeting ads to children, providing in-store play activities, and offering signature characters and other licensed toys and products. The company locates restaurants in prime spots, often near a McDonald's outlet. And Jollibee maintains high standards for fast service and cleanliness.

The company is trying to duplicate its success in the Philippines in other international markets. It currently has restaurants in 10 countries—even in the United

States. Although Jollibee has plans to expand internationally in Asia, the Middle East, and China, its major focus is to be the leading food service company in the Philippines.

The company now serves over 1 million Filipinos a day at its 1,000 restaurants. It has expanded into the pizza–pasta, French café–bakery, and oriental quick service restaurant market segments by acquiring Greenwich Pizza, Delifrance, and Chowking. The basic marketing strategy for all of its restaurants is based on a superior menu lineup, creative marketing programs, efficient manufacturing and logistics facilities, and cheerful and friendly service. The company is highly respected by the Filipino people. In fact, every time a new store is opened, especially overseas, Filipinos form long lines to support the store opening.

Questions

1. Why do you think McDonald's has not been more successful against Jollibee in the Philippines?

2. What would you recommend McDonald's do to increase its market share in the Philippines?

3. What is your evaluation of Jollibee's strategy to expand into Asian, Middle Eastern, and Chinese markets?

4. What marketing strategy would you recommend to Jollibee for successful operations in the U.S. market? How do you think McDonald's will respond as Jollibee enters the U.S. market?

Chapter Two

THE GLOBAL MARKETING ENVIRONMENT

2

After studying this chapter, you should be able to

1 Understand the nature of the marketing environment and why it is important to marketers.

2 Describe the major components of the social environment and how trends in the social environment affect marketing.

3 Understand how the economic environment affects marketing.

4 See how the political/legal environment offers opportunities and threats to marketers.

5 Appreciate the importance of the technological environment to marketers.

6 Understand differences in the competitive environment.

7 Know how changes in the institutional environment affect marketers.

Dell

Michael Dell founded Dell Computer Corporation with $1,000 when he was a college student at the University of Texas at Austin in 1984. Today Dell is the world's leading direct computer systems company with annual revenues in excess of $40 billion and over 34,000 employees.

Why has Dell been so successful? The major reason is that Michael Dell revolutionized the computer industry by introducing the direct model. Prior to Dell, most personal computers were sold through various middlemen—wholesalers and retailers—to the final customer. Dell did not think these middlemen added much value, so he developed a model to bypass them. The basic direct model aims "to deliver a superior customer experience through direct, comprehensive customer relationships, cooperative research and development with technology partners, computer systems custom-built to customer specifications, and service and support programs tailored to customer needs." So if you go to the Dell Web site, you can select from various options to create the exact PC you desire. The computer will then be shipped directly to you. You can also check the Web site to follow your PC throughout the assembly process and keep track of it throughout the shipping process.

Dell now sells PCs and other computer products to business customers, government agencies, educational institutions, and consumers. The company is enhancing the direct model by applying the Internet to its entire business. This allows Dell to be very profitable. It sells low-margin products at low prices, but has much lower operating expenses than competitors.

Dell is the worldwide leader in personal computer market share. It is also the U.S. leader in desktops, notebooks, servers, profits, and growth. The future looks bright as Dell is changing from just a personal computer maker to a diversified IT firm by moving into servers and storage, mobility products, services, software peripheral categories, printers, and flat-screen TVs. In the consumer market it is trying to take advantage of the increasing importance of the personal computer in the digital home. In the business market it is becoming the e-management supplier of everything for small and medium-sized businesses. Dell was named America's Most Admired Company by *Fortune* magazine in 2005. This is quite a feat for a company started in a garage in 1984!

The Dell example illustrates how the marketing environment affects a firm's operations. The **marketing environment** consists of all factors external to an organization that can affect the organization's marketing activities. These factors are largely uncontrollable, although marketers can influence some of them. All marketers face the difficult task of identifying the important elements of the marketing environment for their organization, assessing current and likely future relationships between these factors, and developing effective strategies for a changing environment. This task has become increasingly difficult in recent years, as many elements of the marketing environment change rapidly and unpredictably. The objective of this chapter is to help you understand the important elements and relationships in the marketing environment.

The Marketing Environment

In the contemporary marketing framework diagrammed in Chapter 2 (Exhibit 1–9), the marketing environment appears in the outer circle. We now expand that framework by describing the major elements of the marketing environment. Exhibit 2–1 presents the addition of the social, economic, political/legal, technological, competitive, and institutional environments to the original diagram.

The best way to understand the marketing environment is to place yourself in the middle of the marketing circle. You are now a marketer for some organization and must make decisions about the marketing strategies employed by your organization. However, the decisions you *can* control depend on factors and trends in the marketing environment that you *cannot* control. Thus your task as a marketer is largely to identify opportunities or threats in the marketing environment and then make marketing decisions that capitalize on the opportunities and minimize the threats.

Exhibit 2–1	*Expanding the contemporary marketing framework*

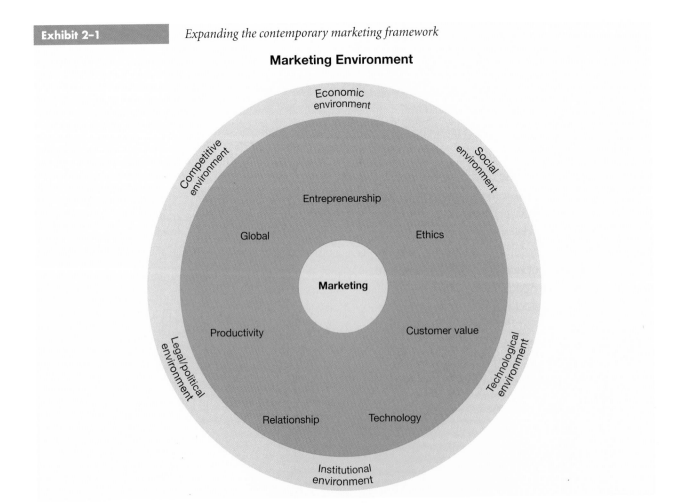

Marketing Environment

Thinking Critically

Select a sport that you like to play or watch:

- Identify at least five marketing environment trends you think will affect the number of people playing or watching your sport in the future.

- Which of these trends represent opportunities? Why?

- Which of these trends represent threats? Why?

- What marketing strategies would you recommend for the sport to take advantage of the opportunities and minimize the threats?

Creation of Market Opportunities and Threats

The marketing environment creates opportunities or threats in two basic ways. First, changes in the marketing environment can directly affect specific markets. A **market** is a group of people or organizations with common needs to satisfy or problems to solve, with the money to spend to satisfy needs or solve problems, and with the authority to make expenditure decisions. Changes in the marketing environment can make markets larger or smaller or sometimes create new markets. Market opportunities typically arise when markets increase in size or new markets are created.

Dell's approach to the server market is a good example. Increased layoffs, higher unemployment, and lower stock prices reduced the number of consumers and organizations willing to purchase PCs. Dell responded to this decrease in the size of the PC market by increasing its efforts in the low-end server market. Many organizations had to have more servers to increase their Internet capacity, even though economic conditions were not good. Dell offered the types of servers needed at a low price. These organizational customers found the low-priced servers very attractive, and Dell's server sales increased during a period when industry sales were decreasing.[1]

The second way the marketing environment produces opportunities or threats is through direct influences on specific marketing activities. Rapid advancements in Internet technology have allowed Dell to reach new markets and to serve customers more effectively and efficiently. Customers can now order customized computers, receive customer service, and get technical support 24 hours a day and seven days a week. Interacting with customers over the Internet is not only more convenient to customers, but is also less costly to Dell. So utilization of the Internet gives customers a better experience and increases Dell's profitability. However, changes in the marketing environment also pose threats. Many companies are using a direct model and incorporating the Internet into marketing operations. This increases the competitive intensity within the industry.

The critical point of this discussion is that marketers need to understand the marketing environment to be able to make good decisions. Changes in the marketing environment may create opportunities or threats either by affecting markets or by directly influencing marketing activities.

Identifying Market Opportunities and Threats

Many firms use **environmental scanning** to identify important trends and determine whether they represent present or future market opportunities or threats. As illustrated in Exhibit 2–2, this procedure consists of identifying relevant factors, determining expected trends, and assessing their potential impact on the organization's markets and marketing activities. This is simpler to say than do because many of the potentially important environmental factors are interrelated, and many of them change constantly.

Exhibit 2–2   *The environmental scanning approach*

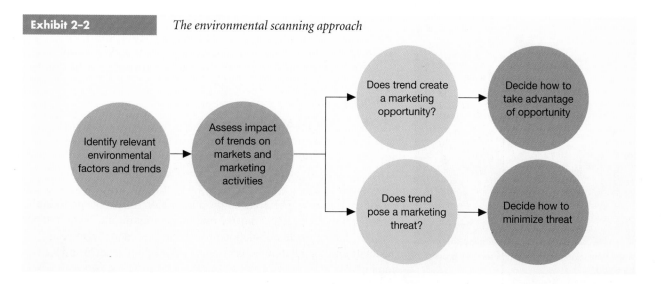

Speaking from Experience

"Hong Kong was in a recession in the early 2000s with consumer confidence and business sentiment low, unemployment high, and real estate prices slumping. The business environment has improved considerably in the last two years. In 2004 the government of China opened the door for Chinese tourists to visit Hong Kong freely from several provinces in the mainland. This has greatly increased retail sales and reduced unemployment. Real estate prices have also increased over 30 percent. These changes have increased consumer confidence and improved business sentiment."

Samuel Chi-Hung Lee
International Marketing Consultant
SamLink International

Samuel Chi-Hung Lee's company has established extensive business networks in Asian Pacific countries, such as Japan, South Korea, Taiwan, Australia, New Zealand, Singapore, Malaysia, Vietnam, and China. He has an MBA and has been involved in the international marketing consultancy business from his Hong Kong base for almost 20 years.

Marketers must continually monitor the marketing environment to identify trends in relevant areas and develop appropriate responses. Some aspects of the marketing environment are more controllable than others. For example, firms can have a direct impact on the legal/political environment through lobbying, campaign contributions, and various political activities. Many companies, therefore, are proactive in trying to influence the legal/political environment in a way that is advantageous for their business. In contrast, firms have little control over the demographic environment, so they must typically react to current and expected demographic trends. The key is to understand what is happening and likely to happen in a firm's marketing environment and then determine the best proactive or reactive actions for the company to capitalize on opportunities and minimize threats.

Social Environment

The **social environment** includes all factors and trends related to groups of people, including their number, characteristics, behavior, and growth projections. Because consumer markets have specific needs and problems, changes in the social environment can affect markets differently. Trends in the social environment might increase the size of some markets, decrease the size of others, or even help to create new markets. We discuss two important components of the social environment: the demographic environment and the cultural environment.

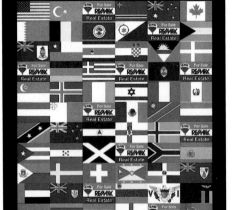

Many firms market products and services around the world.

Demographic Environment

The **demographic environment** refers to the size, distribution, and growth rate of groups of people with different characteristics. The demographic characteristics of interest to marketers relate in some way to purchasing behavior, because people from different countries, cultures, age groups, or household arrangements often exhibit different purchasing behaviors. A global perspective requires that marketers be familiar with important demographic trends around the world as well as within the United States.

GLOBAL POPULATION SIZE AND GROWTH   Population size and growth rates provide one indication of potential market opportunities. The world population is now about 6.4 billion, with around 74 million people added each year. The situation can be summarized as follows. Every second there are 4.1 births and 1.8 deaths, for a net increase of 2.3 people each second. This leads to the addition of 141 people per minute, 8,434 per hour, 202,419 per day, 6.2 million per month, and 74 million per year. The rate of world population growth has slowed in recent years, but the total world population is expected to be 7.8 billion in 2025 and 9.2 billion in 2050.[2]

Exhibit 2–3　　　*The most populous countries in 2025*

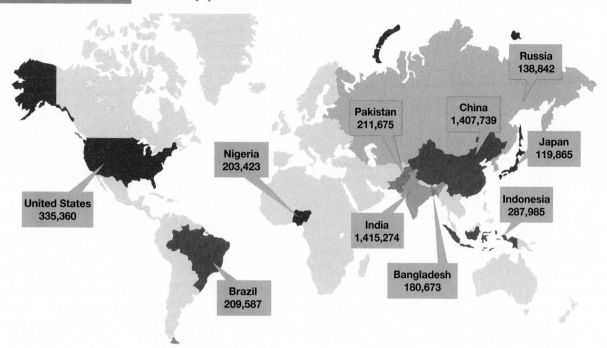

Note: Population in thousands—Year 2025 (estimated).

There is a tremendous disparity in population size and growth rates across countries, as shown in Exhibit 2–3. China currently has the largest population, followed by India, with the United States a distant third. The rapid growth of the Indian population is expected to make it the world's most populous nation. Other countries with large and growing populations are the developing nations of Indonesia, Brazil, Pakistan, Bangladesh, and Nigeria. Most of the world's population growth is in developing countries in Asia, Africa, and Latin America. Population in developed countries is growing at a much slower rate, with some countries actually declining in population. For example, Germany's current population is about 82.4 million. It is expected to decline to 80.6 million by 2025 and 73.6 million by 2050.[3]

These world population statistics make it clear that marketers cannot rely on population growth in developed countries for general increases in market size. The largest markets, measured by population size and growth, are in the developing countries. Yet lower income levels in developing countries may limit the actual market size for many products. Thus marketers will have to look hard to find attractive growth markets in developed and developing countries.

GLOBAL DEMOGRAPHIC CHARACTERISTICS AND TRENDS　Overall world and country population statistics are important, but most marketers target subgroups within these large populations. Trends in population subgroups are therefore typically the most useful to marketers.

An important trend in many countries is growth of the urban population. Current and projected populations for the world's largest cities are presented in Exhibit 2–4. In general, the largest cities and the highest city growth rates are in developing countries such as Mexico, Brazil, and India; however, growth in urban population is evident in many developed countries. For example, in 1900 the U.S. population was 39.6 percent urban and 60.4 percent rural; in 2000 the figures were 79 percent urban and 21 percent rural.[4] This means the largest and fastest-growing markets for many products are located in the urban areas of most countries.

Another interesting trend is the aging of the population in many countries. Past and projected median ages for selected countries are presented in Exhibit 2–5. The aging of the population is especially evident in Italy, Japan, Britain, and the United States. Notice, however, the relatively young populations in the developing countries, such as Nigeria, Mexico, Brazil, and China.

Exhibit 2–4	*The world's largest cities*

City	2000 (in thousands)	2015 (est.) (in thousands)
1. Tokyo, Japan	34,450	36,214
2. Mexico City, Mexico	18,066	20,647
3. New York, U.S.	17,846	19,717
4. São Paulo, Brazil	17,099	19,963
5. Mumbai (Bombay), India	16,086	22,645
6. Kolkata (Calcutta), India	13,058	16,798
7. Shanghai, China	12,887	12,666
8. Buenos Aires, Argentina	12,583	14,563
9. Delhi, India	12,441	20,946
10. Los Angeles, U.S.	11,814	12,904

Exhibit 2–5	*Median age in selected countries*

Country	Median Ages Past and Projected	
	1990	2010
Italy	36.2	42.4
Japan	37.2	42.2
Britain	35.7	40.0
U.S.	32.9	37.4
Korea (North and South)	25.7	34.4
China	25.4	33.9
Brazil	22.9	29.2
Mexico	20.0	26.5
Nigeria	16.3	18.1

Age distribution trends in the United States reflect this aging trend. The largest percentage of growth is occurring in the 45–64 and 65+ age brackets, with slight to moderate decreases in all younger age categories. These trends have important implications for marketers; older consumers have different needs and purchasing habits than do younger consumers. Marketers are responding to different age markets in a number of ways:

- Younger children have trouble peeling or eating whole fruit by themselves. Sunkist Fun Fruits are sliced fruits with no stems in half-cup serving packages with pictures of children on them. Fun Fruits open like potato chip packages, so children find them easy to open and eat the fruit.[5]

- A few years ago few males between 11 and 24 thought about wearing body spray. Now more than 30 percent of them wear body spray, a combination of deodorant and light cologne. Axe Bodyspray has over 80 percent of this $180 million and growing market. But competition is heating up with the introduction of Red Zone Body Spray by Old Spice and Tag by Right Guard.[6]

- Automobile companies are targeting buyers in their twenties and thirties with different models and appeals. For example, the Mazda 3 emphasizes a bold design and tight handling. Honda is reviving its Civic with a snappier, racier design, zippier engine, and sportier suspension.[7]

- The aging of the population has created a large, growing global market for antiaging skin care products. Sales of antiaging skin care products are over $10 billion annually and have grown over 71 percent since 2000. Examples of available products include Perfectionist CP+ (Estee Lauder), Regenerist Perfecting Cream (Olay), and Anew Clinical Line and Wrinkle Corrector (Avon).[8]

Another interesting demographic trend is the changing of household composition in the United States. From almost 80 percent of households in 1950, married-couple households have dropped to about 50 percent, and married couples with kids to around 25 percent. Nearly 30 percent of households consist of someone living alone. And a variety of different household arrangements are prevalent, such as divorced parents sharing child custody, gay couples raising children, single parents, widows and widowers, and cohabitants. The needs and purchasing behaviors of these different household arrangements represent important trends affecting marketers.[9]

Cultural Environment

The **cultural environment** refers to factors and trends related to how people live and behave. Cultural factors, including the values, ideas, attitudes, beliefs, and activities of specific population subgroups, greatly affect consumers' purchasing behavior. Thus marketers must understand important cultural characteristics and trends in different markets.

CULTURAL DIVERSITY   Cultural differences are important in both international and domestic markets. For example, the world's 1.2 billion Muslims want financial institutions that are faithful to Islamic values, such as not charging interest or engaging in short-selling or speculation. However, there are key differences in marketing to Muslims in a Muslim country versus a non-Muslim country. Those living in non-Muslim countries typically balance the local culture and Islamic values. Marketers must, therefore, communicate sensitively with them and use referral and networking approaches to attract customers.[10] A cultural group's characteristics and values affect the types of products it desires and how it purchases and uses those products.

Different cultural groups in international markets often require marketers to develop strategies specifically for them. Campbell's Soup has had some successes and some failures in doing this. The successes include hearty vegetable and fat-free soups in Australia, duck-gizzard soup in Hong Kong, and the Godiva Chocolatier line in Japan. But the company has had some failures due to not understanding cultural differences in some markets. German consumers did not like Campbell's canned condensed soup. They prefer dry soups in envelopes. Polish consumers did not like Campbell's prepared soups because they would rather cook soup at home.[11]

Much of the population and buying power growth in the United States is and will be from multicultural groups. Most of this population growth is accounted for by Hispanics, African Americans, Asian Americans, and Central and Eastern Europeans. The Hispanic population is growing especially fast. It increased by 85 percent since 1990 to 41.3 million, and is expected to reach 102.5 million and be 25 percent of the U.S. population by 2050. Of particular interest to marketers is the buying power of the different cultural groups. As indicated in Exhibit 2–6, each cultural group has substantial buying power now with significant growth projected in the future.[12]

| **Exhibit 2–6** | *Buying power of cultural groups (in billions)* |

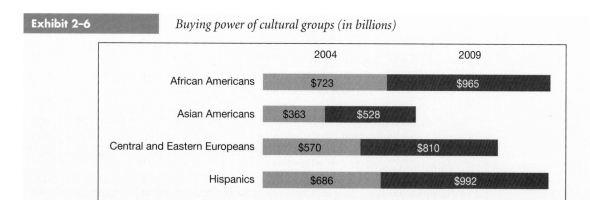

Populations in developed countries are aging, while those in developing countries are much younger. These different demographic trends represent challenging marketing opportunities for many firms.

Another interesting trend is a blending of races and ethnic groups. It is estimated that by 2050, the percentage of the U.S. population that claims some combination of black, white, Hispanic, or Asian ancestry will triple to 21 percent. Singer Mariah Carey and TV news anchor Soledad O'Brien (black, white, and Hispanic) and golfer Tiger Woods (black, white, American Indian, and Asian) are prominent examples of this trend.[13]

This cultural complexity confronts marketers with a continual challenge. Many firms are involved in multicultural marketing. Effective **multicultural marketing** consists of developing a deep understanding of and sensitivity for different cultural markets and the development of relevant products and messages to targeted groups within these markets.[14] Procter & Gamble provides an excellent example of multicultural marketing. P&G established a Multicultural Business Development Organization to market effectively to different cultural groups, especially African Americans and Hispanics. It focused on only 12 brands, but tailored marketing efforts to meet the needs of each cultural group. The results have been impressive, with 6 of the 12 brands ranked number one by Hispanics and five others ranked second.[15] Other examples of successful multicultural marketing include these:

- There are normally many different segments within a cultural market. For example, one study divided the Hispanic market into 19 different lifestyle segments. U.S. Cellular targeted the young, urban Hispanic segment and was able to increase the number of new customers from this group.[16]

- Allstate Insurance segmented the Asian American market into Chinese, Filipino, Indian, Vietnamese, Korean, and Japanese segments. The company targeted the Chinese market, spent a lot of time and money learning about the market, and developed a language-specific integrated marketing communication campaign to appeal to Chinese consumers. This included Cantonese and Mandarin language TV, radio, and print ads; a special Chinese Web site; and the use of Chinese-speaking agents. This marketing approach has been so successful that Allstate has had to hire more Chinese-speaking agents.[17]

- The Central and Eastern European market is about 20 million in the United States, with the largest segments being Polish, Russian, Hungarian, Czech, and Greek. Lufthansa AG, the German airline, is focusing on Polish and Russian Americans. The airline has developed a special Web site where Poles or Russians can book flights in English or their own language. The availability of the site is communicated in radio, TV, and print media that reach Polish and Russian Americans. Online ticket sales to Central and Eastern European countries have more than doubled since the marketing efforts were initiated.[18]

These examples illustrate how different multicultural marketing approaches can be effective in appealing to specific cultural markets and segments.

Women are taking on many new roles and offer attractive opportunities to marketers.

CHANGING ROLES As more women enter the workforce and household compositions change, typical household roles are altered. No longer are financially supporting the household and developing a career solely the responsibility of men. No longer are household chores, child care, or grocery shopping solely the responsibility of women. In many households, roles have shifted and distinctions have become blurred. More men spend time on household and shopping chores, and many women are involved in career development and provide much or most of the financial resources for a household. Tremendous market opportunities exist for firms that can develop effective strategies for appealing to these changing roles.

Take golf as an example. Women now account for about 21 percent of golfers in the United States. And this percentage is growing. Some of this growth is due to more women playing golf as part of their business or professional life. Others play the sport entirely for pleasure. In any case, women spend more than $3 billion annually on golf equipment, clothing, travel, greens fees, and other related products. One study found that women are more likely to take golf lessons, are less price sensitive, and are more concerned about wearing fashionable clothing than are men golfers. This growing, upscale market of female golfers is attractive to marketers of golf products as well as marketers of other products.[19]

EMPHASIS ON HEALTH AND FITNESS Another cultural trend is an increased emphasis on health and fitness. The pursuit of a more healthful lifestyle includes eating more nutritious foods, exercising regularly, participating in various sports activities, and focusing on wellness. This translates into potential market opportunities for firms that provide products and services geared toward improving health and fitness.

The chocolate industry provides an interesting example of potential opportunities. Global sales of chocolate are over $58 billion annually, mostly from not-so-healthful milk chocolate. Barry Callebaut AG is the world's largest manufacturer of cocoa and chocolate.

Multicultural marketing is increasingly important to meet the needs of different cultural groups in many markets.

Cocoa is rich in polyphenols that act as antioxidants and have beneficial effects on cholesterol, cancer, blood pressure, and long-term memory. However, these polyphenols are largely destroyed during the chocolate-making process. Barry Callebaut has patented a process to stop this destruction. Its polyphenol-rich chocolate is currently being tested for health benefits. The company is also working on other more healthful chocolate products, such as chocolates made with added fiber and sugar-free chocolates that taste good. These products are all intended to take advantage of the increased importance of health and fitness to more consumers around the world.[20]

DESIRE FOR CONVENIENCE Changes in household composition, increases in the number of working women, and a general shortage of time underlie an increased desire for convenience. Two-paycheck households often have more money than time. And they are willing to spend this money to avoid spending time doing undesirable chores, such as cooking, cleaning, or auto maintenance. Thus many consumers buy products and services to minimize time devoted to such chores, opening new market opportunities for companies able to meet these needs.

Think of all the products and services that are focused on responding to the increased desire for convenience. Many stores are open for longer hours or even 24 hours; there is an increased use of drive-in windows for fast food, banking, and prescriptions; delivery services exist for dry cleaning,

Excuse me, could we have this magazine when you're done with it?

And while you're at it, give us those old office memos and that 60-page presentation you stuck in a file five years ago and haven't looked at since. We know how to make good use of it all. Since 1974, Weyerhaeuser has been collecting and recycling paper that used to be thrown into landfills – about 60 million tons in all. That's enough to fill the Empire State Building 111 times over. Today, our office paper recycling program serves three million participants, and it's growing every day. To find out how Weyerhaeuser can help your company or small business with recycling, call us at 800-867-2693.

▲ **Weyerhaeuser**
The future is growing
www.weyerhaeuser.com/recycling

Many consumers and businesses are concerned about protecting the environment.

fast food, and groceries; and there is increasing use of the Internet to shop, make purchases, pay bills, communicate with e-mail, and perform many other activities. The desire for convenience is likely to continue to increase in the future. This will create opportunities for marketers to offer their customers more convenient products and services. An interesting example is presented in "Creating Customer Value: Even Convenience Stores Are Becoming More Convenient."

CONSUMERISM   *Consumerism* is the movement to establish and protect the rights of buyers. Some say the consumerism movement will intensify as we move through the twenty-first century. Consumers are more educated, knowledgeable, and organized. They demand better consumer information, quality, service, and dependability, and fair prices. Giving consumers products that work, charging fair prices, being honest, and practicing social responsibility are the best ways to respond to consumerism.

One increasingly important consumer issue is environmentalism. As consumers worldwide become concerned with environmental issues, their purchasing behavior is changing. Successful marketers can respond by developing environmentally safe products and communicating their environmental contributions.

This environmental trend applies to both consumer and business markets. For example, General Electric plans to double its sales of environmentally cleaner products in business markets by 2010. It will also begin to market itself more as a company that produces environmentally friendly products. One example is its "Ecomagination" advertising campaign. Although the focus of these efforts is in the industrial sector, an environmentally friendly image is likely to help General Electric in consumer sales of appliances and lighting products.[21]

Economic Environment

The **economic environment** includes factors and trends related to income levels and the production of goods and services. Whereas demographic and cultural trends generally affect the size and needs of various markets, economic trends affect the purchasing power of these markets. Thus it is not enough for a population to be large or fast growing, as in many developing countries, to offer good market opportunities; the economy must provide sufficient purchasing power for consumers to satisfy their wants and needs.

Economic trends in different parts of the world can affect marketing activities in other parts of the world. For example, changes in interest rates in Europe affect the value of the dollar on world currency markets, which affects the price, and subsequently sales, of American exports and imports.

CREATING CUSTOMER VALUE

Even convenience stores are becoming more convenient

Most of the more than 138,000 convenience stores in the United States made most of their sales from gasoline, cigarettes, fast food, and items consumers picked up between trips to the grocery store. This is changing as more convenience stores are getting larger and offering gourmet coffee, upscale products, and high-end meals. The purpose is to make it more convenient for consumers to do more shopping and eating at these stores. For example, Thorton's Quick Café & Market concept offers branded items in grocery store sizes and fresh salads, sandwiches, and burgers; The Markets of Tiger Fuel has a fancy deli and fresh seafood; On the Run serves a proprietary line of gourmet coffee; and 7-Eleven carries wine, sushi, and prepaid cell phones.

Many developing countries have large and growing segments of middle-class consumers. Many companies are targeting the large group of middle-class consumers in India.

Market opportunities are a function of both economic size and growth. The **gross domestic product (GDP)** represents the total size of a country's economy measured in the amount of goods and services produced. Changes in GDP indicate trends in economic activity. However, changes in economic growth around the world mean that market opportunities are often shifting among countries. Economic growth slowed throughout much of the world in 2001, but recovery began in late 2002. However, there were significant differences in both economic decline and recovery across countries.

Economic growth in the United States and much of the developing world has been about 3 percent annually, but less than that in Japan and parts of Western Europe. Although Japan has the second largest economy in the world, GDP growth in 2004 was only 0.3 percent, with little indication it will pick up in the future. The situation in Western Europe is only a little better, with economic growth around 1.5 percent. Companies such as IBM, Emerson, Sara Lee, and General Motors are responding to this slow growth by scaling back or eliminating operations in Western Europe.[22]

Developing countries, especially China and India, are experiencing faster economic growth. China has averaged a 9.5 percent GDP growth rate during the past two decades. India grew 4.6 percent, but is expecting 5–8 percent GDP growth in the coming years. Not all developing countries are growing this fast. Nigeria and most of the African and Middle Eastern countries are growing much more slowly. However, Siemens, Philips Electronics, Citigroup, and General Electric and many other companies see most of their revenue growth coming from developing countries.[23]

Marketing opportunities can often be found by looking at economic differences within countries.[24] For example, many developing countries have large populations relative to their economic strength; that is, the average consumer does not have much purchasing power. However, subgroups within these countries may have substantial purchasing power, or economic growth may offer substantial opportunities in the future. India, for example, has a large and growing population and a low but growing per capita income. Within this relatively poor country, however, are about 250 million middle-class consumers. The situation in China is similar. The overall per capita income is low, but there is a large, fast-growing middle class of more than 100 million people. General Motors, Procter & Gamble, and Motorola are finding these middle-class markets very attractive for selling cars, shampoo, and cell phones.[25] However, as presented in "Being Entrepreneurial: Creating Opportunities," entrepreneurial companies can find ways to market successfully to the poorest of consumers.

Samuel Chi-Hung Lee, International Marketing Consultant, SamLink International, discusses the marketing opportunities available in China: "Many of the marketing opportunities available to companies in Hong Kong depend on economic growth in China. China's entry into the World Trade Organization

BEING ENTREPRENEURIAL

Creating opportunities

About 65 percent of the world's population earns less than $2,000 per year. Many of these poor are in India living in villages away from urban areas. Most companies are focusing marketing efforts on the middle-class and upper-class consumers in the urban areas. Hindustan Lever is taking advantage of opportunities in these poor, rural areas. It introduced a high-quality candy with real sugar and fruit and sold it for a penny a serving. The product is profitable, and the firm thinks it has the potential to generate $200 million per year in India

and comparable markets in five years. One of the difficulties facing Hindustan Lever is getting products to consumers in these rural areas. The company is using women in these areas to sell its products. There are currently 13,000 poor women selling Lifebuoy soap, Clinic shampoo, and other products in 50,000 Indian villages. These women are not company employees, but entrepreneurs. They receive microcredit loans to purchase the products from Hindustan Lever, and then earn profits from sales to consumers.

(WTO) has had a positive economic impact and created many business opportunities for Hong Kong. Many local and international companies have already moved to the northern Chinese cities of Beijing, Shanghai, and Guangzhou. As China prepares for hosting the 2008 Summer Olympics in Beijing, many more opportunities will be available to Hong Kong and international companies. In the Pearl River Delta of South China, the central government in Beijing has approved a project to build an expressway to link the three cities of Hong Kong, Macau, and Zhuhai."

Political/Legal Environment

The **political/legal environment** encompasses factors and trends related to governmental activities and specific laws and regulations that affect marketing practice. The political/legal environment is closely tied to the social and economic environments. That is, pressures from the social environment, such as ecological or health concerns, or the economic environment, such as slow economic growth or high unemployment, typically motivate legislation intended to improve the particular situation. Regulatory agencies implement legislation by developing and enforcing regulations. Therefore, it is important for marketers to understand specific political processes, laws, and regulations, as well as important trends in each of these areas.

Global Political Trends

In today's world economy, international political events greatly affect marketing activities. Probably the most significant global political trend is the "war on terrorism" led by the United States and a coalition of many different countries around the world. These countries are responding to the September 11, 2001, terrorist attack on the United States, suicide bombings in Israel, terrorist activity in Kashmir and the Philippines, and other terrorist threats. The threat of terrorism and the war on terrorism have changed how people live and companies do business in many parts of the world. For example, many consumers have reduced or changed their normal travel behavior. This has had a negative impact on all aspects of the travel industry, especially the airline industry. In contrast, the need for increased security has generated marketing opportunities for firms providing security products and services.

A second important political trend is movement toward free trade and away from protectionism. One approach is the development of trading blocs throughout the world. One of the most significant is the European Union (EU). It consists of 25 European countries representing 454 million consumers and a combined GDP of $12.5 trillion.[26] The aim is to eliminate trade barriers and to promote easier access to the markets in each participating country. As this development continues, trading blocs have the potential to generate many opportunities for marketers.

The free trade trend goes beyond trading blocs and encompasses a global perspective. The best example of this perspective is the General Agreement on Tariffs and Trade, or GATT. This agreement was signed by 124 countries in 1994 to eliminate trade barriers worldwide. The World Trade Organization (WTO) was established as the watchdog organization, and a world court was set up in Geneva to arbitrate trade disputes. Although results have been mixed, the WTO is making slow but steady progress toward free trade around the world. There are currently 148 members, with China granted membership in 2001. Russia is likely to become a member in the future. The WTO is currently involved in the Doha Development Agenda round of trade negotiations.[27]

There are clear benefits to free trade. For example, studies show that countries with the freest trade have the highest GDP growth.[28] However, achieving free trade in the current environment is difficult for at least two reasons. First, there is often tremendous political pressure to protect specific industries. The United States is one of the major proponents of free trade, but it has established tariffs on imported steel and Canadian softwood lumber and has instituted new farm subsidies.[29] Second, free trade in a global economy requires the free movement of people, goods, and capital across borders. This is difficult to achieve given the need for more security in the war on terrorism. There is likely to be continued tension among the desire for free trade, the political need for some protectionism, and the security requirements for combating terrorism.

Samuel Chi-Hung Lee, International Marketing Consultant, SamLink International, talks about the political environment in Hong Kong since July 1, 1997: "It has been eight years since Hong Kong became a part of China. In March 2005, the first Hong Kong Special Administrative Region Chief Executive, Tung Chee Hwa, submitted his resignation as the political leader in Hong Kong. The first election of a new chief executive will be held in July 2005. Donald Tsang is expected to be elected. He has been a civil servant in Hong Kong for over 30 years. This should not produce much change in the current political situation. However, the people have confidence that he will be able to lead Hong Kong into a new era."

Legislation

Organizations must deal with laws at the international, federal, state, and local levels. U.S. laws directly affecting marketing typically fall into two categories: those promoting competition among firms and those protecting consumers and society. Exhibit 2–7 presents examples of each type.

Laws promoting competition focus on outlawing practices that give a few firms unfair competitive advantages over others. The specific impact of these laws depends on court rulings that may change over time or differ at the state and national levels. One of the highest-profile cases in recent years is *United States v. Microsoft.* The government charged that Microsoft routinely used its monopoly power to crush competitors. The first round went to the government, when U.S. District Judge Thomas P. Jackson released his finding of facts in its favor. Microsoft appealed the verdict and reached a settlement with the Justice Department.

Consumer protection laws generally indicate what firms must do to give consumers the information they need to make sound purchasing decisions or to ensure that the products they buy are safe. For example, the Fair Packaging and Labeling Act requires packages to

| **Exhibit 2–7** | *Key U.S. laws affecting marketing* |

A. Promoting Competition

Act	Purpose
• Sherman Act (1890)	Prohibits monopolistic practices
• Clayton Act (1914)	Prohibits anticompetitive activities
• Federal Trade Commission Act (1914)	Establishes regulatory agency to enforce laws against unfair competition
• Robinson–Patman Act (1936)	Prohibits price discrimination
• Lanham Trademark Act (1946)	Protects trademarks and brand names
• Magnusson–Moss Act (1975)	Regulates warranties
• United States–Canada Trade Act (1988)	Allows free trade between the United States and Canada
• Sarbanes–Oxley Corporate Responsibility Act (2002)	Prevents fraud and promotes corporate accountability

B. Protecting Consumers and Society

Act	Purpose
• Food, Drug, and Cosmetics Act (1938)	Regulates food, drug, and cosmetic industries
• Fair Packaging and Labeling Act (1966)	Regulates packaging and labeling
• Consumer Credit Protection Act (1968)	Requires full disclosure of financial charges for loans
• Child Protection and Toy Safety Act (1969)	Prevents marketing of dangerous products to children
• Fair Credit Report Act (1970)	Regulates reporting and use of credit information
• Fair Debt Collections Practice Act (1970)	Regulates methods for collecting debts
• Child Protection Act (1990)	Regulates advertising on children's television programs
• Americans with Disabilities Act (1990)	Prohibits discrimination against consumers with disabilities
• Do Not Call Implementation Act (2003)	Regulates calls by telemarketers
• Can Spam Act (2003)	Prohibits junk e-mail

The war on terrorism and corporate scandals will have a major impact on marketers and consumers for many years.

be labeled honestly; the Child Protection Act regulates the amount of advertising that can appear on children's television programs.

The business press has been inundated with stories about companies such as Enron, WorldCom, Arthur Andersen, Qwest Communications, Tyco International, and Global Crossing and CEOs such as Martha Stewart, Al Dunlap, Kenneth Lay, and Dennis Kozlowski. These stories report many examples of alleged misreporting of earnings, insider trading, tax evasion, securities fraud, obstruction of justice, and other questionable activities. Some of these activities result in unfair competition; others have an adverse effect on consumers. Because of the global economy, this is a global problem. However, Germany, France, Italy, Finland, Sweden, Hong Kong, Japan, and other countries are implementing different approaches to increase corporate accountability and responsibility.[30] The Sarbanes-Oxley Corporate Responsibility Act was passed in 2002 to prevent fraud and to promote corporate accountability in the U.S.

Regulation and Regulatory Agencies

Most legislation in the United States is enforced through regulations developed by a variety of agencies, and marketers must often work with regulatory authorities at the federal, state, and local levels. Several of the most important federal agencies are described in Exhibit 2–8. Some of these regulatory agencies cut across industries (FTC, CPSC, EPA); others focus on specific

Exhibit 2–8	*Important U.S. regulatory agencies*

Agency	Responsibilities
• Federal Trade Commission (FTC)	Regulates business practices
• Consumer Product Safety Commission (CPSC)	Protects consumers from unsafe products
• Environmental Protection Agency (EPA)	Protects environment
• Food and Drug Administration (FDA)	Regulates food, drug, and cosmetic industries
• Interstate Commerce Commission (ICC)	Regulates interstate transportation industry
• Federal Communications Commission (FCC)	Regulates interstate communications industry

industries (FDA, ICC, FCC). The impact of these regulatory agencies is especially evident in the pharmaceutical industry. The FDA must approve a new drug before it is marketed and can place limitations on its use. Pharmaceutical companies have paid the U.S. government more than $2 billion since 2001 to resolve charges of promoting drugs for uses not approved by the FDA and other fraudulent sales and marketing tactics.[31] This includes one settlement of $875 million and another of $430 million from individual companies.[32]

One area receiving a great deal of regulatory attention is consumer privacy. This includes restricting the use of information consumers provide to companies, as well as protecting consumers from unwanted telemarketing and e-mail (SPAM) solicitations: The FTC is working through many problems in interpreting the Can Spam Act.[33] However, it has announced the first settlements with firms violating the Do Not Call Implementation Act. Two timeshare companies and their telemarketer will pay $500,000 for calling thousands of customers who placed their phone numbers on the FTC's no-call registry.[34]

Technological Environment

The **technological environment** includes factors and trends related to innovations that affect the development of new products or the marketing process. These technological trends can provide opportunities for new product development, affect how marketing activities are performed, or both. For example, advances in information and communication technologies provide new products for firms to market, and the buyers of these products often use them to change the way they market their own products. Using these technological products can help marketers be more productive.

New technologies can spawn new industries, new businesses, or new products for existing business. Firms at the leading edge of technological developments are in a favorable position. Thus marketers need to monitor the technological environment constantly to look for potential opportunities that will improve their positions.

Marketers also need to monitor the technological environment to minimize threats to their companies or industries. New technologies can, after all, *disrupt* entire industries as well as enhance them. For example, optical networks are affecting the telecommunications industry; diagnostic technologies are affecting the health care industry; systems-on-a-chip technologies are pressuring the microprocessor industry; and the Internet is having a significant impact on retailing, financial services, and education.[35]

Consider how the following new and emerging technologies offer potential marketing opportunities:

- Nanotechnology is the ability to manipulate individual atoms to create new materials. The technology has already been used to produce a number of interesting products: automotive sideboards that are stronger and lighter than existing ones, vinyl flooring that won't scuff, mattress covers that won't stain, transparent sunscreen, and tennis balls that last twice as long as normal. Products under development include faster semiconductor chips, implantable devices and biosensors for automatically delivering drug doses, hydrogen cells that can power cars, and tiny robots that could clean oceans and attack germs.[36]

- Developments in horticulture will result in new materials of unprecedented strength and flexibility, new sources of food and medicine, and new approaches for renewable energy. Although these developments are in the early stages, horticulture research has already produced from plants composite materials that are stronger than steel.[37]

- Ultrawideband (UWB) represents tiny pulses of radio signals that can zip through airwaves without interfering

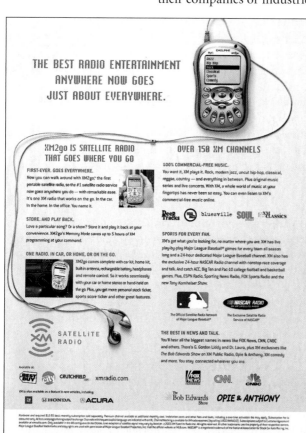

New technologies are the source of many new products and services, such as satellite radio.

with cell phone conversations or broadcasts. Potential applications include a fireman using a UWB "flashlight" to see through walls to locate victims, a camcorder fitted with a UWB chip that could beam home movies to a TV across the room, and a UWB anticollision device that regulates a car's speed, keeping it from getting too close to another car.[38]

Competitive Environment

The **competitive environment** consists of all the organizations that attempt to serve similar customers. Two types of competitors are of major concern: brand competitors and product competitors. **Brand competitors** provide the most direct competition, offering the same types of products as competing firms. For example, Nike is a brand competitor of Reebok, Adidas, and other firms that market different brands of the same types of sport shoes. These firms target the same markets and typically try to take customers away from one another.

Product competitors offer different types of products to satisfy the same general need. Domino's Pizza, McDonald's, and Kentucky Fried Chicken are product competitors. They attempt to satisfy a consumer need for fast food, but they offer somewhat different menus and services. Domino's, McDonald's, and KFC also have brand competitors, which market the same types of fast food to the same customers. Brand competitors of Domino's, for example, are Pizza Hut, Papa John's Pizza, and Little Caesar's Pizza.

The competitive environment for most firms is fierce and often global. Marketers must identify their relevant brand and product competitors in order to identify market opportunities and develop marketing strategies. One trend affecting many industries is the changing competitive landscape. Some product competitors have become brand competitors by expanding their product offerings.

Consider the financial services industry. Banks used to compete against banks, insurance companies against insurance companies, brokerage firms against brokerage firms. Now many banks, insurance companies, and brokerage houses offer a range of financial service products that compete directly with one another. And new competitors are entering the market, especially through the Internet. It is now possible to do banking, buy and sell securities, and purchase many other financial service products online.

The DVD rental business provides an interesting example of how the competitive landscape might develop over time. Let's start with Blockbuster and other retail stores renting DVDs. Then Netflix introduces a DVD rental subscription service over the Internet. Wal-Mart follows suit with online rentals, then Blockbuster; then Amazon.com jumps in. Wal-Mart decides to let Netflix handle its business. But now McDonald's begins offering DVDs from vending machines in some stores. Then MoviebankUSA starts to offer DVDs through kiosks in various neighborhoods.[39] What will happen next? Although complex and difficult, it is extremely important that marketers keep track of the number, types, and actions of competitors.

Institutional Environment

The **institutional environment** consists of all the organizations involved in marketing products and services. These include marketing research firms, advertising agencies, wholesalers, retailers, suppliers, and customers. Specific trends and characteristics of these institutions are discussed in detail in subsequent chapters.

Many organizations are changing how they are structured and managed. These trends in the institutional environment include reengineering, restructuring, the virtual corporation, horizontal organizations, and empowerment. An organization's adoption of any of these concepts means that it is changing some elements of its structure and processes. These changes are likely to affect the amount and types of products the firm needs as well as the purchasing processes it uses.

One trend that continues to increase and expand is outsourcing. Instead of doing everything internally, many companies are outsourcing various business operations to other firms. Because these firms specialize in the particular operation, companies get things done at a lower cost. Outsourcing has moved from being domestic to being international and from basic production operations to R&D and product design. For example, companies in India earn more than $17 billion annually for writing software, collecting debts,

Outsourcing various business and marketing functions is an increasing trend.

Innovation drives everything we do.

From innovative drive systems challenging the electric car land speed record to research on the first "self-healing" power grid, our breakthroughs have proven time and again that today's revolutionary ideas lead the way to greater productivity and competitive advantage for customers tomorrow. Over 100,000 power and automation professionals around the world. Over one million solutions delivered every day. Welcome to the world of ABB.

www.abb.us

© 2005 ABB Inc.

ABB

Marketers need to be innovative to take advantage of opportunities in a dynamic marketing environment.

running call centers to provide customer service, designing semiconductors, and other activities.[40] Companies in Asia and other countries are designing many of the latest electronic products. Taiwanese firms design and manufacture about 65 percent of laptops marketed by Dell, Hewlett-Packard, and Sony.[41] The outsourcing phenomenon is likely to intensify and continue to alter the corporate landscape, providing opportunities and threats for many companies.

Consolidation throughout industries is another important trend. In the future, many industries will consist of a few large firms enjoying most of the market share, plus many small firms, each with limited market share. Some consolidation is occurring in most industries, but it is especially evident in the pharmaceutical, financial services, airline, cellular, and retail industries.

Consolidation has two important implications for marketers. First, organizations must develop marketing strategies to hold their own in a competitive environment consisting of a few large firms and many small firms. Second, they must develop effective marketing strategies to serve both large and small customers.

These and other institutional trends affect the way organizations operate. Marketers that serve organizational customers must examine these trends to identify market opportunities and develop effective marketing strategies. Moreover, these trends affect the competitive structure for all marketers and have important implications for the types of marketing strategies likely to be effective.

The Future

The only certainty about the future is that it will be uncertain, and change will occur at an increasing rate. It will also be more complex. Businesses and consumers now must operate in an era of terrorism and lack of trust. Overlaying these factors on the typical interactions among the social, economic, political/legal, technological, competitive, and institutional environments produces a complex future for marketers. Those that identify the key trends among these factors and understand how these trends interact will be in the best position to take advantage of marketing opportunities and to minimize threats.

Summary

1. **Understand the nature of the marketing environment and why it is important to marketers.** The marketing environment consists of all factors external to an organization that can affect its marketing activities. Elements of the marketing environment are largely uncontrollable, although marketers have influence over some factors. Environmental factors can affect the size and growth rate of markets and can influence marketing activities. Thus changes in the marketing environment offer opportunities and threats to marketers. Identifying and responding effectively to these opportunities and threats is a major challenge.

2. **Describe the major components of the social environment and how trends in the social environment affect marketing.** The social environment comprises all factors and trends related to groups of people, including their number, characteristics, behavior, and growth projections. Its major components are the demographic and cultural environments. The demographic environment refers to the size, distribution, and growth rate of people with different characteristics. The cultural environment refers to factors and trends related to how people live and behave. Demographic factors typically relate to the number of people in different markets, whereas cultural factors generally influence the needs of these markets.

3. **Understand how the economic environment affects marketing.** The economic environment includes factors and trends related to the production of goods and services and the relationships between this production and income levels. The economic environment affects the purchasing power of consumers, which is an important determinant of the size of a market.

4. **See how the political/legal environment offers opportunities and threats to marketers.** The political/legal environment, encompassing factors related to governmental activities and laws and regulations, directly affects marketing activities. Laws and regulations normally present constraints within which marketers must operate. These laws and regulations are closely related to current political trends. Some marketers, however, can identify market opportunities arising from these laws and regulations.

5. **Appreciate the importance of the technological environment to marketers.** The technological environment includes factors and trends related to innovations that affect the development of new products or improving marketing practice. Technological advances are happening so rapidly that marketers must constantly monitor the technological environment to keep abreast of latest developments.

6. **Understand differences in the competitive environment.** The competitive environment consists of all the organizations that attempt to serve the same customers. Brand competitors compete directly by offering the same type of product to the same market. Product competitors compete more indirectly by offering different types of products to satisfy the same basic need.

7. **Know how changes in the institutional environment affect marketers.** The institutional environment consists of all the organizations involved in marketing products and services. These include marketing research firms, advertising agencies, wholesalers, and retailers. As the characteristics of these and other institutions change, so will the marketing strategies necessary to serve different customers and to compete effectively in different industries.

Understanding Marketing Terms and Concepts

Thinking about Marketing

1. How do changes in the marketing environment generate opportunities and threats for marketers?

2. What are the major differences between the demographic and cultural environments?

3. Why are trends in the institutional environment important to marketers?

4. How does the Internet affect the competitive environment facing many firms?

5. Look at "Creating Customer Value: Even Convenience Stores Are Becoming More Convenient." What ideas do you have to make convenience stores more convenient?

6. How do political changes affect regulations and regulatory agencies?

7. What are the most important social trends facing marketers in the twenty-first century?

8. Refer to "Being Entrepreneurial: Creating Opportunities." What ideas do you have for marketing effectively to poor consumers?

9. How are the social and economic environments interrelated?

10. How can new technologies be used to help marketers scan and monitor the marketing environment?

Applying Marketing Skills

1. Identify several marketing environment trends that you think might affect enrollment at your college. Discuss whether each trend represents an opportunity or a threat. What strategy might your institution use to take advantage of the opportunity or minimize the threat?

2. Watch the complete evening news show on one of the major networks. Make a note of significant marketing environment trends examined during the newscast. After the news show is over, suggest the potential effect of each trend on marketing practice. Which trends represent opportunities? Which trends represent threats? Could any of the potential threats become opportunities if a marketer viewed it from an entrepreneurship perspective?

3. Contact a marketing executive at a local company and ask how he or she assesses changes in the marketing environment. Identify who in the company is involved in what types of environmental scanning. Ask the executive to identify the key trends affecting his or her company and what the firm is doing to respond appropriately to these trends.

Using the www in Marketing

Activity One Go to Dell's Web site (*http://www.dell.com*).

1. How does Dell's Web site add value to customers?

2. Using information on the Web site, describe and evaluate Dell's global marketing efforts.

3. What ideas do you have for improving Dell's Web site?

Activity Two As discussed in the chapter, laws and regulations typically are designed to promote competition among firms or to protect consumers and society. Here are some Web sites that present legal information:
Federal Trade Commission (*http://www.ftc.gov*)
FedWorld Information Network
    (*http://www.fedworld.gov*)
Consumer Information Center
    (*http://www.pueblo.gsa.gov*)

United States Information Agency
    (*http://www.usia.gov*)
THOMAS: Legislative Information on the Internet
    (*http://thomas.loc.gov*)
National Archives and Records Administration
    (*http://www.nara.gov*)
Visit several of these sites and then respond to the following questions:

1. Select an example of legislation intended to promote competition among firms. Provide a brief synopsis of this legislation and indicate how the legislation affects marketing practice.

2. Select an example of legislation intended to protect consumers and society. Provide a brief synopsis of this legislation and discuss how the legislation affects marketing practice.

3. Which of these sites would you recommend that marketers monitor on a regular basis? Why?

Making Marketing Decisions

Case 2–1 *Women's NBA: Women's Team Sports Taking Off*

Women's individual sports, such as golf and tennis, have been successful for many years. The same cannot be said for team sports. Prior to 1997, at least three attempts had been made to establish women's professional basketball leagues. All had failed. So why would anyone try again? Because the marketing environment changed.

Women's collegiate sports programs have expanded tremendously in recent years. This has produced a new generation of women athletes and fans. And the stunning success of women athletes at the 1996 Summer Olympic Games in Atlanta added to this interest. The result is the formation of four new women's professional leagues since the Olympics. One is the Women's National Basketball Association (WNBA).

The tip-off of the WNBA was in June 1997. The league initially consisted of eight teams operated by NBA teams in eight cities. The season began after the NBA playoffs in June and concluded with a championship game on August 30.

The WNBA worked hard to make the new league a success. Sponsors were obtained and contracts to televise selected regular season and playoff games were secured. The league advertised during the NBA's regular season and playoff games. The results of these marketing efforts appear to have been successful.

The ninth WNBA season begins with preseason games in 2005. The league started with 8 teams, expanded to 12 in 1999, and now has 13 teams competing. The league drew its 10 millionth fan in 2001. Local, national, and international television coverage reached nearly 60 million fans in 23 different languages in 167 countries. Sponsors such as Nike, Sears, and Anheuser-Busch have extended their sponsorship deals; and new sponsors, such as Gatorade, are being added.

The future looks good as well. WNBA games are televised regularly on ESPN and ABC. A popular Web site (www.wnba.com) is used to communicate with fans, promote the league, and sell merchandise. A major promotional effort titled "This Is Our Game" was implemented in 2005. Promotional spots featured stars such as Diana Taurasi, Becky Hammer, Nykesha Sales, Adia Barnes, and others. The WNBA also wants its players to be viewed as role models and includes them in a variety of community service projects. One is the "WNBA Be Smart—Be Fit—Be Yourself" to promote health and fitness to teenagers. Another is the Breast Cancer Awareness Program.

Questions

1. What trends in the marketing environment helped the WNBA be successful?

2. What trends in the marketing environment represent threats to the WNBA?

3. Why would companies like Nike, Sears, Anheuser-Busch, and Gatorade want to sponsor the WNBA?

4. What role does the WNBA Web site (*www.wnba.com*) play in the league's marketing strategy?

Case 2–2 *Kodak: Looking for Marketing Opportunities*

Kodak introduced its line of EasyShare digital cameras in 2003. The good news is that the cameras were popular with consumers and helped Kodak become the U.S. leader in digital camera sales with $5.3 billion in digital business. The bad news is that because of low profit margins, the digital business generated only $46 million in profits. Contrast this with the high-margin film business with sales of over $8 billion. However, consumer film sales are expected to decline 30 percent this year, with Kodak's film sales off 17 percent.

Kodak is responding to this situation in several ways. Antonio M. Perez suddenly replaced Daniel A. Carp as president in June 2005. Perez had been COO since 2003, but he was previously responsible for building Hewlett-Packard's printing business to over $10 billion in annual sales. He has indicated that Kodak will focus on three basic business areas: consumer imaging, health imaging, and commercial printing.

Kodak is introducing several new products and services in the consumer digital photography market:

- The EasyShare-One will be the newest digital camera. It will allow consumers to store and organize 1,500 shots and e-mail them wirelessly.

- New home photo printers will be introduced, with an emphasis on selling high-margin paper and color cartridges for them.

- The EasyShare Gallery (*www.ofoto.com*) provides a photo repository for its 19 million members, who can order prints and albums.

- Consumers are going to retailers more to make prints. Kodak has installed over 30,000 picture maker kiosks in retail locations. Consumers can print directly from cameras or cell phones.

These changes are expected to increase profits in the consumer digital business significantly.

There are also opportunities in the health imaging and commercial printing businesses. Kodak sells digital radiology machines and software that manages the diagnostic and other information accompanying an X-ray image. Its ultimate goal is to set up information networks for hospitals and entire hospital systems. Even though the digital health care business grew 20 percent last year, Kodak faces formidable competitors, such as General Electric, Phillips, McKesson, and Siemens.

The commercial printing business has potential but is losing money now. It will have to battle Xerox in this market. Kodak's machines can be 40 feet long and cost from $11,000 to $5.5 million. Some can print color copies at 1,000 per minute. The digital technology makes it possible to print custom copies of almost anything at any volume. Direct marketers who want to customize their fliers are an attractive market for Kodak.

The new digital technology has had an enormous impact on Kodak. Achieving acceptable levels of profitability in the new digital businesses will be a real challenge for the company.

Questions

1. What trends in the marketing environment led to Kodak's current situation?

2. Why have the EasyShare cameras been so successful?

3. Which of the marketing opportunities being considered would you recommend Kodak emphasize? Why?

4. What other marketing opportunities can you identify that Kodak might pursue?

Chapter Three

Marketing's Strategic Role in the Organization

After studying this chapter, you should be able to

1 Discuss the three basic levels in an organization and the types of strategic plans developed at each level.

2 Understand the organizational strategic planning process and the role of marketing in this process.

3 Describe the key decisions in the development of corporate strategy.

4 Understand the different general business strategies and their relationship to business marketing, product marketing, and international marketing strategies.

5 Realize the importance of relationships and teamwork in executing strategic plans.

Disney

Disney's long-run objective is to become the world's premier family entertainment company through the ongoing development of its powerful brand and character franchises. Its business is "making people happy by turning fantasy into reality." Already, Disney has become a premier media company, with revenues of $30.7 billion in 2004, including a significant percentage coming from outside the United States and Canada.

The company has four business segments, each with recognizable lines. Its media networks include ABC, ESPN, the Disney channel, the ABC family channel radio and TV channels, and the Toon network. Second, Disney produces and distributes motion pictures and TV animation. Its park and resort operations include the Florida, California, Paris, and Tokyo sites, plus a cruise line. In addition, significant revenues are realized through Disney's extensive licensing of company characters and intellectual property. Each of these areas requires a marketing strategy involving the identification of appropriate market segments and

then design of a market mix offering to effectively appeal to these many and varied segments.

In spite of the obvious Disney brand strength and the company's extensive product line, recent economic events and questionable decisions make Disney an excellent example to follow as its marketing strategy evolves. Questions are now being raised regarding the ability of the company to manage its extensive and complex businesses.

ABC has had significant successes (*Desperate Housewives* and *Lost*), but production costs on other shows have affected profits. ESPN now charges much more profitable rates, and its earnings are high. The sales of DVDs and videos of hits like *Finding Nemo* have been quite significant. The animated production company Pixar provides Disney with 15 percent or more of the Disney studio revenues. Developing marketing strategies for such a complex, varied line of products across so many different market segments remains a challenge for this well-respected, valued corporation.

Why has Microsoft, which has a somewhat uneven record in innovation, become a leader in so many software categories? Why has megaretailer Wal-Mart been able to crush its once larger competitors? Why was Lowe's strategy of cloning its competitor, Home Depot, so successful? The answers to these questions reside in an understanding of marketing strategy.[1]

The complexity of the Disney conglomerate illustrates the importance of a well-designed corporate marketing strategy. The firm consists of unique business units, each offering an extensive array of products and services. Strategies and implementation of strategies must be developed and executed at the corporate, business unit, and product levels. Overall strategy and long-term planning are guided by the firm's vision as stated in its mission statement. At the business level, planning begins with an examination of the current situation, including technological changes and competitive effects. From this analysis, both threats and new business opportunities are identified. Decisions to pursue new opportunities are followed by the establishment of objectives, often stated in terms of market share, sales volume, or profitability. Subsequently, business and marketing strategies are developed to achieve those objectives. Effective execution of strategy in implementation must then occur for objectives to be realized. As such, strategies are made through a great deal of deliberation and rational evaluation of alternative strategies that should be guided by an overall vision of the organization. Here, analysis of the firm' strengths and weaknesses, as well as external threats and opportunities, is crucial to success. As strategies are subsequently implemented, creativity becomes a key aspect of the planning process.[2]

Many of the most familiar firms around the world are complex organizations that market many different products in many different business areas. Marketing efforts require planning and implementation across all the various business segments, business areas, incorporated companies, and profit centers. In today's environment, organizations must frequently cope with unexpected and anomalous events, referred to as *crises,* that create high levels of uncertainty and are potential threats to the viability of the company. The past decade has witnessed tremendous economic and political upheavals, including the outcomes of 9/11, the collapse of Enron and WorldCom, and the turmoil of some foreign currencies, such as the Brazilian real and the Mexican peso.[3]

Often a small company markets a few products to a well-defined market. Although this sort of marketing is not easy, the company directs all its efforts toward the initial products and market. If the firm succeeds and grows, competitors enter with similar products. Over time, the company's opportunities for marketing the same products to the same market decline. To continue growing, the firm must develop new strategies. Typically it must market different types of products to its current market, the same products to different markets, or new products to new markets. The relatively simple single-business, few-products firm becomes a complex multibusiness, multiproduct company.

Michael Porter, the famous Harvard Business School strategy professor, argues that long-term strategy is even more important in uncertain and turbulent times and/or environments. Top marketing managers are constantly faced with the problem of how to trade off competing strategic initiatives. For example, should the firm increase advertising, invest more heavily in loyalty programs, or improve service quality? The ability to financially evaluate the relative strength of these kinds of alternatives is difficult, and decisions are of-

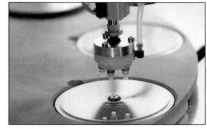

Many corporations have individual business units. GE, a global company, has multibusiness operations in many different markets and for a variety of products.

ten subjective.[4] While change does occur more rapidly now, CEOs have too often downplayed the importance of marketing strategy. However, examples of successful firms, such as Intel, Wal-Mart, and Dell, provide evidence of the importance of a clear strategy and sense of purpose, which then provide firms with sustainable competitive advantage.[5]

The complexities facing Disney and other firms produce many of the key challenges for today's marketers. In this chapter we examine the important role of marketing in the contemporary multibusiness, multiproduct firm. We classify organizations into corporate, business, and functional levels, and discuss strategic planning and strategic decision making at each level. Our focus is on the role of marketing. The chapter concludes with a discussion of teamwork in the execution of strategic plans.

Organizational Levels

The **corporate level** is the highest level in any organization. Corporate managers address issues concerning the overall organization, and their decisions and actions affect all other organizational levels. The **business level** consists of units within the overall organization that are generally managed as self-contained businesses. Often the idea is to break a complex organization into smaller units to be operated like independent businesses. This is the level at which competition takes place; that is, business units typically compete against competitor business units, not corporate levels versus corporate levels.

The **functional level** includes all the various functional areas within a business unit. Most of the work of a business unit is performed in its different functions. A typical university provides a good illustration of different organizational levels. The president, vice presidents, and other central administration positions represent the corporate level. The different colleges within the university, such as the college of business or college of arts and sciences, can be considered business units. There are also different functions performed within each college. The typical functions are teaching, research, and administration carried out by faculty, staff, and administrators.

Organizational Strategic Planning

Strategic planning for multibusiness, multiproduct organizations typically occurs at each organizational level. Strategic plans at higher organizational levels provide direction for strategic plans at lower levels. In a sense, lower-level plans are developed to execute higher-level plans. Because of this relationship, strategic planning must be integrated and consistent throughout levels.

A study of U.S. and South African firms provides a general description of strategic planning.[6] These firms reported that the major benefits of strategic planning are improved performance relative to objectives and a better organizational focus and vision. Most of the firms prepare formal strategic plans at the corporate, business, and product levels, with different functional managers participating in the planning process. These include sales managers, product managers, marketing researchers, production managers, and financial managers. Many firms also incorporate customers into the process. Businesses and departments can be organized any number of ways—around products, brands, categories, geography, markets, or, as explained later, subsidiaries. P&G has a marketing unit just for Wal-Mart. However, and as research suggests, the best organizational structure is one that serves customers most effectively, irrespective of which channels buyers use to access the company.[7]

Types of Strategic Plans

The different types of strategic plans and important strategic decisions are illustrated in Exhibit 3–1. A **corporate strategic plan** provides guidance for strategic planning at all other organizational levels. Important corporate strategy decisions concern development of a corporate vision, formulation of corporate objectives, allocation of resources, determination of how to achieve desired growth, and establishment of business units.

A **business strategic plan** indicates how each business unit in the corporate family expects to compete effectively in the marketplace, given the vision, objectives, and

Exhibit 3–1	*Organizational strategic plans*

Organization Level	Type of Strategic Plan	Key Strategic Decisions
Corporate	Corporate strategic plan	• Corporate vision • Corporate objectives and resource allocation • Corporate growth strategies • Business unit composition
Business	Business strategic plan	• Market scope • Competitive advantage
Marketing	Marketing strategic plan	• Target market approach • Marketing mix approach
	Product marketing plan	• Specific target market • Specific marketing mix • Execution action plan

growth strategies in the corporate strategic plan. Different businesses within the same organization are likely to have different objectives and business strategies. For example, the recent merger of Procter & Gamble and Gillette illustrates corporate strategic thinking. In recent years, the companies improved their bottom lines by cutting costs. Now the combined companies have extra market power that will enhance their ability to create new products, to persuade consumers to buy, and to get retail giants like Wal-Mart to carry their new product additions. In addition, the deal will allow the companies to more effectively pursue developing markets like China and India, which will help propel future sales growth. The merger will also strengthen their pricing position in negotiations with large retailers and pressures from private-label brands.[8] Each business needs to make decisions concerning the scope of the market it serves and the types of competitive advantages to emphasize. Decisions in these areas contribute to a general business strategy.

Each business consists of different functions to be performed, and strategic plans may be developed for each major function. Thus many organizations will have marketing, financial, R&D, manufacturing, and other functional strategic plans. A **marketing strategic plan** describes how marketing managers will execute the business strategic plan. It addresses the general target market and marketing mix approaches. Colgate, which competes effectively with P&G's Crest toothpaste, has benefited from its focused approach and evenly distributed sales worldwide. Colgate's marketing plan includes the maintenance of its "share of voice" in media spending and its strategy to "surround" consumers with samples targeted toward college students and other young adults.[9]

Each business unit has its own product marketing plans that focus on specific target markets and marketing mixes for each product. A **product marketing plan** typically includes both strategic decisions (what to do) and execution decisions (how to do it). At the product marketing plan level, tactical issues related to execution are addressed.

Pitney Bowes, originally founded as a producer of mailing equipment and postage meters, is now a multibusiness, multiproduct corporation. The Copier Systems Division, one of the company's new business units, develops and executes marketing and product plans to compete against Xerox, Canon, Minolta, and Konica. The division's basic business strategy is to target large *Fortune* 1,000 companies and to differentiate its products from the competition on the basis of product quality and efficiency of distribution. Unlike many newcomers to an industry, Pitney Bowes does not claim to offer the lowest prices in the industry.[10]

Planning and the development of brand strategy are focal issues for many managers. Current thinking at P&G regarding the management of brands and the development of brand-level strategies includes the following priorities: (1) continue to innovate; (2) move quickly in introducing new innovations and technology; (3) minimize reliance on Wal-Mart by building relationships with other customers; (4) use multiple media (in-store, print, TV) with messages tailored to the media; and (5) think broadly in terms of solving consumer problems.[11]

The Strategic Role of Brand Loyalty

As described previously in Chapter 1 and as defined by the American Marketing Association, *marketing* is an organizational function and a set of processes for creating, communicating, and delivering value to customers and for managing customer relationships in ways that benefit the organization and its stakeholders.

One of the primary objectives of marketing strategy is generation of market share and the development of a strong customer base. The determinants of market share are multifaceted. However, certain important concepts are recognized as critical. To begin, trust and liking for the firm's brands are the building blocks of success. Trust, in particular, is critical in the establishment of successful exchange relationships and is at the heart of "one-to-one" marketing. From brand trust and affect (liking) come purchase and attitudinal loyalty. That is, a customer base is possible that both purchases the brand(s) regularly and has an enduring positive attitude toward that brand. Strong and positive attitudinal loyalty inhibits competitor inroads as new brands enter the market and enables firms to charge higher prices.[12]

Overall, then, brand loyalty, name awareness, perceived quality, brand assets, and cognitive associations in the minds of consumers form the basis for brand equity. Brand equity provides value to consumers by enhancing the processing of marketplace information, confidence in decision making, and satisfaction. Brand equity provides value to the firm by enhancing the effectiveness of marketing programs, increasing price margins, enabling brand extensions, allowing competitive advantage, and strengthening trade relationships.[13]

For most firms **customer equity,** or the total of the discounted lifetime values of all the firm's customers, is certain to be the most important determinant of the long-term value of the firm. Although customer equity is not the only determinant of firm value (consider assets, property, and R&D capabilities), the firm's customers provide the long-term revenues and profits, and building customer equity should be the focal point for marketing strategy. As such, marketing strategy should determine the most critical drivers of customer equity for brands (quality, service, convenience, or other factors). At the most basic level, customers choose to do business with a firm because of three motivating factors: the firm offers better value, it has a stronger brand, and switching is too costly. Understanding customer equity enables the firm and its managers to use the most important of these motivators to encourage customer retention and to get customers to buy more.[14]

The Strategic Planning Process

Although individual organizations will differ in the way they approach strategic planning, a general process is illustrated in Exhibit 3–2. This process applies to strategic planning at every level. We present it as a step-by-step approach to make it easier to understand strategic planning. In the business world, most organizations are involved in different stages of the process simultaneously and do not necessarily follow such a step-by-step approach.

EXAMINE THE CURRENT SITUATION   First the managers evaluate the existing situation for the corporate, business, marketing, or product level. They typically analyze historical information to describe current strategies and firm strengths and weaknesses, assess recent performance, and evaluate the competitive situation. This background information provides a benchmark for the remainder of the strategic planning process. The planning process enables managers to maintain perspective even in rapidly changing times. For radically new products, the situation analysis pays attention to environmental change that comes from political, economic, social, and technological sources.[15]

Exhibit 3–2	*General strategic planning process*

As part of examining the current situation, firms often engage in benchmarking. **Benchmarking** is a market-based learning process by which a firm seeks to identify best practices that produce superior results in other firms and to replicate those processes to enhance its own competitive advantage. Benchmarking activity includes understanding product and marketing strategy excellence in other firms, as well as the capabilities that produced this excellence.[16]

IDENTIFY POTENTIAL THREATS AND OPPORTUNITIES   Next, the focus changes from what has happened to what might happen. Managers identify key trends in the marketing environment, assess the possible impact of these trends on the current situation, and classify them as either threats or opportunities. Threats represent potential problems that might adversely affect the current situation; opportunities represent areas where performance might be improved. In general, opportunities are most often associated with decisions for which managers perceive they have control over outcomes. Opportunities involving less uncertainty represent pursuits with greater potential for profitability.[17] Thus Specialized Bicycle Components must recognize trends in retailing and changing preferences among consumers. Managers typically rank potential threats and opportunities, addressing the most important ones first in the next strategic planning stage. In the search for opportunities, problems sometimes generate opportunities. For example, the deregulation problems in the California electricity market caused a series of blackouts. In response to these problems, Capstone Turbine has effectively marketed microturbines, the size of refrigerators, to small businesses.[18]

SET OBJECTIVES   Managers must now establish specific objectives for the corporate, business, marketing, and product levels. Typical objectives involve sales, market share, and profitability. The specific objectives should be based on analysis of the current situation and the marketing environment. As we discuss later, objectives at the different organizational levels must be consistent. For example, the sales objectives for all businesses must be set so that meeting them means meeting the corporate level sales objectives.

DEVELOP STRATEGIES   Finally, managers develop strategies for achieving the objectives. These strategies indicate how the organization will minimize potential threats and capitalize on specific opportunities. The strategies developed at this stage represent what an organization plans to do to meet its objectives, given the current situation and expected changes in the marketing environment. A sample product marketing plan is presented in Appendix A at the end of the text.

EXECUTE   A clear strategy and well-crafted programs may still fail if execution and implementation efforts are misdirected or inadequate. Effective execution is enhanced when employees share common values and are properly trained and when sufficient resources and staff are provided to support implementation. Both a sense of organizationwide commitment to the adopted strategy and a sense of commitment by the managers responsible for implementation have been shown to be primary determinants of effective execution.[19] Recent research indicates that the effective implementation of marketing strategy is affected significantly by, again, widespread organizational commitment to the strategy, continuing dialogue between upper-level managers and second-level managers charged with implementation, and employee understanding regarding how individual strategies are consistent with the overall vision and orientation of the firm.[20]

The Role of Marketing

Marketing plays an important role in the strategic planning process for many organizations. Although some marketing positions are represented at the corporate level, most are at the functional level within the business units of an organization. As shown in Exhibit 3–3, however, marketing is involved in strategic planning at all organizational levels.

Strategic marketing describes marketing activities that affect corporate, business, and marketing strategic plans. Strategic marketing activities can be classified into three basic functions. First, marketers help orient everyone in the organization toward markets and customers. Thus they are responsible for helping organizations execute a marketing philosophy throughout the strategic planning process.

Exhibit 3–3   *Role of marketing in strategic planning*

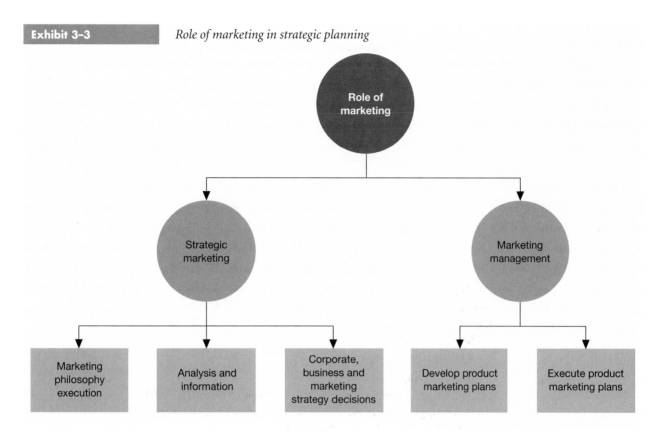

Second, marketers help gather and analyze information required to examine the current situation, identify trends in the marketing environment, and assess the potential impact of these trends. This information and analysis provide input for corporate, business, and marketing strategic plans.

Third, marketers are involved in the development of corporate, business, and marketing strategic plans. Marketing's influence varies across organizations. For organizations driven by a marketing philosophy, marketing necessarily plays a key role in strategic decision making. The trend toward pushing strategic planning responsibility further down the organization is increasing marketing's clout in an organization's strategic planning process.[21]

One typology of recommended business strategies that organizations should pursue includes four alternatives. A *pioneer* strategy involves the identification and exploitation of new product and market opportunities. *Fast followers* imitate pioneers' successful product and development efforts. *Cost leaders* are usually late entrants that engage in aggressive efforts to protect their market positions from competitors. *Customer centrics* create customer value by offering high-quality products supported by excellent service at prices lower than pioneers but higher than fast followers or cost leaders.[22]

Marketing management relates to specific product marketing strategies. It differs from strategic marketing in its basic orientation. Strategic marketing focuses on broad strategic decisions at the corporate and business levels. Marketing management is concerned, by contrast, with specific strategic decisions for individual products and the day-to-day activities needed to execute these strategies successfully. At the operating level, marketing managers focus on customers and the competition as well as on the four Ps of the marketing mix: price, product, promotion, and place (distribution).[23]

The strategic role of marketing and marketing management is now in a period of considerable change and evolution. These changes are due to a number of important environmental phenomena that are affecting how many firms do business. To begin, many well-known companies work closely with dedicated partners on the supply side (often using single supply partners) and the distributor side of their business, expecting their distributors to play proactive roles in the development of services and marketing strategy. For example, on the supply side, Nike now does little manufacturing of its own and focuses largely on marketing. Companies such as this are actually embedded in **business networks,** comprising strategic alliances among suppliers, distributors, and the marketing firm.[24]

Other influences on marketing include the connected-knowledge economy; globalized and consolidated industries; fragmented markets; and demanding customers and consumers. With these changes, new kinds of competitors will emerge; markets will continue to become homogenized across country boundaries; and mass markets will erode in the face of mass customization. Business customers and individual consumers expect diversity and have multiple means of obtaining products, as well as learning about company offerings. Some observers foresee a future in which the Web will enable automated purchasing, anonymous transactions, and the bypassing of most intermediaries.[25]

The role of marketing within the firm is in transition as well. For example, some scholarly observers have predicted that a cross-functional dispersion of marketing activities will occur as the firm becomes market oriented throughout. In a test of this premise, one study of managers across functions (marketing, human relations, operations, accounting, and finance) within their firms revealed that marketing as a separate function still contributes to a firm's financial performance, customer-relationship performance, and new-product performance beyond the performance attributable to the firm's general market orientation.[26] Therefore, an understanding of the strategic planning process is even more important in today's ever-changing marketplace.

Our discussion of organizational strategic planning provides an overview of different types of strategic plans, a general strategic planning process, and marketing's basic role in these areas. With this background, we are now ready to examine the major strategic decisions at the corporate, business, marketing, and product levels.

Marketing Strategy and the Internet

The failure of many dot-com companies, after the promises of many marketing experts that the Internet would rewrite the rules of business, has raised many important questions regarding the lessons firms should learn from Internet business. Internet usage continues to grow globally, and many traditional firms have found viable applications of Web technology. These successes apply to both B2B and consumer-oriented firms. However, the basics of business success remain the same: customers, capabilities, and competitive advantage. Companies must be able to attract and retain profitable customers. Firms must also take advantage of their own unique strengths and capabilities. The maintenance of some distinctive competitive advantage, whether in terms of product and quality advantages, convenience, or price/value, is a must. While online-only firms will certainly exist and succeed, most firms will employ Internet technology in efforts to offer complementary channels and improve existing processes.

The question is not whether firms should employ the Internet. The objective is how to use the Internet profitably as part of operations and marketing strategy. If marketing strategy is defined simply as the firm's identification of desirable market segments and the development of appropriate marketing mixes to appeal to these segments, then the important role of the Internet becomes obvious.[27]

Many businesses are using the Internet to interact with suppliers and large buyers. Internet selling direct to consumers is frequently employed as another channel of communication and interaction. The Internet also expands market coverage and opens up previously unreachable segments and markets. The Internet enables 24/7 convenience, as well as the opportunity to develop more personalized relationships with customers. As Michael Porter argues, the Internet can increase an industry's efficiency by expanding the overall size of the market and improving its position relative to traditional substitutes. Unfortunately, this expansion in market coverage also makes other firms, previously restricted by location, potential competitors.

One of the primary effects of the Internet has been the increased availability of information and the emphasis on price. These changes have certainly made it more difficult for firms to be profitable. As such, the need to develop and maintain an effective marketing strategy consistent with the firm's capabilities and competitive advantages is even more important.[28]

Corporate Strategy Decisions

The key corporate strategy decision areas defined in Exhibit 3–1 are corporate vision, corporate objectives and resource allocation, corporate growth strategies, and business unit composition.

Corporate Vision

A **corporate vision** represents the basic values of an organization. The vision specifies what the organization stands for, where it plans to go, and how it plans to get there. As indicated in Exhibit 3–4, a comprehensive vision should address the organization's markets, principal products and services, geographic domain, core competencies, objectives, basic philosophy, self-concept, and desired public image.[29] Specialized Bicycle, for example, addressed these issues in its stated vision: "customer satisfaction, quality, innovativeness, teamwork, and profitability."

The ability to develop vision depends on the company's understanding of what should be enduring and what is subject to change. Companies that enjoy enduring success, such as Hewlett-Packard, 3M, Motorola, and Procter & Gamble, have core values and core purposes that remain fixed; but they endlessly adapt their strategies and practices to a changing world. A company's **core values** are the small set of guiding principles that represent the enduring tenets of an organization. The Disney Company's emphasis on imagination and wholesomeness reflect its essential core values. **Core purpose** reflects the company's reason for being or its idealistic motivation for doing work. Disney's core purpose is to entertain people; 3M's is "to solve problems innovatively" (see Exhibit 3–5).[30]

Sometimes organizations develop a formal mission statement to communicate the corporate vision to all interested parties. A mission statement can be an important element in the strategic planning process because it specifies the boundaries within which business units, marketing, and other functions must operate.

The mission statement for Ben & Jerry's is threefold: (1) to make and distribute the finest quality all-natural ice cream and related products; (2) to operate the company on a sound financial basis of profitable growth, increasing value for shareholders and creating career opportunities and financial rewards for employees; and (3) to operate the company in a way that actively recognizes the central role that business plays in the structure of society by initiating innovative ways to improve the quality of life of a broad community.[31] The statement emphasizes the importance of quality products, company performance and employee success, and the social responsibility aspects of business.

Exhibit 3–4

Corporate vision components

- Markets
- Products and services
- Geographic domain
- Core competencies
- Organizational objectives
- Organizational philosophy
- Organizational self-concept
- Desired public image

Exhibit 3–5

Core purpose: A company's reason for being

3M: To solve problems innovatively.

Cargill: To improve the standard of living around the world.

Fannie Mae: To strengthen the social fabric by continually democratizing home ownership.

Hewlett-Packard: To make technical contributions for the advancement and welfare of humanity.

Lost Arrow Corporation: To be a role model and a tool for social change.

Pacific Theatres: To provide a place for people to flourish and to enhance the community.

Mary Kay Cosmetics: To give unlimited opportunity to women.

McKinsey & Company: To help leading corporations and governments be more successful.

Merck: To preserve and improve human life.

Nike: To experience the emotion of competition, winning, and crushing competitors.

Sony: To experience the joy of advancing and applying technology for the benefit of the public.

Telecare Corporation: To help people with mental impairments realize their full potential.

Wal-Mart: To give ordinary folks the chance to buy the same things as rich people.

Mission Statement

Unilever's mission is to add Vitality to life. We meet everyday needs for nutrition, hygiene and personal care with brands that help people feel good, look good and get more out of life.

Our deep roots in local cultures and markets around the world give us our strong relationship with consumers and are the foundation for our future growth. We will bring our wealth of knowledge and international expertise to the service of local consumers — a truly multi-local multinational.

Our long-term success requires a total commitment to exceptional standards of performance and productivity, to working together effectively, and to a willingness to embrace new ideas and learn continuously.

To succeed also requires, we believe, the highest standards of corporate behaviour towards everyone we work with, the communities we touch, and the environment on which we have an impact.

This is our road to sustainable, profitable growth, creating long-term value for our shareholders, our people, and our business partners.

Mission statements provide direction for corporate leadership and help guide marketing strategy. At Unilever, a shared vision helps an increasingly diverse workforce make day-to-day decisions about what needs to be done.

Speaking from Experience

Jaye Young
Communications Manager
Michelin

"Michelin has been developing new strategies for over 100 years. Michelin rolled into the tire business by creating the first detachable bicycle tire in 1891. Bicycle repair work was brought down from three hours (plus overnight drying) to just 15 minutes with Michelin's great invention. As the world's mobility has evolved from bicycles to automobiles to trains to commercial trucks to airplanes to heavy earth-moving and agricultural equipment to motorcycles and even to space shuttles, Michelin has diversified its tire technology and expanded its market offering to help lead this mobility evolution. Michelin has recently branched into areas that do not directly involve selling tires. Michelin Lifestyle was launched to develop new mobility-related products and to leverage the Michelin Man in products like windshield wipers, commercial work boots, and driving gloves. In addition, Michelin Business Solutions is a consulting service that markets fleet cost saving from cradle to grave."

Jaye Young of Michelin America's Truck Tires is communications manager for the Michelin division. She holds a bachelor's degree in marketing from the University of South Carolina and has previously held management positions in sales and human resources.

The vision statement for Whirlpool is similar but does not mention the role of business in society: "We create the world's best home appliances that make life a little easier and more enjoyable for all people. Our goal is a Whirlpool product in every home, everywhere. Created by pride in our work and each other; passion for creating unmatched customer loyalty for our brands; and performance results that excite and reward global investors."[32]

Marriott illustrates what some companies are doing. After management developed mission statements for the corporation and hotel division, each of the company's 250 hotels crafted its own mission statement. Staff members at each hotel spent three days participating in "visioning" exercises to develop the mission statements.[33]

Exhibit 3–6 lists questions that a firm's top managers should continually ask themselves in efforts to install a corporate vision for effectively competing in the future. The last two questions form the basis for recent views of successful competition; that is, the firm's comparative advantages and distinctive core competencies are the resources for competitive advantage. **Core competency** reflects a bundle of skills that are possessed by individuals across

Exhibit 3–6

Questions leading to an effective corporate vision

1. Which customers will you be serving in the future?
2. Through which channels will you reach customers in the future?
3. Who will be your competitors in the future?
4. Where will your margins come from in the future?
5. In what end-product markets will you participate in the future?
6. What will be the basis for your competitive advantage in the future?
7. What skills or capabilities will make you unique in the future?

the organization. The core competency FedEx possesses in package routing and delivery rests on the integration of bar technology, wireless communications, and network management. Boeing, the international manufacturer of airplanes, lists three core competencies on its Web site: (1) detailed customer knowledge and focus; (2) large-scale system integration; and (3) lean, efficient design and production systems.[34] For Microsoft, management quality accounts for much of the software vendor's success. Human capital and the resources associated with its thousands of employees represent the key assets driving IBM's performance and the source of its distinctive core competencies.[35] Competitive advantage derived from these core competencies in turn yields superior financial performance.

Corporate Objectives and Resource Allocation

The second major corporate strategy decision area involves setting objectives for the entire organization and assigning objectives and resources to business units and products. Although the corporate vision provides general overall direction for the organization, corporate objectives specify the achievement of desired levels of performance during particular periods. Corporate objectives are established for many areas, but the most visible tend to be financial objectives. Typical financial objectives concern sales growth, profits, profit growth, earnings per share, return on investment, and stock price. Some analysts argue that all actions of the firm should be oriented toward increasing the value of customer assets. Customer assets can be assessed in terms of measures of customer satisfaction and the strengths and weaknesses of customer relationships. The value of customer assets, including newly acquired customers, affects the company's future ability to generate wealth.[36]

Sales and sales growth objectives are often of direct concern to marketers. Although sales-related objectives are set at the corporate level, actual sales are achieved by marketing individual products to individual customers. Therefore, corporate sales objectives influence marketing activities throughout the organization, as illustrated in Exhibit 3–7.

Suppose the corporate sales growth objective is to increase this year's sales by 10 percent over the previous year's total. To achieve the desired results, management must break down this objective into goals for each business unit and product. If all products and business units meet the assigned objectives, assuming generally equal sales across units, the organization will achieve the desired growth.

In Exhibit 3–7, 10 percent of the desired sales growth is assigned to Business 1, 8 percent to Business 2, and 12 percent to Business 3. The sales growth objectives for each business unit are then further assigned to the specific products marketed by each business. The sales growth objectives are not equally divided across products because the various products have different opportunities for increasing sales. But if each product achieves the desired sales increase, the business unit

Exhibit 3–7

Hierarchy of sales growth objectives

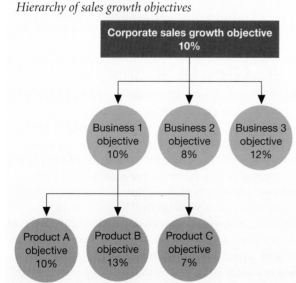

will meet its sales growth objective. And if each business unit does so, the organization will meet its 10 percent objective.

This hierarchy of objectives represents the organization's sales growth plan. Corporate resources are allocated to the business units, and business unit resources are allocated to products. Business 1 receives more corporate resources than some other business units, and Product B receives more of the resources from Business 1 than the other two products it markets. The more sales growth required from a business unit or product, the more resources it typically needs to achieve the desired increases.

Corporate objectives and resource allocation affect marketers in two basic ways. First, marketers are involved in setting the objectives for different organizational levels. Although the amount of marketing participation varies across firms, setting realistic objectives requires the market information and analysis that marketers can provide. Assessments of trends in the size and growth rates of markets and the potential actions of competitors are inputs for setting objectives and allocating resources.

Second, corporate objectives and resource allocation decisions provide guidance for the development and implementation of business and marketing strategies. For example, the marketing managers for Products B and C in Business 1 have different objectives and receive different levels of resources to achieve them. Therefore, they are likely to develop and implement different marketing strategies for their products.

Although growth and new customer generation are traditionally important, companies are increasingly framing objectives in terms of customer relationships and customer retention. Frequently cited corporate objectives based on relationships with customers are (1) retain the most profitable customers, (2) increase sales volume from existing customers, and (3) protect core customers from competition. In fact, **customer relationship management (CRM)** has become a guiding premise of many companies. Briefly, CRM initiatives are designed to achieve a continuing dialogue with customers, across all contact and access points, with personalized treatment of the most valuable customers designed to increase customer retention and the effectiveness of marketing strategies. George Day of the Wharton School of Business summarizes the two important capabilities of successful market-oriented firms:

1. Market sensing capability—how well the organization is equipped to continuously sense changes in its markets and to anticipate the responses of its markets to changes in marketing actions.

2. Customer-linking capability—the skills and processes needed to achieve collaborative customer relationships so individual customer needs are quickly apparent to all functions.[37]

Sadly, many CRM implementations have been expensive failures. Many companies embraced CRM as a cure-all that would make them customer-focused, ignoring the reality that no software can overcome the absence of customer-centric culture. The reasons for these disappointments include focusing solely on technology, ignoring customer lifetime value, and lack of management support.[38]

Corporate Growth Strategies

Corporate growth strategies describe the general approach for achieving corporate growth objectives. Exhibit 3–8 presents four general options.

A **market penetration strategy** represents a decision to achieve corporate growth objectives with existing products within existing markets. The organization needs to persuade current customers to purchase more of its product or to capture new customers. This typically necessitates an aggressive marketing strategy, which means increasing marketing communications, implementing sales promotion programs, lowering prices, or taking other actions intended to generate more business.

A **market expansion strategy** entails marketing existing products to new markets. The new markets might be different market

Exhibit 3–8

Strategic options for corporate growth

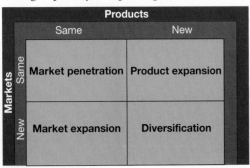

	Products	
	Same	New
Markets Same	Market penetration	Product expansion
New	Market expansion	Diversification

segments in the same geographic area or the same target market in different geographic areas. Specialized Bicycle Components, for example, has expanded into new markets by obtaining expanded distribution through new retail outlets.[39]

A **product expansion strategy** calls for marketing new products to the same market. The organization wants to generate more business from the existing customer base. Nike is not about to abandon athletic footwear, a business it dominates worldwide with more than $4 billion in revenues. However, footwear is a mature business, and Nike is embarking on an expansion strategy to transform itself into a global sports and fitness company.[40] As part of this expansion, Nike plans to offer 82 new stock keeping units (SKUs) in footwear for the committed golfer. These additions will be headlined by 50 Tiger Woods signature models. The expansion into golf products will be accompanied by "Nike Golf" operating as a separate company division with its own unique logo.[41]

One interesting perception in the field of new product introduction is that large, incumbent firms rarely introduce new product innovations. This (mis)perception is referred to as the "incumbent's curse." The belief among many academics and practitioners is that large firms are slow to react and typically introduce only modest, incremental innovations. In contrast, however, a recent historical analysis revealed that most radical innovations for durables and office products introduced since World War II were generated by large incumbent firms.[42]

A **diversification strategy** requires the firm to expand into new products and new markets. This is the riskiest growth strategy because the organization cannot build directly on its strengths in its current markets or with its current products. There are, however, varying degrees of diversification. **Unrelated diversification** means that the new products and markets have nothing in common with existing operations. **Related diversification** occurs when the new products and markets have something in common with existing operations. Blockbuster's move into music retailing has some relationship to video rentals because both are retailing operations in the electronic entertainment business.

DuPont pursues a "sustainable growth" strategy by striving to make more of the world's people its customers, but doing so by developing markets that promote and sustain economic prosperity, social equity, and environmental integrity. To pursue these lofty goals, DuPont's growth objectives are based on the effective use of its scientific resources to enhance the environment. This emphasis has also led to new business opportunities. For example, its floor-covering business unit has shifted its focus from just selling carpet to carpet life cycle planning and removal of old carpet for recycling, as well as installation and maintenance.[43] Whirlpool's growth strategy is based on "building unmatched customer loyalty." Its approach represents a shift from a product-driven organization to a customer-driven focus. This commitment is also evidenced by brand equity measures that include customer perceptions and attitudes along with financial performance measures.[44]

Jaye Young comments on the importance of an international strategic orientation: "Michelin definitely understands that the market is now global. Michelin Group today has factories on every continent and sells its products in more than 170 countries. Although Michelin uses a customized marketing strategy for different countries and even different product lines within those countries, Michelin invests heavily in establishing one recognizable tag line for all countries: 'A better way forward'. The passenger tire group in the United States had invested heavily in 'Because so much is riding on your tires,' and the message has evolved into a great advertising asset. The importance of a global strategy for any company is the correct priority. 'A better way forward' conveys our dedication to the global progress of mobility while being good stewards of the environment. And the best part is that no matter what country you are in, the vision and the message are the same."

Business Unit Composition

In pursuing its corporate growth strategy, an organization may operate in a number of different product and market areas. It does so through business units designed to implement specific business strategies. A **strategic business unit (SBU)** focuses on "a single product or brand, a line of products, or a mix of related products that meets a common market

Thinking Critically

- Identify a company that you think would benefit from strategic corporate growth.

- Discuss how each of the growth strategies presented in this chapter could be implemented by the company you chose.

- Evaluate the potential for success of each growth strategy by identifying the strengths and weaknesses of each, and decide which strategy you think would be most effective overall.

Sony competes effectively with other companies by offering a mix of related product lines.

An overriding decision for many companies is the determination of the firm's mix of strategic business units. Household products, specialty nonfood products, and dressings and sauces represent three of Clorox's strategic business units.

need or a group of related needs, and the unit's management is responsible for all (or most) of the basic business functions."[45] A major structural issue for corporations is whether to group functions together or to operate semi-autonomous business units. One benefit of separate business units is that they force profit and loss responsibility further down the organization and generate more entrepreneurial behavior.

SBUs are sometimes separate businesses from a legal standpoint. For example, Sears at one time consisted of Dean Witter Reynolds (investments), Coldwell Banker (real estate), Allstate Insurance, and the basic retailing business, Sears Merchandise Group. In other cases, corporate management establishes SBUs to facilitate planning and control operations. Additionally, it can change these SBU designations when conditions warrant. General Electric is composed of approximately 20 business units, including aircraft engines, appliances, NBC, and industrial systems. Within the appliance area, as many as 11 product lines have been marketed, including washers and dryers, refrigerators, and microwave ovens.

Changing a firm's business composition is not unusual these days. Corporate downsizing often causes a firm to exit from some business areas. Sears, for example, sold all or parts of its investment, real estate, and insurance businesses to concentrate on its retail business.[46] Whether the corporate decision is to increase or decrease the number of SBUs, once a given business composition is established, separate strategies are developed for each business unit. Ricoh has developed its copier industry portfolio by purchasing companies such as Lanier and Savin. The brand names for these units are then retained to capitalize on their strengths in particular market segments.[47]

Marketing strategy is the emphasis at the SBU level, where the focus is on market segmentation, targeting, and positioning (topics covered in detail in Chapter 7) in defining how the firm is to compete in its chosen businesses.[48] The configuration of a firm's business units can be evaluated in terms of market share and market growth using some variation of the Boston Consulting Group growth share matrix. A very simple depiction of this matrix is shown in Exhibit 3–9.

The matrix classifies the company's portfolio of SBUs into four categories: stars, cash cows, dogs, and question marks. Stars have a large share in growth markets. These products are profitable and require investment by the firm to support their continued performance. In contrast, cash cows have large market shares in slower-growth markets. These products generate significant cash relative to the expenses required to maintain share; hence cash cows provide funds to support other SBUs. Dogs, candidates for deletion or divestment, have modest market shares in low-growth markets. The remaining category, question marks, includes strategic business units that are problems. Ideally, these units with low market share but residence in high-growth markets should be supported and invested in to spur market share. If possible, the question marks should be shifted toward the star cell.

This view has proved useful over the years as a method for organizing and evaluating the mix of SBUs contained in company product/business portfolios. Consideration of strategy at the business unit level enables management to stay in closer touch with customers, competitors, and costs

Simple growth share matrix

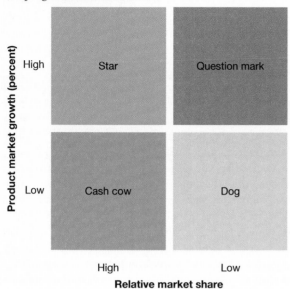

and to maintain strategic focus. Further, this simplistic matrix based on market share and market growth has been expanded to include more complete definitions of market attractiveness (beyond market growth) and business strength (beyond market share).[49] Unfortunately, these business portfolios have been criticized for placing too much emphasis on market share growth and entry into high-growth businesses to the neglect of managing current businesses well.[50]

More recent views of strategy formulation have evolved beyond discussion of star and question mark SBUs. New marketing strategic thinking emphasizes what can be, rather than what is. The emphasis is on identifying opportunities for growth that do not naturally match the skills of existing business units. Companies have begun to redefine strategy generation and to search for creative ways to grow and compete effectively. Instead of figuring out how to position products and businesses within an industry, strategy should focus on challenging industry rules and creating tomorrow's industries, as Wal-Mart did in retailing or as Charles Schwab did in the brokerage business.[51]

Companies now often organize around competency-based SBUs in efforts to establish *sustained competitive advantage*—that is, strategies not simultaneously being implemented by competitors and under conditions that make the duplication of such a strategy difficult. The unique strengths and resources of the firm are used to guide business unit composition in lieu of current marketplace position and growth.[52]

Business Strategy Decisions

The basic objective of a business strategy is to determine how the business unit will compete successfully—that is, how the business unit's skills and resources can be translated into positional advantages in the marketplace. Management wants to craft a strategy difficult for competitors to copy so the business can sustain any advantages it has. For example, some retailers achieve sustainable advantages by selecting the best locations for their retail stores, effectively shutting out competitors from those areas. Other retailers try to gain advantages by offering the lowest prices. Price advantages are often difficult to sustain, however, because competitors can usually match them.

A business strategy consists of a general strategy as well as specific strategies for the different business functions such as marketing. The general strategy is based on two dimensions: market scope and competitive advantage.

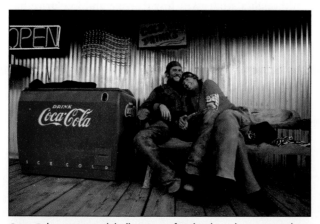

Coca-Cola competes globally using a familiar brand concept and a constant set of soft drink products with expected tastes.

Market Scope

Market scope refers to how broadly the business views its target market. At one extreme, a business unit can select a broad market scope and try to appeal to most consumers in the market. The business might consider all consumers part of one mass market; more likely, it will divide the total market into segments and target all or most of those. An example of a broad market scope strategy is the move by Nike beyond shoes into many sports markets. At the other extreme, a business unit can focus on only a small portion of the market. An example of a focused market scope strategy for a large, known international firm is Honda's introduction of a limited number of new car models compared with the broad offerings of U.S. automobile manufacturers. In some situations, firms find that

deconglomeration is beneficial. Deconglomeration refers to the divestiture behavior of a conglomerate firm and the transformation of its business portfolio to one composed of relatively fewer and related businesses. Research suggests that such a corporate strategy affects business strategies and makes the firm more innovative, as well as competitor and customer oriented.[53]

Competitive Advantage

Competitive advantage refers to the way a business tries to get consumers to purchase its products over those offered by competitors. Two basic strategies are again possible. A business can try to compete by offering similar products and services as competitors, but at lower prices. Succeeding in a low-price strategy typically requires the business unit to have a lower cost structure than that of competitors. Wal-Mart is a good example of a business that prospers with a low-price strategy. It offers the same brands as many other retailers, but at lower prices. Wal-Mart can sustain this advantage and be profitable because it has a very low cost structure and constantly looks for ways to reduce costs. These capabilities lead to competitive advantage. Wal-Mart's low cost structure comes from the firm's operations management skills and purchasing skills. Firms should seek to leverage those distinctive skills or competencies that provide a unique competitive advantage.[54]

A business may also compete through differentiation—that is, offering consumers something different from and better than competitors' products. If it is successful in achieving the desired differentiation, the business can typically charge higher prices than its competitors do. Neiman Marcus, for example, offers a unique product mix and exceptional service to differentiate itself from competition. Consumers are willing to pay higher prices to receive these benefits.

General Business Strategies

Combining the market scope and competitive advantage decisions produces the four general business strategies presented in Exhibit 3–10. The exhibit provides examples of each strategy for the airline industry.[55]

Most of the major airlines, such as American, United, and Delta, employ broad, differentiated strategies. These global carriers compete on many of the same routes but try to differentiate themselves through service, frequent flier programs, and other benefits. These airlines must be price competitive, but their major strategic focus is to find ways to differentiate themselves on nonprice factors.

Although a strategy of broad scope and low price has been seen in the airline industry, several carriers have been

Dell advertises Intel components as part of its alliance with another well-known company.

CREATING CUSTOMER VALUE

FedEx: Customer relationships delivering success

As the market for delivery services flattens, FedEx strives to improve its position by enhancing customer value. As part of its efforts, FedEx has embraced customer relationship management. Billing, claims, and product tracing areas now share information in an integrated approach. Customer satisfaction and the productivity of FedEx's 4,000 plus agents have improved. With its service, the product is created only with an effective interaction between a front-line employee and the customer. The merger with Kinko's chain also enables customers to print directly from Windows desktops to copy centers. In addition, the company is rolling out an online loyalty program that encourages closer relationships with small and medium-sized customers. FedEx also is developing strengths internationally with revenues growing dramatically in China. In support of its service to China, a large center has been established in Anchorage, Alaska.

Exhibit 3–10

General business strategies

unsuccessful in implementing it. Examples are People's Express, Braniff, and Eastern Airlines. These carriers all failed, largely because none could reduce its cost structure enough to be profitable at the low fares.

One airline that might succeed with this strategy is Southwest Airlines. Southwest began as a narrow-scope, low-price airline in 1971, and the company has posted profits for 29 consecutive years. The airline now serves 58 different cities and is expanding into several others. Thus its market scope is broadening. Southwest may be able to do what most other airlines have not: make its no-frills approach work even with a broad market scope.[56]

As Southwest expands its market scope, many major carriers have announced plans to go after the short-haul market. Continental has already entered the short-haul business with CALite. USAir, Delta, and United have similar plans. The major carriers are trying to borrow from the strategies that have made Southwest successful.[57] Delta, for example, has partnered with Air France and Swissair in strategic alliances to expand its offerings. In addition, Delta Connection is affiliated with other southeastern airlines to cover short-haul travel, and it recently purchased Comair, enabling even greater accessibility throughout the eastern United States.[58]

The "Rule of Three" states that naturally occurring competitive forces will create a consistent structure in many mature markets. These three major players often compete by offering a wide range of related products and services and serve most major market segments. Examples include ExxonMobil and ChevronTexaco in the petroleum industry and Gerber, Beech-Nut, and Heinz in the production of baby foods. Sheth and Sisodia argue that smaller players have to carve smaller niche markets that they can serve effectively.[59]

Marketing Strategy Decisions

Recall from Chapter 1 that a marketing strategy addresses the selection of a target market and the development of a marketing mix. The remaining chapters in this book discuss these areas in great detail. Our purpose here is to provide an overview of the two basic types of marketing strategies and to discuss international marketing strategy.

Marketing strategies are developed as functional strategies at the business unit level and as operating strategies at the product level. The two strategies differ in specificity of decisions. Business strategy decisions are relatively general, intended to provide direction for all business-level marketing activities. Product strategy decisions are specific because they guide the actual execution of marketing activities for individual products. Exhibit 3–11 compares the decisions for the two types of marketing strategies.

Business Marketing Strategies

A business marketing strategy must be consistent with the general business strategy. For example, if the general business strategy includes a focused market scope, the target market strategy must concentrate on only a few market segments, perhaps only one. If the general business strategy is low price, the price strategy must be low price. Aside from these

Exhibit 3–11   *Business and product marketing strategies*

Decision Area	Business Marketing Strategy	Product Marketing Strategy
Target market	Segmented or mass approach	Specific definition of target market to be served
Product	Number of different products	Specific features of each product
Price	General competitive price level	Specific price
Distribution	General distribution policy	Specific distributors
Marketing communications	General emphasis on marketing communications tools	Specific marketing communications program

www.landrover.be

New technological features are emphasized in this ad promoting the ability of the Land Rover to handle any environment.

Thinking Critically

- What planning issues would the manufacturer of Saturn automobiles have to confront in deciding whether to use a standardized marketing strategy to promote its cars in Europe?

- What effects would not using a standardized strategy have on marketing costs?

- What possible marketing strategies might BMW implement in the United States as opposed to Europe?

obvious constraints, several strategic options are typically available in each marketing strategy area.

Gillette has had to revamp its marketing strategy because of financial scrutiny from investors, increased internal and material costs, and growing competition. Strategy changes include the elimination of underperforming products, the introduction of new razors for female markets, and enhanced brand support for promising product lines. In conjunction with its ad agency, BBDO, Gillette spent $42 million on ads for its Mach 3 brand in 2001.[60]

Saturn focuses on the broad market but divides it into specific segments and develops strategies for each. It offers a relatively narrow product line with many options available for each product. Pricing is based on value, and dealers typically do not negotiate. Distribution is selective, with only certain dealers chosen to market the Saturn vehicles. Marketing communications are balanced between advertising to inform consumers and get them into the dealers and personal selling to sell the cars.

Social Responsibility as a Strategy

Some companies let social responsibility become a driver of their strategy. Such sincere strategic orientation can be both profitable and admirable. Based on a survey of various stakeholder groups (consider again the new AMA definition of marketing) including

---

BEING ENTREPRENEURIAL

Abercrombie & Fitch: "Tween" the segments

Abercrombie & Fitch realizes that Joe College does not want to hang out with Joey Junior High. As such, A&F has made efforts to remain focused on its primary segment while expanding its appeal to younger market segments. That is, A&F wants to remain cool with college-age and young adults and not become diluted in its A&F positioning from attracting younger patrons. In efforts to appeal to multiple segments, A&F has begun a rollout of a lower-priced chain, Hollister, catering to 14- to 18-year-olds. This line of stores may also compete effectively with the value-oriented American Eagle. A third chain—Abercrombie with a little "a"—is aimed at 7- to 14-year-old customers and has 100-plus stores. These entrepreneurial efforts will require creative strategy in efforts to effectively manage and coordinate different but complementary product lines and market mix configurations.

More recently, A&F has considered ways to grow internationally. As part of that effort, a new brand, Ruehl, is being established. The concept is seen as pitching slightly older customers than A&F and is designed to compete with J. Crew and Banana Republic pricewise, but with more modern styles.

shareholders, employees, minorities, the public, and customers, the best-rated companies included General Mills, Intel, IBM, Avon, and AT&T. The principles underlying socially responsible corporate and marketing strategy include the following:[61]

1. Treating customers with fairness, openness, and quick response to inquiries and complaints.

2. Treating employees, suppliers, and distributors with fairness.

3. Caring about the environmental impact of the firm's activities and supply chain.

4. Behaving in a consistently ethical manner.

Product Marketing Strategies

Product marketing strategies require very specific decisions (see Exhibit 3–11). The target market is defined in detail, the product features and options specified, exact prices established, actual dealers identified, and a detailed communications program developed.

These decisions must be consistent with both the general business and the business marketing strategies. For example, Saturn's target market for each product fits within the market scope of the general business strategy. The unit decides on each product within the business product line, sets prices within the business product guidelines, uses appropriate dealers, and develops a communications strategy similar to the business communications strategy.

International Marketing Strategies

The development of effective global marketing strategies requires creative thinking. Modern marketing typically focuses on developed nations (or developed segments of nations), although most of the world market lies outside these segments. Selling washers to Japanese customers requires understanding how to market to individuals with small homes. Global family networks offer opportunities for products to be purchased for relatives and sent back home. Cellular telephones enable communications among customers previously deemed impossible because of inadequate telecommunications infrastructure.[62]

Marketers must address two key areas when developing international marketing strategies: selecting an entry strategy and deciding on a strategic orientation.

Siemens assumes a global view and adapts its marketing strategy across markets as needed.

ENTRY STRATEGY   An **entry strategy** is the approach used to market products in an international market. The basic options include exporting, joint ventures, and direct investment. Each option has advantages and disadvantages in level of investment and amount of control.

Exporting is a method of selling products to buyers in international markets. The exporter might sell directly to international buyers or use intermediaries, such as exporting firms from the home country or importing firms in the foreign country. Exporting typically requires the lowest level of investment, but it offers limited control to the marketer. Carrier (commercial air conditioners), Caterpillar (construction equipment), and Chrysler (cars) are firms actively engaged in exporting.[63]

At the other extreme is **direct investment,** where the marketer invests in production, sales, distribution, or other operations in the foreign country. This normally requires the largest investment of resources, but it gives the marketer the most control over marketing operations. Wang Laboratories, for example, emphasizes direct investment by operating 175 sales and distribution offices worldwide.[64] The United Kingdom's Cadbury Schweppes PLC purchased Industrias Dulciora SA to give Cadbury the second largest market share in Spain's confectionery market.[65]

Between these extremes are various joint venture approaches. **Joint ventures** include any arrangement between two or more organizations to market products internationally. Options are licensing agreements, contract manufacturing deals, and equity investments in strategic partnerships. Investment requirements and marketing control are usually moderate, although this depends on the details of each joint venture. Examples of joint venture strategies include Apple Computer's licensing of its new PowerPC chip to Asian firms such as Taiwan's Acer; the joint venture for pesticides, named Qingdao Ciba Agro Ltd., between Switzerland's Ciba-Geigy AG and China's Qingdao Pesticides Factory; and the marketing partnership between Delta Airlines and Virgin Atlantic Airways to coordinate flights and give access to London's Heathrow Airport.[66]

INTERNATIONAL STRATEGIC ORIENTATION

Firms operating in international markets can use two different orientations toward marketing strategy. With a **standardized marketing strategy,** a firm develops and implements the same product, price, distribution, and promotion programs in all international markets. With a **customized marketing strategy,** a firm develops and implements a different marketing mix for each target market country.[67] Most international marketing strategies lie somewhere between these extremes, leaning toward one or the other.

These different marketing mixes may involve changes to the communications mix, the product itself, or both. At the corporate level, a **global strategy** views the whole world as a global market. A **multinational strategy** recognizes national differences and views the collection of other countries as a portfolio of markets.

Coca-Cola, for example, uses a largely standardized marketing strategy, where the brand name, concentrate formula, positioning, and advertising are virtually the same worldwide, but the artificial sweetener and packaging differ across countries.[68] Other marketers striving for one brand image and message to appeal to today's worldly consumers include Citibank, McDonald's, Pepsi, and Reebok. For example, Pepsi is recognized for its humor and has applied a similar strategy globally. Likewise, McDonald's is pursuing worldwide the same contemporary approach for promoting to young adults.[69]

McDonald's is one firm that can utilize some of its promotional efforts in the spirit of a global standardized strategy. However, product variations across countries are common.

Some marketing experts suggest the need for caution in the drive to create global brands. In truth, there are very few global brands if you consider the percentage of revenues brands realize outside their domestic markets. Coca-Cola, Gillette, Pampers, Marlboro, Kellogg, and Nescafé derive 50 percent or more of their sales from outside the domestic market. In contrast, many well-known brands are not as global as we often think. For example, Campbell's soup receives only 6 percent of revenues from abroad. In many cases, local and regional brands offer opportunities for company expansion, as foreign markets resist for cultural reasons, particularly following 9/11.[70]

Nissan, in contrast, uses a more customized marketing strategy by tailoring cars to local needs and tastes. One success has been the Nissan Micra, designed specifically to negotiate the narrow streets in England.[71] Similarly, Campbell's Soup gets higher sales by adapting its products to local tastes. For example, sales accelerated when it introduced a cream of chile poblano soup to the Mexican market.[72]

Some companies are moving from customized to standardized marketing strategies. Appliance marketers traditionally customized products for each country. But Whirlpool, through extensive research, found that homemakers from Portugal to Finland have much in common. It now markets the same appliances with the same basic marketing strategy in 25 countries.[73]

The adaptation versus standardization decision is subject to a number of sometimes conflicting factors. Factors encouraging standardization include economy of scale advantages in production, marketing effort, and research and development. In addition, increasing economic integration in Europe and intensifying global competition also favor standardization. In many cases, however, demand and usage conditions differ sufficiently to warrant some modifications in marketing mix offerings. The factors favoring adaptation in international strategy include differing use conditions, governmental and regulatory influences, differing consumer behavior patterns, and local competition. Adaptation is also consistent with the market orientation principles of the marketing concept. Accordingly, standardization may hold only for brands with universal name recognition and for products that require little knowledge for effective use, such as soft drinks and jeans.[74]

One study of 35 companies in Japan, Europe, and the United States that have successfully developed strong brands across countries revealed four common ideas about effective global branding:

1. Stimulate the sharing of insights and best practices across countries.
2. Support a common global brand-planning process.
3. Assign managerial responsibility for brands to create cross-country synergies and to fight local bias.
4. Execute brilliant brand-building strategies.[75]

Executing Strategic Plans
Developing strategic plans is one thing; executing them effectively is another. One route to effective execution of strategic plans is encouraging individuals within an organization to work together to achieve organizational objectives, reflecting the development of relationships within the organization. Two forms of teamwork are important: across the different functional areas and within the marketing function. In addition, comarketing alliances enable pursuit of strategic objectives under certain conditions.

Cross-Functional Teamwork

Traditionally, the different functions within an organization worked largely in isolation. Manufacturers manufactured, engineers engineered, marketers marketed, and accountants accounted. With little direct communication between these functions, their orientations were often more adversarial than cooperative, especially because each function has somewhat different objectives and operates from a different vantage point.

Exhibit 3–12 presents some different orientations between marketing and other organizational functions. The potential difficulties in getting different functions to work

Exhibit 3-12

Business function orientations

Function	Basic Orientation
Marketing	To attract and retain customers
Production	To produce products at lowest cost
Finance	To keep within budgets
Accounting	To standardize financial reports
Purchasing	To purchase products at lowest cost
R&D	To develop newest technologies
Engineering	To design product specifications

together as a team are clear. Why should production care about marketing's interests when it is supposed to produce as much as possible as cheaply as possible? There was no reason for one function to care about another in this type of situation, and typically they did not.

The problem is that if an organization does not produce products that consumers will purchase, it does not matter how low production costs are. More organizations are realizing this and adopting a marketing philosophy, which means that everyone within the organization focuses on satisfying customer needs. This requires teamwork within an organization.

Many organizations have overcome differences in functional objectives and orientations by communicating the importance of teamwork. They reward the meeting of organizational goals such as customer satisfaction instead of merely functional goals such as low-cost production.

An interesting example of cross-functional teamwork is the use of multifunctional teams to work with organizational customers. Companies such as Hewlett-Packard, DuPont, Polaroid, and CIGNA send multifunctional teams from marketing, manufacturing, engineering, and R&D to visit specific customers regularly. The objective is to promote teamwork among employees from different functional areas, to develop a customer focus in all functional areas, to collect useful marketing information about customers, and to improve customer relationships.

Nissan created nine cross-functional teams (CFTs) as a centerpiece of its complete reversal. CFTs represent a powerful vehicle for getting managers to see beyond functional and regional boundaries that define their direct responsibilities. As an example, the sales and marketing team consisted of the executive vice presidents of overseas and domestic sales, plus managers of purchasing and sales and marketing. This group was successful at deciding on a single global ad agency, a reduction in Japanese distribution outlets, and the reduction of marketing costs by 20 percent.[76] One study of 141 cross-functional teams revealed that the success of cross-functional teams in generating innovation is a function of the extent to which members identify with the team rather than with their own functional areas; senior management concern and monitoring; social cohesion among the group members; and team attention to customer input.[77]

Many organizations have emphasized cross-functional teamwork to overcome barriers caused by pursuit of functional objectives, such as low-cost production, rather than long-term customer satisfaction. Hewlett-Packard combines new products with teamwork across functions to enhance market acceptance.

Marketing Teamwork

Even within marketing functions, teamwork is not universal. Different marketing functions often operate somewhat independently—advertising people perform advertising activities, salespeople sell products, brand managers manage their brands, and marketing researchers engage in marketing research. Many firms have little coordination among the different marketing functions. Today, however, the leading organizations are coordinating their marketing efforts and requiring close contact among the different marketing functions.

Many consumer product manufacturers, for example, foster close coordination among brand managers, salespeople and sales managers, and marketing researchers to execute tailored marketing programs for individual retail stores. Working as a team, they uncover information about the customers of each store. The sales and brand managers then work together to execute specific marketing programs for each store to improve sales and profits.

Kodak's reorganization illustrates the importance of marketing teamwork. In changing from a product-driven to a marketing-driven philosophy, the company established a group to integrate marketing functions that had been run separately, such as advertising, sales promotions, public relations, sales, and marketing research. The integrated group works together in developing and executing all marketing plans.[78]

P&G uses a "business management team" approach to run each of its 11 product categories in efforts to encourage global brand success. The teams consist of four managers, headed by an executive vice president, who have line authority for research and development, manufacturing, and marketing in each region. For example, the head of health and beauty aids in Europe also chairs the hair global category team. Because the teams are headed by top-level executives, there are no organizational barriers to carrying out decisions.[79]

Comarketing Alliances

Comarketing alliances include contractual arrangements between companies offering complementary products in the marketplace. The alliance between Microsoft and IBM was instrumental in the growth of Microsoft. Such alliances are increasing in frequency and enable firms to gain specialized resources from previously competing organizations. The success of comarketing alliances depends on the care exhibited in partner selection and the extent to which relationships are balanced in power and benefit both partners. As in relationships between suppliers, customers, and employees, trust and commitment to the relationship in a comarketing alliance engender cooperation and profitable network performance.[80] IBM in just over one year forged 50 strategic partnerships with business software specialists and added $700 million sales revenues through sales of hardware, services, and database programs.[81]

Solution selling, in which products are marketed together to construct a "meal," has become quite popular. Interestingly, this approach has brought together previous competitors, such as Tyson and Pillsbury. Their coordinated effort to sell Sliced and Diced vegetables and chicken involved all aspects of partnering, from using national advertising to encouraging retailer support.[82]

Other alliances include Northwest Airlines and Visa, Kellogg's Pop-Tarts and Smuckers Jelly, and Krups's coffeemakers and Godiva chocolate. So, too, has Quaker Oats partnered with Nestlé in the development of granola bars with candy-bar appeal. Mattel and P&G are combining to share information and to promote their diaper brand, Pampers Playtime. And the cobranding of credit cards (such as Rich's and Visa) by retailers is also increasing; it enhances the visibility of the participating retailer. Determinants of the success of these alliances include prior attitudes toward the two brands and the perceived appropriateness of both brand fit and product fit. More familiar, well-known brands are most effective at generating positive reactions to brand alliances. In particular, a branded component (Intel, NutraSweet) carries a certain equity and signals quality and performance more strongly than conventional attributes.[83] Research suggests that the results of horizontal alliances among competitors regarding joint new product development projects are often enhanced because of increased efficiency in information utilization due to common understanding of marketplace and product category phenomena.[84]

Summary

1. **Discuss the three basic levels in an organization and the types of strategic plans developed at each level.** Organizations can be defined at three basic levels. The corporate level is the highest and addresses issues concerning the overall organization. The business level is the basic level of competition in the marketplace. It consists of units within the organization that are operated as independent businesses. The functional level includes all the different functions within a business unit. Strategic plans are developed at each level. Corporate and business strategic plans provide guidelines for the development of marketing strategic plans and product marketing plans.

2. **Understand the organizational strategic planning process and the role of marketing in this process.** The general strategic planning process consists of examining the current situation, evaluating trends in the marketing environment to identify potential threats and opportunities, setting objectives based on this analysis, and developing strategies to achieve these objectives. Strategic marketing describes marketing activities at the corporate and business levels. Marketing management emphasizes the development and implementation of marketing strategies for individual products and services.

3. **Describe the key decisions in the development of corporate strategy.** The key corporate-level decisions include establishing a corporate vision, developing corporate objectives and allocating resources, determining a corporate growth strategy, and defining the business unit composition. Corporate strategy decisions affect strategic planning at all lower organizational levels. And strategic plans at lower organizational levels are designed to execute the corporate strategy.

4. **Understand the different general business strategies and their relationship to business marketing, product marketing, and international marketing strategies.** General business strategies require decisions concerning market scope and competitive advantage. Market scope can range from focused to broad; competitive advantage might be based on pricing or differentiation. Combining the market scope and competitive advantage options produces four general business strategies. A firm's business marketing strategy must be consistent with its general business strategy. Decisions on market scope and competitive advantage directly affect business marketing strategies. Product marketing strategies must also be consistent with and serve to execute business marketing strategies. International marketing strategies require decisions about entry method and strategic orientation.

5. **Realize the importance of relationships and teamwork in executing strategic plans.** The complexity of today's business environment requires cooperation both across different business functional areas and within the marketing function itself. Cross-functional and marketing teamwork are necessary to execute strategic plans effectively.

Understanding Marketing Terms and Concepts

Thinking about Marketing

1. How does a firm's corporate vision affect its marketing operations?
2. How does marketing differ for a new, single-product venture and a large, multiproduct corporation?
3. What are the basic options for a corporate growth strategy?
4. Review the insert "Creating Customer Value." What factors determine the long-term value of the customers of FedEx?
5. How do business marketing strategies and product marketing strategies differ?
6. What are the keys to effective execution of strategic plans?
7. Consider the various types of Abercrombie & Fitch stores. What are the dangers involved with having different types of stores targeted at different segments?
8. How does an understanding of the marketing environment, as discussed in Chapter 2, help in the development of strategic plans?
9. Why do firms change their business composition?
10. How do corporate objectives affect marketing operations?
11. What is brand equity, and why is it an important part of marketing strategy?
12. How can each of the steps in the strategic planning process enhance the development of a strong customer base?
13. What are the key differences between strategic marketing and marketing management? How do these differences relate to the various organizational levels?
14. What are the benefits and disadvantages of the various strategies for entering international markets?

Applying Marketing Skills

1. Read an annual report for any company. Using only the information in the report, describe the firm's corporate, business, and marketing strategies.
2. Pick a recent issue of *BusinessWeek, Fortune,* or any other business publication. Review it to identify examples of corporate growth strategies used by different firms.
3. Interview a marketing executive at a local firm. Ask the executive what types of strategic plans the firm develops and what is included in each strategic plan. How does this approach coincide with the marketing plan presented in Appendix A?
4. Locate a current advertising campaign that exemplifies a comarketing alliance. Postulate why these two companies decided to partner and what synergies (mutual benefits not available to either product on its own) the comarketing alliance is trying to capture in the market.

Using the www in Marketing

Activity One Go to the home page of Disney.

1. What does the site say about core competencies and corporate vision?
2. How are the businesses organized within the larger corporation?
3. How does the site describe Disney's emphasis on the production of quality products and services?

Activity Two Find the Internet home page of a company that you admire that offers multiple product lines.

1. What company did you choose? Why?
2. What strategic business units make up the company?
3. What is the overall mission for the firm? What marketing strategies are used to support that mission?
4. Describe the primary product benefits used as the focal point for the marketing strategy of one of the company's products.

Making Marketing Decisions

Case 3–1 *Red Bull: The Drink for Generation Y*

As New Age beverages grew in the 1990s, Red Bull entered as an "energy" drink. At one point the firm had 70 percent of the hypercaffeinated market. Industry analysts predict that by 2007, the energy drink market will be just under $1 billion. The thirst for "antiauthoritarian" products and ties to extreme sports have enhanced the trendy appeal of the product. Red Bull's marketing has evolved from word-of-mouth communication to more formal television advertising. The product's slim can and small size make distribution across clubs and similar outlets easy to accomplish. The premium price of about $1.99 offers profitable margins to the Austrian company, as well as its distributors.

Under pressure from new competitors, including SoBe Adrenaline Rush and Amp, experts argue that Red Bull needs to find new ways to market itself beyond its traditional extreme audience. Until recently, the firm successfully targeted 18- to 24-year-olds. However, the edgy image of the brand has limited the appeal to age groups of 30 and above. Some express concern with the drink's use as an alcohol mixer.

In response to increasing competition, Red Bull has altered its strategy by supporting a European PGA event (certainly a nonextreme sport). In 2004 a sugar-free version was introduced in an attempt to appeal to women and carbohydrate-conscious dieters. Market share has dropped to 54.4 percent. Now Red Bull wants to broaden the appeal beyond young male athletes, night owls, and college students.

Questions

1. What is the marketing mix for Red Bull? What markets does Red Bull attempt to reach? How do marketing mix elements and target markets combine to form the firm's marketing strategy?

2. What growth strategies seem to offer the most likely opportunities for the future?

3. What ethical issues are faced by the company?

4. As Red Bull expands to other countries, what international marketing issues must be considered?

Case 3–2 *Virgin Atlantic Airways: Flying toward U.S. Markets*

 Virgin is best known for its competition with the larger and more staid British Airways. Virgin has benefited greatly in Great Britain from its underdog role in competing for the lucrative transatlantic travel business. In the smaller, confined British environment, Virgin has gained wide recognition. The company aggressively promotes and prices air travel fees and services and has developed strong brand recognition. Its corporate reputation, regardless of the business endeavor, is clear: innovation, value for the money, and an element of fun.

Virgin is now applying this philosophy in its efforts to break into the U.S. market. Questions remain, however, about its ability to succeed in the U.S. market, where it will face more competitors and an environment in which companies typically spend a lot more on marketing. One action taken by Virgin was the opening of a 75,000-square-foot megastore in New York's Times Square. The store is described as the world's largest

record, movie, book, and multimedia store. Virgin's soft drink brand, ranked in Great Britain above Pepsi, has been introduced in selected U.S. markets. Its airline does indeed possess considerable name recognition among business travelers in the United Kingdom. Recently Virgin has begun aggressively promoting incentive vouchers that can be purchased and applied for whole or part payments on package holidays, flights, hotel accommodations, and car fares.

Virgin gets much credit for competing with British Airways, and its "cool" image has established a nice niche in the United Kingdom. The cola success has been due to price; the airline success has been due to unique customer services and creative promotions and advertising. Yet the hurdles confronted by Virgin in its efforts to successfully compete in the United States are formidable.

Significant changes are likely to impact the operation and marketing strategy for Virgin Atlantic. Sales of transatlantic flights have been affected by international events. These flights are the lifeline for both British Airways and Virgin Atlantic. Recently the airline made its first flight into Australia and will add aircraft as this important market develops. The company also seeks to improve its presence with strengthened route relationships with Hong Kong and China. International plans also include the possibility of partnering with another company to serve the lucrative Chinese market, as well as newly obtained access to India.

Questions

1. What major obstacles will Virgin face in the U.S. expansion that are not part of marketing within the United Kingdom?

2. What problems occur when products from the same corporate brand (Virgin) are differentiated on different bases (price versus service)?

3. Because of 9/11, how will airlines change their marketing strategy?

Chapter Four

Consumer Buying Behavior and Decision Making

4

After studying this chapter, you should be able to

1 Discuss the importance of consumer behavior.

2 Understand consumer decision making and some of the important influences on those decisions.

3 Distinguish between low-involvement and high-involvement consumer behavior.

4 Understand how attitudes influence consumer purchases.

5 Appreciate how the social environment affects consumer behavior.

6 Recognize many of the individual consumer differences that influence purchase decisions and behavior.

7 Recognize the outcomes of consumers' decisions to purchase or not to purchase and how they affect marketing success.

Visa

Alternatively reviled and adored, the credit card is an integral part of the American and global payment system. Visa credit cards are the world's most used form of "plastic" payment. According to the company's Web site, 2004 was a record year for Visa U.S.A. In the face of a tentative economy, Visa U.S.A. achieved record sales of $956 billion and better than expected revenues of $2.4 billion. Visa's cards are accepted at more than 21 million locations in over 300 countries. As such, Visa is a primary company in the minds and behavior of many consumers. The firm makes purchases and ownership possible while offering consumers credit to support their consumer behavior.

Visa's competition, in addition to American Express, Discover, and MasterCard, is cash and checks. Interestingly, the company's brand managers view their objective as gaining greater control over consumer transactions. Currently Visa outspends all others in terms of media ($319 million). Moreover, its quality rating and awareness levels exceed all other cards. While the Internet potential is enormous, Visa focuses its efforts on traditional in-store purchases. In contrast, American Express and Discover are pressing their presence for use in Internet purchases.

MAN'S BEST FRIEND
Another reason to pay bills automatically with your Visa card.

VISA
it's everywhere you want to be.

Visa obtains revenues from fees associated with cards using the Visa logo and from charge activity. Marketplace acceptance is a key driver of the brand's widespread preference among consumers. Visa's extensive marketing efforts are designed to reinforce that perception among credit users. The overriding objective for Visa is to provide increasing value to consumer users. Its recent efforts are targeted toward affluent consumers with its Visa Signature Card. In addition, Visa International is aiming at Chinese consumers with its 2008 Beijing Olympic Games credit card.

Visa's success is due to the company's ability to adapt to rapidly changing environments and evolving customer needs. Visa's adherence to the principles of the marketing concept has depended on the company's understanding of consumer decision making and the many internal and external factors that affect consumer choices. Marketers are increasingly emphasizing consumer loyalty and retention programs and have allocated marketing budget funds accordingly. These programs go by many names, including loyalty, frequency, retention, and relationship marketing. But all define the same basic concept: identify, segment, and retain profitable customers by communicating and rewarding desired behavior.[1]

In the development and execution of a marketing program, a company must consider consumer preferences, the motivations behind purchase decisions, and subsequent product use. Remember that the marketing concept is based on identification of consumer needs and customer satisfaction. Likewise, building customer loyalty and long-term profitability is not possible without a firm grasp of the company's current and future customers. The success of marketing strategy, including the identification of target segments and the design of marketing mix combinations, depends on knowing what motivates consumers and how they form preferences and make decisions. Even following the many dot-com failures, online marketers, like traditional firms, must understand consumers. Attracting business and keeping consumers are now the greatest challenges. Understanding those consumers is critical.[2]

Consumer behavior is a complex topic and difficult to cover in a single chapter. In fact, consumer behavior is a separate course in many marketing programs. Additionally, the study of consumer behavior has historically been a multidisciplinary phenomenon. Researchers from psychology, anthropology, economics, and sociology, as well as marketing and consumer behavior specialists, have all contributed greatly to our understanding of consumer preferences and decision making.

In this chapter we try to describe many of the most important aspects of consumer behavior. Again, the study of consumer behavior is critical in helping to ensure adherence to the principles of the marketing concept and the development of effective marketing strategy. First we offer a formal definition of consumer behavior and explain why the topic is so important. Then we use a model of consumer decision processes to explore consumer problem solving and decision making. Next we describe important environmental, individual, and situational influences that affect consumer behavior. The chapter concludes with a discussion of the primary outcomes that can follow the purchase and use of products and services, as well as a number of ethical issues that involve individual consumer behavior.

The Nature of Consumer Behavior and Decision Making

Consumer behavior can be defined as the mental and emotional processes and the physical activities that people engage in when they select, purchase, use, and dispose of products or services to satisfy particular needs and desires. The primary means by which consumers obtain goods and services are by buying, trading, renting or leasing, bartering, and gift giving.[3] Identifying and understanding consumer needs and preferences and their determinants are critical in the pursuit of profitable business opportunities.

Today a number of factors make it all the more important to understand consumer markets and individual consumer behavior: the size of the consumer market, ongoing changes in consumer shopping habits and purchase decisions, the continuing emphasis on consumer-oriented marketing, and the design of effective marketing strategy.

Size of the Consumer Market

The U.S. consumer market consists of all individuals in the United States. In 2004, the consumption expenditures for this market were huge: $8.2 trillion out of a total gross domestic product of $11.7 trillion.[4] Demand of this magnitude is well worth understanding. Moreover, competition for consumer dollars will increase as populations in the United States and other countries age, resulting in declining expenditures for some products. Firms that understand consumer behavior will be best able to compete effectively.

Weight Watchers uses unique advertising to appeal to health- and nutrition-conscious consumers.

Changes in the Consumer Market

Of equal importance are changes occurring in the consumer market. Some important growing consumer market segments are detailed in Exhibit 4–1. They include consumers' concern for quality at reasonable and fair prices, for the effects of their purchases on the environment, and for health and diet.

Several fundamental demographic changes will affect the underpinnings of future consumer markets. These include the aging of the baby boom generation, the increasing importance of children as consumers, differences between the haves and have-nots, and society's increasingly diverse population. Household budget expenditures will increase dramatically for health care and computers relative to declining dollars for furniture, food, and apparel.[5]

Other trends that have increased dramatically in the last five years and will continue to increase include the following: the growing importance of convenience items such as bottled water; ready-to-eat consumption such as frozen pizza and refrigerated dinners and fresh salads; and the doubling of sales of health and self-care products. According to the Census Bureau, Hispanics make up the largest growing consumer segment, spending in excess of $400 billion on products and services annually. Importantly, studies show that Hispanics are more loyal to the services, products, and companies that show a direct interest in them through electronic or print advertising.[6]

One of the largest transformations in households has been the changes that have occurred in gender roles and division of responsibilities within the household. The implications of this enormous change for the design of product and service offerings, as well as for the intended audience of advertising, are profound.

Consumers now spend a growing part of their time shopping at the computer, comparing prices, and looking for ideas. In recognition of this phenomenon, retailers are turning to "lifestyle centers" to attract Web-savvy consumers to newly designed malls. Unlike enclosed malls, lifestyle centers offer the shopper the ability to enter quickly and focus more on restaurants, movie theaters, and landscaped environments.[7]

Nowhere are the complexities more obvious than in the food industry. The paradox here is that consumers may want low-fat, low-cholesterol salads for lunch and fish for dinner, but many also choose a hot fudge sundae for dessert. This means that some old-fashioned, middle-of-the-road products like ordinary ice cream are being squeezed by low-calorie frozen yogurts on one side and extra-luscious, super-premium ice creams on the other. An eating evolution that has consumers seeking more healthful and diet-oriented food has forced Kraft to rethink how it markets and to reconsider its product line-up. The firm now offers lower-calorie snacks and reduced-carbohydrate cereals and dressings.[8]

Exhibit 4–1	*Growing consumer markets*

1. Retail line-up changes—three new models: (1) "price-centric retailers"; (2) retailers organized by lifestyle (e.g., the Museum Company); and (3) "occasion-centric" retailers (e.g., gourmet cooking supply).
2. Outdoor living markets—garden, deck, patio, and pool design.
3. Consumer electronics—new digital conveniences.
4. Enhanced experience businesses—spas, travel with theme activities.
5. Anti-aging products and services—as boomers reach retirement.
6. Health as a national hobby—educated consumers are driving changes in health care.
7. High-end sports apparel and equipment—golf clubs, rackets, skis, skates, bikes, etc.
8. Safe packaging, pure contents, and "green" concerns—ecologically enhancing and safety concerns.

Multicultural differences offer opportunities for marketers to capitalize on unique preferences among segments of consumers.

Middle-income consumers are increasingly trading up to higher levels of quality and taste. The consumer segment with incomes above $50,000 possesses approximately $3.5 trillion in disposable income. Companies offer a wide variety of new luxury products and services for this group and have realized high volumes despite relatively high prices. One example is the C-series of brand extensions (new luxury) being offered by Mercedes (old luxury) for the middle-income segment.[9]

Consumer-Oriented Marketing

To become more consumer-oriented and to build long-lasting relationships with their customers, companies need to understand what motivates buyers. This is an important aspect of the marketing concept. Ford Motor Company, for example, focuses on increased customer satisfaction and employee commitment. The company

- Is dedicated to being customer-driven.
- Makes carefully thought-out decisions about the customers to whom each product is to appeal.
- Studies potential customers and what they most want.
- Develops detailed product attributes to fulfill customer wants; doesn't copy what other firms are doing.
- Follows up with customers to confirm that products and marketing programs meet objectives.[10]

As part of this customer orientation, firms are now focusing on customer value and those customers whose long-term values are high. Research has shown that the value of a firm's customers—and by implication, the value of a firm—can almost double when the firm shifts from a low-retention, high-discount orientation to a high-retention, low-discount emphasis.[11]

To consistently deliver high-quality products and services, marketers must understand and respond to continually changing consumer needs and expectations.[12] And marketers with the best understanding and the least biased perceptions of consumer needs will be the most competitive.[13]

Design of Strategy

An understanding of consumer behavior is required for the effective design and implementation of marketing strategy. Knowledge gained through experience and marketing research provides the basis for the development of brand images and market positioning strategies. The success of these efforts determines subsequent brand strength, or what is commonly called *brand equity*—the marketplace value of a brand. A strong, well-known consumer brand, such as Kodak, Gap, Coke, Nabisco, and others, can induce quick and favorable consumer reactions to the particular company's products and enable the successful introduction of new products using the same brand name. Understanding consumer behavior can assist marketers in their efforts at *service recovery*—winning back consumers

ACTING ETHICALLY

Blockbuster's busted campaign

The heavily promoted "No More Late Fees" campaign of Blockbuster met considerable resistance from some state attorney generals' offices. The criticism leading to termination of the campaign was based on allegations that consumers were not being advertised to truthfully and violations of con-

sumer protection laws may have occurred. Blockbuster and all advertisers are obligated to avoid deception and to not mislead consumers. Advertising does not have to be objectively incorrect to be judged deceptive if the advertising leads to incorrect impressions.

Speaking from Experience

Chet Zalesky
President
ConsumerMetrics, Inc.

"Most companies see consumer segmentation as the final phase to a research effort, when, in fact, it is the beginning of marketing effort to help the organization use the information. Too many times companies do not devote enough thought to training the organization on how they can utilize the results of consumer segmentation to develop new services, design more targeted communications, or consider repositioning alternatives."

ConsumerMetrics is an Atlanta marketing research firm that offers general research services but specializes in analyzing complex issues and quantitative analyses. Chet Zalesky earned his Master's of Science in Marketing degree from the University of South Carolina's Darla Moore School of Business.

who defect. Defection can be driven by complaints not handled, the competition offering a better value, or relocation. However, the primary reason for defection is benign neglect. Understanding consumer behavior enhances marketers' ability to know the motivations and needs of consumers and their ability to communicate effectively with consumers.[14]

Understanding E-Customers

The profile of Internet buyers is changing as consumers of all types use the Web for making purchases. Researchers are monitoring consumer behavior on the Internet to understand what drives patronage and decision making, as well as the determinants of loyalty. One survey of 400,000 Internet customers revealed a number of findings. The 10 most important site attributes in order of ranking are product representation, product prices, product selection, on-time delivery, ease of ordering, product information, level and quality of consumer support, product shipping and handling, posted privacy policy, and site navigation and appearance.[15]

Using the Claritas PRIZM segmentation scheme based on a combination of geographic and demographic characteristics, one research study revealed that Web users range from the Blue Blood Estates to the downscale country folk of Rustic Elders. The clusters with the greatest access to the Internet are still early-adopting, upscale consumers. However, many of the clusters with the greatest online activity and time spent online are working-class and lower-income groups. And actually, the number of sites visited monthly by upscale consumers has declined.[16]

Consumers sometimes say one thing and do another. Webvan, an online grocery service, had 6.5 percent of the households in San Francisco order from the company in its first year and a half of operation. However, follow-up orders never achieved sufficient levels to justify the company's elaborate warehouse capabilities. Buying groceries online required more planning and effort than consumers initially anticipated.[17]

Consumer Decision Making

A general model of consumer decision making and influences on these decisions is presented in Exhibit 4–2. The consumer decision process, shown in the center of the model, assumes a conscious and logical decision-making process: from recognition of a need or problem to information search to evaluation of alternatives to purchase. This sequence can be affected by the social environment, individual differences, and situational factors. All have implications for the design and implementation of successful marketing strategy.

The Consumer Decision Process

A consumer's recognition of a *need* or *problem* may stem from an internal desire, the absence or failure of a product, or some external influence such as advertising. It can be as simple as getting thirsty and wanting a soda, or having to replace a used or outdated product or one that has lost its appeal. Advertising may also trigger the consumer's perception

Exhibit 4–2   *A general model of consumer decision making and influences*

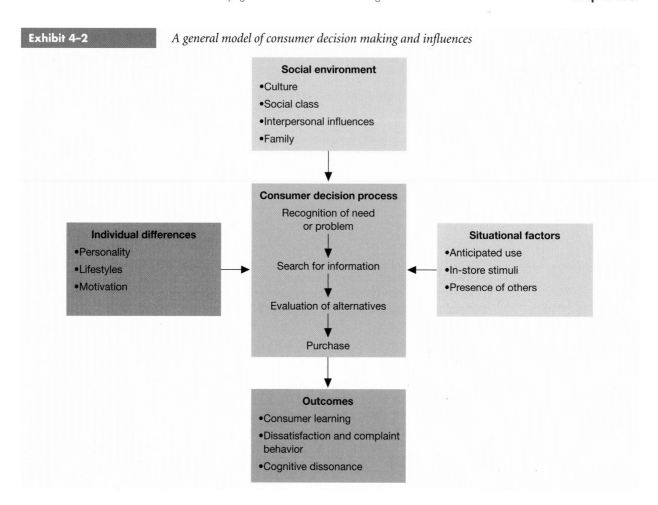

of a need or serve as a reminder. In fact, marketing can influence information search even before consumers are aware of a need or problem through the use of institutional advertising, product image campaigns, and primary demand advertising.

After recognizing a problem, the consumer searches for information. An *internal search* involves a review of information stored in memory. Although readily available, internal information may be incomplete or inaccurate. An *external search* involves gathering information from marketing sources such as advertising or from nonmarketing sources such as friends or *Consumer Reports*. Nonmarketing sources of information may be particularly useful because they are likely unbiased. The degree of search can vary by the number of brands examined, the number of stores visited, the variety of attributes considered, the number of information sources consulted, and the time spent on searching. An understanding of consumer search behavior is important to defining a product's or brand's competition.

Consumer researchers have identified several interesting phenomena regarding search behavior and how search relates to knowledge acquisition by consumers. First, prior knowledge facilitates the learning of new knowledge and increases search efficiency. That is, more expert consumers are likely to search more, not less, than low-knowledge consumers. Experts know the questions to ask and can more easily understand the answers they receive. Relatedly, research suggests that marketers can benefit from teaching consumers the appropriate vocabulary associated with their product categories. This enhanced vocabulary enables consumers to learn more easily new product information and to form more stable brand preferences.[18]

The effects of online search and evaluation are already evident and are profoundly affecting how consumers shop and how firms compete. The Internet acts as a readily accessible source of external information and a facilitator of alternative evaluation. Psychologists and marketing experts have found that consumers who search online are impatient, in control, and quick to shift between Web sites. Consumers in cyberspace are demanding more choices and more information. The most important attributes for encouraging consumers to shop a particular Web site are assurance of privacy, larger price discounts, ability to return products to a physical store, and ability to speak with a customer representative. The shoppingbot phenomenon has also revised the decision-making process. A typical shoppingbot sequence might begin with a series of questions to narrow choices, then offer manufacturer-provided, detailed product descriptions, and end with links to retailers. In other instances, auction sites provide input regarding the possibility of bidding for items.[19]

After searching for information, the consumer evaluates possibilities (products, brands). This *evaluation of alternatives* is based on the individual's beliefs about the products and their features or characteristics. These beliefs form the basis for the consumer's attitudes, which influence both intentions to buy and purchase behavior. Following purchase, outcomes such as feelings of satisfaction or dissatisfaction and the development of brand loyalty may occur.

Consumer behavior is a complex phenomenon, and many internal and external factors may influence an individual decision. Many decisions are motivated by specific needs and values; some involve a conscious, logical decision process; others are made with little or no thought. One in-store field study of 4,200 grocery and mass-merchandiser shoppers revealed the following findings regarding consumer decision making:

1. Fifty-nine percent of purchases were unplanned, 30 percent were specifically planned, and the rest were generally planned or brand switches.

2. In-store decision making is greater for larger households, for higher-income households, and for women.

3. Consumers are more likely to make an unplanned decision when the product is displayed at the end of an aisle.[20]

Two other concepts relate to consumer decision making. First, **conversion rates** are used to describe the percentage of shoppers who are converted into buyers. Conversion rates vary widely depending on the kind of store or department involved. In some parts of the grocery store, conversion rates are near 100 percent. In art galleries, the conversion rates are near zero. Conversion rates in e-commerce are lessened by the "abandoned basket" phenomena. Often consumers get far along the decision process and then walk away. Some reluctance is due to privacy and credit card information concerns. Other reasons are tied to uncertainty among consumers due to their limited ability to evaluate products with confidence. Second, **surrogate shoppers** are involved in a significant portion of consumer decisions. A surrogate shopper is defined as a commercial enterprise, consciously engaged and paid by the consumer or other interested partner on behalf of the consumer to make or facilitate consumer decisions. Familiar examples include financial advisers, travel agents, and wardrobe consultants. Surrogates may perform any or all of the activities involved in consumer decision making—from search to determination of the brand consideration set to choice.[21]

High- and Low-Involvement Decisions

Involvement represents the level of importance or interest generated by a product or a decision. It varies by the situation or the product decision at hand and is influenced by the person's needs or motives. Frequently, involvement is affected by how closely the purchase decision is linked to the consumer's self-concept and how personally relevant the product is to the consumer.

Involvement is an important concept because it affects the nature or complexity of the communications appropriate for promoting products and services. Relatedly, involvement influences the nature of information processing engaged in by consumers. **Consumer information processing** represents the cognitive processes by which consumers interpret and integrate information from the environment.[22]

High-involvement decisions are characterized by high levels of importance, thorough information processing, and substantial differences between alternatives. The choice of a college to attend, the purchase of a home or vehicle, or the purchase of a bike for a sports enthusiast are all examples of high-involvement decisions. As such, high-involvement decisions

Thinking Critically

Think of a purchase where you have gone through each of the four steps in the consumer decision process (see Exhibit 4–2).

- How did you become aware that a need existed for this product or service?

- Was this purchase a result of routinized response behavior, extensive problem solving, or limited problem solving? How might a company's marketing efforts differ under each of these problem-solving situations?

- What influence did your family have on the purchase?

- After purchasing the product or service, did you experience any cognitive dissonance?

Thinking Critically

We all carry attitudes about people, objects, and behaviors. These attitudes can be either positive or negative in direction.

- Why would it be important for a company to understand the attitude consumers have toward its product? How might marketers use this information in marketing communications?

- What role do attitudes play in consumer satisfaction and dissatisfaction?

are consistent with the logical and thoughtful sequence shown in the center of the consumer behavior model in Exhibit 4–2.

High involvement may be caused by a number of personal, product, and situational factors.[23] Again, importance of the purchase to one's self-concept increases involvement. If financial or performance risk is high, the decision is more likely to have high involvement. High involvement is also more likely when a gift is purchased or social pressures occur.

Low-involvement decisions occur when relatively little personal interest, relevance, or importance is associated with a purchase. These decisions involve much simpler decision processes, and less information processing, than the sequence described in Exhibit 4–2. For low-involvement decisions, consumers do not actively seek large amounts of information. Low-involvement purchases may include soft drinks, fast foods, toothpaste, and many snack foods. In these instances, repetitive purchase behavior may develop. Because these decisions involve little risk, trial purchases are often the consumer's major means of information search and product or brand evaluation.[24]

Types of Consumer Choices

Actually, the acquisition of goods and services is made up of many choices. At least six generic choices may be involved in consumer behavior: product, brand, shopping area, store type, store, and to an increasing degree, nonstore source (catalogs, PC and TV shopping).[25] The decision-making processes and the influences on those decisions discussed in this chapter apply to all six of these choices.

The choices consumers now face are enormous. Some experts believe that the choices are too many and that even dropping items (*SKUs* or stockkeeping units) within a product category can actually increase sales. Consumer product manufacturers introduce more than 34,000 new items annually. The typical grocer now stocks more than 40,000 items. The result is Kellogg's Eggo waffles in 16 flavors, nine varieties of Kleenex tissue, and Glad garbage bags that have multiple varieties of ties.[26]

Consumers also must allocate their limited budgets across product categories. The average U.S. metropolitan household devotes half of its spending to housing, utilities, transportation, and food. Other categories allocated at least 5 percent annually are apparel, insurance, health care, and entertainment. So plenty of consumer marketing funds are directed at these categories.[27]

Psychological Processes

Affect and cognition are two psychological processes consumers use in making purchase decisions. **Affect** refers to feeling responses, while **cognition** refers to thinking or mental responses. The two processes are sometimes used together and may support each other. Affect-based decisions are more spontaneous and result from exposure to stimuli in the environment. Affective processes are more likely to occur when products are hedonic in nature.

Cognitively based decisions involve more thought and deliberate processing of information. Under cognitive processing, consumers are more likely to carefully consider brand attribute information and make more reasoned decisions. Cognition is likely to be most important when products are functional and performance-related features are salient.[28]

Attitudes

Attitudes and attitude formation are related to the evaluation stage of the consumer decision process. **Consumer attitudes** are learned predispositions to respond favorably or unfavorably to a product or brand. Most of us take for granted our attitudes toward our favorite restaurant or soft drink. However, attitudes are instrumental in determining which alternative products and brands will be

Jeep employs unique visuals in its efforts to encourage consumer message processing and its distinctive brand positioning.

purchased and used. Attitudes have certain characteristics that make understanding them important to marketers trying to convince consumers to either buy their products for the first time or to remain loyal. First, attitudes have _valence._ That is, attitudes can be positive, negative, or neutral. Firms use creative messages and allocate huge amounts of funds to create or encourage positive attitudes. Second, attitudes that are strongly held or are held with confidence are resistant to change. Therefore, the establishment of positive brand attitudes in the marketplace is a strategic objective for marketers. Last, attitudes can erode over time if not reinforced; hence, one role of advertising, as you will learn in Chapter 17, is to maintain awareness and to reinforce existing positive brand impressions and attitudes. Attitudes are a primary determinant of purchase behavior, and their role in consumer behavior is a frequent area of inquiry for marketing researchers.

An understanding of consumer attitudes has very basic implications for marketing, for two reasons. Attitudes are based on beliefs consumers hold about the attributes or features (price, level of service, quality) of the products they are evaluating. In many instances, these attributes form the basis for the development of marketing strategies. For example, Honda's efforts to grow in North America include the introduction of the Ridgeline high-performance pickup truck with hardy engine, four-wheel drive, and large cargo space. These attributes are part of Honda's new design and are critical product features designed to generate positive consumer attitudes.[29] Also, attitudes are primary causes of behavior, which makes them very relevant to marketers who want to understand why consumers buy—or do not buy—their products.

Consistent with one well-known psychological model, attitudes are often depicted as the combination of beliefs about the salient product attributes that consumers consider in evaluating alternative choices. The model and an example are presented in detail in this textbook's appendix. This theoretical view of consumer attitudes is rich in implications for developing effective marketing strategy. Briefly, attitudes are assumed to reflect the consumer's beliefs about product attributes (such as price, ability to clean, durability) and the weights or evaluation the individual has assigned to the different attributes. This multiattribute view of consumer attitudes helps marketers assess which attributes are important to consumers, the strengths and weaknesses of brands based on those attributes, and areas in which the greatest improvement in attitudes might be realized.

Experiential Choices

So far, we have described consumer decision making as a logical process involving the conscious consideration of product information related to the attributes or the characteristics of the alternatives under consideration. The assumption is that consumers' long-term goals guide their preferences and that they make purchase decisions thoughtfully and logically. Routinized or habitual decision making is the only exception we have discussed to this point. However, consumers frequently make choices based on their emotions and feelings, adding an experiential perspective to the decision process. One such choice heuristic is termed **affect referral.** In such instances, consumers simply elicit from memory their overall evaluations of products and choose the alternative for which they have the most positive feelings. Affect referral explains why so many convenience items are purchased habitually. Another category of buying decisions that are made with little or no cognitive effort is **impulse purchases.** Impulse purchases are choices made on the spur of the moment, often without prior problem recognition, but associated with strong positive feelings.[30]

Consumers also often make irrational choices in which they act against their own better judgment and engage in behavior they would normally reject. These decisions are called _time-inconsistent choices_ and, like impulse purchases, reflect consumer impatience and the urge to splurge. Psychologists have studied these choices as related to dieting and addiction for years. Yet all of us at one time or another have felt the urge to buy when better judgment suggests otherwise.[31]

Principles of Consumer Persuasion

One noted consumer researcher, Robert Cialdini, has studied persuasion extensively and has summarized six rules of persuasion. These principles help explain how marketing firms influence consumers. The six concepts are reciprocation, consistency, social validation, liking, authority, and scarcity. For *reciprocation,* individuals are obligated to repay in kind what they have received. One benefit from product samples, other than product exposure, is the tendency for consumers to feel indebted for the free gift. *Consistency* is demonstrated by the behavior of nonprofit organization supporters who offer monetary contributions following an earlier signing of a petition for that same organization. These two related behaviors (petition signing and monetary contribution) then are consistent over time.

Social validation is evident in advertising that promotes peer approval and social acceptance by others. *Liking* is evidenced by the tendency to say yes to others whom we like. Tiger Woods is an effective company endorser for all types of products (such as Buick and American Express) because of his personal appeal and the fact that he is widely liked. Advertisements that include claims such as "four out of five doctors recommend" embody the persuasive impact of *authority.* Last, consumers are affected by *scarcity* and value products that become less available. For example, purchase limits in the grocery store increase demand in part because of perceived scarcity effects.[32]

Summary Typology of Consumer Decision Making

Professor Hans Baumgartner has done an extensive analysis of consumer decision making. Using three basic dimensions, he identified eight types of different purchases. These three dimensions are thinking versus feeling purchases; low versus high purchase involvement (that is, the degree of buyer care or effort); and spontaneous versus deliberate purchase behavior (how much prior planning or experience is involved?). Combining these three dimensions results in the following eight different purchase behaviors:

1. Extended purchase decision making based on logical and objective criteria.
2. Symbolic purchase behavior based on image or social approval.
3. Repetitive purchase behavior (decisions based on brand loyalty).
4. Hedonic purchase behavior based on simple liking.
5. Promotional purchase behavior because products are on sale.
6. Exploratory purchase behavior due to curiosity or desire for variety.
7. Casual purchase behavior involving little thought.
8. Impulsive purchase behavior.[33]

Influence of the Social Environment   A number of external influences affect

consumer behavior and purchase decision processes. The social environment directly affects sources of information consumers use in decision making and product evaluations. In many instances, personal sources, such as family and friends, may be more credible and influential to consumers than any other source of information.

The most important social influences are culture, subculture, social class, family, and interpersonal or reference group influences. These flows of influence within the social environment are summarized in Exhibit 4–3.

Cultural Influences

Culture refers to the values, ideas, attitudes, and symbols that people adopt to communicate, interpret, and interact as members of society. In fact, culture describes a society's way of life. Culture is learned and transmitted from one generation to the next. It includes abstract elements (values, attitudes, ideas, religion) and material elements (symbols, buildings, products, brands). The process of absorbing a culture is called **socialization.** It continues throughout one's life and produces many specific preferences for products and services, shopping patterns, and interactions with others. Applied to marketing and consumer behavior, it is referred to as *consumer socialization.*

Exhibit 4–3   *Flows of influence within the social environment*

In particular, the culture and subcultures of a country have been shown to affect the appropriateness of different advertising strategies. Using the well-known categories of culture developed by an IBM executive, Geert Hofstede, one researcher discovered that in countries where people are not highly focused on social roles and group affiliation, such as Germany and Argentina, functional brand images are most effective. In countries where social roles are important, such as France and Belgium, images based on social and sensory messages are appropriate. Relatedly, cultures with low individualism (such as Asian countries) are also amenable to social appeals that emphasize group affiliation.[34] Cultural effects have been found also in terms of consumer product innovativeness. For example, consumers in more individualistic and masculine countries tend to be more innovative. Innovativeness decreases in countries scoring high in ethnocentrism, a more favorable attitude toward the past.[35]

The concept of culture has two primary implications for marketing: It determines the most basic values that influence consumer behavior patterns, and it can be used to distinguish subcultures that represent substantial market segments and opportunities.

VALUES   **Values** are shared beliefs or cultural norms about what is important or right. Values, such as the need to belong or to succeed, represent important goals to which consumers subscribe. A society's values are transmitted to the individual through the family, through organizations (schools, religious institutions, businesses), and through other people (the community, the social environment).

Cultural values directly influence how consumers view and use individual products, brands, and services. One typology of values used by consumer researchers is the List of Values (LOV).[36] It includes nine basic values:

- Self-respect.
- Warm relationships with others.

Cultural differences offer opportunities for marketing to appeal to segments within the youth market.

- Self-fulfillment.
- Respect from others.
- Excitement.
- Security.
- Sense of accomplishment.
- Sense of belonging.
- Fun and enjoyment in life.

Another commercial method used to research consumer values is the Values and Lifestyles program (VALS), which identifies eight market segments that share similar end values. This segmentation scheme is explained in more detail in Chapter 7.

Values influence the goals people pursue and the behavior used to pursue those goals. Many marketing communication campaigns recognize the importance of values as the basis for advertising themes and justification for purchase. For example, the desire for recognition and self-fulfillment is frequently used by companies selling self-improvement and exercise products. The sense of belonging forms the basis for marketing many personal and gift products.

SUBCULTURES   The norms and values of specific groups or subcultures within a society are called **ethnic patterns.** Ethnic groups or subcultures may be formed around national, religious, racial, or geographic factors. Members of a subculture share similar values and patterns of behavior, making them attractive marketing targets for specific products and brands.

Unique subcultures often develop in geographic areas of a nation. The southwestern part of the United States is known for casual lifestyles, outdoor living, and active sports.[37] The Southeast is associated with a conservative lifestyle and friendly atmosphere. One system divides North America into "nine nations": the Foundry (industrial Northeast); Dixie; Ecotopia (northern Pacific Rim); Mexamericana (southwestern area); the Breadbasket (Kansas, Nebraska, Iowa, etc.); Quebec (French-speaking Canada); the Empty Quarter (northwestern Canada); the Islands (tip of southern Florida, Caribbean Islands, some Latin American influence); and New England.[38] Each region contains many individuals who share similar values and lifestyles.

The black and Hispanic subcultures, while diverse themselves, are the largest ethnic subcultures. The black subculture is growing in size and spending power. Hispanics make up the second fastest-growing subculture, behind the Asian subculture. Many Hispanics share a common language and a strong family orientation. Conservative Christian areas and Jewish centers also represent subcultures of influence.

Numerous demographic characteristics, such as the following, have been used to identify subcultures:

Nationality—Hispanics, Italians.

Race—African-American, American Indian, Asian.

Region—New England, the South.

Age—elderly, teenager.

Religion—Catholic, Jewish, fundamentalist.

These subcultures include large numbers of consumers who share common values, behavior patterns, and beliefs that relate to consumer behavior. (Note that an individual can belong to more than one subculture.) The consumer socialization of individuals within those subcultures affects their purchase decisions.[39]

Demographic analysis can be used in other ways for understanding consumer phenomena. For example, the enduring characteristics of the generation from which consumers come remain important as individuals age. Marketers are increasingly using these shared generational experiences to reach and effectively appeal to consumer segments. For the Depression generation, that may mean stressing thrift; for the World War II generation, patriotism; boomers are often seen as independent types stretching society's bounds. The point is, as the young get older, their habits stick with them.[40]

Age, a commonly used segmentation variable, also can be used to understand subculture differences. The baby boom, Generation X, and now Generation Y segments share common values much like other cultural subgroups. Even as Generation Y, or those individuals born between 1977 and 1994, reaches adulthood, many companies are positioning themselves to gain a part of this complex and powerful market. Young consumers learn preferences and loyalties that continue for years. In addition, cohort experiences represent shared experiences that form values and life skills through which consumers interpret subsequent experiences. As such, age differences within a year certainly affect consumption and represent different market segments. Moreover, age generations or cohorts share common experiences and represent segments with common values over time.[41]

Gender differences offer obvious segmentation opportunities. One interesting phenomena regarding consumer behavior involves the reluctance of many women to negotiate. Research has found that women's reluctance to negotiate arises even when it comes to commonly negotiated items like automobiles. According to one survey, women are 40 percent more likely than men to accept the first car price the dealer offers.[42]

Social Class Influences

Social classes are relatively homogeneous divisions within a society that contain people with similar values, needs, lifestyles, and behavior. One approach for consumer analysis describes four social classes: upper, middle, working, and lower class, each of which can be further subdivided.[43] Identification with a social class is influenced most strongly by level of education and occupation. Social class is also affected by social skill, status aspirations, community participation, cultural level, and family history.[44] Another recent perspective on social class includes the following four factors impacting social class: social capital (whom you know), credential capital (where you received your degree), income capital, and investment capital (stocks and bonds). One-fifth of Americans are privileged, with job security, high wages, and strong skills. While great variability exists in the remaining 80 percent, many other consumers lack the same stability and high wages.[45] Social classes are relatively stable, but educational experiences and career moves enable individuals to shift from one class to another. Today the middle class is declining in size. Economic conditions have limited upward mobility of the working class and caused many borderline families to fall into poverty.[46]

One recent study asked individuals to classify themselves as lower, working, middle, or upper class. Forty-six and 47 percent categorized themselves as working and middle class,

Timberland recognizes the importance of family influences in this brand advertisement.

respectively. Occupation and education were again the primary reasons individuals gave for their assignments. Research suggests that the working class is becoming younger, more ethnically diverse, and more female. These changes offer opportunities for marketers in their desire to understand consumer behavior and to identify large segments of potential buyers.[47]

Social class influences the types of purchases consumers make and the activities they pursue. Who goes to wrestling matches and who goes to the opera? Who plays polo and who goes bowling? Although preferences change within classes over time, more significant differences in purchases and behaviors occur *between* classes.

Trickle-down theory offers another perspective on social class effects. "Top levels," who determine what is acceptable or hot, are less defined today by social class or money. Rather, many trendsetters are young consumers, many of whom do not have high incomes. One resulting effect of this phenomenon is "cool-hunting," where market researchers covertly observe these trendsetters to learn of the latest styles before these styles reach the mainstream marketplace and culture.

Family Influences and the Family Life Cycle

Family influences play two important roles: in socializing people and in affecting individual purchase decisions. Families are the most influential factor in an individual's behavior, values, and attitudes. Patterns of behavior and values learned early in life are not easily changed. Lifestyles (athleticism, fondness for the outdoors) are usually learned from parents through **childhood consumer socialization**—the process by which young people acquire skills, knowledge, and attitudes relevant to their functioning as consumers in the marketplace.[48]

Individual family members also influence purchase decisions through their performance of different roles within the family. Members of a family or household may assume different roles—and roles may change, depending on the situation. In the choice of toys, for example, parents often determine the acceptable set of brands from which children may select. The parents make the decision to buy, yet the child makes the brand choice. In other cases, all family members may influence decisions to purchase large-ticket items such as homes and automobiles, and increasingly, men and teenagers are doing the grocery shopping; marketers target these shoppers with ads in the magazines they buy.

Developmental timetables are expectations or beliefs about what is normal for a child at a specific age. Socialization differences in terms of developmental timetables have been shown between Japanese and American parents. Specifically, Japanese mothers expect their children to develop consumer-related skills and understanding of advertising later than their U.S. counterparts. In addition, Japanese children are allowed less autonomy in their consumer behavior.[49]

Today the role of children and teenagers within a family, and even as a market themselves, cannot be underestimated. A typical 10-year-old goes shopping two or three times per week with parents. Apparel spending is the fastest-growing category of expenditures, and preferences formed by the young influence brand recognition and success among other age groups. As the number of single-parent households and working mothers has risen, the influence of children has increased as well. In total, over $500 billion in household spending is affected annually, including over $100 million in direct expenditures.[50] A grid showing how family influences relate to different product decisions appears in Exhibit 4–4. It crosses the number of decision makers with the number of users, identifying nine categories of family influence, depending on who makes the purchase decision and who uses the item. Cereal, as shown in cell 4, might be consumed by multiple members of the family but selected by the primary grocery shopper.[51]

Exhibit 4-4

Family buyer and user differences across purchase categories

	Purchase decision maker		
User	**One member**	**Some members**	**All members**
One member	1 Book	2 Dad and Eric buy tennis racquet for Eric	3 Birthday gift
Some members	4 Mom buys breakfast cereal for kids	5 Wine for dinner party	6 Private school for children
All members	7 Refrigerator	8 Personal computer	9 Everyone helps pick toppings on a pizza

Television, the Internet, and other media are affecting teenagers globally. One consequence is a common culture of consumption among young people worldwide. For example, MTV networks are directly influencing the spending habits and brand preferences of young people everywhere. As in the United States and the United Kingdom, well-known brands like Levi's, Nike, and Timberland are preferred worldwide among teenagers and other young consumers.[52]

Family life cycle is also relevant to consumer behavior. It describes the sequence of steps a family goes through: from young, single adults, to the married couple whose children have left home, to, possibly, the retired survivor. The family life cycle suggests ways to develop marketing strategies and design products and services. Household consumption patterns vary dramatically through the family life cycle. Appliances and insurance are bought for the first time during the early stages, for instance. Luxury products, travel, and recreation are typical expenditures for middle-aged adults with no children at home. Companies tailor product variations for specific stages of the family life cycle, such as Campbell's soups or Chef-Boy-R-Dee pasta packaged in smaller sizes for households of single or older consumers.

Changing family life cycles also have implications for product needs and buying behavior. Dramatic increases in age associated with first marriages, women working outside the home, single parents, premarital births, single-person households, childless couples,

The use of popular figures as product endorsers makes use of value-expressive interpersonal influences.

| Exhibit 4–5 | *Transitions in household types* |

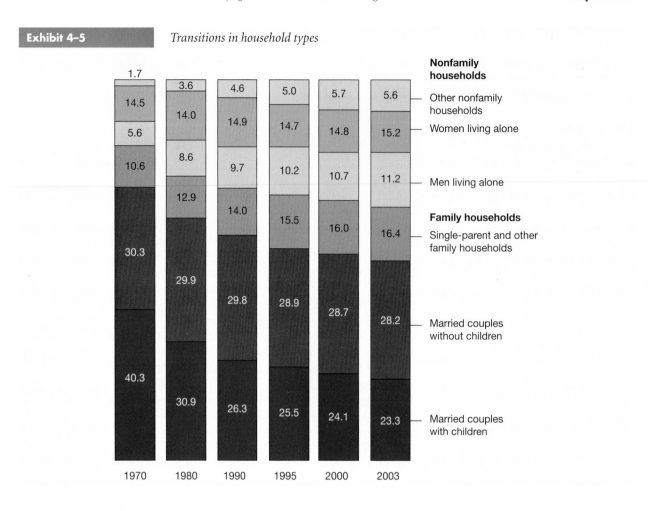

divorces, remarriages, alternative living arrangements, and lower fertility rates have produced striking changes in families and households.[53] Exhibit 4–5 shows the number of households comprising married couples with children at home and single-parent and single-person households as well as the changing nature of households. These numbers may decrease demand for large dining room tables, but they are good news for businesses that sell smaller tables, refrigerators, televisions, cleaning products, and other one-to-a-household items.[54]

Among the changes to the traditional family life cycle, the prevalence of dual-earner households and adult children living at home are phenomena well recognized by marketers. Today companies study dual-income households just as intently as they studied homemakers a quarter of a century ago. For example, college-educated households make large-ticket purchase decisions jointly. Less educated dual-income couples often both work just to buy increasingly expensive necessities. Young adults are now waiting longer to leave the home. In most cases, the prolonged stay enables the young adult to spend wages on luxuries instead of paying rent.[55]

Interpersonal Influences

Marketers also recognize interpersonal influences beyond the family, including friends, coworkers, and others. These sources of influence are often called **reference groups,** or those others look to for help and guidance. As shown in Exhibit 4–6, this influence affects brand and product decisions. They may be groups a person belongs to and ones she or he admires or wants to join. Specifically, reference group influences are greatest for public luxuries regarding both the products consumers buy and the specific brands purchased. In contrast, the limited visibility and functional nature of many private necessities suggests that interpersonal influences are minimal.

Exhibit 4–6	*Reference group influence on product and brand purchase decisions*	

Product / Brand	Weak reference group influence (–)	Strong reference group influence (+)
Strong reference group influence (+)	**Public necessities** *Influence:* Weak product and strong brand *Examples:* Wristwatch, automobile, business suit	**Public luxuries** *Influence:* Strong product and brand *Examples:* Golf clubs, snow skis, sailboat
Weak reference group influence (–)	**Private necessities** *Influence:* Weak product and brand *Examples:* Mattress, floor lamp, refrigerator	**Private luxuries** *Influence:* Strong product and weak brand *Examples:* Video game, pool table, CD player

INTERPERSONAL INFLUENCE PROCESSES   Three types of interpersonal processes—informational, utilitarian, and value-expressive—form the basis for interpersonal influences. **Informational influence** is based on the consumer's desire to make informed choices and reduce uncertainty. When we need to buy a complex product or face a new decision, we often seek information and advice from others we trust.

Utilitarian influence is reflected in compliance with the expectations, real or imagined, of others. These expectations are referred to as *norms*. Compliance to norms occurs in efforts to achieve rewards or avoid punishments. Rewards and punishments in day-to-day consumer behavior involve acceptance and peer approval and disapproval. These normative influences are particularly acute for young people. Sometimes these can be negative influences, such as peer pressure to use drugs, alcohol, or tobacco.

Value-expressive influence stems from a desire to enhance self-concept through identification with others. These influences are seen in the frequent use of popular spokespersons and attractive models in much consumer advertising. Celebrity endorsements from personalities such as Bill Cosby and Britney Spears are intended to encourage identification with these figures through brand purchases. In other instances, products or brands are purchased in support of one's real or desired image.

The latter two forms of influence are sometimes combined into a more general category labeled **normative influence.** Marketers attempt to use normative social influences by showing favorable consequences that can occur when their brands are used or

Peer influences are important determinants of consumer behavior worldwide. Products and services are often purchased consistent with the need to identify with others and/or to express desired images.

unfavorable consequences that occur when not used. What many want, particularly young consumers, is to be acceptable to their peers. So what determines "cool" for teenagers is partly about individuality and partly about belonging. Companies like Levi Strauss spend millions generating associations with their products that reflect positive acceptance among peer groups.[56]

Social influence forms the basis of one principle of persuasion. Robert Cialdini, a noted social scientist, describes this premise as the "principle of social proof." As social actors, consumers rely heavily on the people around them for cues on how to think, feel, and act. For managers, testimonials from satisfied consumers work best when the satisfied consumer spokesperson and prospective buyers share similar characteristics and circumstances. Influence that operates horizontally is often effective, and firms can employ real and imagined peer influences when appropriate.[57]

Individual Differences

A vast number of individual differences can influence consumer behavior. Many people are swayed by various forms of word-of-mouth communications. Individual differences also stem from personality, lifestyles and psychographics, and motivation.

Word-of-Mouth Communications

Some people, traditionally labeled **opinion leaders,** influence consumer behavior through word-of-mouth communications. Opinion leaders were originally viewed as intermediaries between sources of information, such as advertising and other media, and the consumer. Their influence often stems from their involvement and interest or expertise in particular products. Marketers now recognize that communication flows both from and toward opinion leaders. In an application of the opinion leader concept, one research company focuses on the 10 percent of Americans labeled "influentials." This segment of 20 million, by their inclination to use cutting-edge products, their income, their status, and their voice, exerts an inordinate amount of influence on the goods and services adopted by friends, coworkers, and acquaintances. Card issuer First USA has paid college tuition for students at Pepperdine University and the University of Southern California in return for their service as media and public relations spokespersons. The two students were selected based on their academic and extracurricular activities and popularity, hence serving as paid opinion leaders.[58]

Market mavens are another type of information diffuser. These are consumers who know about many kinds of products, places to shop, and other facets of the market, and they like to share this information with other consumers.[59] Unlike opinion leaders, who know a lot about a few products, mavens know something about many products and enjoy discussing them. Market mavenism is a more general concept than opinion leadership in that mavens' influence results from the passing of information and expertise in the course of just making conversation. Mavens do not necessarily adopt new products or even use the products they are knowledgeable about, but they influence other people's choices and diffuse information on new products.

Word-of-mouth communications from friends and family are among the most important influences on consumer behavior. Because of the credibility of word-of-mouth information, others we know can easily affect purchasing decisions, particularly by limiting the choices we consider. More than 40 percent of Americans seek the advice of family and friends when shopping for doctors, lawyers, and auto mechanics. Word-of-mouth information is also crucial to decisions about restaurants, entertainment, banking, and personal services.[60] A recent large-scale study of college students revealed that the influence of word of mouth (44 percent) is twice as influential in new product purchases than either price (22 percent) or advertising (22 percent).[61] Family, friends, and business associates are the primary source of influence on the purchase of personal electronics and computers. Word-of-mouth communications primarily influence consumers at three stages of decision making: awareness, search for information, and decision making. Negative word of mouth is particularly likely following unsatisfactory consumer experiences. Studies reveal that dissatisfied consumers vent their frustration with 5 to 10 other consumers. So it is important for companies to encourage consumers to communicate with their firms, to analyze what customers say in their correspondence, and to respond.[62]

Sometime in the last several decades the influence pattern has shifted from trickle-down from the fashion firms to trickle-up. Using an observational and in-depth interview form of market research, the objective now is chasing the elusive street cool, or "cool-hunting." Nike, for example, introduces new brands faster in efforts to react faster to new ideas from the street. The danger is that the better cool-hunters become at bringing the cutting edge to the mainstream, the more elusive the cutting edge becomes.[63]

The Internet word-of-mouth phenomenon has made the spread of negative information more prevalent. From chat rooms, blogs, and simple lists of addresses, consumers can effectively spread their dissatisfaction to other consumers. In hopes of obtaining positive "word of mouse" some companies send free products to critical reviewers. Companies also solicit, post, and analyze the postings of product reviewers for interested consumers to consider. The power of the Internet is reflected in the ability of everyday consumers to express their opinion on any product.[64]

Personality

Personality reflects a person's consistent response to his or her environment. It has been linked to differences in susceptibility to persuasion and social influence and thereby to purchase behavior. General personality traits related to consumer behavior include extroversion, self-esteem, dogmatism (closed-mindedness), and aggressiveness. For example, dogmatism might limit product trial or the adoption of product innovations for some consumers; aggressiveness may be related to the purchase of certain types of sporty cars and to consumer complaint behavior in reaction to unsatisfactory purchases. Self-esteem is thought to be inversely related to persuasibility—the more self-esteem, the less subject to persuasion—and has implications for the effectiveness of marketing communications.

The notion of *self-concept* is one idea used to explain the products consumers buy and use. Self-concept is the overall perception and feeling that one has about herself or himself. Consumers buy products and brands that are consistent with or enhance their self-concept.[65]

Marketers try to create relationships between their products or services and consumers. Marketers can affect consumers' motivation to learn about, shop for, and buy the sponsored brand by influencing the degree to which people perceive a product to be related to their self-concept. This objective is clear in the many ads that emphasize image enhancement and personal improvement through use of the advertiser's brand of product or service.[66]

Different views of self-concept have been offered. Self-concept has been referred to as actual self-concept, ideal self-concept, and social self-concept, the latter often deemed the "looking glass" view of an individual's self-concept. The notion of ideal, or desired, self-concept reflects the image the individual would like to display to others. The social self-concept reflects the image the individual believes others hold. Consumers purchase, display, and use goods that reflect these views of themselves or that enhance self-concept through the consumption of products as symbols. Possessions play an important role in defining individual identities in today's contemporary Western economies.[67]

Lifestyles and Psychographics

Some outgrowths from attempts to use personality measures to explain consumer behavior are the concepts of lifestyle and psychographics. *Lifestyle* describes a person's pattern of living as expressed in activities, interests, and opinions (AIO statements are discussed in more detail in Chapter 7). Lifestyle traits are more concrete than personality traits and more directly linked to the acquisition, use, and disposition of goods and services.[68]

Psychographics divide a market into lifestyle segments on the basis of consumer interests, values, opinions, personality characteristics, attitudes, and demographics.[69] Marketers use lifestyle and psychographic information to develop marketing communications and product strategies. For example, responses to questions about the frequency of outdoor activity, cultural arts viewing, and opinions on social issues can be related to product use and then used as the basis for advertising themes and other marketing communications.

Chet Zalesky notes, "The basis for segmentation will determine its usefulness throughout the organization. An attitudinal-based segmentation (lifestyles/psychographics) will be useful in advertising, communications, and positioning. On the other hand, a customer needs/benefits-based segmentation will identify unique product benefit segments that can be used to redesign current offerings, launch new offerings, or highlight the need for initiatives to change how the organization interacts with its customers."

Motivation

Motivation refers to a state or condition within a person that prompts goal-directed behavior. Motivation generally occurs with recognition of some need or problem and can affect information search, information processing, and purchase behavior.[70] For example, washing machine owners are not routinely motivated to evaluate washing machine ads. But if their Maytag fails, they will be motivated to evaluate washing machine brands. Motivation involves both energy and focus. Motives themselves may be obvious or hidden.

Researchers frequently cite the classification of motives proposed by Abraham Maslow.[71] In this approach, individuals evolve in their personal growth, with higher-level needs (esteem, self-actualization) becoming important only after lower-level needs (physiological, safety) are satisfied. Any unfulfilled needs are assumed to be "prepotent" and provide the most immediate motivation for behavior. Levels of needs in Maslow's hierarchy and examples of associated product purchases include

Self-actualization needs—Art, books, recreation.

Esteem needs—Clothing, home furnishings.

Love and belonging needs—Mementos, gifts, photographs.

Safety needs—Burglar alarms, seat belts.

Physiological needs—Food, heat, shelter.

Motives that drive consumer behavior are affected by an individual's environment, including marketing communications and reference group influences. Importantly, consumer companies can achieve new levels of growth by addressing customers' higher-order needs. Consumers seek peace of mind and the feelings of security that favored brands offer and that provide a sense of self-definition consistent with their personalities.[72]

Situational Factors

In addition to the social environment and individual consumer characteristics, situational influences also affect consumer behavior.[73] Situational influences can involve purchases for anticipated situations, such as special occasions, and unanticipated occurrences, such as time pressures, unexpected expenses, and changed plans. In-store sales

CREATING CUSTOMER VALUE

Buzzmetrics: Using modern consumer gossip

Buzzmetrics is a New York–based marketing research firm, and specialist in consumer word-of-mouth marketing, that measures consumer feedback through analysis of online consumer dialogue. The company measures the "buzz" surrounding commercial topics by monitoring popular discussion sites and Weblogs. In efforts to build consumer value, brand managers can now be proactive in their public relations efforts by considering the resources offered by Buzzmetrics in terms of their crisis management and prevention services. By collecting online conversation data, the research firm addresses problems associated with negative information being spread by trendsetters and influential consumers. Used by pharmaceutical companies and automotive manufacturers, Buzzmetrics tracks naturally occurring conversations, message boards, blogs, and gripe sites. This information can then be used by firms to address consumer problems quickly.

promotions and advertising can exert situational influences on consumers as they often make buying decisions while shopping. A common in-store situational factor is music, long considered an effective means for triggering moods. One study reveals that grocery store sale volumes were significantly higher with slow rather than with fast music.[74]

Situational determinants of consumer behavior can be summarized as follows:

- Consumers purchase many goods for use in certain situations, and the anticipated use influences choice. Gift giving and social occasions are often important determinants of purchase behavior.

- Situational factors can be inhibitors as well as motivators. Inhibitors that constrain consumer behavior include time or budget constraints.

- The likely influence of situations varies with the product. Consumers buy clothing items, books, and many food products with anticipated uses in mind.

Situational store factors within the retail environment are also important. These store conditions include physical layout, atmospherics, location, the presence of others, the assistance of salespeople, and in-store stimuli. Merchandisers also try to capitalize on situational factors in developing their marketing plans. Gas stations have evolved into multiline convenience stores, for instance, and fast-food chains cater to situational needs with drive-through services.

Advertising often incorporates situational use into its message themes. For example, consider the well-known message "use Arm & Hammer Baking Soda as a refrigerator deodorant." This ad suggests the target brand (Arm & Hammer) as a reasonable choice for the target situation. In contrast, some ads compare the target brand with another product already associated with that situation ("Eat Orville Redenbacher Popcorn instead of potato chips as an afternoon snack"). Other ads compare the use of the target brand in a new situation with its use in a more familiar situation ("Special K breakfast cereal is as good at snack time as it is at breakfast").[75]

Consumer Behavior Outcomes

The study of consumer behavior does not end at purchase. Other phenomena or outcomes may and often do occur. These include consumer learning; consumer satisfaction, dissatisfaction, and complaint behavior; and cognitive dissonance.

Consumer Learning

When marketers set out to influence consumers, they typically try to impart knowledge through advertising, product labels, and personal selling—methods that are efficient and can be controlled by the marketer. Marketers hope consumers will attend to, comprehend, and then remember these messages. Yet consumers also learn by experience. Experiential learning is highly interactive, and consumers often give it special status—experience is the best teacher.

Consumer learning happens when changes occur in knowledge or behavior patterns. Learning as knowledge gained is consistent with the decision process we have described.[76] Learning as behavior is also a critical outcome. Because successful marketing depends on repeat purchase behavior, providing positive reinforcement for the desired behavior is crucial.[77] Briefly, learning involves or is based on the combination of individual drives (needs), cues or stimuli in the environment, responses (consumer behavior), and reinforcement of those behaviors. One outcome of learning from positive experiences is an enhanced base of loyal consumers. Brand loyalty and the loyal relationships between consumers and their favored brands lead to greater profits in many industries. In contrast to constantly courted new consumers, loyal consumers tend to buy more and are more likely to pay premium prices. Moreover, costs to serve them are less.[78]

In addition to learning about brands and marketing organizations, knowledge is also gained by consumers over time regarding the tactics marketers use in persuading us. This **persuasion knowledge** helps consumers to understand why and how marketers are trying to persuade us and to adaptively respond to these attempts. Marian Friestad and Peter Wright, two consumer researchers, describe this learning as developing throughout one's life and resulting from our experiences as consumers with salespeople, family and friends, and advertising and from observing marketers and other persuasion agents.[79]

Consumer Satisfaction, Dissatisfaction, and Complaint Behavior

Consumer satisfaction, dissatisfaction, and complaint behavior are also important outcomes of consumer purchase decision processes. *Satisfaction* and *dissatisfaction* describe the positive, neutral, or negative feelings that may occur after purchase; *consumer complaints* are overt expressions of dissatisfaction. Consumer satisfaction is central to the marketing concept and is a dominant cause of customer loyalty. Increased loyalty enhances revenues, lowers the costs of individual transactions, and decreases price sensitivity. Satisfaction also has benefits within the firm; costs associated with handling returns and warranty claims are reduced, as are those associated with managing complaints.[80]

Judgments of satisfaction and dissatisfaction are generally thought to result from comparisons between a person's expectations about a purchased product and the product's actual performance.[81] At first glance, service and satisfaction appear to be the same concept. Service is what the marketer provides and what the consumer gets. Satisfaction reflects the evaluation of the level of service provided.[82] Purchases that turn out worse than expected result in **negative disconfirmation** and negative feelings. Purchases that turn out better than expected (resulting in **positive disconfirmation**) are evaluated positively. The importance of consumer expectations in the determination of satisfaction cannot be understated. For marketers to be effective, the organization must understand how expectations are formed and the role that competitors have in establishing expectations for the firms in an industry. Moreover, it is critical that marketers monitor expectations and learn the extent to which expectations are static or change over time.[83] These best practices represent business fundamentals of firms that are masterful at exceeding customers' expectations. Deceptively simple for attracting and keeping customers, the practice of exceeding expectations can be applied to both service and nonservice firms.[84]

A simple model of consumer satisfaction–dissatisfaction relationships is depicted in Exhibit 4–7. First, the consumer's prior experiences with products and brands establish expectations. Marketing communications, including advertising, and word-of-mouth communications also influence expectations. When you take your car to be serviced or repaired, what expectations do you have? Consumers thus develop expectations about what a product or service should be able to provide. Comparison between the buyer's expectations and the product or service performance levels results in the confirmation or disconfirmation of expectations and the outcomes of satisfaction or dissatisfaction. These positive or negative feelings serve then as input into the formation of future attitudes and expectations. Although disconfirmation is generally considered the most important determinant of satisfaction, expectations and performance directly influence satisfaction also. This is consistent with research showing that consumers with higher expectations experience higher levels of satisfaction and that performance, independent of positive or negative disconfirmation, exerts a direct effect on feelings of satisfaction.[85] Similarly, research on cars shows that consumers with high product involvement tend to be more satisfied with their purchases than less involved car owners.[86] Regardless, however, firms adopting a *customer value perspective* must employ marketing communications that convey realistic expectations.

Companies now regularly measure satisfaction and recognize it as an important determinant of customer retention. However, the measurement of satisfaction must consider not only what the customer did receive but what he or she could have received. That is, companies must study their competition as well. Overall quality has been shown to be a better predictor of satisfaction than customers' willingness to keep buying.[87] Practitioners

Exhibit 4-7   *A model of consumer satisfaction*

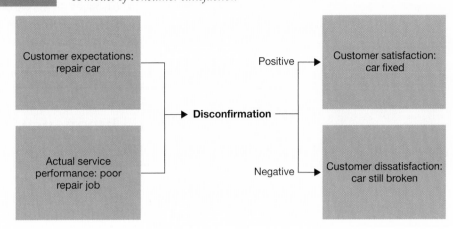

now agree that only stellar performance makes a real difference in customer loyalty. The success of programs that measure satisfaction levels depends on benchmarking against either competitor performance or performance goals established by management. Customer satisfaction measurement is useful for identifying areas in need of improvement to strengthen relationships with customers, as well as subsequent assessment of how efficiently and satisfactorily services and products are being provided.[88]

Recent research reveals a more complicated view of satisfaction than the traditional disconfirmation of expectations model. Based on a series of in-depth interviews with consumers regarding their purchase of technological products, consumer researchers now recognize that satisfaction is often a more dynamic process:

1. Satisfaction judgments evolve and are changeable as products are used.

2. Satisfaction judgments have a social component determined by the satisfaction of others in the household.

3. Emotions are important and yield insights beyond simple comparison standards, such as expectations and performance.

4. Product satisfaction is also related, in some situations, to quality of life and life satisfaction.[89]

Recent research finds that satisfaction is significantly related to firm cash flow. For the average company in a study conducted by researchers analyzing data from the American Customer Satisfaction Index, a one-point increase (measured on a 0–100 index score) increased future cash flow by 7 percent. The impact of satisfaction on cash flow growth was particularly strong for "low-involvement, routinized, and frequently purchased" products and services, such as apparel, hotels, and food and beverages.[90]

Besides influencing subsequent expectations, purchase behavior, and loyalty, dissatisfaction can result in several forms of consumer complaints: **voice responses** (seeking satisfaction directly from the seller), **private responses** (bad-mouthing to friends), and **third-party responses** (taking legal action, filing complaints with consumer affairs agencies).[91] Remember that word-of-mouth personal communications are very credible and influential.

Complaints are customer feedback about products, services, and company performance that marketers should never take lightly. Dissatisfied customers talk to more people than satisfied customers; often dissatisfied customers never make a complaint to the company.[92] Because new customers are harder to find, maintaining satisfaction among existing customers should be paramount.

To gain feedback, some companies even encourage their customers to complain. Companies that know what is bothering their customers have a better chance of correcting problems, retaining sales, and preventing further damage.[93] At Dell Computer Corporation, the mail-order PC marketer, staff and managers meet every Friday morning to review customer

In 15 minutes you could cut out $200 from your car insurance bill.

Save it for a rainy day.   How would I play with my savings?   Get a change of scenery

How would you play with your savings?

GEICO.
geico.com

1-800-841-1598

This Geico advertisement requests consumers to anticipate the outcomes from purchase.

complaints. The Dell vision is that every customer must be pleased, not merely satisfied.[94] In the same way, Coca-Cola wants to hear from its customers when they have a problem. According to its consumer affairs department, "Consumers who have a good experience with our company tell an average of five other people; but those who have a bad experience will tell twice as many people."[95]

Cognitive Dissonance

The final consumer behavior outcome we consider is **cognitive dissonance,** a form of postpurchase doubt about the appropriateness of a decision.[96] Cognitive dissonance may occur over major choices, such as college decisions and purchases of homes and expensive furniture, stereo systems, and appliances. Most students remember some uneasiness about whether they made the best choice of a college to attend. This uneasiness occurs because each alternative has attractive features. Cognitive dissonance is most likely to occur when the purchase is important, perceived risk is high, the purchase is visible, and the decision involves a long-term commitment.

Dissonance can affect postpurchase attitudes, change behavior, and cause additional information seeking. Strategies marketers can use to reduce postpurchase cognitive dissonance include regular programs of follow-up communication with buyers to discourage doubt and reinforce convictions about product strengths; solid service and maintenance plans to provide reassurance and increase postpurchase satisfaction; and warranty agreements arranged after purchase to protect buyers against problems that may occur.

Ethical and Social Issues

Some instances of consumer and business behavior raise ethical and social concerns.

Consumer Behavior

Unethical consumer behaviors include shoplifting and abuse of return policies. Shoplifting losses represent a tremendous cost to retailers and eventually to other consumers as retailers pass on the costs. Abuse of a company's return policies is also unethical; returns should be made only for reasonable problems.[97]

On the positive side, consumers are increasingly incorporating social concerns into their buying decisions. Environmentally concerned consumers show high awareness of label information and product content. Companies often market their products with messages and product information that recognize these environmental concerns.

Other consumer behaviors driven by ethical and social motivations are less personal and more political. For example, 1970s boycotts of infant formula products sold in Third World

Both consumers and marketers have responsibilities to act ethically. This advertisement promotes the importance of not driving after using alcohol.

countries, suspended in the mid-1980s, have reemerged because consumers believe the manufacturer failed to live up to its promise of ethical practice. Minority and gay rights groups use their buying power to express opinions about political issues.[98] "Buy American" campaigns recognize the effects of individual consumer behavior on jobs and local economies. The motivation for many boycotts is simple. Sellers should abide by certain ethical standards. Products produced by child labor or workers severely taken advantage of are an issue that has drawn attention on occasion. Some argue that buyers have responsibilities to be informed about sellers' ethical behavior and to consider that behavior in deciding to make purchases.[99]

Business Behavior

Business behavior is evaluated in terms of two standards: corporate social responsibility and business ethics. For example, firms are expected to provide safe products for reasonable prices. Their actions are not expected to detract from the general well-being of consumers. Efforts to monitor waste and the effects of production on the environment stem from these firm responsibilities. Likewise, marketing practices should not offend individuals or specific groups. Hence liquor and tobacco advertising has been moderated in recent years, and tobacco advertising has been banned from the networks. Many beer companies, such as Coors and Budweiser, now emphasize responsible use of their products. In the area of personal interaction between salesperson and consumer, the salesperson often feels pressure to make the sale, even if it means not being entirely straight with the potential buyer. Principles of both the marketing concept and the Golden Rule, however, underscore the ethical need and the advantages of consistently treating consumers honestly and fairly.[100]

Summary

1. **Discuss the importance of consumer behavior.** Marketers must understand consumer behavior to develop successful strategies and identify target market segments. Furthermore, awareness of emerging trends in the consumer marketplace is essential for quick recognition of and response to problems and opportunities with sound marketing strategies.

2. **Understand consumer decision making and some of the important influences on those decisions.** Consumer behavior describes the mental and physical activities that people engage in when they select, purchase, use, and dispose of products and services purchased to satisfy needs and desires. The traditional view of consumer decision making is sequential: recognition of problem, search for information (either internal or external), evaluation of alternatives, purchase, and postpurchase evaluation.

3. **Distinguish between low-involvement and high-involvement consumer behavior.** Involvement represents the level of importance or interest generated by a product or a decision. A person highly involved in a decision (the purchase is personally relevant) will likely go through the entire decision-making sequence, from problem recognition to postpurchase evaluation. High-involvement decisions are characterized by thorough information processing, significant personal relevance of the decision, and substantial differences between alternatives.

   Consumers with low involvement will probably not engage in an extensive information search. Low-involvement decisions have minimal personal relevance and are likely routine or habitual. Consequently, they require less mental or physical effort than extended or limited problem solving.

4. **Understand how attitudes influence consumer purchases.** Consumer attitudes, which are learned predispositions to respond favorably or unfavorably toward a product or service, are important primary causes of behavior. They are important for both explaining consumer behavior and designing marketing communications for changing consumer behavior. One useful view depicts attitudes toward purchase behavior as a combination of beliefs about the product's attributes and the relative evaluation of those attributes.

5. **Appreciate how the social environment affects consumer behavior.** Social influences on behavior must be understood prior to the development of sound marketing strategies. Social class and family influences affect consumer behavior and can be used to identify market segments.

   The culture in which consumers are raised is also critical in determining the values that matter to them; culture may be used to identify segments with unique needs (subcultures). A great deal of learning also comes from observing and interacting with others (informational interpersonal influence). Some behavior occurs with the expectations of others in mind (utilitarian influences) and some with how they will react to our own behavior (value expressiveness). The latter two are normative social influences. Consumers are also influenced by the situations in which behavior occurs or is expected to occur.

6. **Recognize many of the individual consumer differences that influence purchase decisions and behavior.** Individual consumer differences affect consumer decision making and behavior. These include personality differences; lifestyle differences, which are often measured as consumer activities, interests, and opinions; and differences in motivation.

7. **Recognize the outcomes of consumers' decisions to purchase or not to purchase and how they affect marketing success.** Some of the more important outcomes that occur after purchase are consumer learning, feelings of satisfaction or dissatisfaction, and cognitive dissonance. Learning may result from experience and knowledge gained through advertisements and marketing communications.

   Feelings of satisfaction and dissatisfaction occur when product performance exceeds or falls short of expectations. Dissatisfaction may lead to consumer complaints and loss of future business. Cognitive dissonance is postpurchase doubt about the appropriateness of a decision. It is most likely to occur when the purchase is important or involved, perceived risk is high, the purchase is visible, and the decision involves a long-term commitment.

Understanding Marketing Terms and Concepts

Thinking about Marketing

1. Describe the importance of understanding consumer behavior. How does this understanding relate to the identification of target markets?

2. Outline and discuss the steps involved in the consumer decision-making process. How might this sequence differ for routinized response behavior and limited problem solving?

3. What is low-involvement consumer behavior?

4. Why are consumer attitudes important? What role do consumer beliefs about product attributes play in consumer decision making?

5. Outline the three types of interpersonal influence, and explain how each may affect purchase behavior.

6. Explain how understanding social class and the family life cycle can enhance marketing effectiveness.

7. How does culture affect consumer behavior, and what are the implications for marketers?

8. Discuss the ethical responsibilities that consumers have in the marketplace.

9. Contrast cognitive dissonance with consumer dissatisfaction. What determines feelings of satisfaction and dissatisfaction?

10. How can Web sites be used to generate loyalty, and what characteristics of Internet search and shopping behavior work against customer loyalty?

11. Describe some of the recent changes in consumer markets and why these changes are important for marketers.

12. What are psychographics, and why are they important to marketers? Give an example of how a well-known company can use psychographics to address the needs of consumers.

13. How does word-of-mouth communication impact consumer behavior? What other factors in the chapter may be related to the effectiveness of word-of-mouth communication?

Applying Marketing Skills

1. Think about a recent clothing purchase. What was the motivation behind your purchase? Where would this need lie on Maslow's hierarchy of needs? What word-of-mouth sources did you check when making this purchase? How do you think these sources affected your decision to purchase the article of clothing? How important were your friends in making this decision? How did the visibility and necessity of this product affect the influence your friends had on your purchase?

2. Customer dissatisfaction can result when a consumer's expectation for the performance of a product or service exceeds the performance actually received. Can you think of any instances where you have been dissatisfied with a purchase? What do you normally do when you experience such dissatisfaction? Why is it important that companies try to prevent dissatisfaction from occurring in the first place? When dissatisfaction does occur, what can companies do to lessen the negative consequences?

3. Find examples of ads that exemplify the following consumer behavior concepts: safety needs, consumer satisfaction, family influences, and subcultures.

4. Compare a product's print advertisement in a popular magazine targeted toward the general population with the same product's advertisement in a Latino/Hispanic magazine or an African American magazine. Do the ads emphasize the same product benefits? Are different cultural values used in the message themes for both ads? Do these differences reflect the firm's customer orientation or just opportunistic efforts to capitalize on ethnic identification?

Using the www in Marketing

Activity One Consider one of the following shopping comparison sites: *www.bizrate.com,* *www.mysimon.com,* or *www.bottomdollar.com.* These sources can be used in the selection of untold types of products.

1. How is the information organized, and how do these sources affect the logical decision-making process around which this chapter was organized?

2. How do these sites make a profit or earn revenues?

3. Comment on the search and alternative information generated as it benefits the consumer, as opposed to information obtained from an in-store search designed to benefit the retailer.

Activity Two For Disney, identify the following influences on consumer purchase behavior that Disney is trying to capitalize on:

a. Social influence

b. Family

c. Affect referral

d. Impulse purchase

Making Marketing Decisions

Case 4–1 *Mercedes-Benz: Boosting Volume or Losing Esteem?*

Luxury car makers face a growing market *and* growing competition for younger buyers. Mercedes, Lexus, BMW, Volvo, and Saab all now offer entry-level sedans in the neighborhood of $30,000. Until now, Mercedes's position in the U.S. marketplace has been clear—high style, engineering, and quality at a premium price. No brand says upscale more loudly than Mercedes-Benz. In 2001 Mercedes-Benz posted its best year on record with sales of 206,639 units. The largest increase came from the entry-level CL class of new cars. The focus has shifted to younger owners who seek power and performance as much as leather and style, and a ride more in tune with the Autobahn than 18 holes of golf.

The new sports coupe cars are un-Mercedes-like in several ways. Two-door C230 hatchbacks are $4,000 below any other Mercedes. The shape is almost drag-sterlike, and the interior does not include wood veneer. More emphasis is on performance and maneuverability than other attributes.

Unfortunately, these changes have not all been positive in their effects. Research in Europe and the United States reveals that the quality and satisfaction ratings for Mercedes have been dropping since 1999. J. D. Power recently lowered Mercedes's quality ranking from "good" to "fair." In addition, the quality ratings for competing cars have increased. As noted, worldwide sales have doubled since 1993. However,

all these changes may have hurt the overall brand reputation.

Recently the Daimler-Chrysler–owned Mercedes-Benz has pursued an integrated marketing communication campaign designed to increase awareness among youthful consumers. The ad campaign is being backed by direct mail and online advertising. Efforts are being made to attract Internet users and to include them in mailing lists for direct mail contact. Moreover, Mercedes-Benz is introducing a compact SUV instead of the very small Smart car sold outside the United States. Some industry analysts believe that Mercedes's bet is that, as gases prices escalate, drivers will trade large SUVs for smaller, more fuel-efficient models.

Questions

1. What role does quality play in the formation of attitudes?

2. How might Mercedes preclude any further dilution of its brand in the perceptions of consumers?

3. Comment on the effects of competition from Lexus and other brands on the search for information and decision making by consumers.

4. How do youthful consumers differ from older adults in terms of information search, personal influence, and auto product preferences?

Case 4–2 *Gap Inc.: Appealing to the Global Teenager*

The list of "coolest" brands among U.S. teenagers includes Gap. Included in Gap Inc.'s set of over 2,400 stores are the Gap outlets, GapKids, Banana Republic, and Old Navy Clothing. Best known for casual and active clothing, Gap began in 1969 in San Francisco as a small store named after the "generation gap." During the 1970s, the company expanded its focus beyond sole emphasis on teenagers in efforts to appeal to a larger spectrum of consumers. Now the retail specialty chain

has stores in 48 states, as well as in Canada, France, Puerto Rico, and the United Kingdom. In addition, the company is in the process of opening stores in Japan and exploring other ventures in Asia. Fourth-quarter 1998 sales rose to $3 billion, up 40 percent from the year before.

Japanese customers are not unlike American consumers in their desire for well-known brands for some products. However, cultural and value differences in Japan make competition more difficult. Retailers that are successful expanding across borders typically appeal to a common lifestyle that the company fully understands. Other recent trends are also influencing the purchase of casual clothing. In particular, demand for designer jeans is on the rise, jeans that often are priced at twice what a pair of Gap or Levi jeans cost. And a new array of colors and bright shades are now chic among consumers of all ages.

Gap traditionally had viewed its store windows as the primary means of advertising. As a result, the company's ad spending was below that of many competing retailers. Industry experts questioned the company's reluctance to use radio and television, media popular with the Gap's young target audience.

Gap has recently expanded by adding Banana Republic stores in Japan. This effort is designed to bolster the firm's international segment, which never improved as much as the rest of the firm during the recent turnaround. Consumers in Japan are interested in more high-end clothes, and the new stores reflect Gap's interest in this market as a long-term growth opportunity.

In 2004 Gap issued a "social responsibility" report that reflected a strong sense of honesty and openness. The $6.5 billion clothing retailer found in its 3,000 contracted factories that produce Gap, Old Navy, and Banana Republic brands a series of serious wage, health, and safety problems that affected employees. Problems were found in China, Africa, India, and Central and South America. These admissions engendered both admiration and concerns within the retail clothing industry. Questions remain as to how Gap will address all these problems and the extent to which its forthright approach will yield competitive advantage with consumers.

Experts agree that the stores remain stylish and the advertising has been strengthened. The themes are consistent and confident. The chain has a definite position in the minds of consumers. Unfortunately, marketing problems have detracted from the stores' ability to compete and draw consumers. Questions have arisen regarding merchandising, the assortment of clothes, and quality. Gap Inc. as an organization has a history of improving as needed. However, problems with both fashion and the balance sheet make Gap an interesting strategy case in terms of regenerating its position in the marketplace and in terms of consumer patronage preferences.

Questions

1. What role will the global teenager concept have in Gap's efforts to expand in Japan? Will the modest use of broadcast advertising influence consumer decision making enough to make the Japanese entries successful?

2. Once young consumers in an area learn about a new store's presence, is the decision to patronize the store an extended or limited problem-solving situation?

3. How will culture and subcultural factors affect Gap's performance in non-U.S. areas such as Japan?

4. What must Gap do to reposition itself favorably in the minds of consumers?

Chapter Five

BUSINESS-TO-BUSINESS MARKETS AND BUYING BEHAVIOR

5

After studying this chapter, you should be able to

1 Define the nature of business-to-business buying behavior and markets.

2 Explain the differences between business-to-business buying and consumer purchase behavior.

3 Recognize the different types of buying decisions.

4 Define the different stages of the business buying process.

5 Describe the buying center concept and the determinants of influence within the buying center.

6 Understand the nature of government, reseller, and other institutional markets.

Office Depot

Office Depot, a leading retailer of office products and services, sells more than 10,000 items in 24 countries through 1,200 retail stores, catalog and contract sales, and the Internet. In recent years the company greatly improved its performance by radically modifying the way it buys, stocks, and sells products. Previously the company stocked its retail stores using one buying and distribution system and served its corporate accounts with an entirely different procurement and distribution system. After integrating these separate systems into a single supply system, Office Depot credits the new system (or supply chain) with a 1.8–2.5 percent increase in sales and a $60–75 million reduction in inventory costs.

Office Depot's new supply chain was developed in concert with the company's new retail format, called Millennium 2. This format was designed to help differentiate Office Depot from other large office supply retailers such as Office Max and Staples. Millenium 2 grouped products in highly visible pods with crucial supplies at the outer perimeter of the store and technology and furniture located in the center of the store. This allows customers to get in and out quickly when shopping only for supplies and facilitates more in-depth visits with sales specialists when shopping for more expensive items in the technology and furniture lines.

To make the new supply chain a success, Office Depot invested heavily in information technology. Cross-functional teamwork is also important in this integration of purchasing and logistics, requiring that store managers, inventory managers, and warehouse and transportation supervisors work together with 400 key suppliers to serve the customer. Although Office Depot continues to seek improvements in its supply chain, company executives feel that improvements to date have already given the company a competitive advantage.

Companies like Office Depot spend enormous amounts on products and services for business operations, and then market products and services to other consumer or business buyers. As indicated in the Office Depot example, these firms are making many changes to improve purchasing performance. Companies marketing to businesses and other organizations need to understand purchasing behavior to develop and execute marketing strategies successfully.

In this chapter we define business-to-business buying; discuss its importance; identify emerging trends; examine important business purchasing concepts; describe government, reseller, and other institutional buying practices; and address relevant ethical considerations. As marketers, our objective is to understand what these buyers do and want so we can market to them effectively.

The Nature of Business-to-Business Buying

Business-to-Business Buying Behavior Defined

Business-to-business buying behavior refers to decision making and other activities of organizations as buyers. It involves transactions between buying and selling organizations, and thus is often referred to as *organizational buying.* A primary element in business-to-business buying is the selection of **suppliers, sources, or vendors.** These are interchangeable terms for companies or individuals who sell products and services directly to buying organizations. In practice, industrial or manufacturing firms distinguish between two kinds of purchases: those involving production and operational products routinely needed in ongoing production or maintenance (raw materials, fasteners, bearings, paint) and those involving capital products (milling machines, power-generating devices, computers and telecommunications systems).

Organizations fall into four general categories: *business firms,* including manufacturers of tangible goods and firms that provide services such as health care, entertainment, and transportation; *government markets,* federal, state, and local; *reseller markets,* such as the many wholesalers and retailers; and other *institutional markets,* such as hospitals (profit and nonprofit), educational and religious institutions, and trade associations. Each of these categories includes organizations that purchase from other organizations. Increasingly, business buyers are involved in **supply chain management,** or "the integration of business processes from end user through original suppliers that provides products, services, and information that add value for customers."[1] The basic concept is to cut across organizational and company boundaries to better serve the customer, thereby gaining a competitive advantage. Thus purchasing personnel work with others inside and outside their companies as a key part of supply chain management. In doing so, purchasing personnel may be involved in information gathering and dissemination, negotiating, monitoring the system, evaluating suppliers, and other roles in addition to making purchases.

Supply chain management is distinguished from typical purchasing operations in several ways. In the former, there is a focus on end-to-end processes rather than on individual functional departments such as purchasing, manufacturing, and marketing. Supplier relations require more commitment from the involved parties, and information is more freely shared. In addition to goals for financial performance, targets are set for improved customer satisfaction, and measurement of progress toward these goals becomes more important.

The emphasis on supply chain management has evolved into the broader term **supply management,** defined by the Institute of Supply Management as "the identification, acquisition, access, positioning, and management of resources the organization needs or potentially needs in the attainment of its strategic objectives."[2] According to this definition, supply management extends beyond physical and informational supply chains to include financial flows and working relationships between buyers and sellers. Properly conceived,

Exhibit 5–1	*How business-to-business buying behavior differs from consumer buying*

1. Business-to-business buyers are fewer in number, larger, and more concentrated geographically than consumer buyers. This necessitates heavy emphasis on personal selling and trade advertising in business-to-business marketing.

2. Business purchase decisions often involve a more deliberate or thorough product evaluation and are subject to influence from multiple sources (purchasing, engineering) within a firm.

3. The demand for consumer products drives the purchases made by product manufacturers. Business purchase behavior is thus closely tied to economic fluctuations in the consumer market.

4. The demand for some products is related to the purchase of other products (joint demand). For example, if the demand for business personal computers declines, the demand for software applications and business computer printers may decline also.

5. Purchased industrial products are often complex, expensive, and bought in large quantity. Thus many purchase decisions are based on detailed product specifications or choice criteria. Business markets also make greater use of leasing.

6. There is much more interdependence between business buyers and sellers. This underlies the need to build long-term buyer–seller relationships and leads to greater emphasis on after-sale service.

supply management is aligned with the strategic priorities of the organization and takes an active role in identifying future needs of the organization.

Some organizations approach buying tasks purely as a purchasing function. Others approach them as part of supply chain management, and others incorporate them into the broad activity of supply management. Part of the challenge for business marketers is to determine the buying approaches and processes of specific customers, and to market to them accordingly.

Characteristics of Business-to-Business Buying Behavior

There are some similarities but many differences between consumer and organizational buying behavior and decision making. Principally, consumers buy for their own use and for household consumption. Business buyers purchase for further production (raw materials, components), for use in their firm's operations (office supplies, insurance), or for resale to other customers. Major distinguishing characteristics of business-to-business buying behavior are presented in Exhibit 5–1.

Demand for business-to-business products is often dependent on demand in consumer markets. This phenomenon is referred to as **derived demand.** For example, the demand for many products is derived from consumer demand for new automobiles. When demand for new autos goes up, the demand for products used to make them, such as steel, plastic, and textiles, also goes up. The reverse is also true.

Exhibit 5–2

North American Industry Classification System

Examples of NAICS numbering system

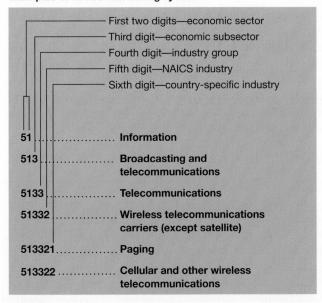

First two digits—economic sector
Third digit—economic subsector
Fourth digit—industry group
Fifth digit—NAICS industry
Sixth digit—country-specific industry

51	Information
513	Broadcasting and telecommunications
5133	Telecommunications
51332	Wireless telecommunications carriers (except satellite)
513321	Paging
513322	Cellular and other wireless telecommunications

Evaluating Business-to-Business Markets

Marketers can evaluate the size and growth rates of consumer markets using demographic characteristics. Many information sources report population statistics by characteristics like age or income level for different geographical areas. These demographic characteristics are not useful for evaluating business markets.

The federal government has developed a numerical scheme called the **North American Industry Classification System (NAICS)** for categorizing businesses. As shown in Exhibit 5–2, NAICS uses the first two digits to identify an economic sector such as the information sector. The third digit identifies an economic subsector (broadcasting and telecommunications), the fourth an industry group (telecommunications), the fifth an NAICS industry (wireless telecommunications carriers, except satellite), and the sixth a country-specific industry—in this case, the U.S. paging industry.

For each classification within NAICS, important economic data are available. These include the number of companies and employees, sales revenues, and percentage of sales occurring in large and small organizations. Such data are useful to marketers for estimating the size and growth rates of business markets. Mexico and Canada also use the NAICS format, which allows comparisons for the entire North American market.

The Importance of Business-to-Business Buying

Business-to-business markets and purchasing behavior are important for two basic reasons. First, the size of business markets offers many opportunities for astute marketers. Second, many firms are trying to increase profits by improving purchasing practices.

Business purchasing far exceeds consumer purchasing in total dollars. Businesses are the prime buyers of raw materials, such as minerals and farm products that are further processed and resold in whole or as part of other products. Businesses and other organizations also purchase services from advertising agents, accountants, consultants, attorneys, airlines, railroads, and so on.

The purchasing budgets of companies such as General Electric, Du Pont, Wal-Mart, and Ford exceed the gross national product of many countries. It is easy to see that businesses represent potentially lucrative markets for the products and services of many suppliers.

Lowering the cost of purchased products can be an effective way to increase profits. Consider this simple example. Assume a firm has annual sales of $100 million and a net profit margin of 5 percent. If this firm wanted to increase profits by $1 million, it would have to increase sales by 20 percent ($20 million sales increase $\times$ .05 net profit margin = $1 million profit increase). This type of sales increase may be difficult to accomplish in the slow-growth markets facing many firms. But if the company reduced costs by $1 million through improved purchasing, it would achieve the profit growth objective. This may be more doable in many situations.

The reality is that most firms are trying to increase profits by both increasing sales and reducing costs. However, more and more firms realize the powerful impact that purchasing improvements can have on profits. As business buyers change purchasing practices, marketers need to be aware of the changes and adapt marketing efforts appropriately.

Trends in Business-to-Business Buying

The purchasing operations at many firms are undergoing substantial changes. Key results of an extensive study about the future of purchasing are shown in Exhibit 5–3. In this study, 160 purchasing executives were asked to identify important trends for purchasing through the year 2008. An examination of Exhibit 5–3 indicates that several key marketing perspectives are particularly relevant for business marketers who seek to effectively meet the needs of purchasers.

Productivity Improvement

Productivity improvement is emphasized throughout many companies. This affects purchasing in at least three major ways. First, firms find that it is often more productive to purchase products and services from other companies than to make the products or perform the services internally. This is called **outsourcing.** Second, corporate downsizing has often involved downsizing of the purchasing function. And third, purchasing is paying greater attention to reducing **cycle time,** or the total elapsed time to complete a business process.

Outsourcing first became popular in the manufacturing sector but has now spread to all sectors of the economy, including services and the government. With many companies

| **Exhibit 5-3** | *Selected purchasing trends 1998–2008* |

1. Electronic commerce
2. Strategic cost management
3. Strategic sourcing
4. Supply chain partner selection and contribution
5. Relationship management
6. Performance measurement

7. Global supplier development
8. Third-party purchasing
9. Competitive bidding
10. Strategic supplier alliances
11. Win–win negotiation strategy
12. Complexity management

pushing for productivity gains, outsourcing for specialized technology functions and applications is on the rise. For example, BellSouth, a *Fortune* 100 communications company headquartered in Atlanta, outsourced its customer service training program to Accenture. The program, titled "Business Excellence through Simulation Training," or BEST, provided 16–24 hours of computer simulation training for 2,000 customer service representatives. Because Accenture's program reduced training time by 13 percent, developed proficient employees more quickly, and led to fewer repeat phone calls, BellSouth expects to save $52 million over a five-year period.[3] In addition to information technology, other popular outsourcing categories include human resource management, facilities management, finance and accounting, corporate security, and some aspects of customer service such as telephone support.[4] As indicated in Exhibit 5–4, several key questions should be addressed in determining if outsourcing would be appropriate.

A primary motivation to outsource is potential cost savings. According to some industry experts, the opportunity to save money through outsourcing is still important, but companies are also using outsourcing to better focus on core competencies and strategic priorities. A common expression heard in the business world is "do what you do best and outsource the rest." According to Michael F. Corbett, a leading outsourcing consultant, "Outsourcing is not simply a by-product of the need to reduce costs. It is an integral part of an organization's strategy for excellence . . . it creates breakthrough thinking through a clearer focus on the organization's core competencies—those things it does best—combined with the unique capabilities of equally talented and focused partners. Seen this way, outsourcing becomes a powerful tool for organizational competitiveness."[5]

Another interesting aspect of outsourcing and its impact on organizational buying is that there is a growing trend toward outsourcing the purchasing and supply chain management functions in larger companies. According to the global managing partner for Accenture's supply chain management consulting division, there is an increased use of outsourcing for these functions, enabling companies not only to save money but to enhance the effectiveness of these functions and thus competitiveness.[6]

Purchasing personnel are often involved in strategic planning, new product development, and other diverse activities. Downsizing the purchasing function has been facilitated by technology, especially the automation of routine reordering from established suppliers. Beyond the gains made possible by technology, productivity improvements have been made by fewer people doing more work.

| **Exhibit 5-4** | *Is outsourcing the solution?* |

Key questions to help determine if outsourcing is appropriate:
- Will outsourcing improve company profitability by lowering labor or procurement costs, reducing the level of capital expenditures, increasing revenues, or enabling economies of scale?
- Do potential suppliers provide a location or expertise that is hard to acquire?
- Can potential suppliers provide a safety margin to reduce supply surpluses and/or shortages?
- Is the function or activity under consideration a core competency for the firm? If not, outsourcing may be appropriate.
- Can the firm's financial risk be reduced through outsourcing?

Business buyers often focus on improving productivity. In this advertisement SAS points out that its software helps increase profits and makes an impact in 94 percent of the largest companies in the world.

Use of Technology

Buyers are increasingly employing technology to improve the productivity of purchasing operations. Reducing cycle time is an important element of the trend toward strategic cost management in purchasing (see Exhibit 5–3). Because time is money, buyers are interested in ways to reduce the purchasing, product development, product delivery, manufacturing, and inventory cycles. Reducing cycle times increases productivity by lowering the costs of doing business and can help increase sales. The use of new technologies often leads to shorter cycle times. For example, Sportsman's Warehouse, an outdoor products retailer with 30 U.S. locations, installed a new computerized inventory management system to reduce cycle time for replenishing retail inventories. The company can now ship to six stores in less time than previously required to ship to four stores. General Motors used wireless technology to link to parts suppliers in developing the H2 Hummer, cutting cycle time for design, engineering, and assembly to two years, an unprecedented feat in the auto industry.[7]

In many industries, computer-to-computer systems link customers and suppliers, allowing automatic replenishment of inventory on a timely basis. Such systems include the shared networks of Wal-Mart and Procter & Gamble, Saturn and its automotive parts suppliers, and numerous hospitals and Allegiance. These company-to-company systems may link companies' private internal systems, which are called intranets. When two or more companies' intranets are linked, this forms an extranet. Increasingly, electronic data interchanges run over the Internet are also referred to as extranets.

Some of the expected advances in organizational buying via the Internet have yet to fully develop. For example, electronic marketplace exchanges, usually referred to as **B2B exchanges,** were heralded as the next revolutionary development in organizational buying. In such an exchange, hundreds and even thousands of suppliers posted their goods and services for sale. The idea was that full disclosure of pricing and product information would ultimately develop a highly competitive marketplace in which organizational buyers would benefit from lower costs. Many of these exchanges were victims of the shakeout in e-commerce that occurred in the past few years. One problem with open-access exchanges is that some suppliers are reluctant to share sensitive information that might be available to competitors.

Although exchanges have yet to have the impact on purchasing that was once expected, they have influenced purchasing practices among companies seeking to be more competitive through cost savings. For example, GlobalNetX-Change LLC and WorldWide Retail Exchange LLC have formed a combined online exchange to help make retailers more competitive with Wal-Mart. This international exchange includes approximately 50 food, drug, and apparel retailers such as Kroger, Walgreen's, Sears, and European retailer Carrefour. The exchange will use online auctions so that retailers can seek the lowest prices from suppliers.[8] For another example of a successful international B2B exchange, see the box "Using Technology: TexYard.com Makes Apparel Industry Exchange Work."

Among the most successful exchanges are eBay, which serves both consumer and organizational buyers, and Free Markets, now part of Ariba Inc. eBay began as a consumer

USING TECHNOLOGY

TexYard.com makes apparel industry exchange work

TexYard.com is an online exchange in the European apparel industry, using computer technology and the Internet to bring buyers and sellers together in a neutral buying environment. This B2B exchange enables buyers to find suppliers more easily, complete transactions more efficiently, lower their administrative costs, obtain competitive pricing, and shorten their time-to-market cycle. TexYard uses auctions that allow buyers to define their needs in detail, from manufacturing specifications to delivery and quality requirements. A key to TexYard's success is that its exchange system greatly reduces the time spent in communicating requests, comparing price quotes from suppliers, and negotiating final prices.

Electronic commerce applications in purchasing

Business buyers frequently use the Internet for these activities:

- Requesting proposals and price quotes.
- Posting bids.
- Transmitting purchase orders.
- Using electronic data interchanges.
- Ordering with electronic catalogs.
- Seeking suppliers.
- Tracking delivery schedules.
- Managing contracts.
- Managing inventory.
- Paying invoices/making payments.

exchange and has become a significant force in organizational buying and selling in recent years. The Ariba Supplier Network includes 120,000 suppliers worldwide and conducts $5 billion in monthly transactions in 115 countries.[9] **Private exchanges,** those that link invitation-only buyers and sellers, are now showing more promise than most of the open-access exchanges. Hewlett-Packard, IBM, and Ace Hardware are among the success stories in the private exchange arena.

Business buyers agree that security is the biggest obstacle to using the Internet in purchasing. But with virtually all business buyers reporting access to the Internet, electronic commerce in business markets is well established and growing rapidly. Exhibit 5–5 indicates how business buyers use the Internet.

A Relationship Perspective

The focus on supplier relationships by buyers is driving the emphasis on relationship marketing by sellers. Many of the purchasing trends reflect the emphasis on buyer–seller relationships (see Exhibit 5–3). These include supply chain partner selection, relationship management, performance measurement, global supplier development, strategic supplier alliances, and win–win negotiation strategies. The goals of strong buyer–seller relationships, as shown in Exhibit 5–6, are to foster innovation and improve business efficiencies. By achieving these goals, customer satisfaction and profitability can be positively influenced.

Buyers are in a rather unique situation because they work directly with suppliers to purchase products for their firm (internal customers) that are used to produce products for external customers. Although it is important for buyers to meet the needs of their internal customers, ultimate success depends on contributing to the success of external customers. Buyers are spending more time with external customers to better understand how the products they purchase from suppliers affect the products purchased by external customers. This helps them make purchases that can both reduce costs and increase customer satisfaction.

Important features of strong buyer–seller relationships

Speaking from Experience

W. Wayne Whitworth
President
Strategic Purchasing Group

"Technology is having and will continue to have a significant impact on both sales and purchasing professionals. Electronic commerce will move the transactional based, nonstrategic purchases to the Internet in a marketplace forum. From the seller's point of view, new skills will be required to service buyers on a more strategic level. Buyers, in turn, will be the visionary link within the supply chain bringing the full resources from strategic partners to manage total cost of ownership and supplier relationships."

W. Wayne Whitworth, C.P.M., is president of Strategic Purchasing Group, a consulting firm specializing in purchasing and supply chain management strategies. He is also director of purchasing for American Commercial Lines. His prior experience includes purchasing management positions with Brown-Forman Corporation and Dover Resources, Incorporated. He is a certified purchasing manager (C.P.M.) and earned his BSBA degree from the University of Louisville and an MBA from Bellarmine College.

Some vendors work to improve relationships with their customers' customers. In this ad, Renaissance Greeting Cards reinforces how it works to strengthen relationships between retailers and their customers.

Ethics are another important element of supplier relationships. Successful relationships must be based on trust. Buyers and sellers share a great deal of information and must trust that this information will remain confidential. Both parties must trust each is working for mutual benefit. Honest and open communication is necessary. Once developed, trust is a powerful asset in a supplier relationship. Once lost, it is very difficult—perhaps impossible—to reestablish.

Cisco Systems, Inc., the computer network company, lost the trust of some of its suppliers when the company asked suppliers to accept its payments without penalty in 90 days, rather than the customary 30. Cisco also pressured suppliers to extend their warranties to three years instead of one year. Although suppliers resented the pressure, they complied with Cisco's demands because they could not afford to lose the business.[10] In the automotive industry, major manufacturers General Motors, Ford, and Daimler-Chrysler are not as trusted as they once were due to demands that many parts suppliers feel are unreasonable.[11]

Maytag provides a contrasting example of how a supplier can build better relationships by earning customer trust. Maytag's goal is to be the preferred appliance supplier to its customers by delivering a rapid, consistent flow of products to its regional distribution centers, which service its retail customers. To accomplish its goal, Maytag collaborates with its trading partners to optimize the flow of products and information. Maytag achieves its position as a trusted supplier through open communications with trading partners and a dedication to continuous improvement. According to Maytag vice president John Nolan, "We never lose sight of the vision, we never stop improving things, but we improve at a rate that we can afford, that isn't too risky, and that allows us to learn as we go."[12]

The final aspect of a *relationship perspective* is teamwork within the firm. Buyers are working more as teams with engineers and other functions in the selection of suppliers. In many respects, buyers orchestrate the purchasing process within their firms. They coordinate the flow of information between the seller and buyer and rely on people within and outside their firm for expertise in evaluating different products and suppliers.

W. Wayne Whitworth, president of Strategic Purchasing Group and director of purchasing for American Commercial Lines, emphasizes the importance of relationships in purchasing: "The traditional role of purchasing will continue to change toward supplier management. This shift will place higher demands on interpersonal skills and the management of relationships with internal and external customers. The very nature of purchasing's new role will require a unique ability to develop collaborative partnerships with internal and external stakeholders to bring new products to market and to reduce total cost of ownership. Bringing multiple disciplines, functions, and cross-functional teams together to promote strategic organizational goals can only be accomplished by building relationships of trust, support, and willingness to adapt to change."

Customer Value Considerations

One of the keys to successful supplier relationships is building customer value. Buyers are interested in suppliers that can add value to their business by continually increasing quality and lowering costs. Quality and cost considerations go beyond just the product being purchased to everything related to doing business together. For more on the importance of customer value in buyer–seller relationships, see the box "Creating Customer Value: Dell Recognizes Top Suppliers."

Graybar, a large distributor of electrical, telecommunications, and networking products, offers an excellent example of how a supplier can distinguish itself by moving from a product focus to a value-added orientation based on expertise, service, and continuous improvement of its offering. In working with Tesoro, a large independent refiner and marketer of petroleum products, Graybar shares its expertise by helping to implement and coordinate continuous improvement teams, meeting regularly at Tesoro's refineries to present new ideas, address operational issues, and implement industry best practices. Graybar also helps Tesoro track expenditures, provide employee education on technical matters, optimize inventory levels, and work on quality assurance programs. Clearly Graybar is more than just a supplier to Tesoro; it is much closer to being a business partner as a result of its value-added orientation.[13]

Environmental Impact

Many buyers examine the costs associated with product disposal and look for ways to recycle or reuse products. These types of programs are likely to be more important in the future, as buyers become more actively involved in the environmental area.

In an effort to make business practices more environmentally friendly and safe, 149 nations are working with the International Organization for Standardization (ISO) to strengthen standards for environmental management. For purchasers there are several implications. First purchasers should identify activities, products, and services that have an environmental impact. This includes recycling programs, emissions to air, discharges to water, use of raw materials, and storage and movement of hazardous materials and the impact of both on land and communities. Purchasers can work with suppliers to reduce excessive packaging, conserve natural resources, and minimize the dangers of products and processes that may harm the environment.

Herman Miller, a manufacturer of office equipment, has worked with suppliers to promote environmentally friendly purchasing practices. Wood is a critical raw material for Herman Miller. Nations with tropical wood forests are a main source of supply. These nations are often developing nations in which indiscriminate logging practices destroy entire forests and various species of wildlife and vegetation. Through its Design for the Environment (DfE) program, Miller promotes sustainability of threatened forests around the world and encourages its suppliers to use environmentally friendly materials and to clearly delineate low-impact disassembly and recycling procedures. The DfE program also has developed an environmental rating tool for new products so that the impact on the environment is directly considered in purchasing decisions.[14]

Thinking Critically

Assume you are the buyer for liquid floor cleaner in the following situations. For each situation, specify what would be the most important purchase criteria that you would use to select a supplier:

- A buyer for a national chain of retail hardware stores.
- A buyer for a large manufacturing facility in Pittsburgh.
- A buyer for a janitorial supplies wholesaler.

CREATING CUSTOMER VALUE

Dell recognizes top suppliers

For the past 12 years, leading computer manufacturer Dell Inc. has recognized its top suppliers, all of whom add significant value to Dell's operations and customers. According to Martin J. Garvin, Dell's senior vice president of worldwide purchasing, "Our suppliers are critical to helping Dell deliver an industry-leading experience to customers who expect nothing but the best quality and value from us." Dell chooses six award winners from thousands of suppliers, basing the selection on quality, global citizenship, continuity of supply, and cost. It is readily apparent that Dell knows what it takes to be a good supplier: the company also has been frequently honored as a top vendor. Most recently Dell received the supplier of the year award from aircraft manufacturer Boeing.

TODAY	TOMORROW	TOYOTA
Reduce manufacturing waste going to landfills	Reduce land going to waste	

Environmental issues are important to many business buyers. The Toyota recycling program keeps 400 million pounds of steel and scrap metal out of landfills around the world.

Types of Buying Decisions

In Chapter 4 we classified consumer decisions on a continuum ranging from extensive problem solving (requiring development of criteria for a decision) to routinized response behavior (requiring only price and availability information). Business-to-business purchase decisions can be classified similarly: straight rebuy, modified rebuy, and new-task decisions.[15] These categories are described in a grid in Exhibit 5–7. Note that the classes are distinguished according to the newness of the purchase decision, the information required, and the need to consider alternatives in the purchase, such as different suppliers.

New-Task Decisions

In **new-task decisions,** as shown in Exhibit 5–7, the buying problem is new and a great deal of information must be gathered. New-task decisions are relatively infrequent for a company, and the cost of making a wrong decision is high. Suppliers must convince the buyer their product will solve the buyer's problem; they cannot count on merely offering a price advantage to win the sale. New-task decisions are generally consistent with the sequence of activities in the buying process (discussed later).

When Wal-Mart contemplates a new-task buying decision, the purchase is considered from all angles. Both product and service suppliers must fill out an extensive questionnaire and submit detailed information about their offerings and their company's operating practices before they will be seriously considered as a supplier. Wal-Mart's supplier development group analyzes the company's financial standing, determines if the supplier qualifies for its Minority & Women-Owned Business Development Program, and specifies various technological, legal, and performance requirements to be met by all suppliers. In addition, the potential supplier's proposal must address a multitude of questions related to cost savings, service improvements, sources for future growth, identification of key competitors, target market characteristics, and

Exhibit 5–7	*The buying decision grid*

Type of Buying Decision	Newness of the Problem	Information Requirements	Consideration of New Alternatives
New task	High	Maximum	Important
Modified rebuy	Medium	Moderate	Limited
Straight rebuy	Low	Minimal	None

Insupplier salespeople provide ideas and programs to help their customers build their businesses. This Colgate-Palmolive salesperson provides advice on in-store displays and merchandising to a retailer in China.

positioning versus competitive products.[16] By requiring so much information of potential suppliers, Wal-Mart increases its chances of making sound new-task decisions.

Modified Rebuy Decisions

Modified rebuy decisions call for the evaluation of new alternatives for purchase decisions. A modified rebuy could involve considering either new suppliers for current purchase needs or new products offered by current suppliers. The amount of information required and the need to consider new alternatives are less than for new-task decisions but more than for straight rebuy decisions. More familiarity with the decision means less uncertainty and perceived risk than for new-task decisions.[17] Purchases of complex component parts from a new supplier are typical modified rebuy decisions. In these situations the firm's buyer, often with some input from management, will make the decision.

Straight Rebuy Decisions

Straight rebuy decisions are the most common type. Products and services bought previously are simply repurchased. Delivery, performance, and price are the critical considerations in a straight rebuy. "Outsuppliers," or suppliers not currently being used, are at a considerable disadvantage in this case because "insuppliers" have achieved their status by fulfilling purchase expectations over time. This being the case, the buyer is often reluctant to spend time evaluating other suppliers or risk changing suppliers. Purchases of office supplies, raw materials, lubricants, castings, and frequently used component parts involve straight rebuy decisions. Business buyers typically make these decisions.

The Buying Process

The buying process is presented in Exhibit 5–8. Like many consumer decisions, the decision sequence begins with problem or opportunity recognition. Problem recognition may be triggered by the depletion of supplies, worn-out equipment, or the need for improved technology. It may arise in various departments: operations, production, purchasing, engineering, or planning. New business opportunities may also generate the need for purchases. Once the firm recognizes a need to purchase, it determines the desired product characteristics and the quantity to buy. Then production, R&D, or engineering personnel determine specific details for each item. These "specs" are the needed levels of product characteristics.

Next the firm searches for qualified sources or suppliers. Information about potential suppliers may be available from salespeople, exhibitions and trade shows, direct-mail advertising, press releases, trade news and trade advertising, word-of-mouth, and professional conferences. Suppliers are evaluated to ensure they can produce and deliver the product as needed and provide service after the purchase. Surveys indicate that buyers are also looking for more than a quality product and excellent service performance in their suppliers.[18] More buyers are expecting that suppliers will work closely with them to improve performance levels, contain costs, and develop new technologies. Buyers also prefer suppliers that will share data and resources to accomplish mutual goals, help improve the buyer's operations, and respond quickly to emergencies.[19] A formal procedure for evaluating suppliers is presented in Appendix B.

| **Exhibit 5–8** | *The business buying process* |

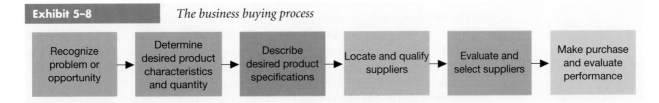

W. Wayne Whitworth, president of the Strategic Purchasing Group and director of purchasing for American Commercial Lines, considers several factors when choosing among potential suppliers: "There are a myriad of factors to consider when evaluating a potential or existing supplier. The most visible and quantifiable are those relating to price and quality. These attributes are readily identified and relatively easy to measure. The most difficult portion to quantify, however, is service since it entails a broad range of activities that are subjective in nature. When evaluating this component, I prefer to examine a supplier's cost contribution. Suppliers are rewarded based on cost savings contributions, innovations, new product development activities, and quantifiable measures that impact our total cost of ownership. The objective of this process is to remove subjective criteria from the evaluation process and recognize those suppliers that continually contribute value added, cost-effective products and services."

Once a decision has been reached, the firm makes the purchase. Typically buyers negotiate the final purchase. Buyers try to get the best deal for their company and often negotiate for better payment terms, delivery schedules, or other benefits. After the purchase is finalized, buyers continually monitor the suppliers' performance.

The business buying process varies according to the type of buying decision. New-task decisions are the most complex and typically follow the process we discussed. Modified rebuy situations are less complex but normally include most of the stages in the buying process. Straight rebuys are usually a reorder from a current supplier.

The Buying Center

Sometimes one individual in a firm makes the buying decisions. Decisions made by a single individual occur most frequently for casual, routine, low-priority, and simple modified repurchase decisions. In many instances, however, purchases are joint decisions of a buying center involving more than just a professional buyer. The **buying center,** a primary concept in business purchasing, includes more than the purchasing department or the purchasing function; it is made up of people throughout the organization at all levels. Moreover, the makeup of the buying center may vary as decisions change.

The number of people and departments represented and the levels of management involved are greater for new-task and complex modified rebuy decisions. The roles that people assume in influencing a purchase decision include initiator, decider, influencer, purchaser, gatekeeper, and user. These terms are largely self-explanatory, except for **gatekeepers,** those who control the flow of information and communication among the buying center participants.

Vendors selling to industrial firms must recognize these multiple roles. The potential supplier may have to reach everyone involved in the decision process. That is, the seller must go beyond engineering and purchasing departments and talk to the gatekeeper, those who influence the decision, and the decision maker, for instance. IBM is a legendary example of how to do this well. IBM salespeople try to identify everyone involved in the purchase decision, the interrelationships among these individuals, the contribution of each, and the criteria each uses in making product or service evaluations.

Global firms face additional challenges because international purchases can make buying decisions and processes even more complicated. Most firms prefer to use overseas purchasing offices, typically staffed with foreign nationals with both purchasing and technical training. Some companies hire import brokers to handle their international purchases.

Buying center members, connected by both workflow and communication networks, receive information from several sources. These sources of information may be personal or impersonal, commercial or noncommercial. Commercial sources come from some *sponsor* that advocates purchase of a particular product or service. Noncommercial personal sources, such as professional contacts, are influential because they include actual users of the product. They also have more credibility because of their likely unbiased perspective.

Marketing efforts targeted toward businesses depend heavily on personal selling. However, commercial nonpersonal advertising through trade publications and other sales literature can stimulate customer leads, enhance a vendor's image, and generally support personal selling efforts. Once again, the Internet can be a valuable source of information for business buyers. With supply chains in Asia often extending from Taiwan to mainland China to the Philippines and the United States, the Internet is a tremendous resource for business buyers. As a result, marketers are rapidly seizing the opportunity to connect with purchasers by adding the Internet to their mix of communication tools for reaching business markets.

Government Markets

An online version of *Commerce Business Daily* alerts vendors to the procurement needs of the U.S. government. Each daily edition contains 500 to 1,000 notices for goods and services to be purchased by the federal government.

In the United States, the **government market** includes federal, state, and local government organizations that purchase goods and services for use in many activities. With total expenditures in the trillions of dollars, the government market is the largest in the world, with the United States federal government the largest customer in this market. The Department of Defense is the federal government's biggest spender, trailed by the Department of Health and Human Services in expenditures.[20] Waste in government purchasing is a perennial topic of discussion, but government buying practices have been reformed significantly in recent years. Taxpayers are less tolerant of frivolous purchases, and government buyers have responded.

The *Commerce Business Daily (CBD)* publishes notices of government procurement needs, contract awards, sales of government property, and other procurement information for the federal government. A new edition of the *CBD* is issued every business day. Each edition contains approximately 500 to 1,000 notices, and each notice appears only once. All federal procurement offices are required to announce in the *CBD* all contracts or subcontracts involving expenditures over $25,000.[21]

Competing for government business is a complex, time-consuming, and often frustrating endeavor. Government purchase decisions are subject to legislative direction and, in the case of the federal government, monitored by outside agencies such as the Office of Management and Budget (OMB). Most governments, whether national, state, or local, purchase through open bids or negotiated contracts. **Bids** are written proposals from qualified suppliers in response to published governmental requirements or specifications. The lowest bidder is typically selected. In some instances, small business suppliers get preferential treatment in bid evaluations. A negotiated contract is reached when a government unit works with a company to determine contract terms.

Reseller Markets

The **reseller market** is made up of firms that purchase goods and in turn sell them to others at a gain. This market includes wholesalers and retailers, totaling approximately 3.5 million companies with more than 20 million employees. Retailers and wholesalers are covered in detail in Chapters 14 and 15.

Retail businesses are everywhere. They make goods and services available to consumers at reasonable prices and in wide assortments. Most goods sold directly to consumers are first purchased by resellers. Wholesale firms tend to be more concentrated in trade centers surrounding larger population areas.

Retail establishments frequently use professional buyers to make their purchase choices. In many instances, say, for grocery chains, salespeople call on the buyers at central wholesale locations. Buyers at other retail firms, such as department stores, frequent trade shows where they place purchase orders directly with manufacturers.

Small retailers not part of large chain or franchise arrangements often band together to make purchases. Through buying group memberships, these retailers get merchandise discounts or rebates they could not typically get on their own.

Assortment and quantity decisions are the cornerstones of retailing and wholesaling success. Resellers must be able to purchase products with significant consumer demand or appeal. Their success also depends heavily on their ability to purchase products that they can resell at prices above their purchase price. Competitive pressures and growing consumer price sensitivity have greatly increased the need to make correct decisions.

Consumer products companies often advertise to both consumer and reseller markets. In this ad, Chomp, Inc., advertises to retailers to acquaint them with Chomp's line of pet food treats.

Other Institutional Markets

Nonprofit organizations must also purchase goods and services to support their activities. These organizations include educational institutions, public and private hospitals, religious and charitable organizations, and trade associations. As buyers, they represent viable marketing opportunities, and many specialized firms meet the needs of these unique market niches. For example, some architects specialize in church or school design and construction. Other companies specialize in supplies for public and private schools. And of course, institutional buyers have standard business needs too. Many firms produce and sell health care equipment and supplies. Concerns about communicable diseases have given rise to an entire industry of protective health equipment such as disposable gloves.

Ethical Issues

As discussed earlier in this chapter, ethics are a constant concern in business-to-business negotiations and transactions. Bribery is a particularly troublesome area. Bribery can take many forms: gifts from vendors to people involved in decision making, "money under the table," and promises for the future. Suppliers offer these financial inducements to increase their chances of being selected by firms. Another related practice in purchase interactions between organizations is **reciprocity.** Reciprocity occurs when firm A purchases from supplier B, who in turn buys A's own products and services. Such practices are illegal if they restrict competition and must not be used in decisions to select suppliers unless the arrangements can be made legally.

Business buyers sometimes visit supplier locations to become more knowledgeable about the products they purchase. Siemens Medical Systems, a supplier of medical equipment, has a fully operational demonstration facility in its New Jersey headquarters.

The important values of fairness, honesty, and trust should influence all negotiations between business purchasers and their suppliers, including the selection of suppliers or vendors. Judgments of suppliers should be made impartially and fairly. Unfair trade promises should not be extracted from companies that are in dire need of business or at some other disadvantage. This is the inverse of price discrimination, when firms unethically and illegally charge different prices to different customers for similar products and services. Purchasers should not unfairly require different suppliers to charge different prices for similar goods and services.[22]

For firms pursuing global markets, the possibility of encountering ethical dilemmas is multiplied many times. Practices in some countries differ dramatically from domestic expectations. In Japan, South Korea, and Taiwan, for example, failure to accept a business gift can imply insensitivity and disrespect. Many international companies have therefore had to develop well-defined policies that address the issue of receiving favors and gifts from overseas suppliers.

Summary

1. **Define the nature of business-to-business buying behavior and markets.** Business-to-business buying behavior refers to the process through which organizations make purchase decisions involving other organizations as suppliers. Increasingly, business buyers are concerned with supply chain management, which integrates business processes from end users through original suppliers, providing products, services, and information that add value for customers. The four broad business markets are business firms, including manufacturers and service providers; federal, state, and local governments; wholesale and retail firms that buy products and then resell them; and institutional firms, including hospitals, educational institutions, and trade associations.

2. **Explain the differences between business-to-business buying and consumer purchase behavior.** Business buyers differ from consumer buyers in important ways. Overall, industrial and business buyers are more geographically concentrated, purchases are larger, decisions are subject to multiple influences and often approached more analytically, and demand is derived from consumer markets and trends in those markets. Organizational buying decisions typically rely on a number of choice criteria, including quality and reliability of performance, price, inventory service, reputation of supplier, and the ability to provide technical and service support.

3. **Recognize the different types of buying decisions.** Business-to-business purchase decisions can be classified into one of three categories, differentiated by complexity: new-task decisions, where the choice criteria must be determined and substantial information gathered; modified rebuys, where new sources of supply may be evaluated for situations previously encountered or the decisions are only moderately complex; and straight rebuys, where products and services bought previously are repurchased from known vendors.

4. **Define the different stages of the business buying process.** The most complex purchase decisions involve this sequence: (1) Recognize the problem or opportunity; (2) determine desired product characteristics and quantity; (3) describe desired product specifications; (4) locate and qualify suppliers; (5) evaluate and select suppliers; and (6) evaluate performance.

5. **Describe the buying center concept and the determinants of influence within the buying center.** The buying center for an organization is responsible for selecting suppliers and arranging purchase terms. It is made up of people involved in routine and nonroutine purchase decisions. They may come from different departments (purchasing, engineering, production) and levels within the organization and may play one or more roles: initiator, decider, influencer, purchaser, gatekeeper, or user. Buying center members vary in their influence on decisions, and a number of factors affect the relative power they hold in business-to-business purchases.

6. **Understand the nature of government, reseller, and other institutional markets.** The primary organizational markets include the government market, resellers, and other institutional firms. The federal government is the largest single purchaser. State and local governments make many purchases as well. Resellers are wholesale and retail firms that purchase goods to resell to other organizations or directly to consumers at higher prices.

Understanding Marketing Terms and Concepts

Thinking about Marketing

1. What are the distinguishing characteristics of business-to-business buying behavior?

2. What is the North American Industry Classification System? How can it be used to assist in marketing to business buyers?

3. Describe some of the current trends in business-to-business buying behavior.

4. Refer to "Using Technology: TexYard.com Makes Apparel Industry Exchange Work." What are some key benefits of using the Internet to facilitate purchasing and supply chain management?

5. Refer to "Creating Customer Value: Dell Recognizes Top Suppliers." From the Dell home page at *www.dell.com,* click on the Small Business link. Locate and document several examples of how Dell adds value in facilitating the purchasing process for small businesses.

6. What are the different types of buying decisions, and how do the information requirements vary across the decisions?

7. What is the general sequence of activities in new-task purchase decisions?

8. What is a buying center? Who are some of its typical members?

9. Contrast personal and impersonal sources of information. How might credibility differ across sources of information that are available to organizational buyers?

10. What is reciprocity? Why might it be illegal?

Applying Marketing Skills

1. Assume you must purchase new personal computers for your medium-sized company. What decision criteria would be involved, and how might the decision be reached?

2. Assume your manufacturing company has made the decision to begin importing critical component parts from country X. It is common practice for companies in that country to offer their customers personal gifts and small amounts of cash for their business. These parts, which are critical to your company's success, can be purchased abroad in country X at a much lower price and at a quality that matches that of current U.S. suppliers' products. What policies should be established for guiding the behavior and decision making of your company's purchasing personnel?

3. Describe how the buying needs of a small retail clothier (the business owner and four employees) might differ from the needs of a manufacturer of industrial forklifts. The manufacturer makes purchases through its buying center. Discuss the likely differences in the decision processes involved for the two businesses.

Using the www in Marketing

Activity One Compare the online purchasing sites for Office Depot *(www.officedepot.com)* and Corporate Express *(www.corporateexpress.com).* Assume you are a buyer for office supplies for a large national manufacturer in the United States and that you want to purchase the majority of your office supplies from one vendor. In making your assessment, compare these attributes: ease of navigation, product availability, customer support, and ease of ordering. Rate each site on each attribute, and make an overall assessment of the strengths and weaknesses of each site.

Activity Two Online auctions have become part of business buying. Go to *www.ebay.com* to investigate an online auction site. Click on the Buy link, then click on the business and industrial category. Select an industry for further investigation, and explore the types of information available for your chosen industry. How useful do you think online auctions could be for business buyers? Based on what you see at www.ebay.com, does it seem that some business buyers might benefit more from online auctions than others? If so, for which product categories would online auctions seem most promising for business buyers?

Activity Three Hewlett-Packard uses its Internet site to appeal to different categories of business and government buyers. Go to *www.hp.com* and compare the information available to government buyers to the information available to small and medium businesses. What specific information does HP offer potential buyers in these two categories? Is it adequate? Are there significant differences in the available information for buyers in the two categories?

Making Marketing Decisions

Case 5–1 *Harley Davidson's Customer-Centered Supply Chain*

Harley Davidson is best known for its high-quality motorcycles; but the company is also getting a lot of press about its customer-centered supply chain. By listening to its customers and getting its suppliers to also listen to customers, Harley has built a strong foundation for its supply chain. In the process, Harley reinforces customer loyalty in a customer base already fiercely loyal to the leading American manufacturer of motorcycles.

Harley's improved supply chain has greatly benefited from advances in computer technology. It has a worldwide extranet that allows dealers to check pricing and product availability, order parts and merchandise, and retrieve service information. Suppliers are also linked via the Web, where they check on business details such as accounts payable, product design, and delivery and monitor their own performance.

In selecting suppliers for its supply chain, Harley expects that all suppliers will practice open communication and participate in important Harley processes such as market research and product development. Suppliers must be dedicated to reducing supply chain costs, provide 24-hour, seven-day accessibility, integrate effectively into the Harley Davidson organization, and align with Harley's strategic direction. In upgrading its supply chain to ultimately meet dealer and consumer needs more effectively, Harley has reduced its supplier base by 80 percent, down from 4,000 to 800. Of these 800, Harley has strategic partnerships with its 125 most crucial suppliers. It has greatly reduced its material costs, product development cycle time, and defective parts percentage. All of these improvements have paid off with a huge reduction in waste and assembly-line slowdowns.

It all starts with the customer, and Harley hits the road to learn from its ultimate buyers. Among the most important venues for listening to the customer are semiannual biker rallies in Florida and South Dakota. Bikers from all over the United States attend these rallies, where Harley sets up booths, display areas, and test rides. Key suppliers join Harley at these rallies to gather customer input through surveys, interviews, and less formal one-on-one conversations with riders. This connection of customers with Harley personnel and suppliers helps ensure that consistent information is passed back from customers to the critical parties in the supply chain.

In addition to the rallies, Harley hosts dealer shows, also attended by supplier representatives. Harley can learn about dealer concerns at these shows, and key suppliers can provide information about technical concerns. All dealer information, as is the case with ultimate consumers at rallies, is documented and entered into the supply chain database for appropriate follow-up. Eventually Harley compares notes with suppliers, and joint decisions are made that better meet the needs of all parties.

The level of detail in this information-gathering process is impressive. For example, Harley riders are sticklers for detail when it comes to paint and chrome. Harley and its suppliers ask for customer input on bike colors and just how much chrome it needs to give the bikes that unmistakable Harley look.

By implementing a customer-centered supply chain, Harley enjoys many benefits. It helps attract world-class suppliers such as Delphi Automotive Delco Electronics Systems, which supplies speedometers, tachometers, cruise control, and other electrical devices. The efficient supply chain also makes it easier for dealers to compete against rival retailers.

Harley supports its dealers through its online RoadStore. RoadStore provides consumers with information about Harley products and also allows shoppers to buy online through authorized Harley dealers. Harley also supports its dealers with advertising, merchandising consultation, and in-store programs. One of its most successful programs is its Rider's Edge New Rider's Course, held in conjunction with selected U.S. dealers. Participating dealers are delighted with the program, which has given them exposure and sales opportunities with a new customer base—females under the age of 35. With its supply chain running at near-optimal levels and the dual focus of its supply chain on dealers and riders, Harley is poised to continue its impressive sales growth. For one thing, dealers and customers are less likely to have to wait for that new Harley: one result of the supply chain improvements is a better match between supply and demand.

Questions

1. How can Harley Davidson marketing and sales personnel interact with its purchasing personnel to further strengthen the supply chain and improve customer loyalty?

2. What is the role of technology in Harley's supply chain? What additional uses of technology can you identify that might be useful to Harley's focus on the dealer and the ultimate customer?

3. Some of Harley's suppliers also supply key Harley competitors. How can Harley be sure these suppliers will not share confidential information with its competitors? How important is trust between suppliers and business buyers?

Case 5–2 *Big Three Automakers Pressure Suppliers*

The relationships between the Big Three automakers (Ford, General Motors, and Daimler-Chrysler) and their suppliers offer some interesting contrasts. On one hand, automakers and suppliers are heavily involved in collaboration on product development and quality improvement. This collaboration is widely viewed as necessary to satisfy changing consumer tastes and compete effectively against other automakers, chiefly Toyota, Honda, Nissan, and to a lesser degree, companies from Germany, Korea, and occasionally other countries.

On the other hand, Detroit automakers have sometimes been adversarial in their relationships with suppliers. The tension between automakers and their suppliers made headline news in the business world throughout the 1990s. General Motors was portrayed as the chief protagonist during this period, led by controversial purchasing chief J. Ignacio Lopez de Arriotura. Lopez approached purchasing as a win–lose proposition, and his goal was for GM to beat its suppliers at the game of constantly trying to buy at lower prices. While a storm of negative publicity surrounded GM's purchasing practices under Lopez, he was able to wring tremendous cost savings out of GM suppliers, and other automotive purchasing groups took notice. None of the major manufacturers could afford to be at a cost disadvantage to the others, a reality that became even more meaningful in the slow economic times of 2000–2002.

Daimler-Chrysler, badly pinched from a profitability point of view, began implementing some of the same tactics GM had used with suppliers. As part of a huge cost-cutting initiative, the company asked suppliers to tear up existing supply contracts and sign new contracts with a 5 percent reduction in costs. Many key suppliers balked, and some privately complained about Daimler-Chrysler's heavy-handed approach to solving its profitability problem. Some went beyond that, saying that they would not give Daimler-Chrysler the first look at new technologies and ideas for new designs.

Another development that irked many major suppliers was the Big Three's move to public exchanges, or electronic marketplaces. Here the automakers could use public exposure to keep competitive suppliers' prices down, and suppliers did not like parading their offerings for all, including their own competitors, to see. The Big Three automakers collaborated to form Covisint, an electronic exchange, which was later sold to Compuware Corporation. Ford and Daimler-Chrysler still utilize Covisint, and their hope is to have all key suppliers active on Covisint—something that many suppliers are not happy with.

In the power struggle to exercise control in the automotive supply market, the Big Three obviously have a lot of economic clout. Ford and General Motors have the two largest purchasing budgets of U.S. corporations, and Daimler-Chrysler's budget is significant as well. But there are thousands of automotive suppliers, and they too have a lot of collective clout. Some of the suppliers are large in their own right. Delphi, a key supplier, has the 17th largest purchasing budget in the United States, well ahead of corporate giants such as Dell Computer, International Paper, and Lockheed Martin. Johnson Controls, another key supplier, has the 38th largest purchasing budget in the United States, ahead of large companies such as Bristol-Meyers, Sprint, and Conoco.

Large suppliers like Delphi and Johnson Controls are called Tier 1 suppliers in the automotive industry. They sell directly to the automobile companies. Tier 2 suppliers are smaller than Tier 1 suppliers, and usually sell to Tier 1 suppliers. They may sell directly to the automakers, but most of the time they sell to Tier 1 suppliers. Tier 3 suppliers sell to Tier 1 and Tier 2 suppliers but rarely directly to the automakers. Tier 1 suppliers are gaining power in the marketplace as they buy up Tier 2 and Tier 3 suppliers. For the automakers' Covisint site to work, a large percentage of Tier 1, 2, and 3 suppliers must participate. Many Tier 2 and Tier 3 suppliers are small businesses and fear that price cuts will put them out of business. Should this happen, a financially healthy supplier would buy them out or simply expand its own business to meet demand. Analysts say that suppliers are gaining clout as the cost-cutting demands of the automakers ultimately create consolidation on the supply side. Already the number of North American suppliers in the past decade has dropped from 30,000 to 8,000, a 75 percent reduction.

Questions

1. Can the Big Three's emphasis on lower costs have any detrimental effects on their ultimate ability to deliver what the consumer wants?

2. Do you see any ethical issues in the way the Big Three conduct their purchasing practices?

3. What can suppliers do to negotiate mutually beneficial contracts with the Big Three automakers? From the suppliers' point of view, what are the pros and cons of participating in Covisint?

Chapter Six

MARKETING RESEARCH AND DECISION SUPPORT SYSTEMS

6

After studying this chapter, you should be able to

1 Understand the purpose and functions of marketing research.

2 Be familiar with the stages of the marketing research process.

3 Discuss different types of research designs, data collection methods, and sources of secondary and primary marketing research data.

4 Understand many of the major issues involved with survey design and sampling.

5 Appreciate the role of marketing research within decision support systems.

IMS Health

IMS Health is the second largest marketing research firm in the United States and the largest provider of research information to the global pharmaceutical industry. With services in over 100 countries, IMS is familiar with the global nature of health care. As the company's self-description asserts, IMS is expertly positioned to supply data and business solutions to organizations throughout the health care environment.

The total revenues for IMS in 2003 were $1.4 billion, with $843.9 million generated outside the United States. Over the past five decades, IMS Health Inc. has evolved to the point where the firm can provide information regarding product movement, buying trends, physicians' prescription patterns, and patient treatment data. In addition, IMS offers information regarding sales force effectiveness, as well as managed care and over-the-counter services. These operations involve the efforts of over 6,100 professionals worldwide.

As part of IMS Health's services, the company offers brand management assistance to pharmaceutical companies. Specifically, IMS Health, with headquarters in Connecticut, assists in identifying market opportunities, determining the optimal mix of products and brands, tracking brand performance, and maximizing brand growth. As such, IMS as a marketing research firm offers many pharmaceutical firms basic marketing information for use in the development and execution of effective marketing strategy.

The hand-built, all-aluminum Acura NSX. As if a 290-horsepower VTEC™ engine, race-tuned suspension and Formula One heritage weren't enough, we enhanced its aerodynamic styling. The NSX. Nothing else comes close. (A)ACURA

Marketing research is used in planning to identify the needs of product users and in problem solving to evaluate the types and styles of products to offer.

Marketing research companies like Information Resources Inc. and ACNielsen are among the largest providers of marketing research data and offer a wide variety of services. Smaller research firms often specialize in industry types or individual services, such as measuring customer retention and customer satisfaction. IRI makes a large portion of its revenues from the sale of product movement tracking data derived from large surveys of grocery stores and drugstores; whereas other research firms provide for their clients individually designed studies that address particular situations or problems. IRI's research enables its customers to monitor sales and promotional activities across product categories, understand the effects of promotions on consumer activity, and identify problems and opportunities in distribution.

The overall objective of marketing research is to reduce risk in decision making by helping management understand its uncertain and changing marketplace and the consumers and competitors that make up its markets. The marketing research process involves the collection, interpretation, and use of data to make decisions. Such understanding makes a firm better able to provide products and services that meet customer expectations and needs. Marketing research enhances communication between a firm and its markets with the aim of improving managerial decision making. The aim of research is not to confirm that decisions already made are correct, but to identify alternative choices and to support the decision-making process.[1]

What Is Marketing Research?

In its definition of **marketing research,** the American Marketing Association recognizes the complexity of the process and the different activities that may be performed.

Marketing research links the consumer, the customer, and the public through information used to

- Identify and define marketing opportunities.
- Generate, refine, and evaluate marketing actions.
- Monitor marketing performance.
- Improve understanding of marketing as a process.

Marketing research

- Specifies the information required to address these issues.
- Designs the methods for collecting information.

Speaking from Experience

Terry G. Vavra
Chairman Emeritus
Ipsos Loyalty, Inc.

"Make no mistake about it, marketing researchers are sometimes criticized for their orientation to objectivity, especially by individuals in positions where personal creativity is viewed as paramount (e.g., brand managers, creative directors). But the tide is turning. Today fewer and fewer upper-level managers will commit company resources based on only one person's intuition. They increasingly demand supportive evidence available only from properly designed research."

Terry G. Vavra has B.S. and M.S. degrees in marketing from the University of California, Los Angeles, and a Ph.D. degree in marketing from the University of Illinois. He is cofounder of Marketing Metrics, which became Ipsos Loyalty

in 2004. Ipsos Loyalty is a global practice focusing on customer satisfaction and retention. Terry is author of five books on marketing, satisfaction, and loyalty.

- Manages and implements the data collection process.
- Analyzes the results.
- Communicates the findings and implications.[2]

This definition emphasizes the generation of information that assists in managerial decision making. We adapted the second half of the definition as an outline for discussing the stages of the marketing research process in this chapter.

Marketing research is useful in planning, problem solving, and control, as shown in Exhibit 6–1. Marketers use marketing research to provide guidance in decision making. This enables them to spend their resources more effectively. Researchers must understand the research process, the marketing process, and the industries in which the firm operates.[3]

| **Exhibit 6–1** | *Kinds of questions marketing research can help answer* |

I. Planning

A. What kinds of people buy our products? Where do they live? How much do they earn? How many of them are there?

B. Are the markets for our products increasing or decreasing? Are there promising markets that we have not yet reached?

C. Are the channels of distribution for our products changing? Are new types of marketing institutions likely to evolve?

II. Problem Solving

A. Product
 1. Which of various product designs is likely to be the most successful?
 2. What kind of packaging should we use?

B. Price
 1. What price should we charge for our products?
 2. As production costs decline, should we lower our prices or try to develop higher-quality products?

C. Place
 1. Where, and by whom, should our products be sold?
 2. What kinds of incentives should we offer the trade to push our products?

D. Promotion
 1. How much should we spend on promotion? How should it be allocated to products and to geographic areas?
 2. What combination of media—newspapers, radio, television, magazines—should we use?

III. Control

A. What is our market share overall? In each geographic area? By each customer type?

B. Are customers satisfied with our products? How is our record for service? Are there many returns?

C. How does the public perceive our company? What is our reputation with the trade?

Take the research team for Stouffers, a national organization that manages private restaurants and clubs, for example. Stouffers researchers must understand the growth and image objectives of the organization, besides identifying new market opportunities and conducting customer satisfaction surveys. Only by knowing the club business can meaningful research be conducted to support the Stouffers organization. Pizza Hut now links its unit managers' bonuses to the results of customer satisfaction surveys. Questions address satisfaction with service, food quality, and other issues.

Answers to important and interesting questions are possible through the use of marketing research. Should McDonald's focus on a clearer market position as opposed to ever-changing menu explorations? The company now faces the need to reawaken its brand diluted by movement away from the initial emphasis on performance and firm management. Could Webvan, the online grocer, have avoided its problems with the consideration of marketing research in lieu of focusing exclusively on developing complex inventory and distribution systems? In the Webvan instance, it is amazing that its substantial investment was made with almost no research into whether consumers would want its service.[4]

Marketing research is often used to evaluate the characteristics and potential of markets prior to making decisions about product introductions and new market entry. Research is helpful in evaluating new product concepts and advertising campaigns under consideration. It is also used to monitor market performance and competitive reaction. VNU Inc. (which includes ACNielsen), one of the largest marketing research firms, provides data to packaged goods manufacturers like Coca-Cola and Nabisco about their product sales. Research is also used to identify and solve problems. Municipalities, for example, frequently conduct marketing research to identify citizens' needs and methods for attracting shoppers to the area.

Most important, marketing research should support a firm's overall market orientation. Research links marketers to markets through information and scientific study. It is used to explore opportunities and problems, monitor performance, refine marketing strategy, and improve understanding of marketing efforts and markets themselves. As such, research enhances a firm's closeness with its customers and enables the marketer to anticipate latent unfulfilled needs and wants.[5]

Marketing Research in the New Millennium

Significant environmental phenomena will affect the marketing research industry in the next decade and beyond. First, the traditional time line of four to six weeks for the typical research project will no longer be acceptable in many cases. However, researchers will still need to balance time pressures with quality. Second, gatekeeper technology, such as caller ID and privacy-related services, will limit researcher access to consumers. And, pending federal and state legislation may restrict the data collection process as well. Marketing research is also becoming more a part of the marketing strategy development process. This shift to more of an advisory role represents less emphasis on the more traditional marketing research roles of testing and evaluation.[6]

Interactivity, e-commerce, and the Internet are certainly affecting the practice of marketing, and likewise are affecting the conduct of marketing research. New consumer information is pouring in at incredible speed from scanners, loyalty program tapes, syndicated data services, and the Internet. Marketing researchers within firms and researchers within the marketing research industry itself are going to be required to adapt to this technological wave of change. The problem is no longer how to get information; the problem today is how will data be managed. As examples, the research departments at Campbell Soup Company and Procter & Gamble have been renamed "Information Management" and "Consumer Market and Knowledge," respectively.

Blockbuster has a database of 36 million households. The information is used to determine movie choices and to cross-promote its affiliates such as Discovery Zone for children. Analyses of these databases also reaffirm Pareto's Law. For example, 13 percent of Diet Coke drinkers represent 83 percent of the product's volume; for Taster's Choice, 4 percent of customers generated 73 percent of sales. These databases and information at the customer level are instrumental in enabling companies to build long-term relationships with their core and loyal segments.[7]

The marketing research industry itself is in transition. Companies like VNU Inc., IMS Health, Information Resources Inc., and Westat hold significant industry market share. These companies are truly global in their customer base and offerings. It is important to note the evolution of firms from market and opinion research firms to suppliers of information, consulting, and data exchange. These changes have made entry into the industry much harder. Previously, small firms could easily exist and succeed, even with minimal capital investment.[8]

The Marketing Research Process

Exhibit 6–2 presents the stages of the **marketing research process.** The sequence begins with an understanding of the problem and ends with analysis and interpretation.[9] The overall objective should be to generate useful, timely, and cost-effective information. That is, the resulting reduced risk and improved decision making should justify the research costs involved. Even a small study involving 500 local telephone interviews can cost more than $10,000 when researcher time and other costs are considered. Consequently, the cost–benefit trade-off of doing research is always an issue for a firm.

Alternative research approaches and methods should not be considered competing but viewed as both substitutes and complements. In fact, in many instances, firms should consider the use of multiple methods in the spirit of "research triangulation." New insights can be gained from research employing different methods (such as focus groups or telephone surveys). Moreover, confidence is enhanced in the validity of findings if results converge from studies conducted using alternative methods. Also, small-scale qualitative information is used as a precursor to subsequent more formal and standardized questioning. For example, a series of small-sample in-depth interviews could be conducted to generate basic understanding of research issues and relationships. Subsequently, large-scale sample surveys could be employed to generate data that enable tests of statistical significance and the identification of quantifiable findings.[10]

Problem Definition

Problem definition is depicted in Exhibit 6–2 as the first step in any marketing research project and is critical to its success. Problems in a business are often defined as differences between the way things should be and the way they are. Both researchers and management (the users of the research) need to understand the research problem clearly. As such, marketing research projects should always begin with clearly stated objectives.

It should be noted that a substantial amount of research is ongoing and is used for general control and planning purposes. For example, the many companies that use data on in-store sales and product movement provided by IRI or VNU engage in research continuously in their efforts to monitor competitive activity in the marketplace. Thus, often in the problem definition stage of the research process, a problem is not formally identified. Instead, ongoing research may lead to identification of a problem, such as declining sales, low turnover, declining brand appeal, or the emergence of competitive offerings.

The problem definition stage is often difficult because the expectations and desires of managers and researchers frequently differ. Researchers generally take an exploratory perspective, whereas managers may prefer research that confirms their expectations and

Exbibit 6–2   *The marketing research process*

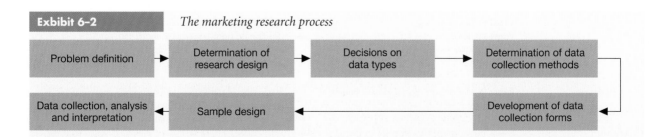

provides few surprises. For best results, all parties involved must take a constructive stance in defining the research problem. They must focus on the real problem and not the symptoms; anticipate how the information will be used; and avoid prescribing a specific study until the problem is fully understood and defined.

Research Designs

Marketing research designs are general strategies or plans of action for addressing the research problem and the data collection and analysis process. The problem definition stage is likely to suggest approaches for determining which marketing research design to use. Research generally has three purposes: exploration, description, and explanation.[11] They result in three general types of research designs: exploratory, descriptive, and causal. Common methods and example studies for each of these designs are shown in Exhibit 6–3.

EXPLORATORY DESIGNS   **Exploratory research** is typically carried out to satisfy the researcher's desire for better understanding, or to develop preliminary background and suggest issues for a more detailed follow-up study.

As shown in Exhibit 6–3, exploratory research can be conducted using literature reviews, case analyses, interviews, and focus groups.[12] Better understanding of a problem might begin with a review of prior research. A researcher working for a bank would not begin a study of the bank's image, for example, without some review of the banking literature on what determines a bank's image. In-depth interviews with individuals who already have some knowledge of the problem may shed some light on the issue.

Interviewing techniques that generate narrative descriptions of consumers' roles in life can be useful in the generation of new innovation ideas. One approach focuses on the conflicts and confusions that consumers report from in-depth interviews regarding their important life "orienting values." Example orienting values include "being professional" or "being cutting edge." Narrative descriptions about pursuit of these defining objectives collected in exploratory interviews and the conflicts that arise in consumers' lives from pursuit of the values represent potential sources of new product ideas.[13]

DESCRIPTIVE DESIGNS   **Descriptive research** is normally directed by one or more formal research questions or hypotheses. Typically a survey or questionnaire is administered to a sample from a population of interest to the firm, such as female household heads or purchasing agents in an industry. Examples include consumer surveys to estimate market potential, segmentation research to identify demographic consumer segments, attitude and opinion surveys, and product usage surveys.

Descriptive studies may be cross-sectional or longitudinal, depending on the timing of the observation. For example, a survey of customers administered at a given time to assess perceived satisfaction with service is a *cross-sectional study*. Consumers who participate in panel studies of purchase behavior over a period of time are involved in *longitudinal research*.

Exhibit 6–3	*Three general research designs*	

Type	**Common Methods**	**Example Studies**
Exploratory designs	Literature reviews Case analyses Interviews with knowledgeable persons In-depth interviews, focus groups	Evaluation of new product concepts, environmental trend analysis, identification of product attribute importance
Descriptive designs	Cross-sectional surveys Panel studies Product movement surveys Store audits Telephone, mail, personal interviews	Market potential, image studies, competitive positioning analysis, market characteristic examinations, customer satisfaction studies
Causal designs	Experimental designs (lab and field studies) Market tests	Evaluation of alternative marketing mix combinations (varying price levels, changing promotional appeals, reallocation of sales force efforts)

NOT ALL OUR GUESTS ARRIVE IN RANGE ROVERS.

At South Seas Plantation, some of our guests actually sail oceans to visit us. But no matter what method of transportation you choose, you'll be welcomed by a Resort and Yacht Harbour that *Motorboating and Sailing* magazine named among the dozen most spectacular cruising grounds in North America.

Located at the end of a private channel at Intracoastal Mile Marker 39, with a 6 ft. low tide depth, our full-service marina can easily accommodate craft up to 110 feet and offers more than 3,600 feet of berthing space. Amenities include fuel, electricity, water, complimentary pumpout facilities, telephone, ice, and cable TV. And the Ship's Store is stocked with supplies, marine charts, groceries, and packaged goods.

So next trip, set your course for South Seas Plantation. Because no matter how you arrive, we promise you'll leave with more wind in your sails. For more information, call your travel agent or 1-800-237-3102.

South Seas Plantation
Captiva Island, Florida

Focus groups are commonly used to explore new concepts and to obtain consumer reactions to ad campaigns under development. South Seas Plantation used focus groups of guests and resort prospects to help make decisions about themes, logos, TV spots, and brochures.

CAUSAL DESIGNS   Exploratory and descriptive studies can help answer certain questions, but identification of cause-and-effect relationships requires **causal research.** Causal designs call for *experiments,* in which researchers manipulate independent variables and then observe or measure the dependent variable or variables of interest.

Suppose a direct marketing company wants to see the effect on sales of increasing its 50¢ coupon to $1. To test this, the company matches two markets, using key variables such as product sales, consumer demographics, and market size. In one market consumers receive the $1 coupon; in the other market they receive the 50¢ coupon. At the end of the experiment, the company compares sales in the two markets and learns that the $1 coupon generates more sales. When it incorporates the cost/profitability of each coupon value into the analysis, however, the company finds the $1 coupon results in a loss, while the 50¢ coupon is profitable. This analysis convinces the company to continue its 50¢ coupon promotion.

Catalog companies have unique opportunities to conduct experimental studies. For example, different versions of the catalogs can be sent to random samples of consumers. This type of design accounts for alternative explanations for results and sample differences. Differences in profits associated with the varying catalog versions can then be easily communicated to managers and explained as effects due to the varying experimental conditions or catalogs.[14]

Data Types

Marketing research methods and data can be categorized in various ways. One description of research categories described total U.S. spending for marketing, advertising, and opinion research in 2004 at nearly $6.4 billion. By segment methods, this spending was broken down as follows: qualitative research—18.2 percent; syndicated research —41.8 percent; and survey research—40.0 percent. The use of syndicated research has increased significantly in recent years.[15]

Marketing research information can also be categorized as either primary data or secondary data. Interrelationships among the different types of data and the various data collection methods are summarized in Exhibit 6–4.

PRIMARY DATA   **Primary data** are collected specifically for a particular research problem. This is the type of information most frequently associated with marketing research, such as survey data from a sample of customers about satisfaction with services. Polls on the standing of political candidates prior to elections are another example. Primary data have the advantage of currency and relevance for a specific research problem. Their primary disadvantage is cost.

| **Exhibit 6–4** | *Data collection methods and examples* |

Sources of Information

Primary Data	**Secondary Data**
Surveys • Mail • Telephone	*Internal Data* • Company records • Data from marketing design support systems
Interviews • Mall intercepts • Personal interviews	*External Data* Proprietary • Custom research • Syndicated services
Focus group observation • Personal • Mechanical	Nonproprietary • Published reports • Census data • Periodicals

Large research firms provide proprietary, secondary research data for use by other firms in analyzing consumer purchase patterns and brand switching. ACNielsen's Homescan panel of 40,000 households tracks consumer purchases at the household level across all types of store outlets.

SECONDARY DATA   **Secondary data** are those already collected for some other purpose and are available from a variety of sources. As a rule, researchers should consult secondary data before collecting primary data. Corporate libraries and outside vendors (firms that specialize in providing research data) provide secondary data. Some public and private universities offer secondary research services. Japanese firms have long recognized the value of secondary data within their firms and regularly use it to compare product movement.[16]

Internal secondary data are collected within a firm and include accounting records, sales force reports, or customer feedback reports. *External secondary data* may be nonproprietary or proprietary. *Nonproprietary* secondary data are available in libraries and other public sources. For example, information from *Sales & Marketing Management*'s "Survey of Buying Power" about population, income, and age groups can help managers estimate market potential and identify likely market segments.

Obviously, the fastest-growing source of secondary data is the Internet. The Internet represents the infrastructure (the machinery, computers, lines, and equipment) that supports what has become known as the World Wide Web or "the Web." Individuals and firms with personal computers, modems, and software access can generate information from both Web sites and home pages around the Web. Information sources include product and company data, business and article reviews, and data from companies such as Dow Jones and Dun & Bradstreet.[17]

Terry G. Vavra talks about the use of available secondary sources of information: "Declining response rates to consumer marketing research are probably the biggest problem marketing research faces. We depend on information collected from individual consumers and businesspeople; failure to respond increases costs and decreases the accuracy of findings. Some would claim that newer technologies (like Internet interviewing) are the answer, but the modality of the interview is a different issue. Industry response rates are becoming unacceptable across all modalities. There are two answers to the problem of declining survey response rates: better discipline (on the part of interviewing practices) and reinforcing the benefits of participation to those who agree."

Primary data are collected for a specific product or situation. In-home surveys, a means of collecting primary data, can provide detailed explanations regarding actual product use.

Online computer databases using CD technology are often free or available in libraries for minimal fees. Many companies now purchase demographic and geographic census data on CD-ROM for use in selecting store sites, mapping sales territories, and segmenting markets.[18]

Syndicated secondary data are provided by commercial marketing research firms that sell their services to other firms. Commercial firms can establish *diary panels* of representative households that record product and brand purchases. These data can help companies evaluate market share and purchase patterns. **Scanner data** obtained from Universal Product Code (UPC) information read in grocery stores provide timely information on actual purchase behavior. Scanner information is forecast to eventually enable companies to model their decisions and to allow management to allocate advertising and

When you're looking for a path to reliable research services –
find a partner who knows the road.

If it can be measured, tested, and tabulated, chances are JRA
has already been there. With innovative technologies and comprehensive
facilities, JRA has the expertise needed for executing the most challenging
project throughout the United States and the world. JRA is the partner
you need to lead you on the path to success (and reliable results).

JRA

J. RECKNER ASSOCIATES, INC. WORLDWIDE HEADQUARTERS

Purchase data collected on samples of consumers can identify what consumers are buying, who are new adopters, and which firms represent the competition.

promotional dollars across actions to achieve optimal marketplace performance.[19]

Advances like these enable retailers to monitor product movement and to assess the effectiveness of advertising and in-store promotions. Several firms, including Nielsen and Information Resources Inc., developed proprietary systems that combine information on product purchasing behavior with TV viewing behavior to produce **single-source data.**[20]

Computer technology is used in novel ways to combine U.S. census data with internal customer data. For example, *geographic information systems (GIS)* provide digitized maps that can be displayed on computers.[21] There is a huge difference between a stack of printed customer names and addresses and a color-coded map showing where the customers are located. GIS systems save marketing researchers hours of tedious plotting. GIS maps were used in the Clinton/Gore presidential campaign to improve volunteer and media efforts.[22]

Geographic displays have significant potential for marketing research use. The Bureau of Census now sells street maps with economic and population data detailed to city blocks on compact disks. Programmers can mesh customer data with these spatial databases, allowing display of three-dimensional plots of customers. Chemical Bank uses GIS to ensure the bank acts in a socially responsible manner and lends money fairly in poor neighborhoods.[23]

Data Collection Methods

Some of the more popular methods of primary data collection include focus groups, telephone surveys, mail surveys, personal interviews, mall intercepts, and Internet surveys. Their principal advantages and disadvantages are summarized in Exhibit 6–5.

FOCUS GROUPS   The most common exploratory procedure is the **focus group.** Focus groups usually comprise 8 to 12 individuals led by a moderator in a focused, in-depth discussion on a specific topic. Usually lasting no more than two hours, the sessions are designed to obtain participant feedback on a particular subject. Focus groups of consumers are well suited for examining new product concepts and advertising themes, investigating the criteria underlying purchase decisions, and generating information for developing consumer questionnaires.[24]

The guidelines for using focus groups often vary by the research problem or situation of the firm. For example, groups of executives who may hold strong opinions or teenage consumers who can be shy argue for mini–focus groups of four to six participants. Also, focus groups need not necessarily be homogeneous demographically. The rule of thumb is that subjects should be comfortable with one another and that some diversity is beneficial. In many cases, budgets do not afford the luxury of separate focus groups, which can run as high as $20,000, for each demographic group in each market.[25]

USING TECHNOLOGY

Cyber shopping and conjoint analysis

Conjoint analysis is a frequently applied research technique that involves soliciting consumers' opinions about various stimuli, often product configurations. Consumer preferences (often rank-order data) for various combinations of products are decomposed to produce feature or attribute preferences. Researchers can identify the relative contribution of price, service, size, warranty level, and other attributes to determine which are most important to product references. Lands' End has made novel use of this approach via a simple questionnaire included on its Web site. For example, six pairs of outfits are shown to the shopper, who chooses a preferred outfit from among each pair. Through conjoint analysis of these choices and the answers to a few other questions, the site sorts through 80,000 apparel options and presents the most suitable ones to the consumer.

| Exhibit 6–5 | | *Advantages and disadvantages of frequently used data collection methods* |

Method	Advantages	Disadvantages
Focus groups	• Depth of information collected • Flexibility in use • Relatively low cost • Data collected quickly	• Requires expert moderator • Questions of group size and acquaintanceships of participants • Potential for bias from moderator • Small sample size
Telephone surveys	• Centralized control of data collection • More cost-effective than personal interviews • Data collected quickly	• Resistance in collecting income, financial data • Limited depth of response • Disproportionate coverage of low-income segments • Abuse of phone by solicitors • Perceived intrusiveness
Mail surveys	• Cost-effective per completed response • Broad geographic dispersion • Ease of administration • Data collected quickly	• Refusal and contact problems with certain segments • Limited depth of response • Difficult to estimate nonresponse biases • Resistance and bias in collecting income, financial data • Lack of control following mailing
Personal (in-depth) interviews	• More depth of response than telephone interviews • Generate substantial number of ideas compared with group methods	• Easy to transmit biasing cues • Not-at-homes • Broad coverage often infeasible • Cost per contact high • Data collection time may be excessive
Mall intercepts	• Flexibility in collecting data, answering questions, probing respondents • Data collected quickly • Excellent for concept tests, copy evaluations, other visuals • Fairly high response rates	• Limited time • Sample composition or representativeness is suspect • Costs depend on incidence rates • Interviewer supervision difficult
Internet surveys	• Inexpensive, quickly executed • Visual stimuli can be evaluated • Real-time data processing possible • Can be answered at convenience of respondent	• Responses must be checked for duplication, bogus responses • Respondent self-selection bias • Limited ability to qualify respondents and confirm responses • Difficulty in generating sample frames for probability sampling
Projective techniques	• Useful in word association tests of new brand names • Less threatening to respondents for sensitive topics • Can identify important motives underlying choices	• Require trained interviewers • Cost per interview high
Observation	• Can collect sensitive data • Accuracy of measuring overt behaviors • Different perspective than survey self-reports • Useful in studies of cross-cultural differences	• Appropriate only for frequently occurring behaviors • Unable to assess opinions or attitudes causing behaviors • May be expensive in data collection time costs

Interestingly, focus groups have become so common that at least 10 episodes of TV sitcoms have employed focus groups as part of their plot. Unfortunately, these depictions are misleading. Multiple groups are typically required before large decisions are made. Participants must be screened for appropriateness, and unbiased and competent moderators are a necessity. Further, groups should not become dominated by a single or few strong participant personalities.[26]

P&G uses research to make most new product decisions; $150 million is spent on 4,000 to 5,000 studies per year. Focus groups comprise a large portion of this activity. Outside firms specializing in focus group research are often employed to recruit and screen participants. As part of these studies, residents of Cincinnati, the home of Procter & Gamble, are a frequent source of study subjects, testing products from Pampers to cleaning products.[27]

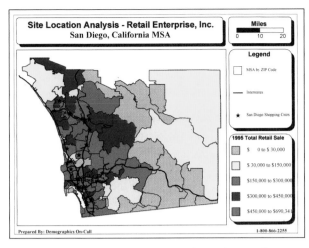

Geographic information systems provide digitized maps of customer markets that are easily color coded to display differences in an area's effective buying income or other characteristics. These systems have been used effectively in selecting retail sites.

Online focus groups provide the ability to incorporate consumers widely dispersed geographically and to obtain quick responses. In addition, technological advances can now provide visual stimuli and are more convenient for consumer group participants. Online focus groups, however, do not normally provide the ability to observe the group members' nonverbal responses, and typed feedback may differ from vocal expressions and opinions. Some companies are using online bulletin boards in efforts to obtain thoughtful responses to research questions.[28]

Focus groups, along with some research information obtained from in-depth interviews and the observation research methods described later, provide **qualitative data.** Qualitative data are characterized by the depth of responses obtained and richness of description. The open-ended nature of the responses, coupled with typically smaller samples, makes predictions and generalizations tentative or difficult. However, qualitative information from focus groups, for example, is particularly useful in exploratory studies where problem understanding and initial insights are needed.

In contrast, descriptive surveys using large-sample telephone surveys or salestracking data from store panels such as IRI yield **quantitative data.** These data, collected using structured response formats, can be easily analyzed and projected to larger populations. For example, quantitative information from political polls can be used to predict voter opinion. Marketing surveys can be used to identify the content and rank order of reasons underlying customer satisfaction.

TELEPHONE SURVEYS   Telephone interviews are relatively cost-effective; a large number of them over a wide geographical area can be conducted quickly and efficiently. Many firms use telephone interviews as their primary means of conducting survey research.

Telephone interviews also enable centralized control and supervision of data collection. *Random digit dialing* and *plus-one dialing* methods have become increasingly popular in the telephone interview process. In one popular version of random-digit dialing, four random digits are added to three-digit telephone exchanges. In plus-one dialing, a telephone number is randomly selected from the local directory, and a digit or digits added to it. This enables the inclusion of unlisted numbers in the sample and increases the likelihood of sampling a working number.

Problems with the use of telephone interviews limit their effectiveness. Questionable ethical practices, such as the use of marketing research as a sales ploy, hurt the research industry. There are major differences between telemarketers soliciting for a product or service and researchers seeking consumer opinions. Unfortunately, these differences are often unclear to potential phone respondents and legislators.[29] Both the European Society for Opinion and Marketing Research (ESOMAR) and the Council of American Survey Research Organizations (CASRO) have called for self-regulation among companies doing telephone interviews

BEING ENTREPRENEURIAL

Online market research

Unilever is turning to the Internet for a faster, more cost-effective method for judging consumer perceptions, attitudes, and willingness to buy. The advantages of online research over telephone and face-to-face interviewing are increasingly recognized by consumer companies like Unilever, which now allocates 30 percent of its research study budget for online research. Surveys conducted online are much less costly per respondent; enable the delivery of video, sound, and photos; allow real-time delivery of results; and enhance participation due to their convenience and anonymity. Unilever executives are surprised at the willingness of consumers to participate and the depth of their responses. As part of its online research, Unilever is now conducting some new concept and package testing using online survey methods and feels that the research enhances its ability to act quickly while still reducing the risks in decision making.

Personal interviews enable the collection of in-depth information in one-on-one situations. Such interviews can be conducted in-house or in-store. For in-store situations, researchers may actually observe behaviors and choices as evaluations and decisions are made.

to stem the growing backlash against researchers.[30] Many states are contemplating legislation to restrict telephone survey research. In addition, the breadth and depth of information that can be obtained from telephone interviews are limited.[31]

MAIL SURVEYS   Mail surveys can obtain broad geographical market coverage, are generally less expensive per completed survey than other methods, and can be used to collect data rather quickly. Surveys can address a range of issues in a single questionnaire. However, studies based on mail questionnaires, and to lesser degrees those using telephone and personal interviews, suffer from nonresponse. Inaccurate mailing lists, questions about who exactly answers the survey, and the inability to handle respondent questions are additional shortcomings of mail surveys.

Although mail questionnaires are relatively inexpensive, conducting a mail survey can involve investments that may be prohibitive for smaller firms. Costs can be reduced by a number of means. For example, Plymart Company, a large southeastern building supply company, chose a university professor over an independent marketing research contractor to design and administer a survey of customer perceptions. The results persuaded management to add framing supplies, which increased sales by 22 percent. For less than $5,000, the company received $100,000 worth of information.[32]

PERSONAL INTERVIEWS   Personal interviews involve one-on-one interactions between a consumer, customer, or respondent and the researcher or some field interviewer paid to conduct the interviews. Personal interviews have relatively high response rates. In addition, they are conducive to the collection of substantial in-depth information and provide visual stimuli such as products and advertisements. Some researchers believe personal interviews are even more flexible than focus groups in that questioning adjustments can be made between interviews if necessary.[33] In addition, shy respondents can have their say, and sensitive topics can be more easily covered than in focus groups.

Disadvantages of personal interviews include the time and travel costs, concerns of personal safety of the interviewer, and inability to cover a wide geographical area. Although personal interview response rates average 70 percent, participation varies widely over types of neighborhoods. People living in metropolitan areas tend to be the least responsive.[34]

MALL INTERCEPTS   The shortcomings of personal interviews have led to increased use of **mall intercept interviews.** In a mall intercept, consumers are approached and interviewed while on shopping trips. One-on-one interaction provides the chance to show visual cues, while overcoming many of the time, travel, and safety concerns associated with door-to-door personal interviewing. Research has shown mall intercept interviewing to provide findings and quality of responses similar to telephone and mail survey collection methods.[35]

Technological advances have enhanced the productivity of mall intercept research. MarketWare Corporation solicits participants for their "virtually real shopping" simulation: "strolling" through store aisles via computer screen. Research can be conducted on any number of variables simultaneously, such as price, package information, and shelf location.[36]

INTERNET SURVEYS   The Internet is fast becoming a popular means of conducting survey research, as are modified focus group discussions. With technology changing rapidly, the future of Internet-based research is both promising and hard to predict. The primary methods of online research are (1) online surveys in which respondents participate on-site following some solicitation or agreement to visit that site and (2) e-mail surveys.[37] However, and as shown in Exhibit 6–5, Internet-based survey research has its advantages and disadvantages like other methods of conducting surveys. On the positive side, research can be done faster, easier, and more cheaply than surveys conducted by mail, in the mall, or over the phone. The

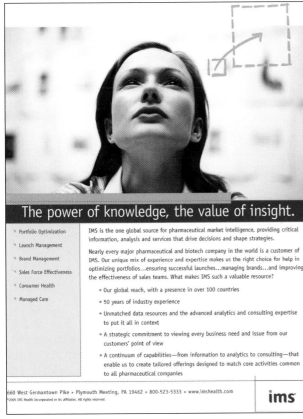

The power of knowledge, the value of insight.

- Portfolio Optimization
- Launch Management
- Brand Management
- Sales Force Effectiveness
- Consumer Health
- Managed Care

IMS is the one global source for pharmaceutical market intelligence, providing critical information, analysis and services that drive decisions and shape strategies.

Nearly every major pharmaceutical and biotech company in the world is a customer of IMS. Our unique mix of experience and expertise makes us the right choice for help in optimizing portfolios...ensuring successful launches...managing brands...and improving the effectiveness of sales teams. What makes IMS such a valuable resource?

- Our global reach, with a presence in over 100 countries
- 50 years of industry experience
- Unmatched data resources and the advanced analytics and consulting expertise to put it all in context
- A strategic commitment to viewing every business need and issue from our customers' point of view
- A continuum of capabilities—from information to analytics to consulting—that enable us to create tailored offerings designed to match core activities common to all pharmaceutical companies

660 West Germantown Pike • Plymouth Meeting, PA 19462 • 800-523-5333 • www.imshealth.com
©2005 IMS Health Incorporated or its affiliates. All rights reserved.

ims

Some Internet panels use incentives to encourage respondent participation. Questions still arise regarding the representativeness of Internet samples due, in part, to self-selection biases.

surveys are less intrusive and more convenient for respondents, and the potential exists to present visual cues, unlike traditional telephone interviews.

Concerns have been raised regarding privacy and validity. Regarding the latter, the primary concern for now is that Internet surveys provide largely self-selected, convenience samples. Sample frames are more difficult to define than for telephone and mail surveys. Relatedly, most Internet surveys are volunteer-based, as participants can select which studies interest them. Hence care must be taken to ensure that Internet surveys are not just 1-800 or 1-900 polls.[38]

American firms are increasingly reducing the use of telephone surveys, partly because of the external pressure related to do-not-call legislation and partly because of cost savings. Internet research, particularly among an audience primed to respond, such as a company's own customers, can yield fast, inexpensive, but valuable feedback on product and marketing communication concepts. However, care in constructing online surveys should be taken. Invitations to participate and the surveys themselves should avoid unnecessary length. One recent study was effective at reaching physicians, a target audience notoriously difficult to study, regarding their use of PDAs in the treatment of patients.[39]

PROJECTIVE TECHNIQUES AND OBSERVATION

Marketing researchers sometimes use projective techniques and observation for data collection. **Projective techniques,** such as word association or sentence completion, allow a researcher to elicit feelings that normally go unexpressed. They may be particularly useful in eliciting honest opinions about sensitive subjects. They can be used effectively in focus groups, mall intercepts, and personal interviews. In one application, consumers are asked to react to different forms of an advertisement or pictures without any brand or product information included in the mock-up. Reactions are reassessed when brand names are added.[40]

Observation research monitors customer behavior by a researcher or by video camera. Much can be learned by unobtrusively observing how customers use a firm's or its competitor's products. In some instances, observation may provide more accurate information than might survey data.[41] Observation research is also useful when traditional survey methods may not reveal the process by which goods and services are bought and used.

In another form of observation research, mystery shoppers evaluate the consistency and quality of services offered. Banks frequently use this practice to evaluate the service quality provided by their tellers and service personnel. The spread of digital cameras has made the use of mystery shoppers more high-tech and effective in their data gathering. Photos, which can be transmitted quickly, provide more detail and less subjectivity in the research information gathered by mystery shoppers in their observations of product and service quality.[42] Field observation requires patience, discipline, and enthusiasm on the part of the observer. However, in-store observations coupled with a few open-ended questions can yield insights into the role of price, the importance of ingredients, the effects of packages, and so on. In all cases, the researcher or field worker is there when the consumer or buyer behavior happens.[43]

The Portable People Meter, a pagerlike device that clips to consumer panel members, enhances observation research via another interesting use of technology. The device monitors the environment and takes note of audio channels of radio and television broadcasts. The PPM records the time and duration of exposure and transmits the data to Arbitron when returned each night to its charger base.[44]

Ethnographic research attempts to record how consumers actually use products, brands, and services in day-to-day activity. This form of direct observation, called *ethnography,* is based on techniques borrowed from sociology and anthropology. For example, a researcher may actually enter a consumer's home, observe consumption behavior, and record pantry and even garbage content, which can result in the collection of realistic data and richer descriptions of consumer behavior.[45]

One form of ethnographic research employs the use of pictures. Consumers are recruited to select pictures that convey their deeper feelings about a concept. This research, designed by Professor Jerry Zaltman of Harvard, is designed to help companies learn what consumers really want and to enhance the marketer's ability to develop campaigns that resonate with consumers on an emotional level. Selected individuals are asked to bring to the research site pictures that serve as metaphors for the deeper thoughts consumers have regarding a concept. This technique has been used successfully to assist Pittsburgh in promoting the arts and Kraft in designing foods for after work.[46]

The richness of explanation and unique perspectives possible from ethnographic research observation have helped some of the largest marketing firms. For example, Procter & Gamble placed cameras in 80 households in the United Kingdom, Italy, Germany, and China to record their daily habits. Best Western paid 25 over-55 couples to tape themselves in cross-country trips. After observing how 64 households balanced complicated schedules, 3Com designed an extremely compact electronic home organizer.[47]

Data Collection Instruments

The collection of marketing research information typically involves construction of a data collection instrument called a *survey* or *questionnaire*. Once a survey has been drafted, the instrument should be pretested on a representative sample and revised accordingly. The final instrument should consist of unambiguous, concise, and unbiased questions that respondents will be able and willing to answer.

Data collection instruments vary in structure. The degree of structure is influenced both by the research design (exploratory versus descriptive) and the method of data collection (focus group versus mail survey). Questions may take an open-ended, multiple choice, or scaled response format. Examples of questions and response formats are shown in Exhibit 6–6.

Exhibit 6–6	*Types of questions used in survey research*

Scaled

Likert agree-disagree

I favor the increased use of nuclear power. (Circle one)

Strongly   Agree   Neither agree   Disagree   Strongly
agree   nor disagree   disagree

Semantic differential

For me, tennis is . . .

Important _____ : _____ : _____ : _____ : _____ : Unimportant

Multichotomous (multiple choice)

Which of the following is the primary reason you selected our bank for your personal checking account?

_____ Location   _____ Service
_____ Interest rates _____ Other (Please specify)
_____ Reputation

Categorical

Which of the following categories includes your total income for 200x? (Please check)

_____ $30,000 and under
_____ $30,001–$35,000
_____ $35,001–$50,000
_____ $50,001–$65,000
_____ Over $65,000

Open-ended

What suggestions can you make to improve our service? _____

"Margaret, I want to know the real you...subject to a sampling error plus or minus three percentage points, of course.

Sampling and nonsampling errors may affect marketing research results. When even carefully selected probability samples do not exactly mirror the population, sampling error occurs. Nonsampling errors are due to such factors as interviewer bias, nonresponse bias, and improperly worded questions.

Errors in question design include at least five types:

- *Double-barreled wording:* "How would you rate the handling ability and gas economy of your new Toyota?" (very good, good, fair, poor, very poor)

- *Loaded wording:* "Given the growing rate of product recalls, how likely would you be to complain about problems with a new car purchase?" (likely, unlikely)

- *Ambiguous wording:* "Have you purchased a home appliance within the last six months?" (yes, no)

- *Inappropriate vocabulary:* "Do you feel the current discount rate is too high?" (yes, no)

- *Missing alternatives:* "Which of the following includes your age?" (25 and under, 26 to 49, and over 50)[48]

The emphasis on brand equity, marketing return on investment (ROI), and the long-term value of customers has increased both the importance of marketing research and the range/complexity of the types of variables and questions that market research now often addresses. A complete listing of all types of required measures is beyond the scope of this text and course. However, an ongoing program of research to assess marketing effort ROI would include measures of brand awareness, brand image, and customer satisfaction from current and potential customers. Measures related to transactions would include revenues per sale, transaction profitability, and costs per sale. Presale data would include initial response rates and leads generated from marketing communication programs. Ongoing measures would include customer retention rates and over time purchase data.[49]

Sample Design

The decisions and sequences involved in sampling are presented in Exhibit 6–7. The particular purpose of any research greatly influences the nature of the sampling process; of course, the population or group to be studied is determined by the issue of interest. If a wholesale bakery experiences declining product sales at the store level, it would want to sample individual purchasers and users of bakery products. Researchers might decide to sample household heads who regularly purchase bakery products.

Sampling saves money and time in that a smaller subgroup (or sample) is assumed to represent a larger population. Inferences from sample responses are then made to the population. The quality of these projections depends largely on how representative the sample is.

In B2B research situations, it will often be necessary to survey multiple informants within the organization. For example, senior executives are appropriate for strategic vision issues, while boundary personnel who interact directly with the firm's customers may answer questions tied to daily operations. In one study for a health care product marketer,

| **Exhibit 6–7** | *Sampling decisions and data collection issues* |

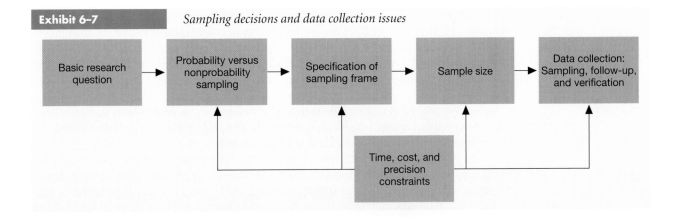

researchers surveyed both hospital physicians and administrators. Compiling appropriate sample lists of customers is surprisingly difficult in marketing research for business-to-business firms.[50]

PROBABILITY SAMPLING   In **probability sampling,** each person or unit in the population has a known, nonzero chance of being selected by some objective procedure. Probability samples are desirable because the use of an objective, unbiased selection technique enhances the representativeness of the sample. There are several probability sampling approaches. In *simple random sampling,* each unit has an equal chance of being selected, such as the use of a random number table to select phone numbers. *Stratified sampling* occurs when the population is divided into mutually exclusive groups, such as consumers with different income levels, and random samples are taken from each group. *Cluster sampling* consists of organizing units into smaller groups or clusters, such as similar neighborhoods or census tracts, then selecting clusters randomly and including each house in the selected clusters in the sample.

NONPROBABILITY SAMPLING   In **nonprobability sampling,** the selection of a sample is based on the judgment of the researcher or field worker. When funds or time are limited, or when only preliminary insight into a problem is needed, nonprobability samples may be appropriate. Nonprobability samples include convenience samples: for instance, the use of student samples in academic research; quota samples, in which a sample is selected to conform to some known distribution such as half female or 30 percent minority; and judgment samples, in which sample members are selected because researchers believe they bring some unique perspective to the research problem.

SAMPLING FRAME   Once the type of sample and the target population have been determined, the **sampling frame** is specified. The sampling frame is the outline or working description of the population used in sample selection. A frequently used sampling frame is the telephone book. For business-to-business marketing research, customer or firm lists might serve as the sampling frame. Today firms often purchase sample lists from companies that specialize in providing them. Care must be exercised in selecting a sampling frame (say, a telephone listing) to minimize the exclusion of relevant population members. For example, telephone directories do not include unlisted households and households without telephones.

SAMPLE SIZE   The desired **sample size** is based on a combination of factors: the anticipated response rate, the variability in the data, cost and time considerations, and the desired level of precision.

In practice, a sample size is often some even number (say, 500 or 1,000) large enough to give the user confidence in the results, on which he or she will base decisions. As a rule, researchers may benefit by taking smaller samples selected by more rigorous but possibly more expensive probability sampling procedures. That is, research users will be more confident in the representativeness of samples selected by some unbiased selection process.

RESPONSE RATES   A disturbing trend in the past quarter century has been the slow but steady decline in sample cooperation. A recent study by the Council for Marketing and Opinion Research (CMOR) estimated that 45 percent of consumers refused to participate in a survey. This estimate does not include the use of caller IDs and answering machines to avoid telephone surveys—factors that would have made the annual refusal rate estimate much higher.[51] The causes of this trend include an increase in the percentage of working women, the increase of telemarketing, and the spread of screening devices. High-quality samples will be possible only with greater cost and effort. The changes required to generate higher response rates will include increased compensation to respondents and interviewers, more contact attempts to locate respondents, and greater use of mixed modes of survey administration, including e-mail and Internet research.

The primary concern with nonresponse is the realization that nonrespondents differ from respondents in their opinions about the issues being studied and in their demographic composition. Hence it is necessary to contact a subset of nonrespondents so that findings can be adjusted. In addition, the computation of response rates is required and should be included in marketing research reports and summaries. For example, the response for a telephone survey can be computed as follows:

$$\text{Response rate} = \frac{\text{Number of complete from those contacted}}{\text{Number of complete} + \text{Number of refusals} + \text{Number of terminations}^{52}}$$

Fieldwork

Fieldwork is the process of contacting respondents, conducting interviews, and completing surveys. In the case of mail surveys, field workers must prepare mailing labels, develop introductory and follow-up letters, and carry out the mailings. Telephone surveys, personal interviews, and mall intercepts require the recruitment and training of interviewers to collect the data from the designated sample.

In many instances the data collection process, and perhaps data analysis, will be subcontracted out to a supplier or field service firm. That is, the actual interviews may be performed by a company that specializes in collecting marketing research data. Under these circumstances, the subcontractor supervises the data collection process and verifies the quality of the information collected. This should include verifying that the interviews were indeed conducted and that the responses to certain key questions are valid or correct.

Terry G. Vavra underscores the pitfalls of failing to monitor data collection fieldwork: "Although many research projects are well conceived and designed, all too frequently they fail where 'the rubber meets the road'—the fieldwork component. Much fieldwork is subcontracted to specialty fieldwork companies (such as telephone interviewing firms). As researchers look for cost efficiencies in conducting their fieldwork, they often rely on poorly trained and inadequately supervised field staffs. As you become involved in marketing research, monitor very carefully how your data are collected from respondents. Fieldwork is often the weakest link in the research process chain."

Analysis and Interpretation

There are a variety of techniques for analyzing marketing research data, ranging in complexity from straightforward frequency distributions, means, and percentages to complex multivariate statistical tests. Statistical analyses typically look at group differences (males versus females, users versus nonusers) or the strength of association between marketing variables (advertising and sales, prices and sales). The most frequently used statistical tests include those of mean differences (t-tests, analyses of variance) and correlation tests (chi-square cross-classification tests, Pearson correlations, regression).

The types of analysis to be performed on the data should be anticipated at the design stage so the appropriate data collection forms are developed. As a rule, managers prefer simple, understandable presentations of findings. Reports should focus on the original problem and objectives of the research.

Changing Technology

Technology has both positive and negative effects on the conduct of marketing research. As mentioned previously, scanner data and the ability to collect single-source data from households are dramatically affecting the research industry. On the positive side, the availability of computer-assisted telephone (CAT) interviewing has enhanced sampling, data entry, and data processing. Interviewers can read questions from a computer screen and record answers directly on the computer. This process results in instantaneously updating data. Moreover, WATS services have lowered the cost of telephone surveying. Yet technology has some negative effects on the use of telephone interviews too. Answering machines and voice-mail responses inhibit both consumer and business-to-business telephone research.[53] Call waiting also hampers the conduct of telephone surveys and is another factor contributing to the decline of telephone response rates. Sadly, the large increase in telephone sales calls and the difficulty of distinguishing between sales calls and survey research are the primary determinants of declining response rates.[54]

Technology is affecting other aspects of marketing research as well. For example, videoconferencing capabilities enable clients from a distance to monitor focus groups and provide the opportunity to involve more participants in observation. The savings from videoconferencing result because clients do not have to travel to locations to view focus group sessions. Breakthroughs in technology have also increased the potential for using faxes in survey research. Early research on survey effects suggests that fax surveys could make the administration of short questionnaires less expensive and faster than mail surveys. Likewise, e-mail offers the potential for increasing survey efficiency. Last, freestanding touch-screen computers at retail kiosks are now programmed to administer complicated surveys, show full-color images and video clips, and play stereo clips. With little need for instruction, in-store patrons freely use the interactive kiosks without reservation.[55]

International Considerations

Rote application of U.S. research practices to other countries is not likely to be appropriate. Firms operating globally must understand that cultural and economic differences between countries add a layer of complexity. One researcher identified eight common errors in conducting an international research project:[56]

1. *Selecting a domestic research company to do international research*—It is best to choose a company with experience in conducting global research.

2. *Rigidly standardizing methods across countries*—In certain countries, postal problems present unique difficulties; and in many countries, communications systems are inadequate for telephone interviews.

3. *Interviewing in English around the world*—Depth of responses is greatest when the local language is used.

4. *Implementing inappropriate sampling techniques*—Probability sampling designs are difficult to implement in many foreign countries.

5. *Failing to communicate effectively with local research companies*—Everything should be put in writing, and all deadlines should be specified exactly to avoid delays.

6. *Lack of consideration given to language*—For some research studies, measurement instruments should be "back translated" to ensure equivalence in meaning.

Conducting research across cultures can be difficult. International marketing researchers encounter such added problems as language differences, product use differences, and technological differences that limit data collection alternatives. This campaign for noise-insulated windows was based on an understanding of cultural concerns.

7. *Misinterpreting data across countries*—Cultural and ethnic differences can affect response, the meaning of concepts, and even responses to measurement scales. For example, Asians may use the midpoints of scales, whereas the English tend to understate responses.

8. *Failing to understand preferences of foreign researchers regarding the effective conduct of qualitative research*—For example, Europeans expect focus group moderators to have training in psychology; Asian mixed-sex group discussions do not yield useful information.

Conducting research using Japanese participants in particular requires some adjustment of American and European methods. Moderators or interviewers must repeatedly reassure Japanese respondents that negative statements are acceptable. Open-ended questions, lacking some illustration, will not elicit adequate responses from Japanese consumers. Nonverbal responses, such as body movement and facial expressions, often yield more information than will verbal answers.[57] Responses to scale items can vary across cultures as well. Three respondents, all equally likely to buy a product from a market test, may give different responses based on their interpretation of rating scales. Interpreting these meanings in global research can become even more difficult. For example, in a study of Brazilian and Japanese consumers, a "5" from a seven-point scale corresponded to 75 percent probability of purchase. For the Japanese data, a score of about 3.8 corresponded to a 75 percent probability of purchase.[58] One rule of thumb used by some research practitioners is that the farther north you go in the Americas, the more reserved consumers are in expressing their opinions. High scores are given in Latin America; in America, average scores are given; and in Canada, less favorable ratings are typical.[59]

Research in Latin America exemplifies many of the difficulties in conducting research across cultures and companies. Most companies in Latin America use nonprobability quota samples across income categories. In addition, only about 18 percent of the population has telephones, which further complicates the collection of data. Safety concerns and inaccessible rural areas also limit the effective collection of marketing research information.[60]

Evaluating Marketing Research

A research proposal is often developed prior to conducting a research study. These proposals outline the purpose of the research, the activities of the project, the costs and time constraints, and the likely implications or outcomes. The most important questions to ask in evaluating a research design prior to conducting research are presented in Exhibit 6–8.

Once a research project has been completed, the validity and reliability of the procedures used should be evaluated. **Validity** of questions on a survey refers to the extent to which the measures truly assess the concepts being studied. Consider the item, "I like BMW sedans." Results showing significant agreement with this statement would not be a valid measure of consumer opinions about purchase attitudes; rather, they would indicate an overall liking for the brand. **Reliability** reflects the consistency of responses or the extent to which measurement results are reproducible. A related validity issue, and important in determining the value of many research projects, is the concept of external validity. *External validity* reflects the extent to which the results from a research study can be generalized to other contexts, situations, and populations.[61]

| **Exhibit 6–8** | *Evaluating the research design* |

| Will the design provide information that addresses the research problem and needs of the decision maker? | → | Are the anticipated implications from the research actionable? | → | Will the value of the information justify the research cost? | → | Will the findings be limited by questions about the validity and generalizability of the results? | → | Are all aspects of the proposed research process and the use of the research ethically sound? |

As an example, firms should consider the following in efforts to increase the validity and benefits of their marketing research. First, study more than just your own firm's products. Competitive products should be studied as well to provide insights into likely consumer brand-switching behavior. Second, study the product and any associated services. Many consumer defections are caused by problems with service. Third, research should also ask about more than satisfaction. Questions about loyalty, for example, should be included in most research studies of consumer satisfaction.[62]

Ethical Issues in Marketing Research

Research ethics are increasingly debated. The American Marketing Association (AMA), the Advertising Research Foundation (ARF), and the Council of American Survey Research Organizations (CASRO) are collaborating on a code of ethics. Self-regulation among firms conducting research is increasingly being called for in efforts to improve the practice of marketing research. If these efforts are not successful, respondent cooperation will continue to erode.[63]

Thinking Critically

Much debate has centered on the ethical implications of using children in marketing research. Although companies such as Nickelodeon have successfully used various methods of gathering data from children, many people consider this unfair exploitation. Discuss whether you think marketing research involving children is ethical. Regardless of your opinion about the overall ethics of marketing research with children, describe a situation in which you feel marketing research with children would be acceptable.

Questionable tactics in marketing research that are frequently criticized include excessive interviewing, lack of consideration and abuse of respondents, and delivering sales pitches under the guise of marketing research.[64] The latter is particularly important for the research industry, as two-thirds of Americans consider survey research and telemarketing to be the same thing.[65] Legislation that now addresses only unsolicited commercial telephone calls could easily be extended to cover survey research.[66] Legislation already exists in most European Community nations that restricts the research industry by protecting privacy rights of consumers.

Ethical considerations are involved in researchers' relationships with all parties in the process, including respondents, the general public, and clients. First, marketers have the responsibility to treat respondents fairly by being candid about the nature and purposes of the research, by not using research as a sales ploy, and by not violating the confidentiality of respondents' answers. Researchers' obligations to the general public include being unintrusive, being considerate, and protecting the rights of privacy.

At the same time, researchers have a responsibility to gather accurate and reliable data for their clients.[67] Researchers should not manipulate findings to present a more favorable image of themselves or the firm. The significance of results should not be overstated. Questionable research practices, such as incomplete reporting of results, misleading reporting, and nonobjective research, can bring the integrity of the entire research process into question. For example, a cigarette ad once claimed that "an amazing 60 percent" of a sample said Triumph cigarettes tasted "as good as or better than Merit." Although this statement was technically correct, the results also indicated that 64 percent said Merit tasted as good as or better than Triumph, which was not reported to the public.[68]

Another issue is the subsequent use of data and the confidentiality of information collected for a client by a firm specializing in marketing research. Data collected for one client should not be made available to other clients.

Marketing Decision Support Systems (MDSS)

Glaxo Inc., a pharmaceutical maker in Research Triangle Park, North Carolina, spends about $2 million a year on its sales and marketing decision support system for hardware, software, user training, and personnel. Donald Rao, manager of market analysis and decision support at Glaxo, claimed a return on investment of 1,000 percent since the system's development in 1987. The system provides detailed data on physician locations within sales territories, which allows managers to fine-tune marketing plans and product sample allocations. In addition, it allows substantial savings in managerial time.[69]

Like Glaxo, many firms view all marketing data and information as part of a larger entity called a **marketing decision support system (MDSS).** All activities and computerized elements used to process information relevant to marketing decisions are components. These systems are now commonplace in many *Fortune* 500 business-to-business giants in industries such as airlines, banking, insurance, and pharmaceuticals.

Exhibit 6–9   *Marketing decision support system*

Marketplace
Social environment
Economic environment
Political/legal environment
Technological environment
Competitive environment
Institutional environment

→

Decision support system
Internal
Secondary data
Marketing research department
Marketing intelligence
External
Syndicated data
Nonproprietary secondary data
External marketing research

→
←

Managerial decision making and firm behavior

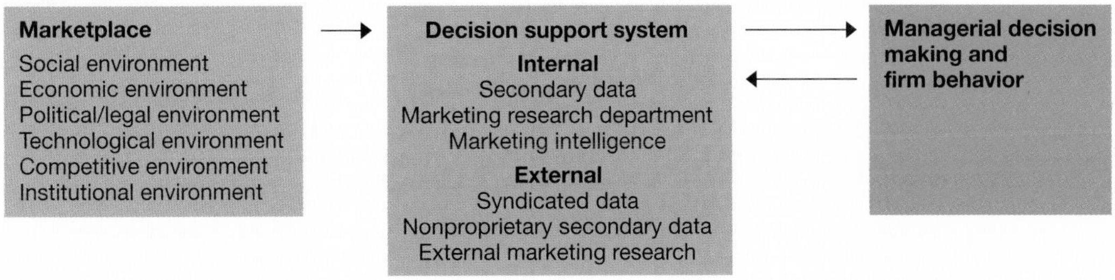

A schematic overview of an MDSS is shown in Exhibit 6–9. Such systems represent a comprehensive perspective allowing a combination of different sources of information from different departments. MDSSs are useful for both manufacturing and service companies.

Marketing decision support systems are generally designed to[70]

- Support but not supplant management decision making.

- Apply to semistructured decisions of middle and upper management, such as pricing, promotion, and location decisions.

- Provide interaction between and among people and systems.

- Center on a segment of related decisions (the allocation of marketing effort and resources).

- Be user-friendly.

An MDSS is designed to enhance managerial decision making and firm performance by providing relevant, timely internal and external information. Input comes from many sources: the economic environment, social trends and changing consumer tastes, and the legal environment. Data from consumers, customers, and competitors are relevant. Prior experiences and decisions are also fed back into the system. Even permanent links with customers are now included in some MDSSs. For example, a system linking Levi Strauss and Milliken, a textile manufacturer, significantly reduced costs for both companies and enabled Levi Strauss to respond to fashion changes and bring new products to market more quickly.[71]

External marketing research data may come from syndicated sources or various nonproprietary sources of secondary data. Syndicated market databases are useful for comparison with internal sales data to gauge market penetration. Internal data normally come from the marketing research department's own input, accounting records, and sales force reports. Amazon.com has an incredible database management system that generates internal research that the company uses in pricing and product decisions.

Computer technology now enables a variety of outputs from an MDSS. Output might include forecasts of sales, comparison of sales relative to forecasts, analysis of competitor performance, estimation of market potentials, evaluation of advertising effectiveness, and monitoring of consumer expectations and satisfaction. Some researchers predict that in the coming decades, a growing proportion of marketing decisions will be automated by ever more powerful combinations of data, models, and computers. As such, some aspects of marketing decision support systems will involve marketing decision *automation*. These changes will occur as firms condense their marketing activities into smaller units (individual stores, customers, and transactions). The resulting amount of data and numerous decision-making points can be more effectively handled by automated systems.[72]

Database Marketing

A significant technological innovation is **database marketing,** the collection and use of individual customer-specific information to make marketing more efficient. The term *database* refers to customer/prospect information stored in a computer with software to process the information. Computer technology provides the ability to pull apart and recombine information in ways previously impossible. Knowing which customers are predisposed to which products allows a firm to tailor marketing efforts to individual customers.

Database marketing can be instrumental in the success of companies' direct marketing efforts. In many cases, customers respond to such efforts by making orders and inquiries via toll-free phone numbers. Companies use marketing research principles in developing customer databases and analyzing the information obtained from customer responses to direct marketing efforts, such as telemarketing and direct mail. This information can enable a company to tailor individual messages at the customer level. Database marketing extends the traditional customer address list by including purchase records, demographics, psychographics, and information on media use. Note, however, that consumer advocates and government officials are increasingly raising ethical concerns about individual privacy as a result of the use of such data.

Data mining is defined as the process by which customer descriptions are derived from company databases by the use of analytical procedures that discover patterns with the company's own data sets. Harrah's casinos have used this process to increase service and rewards to profitable slot machine customers. As such, gaming machines now account for 80 percent of Harrah's profits, and the company is now second in the industry (behind only MGM). Information at the customer level on age, distance from home, gender, and the games played is accumulated through the cards used in the playing of slot machines. Direct marketing offers are then designed to reward the most profitable patrons and to encourage their return.[73]

One extension of the use of information at the customer level has been the evolution of **customer relationship management,** commonly referred to by marketers as **CRM.** The shift in emphasis to customer relationship management from a transaction orientation has been one of the significant developments in the practice of marketing. Linking research and CRM systems can be very beneficial to the marketer. To merge CRM and marketing research, organizations must create unified systems that hold information on customer characteristics and historical transaction data, as well as data that reflect consumer preference ratings, perceptions, and behavioral intentions. Use of this detailed customer information enables marketers to better understand the customer and to effectively target better-defined segments and even individual customers with tailored offers.[74]

Terry G. Vavra comments on the new emphasis on returns for marketing expenditures: "ROMI—return on marketing investments—is becoming a major criterion by which marketing efforts are being evaluated. Unfortunately for marketing research, most traditional directors of marketing research departments have taken the value of their departments as a given. They've failed to collect evidence documenting the contribution their department and their programs have made to organizations' performance. Lacking such evidence, CEOs are increasingly scrutinizing their MR budgets, assuming these are costs that can easily be cut for the sake of increasing momentary profitability. Unfortunately, as MR programs are downsized, businesses will learn the hard way of the difficulties of operating in informational vacuums. It's imperative that all marketing research professionals track the contributions of their programs to the performance of their employer and maintain records to justify their existence should their contributions come under question."

One important aspect of database marketing is the ability to evaluate return on investment (ROI) of marketing expenditures. By merging descriptive attitudinal data with behavioral purchase records, direct marketers can both target mailings and craft messages to their most profitable customers. The behavioral data can be used to estimate incremental purchases from a targeted campaign with certain estimated costs. Moreover, such information, as expected return on investment, can be used to argue for additional resources and support for marketing effort within the firm.[75]

With better targeting of prospects for products and promotions, database marketing clearly contributes to increased efficiency. When practiced properly, database marketing yields double-digit response rates, compared with 2 to 4 percent for "junk mail."

Database marketing involves the collection and use of individual customer-specific information.
Catalog companies now analyze individual customer purchase patterns to tailor their direct marketing
efforts.

For example, Hilton Hotels offers targeted promotions to senior citizens in its Senior
Honors program, prompting almost half of the members to take previously unplanned
trips that include stays at the Hilton.[76]

Last, the development and use of databases comprising information on individual customers raises ethical concerns regarding privacy. First, marketers must thus continue to
work at self-regulation regarding privacy protection. Second, it should be noted that firms
that build their databases from within, as opposed to purchasing lists from other sources,
are able to maintain the privacy of their customers. Third, customer permission and notification should be regularly sought. And fourth, firms should take into consideration that
customers generally want firms to reduce the volume of catalog and advertising mail while
simultaneously increasing the relevance of that information.[77]

Summary

1. **Understand the purpose and functions of marketing research.** The function of marketing research is to generate information that assists the firm's managers in making decisions. Marketing research helps managers respond to the ever-changing environment in which businesses operate. It is useful in problem solving, planning for the future, and controlling or monitoring ongoing performance. Marketing research links the marketer, the customer, and the public through information used to: identify and define marketing opportunities; generate, refine, and evaluate marketing actions; monitor marketing performance; and improve understanding of marketing as a process.

2. **Be familiar with the stages of the marketing research process.** There are six stages of the marketing research process, through which primary data are generated to address a specific marketing problem or issue. In the first stage, problem definition, both the researcher and the user develop a clear conception of the problem that the research is intended to address.

   The second stage is specification of the appropriate research design, which is then used in the third stage, determination of the types of data to be collected and the methods of collection.

   In the fourth stage researchers develop a data collection form, often a survey or questionnaire. In the fifth stage researchers design the sample, specifying the fieldwork required to collect the data. Finally, the data collected are analyzed, summarized, and presented to the users or firm management.

3. **Discuss different types of research designs, data collection methods, and sources of secondary and primary marketing research data.** Exploratory research designs are used to obtain general familiarity with a topic or problem. Focus groups, literature reviews, case analyses, interviews with knowledgeable individuals, and convenience sampling are examples of exploratory research.

   Descriptive designs are typically guided by some specific research question or hypothesis. Cross-sectional designs involve surveys administered at a given time. Longitudinal designs examine research questions over time through repeated measures of a common sample. Causal designs involve experiments, in which researchers manipulate independent variables of interest, such as price or advertising.

   Marketing data can be primary or secondary. Secondary data may be either internal, coming from within the firm, or external. External secondary data may be either nonproprietary (noncommercial) or proprietary.

4. **Understand many of the major issues involved with survey design and sampling.** Each survey method has advantages and disadvantages. The different survey methods include telephone interviews, mail questionnaires, personal interviews, and mall intercepts. Researchers must carefully construct items or questions in a survey to ensure that the data collected are reliable (yield consistent responses) and valid (reflect the concepts being studied).

   Researchers can use probability or nonprobability samples, depending on the objectives, characteristics, and budget of the research. Probability samples are selected by some objective, unbiased process. Simple random samples are the most typical example.

   To assemble a nonprobability sample, the judgment of the researcher enters into the selection. Examples of nonprobability samples are convenience samples and quota samples. The researcher must decide on the population to be sampled, the sample size, and the sampling frame.

5. **Appreciate the role of marketing research within decision support systems.** Within the firm, the marketing decision support system (MDSS) consists of all activities and the hardware and software regularly used to process and provide marketing information relevant to marketing decisions. The firm may also employ outside agencies to provide marketing input.

Understanding Marketing Terms and Concepts

Thinking about Marketing

1. How might a clothes manufacturer employ focus groups in its search for what is "cool"? Would observation be a better approach?

2. What is the purpose of marketing research? What are the primary stages of the marketing research process?

3. Explain differences among exploratory, descriptive, and causal designs, and give examples of each.

4. Differentiate these pairs of concepts:
   a. Cross-sectional versus longitudinal designs.
   b. Secondary versus primary data.
   c. Field market tests versus simulated market tests.

5. Describe the primary advantages and disadvantages of mail surveys, telephone interviews, personal interviews, and mall intercepts. What advantages are offered by virtual shopping technology over simulated test markets?

6. What are the different types of probability and nonprobability samples? Give examples of each.

7. What is the difference between projective techniques and observation research? What is ethnographic observation?

8. What factors determine sample size? What is involved in fieldwork?

9. What is an MDSS? Describe its primary advantages.

10. Identify three ethical issues in marketing research. Cite some concerns faced by firms conducting marketing research.

11. What are some of the emerging environmental factors that are affecting the role of and techniques used for marketing research? How can marketing researchers successfully adapt to these changes?

12. Describe the specific concerns and mistakes companies often make when conducting international marketing research.

13. How are marketing research designs and the results obtained from data collection evaluated?

Applying Marketing Skills

1. Develop a sampling plan to conduct a telephone survey of residents in the county where your university is located. Assume you want to investigate opinions about the construction of a nuclear power plant in a nearby county. Who should be interviewed? How will the sample be drawn?

2. A manufacturer of roller blades is interested in assessing the satisfaction of its retailer customers. What are the advantages and disadvantages of the alternative data collection methods in gathering customer satisfaction data for the firm?

3. Suppose you were considering selling a new personal data assistant (PDA) that was designed specifically for university students. To ensure that you are successful, it would be necessary to determine the student makeup of the university, whether the students would be willing to buy the PDA, and how best to inform the

students about the product. What types of marketing information would you need to consult? Where would you obtain this information? What information would be available only through primary data collection, and how would you collect it?

4. Research Incorporated, a regional marketing research firm that does tailored primary research projects in California, has been contacted by ABC Company for what appears to be a very profitable research project involving the demand for catalog shopping services. Research Incorporated recently completed a similar project for XYZ Company, a competitor of ABC. Both ABC and XYZ are large retail discount chains with over 50 stores in the Southwest. Should Research Incorporated accept the project? Should the information obtained for XYZ be given or sold to ABC?

Using the www in Marketing

Activity One This chapter is organized around a description of the marketing research process. Consider this explanation as you access the IMS Health site.

1. IMS Health is one of the world's largest research firms. What can be learned about information on the Internet as a source of secondary data?

2. What services does IMS offer regarding data for its prescription drugs?

Activity Two Consider the Web site of TNS NFO.

1. What services and products are offered by the company?

2. Do its information services represent primary or secondary data?

3. What kinds of companies could make the best use of the information this company provides?

Making Marketing Decisions

Case 6–1 *Bayer: Aleve and the Road to Recovery*

Bayer inherited the poorly performing Aleve pain reliever from Procter & Gamble in 1996. The brand had never achieved more than a 6 percent market share. Later, the Bayer team hired CLT Research Associates to conduct 800 in-home interviews, a random sample of men and women ages 18 to 75, who had used a nonprescription pain reliever in the last year. CLT discovered that 24 percent of the sample were "pain busters"—consumers who are heavy users of pain relievers. Additional research was conducted to identify the various statements about Aleve that could be used to convince this segment to buy Aleve. Bayer managers also analyzed data from Medioscope—a syndicated source for OTC drug data—Nielsen Panel data, and Simmons, as well as information from focus groups.

Subsequently, BBDO designed Aleve's "Dramatic Difference" campaign that was successful in substantially raising sales and brand aided and unaided recall. New campaigns emphasize the need for only two dosages all day long. Empowering consumers to rid themselves of pain seems to have been just the medicine Aleve needed.

Aleve is presently number three in market share, with $145 million in sales in the $2 billion analgesic tablet category. Tylenol dominates the category with sales of $541 million. In a shift of advertising strategy, Bayer Inc., the parent company, now promotes Aleve's brand origin as a prescription pain reliever that provides long-lasting relief rather than comparing it directly to other over-the-counter competitors.

Questions

1. How do different types of research complement each other in diagnosing brand problems?

2. What types of research are needed to monitor Aleve's performance in today's marketplace? What role does repeat purchase play in the brand's success?

3. What types of research might be conducted in efforts to develop strategies for improving market share relative to Tylenol?

Case 6–2 *Adidas: Running Risks*

 In the pursuit of leadership in the sporting goods industry, the German-based Adidas-Saloman continually focuses on building its brands. Its segments of interest include performance athletes, lifestyle consumers, fashion-conscious consumers, and freestyle athletes. The company's objective is to anticipate and fulfill consumer needs and desires in the pursuit of building powerful brands. In 2004 the company realized net sales and gross profits of $6.5 billion and $3.0 billion, respectively. The company employs over 17,000 workers and is truly a global corporation.

The extensive, varied marketing efforts of Adidas provide a unique opportunity for the use of marketing research. For example, the company has introduced a $250 high-tech shoe, Adidas 1, which contains a sensor that adjusts cushioning for different surfaces. The company believes the technology could be its iPod, eventually being included in its soccer and basketball shoes and demanded by all youth. The hope is that the innovative shoe will enhance the ability of Adidas to compete more effectively against Nike and Reebok. Its strategy is to introduce the technology into high-priced models to establish credibility before incorporating the technology into lower-priced shoes. The question remains, however: Will consumers pay $250 for a shoe?

Adidas has also gained permission to outfit the Chinese 2008 Beijing Olympics team. This noteworthy achievement is being focused on in a nationwide campaign in China driven largely by public relations events. In addition, the sports brand, which has 1,300 own-branded stores, has decided to expand to 4,000 stores as part of an aggressive growth strategy. In addition, Adidas has partnered with Goodyear. The tire company used its Eagle F1 tire treads to inspire designs for Adidas's trendy Tuscany shoes.

Questions

1. What role might marketing research play in helping the company evaluate these diverse marketing efforts and the development of new products?

2. How will consumers value the technological advantage embodied in the Adidas 1 shoe?

3. How might cultural phenomena affect the nature of any research that might be proposed to evaluate new brand acceptance?

4. What types of studies might be conducted to determine price elasticity for its new shoe brands?

Chapter Seven

MARKET SEGMENTATION AND TARGETING

After studying this chapter, you should be able to

1 Define and explain market segmentation, target markets, and product differentiation and positioning.

2 Understand the criteria used for evaluating the likely success of a segmentation strategy.

3 Know the role of market segmentation in the development of marketing strategies and programs.

4 Describe the issues involved in product and brand positioning.

5 Understand the alternative bases for segmenting consumer and business-to-business markets.

6 Evaluate alternative approaches for pursuing segmentation strategies.

Acxiom

Acxiom is a world leader in consumer information and information management. The company offers its clients the ability to effectively analyze their customer base. As such, Acxiom enhances the capability of firms to pursue customer relationship management objectives and to strengthen overall their own customer relationships. As the company's Web site states, Acxiom makes it easy for firms to keep their best customers by building knowledge about what customers like and how best to communicate with them.

This increased understanding of customers' needs and preferences assists greatly in the development of market segmentation strategies—the topic of this chapter.

The publicly traded company is the world's largest processor of consumer data, and its customers include the top credit card issuers, as well as many major retail banks, insurance companies, and automakers.

Acxiom's current information resources enable companies to develop in-depth profiles of their customers and to design marketing programs for efficiently reaching profitable target market segments. Of note, the future is bright. In addition to Acxiom's presence in the United States, the company is expanding in Europe and Asia. Moreover, Acxiom is often listed as one of the best companies to work for and is frequently cited as a leader in protecting the privacy of consumers.

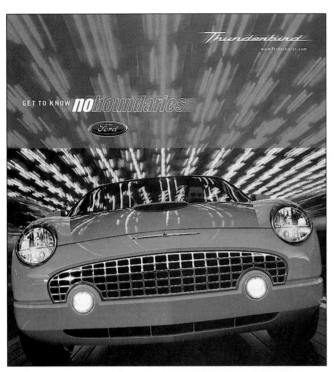

Market segmentation involves identifying market segments that will respond differently to varying marketing mix combinations. Ford offers products and communications designed to appeal to car buyer segments formed on the basis of desired end benefits.

Market segmentation is among the most popular and important topics in the entire field of marketing. Market segmentation is consistent with the marketing concept and enhances a firm's ability to understand its core customers or who its core customers will be in the future. As such, segmentation helps the marketer identify important consumption patterns. Furthermore, market segmentation strategies are necessary both for consumer goods and services marketers and for firms operating in business-to-business markets. Segmentation starts with the notion that a company is not able to be all things to all customers. Customers must be treated differently based on the firm's knowing what a customer wants and its ability to profitability deliver those needs.[1]

In this chapter we explore the concept of market segmentation and how firms develop their market segmentation strategies. We define target markets and product differentiation and positioning, and we discuss the stages involved in developing a segmentation strategy.

Market Segmentation, Target Markets, and Product Differentiation

Mass markets and widespread brand loyalty, once taken for granted in business, have given way today to market segments of widely varying tastes, needs, and sensitivity to competing products. The emergence of these fragmented markets, new economic demands, changing technology, and intense international competition have altered the ways firms compete. The presence of increased information about customers and buying patterns (from studying everything from loyalty program data to cheap Internet surveys) and the availability of more sophisticated analytical procedures have enhanced the ability of firms to target specific, profitable market segments with tailored and attractive marketing mix combinations.[2]

In this section we distinguish between market segmentation, target markets, and product differentiation. Throughout the section and the chapter, issues related to market segments, target segments, and targeting are discussed. Although similar terms, these reflect different concepts. Briefly, *market segments* are groups of prospective customers who share similar needs and wants. No firm can operate in every market and satisfy every need, nor can firms operate effectively within very broadly defined markets. Thus *target segments* represent those groups the firm selects to focus on with separate marketing mixes. *Targeting* then involves selecting market segments to emphasize and designing efforts to appeal to the unique differences and motivations that define those selected segments.

Market Segmentation

Firms often pursue a market segmentation approach to meet today's market realities. As discussed in Chapter 1, a market is a group of consumers or organizations with which a firm desires to create marketing exchanges. **Market segmentation** divides a market into subsets of prospective customers who behave in the same way, have similar wants, or have similar characteristics that relate to purchase behavior. The overall market for a product consists of segments of customers who vary in their responses to different marketing mix offerings.

Market segmentation attempts to explain differences among groups of consumers who share similar characteristics and to turn these differences into an advantage.[3] As such, marketing effectiveness is enhanced by an understanding of who the firm's best customers are, what's on their minds, where and how they can be reached, and what they are buying.

A segmentation strategy can be pursued through variations in some or all aspects (product, marketing communications, price, distribution) of the marketing mix elements. For example, many widely purchased products such as soft drinks, computers, and clothing involve variation in both product and marketing communications to reach market segments and increase sales. In other instances, a single product may be marketed to different segments using different marketing communication campaigns. For example, a pharmaceutical manufacturer may promote the same new drug product to physicians, pharmacists, and hospitals using a different communication program for each. Sheraton's loyalty programs, costing up to $50 million annually, are based on the data-based segmentation scheme comprising business travelers and leisure guests.[4] Young men and mothers are two key segments that McDonald's has made a focus.[5]

A number of factors are making understanding market segmentation more important:

- Slower rates of market growth, coupled with increased foreign competition, have fostered more competition, increasing the need to identify target markets with unique needs.

- Social and economic forces, including expanding media, increased educational levels, and general world awareness, have produced customers with more varied and sophisticated needs, tastes, and lifestyles.

- Technological advances make it possible for marketers to devise marketing programs that focus efficiently on precisely defined segments of the market.[6]

- Marketers now find that minority buyers do not necessarily adopt the social and economic habits of the mainstream. For example, many Hispanics speak both Spanish and English and retain much of their culture even as they adapt to U.S. lifestyles, while many others remain in Spanish-speaking enclaves in Hispanic states like Texas and California.[7]

- Roughly 4 in 10 residents in the United States identify with some segment or niche group that does not reflect the white, heterosexual consumer that historically defined the marketing mainstream.[8]

Market segmentation is appropriate not just for firms marketing tangible products; nonprofit and service organizations also find it useful. For example, realizing that it had many different types of donors and volunteers, the Arthritis Foundation looked for an effective way to reach the right person, at the right time, with the proper request amount, and with the right message. To address the diversity in possible donors and volunteers, the foundation identified 12 categories of individual households defined by location, housing type, and income. The foundation found the segment labeled "urban gentry" (upper-income city dwellers) four times more likely than any other group to contribute both money and time.[9]

International marketing may be based on the cultivation of **intermarket segments,** which are well-defined, similar clusters of customers across national boundaries. This view of segmentation allows firms to develop marketing programs and offerings for each identified segment on a global basis.[10] Reliance on a single standardized global strategy can cause a firm to miss important target markets or to position products inappropriately. Similarly, customizing marketing strategy only to individual countries may result in a firm's losing either potential economies of scale or opportunities for exploiting product ideas on a wider scale.[11]

Some consumer product businesses, such as McDonald's, Coca-Cola, and Colgate-Palmolive, use globally standardized products and marketing themes for some of their products. For most consumer products and brands, however, international marketing benefits from segmentation principles. In these instances, customized strategies may be developed for different countries or groups of countries. One recent study of soap and toothpaste preferences, for example, revealed four segments across consumers in the United States, Mexico, the Netherlands, Turkey, Thailand, and Saudi Arabia. The largest segment comprised substantial numbers of consumers from Saudi Arabia, Mexico, and the Netherlands. These people all shared preferences for selected product benefits.

Speaking from Experience

Christine Dickhans
Assistant Visual Merchandiser
Hanes

"Hanes has sold over 1 billion T-shirts, underwear, and socks to consumers around the world, so understanding different consumer needs is essential. It is imperative for Hanes to know what different consumer segments are looking for in its product mix, and also to know what each segment is looking to get out of the product once it is bought.

As such, Hanes develops in-depth profiles of consumer segments so that we can better serve their needs. Through AIO statements used in marketing research, Hanes found that the typical consumer wants to find a high-quality T-shirt but does not want to pay midtier prices and prefers not to search extensively. We have found that our consumers are not only price conscious but also time conscious. Usually this consumer is a busy mom trying to shop not only for herself but for everyone in the family."

Christine Dickhans, Assistant Visual Merchandiser, earned a bachelor of science degree in marketing from the University of South Carolina and now works for the Hanes Division of Sara Lee Branded Apparel—Americas, in Winston-Salem, North Carolina.

Many international marketers believe that teenagers represent the first truly global segment. Teens worldwide show remarkably similar attitudes and preferences. There are similarities in the way teens look and the consumption patterns they exhibit. The emergence of this common ground will make marketing to this global segment more efficient. However, companies must still acknowledge subtle differences in culture and national preferences, particularly in the advertising messages used to promote nonlocal brands.

India has a very heterogeneous population, but the mere size of the market is attractive to consumer goods marketers. With a population exceeding 1 billion, the potential demand is obvious. Consumer goods marketers like Pizza Hut, Kentucky Fried Chicken,

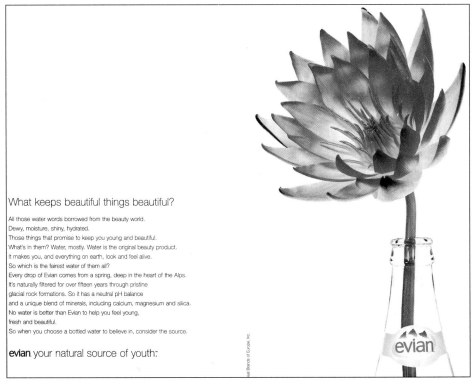

What keeps beautiful things beautiful?

All those water words borrowed from the beauty world.
Dewy, moisture, shiny, hydrated.
Those things that promise to keep you young and beautiful.
What's in them? Water, mostly. Water is the original beauty product.
It makes you, and everything on earth, look and feel alive.
So which is the fairest water of them all?
Every drop of Evian comes from a spring, deep in the heart of the Alps.
It's naturally filtered for over fifteen years through pristine
glacial rock formations. So it has a neutral pH balance
and a unique blend of minerals, including calcium, magnesium and silica.
No water is better than Evian to help you feel young,
fresh and beautiful.
So when you choose a bottled water to believe in, consider the source.

evian your natural source of youth:

Evian's multinational campaign recognizes the existence of segments across country lines. The ads are included in women's magazines in Switzerland, Japan, France, Spain, Singapore, Italy, Austria, Hong Kong, Germany, the United Kingdom, and the United States.

Honda, and General Motors have simplified their strategies by focusing on the middle-class segment of the 250 million well-educated, Westernized residents of the largest cities.[12]

Target Markets

Market segmentation lets a firm tailor or develop products and strategies to appeal to the preferences and unique needs of specific groups of customers. These groups are typically referred to as *target markets:* groups of consumers or organizations with whom a firm wants to create marketing exchanges.[13] Examples include the elderly, the Hispanic, or the college student markets, each of which can be targeted for specific products and reached through specific marketing programs. **Targeting** involves selecting which segments in a market are appropriate to focus on and designing the means of reaching them. Appealing to an entire market is often too costly. Moreover, a focus on certain markets can increase the efficiency and effectiveness of marketing efforts. However, a firm should target only those markets it can effectively reach and serve. Finely defined segments with their own marketing mix strategies should be justified only on a return-on-investment evaluation.

For example, targeting Hispanic markets requires an in-depth approach. Geico first encountered difficulties in one of its Web sites by converting the site to Spanish without corresponding language use in messages sent in reply to Web site interactions. Lead sales and service were disappointing and reduced the impact of the insurance company's initial targeting efforts.[14] In the airline industry, multiple segments exist within the segment of fliers that accounts for a large percentage of flights taken. One segment routinely pays full fares due to last-minute arrangements. Another segment systematically plans in advance and takes advantage of loyalty programs.[15]

As we will see later in this chapter, segmentation may be appropriate for businesses of all sizes, not just for large firms with many products. Many small- and medium-sized companies find it better to concentrate on gaining a large share of one segment or a few, rather than small shares of all possible segments in a product market. For example, Liberty Bank of Philadelphia generates profit from a market segment overlooked by many of its competitors: small businesses.

Product Differentiation

Related to market segmentation is **product differentiation.** Product differentiation exists when a firm's offerings differ or are perceived to differ from those of competing firms on any attribute, including price. A product differentiation strategy positions a product within the market. Marketers attempt to position a product or service in customers' minds—to convince customers the product has unique and desirable characteristics. By developing these perceptions, marketers seek to establish a competitive advantage relative to competing firms that offer similar products or brands.

In the mid-1980s, for example, brands in the frozen entrée market were differentiated on convenience, and consumers traded taste for that convenience. Stouffer's changed that balance by introducing a line of entrées positioned on taste but offered at a premium price. By focusing on a key benefit previously missing from other frozen dinners, Stouffer's expanded the market and became the category leader. Product differentiation and positioning are explained in more detail later in this chapter.

From Mass Marketing to Mass Customization   Among the most notable changes in this century has been the shift from mass marketing to **mass customization.** Companies like Dell Computers have proved that complex manufactured products can be made to order. Now companies throughout the world have embraced mass customization in an attempt to satisfy the diverse needs of their customers and to provide unique value. The concept is made possible by advances in manufacturing and information technology that enable firms to provide product variety and customization through flexibility and quick responsiveness.

Various approaches have been used, and these approaches can range in the extent to which interactions with customers occur. "Collaborative customizers" conduct direct dialogue with customers to determine their needs and to identify the precise offering that is required to satisfy those needs. Other firms only package the offering individually in what is termed "cosmetic customization." The National Bicycle Company of Japan serves both ends of the mass market to mass customization continuum by operating two separate manufacturing facilities. The mass production facility caters to its large market segment and is organized around traditional production facility efficiency. The mass custom bicycle plant is directly linked to retail outlets where customers can choose from 8 million possible variations.[16]

One summary of the possibilities describes the alternatives as follows. At the least specific level, mass marketing involves the company offering a standard product to markets worldwide, such as Diet Coke. Companies that practice target marketing focus on niches in the market. Godiva Chocolate is directed at a more focused market comprising consumers with specific tastes. Sometimes companies focus on market cells, many more in number and varied in description than typical larger target markets. As explained in Chapter 6, these cells are derived from company databases through the process of data mining, which uses sophisticated analytical and statistical procedures to discover interesting patterns within company data sets. Data mining enabled Capital One to market 7,000 different MasterCard and Visa variations.

In developing mass customization strategies, firms face a number of challenges. These potential problems include obtaining information from customers, identifying the tangible and intangible factors that are important to each customer, dealing with higher customer expectations, limiting the complexity of options to a reasonable number, and pricing customized offerings.[17]

When Is Market Segmentation Appropriate?   Market segmentation can be useful for both new ventures and mature brands. In the case of new products, marketers target segments likely to respond positively to the introduction. Products that have been on the market for a while face an increasing number of competitive offerings, making it more difficult for any mass marketer to dominate in its product categories. Some frequently used approaches include developing brand line extensions, repositioning the product for additional uses, or identifying the needs of a particular segment, or segments, and developing marketing strategies for each.[18]

The frozen entrée category again provides an example of a combined approach. Once Stouffer's successfully introduced its line of frozen entrées, the competitors came running. Stouffer's built on its success by extending its product line, tapping another key segment in the marketplace: the weight-conscious consumer. Stouffer's Lean Cuisine frozen entrées offered this segment low-calorie, tasty meals and the convenience of quick preparation. The frozen entrée category continues to be one of the most competitive in the grocery store, but Stouffer's maintains dominance through its target marketing approach.

A market segmentation strategy is not always appropriate, however. Advertising and marketing research practitioners suggest segmentation may not be useful when the overall market is so small that marketing to a portion of it is not profitable, or when the brand is dominant in the market and draws its appeal from all segments.[19] Segmentation strategies fail most often when firms target consumers on the basis of simple demographics, or in the case of B2B marketing, "firmographics," yet the segments do not buy different products or respond differently to alternative marketing communications. Segmentation built around income differences, for example, can easily result in a direct mail list. The problem is that simple demographics may not correlate well with customer behavior.[20]

Criteria for Effective Segmentation

Successful execution of a market segmentation strategy depends on the presence of several characteristics in the overall market and its various segments. In determining strategies to pursue, marketers should judge potential segments against five criteria: measurability, accessibility, substantialness, durability, and differential responsiveness.

Hispanic Americans represent a substantial and responsive demographic segment. Telefutura makes effective use of market segmentation by targeting this growing, lucrative consumer segment.

MEASURABILITY   **Measurability** reflects the degree to which the size and purchasing power of segments can be assessed. Measurability is enhanced if segments are defined by concrete variables enabling easily obtainable data. Demographic characteristics, such as income and age, are examples. Firms can use such data to reach segments and to estimate the size and potential of target markets. Marketers recognize that the age of the populations of advanced Western economies is changing. Data from the European Commission indicate that around 30 percent of the population in many countries is over age 65. Estimates of the percentage over 65 in 2050 are Italy and Spain—70 percent, Germany—57 percent, France—53 percent, and Britain—49 percent.[21]

ACCESSIBILITY   **Accessibility** describes the degree to which a firm can reach intended target segments efficiently. That is, the selected market segments must be reachable with unique marketing communications and distribution strategies. The Hispanic market is an example of a growing segment that can be reached by specific media (newspapers, radio, television). The growth of cable and satellite television programs for targeted audiences gives advertisers the opportunity to access in-language television audiences. In another example, previously successful albums now available on CDs, such as Led Zeppelin albums, are marketed to middle-aged consumers by ads on the cable channels ESPN and Arts and Entertainment.[22] Accessibility relates to the communication channels used by buyers. To understand customer communication characteristics, sometimes referred to as "infographics," marketers should consider three questions: Where do customers go for information? How do they like to communicate? And how do they prefer to buy?[23]

SUBSTANTIALNESS   **Substantialness** refers to the degree to which identified target segments are large enough or have sufficient sales and profit potential to warrant unique or separate marketing programs. The growing Hispanic population is a sizable market that merits specifically designed products, advertising campaigns, and even distribution approaches. The 2000 census shows that Asian Americans are the fastest-growing racial group. Regarding segmentation and buying power, Asians have the highest education level and household income, own expensive homes, and are among the most tech-savvy.[24] Substantial buying power and continuing growth have influenced companies to reach out to

Market segments are often defined in terms of price sensitivity. Hartmarx Corporation offers multiple product lines to various price-sensitive segments. These offerings include Hart Schaffner & Marx and Hickey-Freeman, the latter of which appeals to the more price-conscious segment.

six segments of Asians (Chinese, Filipinos, Indians, Vietnamese, Koreans, and Japanese) using predominantly four strategies: language-specific promotions, grassroots marketing, Asian television ads and programs, and Web site innovations. For example, Allstate has launched a Web site called w*ww.Chinese.Allstate.com* for Chinese consumers to learn about Allstate in their native language.[25]

DURABILITY   **Durability** has to do with stability of segments—whether distinctions between segments will diminish or disappear as the product category or the markets themselves mature.[26] The development of differentiated products, communication campaigns, or distribution strategies often involves considerable financial and time commitments. Segments selected for targeting should offer reasonably enduring business opportunities. The Hispanic market meets this criterion, as it is a significant and, perhaps more important, a growing segment of the population. Current population trends indicate the Hispanic population will be a key segment for marketers for many years to come. Another is the aging U.S. population. This segment is ripe for targeting products and services oriented toward health and conservation of income.

DIFFERENTIAL RESPONSIVENESS   **Differential responsiveness** refers to the extent to which market segments exhibit different responses to different marketing mixes.[27] If segments do not respond differently to varying marketing communications or product offerings, there is little need to segment. People interested in price will respond differently to low prices than people who seek high quality and assume price and quality are related.

Hartmarx Corporation provides a good example of the way a manufacturer segments target markets by price sensitivity. Hartmarx, a national producer and marketer of men's and women's fashions, developed brands and strategies to fill unique market voids.[28] Once Hartmarx acknowledges that different groups of consumers are sensitive to different price levels, it designs marketing strategies to differentiate variations in product (quality), communications (types of ads), and distribution (types of retail outlets). For example, the company targets Hart Schaffner & Marx to the upscale segment. Jaymar dress slacks and Sansabelt slacks are sold to the moderate segment. Kuppenheimer Men's Clothiers and Allyn St. George are included in the popular value offerings. Each brand name provides a product designed for different price-sensitive segments. Exhibit 7–1 is an example of how a retailer might segment men's clothing by price range.

Satisfying the Segmentation Criteria

By satisfying these various criteria, a company can choose market segments that can be described in managerially useful terms (measurability); that can utilize its communication and distribution channels (accessibility); that are sufficient in profit potential (substantialness); that will persist for some reasonable period (durability); and that vary in their reactions to different marketing efforts (differential responsiveness).

The Hispanic market provides a good example of combining segmentation criteria to evaluate a market. Although there are subsegments within it, the overall Hispanic market possesses unique cultural characteristics that make it an attractive target segment. The unique language and cultural characteristics of this market clearly make the segment measurable and responsive to appeals designed directly for it. Hispanic Americans accounted for over one-fourth of the population by the end of 2000; the market thus represents both a

| Exhibit 7–1 | *Hypothetical retail market segments and price points* |

Retail Market Segments	Business Clothing			Furnishings		Casual Wear	
	Suits	Jackets	Dress Slacks	Dress Shirts	Neckties	Sport Shirts	Casual Slacks
Upscale	$600 & over	$475 & over	$150 & over	$55 & over	$45 & over	$47.50 & over	$95 & over
Upscale moderate	$450–$600	$350–$475	$100–$150	$39.50–$55	$37.50–$45	$37.50–$47.50	$65–$95
Moderate	$375–$450	$250–$350	$75–$100	$30–$39.50	$25–$37.50	$32.50–$37.50	$45–$65
Value conscious	Under $375	Under $250	Under $75	Under $30	Under $25	Under $32.50	Under $45

substantial and durable opportunity. The market is also accessible—both broadcast (radio, television) and print (newspapers, magazines) media reach the Hispanic community efficiently with specialized ads.

Wal-Mart, Sears, McDonald's, Ford, General Motors, and PepsiCo target Mexico for expanded export and local operations. McDonald's earmarked $500 million to open 250 new restaurants in Mexico, and relaxed trade restrictions have opened opportunities for Ford and GM to export luxury automobile models.[29] By 2010, one in five teens will be Hispanic. While all young consumers are hard to reach with their ever-growing assortment of media channels, Hispanic youth are even more difficult to target. Unlike their non-Hispanic counterparts, many Hispanic youth are bilingual and have access to another set of media. Previously, Spanish-language media were sufficient for marketing to Hispanic adults.[30]

In fact, ethnic commonalities make marketing in native languages to subcultures within countries worldwide, particularly in the United States, worthwhile. For example, the purchasing power of Arab, Asian, Hispanic, Russian, Eastern European, African, and Caribbean immigrants in the United States is now over $400 billion. Cultural differences exist within countries, and businesses that market to other countries should recognize segment differences. Like India, China has a very large population, and firms look at China as having a 1.3 billion-plus population. However, the most important market for a lot of products is the 200–250 million middle-class, urban residents in the major cities along China's east coast.[31]

Stages in Developing Market Segmentation Strategies

Stages required in the development of a market segmentation strategy are summarized in Exhibit 7–2. The organization's core business determines the product or service market in which it operates, be it the restaurant industry, computer software, lawnmowers, cleaning services for office buildings, or whatever. Given its overall product or service market, a firm identifies the distinguishing characteristics, or **bases of segmentation,** for the segments within that market. After describing these segments, the firm evaluates them for potential and likely success, then selects the key segment or segments to target. Finally, the firm develops marketing mix strategies, including various product and service forms, and price and distribution strategies and communication appeals for each segment.[32]

Bases for Segmentation

Logical bases to define market segments have to do with characteristics of the firm's customers or their behaviors. Exhibit 7–3 describes some of these bases for both consumer and business-to-business marketing situations.[33] The Levi Strauss strategy uses some of the most easily identified consumer segmentation bases, including age, race, and gender. Brand-loyalty segments and the heavy-user segment are among the most important and now are the focus of many customer retention efforts. For business-to-business marketing, computer companies provide an example. They frequently organize their selling efforts around different industries, such as banking, insurance, and educational institutions. Companies need to identify which variables help predict attitudes and behaviors. For consumer markets, this process means trying to understand

| **Exhibit 7-2** | *Developing a market segmentation strategy* |

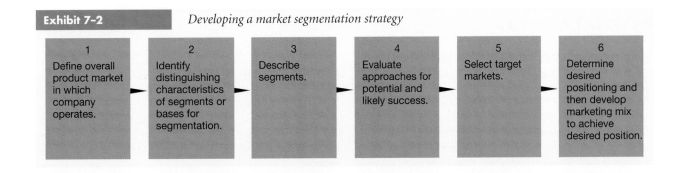

1	2	3	4	5	6
Define overall product market in which company operates.	Identify distinguishing characteristics of segments or bases for segmentation.	Describe segments.	Evaluate approaches for potential and likely success.	Select target markets.	Determine desired positioning and then develop marketing mix to achieve desired position.

| Exhibit 7–3 | *Frequently used consumer and business-to-business segmentation bases* |

Consumer Marketing

User-Related

Demographics: age, gender, race, income, education, family size, family life cycle stage
Social class: lower, middle, upper
Culture: religion, nationality, subculture
Geographic: region, state, metropolitan location and size, urban versus rural
Lifestyles and psychographics: quiet family person, traditionalist attitudes, progressive, conservative

Behavioral

Benefits: desired product attributes
Usage: users versus nonusers, light versus heavy
Price or promotional sensitivity: high versus low
Brand loyalty: loyal versus nonloyal
Buying situation: kind of store, gift giving (kind of shopping)
Economic: profitability and potential

Business-to-Business

User-Related

Customer size: annual sales
Geographic location: Northeast versus West Coast
Organizational structure: centralized versus decentralized
Stage of buying process: decision at hand versus initial stages of decision making
Attitude toward vendor: current purchaser versus new account
Buying decision criteria: price versus quality
Type of product: installations, supplies, services, raw materials, component parts
Type of organization: manufacturing, government, public utility

Behavioral

End use: resale versus production component
Usage: users versus nonusers, light versus heavy
Product/service application: insurance versus banking
Economic: profitability and potential

---

consumer motivations for purchase and segment descriptors, such as demographics, lifestyle variables, and desired benefits.[34]

DEMOGRAPHICS   For consumer marketing, demographic segments are particularly significant. Some products are targeted for teenagers and others for the elderly; others are designed for young couples just beginning a family. Vacation decisions are uniquely related to family life cycle characteristics, with children having significant input even at young ages. Marketing researchers often rely heavily on occupation and education to form social class segments.

ACTING ETHICALLY

Segmentation and data privacy

Data mining and data-based market segmentation practices are employed by many companies. Even pursuit of the principles associated with customer relationship management requires the extensive analysis and use of information collected at the individual customer level. In many instances, the information obtained is for individual consumers. Although these practices benefit firms in their ability to provide more effective product offerings, issues related to privacy are being raised by lawmakers who seek greater data protection. Identity theft and improper use of private information are increasing pressures to control how personal information is made available and used. The safety of personal financial data is a top priority following recent incidents in which data brokers misused or lost personal records.

The demographic makeup of the typical American household continues to change. Married couples are now barely the majority. Households are growing more slowly and getting older. College-educated people earn a lot more than less educated consumers, and sadly, the gap between these two groups is growing wider. More and more jobs are being found in service industries, and the population shift to western and southern states continues.[35] The substantial income of many middle-class consumers has enabled the growth of "new luxury" brands as consumers trade up. Successful brand examples include Starbucks, Panera Bread, Sam Adams, Pottery Barn, Aveda, and BMW.[36]

These trends and demographic phenomena are important to marketers' understanding of segment characteristics. For example, age differences are often used individually or with other demographic variables, such as gender, income, and education, to describe market segments. Five generations are often used to categorize age differences:

- *The millennial generation*—Born between 1977 and 1994, this large new generation numbers 70 million.

- *Generation X*—Born between 1965 and 1976, this well-educated, media-savvy generation now makes up the young adult population of the United States.

- *Baby boom generation*—Born between 1946 and 1964, this is the largest single generation of Americans and remains a focus of marketers.

- *Swing generation*—Born between 1933 and 1945, this small generation of Americans now holds top positions in business and government.

- *World War II generation*—Born before 1933, the oldest consumers are the most affluent in history.[37]

- *Generation Y*—The children of baby boomers, aged 16 to 24 years in 2005. Greater in number than the boomers, about 63 million will be buying cars by 2010. Firms need to build relationships with them just as they did with their parents.[38]

Three of these age groups are particularly important in marketing: teens, Xers, and boomers; and similarities among these groups offer unique insights into differences in consumer behavior. Of note, teens spend over $65 billion each year of their own money and influence considerably more in aggregate expenditures by either spending their family's money or determining how their parents make decisions.

Xers are more likely than boomers to seek a balance between leisure and work activities as young adults. They care deeply about buying "cool" brands that match their own image needs and often serve as trendsetters for the population at large. In addition, following their college years, young adults now more often live at home as their careers are formed; hence they have considerable discretionary income. This group actually consists of three significant and overlapping submarkets: college and graduate students, up-and-coming professionals, and married couples. Firms that have been successful in reaching this group typically use the Internet as part of a larger campaign, particularly TV advertising. However, care must be exercised in the design of these campaigns because Generation X consumers are often cynical about advertising.[39]

With boomers continuing to age, the marketing opportunities associated with an aging population are profound. Previous generations retired and lived off fixed incomes. Boomers are expected to continue working in

WHEN YOU USE HI WHITE, IT SHOWS.

Many products are designed for the growing and lucrative segment of consumers over 50.

Thinking Critically

- Identify a company that you think would benefit from strategic corporate growth.

- Discuss how each of the growth strategies presented in this chapter could be implemented by the company you chose.

- Evaluate the potential for success of the growth strategies by identifying the strengths and weaknesses of each, and decide which strategy you think would be most effective overall.

the marketplace and to place a positive spin on aging. Consequently, products and services that appeal to older consumers with younger, positive self-images will be effective. Moreover, major life events like diet changes, divorce, and retirement open fertile ground for marketers.[40]

The presence and surprisingly the absence of children in families have become noticed by marketers in their efforts to identify potentially profitable market segments. The generation comprising the children of baby boomers, more than 79 million strong, will have purchasing power beyond their parents. Almost 30 million are already in their teens and spend an estimated $150 billion annually, and influence another $300 billion in spending by their parents. In contrast, families who have made the conscious decision to not have children represent a lucrative and neglected market segment as well. According to *American Demographics,* childless couples spend more per person in almost every consumer category than their married-with-children counterparts. Their unique buying power and growing size warrant marketer attention in certain segmentation situations.[41] Another unique market segment is the "twixters." Twixters are an emerging market of young consumers between the ages of 21 and 29 who continue to live with their parents and who have substantial discretionary income. This segment is present in many developed countries including Canada, Japan, France, Germany, and the United States.[42]

GEOGRAPHICS   Geographic differences are sometimes important in the development of marketing strategies. For example, cellular phone marketers use geographic analyses to evaluate their distribution effectiveness. In addition, gaps in geographic coverage can also signal effective area campaigns by cellular phone competitors that must be countered.[43]

One method of categorizing geographic differences uses census data to identify metropolitan areas. There are three types: **metropolitan statistical areas** (MSAs), **primary metropolitan statistical areas** (PMSAs), and **consolidated metropolitan statistical areas** (CMSAs). MSAs must have a city with a population of at least 50,000 or be an "urbanized area" with 50,000 people that is part of a county of at least 100,000 residents. The largest designation is CMSA. These are the approximately 20 largest markets in the United States that contain at least two PMSAs. PMSAs are major urban areas, often located within a CMSA, that have at least 1 million inhabitants. New York, Los Angeles, and Chicago are among the largest CMSAs. Populated areas within these markets, such as Marietta near Atlanta and Ventura near Los Angeles, represent PMSAs.

The combination of geographic information and demographic characteristics is called **geodemographics.** Ample published geodemographic data are available that firms can use in evaluating the size of potential market segments. Products are often directed toward geographic markets, particularly when tastes differ between regions. Further, it is important for marketers to know which areas are the fastest growing and represent the greatest future opportunities.

Christine Dickhans notes the following trends: *"Currently the largest segment for Hanes's consumer products (T-shirts, underwear, socks) is the baby boomer generation. Because our products are made for the basic needs of everyday life and they are usually at the opening price point, baby boomers know Hanes will have exactly what they need for the price that they want to pay. While this generation is more price conscious, and the Generation X and the Millennials are not, boomers will pay the price if the products are what they are looking for. The younger generations are more tech-savvy. For instance, when Hanes designs a clothing line for younger generations, we must include media pockets to capture that type of consumer."*

Firms use geodemographic data systems to integrate geographic information with census data. The fundamental premise in such geodemographic systems is that households in neighborhoods share similar lifestyles ("birds of a feather flock together") and that such neighborhoods repeat themselves, allowing similar neighborhoods to be classified into market segments.[44] Using a geographic information system (popularly labeled GIS), the lifestyle cluster system groups households into one of 40 residential types. Marketers can append lifestyle codes to customer records to expand their customer profiles and to enhance the study of the relationship of lifestyles to purchasing patterns.[45] Southwestern Bell Corporation (SBC) uses geodemographic analysis to develop marketing strategies for its European cable operations in the United Kingdom. The company uses the data to identify neighborhoods susceptible to sales through direct marketing campaigns and to screen bad-debt areas.[46]

Geographic clusters reflect segmentation targets that enable marketers to more efficiently employ their resources. Consider your own neighborhood. The cars and homes are probably of similar value. The mailboxes contain many of the same magazines, the cabinets the same products. The households have similar incomes and educations, as well as attitudes and product preferences.[47]

Cultural differences between countries have been used to identify segments comprising countries assumed to share similar values. Hofstede's classification scheme proposes five cultural dimensions for classifying countries: individualism versus collectivism, power distance, uncertainty avoidance, masculinity, and long-term orientation. For example, Austria, Germany, Switzerland, Italy, Great Britain, and Ireland form one segment that is medium high on individualism and high on masculinity. These cultural characteristics suggest preferences for high-performance products and a "successful achiever" theme in advertising. Similar comparisons have been made in terms of individualism–collectivism for Japanese versus U.S. consumers.[48]

PSYCHOGRAPHICS AND LIFESTYLES   **Psychographic or lifestyle research** attempts to segment customers according to their activities, interests, and opinions.[49] Such research uses survey responses to items concerning individual *activities, interests,* and *opinions*—called **AIO statements**—to develop in-depth profiles of consumer groups or segments. By tapping into a consumer's preferences and learning where her/his passions lie, firms increase the reception of their messages. If marketers can adopt the proper focus and promote benefits that sustain or become a part of the customer's lifestyle, then selling products and services is enhanced.[50] Here are examples of AIO statements:

- "A person can save a lot of money by shopping around for bargains" (price conscious).
- "An important part of my life is dressing smartly" (fashion conscious).
- "I would rather spend a quiet evening at home than go to a party" (homebody).
- "I am uncomfortable when my house is not completely clean" (compulsive housekeeper).[51]

Psychographic research has been used successfully in a variety of segmentation applications. This segmentation approach evolved as marketing researchers began to recognize that demographic and geographic segmentation schemes did not provide the depth of understanding needed to adequately describe profitable primary target markets. Economic changes had blurred class distinctions, and the increasing saturation of product categories had led to fewer physical differences between competing brands.[52] As an example, one study of women over 65 combined psychographic research with an analysis of segments identified by media preferences. This study of the growing over-65 market described the following media consumption patterns:

- *The engaged*—High levels of newspaper readership and high viewing levels of television news programming.
- *The autonomous*—Moderate levels of newspaper readership, and low use of media in general.
- *The receptive*—High viewing levels of television comedy programs and moderate levels of newspaper readership.[53]

A follow-up study using responses to a series of AIO agree–disagree statements provided a richer description of lifestyles within these segments. For example, women in the engaged segment were heavier users of cosmetics, considered cooking and baking extremely important, and were quite negative toward large companies and business practices.

Psychographic analyses have also been used to identify the defining events that will shape the 70 million-plus Generation Ys. The most noteworthy of the events included Columbine, Oklahoma City, the Clinton

Avonite targets business customers and stresses desired end benefits sought by B2B market segments.

TOUGH.

Avonite *Innovations in solid surfacing.*

Business-to-business situations can benefit from segmentation practices. For example, Johnson & Johnson targets minority businesses in efforts to build relationships.

impeachment trial, and 9/11. The MTV style of programming affects marketing and advertising messages. Shorter attention spans and information overload are the outcome of the current media environment faced by this developing and large segment of consumers. Relative to their Gen X predecessors, 18- to 24-year-olds are active channel surfers, interact more with technology, possess more positive attitudes toward their ability to make money, and like to spend.[54]

A popular application of the lifestyle and psychographic approach to segmentation is the **Values and Lifestyles Program** of SRI International. VALS segments consumers into eight groups: actualizers, fulfilleds, believers, achievers, strivers, experiencers, makers, and strugglers. Firms can use this system to effectively develop advertising and promotional campaigns, including the selection of media and the design of message content. As shown in Exhibit 7–4, the groups are arranged along two dimensions: self-orientation and resources. Self-orientation refers to the attitudes and activities people use to maintain their social self-image and self-esteem. Resources include attributes such as education, income, age, energy, self-confidence, and even health.[55] For example, the actualizers, the smallest segment at 8 percent of the U.S. population, have the highest incomes and self-esteem. The remaining seven segments each represent from 11 to 16 percent of the population.[56]

BENEFIT SEGMENTATION Many firms segment markets according to the particular attributes or benefits that consumers want.[57] **Benefit segmentation** enhances the design and marketing of a product to meet expressed consumer needs for quality, service, or unique features. In fact, benefit segmentation is most consistent with assumption of demand variation between segments. For example, Apple targeted a segment that wanted easy-to-use computers—consumers put off by what they saw as complications in operating other PCs. Defining this niche and simplifying the process of learning built Apple into a major factor in this market.

Benefit segmentation is consistent with the provision of *customer value* and the marketing concept—that is, to be customer-oriented and to provide consumer benefits to generate long-term customer satisfaction. The belief underlying benefit segmentation is that true segments are best described in terms of the causal factors or basic reasons for purchase.[58]

Benefit segmentation works in marketing services as well as products. Through its novel promotional messages, IBM markets itself as a provider of much-needed benefits to many companies—information systems that do not threaten the firm's employees and that make computer technology a real contributor to the firm's performance.

ECONOMIC SEGMENTATION Firms are increasingly segmenting their customers based on the profit potential associated with individual accounts. Such economic segmentation occurs in both consumer marketing situations and business-to-business competitive markets. As shown in Exhibit 7–3, economic considerations are a behaviorally based segmentation characteristic. For example, banks often segment their customers into A, B, and C categories based on profitability data generated through information

Exhibit 7–4

Eight values and lifestyles segments

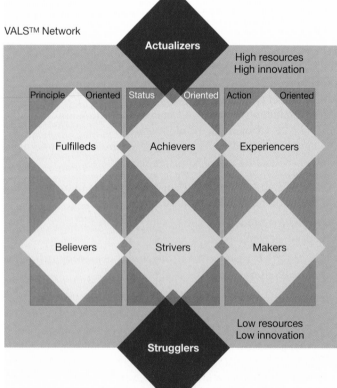

on customer accounts and their previous account activity. The low revenue/low profit customers will receive minimum service, and in the case of banks, may be charged higher fees. In contrast, high revenue/high profit customers are targeted with personal communications, while direct mail is used for moderate revenue/moderate profit accounts. Factors such as cost of retention, potential for expansion, and customer contributions to profits are instrumental in determining these segment identifications.[59] Data from the University of Michigan's Business School and its American Customer Satisfaction Index have documented a steady decline in service satisfaction for airlines, banks, stores, hotels, personal computer companies, and telephone services. One reason for these declines is the uneven way in which customer segments are treated. Financial institutions prefer day traders and heavy card users who pay substantial interest charges. At Charles Schwab, Signature clients, who process $100,000 in assets or trade at least monthly, never have to wait more than 15 seconds to get a call answered.[60]

The most frequently used B2B segmentation variables are firm demographics, purchasing approaches (buying center approaches), and purchase characteristics (specific applications, product urgency, order size). An economic value approach bases segmentation on how the firm's customers deliver value to their customers. FedEx, for example, segments its customers based on their needs for parcel security and on-time arrival. In addition, it is important to focus on segments for which the marketer can provide superior value relative to competitors. A value-based segmentation approach, based on the differentiation or competitive strengths of a firm, enables the firm to realize premium prices and frequent repeat business.[61]

INTERNATIONAL SEGMENTATION   Segmentation is an important part of international marketing as well. Firms can employ one—or some combination—of three approaches. First, companies may use a single standardized strategy in all international marketing. Second, customized strategies may be developed for different countries or groups of countries. In these cases, the countries represent different segments. Third, and as explained earlier, intermarket segments, comprising similar clusters of consumers across national boundaries, may be identified. Variables that are typically used to form country segments include income and GNP per capita, telephones and TV sets per capita, percentage of population in agriculture, and political stability. For example, a company considering the sale of durable electronic products (VCRs and CD players) identified two important segments formed by combining countries: (1) Holland, Japan, Sweden, and the United Kingdom; and (2) Austria, Belgium, Denmark, Finland, France, Norway, and Switzerland. Those segments were found to share similar patterns of new product adoption and hence were addressed with similar marketing efforts.[62]

Global marketing emphasizes the following: (1) cost efficiencies resulting from reduced duplication of efforts, (2) opportunities to transfer products, brands, and ideas across subsidiaries in different countries, and (3) the emergence of global customer segments, such as teenagers and the global elite. Global segmentation then is the process of identifying specific segments of customers, such as country groups or consumer groups across countries, with homogeneous attributes who are likely to exhibit similar buying behavior.[63]

Combining Bases of Market Segmentation

Exhibit 7–5 diagrams one way a firm might combine consumer characteristics to decide on a market segmentation strategy. Here a two-stage process begins with research designed to identify the heavy users of a product or service. If the heavy-user segment has unique or consistent demographic characteristics, such as income or education, the firm's decisions about how to reach that segment (which magazines or television programs can be used efficiently) are easier. Similarly, identifying certain lifestyle characteristics of the heavy-user segment gives the firm additional insight about which product configuration or advertising theme is likely to be successful.

Exhibit 7–6 gives another approach for combining different variables to describe segments of teenage consumers. Nissan's 2002 campaign for its upgraded Maxima targets married men in their late 30s who make $125,000 plus and love driving a more powerful automobile. This demographic segment was marketed to by advertising on cable channels

Exhibit 7–5   *A two-stage segmentation example*

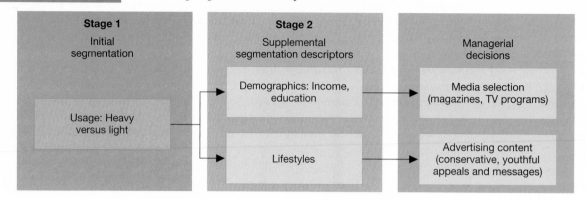

Exhibit 7–6   *Teen segmentation bases*

Teen Segment	Key Definers	Activities and Purchases
Thrills and chills	Fun Friends Irreverence Sensation	Eating out Going to bars Attending concerts Fast food Acne medication Perfume/cologne Body rings Hair dye Tobacco Alcohol
Resigned	Friends Fun Family Low expectations	Drinking Smoking Heavy metal music Fast food Low-ticket clothes Hair dye Tobacco Alcohol
World savers	Environment Humanism Fun Friends	Attending plays Camping/hiking School clubs Going to bars Doing something creative
Quiet achievers	Success Anonymity Anti-individualism Social optimism	Studying Listening to music Visiting museums CDs Stereo equipment
Bootstrappers	Achievement Individualism Optimism Determination Power	Studying Housework Spending time with family Visiting relatives Attending religious services Premium brands Luxury goods
Upholders	Family Custom Tradition Respect for individuals	Reading books Spending time with family Visiting relatives Playing/watching sports

such as A&E, Discovery, and the History Channel. Print ads were placed in *Smithsonian, Fortune,* and *Forbes.*[64]

Basically then, firms identify and combine distinguishing buyer segment bases to

- Help them design product or service offerings to market to targeted consumer segments.
- Help them choose media vehicles.
- Help them develop marketing themes for use in communicating to a particular segment or segments.

Segmentation Strategies

Strategies for engaging in segmentation are often categorized as undifferentiated, differentiated, or concentrated. These approaches give firms alternative methods for enhancing the execution of their marketing programs. These strategies range from appeals based on "mass marketing" to strategy focused on predetermined target markets. From our earlier discussion, other more specific segmentation approaches target large numbers of market cells, or involve customer-based marketing, in which mass customization is used to combine basic product modules in different ways for each customer; or customized marketing is used, in which products are developed from scratch for each individual customer. Exhibit 7–7 is a schematic view of the three approaches.

UNDIFFERENTIATED STRATEGY   A company adopts an **undifferentiated strategy** when it markets a single product using a single communication and distribution mix for the mass market. Neither the product nor the promotional theme is varied or differentiated. Undifferentiated approaches are most often used early in the life of a product category. Initial product introductions, such as the early introduction of the automobile, often use a single mass-marketing approach. The undifferentiated strategy offers some advantages because of economies of scale but opens the firm to competition. Today even water is marketed in brands to different segments. Truly undifferentiated strategies are largely a theoretical impracticability, or at least a phenomenon that occurs infrequently.

DIFFERENTIATED STRATEGY   At the other end of the scale is the **differentiated strategy,** under which a firm uses different strategies for most or a large number of different segments. Identifying segments where others see an undifferentiated mass market creates opportunities for innovations in marketing strategy based on meeting customers' needs more precisely.[65] In some cases, a unique product and communications campaign may be developed for each segment. In other instances, a common product may be marketed to different segments with varying communication strategies. Of note, a differentiated strategy does not simply mean a change in product, although it may. Frequently, variations in multiple aspects of the marketing mix are involved. The Hartmarx and Levi Strauss approaches, with their multiple product versions and advertising campaigns, are examples of complex segmentation schemes. Differentiated strategies are often the choice of companies such as soft drink manufacturers and life insurance firms, which offer many product versions to meet different preferences. McDonald's, for example, embodies segmentation principles in its offerings. Happy Meals and playgrounds are offered for children, while nutritional information on trays and commercials showing parent–child interactions are targeted toward adults. Likewise, traditional burgers are offered along with more healthful salads and sandwiches. Although a differentiated strategy is often useful for increasing sales and profits, continual adjustments to segmentation programs may prove expensive.

CONCENTRATED STRATEGY   A firm pursues a **concentrated strategy** when it seeks a large share of just a few profitable segments, perhaps only one, of the total market. With such a strategy, a company concentrates more on serving

Exhibit 7–7

Three alternative market segmentation strategies

segments innovatively and creatively than on pricing.[66] Indeed, the essence of marketing strategy for many companies is choosing which segments to focus on. Is the firm a high-end differentiator, or does the company serve the price-sensitive consumer with a low-cost approach?[67] American Express, for example, has traditionally sought upscale instead of middle-income customers. Thus the company concentrates its advertising resources in pursuit of a large share of the higher-income consumer market.

COUNTERSEGMENTATION STRATEGY **Countersegmentation** is an alternative strategy to traditional segmentation approaches. It involves combining market segments and assumes an increasing consumer willingness to accept fewer product and service variations for lower prices. Countersegmentation is seen in the move toward generic brands and retail superstores and warehouse stores and reflects segmentation by demand for low price. Sam's outlets and Toys "Я" Us appeal to a broad range of consumers and do not emphasize finely focused target segments. Countersegmentation is seen also at IBM and Chrysler, which have streamlined their product lines by combining operations and eliminating some brands.

FACTORS INFLUENCING SEGMENTATION STRATEGY A number of market, product, and competitive factors may influence a firm's choice of segmentation strategy. They include size and type of the market and a variety of competitive factors.

If consumers are not particularly sensitive to product differences, an undifferentiated strategy may be appropriate. But if the firm sells to an overall product market with many different segments, a differentiated or concentrated approach is the better choice. Two product-related factors are also relevant: stage in the product life cycle, and the degree to which the product may be varied or modified. If the product is new, a concentrated segmentation strategy may be best—that is, offering only one product version or a few at most. If the firm's interest is to develop primary demand, an undifferentiated strategy may be appropriate. In the later stages of a product's life, large firms tend to pursue a differentiated segmentation strategy.

For example, consumer product giant Procter & Gamble pursues a differentiated strategy in the laundry detergent category. P&G markets powdered laundry detergents such as Cheer and Tide to different segments of the product market. The company constantly differentiates its products within and across brands to address the segments vital to its success. Potential growth segments are prime candidates for differentiated products. When the liquid detergent segment was growing, P&G introduced a liquid version of Tide; later the company addressed another potential growth segment with Concentrated Tide.

Competitive factors are particularly important in a firm's market segmentation strategy. If its major competitors pursue an undifferentiated approach, a firm may decide to engage in a differentiated or concentrated approach. If a firm has many competitors, its best strategy may be to concentrate on developing strong brand loyalty and buyer preferences in one target segment or perhaps a few. Finally, a firm's size and financial position can influence the choice of strategy. Smaller firms with relatively limited resources often find it necessary to pursue a concentrated segmentation strategy.

A firm adopting an undifferentiated approach or pursuing only the largest segments may well invite substantial competition. This is the **majority fallacy:** although large "majority" segments may appear to offer a firm potential gains, pursuing only them may involve confronting overwhelming competition. In this case it is better for a firm to pursue a concentrated strategy, focusing on one segment or a few, to obtain larger shares of markets in which it can compete effectively.

Targeting Market Segments and Positioning Products

Once a firm has chosen its overall market segmentation strategy, it then must select specific segments and position products for effective appeal to those segments. Factors that affect the choice of a segmentation strategy also influence which specific segments should be targeted.

Firm and market potentials and forecasts

	Best Possible Results	**Expected Results for Given Strategy**
Industry Level	Market potential	Market forecast
Firm Level	Sales potential	Sales forecast

Estimating Segment Potentials

To estimate market potential and likely sales, the firm should distinguish between firm and industry potentials and between forecasts of the best possible results and expected results. As Exhibit 7–8 shows, **market potential** is the maximum amount of industry sales possible for a product or service for a specific period. The **market forecast** for that same period is a function of the amount of marketing effort (expenditures) put forth by all companies competing in that market. Total market potential then represents an upper limit on total sales. **Sales potential** is the maximum amount of sales a specific firm can obtain for a specified time period.

To produce a sales forecast, a company should screen out market segments that represent insufficient potential sales and analyze further the remaining segments. Company forecasts must consider competitive activity and the availability of channels of distribution and marketing media. What brands are already in the market? What are the strengths and weaknesses of the competition? What distribution outlets and supporting channels of distribution are available? What is the cost of access to the appropriate media? Here is one set of steps firms can use to estimate potential for a segment:

1. Set time period of interest.
2. Define product level.
3. Specify segment characteristics or bases.
4. Identify geographic market boundaries.
5. Make assumptions about marketing environment (uncontrollable factors such as competitive activity).
6. Make assumptions about company's own marketing efforts and programs (controllable factors).
7. Make estimates of market potential, industry sales, and company sales.[68]

Exhibit 7–9 sets out data on market potential for pizza across four age groups. Population information of this sort is obtainable from U.S. census or state records. The product purchase percentage data can be obtained from an annual "Survey of Buying Power" in *Sales & Marketing Management*. The use of these data is explained in Appendix B.

Developing Forecasts

Forecasts represent the amount the company expects to sell in a market over a specific time period. The period will vary by company and use of the forecast. Forecasts are used to evaluate opportunities, budget marketing efforts, control expenditures, and assess subsequent

Estimating market potential for frozen pizza for Arizona and Colorado (in thousands)

Age Group	Percentage Purchasing Frozen Pizza	Population		Potential Pizza Sales	
		Arizona	**Colorado**	**Arizona**	**Colorado**
18–24	10.4	384	341	39.94	35.46
25–34	25.8	634	607	163.57	156.61
35–44	24.3	568	622	138.02	151.15
45–54	14.5	381	384	55.25	55.68
				396.78	398.90

sales performance. High forecasts can lead to excessive investment and expenditures, whereas low forecasts can result in lost opportunities.

There are a number of methods for forecasting sales, some of which are explained here. These methods can be grouped into *qualitative* procedures, which employ judgmental opinion and insight, and *quantitative* methods, which use historical data to make trend extensions or numerical estimates of forecast sales. The primary qualitative forecasting methods are a survey of buyers' intentions, expert opinion, and a composite of sales force estimates. The primary quantitative methods are trend analysis, market tests, and statistical demand analysis.

A **survey of buyers' intentions** is useful in certain situations. Under this method, forecasts are based on surveys of what consumers or organizational buyers say they will do. First, the buyers must have well-formed intentions and be willing to follow those intentions. In addition, they must be willing to disclose their intentions accurately. These conditions are most often satisfied for durable consumer goods and for large purchases in business-to-business marketing.

Expert opinion represents another qualitative or judgmental approach to forecasting. Using this approach, analysts ask executives within the company or other experts to provide forecasts based on their own judgments or experiences. This can be a quick and perhaps inexpensive method; however, the forecast accuracy depends on the knowledge of the executives or experts involved and their ability to provide realistic estimates.

A **composite of sales force estimates** provides another means of forecasting sales. Under this method, sales representatives give forecasts for their individual territories, which can then be combined across territories. Sales reps have unique exposure to the competition and market trends. Plus, these estimates can be obtained cheaply and regularly. However, reps may give low forecasts in efforts to keep their own sales quotas low.

Trend analysis, a quantitative forecasting approach, often referred to as *time-series analysis,* examines historical sales data for predictable patterns. If the environment is reasonably stable, extrapolating past sales data can provide a quick and efficient means of making forecasts. Often the firm will identify trend, cyclical (economic cycles), and seasonal effects in its past sales pattern. Exponential smoothing is a frequently used form of trend analysis in which the most recent sales data are weighted most heavily in determining each new forecast. The major problem with time-series or trend analysis is that the firm is assuming that what happened in the past will continue in the future, making no attempt to determine what caused the sales.

When the firm is uncertain about its subjective judgment or the ability of past data to forecast the future, a market test may be necessary. Market tests are particularly useful for evaluating the likely success of new product introductions. **Market tests** involve marketing the product in test locations using the planned communication, pricing, and distribution strategies. Forecasts for other areas can then be obtained from sales in the test markets.

Statistical demand analysis involves developing forecasts from the factors thought to be most important in determining sales. In this method, sales are forecast from equations in which price, advertising and sales promotion, distribution, competitive, and economic factors serve as independent variables. Regression analysis is the most frequently used estimation procedure. Statistical demand analysis is advantageous in that it forces the firm to consider the causal factors that determine sales. Also, the relative importance of the independent factors can be evaluated. Although computers have made demand analysis readily available to forecasters, the usefulness of the method depends on appropriate application. Some sophistication in data analysis procedures is clearly a prerequisite to their use.

Forecasting is not a rigorous science, in spite of the availability of some very sophisticated methods. When using any of the methods described, forecasters should be careful to avoid several common errors. These errors include the failure to carefully examine any assumptions made, such as anticipated social and technological changes; excessive optimism that inhibits consideration of the downside risks involved; failure to specify the time frame involved and the intended purpose of the forecast; and the failure to blend both quantitative and qualitative methods so that mechanical extrapolation is combined with reasoned judgment.[69]

Thinking Critically

- The past decade has seen significant market share loss for Levi Strauss & Co. as it tries to market products to entirely different market segments. On the one hand, it is interested in selling Dockers brand pants to the baby boomer generation while at the same time maintaining focus on its core jeans products for the teenage market. What are some of the difficulties that a company might face following such a dual strategy? What factors might be influencing Levi Strauss & Co. to follow this differentiated strategy of targeting two diverse markets?

- Thinking about the millennial generation (Generation Y) and Generation X, in what ways are these two groups different? How might the products and advertising programs targeted at these two groups differ? How do these two segments rate according to the five criteria for effective segmentation?

Targeting Market Segments

To select target segments, the firm must consider a combination of factors, including the segment's potential sales volume and profits, any competition currently selling to the segments, and the firm's abilities and objectives.

Although large segments with a substantial number of buyers seem to promise high potential sales volume and profits, smaller segments served by a unique marketing mix may also provide lucrative business opportunities. Specialty stores in large malls serve many of these segments. For example, General Nutrition Center targets health-conscious people, and Lady Foot Locker, women sports enthusiasts.

Large markets may also attract the greatest number of competing firms (the majority fallacy). In general, a firm will have to assess market potential in light of competitive issues. If the firm has a competitive advantage that cannot be easily copied, it may attempt to approach the larger market segments.

Selection of target markets has a lot to do with a firm's objectives and distinctive competence. A firm specializing in innovative technological products, for example, may compete on total value rather than on price alone, focusing on one segment or a few segments where high-quality, innovative products appeal.

Targeting also requires designing advertising and promotional mixes to reach the intended segments. Resources are wasted if the advertising results in duplication of audience or reaches nontarget market consumers. Accurate identification of the

---

S3 - Inner Suburbs

The four clusters of the S3 Social Group comprise the middle income suburbs of major metropolitan areas, straddling the United States average. Otherwise, the clusters are markedly different. Two clusters have more college-educated, white-collar workers; two have more high school-educated blue-collar workers; two are young; one is old; one is mixed; but all show distinct, variant patterns of employment, lifestyle, and regional concentration.

23 Upstarts and Seniors   Middle-Income Empty Nesters

Cluster 23 shows that young people and seniors are very similar if they are employable, single, and childless. *Upstarts and Seniors* have average educations and incomes in business, finance, retail, health and public service. Preferring condos and apartments, they live in the Sunbelt and the West.

Middle (28)   Age Groups: 25-54, 65+   Predominantly White

24 New Beginnings   *Young Mobile City Singles*

Concentrated in the boomtowns of the Southeast, the Southwest, and the Pacific coast, *New Beginnings* is a magnet for many young, well-educated minorities who are making fresh starts. Some are divorced, and many are single parents. They live in multi-unit rentals and work in a variety of low-level, white-collar jobs.

Middle (29)   Age Groups: 18-44   Ethnically Diverse

25 Mobility Blues   *Young Blue-Collar/Service Families*

These blue-collar counterparts of *New Beginnings* are young, ethnically mixed, and very mobile. Many are Hispanics and have large families with children. These breadwinners work in transportation, industry, public service, and the military.

Middle (41)   Age Groups: Under 18, 25-34   Ethnically Diverse, High Hispanic

26 Gray Collars   *Aging Couples in Inner Suburbs*

The highly skilled blue-collar workers of Cluster 26 weathered the economic downturn of America's industrial areas and now enjoy a resurgence of employment. Their kids grew up and left, but the Gray Collars stayed in the Great Lakes "Rust Belt."

Middle (42)   Age Groups: 65+   Ethnically Diverse

This segmentation description summarizes major target market segments defined in terms of geodemographic characteristics.

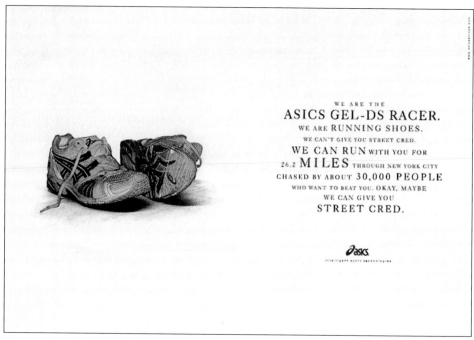

Segmentation schemes involve identifying groups defined in terms of geodemographics and desired end benefits, as in this Asics advertisement.

marketing segments appropriate for a particular product is critical if firms are to target those segments efficiently.

Technology brings new precision to both the selection of specific target segments and the ability to reach them. When Buick's analysis of the large station wagon segment revealed that upscale suburbs, particularly in the Midwest and Northeast, were potentially lucrative markets, it targeted consumers with ads in magazines sent to the relevant zip codes. Targeted ads promoting the Roadmaster station wagon ran in issues going to 4,940 of the more than 40,000 U.S. zip codes. That was 20 percent of U.S. households, but those households represented 50 percent of the buyers of large wagons.[70]

The benefits of targeting are prevalent in the marketplace—the grocery, clothing, and shoe industries included. For example, in-store scanners and grocery card loyalty programs are enabling grocery retailers to more precisely target their consumers. In an application of economic segmentation, Sav-O's Piggly Wiggly stores are focusing on the top 50 percent of their customers, who represent 90 percent of their business. These customers are targeted with special promotions and advertisements designed to increase their transaction numbers per store visit. Moreover, data on the preferences of these desirable consumers are useful in determining shelf space allocations among competing brands. Targeting specifically toward baby boomers has also enabled New Balance to compete successfully with Nike in the very competitive athletic shoe market.[71]

Positioning

Once segments have been selected and targeted, the firm must position its products and services in the minds of its customers. **Positioning** a product or service involves designing a marketing program, including the product mix, that is consistent with how the company wants its products or services to be perceived. The strategy a firm adopts is driven then by the desired positioning. Positioning aims to influence or adjust customer perceptions of a product or brand. An effective position lets a brand occupy a preferred and unique position in the customers' minds while being consistent with the firm's overall marketing strategy.[72] As such, positioning involves the selection of target segments and the formulation of product attributes that make up the brand. Recently Snackwell's successfully halted dramatically falling sales volume by repositioning itself. This repositioning included product reformulation, an increased marketing budget, and a drastic

Gender and age are used in the fashion industry to define market segments.

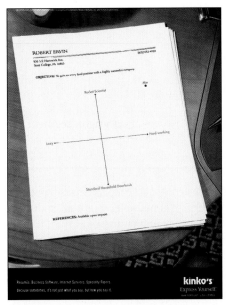

This Kinko's advertisement depicts a humorous perceptual map that makes the important point that even students must "position" themselves in the marketplace.

shift in advertising redirected toward the brand's new core audience—women. Nabisco is also building its relationship with its primary target market by creating a Web site directed at women and an ongoing direct mail campaign augmented by women-targeted promotions.[73]

Positioning a new brand requires distinguishing it from other brands. Customers must perceive it as sharing important attributes with other brands in the product category but as being superior on differentiating attributes.[74] **Repositioning,** called for when a firm wants to shift consumer opinions about an existing brand, requires development of new marketing programs. A number of nostalgic brands have been revived and repositioned in recent years. Oxydol detergent, Breck shampoo, and Fanta soda have all been reintroduced based on the belief that there remains some leverageable brand equity associated with these decades-old brands that will prove profitable for some segment or segments.[75]

Product attributes, price, and image enhancements are major components in positioning. **Perceptual maps,** spatial representations of consumer perceptions of products or brands, are often used to evaluate brand positions in a market. Exhibit 7–10 is a perceptual map for the soft drink market. Brands are positioned on the map according to consumer perceptions of price and brand expressiveness. Note that over time a brand's market position can shift.

Perceptual maps often show positions for competitors' brands. They also convey to a company how much it must change consumer perceptions to achieve parity with or differentiation from competitors. By combining segmentation and positioning research, a company can learn which segments are attractive and how consumers in specific segments perceive the company's products relative to competing products and brands.[76]

Micromarketing

The ultimate in target marketing is **micromarketing,** which frequently combines census and demographic data to identify clusters of households that share similar consumption patterns. The **PRIZM** market segmentation system is one example. Demographic descriptions of county, zip code, and census tract locations combined with information about area values, preferences, and purchasing habits enable companies to pinpoint likely or desired customers. Firms use micromarketing to increase the productivity of their marketing expenditures. Micromarketing enhances the effectiveness of marketing efforts by enabling marketers to

- Identify potential markets for direct selling through mail and telemarketing campaigns.

CREATING CUSTOMER VALUE

"Priceless" MasterCard

MasterCard, one of the world's most recognized and respected brands, is constantly striving to increase customer loyalty as well as the value of its customers. The company's customers include 25,000 financial institutions serving consumers in 210 countries. As part of its objective to serve consumers, principles of market segmentation are employed. These principles are recognized in extensions of the award-winning ad campaign aired worldwide titled "Priceless." For example, the company recognized that only one-third of the $440 billion U.S. market has credit cards. In recognition of this attractive credit opportunity, MasterCard launched a major campaign using a variation of the "Priceless" theme coupled with education intended to help U.S. Hispanic newcomers employ credit responsibly. The question remains of whether editing a mainstream campaign for a niche market will be effective. Mastercard has also developed a Web-based ATM location service to give customers greater information about its 900,000 Cirrus locations. In addition, a new movie theater reward program is designed to reach the younger, less affluent segment of credit card consumers.

Exhibit 7-10

Perceptual map of 15 soda beverages

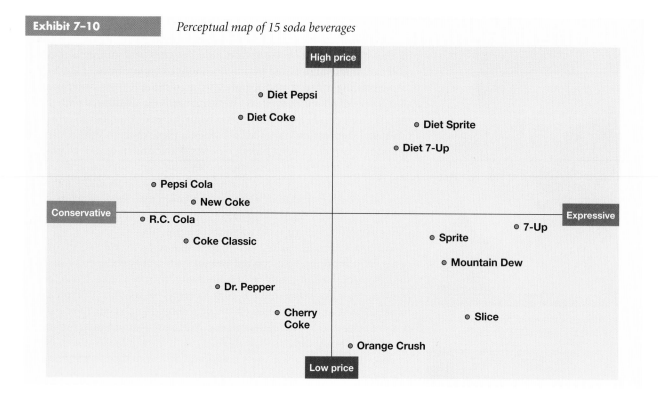

- Profile their customers by matching them to demographic and lifestyle clusters.
- Learn which areas offer the greatest potential in site selection for new stores or offices.
- Tailor their advertising themes and plan their media.[77]

Market Segmentation and Ethics

Targeting selected market segments can provide substantial benefits to both marketers and consumers: The marketer gains sales and the consumers receive the particular products and services they most want and value. Yet segmentation practices can be so effective that they are fraught with opportunities for exploitation. Marketers must consider the ethical issues associated with some segmentation and targeting practices.

Advertising to Children

Advertising to children, a large and influential market segment, can stimulate demand for expensive and unnecessary products. Such advertising has been criticized for developing unrealistic expectations and demands for some youthful consumers who can least afford unnecessary expenditures. Demand for expensive athletic shoes or certain kinds of jackets or jewelry is easily fostered. Further, very young children sometimes have difficulty differentiating between program content and commercial messages.

Reaching children, whose influence and discretionary funds growth exceed inflation, is big business. However, some of the member countries of the European Union believe that overtly selling to children via television advertising is unethical. As an example, the British Independent Television Commission states that ads targeting children must not

- Take advantage of their natural credulity.
- Lead them to believe they will be inferior if they do not have the advertised product.
- Harm them.
- Force them to pester their parents.

The same concerns hold in the United States for young consumers. The results from congressional legislation and government restrictions will place tight reins on the ability of firms to collect information from children via the Internet. In particular, the Children's Online Privacy Protection rules are a response to parental concerns and a Federal Trade Commission study regarding the susceptibility of children to marketing tactics, predominantly those associated with interactive communications available on the Internet.[78]

Harmful Products

Marketing harmful products, such as cigarettes and alcohol, to young people raises important ethical issues. Some brands of cigarettes, such as Virginia Slims, are positioned to attract young women. Models in cigarette and beer ads are youthful, active, and attractive individuals. Messages for these products often emphasize the social acceptability of smoking and drinking, minimizing the impact of package warnings regarding the negative effects of their use.

Privacy Issues

As marketers are increasingly able to target precise consumer segments, concerns about privacy arise. Consumer purchase histories, credit histories, and telephone numbers can be combined for use in developing and targeting direct marketing campaigns. Care must be exercised in the use of this information.

Product Proliferation

Over 30 food products are introduced every day, or 25,000-plus per year in packaged goods, including food, beverages, health and beauty aids, household products, and pet products. Is this ever-increasing proliferation needed? The continuing segmentation of markets and products to serve those markets seems endless. Consumers are often bewildered by the number of choice alternatives.[79]

Some researchers and practitioners are now arguing for a plan labeled the "efficient consumer response." One pillar of this grocery industry recommendation is **efficient assortment.** While product issues are addressed in the three chapters that follow, keep in mind that the practice of developing finer and finer product distinctions designed in part to appeal to more specific market segments has been questioned from both the perspective of improving consumer decision making and retailer performance. In fact, a number of studies have shown that the number of brands and brand sizes (that is, stock-keeping units) can be reduced without affecting sales or consumers' perceptions of variety. In addition to simplifying decisions for consumers, cutbacks in category SKUs allow the retailer to reduce the occurrence of out-of-stocks, to cut back on stocking frequency, and to lower warehouse costs. For example, one summary of industry research reported a study in which the number of alternatives of cat-box filler was reduced from 26 to 16. There were no effects on category sales, but savings in logistics costs increased operating profit 87 percent.[80]

Summary

1. **Define and explain market segmentation, target markets, and product differentiation and positioning.** Market segmentation is used when consumer groups (segments) share needs or preferences that differ from other segments. Market segmentation strategies attempt to take advantage of these differences and to meet each segment's demands. The segments served by firms are often called *target markets.*

    Product differentiation exists when customers perceive that a firm's product offerings differ from those of competing firms on any physical or nonphysical attribute. Positioning a product within a market is the process of exercising a differentiation strategy to convince consumers that the product has unique desirable characteristics.

2. **Understand the criteria used for evaluating the likely success of a segmentation strategy.** Five criteria are relevant in the design of a market segmentation strategy. *Measurability* refers to the extent to which the size and purchasing power of segments can be defined. *Accessibility* is the degree to which firms can efficiently reach intended target segments. *Substantialness* addresses the size of the target segment and its potential sales and profits. *Durability* refers to persistence—the extent to which segments will persist over time as good business opportunities. *Differential responsiveness* is the degree to which market segments differ in their response to varying marketing mix combinations.

3. **Know the role of market segmentation in the development of marketing strategies and programs.** Market segmentation can be useful for both new and mature products or services. New products can be targeted to segments promising opportunities for introduction and growth. Mature brands can be repositioned, extended, or marketed to appeal to specific segments. An appropriate market segmentation strategy can help marketers focus on growth and expansion opportunities in an increasingly competitive marketplace.

4. **Describe the issues involved in product and brand positioning.** After determining the segmentation strategy, the marketer must take care in selecting the appropriate segments and positioning the firm's

brands for those segments. *Positioning* refers to consumers' perceptions of the particular product or brand in relation to its competitors. Overall, the firm must identify the existing competitive products and brands within a market. It then must assess which attributes determine product preferences for the brands in that market. An examination of the fit between existing preferences and beliefs, ideal preferences, and brand capabilities will assist the firm either in positioning a new brand or in repositioning an already available brand.

5. **Understand the alternative bases for segmenting consumer and business-to-business markets.** Variables used to develop segmentation schemes may be either user- or behavior-based, and they may apply in either consumer or business-to-business marketing situations. User-related characteristics include demographic and psychographic variables for consumers, and customer size and geographic location for business-to-business applications. Behavior-related characteristics include benefits desired and extent of usage for consumers, and product application for business-to-business markets.

6. **Evaluate alternative approaches for pursuing segmentation strategies.** Segmentation strategies are of three types: undifferentiated, differentiated, and concentrated. An undifferentiated strategy uses only one combination of marketing mix variables to meet the demands of the entire market. This strategy is appropriate if consumers are insensitive to product variations, if the competition is light, or if the product itself cannot be easily varied.

    A differentiated strategy uses different marketing mix combinations to meet all or many of the segments constituting a market. A concentrated strategy aims to achieve a large share in just one or a few segments.

    In practice, many firms evolve from using an undifferentiated or concentrated strategy to adopting a differentiated approach, either as the firm can produce variations of the product or as the product develops beyond its introductory stage. An alternative approach, countersegmentation, combines market segments to provide lower-priced products with fewer product variations.

Understanding Marketing Terms and Concepts

Thinking about Marketing

1. What is market segmentation, and how does it differ from product differentiation?

2. How might a marketer attempt to differentiate a product from competing products?

3. What are the criteria for segmenting a market, and what is meant by each one? Contrast differential responsiveness with segment accessibility.

4. Describe the different bases for segmentation. In doing so, explain the differences between user-related and behavior-related characteristics. How does PRIZM, described in Case 7–1, make use of these bases?

5. What bases might be used to define segments for these products: cassette recorders, hand calculators, personal computers, and public universities?

6. What is benefit segmentation? How does demographic segmentation differ from psychographic segmentation?

7. Define the different segmentation strategies. Compare and contrast each strategy with the others, and explain the conditions under which each may be appropriate.

8. What implications does the majority fallacy hypothesis have for the pursuit of a concentrated segmentation strategy?

9. How might Fingerhut use its databases to strengthen its marketing efforts?

10. Why is the practice of market segmentation and targeting now more important than ever?

11. What are some factors that make market segmentation especially important for marketers? How do these factors affect intermarket segments?

12. Discuss the shift from mass marketing to mass customization. What are some of the segmentation challenges involved with mass customization?

Applying Marketing Skills

1. Compare the audiences of *Time* and *Rolling Stone* magazines. How does advertising in these magazines relate to market segmentation?

2. A large U.S. manufacturer of heavy-duty carpet for use in office buildings is considering expanding its marketing efforts to include European countries. The company has segmented its marketing efforts geographically and by company size. What market segmentation decisions does the company face as it expands its efforts to include both Eastern and Western European countries?

3. Using the concepts discussed in Chapter 6, "Marketing Research and Decision Support Systems," what type of study might be conducted to identify market segments within the overall market of consumers who regularly purchase financial services by selecting stocks and bonds?

Using the www in Marketing

Activity One Considering the VALS Web site (*http://www.sric-bi.com*). Select the Values and Lifestyles Program, and then at the bottom of the page click on "Find your own VALS-type now."

1. What demographic descriptors are used to define the VALS segments?

2. Comment on the number and nature of the agree–disagree attitude statements. Do your

responses reflect stable or temporary opinions about yourself? Were you surprised by your own VALS categorization? How do your own values and lifestyle compare with others?

3. What other information must companies have before this segmentation scheme is useful in a practical sense?

Activity Two Many e-commerce companies are now using heavy advertising to market their online

services. Consider the Barnes & Noble site: *http://www.barnesandnoble.com.*

1. What aspects of this site are designed to develop a "loyal" segment?

2. How does Barnes & Noble compete with *Amazon.com?*

3. What behavioral segmentation characteristics of online book buyers would be helpful in the design of marketing strategy?

Making Marketing Decisions

Case 7–1 PRIZM by Claritas: You Are Where You Live

For the past two decades, the Alexandria, Virginia–based company Claritas Inc.'s geodemographic segmentation product, PRIZM (potential rating index by zip market), has been one of the most highly used tools to identify consumers. PRIZM is a micromarketing tool that categorizes consumers into lifestyle segments. The basic notion behind PRIZM is that "birds of a feather flock together"; that is, people who live together often purchase the same types of items. The original designer of the PRIZM database, Jonathan Robbin, categorized U.S. Census Bureau data in zip codes and analyzed each for social rank, mobility, ethnicity, family life cycle, and housing. These data are supplemented by market research surveys and other statistics obtained from the ACNielsen Co. Currently PRIZM also segments consumers by block tracts and zip-plus-four. The newest version of the PRIZM software consists of 62 consumer segments. This growing number of consumer segments is an indication of the increasing economic and ethnic complexity within consumer markets. Based on the concept that people with similar demographic traits tend to behave similarly in the marketplace, Claritas mines America's households to build snapshots of an increasingly diverse population.

The 62 clusters are organized into 15 standard social groups, indicated by the degree of urbanization, from the rural countryside to urban high-rises. The 15 groups cover the range of affluence, from "rural landed gentry" to "urban cores." Survey Sampling, Inc., adds PRIZM codes to its random telephone samples to add lifestyle information such as interests, hobbies, education, and spending patterns. By identifying the neighborhood types where existing customers are located, accurate predictions can be made about where prospective customers are located.

This information can then be used in designing direct mail campaigns, media planning, site analysis, product positioning, and customer relationship management (CRM) campaigns.

Users of PRIZM include restaurant chains, banks, and stores in search of the best locations for new outlets. For example, Premier Bank in Baton Rouge, Louisiana, merges PRIZM with its internal database to find neighborhoods with households that match the traits of its best customers. Additionally, direct marketers develop target mailings based on information provided by PRIZM. Finally, advertising agencies explore the PRIZM database for insights concerning consumers. As another example, Cabin cruise lines used information provided by Claritas to develop a direct mail promotion for one of its summer cruise destinations. Only those households fitting the profile of its most profitable customers were targeted with the promotional offer. The campaign resulted in increased occupancy rates of 15 percent and increased revenues of 20 percent. Follow-up analyses indicated a return on investment (ROI) of over 40 percent.

Having successfully developed the original PRIZM software, Claritas Inc. has recently introduced a segmentation system that can accurately profile a market's workday population as well as illustrate the difference between the area's daytime and nighttime demographics. This segmentation product, Workplace PRIZM, gives marketers valuable information concerning the daytime demographics of an area. Therefore, companies can evaluate whether their products and services are needed for the daytime population.

The development of the Workplace PRIZM software was based on the original PRIZM residential tracts. Workplace PRIZM weights the original tracts by the percentage of residents commuting to specific employment tracts. These newly developed workday tracts are often quite different than the original population tracts.

Overall, the PRIZM system is based on the theory that by knowing the location, education level, traits, and habits of each cluster in a community, retailers and shopping center marketers can market to specific clusters. Therefore, the use of PRIZM software as a consumer segmentation tool should provide valuable information about consumers.

Questions

1. Why is PRIZM software an effective marketing tool?

2. How does the PRIZM approach satisfy the criteria for effective segmentation?

3. How might cultural changes involving the Hispanic and Asian populations affect the effectiveness of PRIZM?

4. What are the advantages of the newly developed Workplace PRIZM software?

Case 7–2 *Marriott International: "Suite Deals"*

 Marriott International is a worldwide operator and franchiser of hotels and senior living communities. Marriott has subsidiaries in 65 countries and regions and is the world's leading hotelier in terms of annual revenues. The lodging business includes over 2,600 operated or franchised properties. Marriott, which operates nine chains of hotels and suites, focuses its hotel marketing efforts on two groups: middle-class families and business travelers. Unlike other hotel competitors, Marriott uses separate brand names on its different lines. Examples of its product mix, approximate prices, and the intended target market for each are as follows:

Fairfield Inn—$45–$65; the economizing business and leisure markets.

SpringHill Suites—$75–$95; members of business and leisure markets looking for more space, amenities.

Courtyard—$75–$105; the "road warrior."

Residence Inn—$85–$110; travelers seeking residential-style hotels.

Marriott Hotels/Resorts—$90–$235; members of the discerning business and leisure markets.

Ritz-Carlton—$175–$300; senior executives and others looking for luxury.

Recently Marriott restructured its management to ensure more effective coordination of its complex oper-

ations. Specifically, three business categories were established, each headed by a senior VP: full service (e.g., Marriott Hotels), extended stay (e.g., Residence Inns), and select services (e.g., Courtyard, SpringHill). This organization allows shared resources for such activities as strategic development, market analyses, and the Rewards loyalty program. Category teams structured around these three groupings should enhance decision making and implementation of marketing changes and strategies.

The SpringHill introduction is one of Marriott's most recent product line additions. Marriott is continuing to expand and improve its lodgings, including rebranding its spas under the "Revive" name. Other expansion will include mixed-use projects in which both hotel guests and permanent residents will be involved. Serving such different segments within the same location and facility raises questions about shared utility costs, parking, and other services.

Questions

1. What are benefits and drawbacks from such a diverse offering of hotel chains?

2. What segments remain untapped?

3. To what extent does price sensitivity affect choice of alternatives within the line of hotels and suites?

4. What are the bases that could be used to segment the market for all types of hotel patrons?

Chapter Eight

PRODUCT AND SERVICE CONCEPTS

After studying this chapter, you should be able to

1 Understand the differences between goods and services.

2 Differentiate between consumer and business products, and discuss the different types of each.

3 Recognize that marketers need to appreciate the perspective of the consumer.

4 Define and discuss the importance of product quality, product design, branding, packaging, and customer service.

5 Explain how the different product components need to be integrated to meet the needs of customers.

Frito-Lay

Frito-Lay is a worldwide marketer of snack foods. The history of Frito-Lay is especially interesting. Elmer Doolin started The Frito Company in 1932 based on the new product Frito Corn Chips. Herman W. Lay founded the H. W. Lay & Company in 1938 to market potato chips. In 1945 The Frito Company granted H. W. Lay & Company an exclusive franchise to manufacture and distribute Frito Corn Chips in the Southeast. The two companies developed a close affiliation and merged in 1961 to form Frito-Lay Inc. In 1965 Frito-Lay Inc. and the Pepsi-Cola Company merged into PepsiCo. Frito-Lay remains a separate operating division of PepsiCo, producing almost 60 percent of the parent company's profits.

Today Frito-Lay has sales in excess of $9 billion a year. The company has many well-known brands such as Lay's, Ruffles, Doritos, Tostitos, Fritos, Rold Gold, and Sun Chips. Nine of Frito-Lay's brands are among the 10 best-selling snack food brands in major U.S. supermarkets. Lay's and Ruffles potato chips and Doritos tortilla chips are the leaders in the potato chip and salty snack food categories. Doritos, Cheetos, Lay's, 3D's,

and Ruffles are global brands. The company has more than 15 brands with sales in excess of $100 million annually.

Frito-Lay continually adapts to changes in the marketing environment. One example is "Lay's Tastes of America" promotion. It introduced Lay's Potato Chips in flavors that celebrate regional tastes across the United States, such as San Antonio Salsa, New Orleans Cajun Gumbo, Coney Island Hot Dog, and Wisconsin Cheddar. Another example is offering Go Snacks. These are snack foods in mini shapes and special packaging to fit the need for convenience in the active, fast-paced, go-anywhere lifestyles of today's consumers. A final example is the introduction of low-fat, natural, and organic chips, removing all trans fats from its brands, and selling low-carb Doritos, Cheetos, and Tostitos as a response to the consumer health and fitness trend.

Frito-Lay is noted for the quality of products it provides to consumers and the exceptional service it gives to retail customers. The company's basic business philosophy is: "Make the best product possible; sell it at a fair profit; and make service a fundamental part of doing business."

The Frito-Lay example illustrates the importance of product and service concepts to a company's success. Frito-Lay meets the needs of different customer segments by offering many different brands in different shapes, flavors, and packages. Product quality and customer service have been emphasized throughout the company's history. We examine these key product and service concepts by defining different types of products and then discussing the critical components of a product: quality, design, branding, packaging, and customer service.

What Is a Product?

The term **product** is defined as an idea, a physical entity (a good), a service, or any combination of the three that is an element of exchange to satisfy individual or business objectives.[1] From a marketing viewpoint, the key element of this definition is "to satisfy individual or business objectives." Individuals and businesses purchase products to solve problems or satisfy needs. That is, products provide benefits. Successful marketers focus on the benefits products supply to customers.

Let's examine the term *product* from a consumer's viewpoint. Say a consumer bought some product—maybe purchased a notebook for a course, or bought lunch at a local restaurant, or perhaps picked up some dry cleaning. Why did the consumer make each purchase? The major reason is the consumer received value from the benefits offered by the purchased product. The notebook, the lunch, and the dry cleaning provided benefits—the ability to take notes in class, to satisfy hunger, and/or to have clean clothing. The specific features of each product (the type of notebook, specific restaurant and meal, characteristics of the dry cleaner) are important only insofar as they are translated into the specific benefits the consumer values.

While reading these three chapters in Part Four, it is critical to think about products from a customer's viewpoint. Customers purchase products for their benefits, and astute marketers emphasize product benefits in their marketing efforts. For example, focusing on customer benefits is the basic marketing philosophy of Hewlett-Packard: "Many companies build a product and look for a market. We listen to our customers, research their needs, and build products that provide solutions for their problems."[2]

Consumers purchase products to receive benefits. The Sonic can help users eliminate plaque, clean sensitive places, and vitalize gums.

Types of Products

Marketers often classify products into specific categories. We focus on two categories: goods and services, and consumer and business products. We then discuss different types of consumer and business products.

Goods and Services

Goods are usually defined as physical products such as cars, golf clubs, soft drinks, or other concrete entities. **Services,** in contrast, are normally defined as nonphysical products such as a haircut, a football game, or a doctor's diagnosis. Products, however, do not necessarily fall into one category or the other. Almost all products incorporate some characteristics of both goods and services.

Consistent with the new definition of marketing, the latest thinking suggests that marketers should move from a goods-dominant view to a services-dominant view. A goods-dominant view assumes that marketers build value into a product through the features

| Exhibit 8–1 | *The goods/services continuum* |

| Paper
Truck
Production
equipment | Auto repair
Uniform rental
Restaurant | Health care
Haircut
Accounting |

Goods ◄───► **Services**

included in it. A services-dominant view is based on the idea that consumers define and cocreate value through the purchase and use of products. Thus a good is merely an appliance for producing services desired by consumers. For example, toothpaste is an appliance for preventing cavities or whitening teeth. The value a consumer derives from toothpaste is defined by the experience the consumer has in purchasing and using the toothpaste.[3] An example of this new thinking is mass customization. Firms practicing **mass customization** allow consumers to cocreate value by designing products to meet their specific needs. "Using Technology: Mass Customization" provides examples of how technology facilitates this process.

A useful way to view goods and services is on a continuum, as presented in Exhibit 8–1. Where a product lies on this continuum affects how it should be marketed, because goods and services possess several unique characteristics. The more a product lies toward the services end of the continuum, the more it is intangible, perishable, inseparable, and variable in quality. The more a product lies toward the goods end, the more it is tangible, storable, separable from the producer, and standardized in quality.

The purchase of a soft drink such as Pepsi-Cola in a restaurant can illustrate these differences. The soft drink is a good. It is tangible; it can be touched when it is served from the can. The restaurant can stockpile cases of Pepsi-Cola to serve when needed. The companies manufacturing and distributing the Pepsi are separated from the customer when the product is consumed. Finally, the quality of the Pepsi is expected to be the same from can to can because the manufacturing process is standardized.

The service provided by the restaurant, however, is different. The activity of serving the Pepsi is not tangible; it cannot be touched. The restaurant cannot store the service provided by a waiter; if there are no customers, the potential service of a waiter is wasted. The waiter's service cannot be separated from the restaurant, and it is performed in the presence of the customer. Consumers consider the waiter and the restaurant to be the same. And finally, the service provided by the same waiter to different customers, or by different waiters, is likely to vary in quality.

GOODS AND SERVICES STRATEGIES   Although the tangibility, perishability, separability, and variability characteristics differentiate many products and services, new technological developments are blurring some of these differences. Some services have

USING TECHNOLOGY

Mass customization

Technology developments have made it easier for firms to allow customers to cocreate value by being actively involved in the design of products:

- Ralph Lauren allows customers to create their own polo shirts online by selecting from 17 colors and 6 logos.

- Nike iD makes it possible for customers to design a specific pair of running shoes online. The customer can select from seven styles, thousands of color combinations, and eight characters for a personal brand.

- M&Ms Masterfoods lets customers customize various candies online. Customers can select from 13 colors and can add a slogan on one side of the candy. The "m" trademark must be on the other side.

Advances in Internet and manufacturing technology make it possible for these products to be designed and manufactured to the specifications of each customer. Customers pay more for customized products, but they receive more value from the process and final product.

| Exhibit 8–2 | | *Characteristics and strategies for services* |

Service Characteristic	Service Strategy	Examples
Intangible	Associate the service with something tangible.	General Motors's Mr. Goodwrench; models of buildings prepared by architects.
Perishable	Manage demand to utilize supply.	Reduced prices for afternoon movies; lower rates for off-season accommodations at tourist attractions.
Inseparable	Capitalize on advantages of person providing the service.	Motivating service providers through compensation and recognition programs; continual training of all customer contact personnel.
Variable	Standardize service delivery as much as possible.	Use of technologies, such as automated teller machines, to provide service; implementation of quality improvement programs.

characteristics similar to those of goods. For example, online databases are services; but the information provided is tangible, it can be stored until a customer needs it, the provider of the service is separated from the user, and there is little service variability.

In addition, the service content of many goods is a key component of the value received by customers. Take computers as an example. The hardware is clearly a good, but much of the value provided to customers is through the services accompanying the good, such as customizing a system to meet the specific needs of a customer. These services might include installation, software modifications, training, and ongoing support.

As suggested earlier, it is important to think about products from a customer's viewpoint. Customers are making purchases to satisfy needs or solve problems. Increasingly, this often requires marketers to offer products that represent a mix of goods and services. It is still important, however, to understand the typical differences between goods and services and how these characteristics lead to different strategies for the goods and service components of a product offering. We discuss these differences here and present specific strategies for services in Exhibit 8–2.

TANGIBILITY   One of the most interesting differences between goods and services relates to tangibility. Because goods are tangible, marketing strategies typically emphasize the intangible benefits derived from consuming the product. For example, many ads for Coke convey an intangible excitement associated with drinking the product. On the other hand, because services are intangible, marketers often try to associate them with something tangible. This approach is evident in the insurance industry: Consider the "good hands" of Allstate, the "rock" of Prudential, the "cavalry" of Kemper, and the "good neighbor" of State Farm.

The production and consumption of services are often inseparable. Singapore Airlines emphasizes the importance of its flight attendants in delivering services to customers.

PERISHABILITY   Perishability also has an important effect on the marketing of services. Services cannot normally be stored, so marketers of services use different strategies to manage demand. For example, higher prices are charged when demand is expected to be high, but prices are lowered when demand is expected to be low.

Airlines offer a good example of this type of strategy. Passengers flying to the same destination often pay very different fares, depending on flight schedule and time of booking. During holiday periods, fewer discounted tickets are available. Various types of discounted tickets are offered at other times to fill planes that would otherwise fly with empty seats not purchased at regular fares. The earlier customers make reservations and pay for tickets, the lower the fare. Low fares also go to those on standby—that is, customers willing to wait for an available seat after all reserved passengers are boarded. Airlines use standby to generate revenue for seats that have not been purchased in advance and would otherwise go to waste.

SEPARABILITY Goods like tennis racquets, tuxedos, or tomatoes can be produced, stored, and then sold to customers. Services, on the other hand, are typically produced and consumed simultaneously. For example, a dentist produces dental service at the same time the patient consumes it. The customer, then, tends to see the person and the business providing the service as one and the same. Thus bank tellers are the bank, nurses or billing personnel are the hospital, and salespeople are the firm.

The close relationships between the production and consumption of services and between the person and the business providing the service have significant implications. Whether a business provides goods or services, it must be concerned with the management of service employees. Every employee who has contact with customers is part of the firm's service offering. Therefore, effective management and training of employees who see customers is critical for providing quality services. Training of executive-level managers is not enough; service employees at all levels need the appropriate attention if they are to "be" the company.

VARIABILITY The difficulty of standardizing services, especially when they are delivered by people, has important implications for marketers. Even well-trained and professional service providers have bad days. Therefore, there will always be some variability in service quality. However, leading firms analyze their service processes and develop standards and procedures to minimize variability to the extent they can.

Consumer and Business Products

Another important distinction is between consumer and business products. This categorization is based on the way a product is used, and not on the specific characteristics of the product. **Consumer products** are those purchased by consumers for their own personal use. **Business products** are those purchased by a firm or organization for its own use. Thus, the same product could be classified differently depending on the purchase and use. For example, if Elena buys a pencil to use at home, it is considered a consumer product. If Elena's employer purchases the same pencil for her to use at work, it is considered a business product.

We have seen that the buying behaviors of consumers and businesses differ in important ways. These differences motivate different strategies, depending on whether a product is marketed to consumers or businesses. Take Singing Machine as an example. The company began by trying to market $2,000 karaoke machines to nightclubs. After limited success, it switched its focus to home karaoke machines. These machines are connected to TV sets and play special compact disks that allow users to read lyrics on the screen. A marketing tie-in with MTV, distribution through retailers like Best Buy and Target, and a price under $300 have made the product a success. Sales grew 83 percent annually for three years, reaching $59 million in 2001.[4] The move from a business to a consumer product made a major difference for Singing Machine. There are also different types of consumer products and business products, as Exhibit 8–3 demonstrates.

TYPES OF CONSUMER PRODUCTS There are millions of consumer products, and they can be classified in a number of ways. One especially useful approach is to classify products according to how consumers shop. Such an approach is valuable because it suggests that specific marketing strategies are relevant for a particular consumer product category. Relevant shopping behavior by category is described in Exhibit 8–4. Of course, the same product can be classified differently by different buyers.

Convenience products are items consumers do not want to spend much time shopping for. Buyers of convenience products typically want to make a quick purchase at the most convenient location. Although they may prefer a specific brand, they will buy something else if that brand is not available. Convenience products are normally low-priced, often-purchased goods. They might range from staples (toothpaste, bread, or mustard) to products bought on impulse (chewing gum, magazines, or candy bars) or in an emergency (umbrellas, antifreeze, or snow shovels).

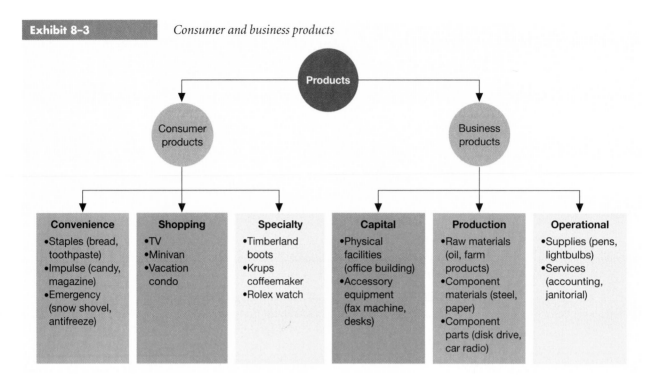

Exhibit 8–3   *Consumer and business products*

A key to marketing convenience products is to obtain extensive distribution. Marketers should make such products available at all convenient locations so consumers will be able to find the brand they want and not have to switch to another. Widespread distribution is especially important for products bought on impulse because consumers purchase them only when they see them during their shopping trip. Distribution is also important for products bought in emergencies.

Soft drinks are convenience products for most consumers. Although consumers might prefer Coke over Pepsi or vice versa, they tend to switch to the other if the preferred brand is not available. Coke and Pepsi marketing strategies are designed to ensure that their brands are readily available. Thus the brands are marketed through all types of retail outlets, restaurants, vending machines, and at the checkout counters in many grocery stores.

Shopping products, in contrast, are items consumers are willing to spend time shopping for. When consumers perceive all the product alternatives as similar, they often shop around for the best price. A family might shop at several electronics stores, for example, to get the best deal on a television. For other shopping products, consumers might see alternatives as differing in important ways and shop for the one that best meets their needs. A family might shop at Honda, Toyota, and Ford dealerships to determine which minivan suits them, as well as to obtain the best price.

Consumers are willing to spend time shopping if the purchase is important to them, particularly if the product is expensive. For marketers, the key strategic implication is to facilitate the shopping process. Typically, a shopping product needs to be readily available but not as widely available as a convenience product. Distribution outlets for a shopping product should provide extensive information to help consumers in the purchase decision. This may be accomplished with knowledgeable salespeople and informative communications and promotional materials. Salespeople and printed brochures for car models at dealerships illustrate typical marketing approaches for shopping products. Locating several car dealers in the same general area also would help to facilitate the shopping process.

The Internet has, however, changed the purchasing process for shopping goods. Consumers do not have to physically visit retail stores to get information about

Exhibit 8–4

Types of consumer products

	Prefer Specific Brand	Willing to Shop
Convenience	May	No
Shopping	No	Yes
Specialty	Yes	Yes

shopping goods. They can now "click" to many different sites to get needed information and then decide to make the purchase online or at a retail store. Consumers still spend time on shopping good purchases, but the Internet makes it possible for them to get more and better purchasing information in a convenient manner.

Specialty products are different in that consumers both want to purchase a specific brand and are willing to look to find it. They are willing to neither switch brands, as they are for convenience products, nor shop to evaluate product alternatives, as for shopping products. They want one brand, and they will travel to buy it.

Marketers might limit distribution of specialty products to exclusive outlets and can typically charge high prices. Such marketing efforts should focus on maintaining the loyalty of customers and the image of the product. Certainly, most marketers would enjoy selling a brand considered a specialty product. These are rare circumstances, however, for few consumers are committed to only one brand in many product categories.

TYPES OF BUSINESS PRODUCTS Classifying business products is difficult because a vast number of different products are used by for-profit firms, nonprofit organizations, and government agencies. Our categorization groups products according to the way they are used in the operation of a business (see Exhibit 8–3).

Capital products are expensive items used in business operations but do not become part of any type of finished product. Because they are used over long periods of time, their cost is normally depreciated or spread over some useful life rather than expensed completely in the year of purchase. Capital products range from physical facilities, such as manufacturing plants, office buildings, and major equipment, to accessory equipment such as desks, copy machines, fax machines, or fork-lifts.

The purchasing process for capital products may be long and involve many individuals. Marketers of capital products emphasize personal selling as the major communication tool. Prices are often negotiated, and sometimes businesses decide to rent or lease capital products rather than buy them outright.

Production products become part of some finished product. Raw materials, such as coal, oil, or farm products, are the basic type of production product. Component materials and component parts are also production products. Component materials are products that require further processing to be included in the finished product. Examples are steel, paper, and textiles. Component parts are fabricated for the finished product. They may require some minor processing or be used as is in the finished product. Thermostats and disk drives are examples.

The purchasing process for production products is extensive but typically less involved than for capital products. Businesses want to receive quality production products when they are needed; otherwise the production process may be interrupted. Marketers of production products therefore must emphasize both product quality and reliability in meeting delivery schedules. A buyer does not necessarily select the supplier with the lowest initial price. Increasingly, the long-run cost of doing business with suppliers is more important to firms than the short-run price of the product.

Operational products are used in a firm's activities but do not become part of any type of finished product. Maintenance, repair, and operating supplies are considered operational products. These include lightbulbs, cleaning materials, repair parts, and office supplies. Also included are services such as accounting, engineering, and advertising that are purchased from outside vendors rather than provided within the business.

The purchasing process for many operational products is the least extensive for any business product. After an initial purchase, and assuming the business is satisfied, subsequent purchases may be straight rebuys; that is, the buyer merely places an additional order with the same supplier. Thus it is important for a seller to get the initial order and to ensure that the buyer is satisfied with all aspects of the purchase. If this happens, it is almost impossible for a competitor to get its foot in the door.

Capital products are expensive items used in business operations. Komatsu markets construction equipment to business customers.

Product Components

We have said that consumers purchase products to satisfy needs. Another way to say this is that people really want a "bundle" of benefits when they purchase a product, and different consumers are likely to want different benefits from the same type of product. For example, some consumers purchase Rollerblade skates for fun, others as a way to increase health and fitness, and others because of the excitement involved with in-line roller skating.

To provide the benefits consumers want, marketers need to integrate the components that make up a product effectively. These consist of the product and customer service features illustrated in Exhibit 8–5. Product features include quality, design, branding, and packaging. Customer service encompasses various purchase and usage services. Different blends of product features and customer service provide different benefit bundles.

Credit cards offer a good example. Although all credit cards provide a basic benefit (credit), they offer different mixes of benefits to appeal to specific consumers. Credit cards differ in annual fees, rewards for use of the card, payment terms, design of the card, brand name, and services provided. All these components interact to produce the product, or the benefits, consumers purchase.

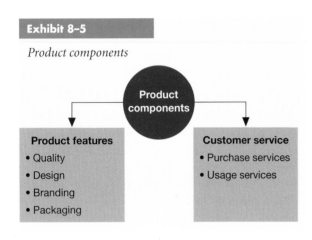

Exhibit 8–5

Product components

Product components

Product features
- Quality
- Design
- Branding
- Packaging

Customer service
- Purchase services
- Usage services

Quality

As a product component, product quality represents how well a product does what it is supposed to do as defined by the customer. Rational, a German manufacturer of computer-controlled ovens that combine convection and steam heat, recognizes the importance of defining product quality from the customer's viewpoint. Everywhere in the plant, signs say, "Gut genug? Der Kunde entscheidet" ("Good enough? The customer will decide").[5]

Consumers define quality in different ways. Clothing quality might be defined in terms of how the clothing looks and fits and how durable it is. Elements of quality in writing instruments could be how well the instrument writes, how it looks and feels, and how long it lasts. Automobile quality dimensions are related to safety, reliability, dependability, comfort, prestige, and other factors. The important point for marketers is to identify their target market's important quality characteristics and make sure their products deliver on these factors.

The importance of quality is evident in the automobile industry. J.D. Power conducts quality studies of automobile brands. Two of its most publicized ratings are the Initial Quality Survey (number of customer complaints in the first 90 days of ownership) and Vehicle Dependability Study (number of problems during three years of ownership). These are objective assessments of quality. Sometimes consumer perceptions of quality are different than the objective evaluations. For example, consumers generally perceive lower quality from many American brands, even though objective quality assessments indicate significant quality improvement in recent years. In fact, Cadillac and Buick were in the top five in the 2005 Initial Quality Survey.[6] Three examples illustrate the importance of both objective evaluations and subjective perceptions of quality.

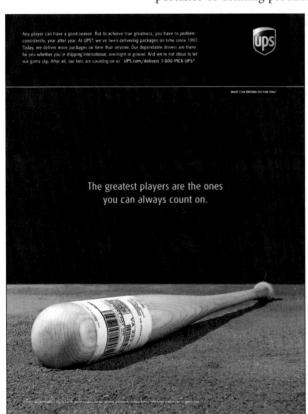

Quality is important for services. UPS emphasizes the dependability of its delivery service.

Speaking from Experience

Doris K. Christopher
Founder
The Pampered Chef

"Satisfying the needs of customers is the key to our success. The philosophy of direct selling is based on one-on-one interaction with customers. Through this direct interaction, customers provide feedback directly to the company regarding product quality, design, and service. At the Pampered Chef we believe that our products should earn the right to be in your kitchen. We say 'This is a good product, now how can we make it better?' We've made our mark by listening to our customers, improving our products, and offering them at competitive prices."

Doris started The Pampered Chef as a direct seller of high-quality kitchen tools in her suburban-Chicago basement in 1980. She grew the company to over $700 million in annual sales and sold it to Berkshire Hathaway. Doris has served as the chairperson of the Direct Selling Association, was named a regional winner of Ernst & Young's National Entrepreneur of the Year Award, and wrote *Come to the Table: A Celebration of Family Life.* She earned a B.S. in Home Economics from the University of Illinois at Urbana–Champaign.

Thinking Critically

You have decided to open a pizza restaurant that would provide customers with the highest-quality pizzas.

- What are the characteristics of a quality pizza as defined by most customers?

- How do you evaluate the quality of the pizzas offered by the existing pizza restaurants (Pizza Hut, Godfather's, Papa John's, etc.)?

- What do you plan to do to make your pizzas higher quality than what competitors offer?

- Nissan experienced losses in the late 1990s. The company decided to turn things around by introducing many new models. This strategy was successful as the company generated thousands of new customers for the 13 new vehicles it introduced since 1999. The company also returned to profitability. However, it fell from sixth to eleventh on the Initial Quality Survey with more customer complaints than the industry average. The company is trying to improve its product quality to keep its new customers and to reduce warranty costs.[7]

- When the Korean carmaker Hyundai entered the U.S. market, its cars were of low quality. The company decided to try to improve quality to "Toyota levels." Among other things, it increased the quality team from 100 to 865 workers and held twice-monthly quality meetings. This approach is apparently paying off. Five years later, Hyundai came within one complaint of Toyota in the Initial Quality Survey. It still lags behind many brands in the Vehicle Dependability Study, but it is working to improve this score. With a 10-year drive train warranty and 5 years on everything else, and improving quality, Hyundai has seen sales and profits increase significantly.[8]

- Mercedes's situation was almost the opposite of Hyundai's. Mercedes was a quality leader for many years. However, when Toyota and Nissan introduced lower-cost luxury cars, Mercedes changed its engineering approach to respond quickly to this competition. Unfortunately, the new cars generated many consumer complaints, and Mercedes dropped to number 26 in the 2003 Vehicle Dependability Study. Before it lost customers, the company moved quickly to solve the quality problems and moved back to a top five position in 2005. The newest models are receiving rave reviews from consumers and high scores from J.D. Power.[9]

Although the three automobile examples are different, product quality played a critical role in the marketing success of each company. The lessons are similar for most industries. Determining the important quality elements for targeted customers, working hard to improve quality in these areas, and communicating the quality improvements to customers are difficult tasks—but essential for success in today's competitive marketplace.

Design

Product design includes the styling, aesthetics, and function of a product. How a product is designed affects how it looks, how it works, how it feels, how easy it is to assemble and fix, and how easy it is to recycle.

Product design decisions can be pivotal in a product's success. Consider the impact on Motorola. Motorola lost its lead in the mobile phone market in 1998. It was slow to shift to digital, but it also produced many plain phones that did not appeal to customers. New CEO Ed Zander wanted to create more hip phones, so he moved the product design team to trendy offices in downtown Chicago. The designers responded with Razr V3, a superthin

Product design is an important component of both goods and services.

phone in an elegant clamshell. Although the Razr V3 has the same basic functions as other phones, it sells for around $350 and has been a hit in Europe and North America. Motorola sold 1.2 million Razr V3s in the first quarter of 2005 and increased its overall mobile phone market share by 1.4 percent.[10]

Product design is also important for services as it affects the consumer's experience. Kaiser Permanente, the largest HMO in the United States, worked with IDEO, a design firm, to improve the health care experience for customers. An assessment of the current situation indicated many problems, such as difficulties in checking in, uncomfortable waiting rooms, and examination rooms that were too small and intimidating. Based on these findings, Kaiser decided to make some design changes. It made the waiting rooms more comfortable, posted signs in the lobby with check-in instructions, enlarged the examination rooms, and added curtains for privacy. This new design improved the patient experience significantly.[11]

Much of the current focus on product design is to improve the performance of a product and to reduce the cost of producing it. Boeing did this when it designed the fighter jet for the twenty-first century. The design was very innovative with an unusual modular wing, a front-mounted engine, and stealth capabilities. This design improved jet fighter performance, but it also significantly reduced production costs.[12] Seagate automated its production process and standardized the key specifications for disk drives. These changes make it possible for the company to design and produce all types of drives quickly and at low cost. Seagate has used this advantage to respond to marketplace changes quickly. It designed one-inch drives for music players and larger drives for laptops and is generating sales growth in both areas.[13]

Another emphasis in product design is to add more features but make it easier for customers to use the product. Whirlpool is trying to do this with kitchen appliances. One approach is to make the control panels for all appliances have a common look, feel, and function. Once customers learn how to use one Whirlpool appliance, it will be easy for them to use other Whirlpool appliances. Another approach is to simplify the control panels. Current microwave ovens have 75 separate functions. The plan is to increase the number of functions to 250 but to present them to users in layered small groups. Preliminary tests show that customers are able to access the 250 functions in less time and with 30 percent fewer errors.[14]

Product design is becoming increasingly important for all types of products. Products receiving recent awards for exceptional design and commercial success include these:

- LiveStrong Wristband created by the Lance Armstrong Foundation with more than 5 million sold.

- Virgin Atlantic's Upper-Class Cabin, which increased revenue by 30 percent.

- Apple's Flat-Panel iMac G5 monitor, which doubled iMac unit sales.

- Google Gmail with 54 percent of customers coming from Hotmail and 33 percent from Yahoo!

- Fiskars Posthole Digger, which captured 25 percent of the market in 10 months.

These examples illustrate the important role of product design as a component of both goods and services.[15]

Branding

It is critical that a firm identify its products to distinguish them from similar products offered by competitors. This is the **branding** process. Several key terms need defining for this discussion:

- **Brand**—A name, term, sign, symbol, design, or combination that a firm uses to identify its products and differentiate them from those of competitors.

- **Brand name**—The element of a brand that can be vocalized, such as IBM, Tide, Snickers, or Diet Coke.

- **Brand mark**—The element of a brand that cannot be vocalized, such as the MGM lion, the Buick symbol, or the Nike Swoosh.

- **Trademark**—A brand or part of a brand that is registered with the U.S. Patent and Trademark Office. This registration gives the owner exclusive rights to use the brand and may even preclude other firms from using brand names or marks that are similar.

The global marketplace and new technologies are adding to the complexity of protecting brand names and brand marks. For example, World Wrestling Federation Entertainment Inc. had been using *wwf.com* as its Internet address and "WWF" as its logo. However, the World Wildlife Fund had been using the "WWF" initials in its marketing materials and Internet address for many years. The "WWF" initials were generally understood to represent the World Wildlife Fund in many countries around the world. An initial court and an appeals court in the United Kingdom found this to be the case and ordered the World Wrestling Federation to remove the "WWF" from its Internet address and logo outside the United States.[16]

The situation should be improved by the Madrid Protocol, an international system for registering trademarks administered by the World Intellectual Property Organization (WIPO). More than 70 countries, including the United States, have joined the Madrid Protocol. This treaty makes it easier and cheaper for firms to extend trademark protection to the member countries. A firm can file one basic application in its home country, have it extended to other countries, and pay a reduced fee.[17]

IMPORTANCE OF BRANDING   Branding is important to both consumers and marketers. From a consumer's viewpoint, branding facilitates buying. If there were no brands, consumers would have to evaluate the nonbranded products available every time they went shopping. They could never be sure they were purchasing the specific desired products and would have difficulty evaluating the quality of some. When selecting from among branded products, consumers can purchase specific ones and be reasonably certain of their quality. However, there are differences in the importance of brands across countries and products. One study found that consumers in England, Scotland, and Wales preferred branded products more than consumers from the Czech Republic, Hungary, Poland, and the Slovak Republic for cosmetics, clothing, and food products. Interestingly, there was a high level of brand preference in all of these countries for consumer electronic products.[18]

Branding also provides psychological benefits to consumers. Some buyers derive satisfaction from owning brands with images of prestige. These brands convey status. Examples are Rolex watches, Mercedes-Benz automobiles, and Waterford crystal.

Building strong brands and protecting brand names and brand marks is critical for many firms. P&G presents many of its successful brands in this picture.

From a marketer's viewpoint, branding has considerable value. A brand can be used to represent the benefits of a product, including those associated with specific product features and those relevant to the product purchase and use experience. This can make it easier to differentiate a company's product from competing offerings. Branding also facilitates and focuses a firm's marketing efforts. Chinese companies are beginning to realize the potential value of brands. Haier (appliances), Legend (personal computers), Kejian (cell phones), TCL (consumer electronics), and other companies are trying to build their brands outside China, much as Japanese and Korean firms did with the Sony, Samsung, and Sanyo brands. Building these brands is expected to lead to increased sales and profits worldwide for these Chinese companies.[19]

BUILDING BRANDS   Many firms focus considerable effort on building brands. However, sometimes too much attention is paid to the brand and not enough to the customers of the brand. As discussed in Chapter 1, the ultimate goal is to increase customer equity. Building brands is a means to attract and retain profitable customers. A brand has little value in and of itself. Its value depends on the relationships it has with targeted customers. For example, the brand WiLL in Japan is owned and managed by a consortium of companies. The brand targets new-generation women in their twenties or thirties who like things that are genuine and fun. Products include WiLL Vi (a car made by Toyota), WiLL PC (made by Panasonic), and WiLL beer (brewed by Asashi). The WiLL brand has value because the various products create value for the target market. Because the purpose of the WiLL brand is to increase customer equity, the consortium companies will continue to introduce products under the WiLL brand to expand relationships with these customers.[20] A basic brand-building process is presented in Exhibit 8–6.

To build a strong brand, marketers need to first determine an identity for the brand. A **brand identity** is the brand concept from the marketer's viewpoint. It should define the brand in simple, clear terms. All aspects of the brand-building process should support and reinforce the brand identity. Examples of effective brand identities are strong, reliable products backed by serious, competent people (Caterpillar) and thicker, creamier, and pricier than any other ice cream (Haagen-Dazs).[21] A good brand identity distinguishes the brand from others in the market by communicating characteristics important to target customers. This is a critical step in the brand-building process, but some companies may not be achieving this differentiation: One study found that consumers perceived more similarities than differences among many competing brands.[22]

The next step consists of three interrelated activities. Marketers must ensure that targeted customers are aware of the availability of the brand (**brand awareness**), have an accurate perception of the brand's characteristics that matches the brand identity (**brand image**), and understand the benefits from purchasing and using the brand (**brand promise**). Achieving these objectives typically requires an integrated marketing communications effort. All marketing communications need to communicate the brand identity consistently.

An example of this step is the Roundhouse brand. The Roundhouse brand was created for a company that provides electronic data interchange (EDI) services to the fashion industry. The brand identity was to solve clothing replenishment problems for customers in the fashion industry. All marketing communications included the taglines "Suddenly, IT is sexy" to reinforce the EDI services and "We know the business" to support the fashion industry focus. To generate brand awareness, print ads were placed in *Women's Wear Daily;* postcards and e-mail were sent to potential prospects; and several public relations efforts were implemented. An eight-page brochure was then mailed to the top 100 prospects to establish an accurate brand image. Finally, salespeople followed up with these prospects to communicate the brand promise and close the sale. A brand

| Exhibit 8–6 | *Brand-building process* |

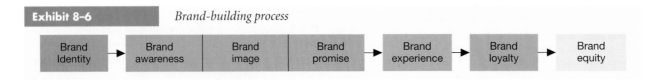

Web site was also developed to reinforce all marketing efforts. After two months, the brand-building effort brought in 15 new customers, increased sales by 50 percent, and doubled profit margins.[23]

Many firms think the brand-building process ends here because new customers have been added and sales and profits are increasing. Brand building is, however, more than an effective integrated marketing communications program. Marketing communications can attract customers and generate transactions, but more is needed to develop and expand relationships with customers. Firms need to ensure that the **brand experience** customers have in purchasing and using the product meets or exceeds the brand promise. If customers receive the promised benefits, their brand experience is good and the basis for future purchases is established. Ideally, the customers exhibit **brand loyalty** and select the brand on all or most purchasing opportunities.

Let's return to the Roundhouse example. The firm was successful in generating brand awareness, establishing the desired brand image, and communicating a relevant brand promise. New customers were added, and sales and profits increased. Despite these favorable signs, the success of the Roundhouse brand-building efforts will depend largely on the brand experience of customers. If customers have a positive brand experience, they will continue to use the Roundhouse service, with many becoming brand loyal. If customers have a negative brand experience, the initial brand-building successes will be lost as the customers switch to another brand. It will also be extremely difficult to get these lost customers back in the future.

The more brand loyal customers a brand has and the more brand loyal these customers are, the higher the **brand equity,** or the value the brand has in the marketplace. Brand equity has a financial dimension, especially important in any merger or acquisition transaction. The world's most valuable brands are presented in Exhibit 8–7.

Brand equity is also important because it is closely related to customer equity and affects marketing efforts. The same marketing strategy and level of expenditures used for different brands are likely to have different results, depending on brand equity. Typically, marketing efforts built on an established positive brand awareness, image, promise, and loyalty—or high brand equity—are more successful than those conducted by firms with low brand equity.

Building strong brands is extremely important to many companies. The typical approach is to focus efforts on marketing communications to generate brand awareness, to develop a desired brand image, and to get consumers to purchase the brand. This is important, but it is only part of the brand-building process. Research indicates that strong brands are built on the favorable experiences consumers have with a firm's products and services. Effective marketing communications can only drive consumers to an Internet site or retail store or to try a product or service. Brand loyalty and brand equity depend on the experiences consumers have once at the Internet site or retail store, or when the product or service is purchased and used.

Exhibit 8–7	The World's 10 Most Valuable Brands	

Rank	Brand	2004 Brand Value ($billions)
1	Coca-Cola	67.4
2	Microsoft	61.4
3	IBM	53.8
4	GE	44.1
5	Intel	33.5
6	Disney	27.1
7	McDonald's	25.0
8	Nokia	24.0
9	Toyota	22.7
10	Marlboro	22.1

T. Rowe Price is a mutual fund company that focuses on increasing customer equity by building brand equity. It emphasizes a positive brand experience by achieving consistent financial performance for its investors. The uncertain stock market in recent years led many mutual fund companies to increase advertising to stimulate growth. Not T. Rowe Price: The company actually cut its ad budget by 27 percent. Instead, it continued to focus on achieving consistent financial performance and providing customers with valuable information and services. A quarterly newsletter presents articles about different financial management topics that customers like; circulation is up 30 percent. The company also has an advisory services team that conducts personal telephone interviews with clients rather than have them complete and submit forms, as most competitors do. This attention to consistent financial performance and personalized customer service resulted in T. Rowe Price being at the top of a recent brand loyalty study of mutual fund companies.[24]

Doris Christopher, Founder, The Pampered Chef, discusses the brand-building process: "Building brands is important for many firms. In the direct-selling industry, to build a brand means to build a trusting relationship with customers. Customers will continue to buy products from companies with whom they have good experiences. The Pampered Chef believes in building brands through fulfilling promises. We make a promise to our customers that with every product we sell they will get the best quality product at the best price, with service that exceeds their expectations."

TYPES OF BRANDS Marketers must decide early whether to brand a product, and if so, which type of brand to use. **Generics** are products that are typically not branded. They are normally labeled instead by their generic name and may be of lower quality and cost less than branded competitors.

The pharmaceutical industry offers an interesting example of generic and branded products. Branded drugs receive patent protection to allow the company time to recoup the costs associated with getting the drug approved and marketed. Once the patent expires, the branded drug company can introduce an "authorized generic version" and receive exclusive generic rights for 180 days. If the branded company does not do this, the first generic company to get FDA approval can receive the 180 days of exclusive rights. After the expiration of exclusive rights, generic companies can get FDA approval to introduce a traditional generic product (contains the active ingredient of the branded drug and acts the same way in the body as the branded drug) or a branded generic product (contains the same active ingredient, but acts differently in the body by lasting longer, including other compounds, or the like).[25] The number of generic drugs in the United States is growing rapidly because of expiring patents and low prices to consumers. Although more prescriptions are filled by generic products, total dollar sales of branded drugs are still higher than for generics. About one-third of generic drug sales are from branded generics.[26]

If a firm decides to brand its products, it can choose one of two types of brands. The first and most familiar type is a **manufacturer brand.** Sometimes referred to as a **national brand** or **regional brand,** it is sponsored by the manufacturer of the product. The manufacturer is responsible for the product's quality and marketing. Many firms, such as P&G, IBM, Gillette, and Xerox, use manufacturer brands for their products.

The other type is a **distributor brand.** Also called a **store brand, private brand,** or **private label,** it is sponsored by a distributor such as a wholesaler or retailer. Although the manufacturer's name may be indicated somewhere on the label, the distributor is responsible for the product's quality and marketing. Familiar store brands are Craftsman tools (Sears) and President's Choice grocery products (Loblaw). Many distributors are introducing their own brands. The lower marketing costs for private label brands make it possible for distributors to maintain high profit margins while charging lower prices than for manufacturer brands.

Intense competition today between manufacturer and distributor brands has been termed the *battle of the brands.* Initially, the mass marketing power of large manufacturers gave them the edge in this battle. Recently, however, large retailers with tremendous amounts of consumer purchasing information have improved their position substantially.

Thinking Critically

The increasing attention given to private brands by many retailers is causing problems for manufacturer brands.

- What strategies would you recommend manufacturers employ in order to strengthen their brands and combat the increasing penetration of private brands?

- What strategies should retailers use to offer the best mix of manufacturer and private brands?

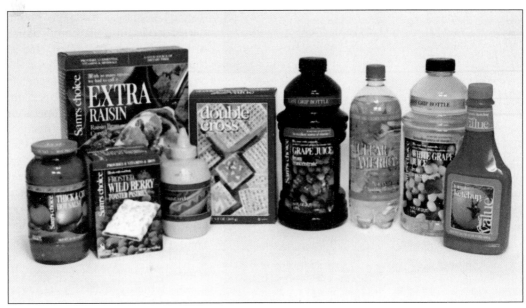

Private labels allow retailers to charge low prices and earn high profit margins. Sam's Choice and Great Value are distributor brands of Wal-Mart.

The competition for market share involves the value provided to consumers. They typically perceive manufacturer brands as of higher quality than distributor brands. Yet the quality and cost differences vary considerably. When consumers perceive large quality differences, manufacturer brands may provide the most value and are purchased. When consumers perceive small quality differences, then distributor brands may provide the best value and are purchased.

More and higher-quality store brands are being introduced. Sales of store brands have been increasing about 8.5 percent versus only 1.5 percent for national brands. In the United States about 20 percent of purchases are store brands, but this figure is around 40 percent in Europe. Successful store brands include Kirkland (Costco), Ol' Roy dog food (Wal-Mart), Charles Shaw wine (Trader Joe's), Michael Graves housewares (Target), and B&N Classics (Barnes & Noble).[27] Because of the success of many of these private labels, companies such as Kraft Foods are dropping some national brands that cannot maintain a strong position in a product category.[28] The battle between manufacturer and distributor brands is likely to intensify in the foreseeable future.

CHOOSING A BRAND NAME Choosing an effective brand name is an important decision for both manufacturer and distributor brands. The brand name communicates a great deal, which can facilitate brand awareness and brand image. In general, an effective brand name suggests something about the product's benefits; is easy to pronounce, recognize, and remember; is distinctive in some way; and can be translated into other languages. Ideally, a brand name should help to communicate to consumers the major benefits of the firm's product. If this is achieved, the brand name helps to link brand awareness with brand image. As consumers become aware of the brand name, they begin to associate it with specific product benefits.

There are some interesting trends in naming brands over the years. In the early years founders' names were used to communicate traditional ideals of quality and craftsmanship. Examples include Heinz (1869), Ford (1903), and Kellogg's (1906). Later, large firms with long names began to employ acronyms, such as RCA (1919), TWA (1930), and IBM (1947). The trend moved toward abstract names that implied high-tech precision. Xerox (1961), Exxon (1972), and Microsoft (1975) are examples. The 1990s saw the emergence of absurd, meaningless umbrella names, such as Yahoo! (1994), Google (1998), and Vivendi (1998). The 2000s are bringing an emphasis on names that have meaning. JetBlue is a good example of this trend. The company's strategy is to offer budget travelers a stylish way to fly. The name Blue was selected to communicate clear skies and serenity and Jet

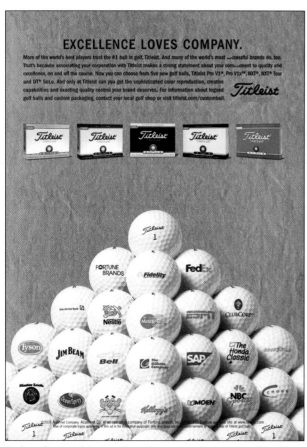

Co-branding combines two brand names on the same product. Many companies like to be associated with a brand like Titleist.

to emphasize fast air travel. The brand name and company started service in 2000. Competitors tried to follow suit, with Delta's Song and United's Ted used to name the discount operations of these airlines.[29]

As more companies operate globally, international considerations are increasingly important in selecting a brand name. This is not easy. Sometimes companies must use different names in different international areas. For example, Mitsubishi's SUV is named Pajero in most of the world. However, in Spanish this means "wankermobile," so the name was changed to Montero in Spain, Latin America, and the United States.[30] General Motors, on the other hand, is trying to change the name of its Korean Daewoo brand to Chevrolet around the world. Preliminary research indicates that the Chevrolet name enjoys a good global image, and sales have gone up in every area where the name has been changed from Daewoo to Chevrolet.[31]

An alternative to developing a brand name is to license an existing name or logo. **Licensing** typically consists of the right to use a trademark in exchange for paying royalties on the sales of the licensed product. The licensing industry in the United States is over $70 billion with Disney, Sony, and Procter & Gamble being big players. The company purchasing the licensing rights gets an established brand name for its product. The licensing company gets income from royalties, but also gets brand exposure and opportunities for brand extensions. For example, P&G has built its Iams pet food line into a pet nutrition and health company through licensing.[32]

Another approach is **co-branding,** where two brand names are used on a product. The objective is to capitalize on the brand equity in each brand as a way to appeal to defined target markets more effectively. Co-branding has become commonplace in the credit card industry. For example, the Visa brand name is often combined with another brand name to focus on specific markets. The other brand might be another company trying to generate sales for its products, such as Ford, Traveler's Advantage, or Churchill Downs, or a nonprofit organization trying to generate revenue, such as your university or its alumni association. Another example of co-branding is the inclusion of "Intel Inside" on specific personal computer brands. Some interesting co-branding relationships have been introduced. The Ferrari logo and Acer laptops, Goodyear and Adidas on Tuscany shoes, and Nickolodeon and Holiday Inn at Nickolodeon Family Suites are examples.[33]

Packaging

Packaging is an important component for many products. A *package* is the container or wrapper for a product. It typically includes a *label*, a printed description of the product on the package. Packaging is important to both consumers and distributors of a product. A product's package might perform a number of different functions, including protecting the product until consumed, storing the product until consumed, facilitating consumption of the product, promoting the product, and facilitating disposal of the product.

Because many retailers are self-service sellers, a product's package must communicate the brand's image and help to sell the product. Distinctive packages help capture the attention of consumers as they view competitive products. Both package and label also provide important information

Packaging is an important component of many products. Black & Decker uses different packages for its different brands.

that consumers use in evaluating competing brands. For example, the concern for health has led the FDA to mandate that food manufacturers state the total amount of trans fat used in their products. Although all companies will have to do this, some companies are doing this sooner to gain a competitive advantage. Frito-Lay changed its recipes by switching to cooking oils that are free of trans fats. The company has already designed new labels that state zero grams of trans fat.[34]

Black & Decker markets Quantum tools to the do-it-yourself market and DeWalt tools to the professional market. The Quantum package appeals to the dominantly masculine market and has a photograph of the product and the Black & Decker name prominently displayed on the package because the Black & Decker name has credibility in the nonprofessional market. Packaging for the DeWalt products features a neon yellow background and black type and has no references to Black & Decker because professionals do not associate the Black & Decker name with professional tools. The different packages have helped to increase sales of both brands by appealing to the targeted market segments.[35]

Innovations in packaging offer ways to differentiate brands that consumers might otherwise perceive as very similar. An example is Annie's Homegrown. The company markets food products that contain no artificial ingredients. One of its successful products is white-cheddar macaroni and cheese. This product has a purple package with a friendly rabbit on it to differentiate it from the blue boxes used by market leader Kraft Foods.[36]

Packaging innovations can make a product more convenient or attractive and lead to substantial sales increases. When Dean Foods created a tall, grippable milk bottle package for its Milk Chug product, sales of white and flavored milk soared. Dutch Boy had similar results when it changed from the typical metal paint can to a side handled, spout-pourable, square plastic container for its paints.[37] Blue Q has built a $9 million business by putting mundane merchandise into entertaining packages with exciting graphics, charismatic characters, and witty phrases.[38] A final example is the energy drink market. Part of Red Bull's success is the use of an 8.3-ounce slim can instead of the traditional 12-ounce can. Other energy drink makers have followed suit and are increasing the can size. In fact, the 16-ounce can is currently the fastest growing, but this may not last long because BooKoo now comes in a 24-ounce can.[39]

An ecological concern is critical to packaging success in the current environment. Many consumers complain about packages that use too much material or material that is difficult to dispose of. Compact disks were introduced with excessive packaging, and many people remember the flap over McDonald's Styrofoam containers. Today the CD industry uses a new standardized package that is much smaller than the original versions, and McDonald's now packages all its hamburgers in paper wrappers. There are many opportunities for marketers to develop innovative packages that help sell a brand, improve its function, and have environmental advantages.

Customer Service

The final product component is **customer service,** which describes the assistance provided to help a customer with the purchase or use of a product. Customer service applies to both goods and services. For example, a consumer purchasing phone lines from BellSouth for a

CREATING CUSTOMER VALUE

Giving customers what they want

Avis has achieved the highest level of brand loyalty in the rental car industry. Hertz, the market leader, spends about $53 million annually on advertising and provides good customer service. Avis spends only around $9 million a year on advertising but gives customers exactly what they want. Its objective is to manage the entire rental car experience in a way that delights customers. Delighting customers increases customer equity.

Each year Avis determines the set of factors that car renters care about the most. This year the factors are price, convenience, safety, and customer service. The company then breaks the entire car rental process into more than 100 incremental steps and looks for ways to infuse the important factors into these steps. One example from this process is the Avis Preferred service program. This was the first in the industry, and it reduces the time it takes a customer to pick up a car at an airport by 5 to 10 minutes. Customers love it; more than 1 million have signed up. Avis advertises "We Try Harder," and it does!

"OUR NEW DESK CLERK
LENT HIS CUFF LINKS
TO A GUEST FOR
A CRUCIAL MEETING.
INSTANTLY
WE KNEW WE HIRED
THE RIGHT GUY."

Bill Marriott

That's a true story. There are many others. They are just one
of the many reasons frequent business travelers prefer Marriott.
Call your travel agent or 1-800-228-9290.

Marriott
WE MAKE IT HAPPEN FOR YOU.

Providing exceptional customer service is one way to
gain competitive advantage. Marriott celebrates how
one employee did something exceptional to help a
hotel guest.

new home is buying the basic service of being able to communicate by
phone from specified locations within the home. These are the basic features of the phone service. However, customer service concerns all the
contacts the customer has with BellSouth employees. This includes the
person taking the order and the employee installing the phone line. For
instance, customers might evaluate the service according to how well the
service options were explained, whether the installer arrived on time,
and whether the work was completed as promised.

For many products, especially business goods, customer service differentiates competitors. Many successful companies differentiate
themselves from competitors by providing better customer service regardless of whether marketing goods or services. Providing exceptional customer service can give a firm a marketing advantage. Because
competitors can quickly copy changes in basic product components,
the key to success in many industries is beating the competition in customer service. An innovative customer service can sometimes provide
exceptional and unique value to customers, as indicated in "Creating
Customer Value: Giving Customers What They Want."

Few things can help a firm more than giving customers exceptional
service, even under trying conditions. An example will illustrate. The
warehouse manager of Miller Business Systems received an order for
20 desks, 20 executive chairs, 40 side chairs, and 20 file cabinets that the
customer wanted delivered and set up later in the afternoon. But there
were no trucks or employees available to make the delivery. On hearing about the problem, the president had the warehouse manager rent
a truck, and the two delivered and installed everything that afternoon
as requested. It was an unusual situation, but what to do was clear: "If you promise a customer, deliver."[40]

**Doris Christopher, Founder, The Pampered Chef, emphasizes the importance of
providing customers with excellent service:** "Selling a product is only the first step
in building a relationship with customers. Many times when customers take home
a product they are unsure how to use it. At The Pampered Chef we make sure this
does not happen. At our Kitchen Shows, the customer has the opportunity to try
the product before he or she buys it. We also ensure that once the customers get
the product home, they know how it will meet their needs in the kitchen. With
each product we provide easy-to-read instructions detailing how to properly care
for and use it, along with recipes that utilize the product. Our Kitchen Consultants
also offer ongoing customer service and support after the sale."

The critical task facing marketers is to combine quality, design, branding, packaging,
and customer service components into an effective product offering. A product must meet
the needs of the target market and also have advantages over competitors on important
product components. Moreover, businesses must constantly be ready to alter product
components to adapt to a dynamic marketing environment.

Summary

1. **Understand the differences between goods and services.** Products can be viewed as a continuum, with goods at one end and services at the other. Goods are physical products; services are nonphysical products. Goods are more tangible, nonperishable, separable, and standardized than services. Most products represent a mixture of goods and services.

2. **Differentiate between consumer and business products, and discuss the different types of each.** Consumer products are those purchased by consumers for their personal use. Business products are those purchased by a firm for its own use.

   Different types of consumer products include convenience, shopping, and specialty products, which differ in the amount of shopping consumers are willing to undertake. Consumers are not willing to shop for convenience products, will shop to make the best purchase for shopping products, and will shop to purchase a specific product for specialty products.

   Business products include capital, production, and operational products. Capital products are expensive goods that do not become part of a company's finished product. Production goods become part of a finished product; operational goods are used in a company's operations but do not become part of a finished product.

3. **Recognize that marketers need to appreciate the perspective of the consumer.** People purchase products to satisfy needs or solve problems. They perceive products as bundles of benefits that can help them satisfy needs or solve problems. To view products from the customer's perspective, marketers must focus on the benefits that product components provide to customers.

4. **Define and discuss the importance of product quality, product design, branding, packaging, and customer service.** Marketers need to look at products as consisting of various components that provide benefits to consumers. The major components are product quality, product design, branding, packaging, and customer service. Product quality could be described as an assessment of how well a product does what it is supposed to do from the customer's viewpoint. Product design includes how the product looks and feels, and how easy it is to assemble and use.

   Branding describes the way a firm identifies its products from those offered by competitors. Packaging addresses the container or wrapper for a product and any labeling that might be provided. Customer service refers to any activity intended to facilitate the purchasing or use of a product.

5. **Explain how the different product components need to be integrated to meet the needs of customers.** Marketers must integrate all product components to offer the bundle of benefits desired by customers. Marketers can achieve competitive advantages by skillfully mixing the different product components into an effective, complete product offering.

Understanding Marketing Terms and Concepts

Thinking about Marketing

1. What are the basic differences between goods and services?
2. Why is it important to differentiate between consumer and business products and among different types of each?
3. Refer to "Using Technology: Mass Customization." How do these examples represent a blend of goods and services?
4. Refer to "Creating Customer Value: Giving Customers What They Want." What are other things Avis can do to build customer equity?

5. Why is brand equity important?
6. Explain what product quality is. Why might it be important to your classmates?
7. Explain how firms can develop competitive advantages through customer service.
8. How does a global perspective affect product component decisions?
9. Why is it important to incorporate environmental issues into packaging decisions?
10. How are customer value and customer service related?

Applying Marketing Skills

1. Go to a large chain supermarket. Select any one specific product and identify the manufacturer brands, distributor brands, and generics that this store stocks. List each specific brand under each type and compare the product components for each. Summarize your findings to report the results.
2. Assume you have developed a new type of microwave popcorn that tastes as good as competitive products but takes only half the time to prepare. Develop a

manufacturer brand name for this product. Compare the name you have chosen with brand names for other microwave popcorn brands. Discuss why you think your brand name will be effective.

3. Look through the ads in the local newspaper. Identify all the examples of customer service you find. Summarize your findings into a list of the ways marketers are using customer service to differentiate their products.

Using the www in Marketing

Activity One Go to Frito-Lay's home page (*http://www.fritolay.com*).

1. For most consumers, are Frito-Lay's products convenience, shopping, or specialty products? Citing evidence from the Web site, is Frito-Lay's marketing strategy consistent with your classification?
2. How would you evaluate the brand names of Frito-Lay products? Which are the best? Why?
3. How does this Web site help Frito-Lay provide added value to customers and retailers?

Activity Two The most obvious examples of product design are for physical goods such as cars and home appliances. However, product design is also important for services. View the following Web sites:

Yahoo! (*http://www.yahoo.com*)
MSN (*http://www.msn.com*)
AOL (*http://aol.com*)

1. How does product design apply to these services?
2. Compare the design of each of these sites.
3. What recommendations do you have to improve the design of each site?

Making Marketing Decisions

Case 8–1 *IBM: Integrating Goods and Services*

IBM has traditionally been involved in marketing goods such as computers and servers. It recently began offering various services such as consulting. One new idea is to use technology to integrate services into some of its products.

Computer networks can be temperamental, as all computer users know. Mechanical failures, software glitches, and traffic bottlenecks are normal problems. The

typical solution in many organizations is to contact the technical services department to get the problem fixed. But the cost of maintaining an adequate technical services department is high and growing. And many of the tasks performed by the technical people are tedious and labor intensive. Examples include updating software, changing settings, formatting drives, and many others.

IBM is trying to improve this approach by developing hardware and software systems that can take care of themselves. This is called *autonomic computing*. Robert Morris, director of IBM's Almaden Research Center, explains: "Systems will self-manage and self-repair, learning from mistakes, always aware of what can help them get things done." IBM's newest servers already use autonomic systems to configure themselves on networks and to order replacement parts when needed. Research is under way to expand the use of autonomic computing in many different ways.

All of this sounds good, but what happens if something goes wrong? One of the causes of the 1987 stock market crash was that automated stock-trading programs continued to sell shares even as the market continued to fall. Other potential catastrophes are possible. IBM recognizes this and plans to build self-checks and safety protocols into the systems.

One potential benefit to organizations using autonomic computing systems is that fewer people will be needed to keep complex computer systems running. This could reduce the cost of technical service departments dramatically. But if technical service workers think they will lose their jobs, will they embrace the autonomic systems and help get them established in an organization?

IBM calls its autonomic computing services effort Project eLiza. As its research develops more applications, the potential to make it easier and less expensive for organizations to keep complex computer network systems running smoothly increases. The addition of autonomic computing services to IBM hardware should make the products more valuable to customers.

Questions

1. What is your assessment of the value of the autonomic computing services being developed by IBM? What problems need to be addressed? How?

2. What markets would you recommend that IBM target initially? Why?

3. What key quality elements should IBM emphasize in marketing the autonomic computing services?

4. Should products that include the autonomic computing services be branded? Why or why not? If so, what brand name would you suggest? Why?

Case 8–2 Columbia Sportswear: Designing Quality Products

Gertrude Boyle, known as Gert, had helped her husband operate Columbia Sportswear Company in its early years. For example, she sewed the company's first fishing vest at her kitchen table. It included many pockets because customers wanted more places to store flies, pliers, and fishing line. Unfortunately, her husband died of a heart attack in 1970. She tried to sell the company but could not get a good price. So with the help of her son, Timothy Boyle, she decided to run the company.

Gert and Timothy began by listening to customers and innovating. Quad jackets for hunters were one success. These jackets represented an innovative design that featured a weatherproof outer shell and an insulated inner jacket that could be worn together or separately. A similarly designed Bugaboo ski jacket was another success. This approach led to high-quality outdoor sportswear at lower prices than the major competitors, Patagonia and North Face.

Columbia also used an innovative advertising approach to communicate to customers. The humorous ads are called "Mother Gert" ads and include Gert and Timothy in various situations. Usually "Mother Gert" is portrayed as a tyrant who makes sure that the company's products live up to her tough quality standards. Her favorite line is "Old age and treachery will overcome youth and skill."

High-quality, well-designed clothing at reasonable prices, effective ads, and rapid expansion of the outdoor sportswear market helped Columbia increase sales and profits. The company went public in 1998, with its stock price doubling in the following four years.

It may be difficult to continue this type of growth. Warm winters and a depressed economy in the United States have slowed growth to 2 to 4 percent. This is not expected to improve much in the near future, so the firm is looking for new growth approaches. One is to lessen the company's reliance on weather-related clothing. Footwear and sportswear are being considered. Another option is to expand into overseas markets, with Europe a first choice.

Gert is now 78 years old, but she has no intention of retiring. She has built one of the world's largest outdoor apparel companies during the past 32 years. She and Timothy will, however, have to develop a strategy to continue growth in the future.

Questions

1. What are the key components of the company's products?

2. Why is design such an important element of outdoor sportswear?

3. Would you recommend expansion into footwear or sportswear? Why or why not?

4. Would you recommend international expansion? Why or why not?

Chapter Nine

DEVELOPING NEW PRODUCTS AND SERVICES

After studying this chapter, you should be able to

1 Recognize the different types of new products.

2 Discuss the different sources of new products.

3 Understand the stages in the new product development process.

4 Describe the way marketing research is used in the new product development process.

5 Appreciate the keys to new product success.

3M

3M is a $20 billion company with more than 67,000 employees who create, manufacture, and sell products in 200 countries around the world. The company has operations in more than 60 countries. Some of 3M's products, such as Scotch Magic Tape, are well-known brands purchased by individual consumers and organizations. Other products are components for automobiles, computers, and other products purchased only by business customers.

The real distinguishing characteristic of 3M is its continuous emphasis on innovation. One of the company's major objectives is to generate 30 percent of each year's sales from products that are less than four years old. This means that 3M must continually develop and introduce successful new products. Thus one of the driving principles at 3M is "the promotion of entrepreneurship and insistence upon freedom in the workplace to pursue innovative ideas." Efforts are directed toward listening to commercial partners and consumers to identify problems to be solved and needs to be satisfied. Then products are developed to solve these problems and satisfy these needs. The objective is to make people's lives better by providing new products with superior features, advantages, and benefits.

3M celebrated its 100th birthday in April 2002 using the theme "A Century of Innovation." Despite its success in new product development, the company is involved in several changes. Jim McNerney was hired from General Electric as the first outsider to become chairman and CEO at

3M. He arrived during the tough economic times of 2001. Although 3M's performance held up better than that of many other manufacturers, the new CEO targeted sales and profit growth of over 10 percent annually.

3M is achieving growth through international expansion and new product innovation. Much of the international growth is coming from the developing economies of China, Russia, Eastern Europe, Brazil, and India. Recent innovative new products include Post-it Super Sticky Notes, Scotch Transparent Duct Tape, optical films for LCD televisions, and a new family of Scotch-Brite Cleaning Products. Future new products are expected from emerging technologies, such as track and trace, nanotechnology, separation and filtration, and sensors and diagnostics. 3M is also moving into the service area. One example is its Strategic Intellectual Asset Management business. This business helps companies solve research and development challenges by identifying and licensing appropriate 3M technologies.

3M provides an especially interesting example of the importance of new product development. If the company generates 30 percent of sales from products less than four years old, then over $6 billion of its $20 billion total sales come from relatively new products. To meet this objective year after year, 3M must continuously churn out new products and effectively market many of them. New products are clearly the key to 3M's growth and success.

In this chapter we examine new product development. We begin by discussing the types and sources of new products. Then we discuss the various stages of the new product development process. Finally, we suggest several keys for successful new product development.

New Product Overview

New product development is a key element of success for many firms. The iPod was a big winner for Apple.

Developing successful new products drives sales and profit growth for many companies. Research indicates that companies leading their industries in profitability and sales growth gain 49 percent of their revenues from products developed in the most recent five years. Companies at the bottom in sales and profit growth achieve only 11 percent of sales from new products.[1]

Another study of 2,000 companies predicted that new products would account for 37 percent of total sales in the future, up from the then-current level of 28 percent.[2] This seems reasonable because companies often set specific goals for new products. We have already mentioned 3M's new product goals. Rubbermaid is an additional example. Rubbermaid wants to enter a new product category every 12 to 18 months and expects to get 33 percent of sales from products introduced within the past five years.[3]

Companies also develop new products to respond to changing customer needs and competitor actions. For example, more health-conscious consumers are turning to "fast casual" restaurants like Panera Bread and Baja Fresh for lunch. This is taking market share from the fast-food chains. In response, McDonald's, Wendy's, and others are offering more healthful menu alternatives. Main-dish salads are one example, with sales up around 14 percent.[4]

Despite the importance of developing new products, a large percentage of them fail. Although different statistics are often reported, studies indicate that around 50 percent of new products fail.[5] Whatever the exact figure, new product failures are costly. The failures of Ford's Edsel, DuPont's Corfam, Polaroid's Polarvision, RCA's Videodisc, Cadillac's Allante, and IBM's PCjr cost each company millions.

These and other costly failures motivate companies to improve their new product development process. The aim is to decrease the percentage of new product failures, reduce the cost of development, and shorten the time required to get new products to market. These objectives drive most of the changes companies are making in the new product development process. Herman Miller, for example, incorporated customers, cross-functional teams, and computer software to develop new office furniture that satisfies customer needs. This approach shortened the new product development cycle by 50 percent, lowered costs substantially, and led to an 11 percent sales increase in a sluggish market.[6] A study of consumer product manufacturers found that most are shortening product development time to meet the needs of retailers. Study results indicated that 36 percent had one- to three-month development cycles, 36 percent had three- to six-month cycles, and 28 percent took six months to a year for new product development.[7]

Speaking from Experience

"Getting new products to market quickly is critical to success in today's business environment. If you can't be the first to market, you run the risk of your competitor being several jumps ahead by the time you introduce a new me-too product. Small, innovative companies with first-to-market products often find themselves acquired by larger companies who are willing to pay high premiums for the advantages of early market entry. The challenge Lucent faces in the communication industry is in being able to take advantage of technological advancements while not forcing your customer to continuously replace costly infrastructure. The difficulty lies in anticipating technological advances and being able to integrate them into existing products. Lucent is no longer just in the business of producing telephones. Today we must compete in unfamiliar industries such as cable, the Internet, and wireless data transmission."

L. A. Mitchell
Account Executive for Large
Business Accounts
Lucent Technologies

L. A. Mitchell is Account Executive for Large Business Accounts at Lucent Technologies. She has worked on developing sales forecasts for new and existing products, developed marketing plans for various sales teams, and currently assists local phone companies in marketing communications features to large business accounts. L. A. earned her M.S. in marketing from Colorado State University.

Types of New Products

At first glance, defining a new product would seem to be easy. Yet the term *new* can be defined from different vantage points and in a number of ways. The first issue is, new to whom? The first time a customer uses a product, it is a new product to him or her, even if it has been available and used by others for a long time. In this case, though the product newness affects the customer's purchasing behavior and the firm's marketing strategies, it does not have a major impact on an organization's new product development process.

What does directly affect this process is how new the product is to the organization. And even from an organizational perspective, there are degrees of newness. Exhibit 9–1 presents several categories of new products, organized by how new they are to the company developing and marketing the product.

New-to-the-world products are the only ones that are new to both consumers and organizations. These products have never been offered before to any group of consumers; if successful, they spawn a completely new industry. Obvious examples are the introduction of the first car leading to today's automobile industry, the first airplane and the aircraft and airline industries, and the first microcomputer and the personal computer industry.

The other types of new products in Exhibit 9–1 describe products new to the marketing firm but not new to some other firms or to consumers. From the firm's point of view, the product could be a new category entry, an addition to an existing product line, an improvement to an existing product, or a new use of an existing product.

A large percentage of new products introduced each year are in the less innovative categories, particularly in many consumer product areas. One study found that of the 15,866 health, beauty, household, food, and pet products introduced, nearly 70 percent were different varieties, formulations, sizes, or packages of existing brands; only 5.7 percent of new products in these categories represented breakthroughs in technology, formulation, packaging, or even positioning.[8]

Moving down the list of product types from new-to-the-world products to repositionings, the product is less new to the firm. This means that its development and introduction are less risky too because the firm is building on areas of experience. Lower risk also typically makes the new product development process shorter and less rigorous.

An interesting trend for lowering risk is to capitalize on nostalgia by reintroducing products that were popular in the 1950s through the

When we started making tires, this was the closest thing to a car.

The year was 1894. And we had just made America's first successful rubber carriage tire.

A few years later America would trade horses for cars, and we'd start making car tires instead of carriage tires. And the more cars they'd make, the more tires we'd make.

Today, we make more high-mileage aftermarket tires than anyone else in America. For cars, trucks, and tractors that would have seemed like science fiction to Mr. Kelly back in Springfield, Ohio in 1894.

But we all had to start somewhere. And someone had to be first.

The Kelly-Springfield Tire Company

America's Oldest Tire Company

New-to-the-world products create new industries. The Kelly-Springfield Tire Company was established when the automobile was introduced to replace travel by horse with travel by car.

Types of new products

- **New-to-the-world products:** Product inventions, such as Polaroid instant camera, the first car, rayon, the laser printer, in-line skates.
- **New category entries:** Products new to the firm but not to the world, such as P&G's first shampoo, Hallmark gift items, AT&T's Universal Card.
- **Additions to product lines:** Line extensions or flankers on the firm's current markets, such as Tide Liquid detergent, Chrysler K cars.
- **Product improvements:** Current products made better; virtually every product on the market today has been improved, often many times.
- **Repositionings:** Products retargeted for a new use or application, such as Kellogg's Frosted Flakes cereal (now targeted to adults), and pork repositioned by National Pork Producers in recent years from being similar to beef to being the "other white meat."

1980s. These are typically brands that were successful in the past but have faded away. The challenge is to build on positive brand associations from the past, but to adapt to the needs of current customers. Examples include Triumph and Indian motorcycles, the Nissan Z and Ford Thunderbird, Tang powdered orange drink, Doan's backache pills, Lavoris mouthwash, Breck shampoo, and Care Bears.[9]

Remember that in our discussion of the new product development process we use the general term *product* to refer to both goods and services as well as to consumer and business products. The stages in the new product development process generally apply to all types of products. Examples throughout the chapter include goods, services, and consumer and business products.

Sources of New Products

Firms can obtain new products in a number of ways, with the two extremes being through external sourcing or through internal development. **External sourcing** is any approach by which a firm receives either ownership of another organization's products or the right to market the products of another organization. In such a case, products are new to the firm but not to consumers.

A number of alternative arrangements describe external sourcing. In an acquisition, the buying firm purchases another firm to obtain ownership of all the latter's products. The buying firm owns these products and may either merge them into its existing operations or allow the acquired firm to continue current operations. Newell Rubbermaid represents a good example of this approach. The Newell Co. started as a drapery hardware manufacturer. Since the 1960s the company has acquired 75 consumer product companies. During the 1990s the company made 18 major acquisitions, adding $2 billion in sales. The most noteworthy was the acquisition of Rubbermaid, completed in March 1999. This acquisition led the company to change its name to Newell Rubbermaid. Newell Rubbermaid generates sales in excess of $6 billion annually by manufacturing and marketing consumer products through mass retailers and home centers. Its acquisitions over the years have added many new products into the corporate family, such as Rubbermaid plastic products, Anchor Hocking glassware, Levelor blinds, and Rolodex files.[10]

Acquisitions are an increasingly important way for companies to get new products. Recent examples include Medco Health Solutions purchasing Accredo Health for new biotech medication products;[11] Sun Microsystems acquiring Storage Technology to obtain data storage products;[12] and Citigroup buying the credit card businesses of Federated Department Stores to get private label credit card products.[13] Even China is getting into the act. Chinese entrepreneurs are searching the United States for acquisitions that will provide them with new products. One successful example is Lenovo's purchase of IBM's personal computer products.[14]

Collaborative ventures are an increasingly important approach for developing new products. NTT and Verio have formed a collaborative venture to meet the Internet needs of their customers.

Other arrangements can be classified as some type of **collaborative venture.** Collaborative ventures allow two or more firms to share in the rights to market specified products. Often-used collaborative arrangements include strategic partnerships, strategic alliances, joint ventures, and licensing agreements. Although collaborative ventures can be successful, some studies report failure rates as high as 70 percent.[15]

Microsoft and SAP AG recently announced a collaborative venture to jointly develop and market a new product code-named Mendocino. The new product will integrate Microsoft's Office suite of desktop applications with SAP's suite of enterprise resource planning applications. This new product is expected to help the companies compete more effectively against IBM and Oracle.[16]

Internal development means that a firm develops new products itself. The firm may work with other firms for some parts of the process; it might subcontract product design, engineering, or test marketing to other firms. Or it might work in partnership with another firm throughout the entire process. The key point is that in internal development the firm is directly involved in the development of a new product, even though it may not accomplish every step by itself.

Internal development is riskier than acquiring new products from external sources. A firm developing new products assumes all or most of the costs and risks involved. When acquiring through external sources, a firm purchases or receives the rights to sell products that have a history in the market. External sourcing requires a firm to identify products of other firms, make the necessary agreements to obtain the desired products, and market them. Many firms use both external sourcing and internal development for new products.

New Product Development Process

A new product development process can be conceived as consisting of the seven stages presented in Exhibit 9–2. The process is presented as a logical series of steps for discussion purposes. In reality, the lines between each step are often blurred as companies are involved in different stages at the same time; sometimes they even eliminate specific stages. Also, the specific process for any one product will vary by company, industry, and type of new product.

Two issues related to the new product development process deserve some discussion. First, as a firm moves from one step in the process to the next, costs increase substantially. A major objective is to weed out potential failures as early as possible without eliminating products that might be successful. This is a difficult balancing act, but one that cannot be avoided. Rigorous analysis to evaluate products at each stage and to determine which warrant further attention can help firms be both productive and successful in developing new products. Because of this, each stage requires a go or no-go decision. Research indicates that firms are making no-go decisions sooner in the process. One study found that about 73 percent of new product ideas made it to the product development stage in the past. However, companies with a more rigorous new product development process had only about 29 percent of their ideas make it to the product development stage.[17]

The second issue of note is that the traditional approach to new product development has been a functional, linear process as shown in the top half of Exhibit 9–3. Typically each functional area works on specific stages of a process in isolation. When one step is concluded, the results go to the following functional area for the next step. For example, R&D might conceive a product idea and give it to the design function, which would design the product. Design passes it to engineering, which develops engineering specifications and gives it to manufacturing to produce. Manufacturing produces the product and gives it to marketing to sell. Although this type of approach has resulted in some successes, the process can be slow and costly.

| **Exhibit 9–2** | *New product development process* |

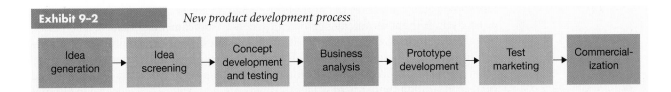

Idea generation → Idea screening → Concept development and testing → Business analysis → Prototype development → Test marketing → Commercialization

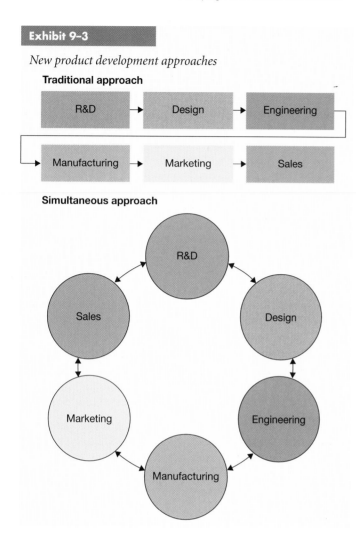

Exhibit 9–3

New product development approaches

Traditional approach

Simultaneous approach

Many firms have improved the new product development process by adopting a multifunctional, simultaneous approach as shown in the bottom half of Exhibit 9–3. This approach requires all relevant functions to work together during all stages, with several steps typically performed simultaneously. Some firms benefit from including suppliers, distributors, customers, and other interest groups.

3M has formalized this approach through its Pacing Plus initiative. This initiative is intended to accelerate the development of high-impact new products and bring them to market faster. Criteria for qualifying for the Pacing Plus program are new product development projects that change the basis for competition in new or existing markets, offer large sales and profit potential, receive priority access to 3M resources, operate in an accelerated time frame, and employ the best available commercialization processes. About 25 Pacing Plus programs are under way for products ranging from microflex circuits for electronic products to films that increase the brightness of notebook computer screens.[18]

Voyant Technologies developed an interesting teamwork approach. The company established the position of new product officer to coordinate the efforts of engineers and product managers. Joint meetings with engineers and product managers intermingled led to more cooperation throughout the new product development process. This teamwork approach produced three new products, improved time to market by 40 percent, and reduced R&D development costs by 20 percent.[19]

Idea Generation

Idea generation is the initial stage of the new product development process. A new product begins as someone's idea. Firms typically generate a large number of ideas relative to the number of successful products introduced.

One study found that almost half of the best new product ideas come from employees, with customers, suppliers, and competitors contributing the other half. Companies such as W. R. Grace, Georgia-Pacific, Sun Life Financial, and Chevron Texaco use online brainstorming sessions for employees at various locations to generate solutions to customer problems. The technology allows everyone to interact and share ideas. W. R. Grace ran 34 of these online sessions and generated 2,685 ideas that yielded 76 new products.[20]

By watching customers use existing products, firms can generate ideas for new products. Grace Performance Chemicals supplies materials and chemicals to the construction and packaging industries. The company asked its salespeople to observe the ways customers used its products, especially innovative and unexpected uses. The sales reps collected 134 different anecdotes. The company analyzed these examples with idea management software and identified seven ideas for potential new products.[21]

In addition, technological developments can be a useful source of new product ideas. Firms think about ways they might transform emerging technologies into successful new products. Even the government is getting into the act. Government agencies of all types are introducing a growing number of electronic services. It is the beginning of the e-government era. The state of Georgia offers citizens the opportunity to purchase hunting, fishing, and boating licenses over the Internet. College students can apply for financial aid from an Education Department student aid Web site. The National Science Foundation is

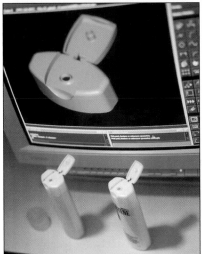

Reducing new product development time can produce a competitive advantage for many firms. Companies use various approaches to test new products.

currently conducting a study of the feasibility of "cybervoting." These new electronic services provide convenience to citizens while also reducing the cost of government. For example, Maryland saved $1.6 million when 250,000 professionals renewed their annual licenses online.[22]

New product ideas can also come directly from customers. Formal marketing research approaches can be useful, but interacting with customers in various ways can generate successful new product ideas. Harley-Davidson talks with customers at product demonstration rides, at H.O.G. (Harley Owners Group) Rallies, and on factory tours.[23] MySpace is a social networking Web site with more than 14 million members. It is growing quickly and has been adding about 65,000 new members a day. The first time a new member signs on, the president of the company appears and asks, "What features do you want to see on MySpace?" Five thousand responses are received each day, with the best ones incorporated into the service.[24]

Companies can also get new product ideas by analyzing the products offered by competitors. The focus is on new products or improvements to existing products that can differentiate a firm from its competition. Analyzing a firm's new product failures can also lead to good ideas. Eli Lilly has a formal process for examining every new drug product that failed; it uses this information to identify potential new uses for the drug. This process has been very successful. One example is Evista, which failed as a contraceptive but now brings in over $1 billion annually as a drug for osteoporosis.[25]

L. A. Mitchell, Account Executive for Large Business Accounts, Lucent Technologies, discusses sources for new product ideas: "New product ideas can come from just about anywhere. Lucent has entire organizations whose sole function is to continually explore and develop new product ideas. These organizations frequently employ focus groups, surveys, and other marketing research techniques to generate new ideas. Some of the best ideas come from needing to solve a significant customer problem. For example, the increase in automobile accidents due to people talking on cell phones while driving generated many ideas for new products and features. This led to products that allow cell phones to be used "hands free" and new features that make it possible to dial a number by simply speaking the name of the person or business you wish to call."

Idea Screening

Because the idea generation stage is relatively inexpensive, the major objective is to create a large pool of ideas for potential new products. The purpose of **idea screening** is to evaluate the idea pool and reduce it to a smaller, more attractive set of potential new products. The ideas should be screened for consistency with company vision and strategic objectives, potential market acceptance, fit with the firm's capabilities, and possible long-term contribution to profit. A major objective is to eliminate as early as possible ideas that have little chance of resulting in successful new products. Ideas that remain after screening move to the next stage in the new product development process.

Mattel launched Project Platypus to bring together 15–20 employees from engineering, design, marketing, and copywriting to invent original new toys. The employees leave their jobs for three months and move out of Mattel headquarters to a nearby building with open-plan offices. Group sessions are designed to generate creative ideas and then to refine them into specific new products. The first output from this process was Ello, a construction and activity toy for girls. Mattel hopes Project Platypus will produce two to three viable product ideas each year.[26]

A popular idea-screening approach is to use a checklist. The basic procedure is to identify the factors that are important to a firm and to evaluate each new product idea against each factor. Adding the individual factor scores for each idea produces an overall idea-screening score. The higher this score, the better the new product idea. Sometimes firms

Exhibit 9–4							

3M's idea-screening checklist

	Scale						
Factor	**0**	**1**	**2**	**3**	**4**	**5**	**Rating**
Customer need		Nice	Definite utility		Critical		5
Competition		Many	Limited		None		4
Technology		None in 3M	Within 3M		Within ISD*		4
Marketing		None in 3M	Tape Group		ISD		5
Manufacturing		None in 3M	Equipment modification		Existing equipment		4
Price versus competition		Competitive advantage	Neutral		Strong 3M		3
Performance versus competition		Strong competitive	Neutral		Strong 3M		5
					Total		30

*Industrial Specialties Division.

have a cutoff score; they drop ideas scoring below the cutoff and retain those scoring above for further development. Or companies might rank the idea-screening scores from highest to lowest and focus efforts on the ideas with the highest scores.

Exhibit 9–4 presents an example of a checklist used by 3M. 3M decided that customer need, competition, technology, marketing, manufacturing, price versus competition, and performance versus competition are important factors. The company rates ideas against each factor on a scale ranging from zero to five. The individual factor ratings are then summed to produce a total score. As shown in the exhibit, the example idea is evaluated very high on each factor, for a total score of 30. On the basis of this score, a go decision is likely. If the score had been very low, say 15, the new product idea would not have been developed any further.

The key to the success of the idea-screening checklist is to identify all of the factors that are important for a new product. As indicated in Exhibit 9–4, these factors are typically related to the customer, competitor, and company characteristics related to new product success. However, other factors can be included, as presented in "Acting Ethically: Incorporating Values in New Products."

Concept Development and Testing

Concept development is the process of shaping and refining the idea into a more complete product concept. In the generation and screening stages, the product idea is typically very general, perhaps a soft drink with added nutrients for health-conscious consumers or

ACTING ETHICALLY

Incorporating values in new products

Aveda is a high-end organic cosmetics company established in 1978. The company was founded by Horst Rechelbacher to produce natural cosmetics in an environmentally responsible way. Estee Lauder purchased Aveda in 1997 but allowed the company to maintain its core values. This was a good move: Aveda sales have doubled in the past two years. Aveda incorporates its values into all of its products. For example, the checklist used to screen new products ensures that all product ingredients aren't harmful to the environment or indigenous communities. It once dropped a successful perfume line because the source of one ingredient was not traceable. Four years later it found an environmentally friendly source and re-launched the perfume product line.

Thinking Critically

Identify a new product you think has the potential to be successful. Develop a concept statement for this new product with at least two variations of the product. If possible, draw pictures of each product variation. Then develop a short concept test and administer it to at least five other students. Evaluate the results of this exercise:

• What information did the concept test provide?

• Given this information, what would you do next if you really wanted to develop and market this new product?

a direct-mail service for marketing textbooks to students. The evaluation of product ideas to this point is generally done by people within the firm, with little if any assessment by potential customers.

The major objective of concept development and testing is to formalize product concepts and have them evaluated by potential customers. Formalizing the product concept means describing the basic product idea in detail. This usually entails describing all of the product's components, including its projected price. If possible, a picture of the product should be included with the concept description. Exhibit 9–5 presents a product concept for a new aerosol hand cleanser.

Concept tests are then used to get potential customers to evaluate the product concept. Sometimes multiple variations of the basic product concept are provided so consumers can indicate which they like best. In other cases (see Exhibit 9–5) consumers are asked to respond to various questions about only one product concept. Besides assessing the concept provided to them, consumers might be given an opportunity to suggest improvements. Concept tests are most often conducted as personal interviews, but they can be performed through mail surveys.

If the concept tests indicate a low level of consumer acceptance and low likelihood of purchase, the firm makes a no-go decision. If the tests indicate a high level of consumer acceptance and high probability of purchase, the firm makes a go decision. The results of the concept test in Exhibit 9–5 indicate a generally positive response from consumers and a go decision to proceed to the next stage of the new product development process. The results of the tests may also provide ideas for revising the concept to better meet the needs of consumers.

Business Analysis

Ideas that survive concept development and testing are subjected to detailed business analysis. The **business analysis** stage of the new product development process calls for preparing initial marketing plans for the product. This requires developing a tentative

Exhibit 9–5

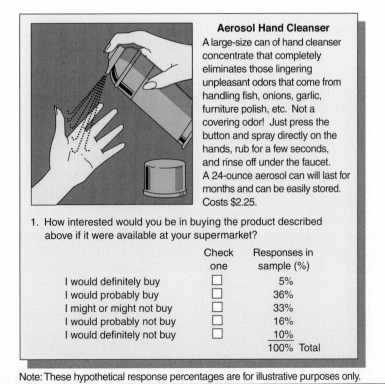

Aerosol Hand Cleanser
A large-size can of hand cleanser concentrate that completely eliminates those lingering unpleasant odors that come from handling fish, onions, garlic, furniture polish, etc. Not a covering odor! Just press the button and spray directly on the hands, rub for a few seconds, and rinse off under the faucet. A 24-ounce aerosol can will last for months and can be easily stored. Costs $2.25.

1. How interested would you be in buying the product described above if it were available at your supermarket?

	Check one	Responses in sample (%)
I would definitely buy	☐	5%
I would probably buy	☐	36%
I might or might not buy	☐	33%
I would probably not buy	☐	16%
I would definitely not buy	☐	10%
		100% Total

Note: These hypothetical response percentages are for illustrative purposes only.

marketing strategy and estimating expected sales, costs, and profitability for the product. A product idea reaching this point has passed general company screening criteria and been accepted by consumers. The purpose of the business analysis is to determine if it makes business sense to introduce the product.

The firm must assess whether it can market the new product profitably. This requires estimating costs, which is difficult but easier than forecasting sales. Several types of sales estimates may be necessary. For infrequently purchased products, such as appliances, production equipment, or personal computers, the firm must estimate initial sales and long-term replacement sales. For frequently purchased products, like toothpaste, business supplies, or cookies, it must forecast both first-time sales and repeat sales over time.

The firm must attempt to predict sales over several purchasing cycles because the ultimate success of a new product depends on consumers' trying the product and then re-purchasing it. Pillsbury's experience with Oven Lovin' Cookie Dough shows what can happen. Within months of introduction, the product was available in 90 percent of supermarkets and sales were growing. In less than two years, however, sales crumbled. After using the product, consumers did not think it was much different from the dough they were using previously, so they switched back to their old product.[27]

Because it is so difficult to estimate new product sales and costs, the real value of the business analysis is in identifying products that are not likely to succeed commercially. Consumers might like the product, and it might meet the firm's general criteria, but the market might be too small or the marketing costs too high for the new product to have a reasonable chance of long-term profitability. If this is the case, the firm makes a no-go decision. Although a no-go decision at this point has some costs, it can save the firm the very high costs associated with the remainder of the new product development process. A go decision means that the new product offers the potential profitability to warrant continued development.

Chrysler provides an example of a no-go decision. The company put together a formidable team to develop a luxury car code-named LX. The LX would be a rear-wheel drive luxury car with a new 32-valve V-8 engine of over 300 horsepower. The car would be fast, but it would handle well and be able to compete with BMW, Mercedes, Jaguar, Lexus, Infiniti, and Cadillac. Everyone was excited about the project as Chrysler moved closer to actually producing the car. However, after analyzing the market, management concluded that increased competition would reduce margins to a level where the product would not generate sufficient profits. Although everyone involved wanted to produce the car, management made a no-go decision because of the limited profit potential.[28]

Thinking Critically

Select any product that you use often, such as a computer, VCR, television, or automobile. Construct a QFD matrix for this product. On the horizontal axis, list at least five characteristics of the product. On the vertical axis, list at least five benefits you desire from using the product. Once the matrix is developed, place an X in each box to indicate where a specific product characteristic provides a specific benefit.

Evaluate the results:

- How well do the existing product characteristics translate into specific benefits to you?

- Can you come up with any ideas for additional product characteristics that would produce additional benefits for you?

Prototype Development

Prototype development means converting the concept into an actual product. The objective is to use the information obtained from the concept tests to design an actual product that can be further tested. New product costs begin to escalate at this stage because developing a prototype normally requires a considerable investment. Product ideas that make it to this stage should have a high probability of succeeding. Firms are doing a better job of weeding out poor product ideas earlier in the development process.

Firms need to focus on two areas during prototype development. The first is to design the product to satisfy the needs expressed by consumers in the concept tests. One approach is through **quality function deployment** (**QFD**), a procedure that links specific consumer requirements with specific product characteristics. A simplified QFD matrix for a new copier product to be marketed to business users is presented in Exhibit 9–6. In this example, each product characteristic is designed to provide at least one benefit desired by customers. This approach directly links product features to customer requirements.

The second area is to build quality into the product. In the past, a product would be designed and then given to manufacturing to produce. Sometimes it would be difficult and costly to produce to the design specifications. Now many firms include people from product design, engineering, and manufacturing in designing the prototype. Manufacturing considerations are incorporated directly into product design. This approach ensures not only that the prototype will satisfy customer needs on paper, but that it can be produced

Exhibit 9–6   *Product function deployment matrix*

NEW COPIER PRODUCT Product Characteristics						
Customer requirements	Multiple-size paper tray	Touch controls	Energy-efficient	Slip-in toner cartridges	Long-term warranty	High speed
Fast copies						X
Versatile	X					
Durable		X	X		X	
Low maintenance		X	X	X		
Easy to operate	X	X		X		X
Low operating cost			X			

X = Specific product characteristics designed to meet specific customer requirements.

to the desired quality level. An interesting example of developing prototypes is presented in "Using Technology: Building Prototypes with Technology."

Test Marketing

Once a product prototype is developed, it can be tested. **Test marketing** involves testing the product prototype and marketing strategy in simulated or actual market situations. Test marketing can be both expensive and risky. Full-scale test marketing can cost over $1 million and last up to 18 months. Competitive reactions have taught even savvy marketers like Procter & Gamble to be cautious in their testing. Several years ago, P&G was testing a ready-to-spread frosting brand. Taking note of the test, General Mills rushed to introduce its own Betty Crocker brand, which now dominates the market.[29]

The two primary methods for testing are simulated test marketing and standard test marketing. **Simulated test marketing** refers to evaluating a new product in situations contrived to be similar to how consumers would purchase and use it. A typical simulated test involves intercepting shoppers at a high-traffic location in a mall. Surveyors ask them about their use of various products and expose them to a concept or commercial for a new product. Respondents then participate in a shopping exercise during which they can purchase the new product. After the exercise, they are asked about their

USING TECHNOLOGY

Building prototypes with technology

Paul Budnitz grew Kidrobot from nothing to over $5 million annual sales in just three years. Maintaining growth requires the continuous introduction of new robot characters. The company employs various types of technology to build prototype characters. The characters are initially sketched using an electronic drawing program. It may take several iterations to get a good design that is sent electronically to everyone involved, usually the designers in New York and the manufacturers in China. Then the final details are worked out by everyone interacting via a Web-based conferencing application. Once the final design is decided, it is sent electronically to engineers in China. The engineers translate the design into clay or wax prototypes and ship them to New York. The prototypes are evaluated; changes are made and sent electronically to the manufacturer in China; and the new character is off the production line in 30 days.

purchases. They are then contacted at a later date about their use of and intentions to repurchase the product.

In **standard test marketing,** a firm tests a new product and its marketing strategy in actual market situations. The size and number of test markets depend on the need for reliable information, the costs associated with test marketing, and the potential reactions from competitors. Selected test markets should represent the characteristics of the target market for the new product. A typical approach is to execute the marketing strategy for the new product in the selected test markets and to carefully track results. Sometimes firms vary elements of the marketing mix in different test markets to identify the most effective marketing strategy.

The introduction of a new product begins the commercialization stage of the new product process.

Ameritech uses an interesting approach to test marketing. It goes to small towns in its region and has the citizens test new products and services. For example, the company enlisted more than 100 people in Woodstock, Illinois, to evaluate its Clearpath digital cellular service. The feedback from these test-market towns has provided useful information for improving Ameritech's new products prior to launch. Interestingly, people from these towns who have actually participated in the test-marketing programs are often used in Ameritech's "Human Factors" advertising campaign. These ads show the people using the new products in sometimes humorous ways. The underlying logic behind the test marketing and advertising is that "if technology doesn't work for people, it doesn't work."[30]

Test marketing represents the final exam for a new product. If the new product passes this exam, a go decision will lead to the commercialization stage. If the new product fails this exam, a no-go decision will lead to dropping the new product or going back to the drawing board to make significant changes. Even though test marketing is expensive, it is typically much less costly than commercializing the product. So a firm is much better off stopping an unsuccessful product at this stage than during the commercialization stage.

Commercialization

During the **commercialization** stage, the firm introduces the product on a full-scale basis. The level of investment and risk is generally the highest at this stage. Investments in production, distribution, and marketing support can be extremely high. However, the firm can reduce some of this risk by performing the other stages of the new product development process appropriately. Successful commercialization requires understanding consumer adoption, timing decisions, and coordinating efforts.

CONSUMER ADOPTION   The **adoption process** describes the steps consumers follow in deciding whether to use a new product. The stages in the adoption process are presented in Exhibit 9–7. Marketing strategies must be designed to move consumers through these stages to achieve the adoption of new products.

Research suggests two important considerations about the adoption process. First, consumers differ in their rates of adoption. There is usually a small group of consumers who are the most willing to adopt new products. Typically called **innovators,** they normally represent the first 2.5 percent of the adopters. Identifying the innovators and targeting marketing efforts to this group are keys to successful commercialization of a new product.

Second, the characteristics of a new product affect its rate of adoption. The more complex the product, the slower the rate. For example, it takes 5 to 15 years before new electronic technologies (VCRs, cable TVs, PCs, cell phones) catch on among consumers and penetrate a large portion of the market.[31] The rate of adoption is facilitated, however,

Exhibit 9-7	*Consumer adoption process*

Consumer Adoption Stage	Marketing Strategy Objective
Awareness	Communicate the availability of the new product.
Interest	Communicate benefits of new product to gain consumer interest.
Evaluation	Emphasize the advantages of new product over alternatives currently on the market.
Trial	Motivate consumers to try the new product.
Adoption	Make sure consumers are satisfied with use of the new product.

when the new product is compatible with existing products, has clear and readily observable advantages over those products, and can be tried on a limited basis. Marketing strategies should capitalize on the characteristics that facilitate adoption and minimize the characteristics that slow adoption.

L. A. Mitchell, Account Executive for Large Business Accounts, Lucent Technologies, talks about facilitating the adoption of new products: "Even good new products can become old products very quickly if the customer has difficulty in accepting the new product. High-tech products traditionally have very high initial costs. For these new products, Lucent targets customers in very competitive industries where product differentiation is critical to a company's success. It is here that we will most likely find early adopters willing to take on new products. In order to capture the early adopter market, we need to present a product that can integrate quickly into the customer's product offering and demonstrates a quick return on investment or a significant competitive advantage."

TIMING   In most cases a firm can introduce a new product on its own timetable. One strategic consideration for new products in new product categories or industries is whether to be an early entry. Gillette (in safety razors) and Sony (in personal stereos) performed well as first movers. However, Xerox (in fax machines) and eToys (in Internet retailing) were failures. The appropriate strategy depends on many factors including the pace of technology evolution, the pace of market evolution, and the resources and capabilities of the firm. When technology and market evolution are slow, the likelihood of

Celebrate the first plasma TV with a built-in High-Definition Digital Video Recorder.

WITH THE LG INTEGRATED PLASMA HDTV, LIFE'S MORE EASILY PAUSED.

Or played - stopped - replayed - saved! LG once again re-writes the rules with the world's first plasma HDTV to feature a built-in High-Definition HDD Digital Video Recorder. Now you'll never miss out on a moment again.

LGusa.com/PlasmaDVR

LG   Life's Good

Adoption of new products is facilitated if the new product has clear advantages over existing products. LG Electronics emphasizes the features of a digital video recorder built into its plasma HDTV.

gaining a long-term advantage by being first to market is high. When technology and market evolution are fast, it is hard to achieve a long-term advantage from being first, even for firms with considerable resources. If technology evolution is fast and market evolution slow, it is also difficult to gain a first-mover advantage unless a firm has considerable resources and strong R&D and new product development capabilities. The best opportunity for first-mover advantage is when market evolution is fast, technology evolution is slow, and the firm has strong marketing capabilities and adequate resources.[32]

Many firms preannounce the introduction of new products because this provides some hype for the product and company and can allow customers and partners to prepare for the new product. The benefits of a new product preannouncement are considerable. However, once this is done, it is critical that the new product be introduced on time. Many preannounced new products are delayed or canceled, especially in technology-intensive industries. Studies indicate that these delays and cancellations can hurt a firm in its relationships with customers; and, they have also been found to have a negative impact on the firm's stock price.[33]

COORDINATION   As the new product development stages have progressed, a marketing strategy for commercialization has evolved. A firm needs to coordinate all functions to implement this strategy effectively. Production, distribution, and all other marketing and company efforts must ensure that sufficient product is produced and available to satisfy the demand generated from the commercialization strategy.

One study found that new product launches were more likely to succeed when the firm had a structured commercialization process that was understood by everyone involved and when there was frequent communication within and across department and divisional boundaries. It is also important that the product launch be given priority status with objectives set and specific responsibilities for all tasks assigned. The results of another study suggest that this type of coordination can be best achieved through the use of cross-functional teams, but by adding some team members with successful experience in launching new products. This approach keeps the original team together but adds additional expertise.[34] Once the product is introduced, tracking results and providing feedback are critical.[35]

Keys to New Product Success

Studies of new product introductions identify a number of reasons for failures and successes. Many executives are not satisfied with the speed of new product development in their companies and have difficulty in planning and budgeting for new projects. Front-end planning is critical to improving the new product development process.[36] A synthesis of these studies provides the keys for new product success, as presented in Exhibit 9–8.[37]

Many of these keys to new product success are consistent with the perspectives emphasized throughout this book. New product development should be market-driven and customer-focused, aimed at developing superior products that offer consumers unique benefits and exceptional value. The predevelopment efforts, such as idea screening, concept development and testing, and business analysis, appear to be critical to new product success. In fact, establishment of a disciplined and rigorous new product development process, effectively executed at each step of the process, is an important determinant of success.

Organizational Approaches

Research results suggest several interesting relationships between different organizational approaches and new product success. For less innovative products, studies indicate a positive relationship between firms practicing a market orientation and new product success.[38] However, the firms most successful in introducing innovative new products tend to integrate a market orientation with creativity and an entrepreneurial perspective.[39]

There is also evidence that the use of cross-functional new product development teams increases the chances of new product success and reduces the cycle time for new products. Companies use different approaches for their new product development teams. Harley-Davidson employs a matrix organization within the new product development center that maximizes the diversity of functional area involvement and integration throughout the new product development process.[40] Dow Chemical Company implements a Speed Based Development Philosophy to introduce successful new products three to five times faster than in the past. This is a flexible approach that has the right leadership choose the right people to use the right skills to do the right execution. Over $1 billion in sales have been generated from new products using this approach.[41]

Teamwork across functional areas is essential for new product success. The emphasis throughout the process should be on producing products that offer the quality and value desired by consumers. In many cases, this means constant awareness of how new technologies may be used to solve customer problems. Although many of

Teamwork is often required to make the new product development process successful. Thermos used a cross-functional team to develop a new electric grill that won four design awards.

Keys to new product success

- Number one factor: unique, superior, differentiated product that delivers unique benefits and superior value to customer.
- Market-driven and customer-focused new product process.
- More predevelopment work before development gets under way.
- Sharp and early product definition.
- Right organizational structure.

- New product success is predictable: Use profile of winner to sharpen project selection decisions.
- New product success is controllable: Emphasize completeness, consistency, quality of execution.
- Speed is everything! But not at the expense of quality of execution.
- Companies that follow multistage, disciplined new product game plans fare much better.

the keys to success seem obvious, the majority of new products still fail. The reason for many of these failures may be that firms did some of the obvious things wrong or failed to do them at all.

Marketing Research Support

Marketing research can make important contributions to the new product development process. Concept tests and test marketing were discussed earlier in this chapter, and other marketing research approaches were covered in Chapter 6. Exhibit 9–9 highlights some of the types of marketing research that might be used throughout the new product development process.

Prelaunch activities refer to marketing research studies prior to commercialization. These types of studies typically introduce consumer input into the decisions made at each stage of the new product development process. *Rollout studies* are performed after the product has been introduced in the commercialization stage. These studies assess consumer response to the new product and its marketing strategy.

The successful introduction of Banana Nut Crunch illustrates the important role that marketing research can play. The cereal maker, C. W. Post, wanted to develop a banana-flavored cereal. Bananas are America's favorite cereal fruit, and consumers had responded favorably to the banana-flavored cereal concept. The initial cereal included dried banana pieces, but this flopped in product tests. Then the idea to make the cereal like banana-nut bread was generated. Consumers responded positively to this new concept. Prototypes were produced and tested in several hundred households. Again, the response was positive. Banana Nut Crunch was then introduced, and tracking studies indicated strong initial and repurchase demand. Today the cereal is a strong success and one of Post's hottest brands. Information provided by consumers through various marketing research approaches produced the key information to make the product introduction successful.[42]

Successful New Products

Although many new products are failures, there are always many interesting successes. Let's conclude our discussion of new product development by looking at several products selected as "The Best Products for 2004":[43]

- The Aliph Jawbone Handset includes two microphones that make it possible to use a cell phone in noisy places.
- Hewlett-Packard's Photosmart R707 Digital Camera is a pocket-sized, 5.1 megapixel camera that lets the user fix red eye on the camera.
- The Ryobi AIRgrip Laser Level uses a tiny vacuum to stick to walls and can be turned for horizontal and vertical leveling.
- Maytag's Neptune Drying Center has a drying cabinet on top of a tumble dryer.

Introduced wireless Internet access to air travel.
Brought real-time surfing to every seat.
Made an airplane feel like a cyber cafe.
All for this one moment.

Access e-mail, work online or check the latest news with FlyNet.? Just bring your laptop. Visit **lufthansa-usa.com** for FlyNet availability.   There's no better way to fly.   ✈ **Lufthansa**
A STAR ALLIANCE MEMBER ✧

Lufthansa introduces a new service to improve its customers' flying experience.

| Exhibit 9–9 | *Marketing research support for new products* |

Prelaunch		**Rollout**	
• Focus groups	• Name and package evaluation	• Awareness, attitude studies	• Product refinement tests
• Market definition studies	• Product tests	• Usage studies	• New advertising strategy tests
• Target segment identification	• Copy tests	• Tracking studies	
• Concept tests	• Simulated test markets		
	• Test markets		

- The Oral B Brush-Ups Finger Toothbrush is a disposable toothbrush that fits on a finger with toothpaste built in and no need for rinsing.

- Honda's CRF 250K Motorcycle is a race-ready, off-road bike that meets emission standards in all states.

Summary

1. **Recognize the different types of new products.** Products differ in how new they are to customers or to the firm introducing them. From a firm's perspective, new products can be classified as new-to-the-world products, new category entries, additions to product lines, product improvements, or repositionings.

2. **Discuss the different sources of new products.** New products can come from external sources or be developed internally. External sourcing includes acquisitions or various types of collaborative arrangements allowing a firm the right to market the products of another firm. Internal development occurs when a firm is directly involved in the development of new products. The firm might work with other firms on some new product activities, but it is actively involved in the process.

3. **Understand the stages in the new product development process.** The new product development process consists of the interrelated stages of idea generation, idea screening, concept development, business analysis, prototype development, test marketing, and commercialization. As a firm moves through this process,

costs rise substantially. A prime objective is to eliminate potential product failures as early as possible and to spend time and resources on the ideas with the largest chances for success.

4. **Describe the way marketing research is used in the new product development process.** Marketing research goes on throughout the new product development process. Specific types of marketing research are valuable in the prelaunch stages. These studies help to assess market acceptance of the product and the likely success of particular marketing alternatives. Different marketing research approaches are used to monitor and evaluate results during the commercialization stage.

5. **Appreciate the keys to new product success.** A synthesis of new product research suggests the nine keys to new product success presented in Exhibit 9–8. In general, the keys to success are market orientation, customer focus, effective execution of a rigorous new product development process, adoption of a multifunctional new product organizational approach, and development of products that deliver the benefits and value desired by consumers.

Understanding Marketing Terms and Concepts

Thinking about Marketing

1. How does the new product development process differ for different types of products?

2. What are the advantages and disadvantages of using external sources for new products?

3. Review "Acting Ethically: Incorporating Values in New Products." What other noncommercial factors might a firm incorporate into its idea-screening process for new products?

4. Should all new products be test marketed? Why or why not?

5. What should be included in a business analysis for a new product?

6. Reread "Using Technology: Building Prototypes with Technology." What are the specific benefits of

information and communication technologies in the development of prototypes for new products?

7. Describe the use of marketing research throughout the new product development process.

8. What factors should be considered during the idea-screening stage of the new product development process?

9. How is the development of new services likely to differ from the development of new goods?

10. How is the development of consumer products likely to differ from the development of business products?

Applying Marketing Skills

1. Assume that students are complaining about how hard it is to get information about scheduled school events. Being entrepreneurially oriented, you would like to develop a product to solve this problem. Go through the idea generation, idea-screening, and concept development stages of the new product development process. Bring one or more new product concepts to class for testing.

2. Contact a local firm in your area that is active in new product development. Interview people at the firm, and find out as much as possible about the company's new product development process.

3. Identify a recent new product that you think has been very successful. Select a product that allows you to obtain information from both published sources and company officials. Evaluate how well the firm introducing this product followed the keys to new product success presented in Exhibit 9–8.

Using the www in Marketing

Activity One Go to the 3M Web site (*http://www.3m.com*).

1. Select one of the inventors in the "Our Pioneers" section. Describe the invention and how it led to new 3M products.

2. Based on information available from the Web site, why do you think 3M has been so successful in developing new products?

3. What are 3M's plans for new product development in the future?

Activity Two The Product Development and Management Association (PDMA) is an interesting organization. It can be accessed at *www.pdma.org*.

1. What is the purpose of PDMA?

2. What benefits does PDMA provide to its members?

3. Click on the *Visions Magazine* section. Review the articles from recent issues and compare them to the topics covered in this chapter. What new product topics are emphasized in these issues?

Making Marketing Decisions

Case 9–1 Eclipse Aviation: Developing an Innovative Jet

Eclipse Aviation was founded by former Microsoft executive Vern Rayburn. The company is trying to develop a twin-engine jet that could revolutionize the aviation industry. The jet would resemble a luxury sedan and be equipped with the latest flight controls and safety features. It could fly almost 450 miles per hour at altitudes up to 41,000 feet but would be small and maneuverable enough to land at almost every small airport. The cost of operating the jet would be about 40 percent of what it costs to operate today's cheapest jet. And the price of the Eclipse 500 would be about $850,000!

The company has been working on the jet for four years. The design has passed computer-simulated tests, so a prototype has been built. The Eclipse design team includes about 180 engineers to get the design right.

New government regulations regarding security for private jets will also have to be addressed. Eclipse plans to train all Eclipse 500 pilots rather than have it done by flight training schools. This would give the company more control and help to minimize any safety or security problems.

The Eclipse 500 has been undergoing a series of flight tests. As of April 2005, it had flown 112 sorties and 127.4 flight hours. Its first public appearance was a 3,000-mile round trip between Albuquerque, New Mexico, and Lakeland, Florida. The current plan is for all the testing to be completed and certification received by the end of March 2006.

Some good news came on April 25, 2005, when DayJet Corporation was launched and announced the purchase of 239 Eclipse 500s in the first two years of a five-year purchase contract. DayJet offers "Per-Seat, On-Demand" jet service for short-haul, regional travel.

Why so much interest in the Eclipse 500 jet? If the jet delivers as promised, it has "dynamite potential" and "could change the industry," according to an aerospace analyst at Morgan Stanley. First, private pilots currently flying piston-engine planes could move up to the level of executive travel. Second, the low purchase price and low operating expenses could open up a new market for private jet service. More individuals and companies would be able to purchase jets outright or become involved in some type of fractional ownership program of the Eclipse 500 than are able to for available private jets.

The most intriguing opportunity is for the Eclipse 500 to be used as an air taxi for average travelers. A traveler would call an air taxi service to make a reservation. An Eclipse 500 would then pick up as many as six passengers at the local municipal airport and deliver them to any other municipal airport. And the cost for this service would be similar to a commercial airline coach seat!

Questions

1. How has Eclipse Aviation followed the new product development process?

2. Would you recommend that the company focus on upgrading existing private jet travelers or getting new private jet travelers? Why?

3. How would marketing strategies differ for existing versus new private jet travelers?

4. What is your assessment of the air taxi concept? How would you recommend this new approach be marketed?

Case 9–2 PaperPro: Turning a Problem into an Opportunity

In 2003 Todd Moses quit his job and moved back to his parents' house with his pregnant wife to save money. Todd wanted to become an entrepreneur and set up an appointment with a venture capital firm to see if it would fund his idea for a chain of gourmet wrap restaurants. He was running a little late for the meeting, so he hurriedly tried to staple the pages of his business plan together. Everything needed to look perfect because he was trying to raise $5 million from the venture capital firm.

On his first attempt, the staple went only halfway through the 19-page document. On his second attempt the stapler jammed. Todd tried to pull out the jammed staple, but cut his finger and blood got on his business plan. He threw the stapler against the wall and left for the meeting. Upon arrival, he apologized for being late and for not having enough copies of his business plan. The meeting did not go as well as he had hoped.

That night Todd was still mad about the stapler incident. He couldn't sleep, so he went to the Internet to research staplers at Web sites for Staples and Office Depot. All of the available staplers seemed like the one he had used. The next day he tracked down Joel Marks, a mechanical engineer who had designed a spring-loaded mechanism for an industrial stapler. Joel agreed to help Todd build a desktop stapler that would work better than what was available in exchange for equity in any new company. Typical office staplers require 30 pounds of force to bind 20 pages of paper. Todd and Joel designed a compact recoil spring that would store enough energy to bind 20 pages with only seven pounds of force. With this stapler a person could staple 20 pages using one finger, even just a pinkie.

Todd established a company called Accentra and contracted with a manufacturer in Taiwan to produce the new stapler with the brand name PaperPro. He then met with 120 potential distributors; 119 agreed to carry the product. By the end of 2004 PaperPro was available through Office Depot, Office Max, and catalogs. Staples carried it under its store brand One-Touch. Three models were available, retailing between $9.99 and $29.99. Sales were brisk. Even Wal-Mart started to carry PaperPro. Sales could top $50 million this year with the product now being distributed in 60 countries.

In the meantime, Swingline, the market leader in staplers, noticed a significant drop in its market share. The company conducted several marketing research projects with stapler users to try to identify the cause of the market share drop. The biggest complaint from Swingline stapler users was that their staplers were prone to jamming. Swingline made some improvements and introduced five new stapler models, including one with an ergonomically contoured grip. The new products have helped to revive Swingline's market share.

Questions

1. How did Todd Moses identify his idea for a new product?

2. What stages of the new product development process did Todd go through to get the PaperPro stapler commercialized?

3. How could Todd have improved the new product development process he used?

4. How should Todd and Accentra respond to the introduction of new staplers by Swingline?

Chapter Ten

PRODUCT AND SERVICE STRATEGIES

10

After studying this chapter, you should be able to

1 Understand the different characteristics of a product mix.

2 Recognize the stages and characteristics of the product life cycle.

3 Identify appropriate marketing strategies for products in different life cycle stages.

4 Describe the limitations of the product life cycle concept.

5 Discuss different product-mix and product-line strategies.

Starbucks

The first Starbucks coffee shop was at Pike Place Market in Seattle in 1971. The concept was successful, and 165 Starbucks locations were open in 1992 when the company went public. The chain now has more than 9,000 retail locations in the United States and internationally. The Starbucks strategy is to create a unique experience based on mellow ambience, premium coffee beans, and coffee beverages.

Future sales and profit growth of around 20 percent annually is expected. The long-term goal is to have 30,000 stores, with about 1,500 new stores opened each year. Although there is still room for more stores in metropolitan areas, Starbucks is moving into smaller cities and sees many opportunities along the 165,000 miles of roadway in the United States. There are many international opportunities as well. For

example, only 150 stores have been opened in China, but the company expects to have over 2,000 Chinese stores in the future.

Starbucks is also increasing its product mix to connect better with customers and improve the Starbucks experience. As expressed by chairman Howard Schultz, Starbucks "is not in the coffee business serving people, it is in the people business serving coffee." Recent product and service additions to its stores include Tazo premium tea, wireless Internet access, the Hear Music platform, and Torrefazione Italia Coffee.

Store sales are complemented by Internet sales, especially for merchandise like espresso machines. In addition to stores, Starbucks has a variety of partnerships to market other products, such as Frappuccino coffee drinks, Starbucks DoubleShot coffee drink, Starbucks Coffee Liqueur, and a line of superpremium ice creams.

The Starbucks Card is a successful example of integrating Starbucks stores and its Web site. Customers can order a card and make deposits on the Web or in stores. Then they can use the cards to make Web or store purchases. More than 52 million cards have been activated. The cards are so popular that some companies use them in their employee reward and incentive programs.

Starbucks is proud of its social responsibility efforts to champion business practices that produce social, environmental, and economic benefits to the company and communities globally. For example, the Starbucks Make Your Mark program matches volunteer hours with cash contributions to designated nonprofit organizations. In January 2005 the World Environment Center (WEC) presented Starbucks with its Gold Medal for International Corporate Achievement in Sustainable Development.

The future looks bright for Starbucks to add more retail stores, expand its product mix, and leverage its Web site to build customer equity around the world.

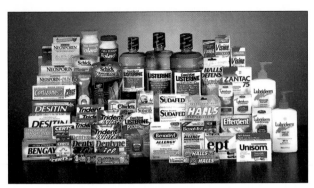

Most companies market many different products. Pfizer Consumer Healthcare shows some of the many products in its product mix.

The experiences Starbucks has had illustrate the challenge of marketing multiple products and services, where success depends on developing and implementing effective strategies for specific products, individual product lines, and the entire product mix. The task becomes even more difficult for companies such as Starbucks because product strategies for their stores must be integrated with those for electronic commerce. But this task is faced by more and more firms.

Even small, entrepreneurial firms based on a single product normally add new products to achieve growth objectives. One reason for this is that once a new product passes the commercialization stage and is introduced into the market, it typically goes through some type of life cycle. At the later stages of this life cycle, sales and profits decrease significantly. Thus firms introduce new versions of existing products to extend this life cycle or new products in other areas to meet company growth objectives and take advantage of market opportunities. Smart companies employ effective product and service strategies to direct this growth.

In this chapter we introduce the product mix concept and discuss strategies for individual products, product lines, and the overall product mix. We emphasize the role of the product life cycle as a basis for strategy development.

Product Mix

A **product mix** is the total assortment of products and services marketed by a firm. Every product mix consists of at least one product line, often more. A **product line** is a group of individual products that are closely related in some way. An **individual product** is any brand or variant of a brand in a product line. Thus a product mix is a combination of product lines, which are combinations of individual products.

A product mix, relevant product lines, and individual products can be defined at different levels. In Chapter 3 we discussed organizational strategic planning at the corporate, business, and marketing levels. At the corporate level, the product mix would be defined as all products marketed by the entire corporate entity, with each business unit typically representing one or more product lines. Each business unit, however, also has its own relevant product lines made up of related products. For example, General Electric is

Exhibit 10–1   *Product mix characteristics*

Kodak Camera **Product Mix**			
One-Time-Use **Cameras**	**Digital** **Cameras**	**Professional** **Cameras**	**Medical Cameras**
•Kodak Zoom •Kodak Plus Digital •Kodak High Definition •Kodak HQ Maximum Versatility •Kodak Water and Sport •Kodak Power Flash •Kodak Advantix Switchable •Kodak Black and White •Kodak Fun Saver 35 Flash •Kodak Max Outdoor	•Easyshare C360 •Easyshare C340 •Easyshare C330 •Easyshare C310 •Easyshare C300 •Easyshare CX7530 •Easyshare CX7430 •Easyshare CX7330 •Easyshare CX7300 •Easyshare CX7220 •Easyshare Z7590 •Easyshare Z760 •Easyshare Z740 •Easyshare Z730 •Easyshare Z700 •Easyshare DX7630 •Easyshare DX7590 •Easyshare DX7440 •Easyshare DX6490 •Easyshare V550 •Easyshare V530 •Easyshare LS753 •Easyshare LS743	•Kodak Pro SLR/C •Kodak Pro SLR/N	•Kodak 1000 Intraoral Video Camera •Kodak RVG 6000 Digital Radiography System •Kodak 8000 Digital Panoramic System •Kodak Directview DR 9000

Product Line Length (left vertical axis label)

Product Mix Width (bottom label)

organized into 10 business units. The appliance product mix consists of the following product lines: refrigerators and freezers, electric cooking, gas cooking, microwaves, washers and dryers, dishwashers, compactors and disposers, venting systems, water systems, room air conditioners, dehumidifiers, small appliances, and electronics. The gas cooking product line is made up of various free-standing ranges, single wall ovens, slide-in ranges, and cooktops.[1]

Any product mix can be defined in terms of width, length, and consistency. Exhibit 10–1 illustrates these characteristics for the camera product mix at Kodak. **Product mix width** refers to the number of product lines in the product mix. The more product lines, the wider the product mix. The camera product mix is relatively narrow because it consists of only four product lines: one-time-use cameras, digital cameras, professional cameras, and medical cameras.

Product line length refers to the number of products in a product line. In the Kodak example, the digital cameras product line is the longest, with 23 products. The professional cameras product line is the shortest, with only two products. It is also sometimes useful to talk about the average product-line length across a firm's product mix. For Kodak cameras, the average product-line length is 9.75: there are 39 products organized into four product lines.

Product mix consistency refers to the relatedness of the different product lines in a product mix. The product mix throughout Kodak is consistent because all of the products are related to imaging. So even if we expanded our focus to the corporate level, the product mix would still be relatively consistent. The products would not all be cameras, but they would be associated with imaging.

Firms marketing multiple products and services must devise strategies for individual products, specific product lines, and the overall product mix. Key strategies at each level are presented in Exhibit 10–2. Although we discuss each level separately, the strategies are interrelated. Effective firms integrate product and service strategies across these levels. "Being Entrepreneurial: Developing an Effective Product Mix" provides an interesting example in the footwear industry.

| Exhibit 10-2 | *Product and service strategies* |

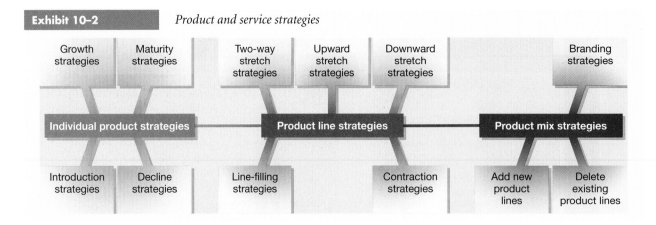

Individual Product Strategies

An important factor in the development of marketing strategies for individual products is the product life cycle. The **product life cycle (PLC),** like the biological life cycle, describes the advancement of products through identifiable stages of their existence. The stages are introduction, growth, maturity, and decline, as shown in Exhibit 10–3. The product life cycle concept applies best to new product forms; it does not work as well to describe stages for general product classes or for the specific life of individual brands. Thus the product life cycle concept is of most value for product forms such as portable telephones, cellular telephones, or video telephones. The concept is less useful in analysis of the specific brands of telephones.

The product life cycle concept is based on four premises:

- Products have a limited life.
- Product sales pass through distinct stages, each with different marketing implications.
- Profits from a product vary at different stages in the life cycle.
- Products require different strategies at different life cycle stages.[2]

Before discussing relevant stages, characteristics, and marketing strategies, we should examine the diffusion process as a basis for the product life cycle concept.

Diffusion Process

When a new product form, such as the cellular telephone or the compact disk, is first introduced to the market, consumers go through a process in determining whether to adopt it. We discussed this process and factors that facilitate adoption in Chapter 9. Research suggests

---

BEING ENTREPRENEURIAL

Developing an effective product mix

After being pushed aside by L. A. Gear, Robert and Michael Greenberg have created a successful footwear company. The typical footwear company has a product mix of 100 to 200 selections within a specific type of shoe class, such as athletic shoes. Skechers USA produces over 2,000 selections for all kinds of shoe buyers and many different types of shoes. For example, its product mix includes athletic shoes, clunky boots, basic brown shoes, trendy platforms, steel-toed sneakers, fuzzy slippers, and others. These shoes are sold to men, women, teens, and kids through retailers like Athlete's Foot, JCPenney, Sears, its own retail stores, and over the Internet.

One reason for its success is that it pays special attention to young women because they tend to buy shoes for all members of a family when shopping for themselves. It also aims its styles at teens and young adults and responds to changing needs quickly. For example, when clunky shoe styles lost popularity, the company immediately launched a "sexy and frivolous" line called Skechers by Michelle K targeted to trend-conscious women in the 18–34 age bracket. Skechers has also been able to keep prices lower than competitors. Recent new products include Marc Ecko Footwear and 310 Motoring fashion product lines. Skechers continues to design, develop, and market lifestyle footwear that appeals to trend-savvy men, women, and children.

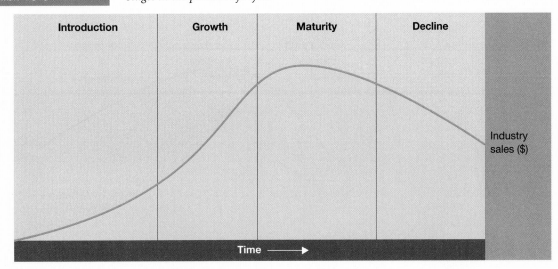

Exhibit 10–3   *Stages in the product life cycle*

Exhibit 10–4   *Diffusion process*

| **Innovators:** 2.5% Venturesome; highly educated; use multiple information sources | **Early adopters:** 13.5% Leaders in social setting; slightly above-average education | **Early majority:** 34% Deliberate; many informal social contacts | **Late majority:** 34% Skeptical; below-average social status | **Laggards:** 16% Fear of debt; neighbors and friends are information sources |

that different groups of consumers adopt innovations at different rates. Some consumers adopt a new product when it is first introduced; others wait until the innovation has been on the market for some time. These different adoption rates mean that it typically takes time for an innovative new product form to diffuse throughout a market. The **diffusion process** describes the adoption of an innovation over time.

The general diffusion process is presented in Exhibit 10–4, which describes five different adoption groups. As discussed in Chapter 9, **innovators** are the first to adopt a new product; they represent about 2.5 percent of a market. The diffusion process then moves to the **early adopters** (13.5%), **early majority** (34%), **late majority** (34%), and finally the **laggards** (16%). The types of consumers in each group differ depending on the type of innovation. However, as shown in Exhibit 10–4, consumers within each category have several common characteristics.

The different categories of adopters in the diffusion process are one reason new products go through life cycles. As an innovative product diffuses through these adopter categories, competitors enter the market and marketing strategies change. The interaction of the diffusion process and firm competition means that marketers face a different situation at each stage of the product life cycle (see Exhibit 10–5).

PLC Stages and Characteristics

The **introduction stage** starts with the launch of a newly developed product into the marketplace. Thus the introduction stage of the product life cycle extends the commercialization stage of the new product development process discussed in Chapter 9. Sales growth in the introduction stage is often slow because innovators typically represent a small portion of the market. Profits are low or nonexistent because of heavy expenses incurred in product development and intensive marketing to launch the product. There are no direct competitors for the first market entry, but competitors will likely enter over time.

Exhibit 10–5   *PLC stages and characteristics*

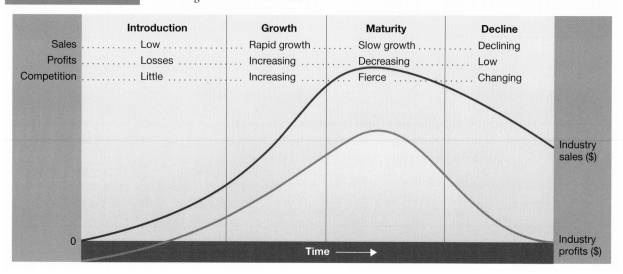

Ideally, a new product would remain in the introduction stage for only a short time. However, some products never get out of this stage or remain in it for much longer than desired. A case in point is the introduction of handheld computing products. Apple's Newton MessagePad was among the first entries in this market. Adoption was much slower than expected because consumers did not perceive sufficient value from the initial product. Apple responded by introducing new models, the Newton MessagePad 110 and 2100, with many new features. However, consumers did not value these new features either, and sales of handheld computing products languished. The situation changed when 3Com Corporation introduced its Palm Pilot 1000 and Palm Pilot 5000 handheld products. These products were simple, easy to use, extremely portable, and able to be automatically synchronized with the data on a personal computer. Consumers saw real value in these products, and sales took off.[3]

The second phase in the product life cycle is the **growth stage.** During this time, sales and profits increase rapidly. Innovators, early adopters, and the early majority buy the product. Recognizing the potential for profits, additional competitors enter the market with different product versions. The number of competitors and the rate at which they enter affect how long the growth stage will last. It will be shorter the faster competitors enter the market and the more aggressive their marketing strategies. As handheld computing products began to grow, competitors such as Handspring, Compaq, Sony, and Dell entered the market. All of these competitive products had some basic features, but each marketer tried to differentiate its product in some way. Some provided the core features at a lower price; others added features and kept the price relatively high. A convergence of technologies also began as some PDAs added e-mail and cell phone features, and cell phones added e-mail, digital photography, and PDA features. For example, the Sprint PCS Treo 650 integrates a cell phone, PDA, Internet and e-mail, and digital photography into one handheld device.

When the marketing efforts of all competitors begin to get adoptions from the late majority, the **maturity stage** begins. Profits peak, then begin to decline, reflecting intensified competition, especially on price. Competition becomes even more fierce during the latter part of the maturity stage, when laggards adopt the product. The market gets saturated, so increased sales come more from taking business away from competitors than from getting business from new adopter categories. Most companies market products in the maturity stage of the product life cycle.

When falling sales persist past the short run, a product enters the **decline stage.** Profits decline and competition is changing. A product can reach this stage for a variety of reasons. Most consumers who could buy the product may have done so. Another reason may be a shift in consumers' tastes, which is common in the clothing industry. Sales can also decline because of technological advances. The rotary telephone, for example, has largely been replaced by touch-tone phones that make it easier and quicker to place a call. Compact disks and digital audiotape formats hastened the decline of long-playing records. Digital imaging could have the same effect on film photography.

PLC Length and Shape

The length of a product life cycle depends on how well the product meets the needs of the marketplace. Products such as the basic household refrigerator have endured for a long time by offering consumers a good value. For less than $1,000, consumers can buy 20 years or more of convenient food storage.

In many industries, technology is advancing rapidly, which tends to shorten product life cycles. The life cycle for laptop computers was only a few years, as technology paved the way for the introduction of equally powerful but smaller notebook computers. The product life cycles for styles, fashions, and fads are similarly shorter than for many other products.

Life cycle curves for styles, fashions, and fads differ from traditional product life cycle curves, as shown in Exhibit 10–6. A *style* is a unique form of expression defined by certain characteristics of the product. Decorating is a good example. There are different styles of furniture and home furnishings, such as early American, contemporary, and French provincial, and one style or another goes in and out of vogue over time. The product life cycle curve for a style fluctuates, reflecting periods of renewed and waning interest by consumers.

Fashion is a component of style. It reflects the more currently accepted or popular style. Fashions tend to follow the typical product life cycle curve. A few consumers interested in differentiating themselves from the norm start a trend. Soon more consumers follow the lead of these innovators in the desire to copy the latest fashion. The mass market adopts the popular fashion as the norm, and eventually the fashion goes into decline as the cycle starts over with another new and different fashion. This is especially evident in the apparel industry—ask Levi Strauss. Levi's sales slid from over $7.1 billion in 1996 to about $4.2 billion in 2001 with its men's and women's market share down from 18.7 percent to 12.1 percent. The reason was that young consumers perceived Levi's jeans to be for the middle-aged. These consumers wanted more fashionable jeans like those from Seven and Blue Asphalt.[4]

Fads are a subcategory of fashion. Fads have dramatic product life cycles. They capture attention and grow quickly, but last only a short time and attract a limited number of consumers. Fads do not last long because of their limited benefits. They merely satisfy the need to be different and interesting. Some examples of fads are Cabbage Patch dolls, high-power water pistols, and games such as Trivial Pursuit. The life cycle of a fad is thus a very steep curve over a short period.

Sometimes it is difficult to determine if a sharp gain in sales is a fad or whether sales growth will continue. Harley-Davidson faced this situation when its large motorcycles

| **Exhibit 10–6** | *PLC for styles, fashions, and fads* |

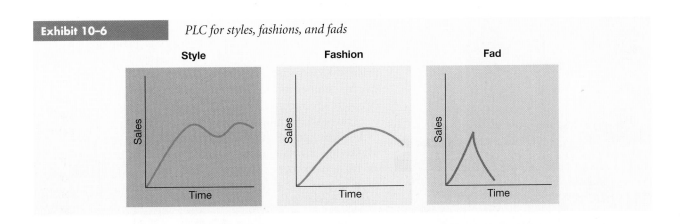

Exhibit 10-7		PLC marketing strategies
Stage	**Objective**	**Marketing Strategy**
Introduction	Awareness and trial.	Communicate general product benefits to consumers and channel members.
Growth	Usage of firm's brand.	Specific brand marketing communications, lower prices, and expanding distribution.
Maturity	Maintain market share and extend life cycle.	Sales promotion, lower prices, expanding distribution, new uses, and new versions of product.
Decline	Decide what to do with product.	Maintain, harvest, or divest.

gained popularity and stretched production capability. Management was contemplating a large expenditure to increase production but was concerned that the sales spike was due to a short-lived fad. Further analysis indicated this was not the case; Harley-Davidson increased production capacity, and sales have continued to grow.

Shortening lengths of product life cycles and their different shapes increase the complexity of marketing decisions. Firms respond to these trends by developing marketing strategies to take advantage of each life cycle stage. Some marketing strategies for each stage in a typical life cycle (Exhibit 10–5) are presented in Exhibit 10–7.

Introduction Strategies

The overall objective in the introduction stage is to increase awareness and stimulate trial of the new product. If there are no competitors, marketing efforts focus on generating **primary demand,** or demand for the new product form. As competitive brands are introduced, the focus shifts to generating **secondary demand,** or demand for the firm's specific brand.

Business

NOKIA 9300

The Nokia 9300 smartphone— created for a new generation of leader.

Stylish and compact on the outside, exceedingly smart within. The Nokia 9300 enhances your worklife while complementing your lifestyle. Find out more at nokiaforbusiness.com/amer/9300

- Widescreen viewing and full keyboard
- Email with attachments
- Instant messaging
- Full PDA functionality with calendar, contacts, and PC Sync
- Office applications
- High-speed data transfer via EDGE (EGPRS)
- Handsfree speakerphone
- HTML web browsing

Class

NOKIA CONNECTING PEOPLE

Marketing strategies during the growth stage typically focus on the competitive advantages of a firm's brand.

Two different pricing strategies are possible. Firms often set high introductory prices for new products to quickly recover the costs associated with development and introduction. Examples of this type of strategy are seen frequently in high-tech products. Most technologically advanced products start out at a high price that innovators are willing to pay. VCRs, home computers, and cellular phones, for example, were all introduced at a high price. Firms modified their pricing strategies as these products moved through the life cycle, making them much more affordable to the mass market.

Another strategy is to set a low introductory price. This approach is intended to generate faster market penetration. Because of the low price, it will take longer for a firm to recover new product development costs. However, the low-price strategy can lead to a larger market share and long-term profits. P&G normally introduces new products at a high price and then cuts the price as competitors move into the market. However, it changed its approach for the extremely successful launch of the Crest SpinBrush electric toothbrush. It used a low introductory price of $5 to gain market share quickly and make it less attractive for competitors to enter the market. The results of this strategy were spectacular. The Crest SpinBrush achieved global sales in excess of $200 million.[5]

Distribution in the introduction stage is typically limited. Marketing efforts must be targeted to channel members as well as final customers. Marketers use different communication tools to persuade resellers to stock the product and to get consumers to try it.

Introducing new and improved versions of a product is one strategy for extending a product's life cycle. Cheerios began as Cheerioats in 1941 and has been improved many times to extend its life cycle to over 50 years.

Growth Strategies

When a product enters the growth stage, the firm's basic objective is to build consumer preference for its brand. Because of the favorable characteristics of the growth stage, many competitors are likely to enter the market. These competitors usually challenge existing brands by offering improved versions of the product. An example is digital music players. The introductory stage began when several firms introduced MP3 players. Sales did not take off until Apple came out with its iPod and took over about 60 percent of the market. During the growth stage, a number of competitive products were introduced. Sony's NW-HD3 Network Walkman, Toshiba's Gigabeat MEG F20, and Creative Technology's Creative Zen Micro are examples. Each of these firms tried to differentiate its product in some way from the iPod so that it could get business from the expanding market and take customers away from Apple.[6]

Increased competition often results in the lowering of prices, especially toward the end of the growth stage. Even the market leader might lower price. For example, Apple introduced the iPod mini and the iPod shuffle as scaled-down, lower-priced versions of the iPod.[7] In addition, marketers usually expand distribution to make it easier for consumers to purchase the product. Communication efforts emphasize the competitive advantages of each firm's brand.

Thinking Critically

Select a product that you use and think is in the maturity stage of its life cycle:

- Propose three different strategies to extend the life cycle for this product.
- Which of these strategies would you recommend to the marketer of this product? Why?

Maturity Strategies

The overall objectives at the maturity stage are to defend market share and extend the product life cycle. With the diffusion process nearing completion, opportunities to get new adopters are limited. Marketing efforts focus more on taking customers away from competitors than bringing new adopters into the market. But this is difficult and costly. Several strategies might be used during the maturity stage.

One popular strategy is to offer incentives to consumers for purchasing the firm's brand. These include lowering the brand's price relative to that of competitors or using sales promotions, such as coupons or rebates, to reduce the brand's price. Although incentives can produce more sales from existing customers and take sales from competitors, their cost reduces a firm's profit margins.

Another approach is to get consumers to use the product in different ways. This strategy can lead to more purchases from existing customers or might extend the product life cycle by bringing new consumers into the market. For example, Arm & Hammer successfully expanded the uses of its baking soda product. Originally used in cooking, baking soda is now used as a deodorizer in refrigerators, in carpet cleaning, in toothpaste, in antiperspirants, and most recently in wintergreen-flavored gum. Eagle Brand Sweetened Condensed Milk has followed a similar strategy. It has been used for more than a century in pumpkin pies. The brand is now being marketed to busy cooks for use in all types of recipes, such as no-bake bars and shareable crumble treats, and as an after-school beverage.[8]

A typical approach is to extend the life cycle by continually introducing new and improved versions of the product. Because these new versions are not new product forms, they do not start a new product life cycle. They do, however, help prevent the product from moving into the decline stage. Procter & Gamble uses this strategy often. For example, P&G has improved Tide detergent many times during its long history.

A final approach is to reposition the product. This might be achieved by associating it in a more positive way with consumers. For example, Sony repositioned its household robots from an imperfect robot that could not perform simple chores to a lovable but useless pet. Sales of its doglike AIBO took off. Repositioning can also be achieved by combining features from different product categories into the product. The integration of PDAs, cell phones, and digital cameras, discussed earlier in this chapter, is an example of this strategy.[9]

The sales, profit, and competitive characteristics of the maturity stage produce a difficult situation for marketers. Marketing strategies used in the introductory and growth stages are not normally successful in the maturity stage. Firms often try many different strategies to maintain market share and extend the product life cycle.

Decline Strategies

When a product reaches the decline stage, marketers must make tough decisions on what to do with their brand. Sales and profits are decreasing and competition is strong. However, the picture can change depending on what competitors do. If many competitors decide to leave the market, sales and profit opportunities increase. If most competitors stay in the market, opportunities are limited. Thus the appropriate strategy depends a great deal on the actions of competitors.

Three basic strategic choices are available: maintaining, harvesting, or deleting the product. *Maintaining* refers to keeping a product going without reducing marketing support, hoping that competitors will eventually leave the market. Some people, for example, still prefer (or can only afford) black-and-white televisions. Similarly, rotary or dial telephones persist in some areas of the country for reasons of technology.

A *harvesting* strategy focuses on reducing the costs associated with a product in the decline stage as much as possible. Advertising, sales force time, and research and development budgets are limited. The objective is to wring out as much profit as possible during the decline stage.

Finally, *deleting* refers to dropping a product altogether. A firm might withdraw the product from the market, ending its life cycle, or might be able to sell it to another firm. Deleting products is difficult for many firms, but it may be the best strategy. The resources expended on a product in the decline stage may produce only minimal returns. Profit can normally be increased by allocating these resources to products that will produce higher returns.

Limitations of the PLC

The product life cycle is meant to be a tool to help analyze the characteristics of products and design marketing strategies. The concept, however, has limitations. Marketers should be aware of these before jumping to conclusions based solely on the product life cycle.

First, remember that the life cycle concept applies best to product forms rather than to specific brands. If marketers look only at the brand and not the overall product form, they may not see the whole picture. Brand sales can fluctuate for reasons unrelated to the product life cycle.

Second, the life cycle concept may lead marketers to think that a product has a prede-termined life, which may produce problems in interpreting sales and profits. A dip in sales, for example, may be taken to mean that a product is entering the decline stage. Managers could prematurely drop the product when the dip represents only a temporary blip in the marketplace. Many products have survived for decades without decline because they were managed correctly. Ivory Soap (introduced in 1879) and Morton's Salt remain stalwart competitors. In other cases, declining products can experience a jump in sales with some new development in the environment, as was the case with cereals. When medical research seemed to show that oat consumption reduces cholesterol, sales of Quaker Oats soared.

The final and most important limitation of the product life cycle is that it is merely a descriptive way of looking at the behavior of a product. There is no way the life cycle can predict the behavior of a product. That is, the product life cycle has limited relevance for forecasting future performance. Rather, marketing strategies help move a product along the life cycle. It is an interesting paradox that the strategies marketers adopt are both a cause and a result of the product's life cycle.

Product-Line Strategies

Individual products that are related in some way form product lines. Firms must integrate strategies for individual products within the strategy for a product line. The basic strategic alternatives are to increase or decrease the length of a product line.

Increasing the Product Line

Most firms have growth objectives, so they tend to adopt strategies that add products to a product line. Because few firms have product lines that cover all market segments, they focus on where to add products. Sometimes additions to product lines are needed to keep customers coming back.

A **downward-stretch strategy** is an attempt to add products to the lower end of the product line. Luxury car makers are introducing lower-priced cars to get new customers. For example, Mercedes C-Class cars cost around $30,000. Compare this to other Mercedes cars that sell for $100,000 or more. The strategy is designed to get consumers to try a luxury car at the low end and then to sell them higher-priced luxury cars in the future.

An **upward-stretch strategy** is just the opposite: Products are added at the higher end of a product line. This has been a favorite approach for Japanese companies in the U.S. market. All the Japanese car marketers initially entered the U.S. market at the low-priced end. As companies achieved success with these products, they gradually added higher-priced products. Now most Japanese companies market products at all levels, even at the luxury end of the market with products such as Lexus and Infiniti.

An interesting example of an upward-stretch strategy is the Boeing Business jet service offered by Deutsche Lufthansa. Instead of just offering a few business class seats on a 247-passenger plane, Lufthansa has introduced private business class service for all 48 seats on the plane flying from Newark, New Jersey, to Dusseldorf, Germany. No crowds, good food, and personal Sony watchman movie players—all for $5,900. The flights are about 60 percent full and already profitable.[10]

A **two-way-stretch strategy** entails adding products at both the high and low ends of the product line. Firms that have focused on the mass market might use this strategy to appeal to both price-conscious and luxury-seeking consumers. Marriott has used this strategy for its hotel product line, adding Marriott Marquis at the high end and Courtyard and Fairfield Inn at the low end. Marriott's product line now cuts across most segments of the lodging industry.

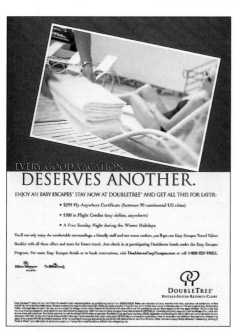

A downward-stretch strategy adds products to the lower-cost end of the product line. Doubletree appeals to customers who value a lower price and fewer amenities than upper-end Hilton customers.

Many firms market multiple products and services to meet the diverse needs of their customers.

A **line-filling strategy** involves adding products in different places within a product line. A firm might use this strategy to fill gaps in its product line that are not at the high or low end. Honda has always trailed import rival Toyota in U.S. sales, even though its Accord is very successful. One reason is that Honda did not have a pickup truck to compete with Toyota's Tacoma or Tundra or the pickups offered by General Motors or Ford. This changed as Honda introduced the Ridgeline pickup truck in March 2005; it hopes to sell 50,000 a year in the United States.[11]

A key concern in adding products to a product line is evaluating whether a new product will add new sales or take sales away from current products in the line. **Cannibalization** occurs when a new product takes sales away from existing products. A great deal of cannibalization shifts sales from one product to the new product, with little overall gain for the firm.

Strategies for adding products to a product line are typically most successful when cannibalization is low. For example, Anheuser-Busch introduced Budweiser Select as an upscale beer to help it recapture lost market share. The strategy was to position Bud Select as an alternative to Miller Lite. Distributors were asked to place Bud Select next to Miller Lite and away from Bud Light. Initial results suggest that this strategy is not working. Bud Select has been successful as it captured a healthy 2 percent market share. However, it appears that most of Bud Select's sales have come at the expense of other Anheuser brands and not Miller Lite. This cannibalization led to a drop in the firm's profits.[12]

Jack Kennard, Senior Vice President, Executive Director of Global Brand Development, Brown-Forman Beverages Worldwide, talks about increasing a product line: "Effective strategies for increasing a product line should enhance product image and satisfy different customer needs. Brown-Forman has used upward-stretch strategies to increase sales and enhance product image. For example, our best-selling brand is Jack Daniel's Tennessee Whiskey. We successfully introduced Gentleman Jack Tennessee Whiskey as a premium quality addition to the original line. Then Jack Daniel's Single Barrel Tennessee Whiskey was released as a new superpremium product. Cannibalization has been zero, as these new product "family members" met different customer needs, boosted volume and profit, and enhanced brand image both within the United States and internationally."

Decreasing the Product Line

Firms must consider deleting products when they are not successful, when they have reached the decline stage of the life cycle, or when the costs of marketing long product lines are high. Such **product line contraction** is normally painful but often necessary to improve performance.

The more products a company sells in a product line, the higher its marketing expenses tend to be. Deleting products reduces expenses and can lead to improved profitability. Many packaged-food companies are weeding out slow-selling products. For example, General Mills plans to drop 20 percent of its products. It is doing this to reduce costs, but also because Wal-Mart and other large grocery retailers are willing to give shelf space only to the fastest-selling products. And, as discussed in Chapter 8, these grocers are giving more shelf space to their own private labels.[13]

Product-line strategies are extremely important, and they are the result of complex and difficult decisions. The products in a product line represent a firm's offerings to its customers. As customer needs change or competitors introduce new products, a firm must be able to respond. One proper response might be to add products to a product line; another response, to delete some.

Product-Mix Strategies

The product mix consists of all product lines and individual products marketed by a firm. Most firms market multiple product lines with many products in each line. However, sometimes companies can be very successful by having a limited product mix. An example of how one company has done this is presented in "Creating Customer Value: A Small Product Mix."

Thinking Critically

Adding product lines to a product mix is a difficult task. Although there are some reported successes, there appear to be many more failures. Assume that you were asked to advise a company that was considering the addition of a product line.

- What are the key factors this firm should consider?

- How can the company best evaluate these factors to arrive at a decision?

- What strategy would you recommend to introduce this new product line?

Strategic Alternatives

The basic product mix strategic alternatives are to add new product lines or to delete existing ones. Many firms achieve growth objectives by expanding the product mix through the addition of new product lines. Successes are most likely to occur when a new product line has some similarity to existing product lines.

For example, Nike's apparel division has been doing well by marketing clothes to athletes. The new strategy is to move beyond this into the market for sporty street apparel. Women will be the main target. Nike thinks that by combining its high-tech athletic materials with casual fashion it will have an advantage over competitors. The sporty street apparel product line builds on some of Nike's current strengths.[14]

Although expanding into new product lines might seem to be an easy growth strategy, many firms find such success elusive. Adding new product lines can be risky. The more different a new product line is from existing lines, the more risk is involved. This is especially true for firms that move into products outside their areas of expertise. The popular business press presents almost daily examples of firms that have downsized by dropping unrelated product lines. For example, Ford Motor Credit is getting out of online brokerages, mortgages, and commercial lending to focus on financing sales of Ford vehicles and dealer loans.[15] Bank of America is dropping auto leasing and high-risk mortgages to emphasize product lines with less risk and more profit potential.[16]

Deleting product lines is another strategic alternative. Usually this is done to improve performance by focusing efforts in more profitable areas. For example, Bristol-Myers Squibb plans to sell its consumer over-the-counter drug product line. It wants to focus on prescription drugs that treat and prevent disease. This will require more time and effort in

CREATING CUSTOMER VALUE

A small product mix

ING Direct opened five years ago in the United States but has already generated 2.2 million customers and $29 billion in deposits. It pays the highest rates on savings accounts, and savings accounts are just about the only product it has. ING Direct does not offer checking accounts, has no real branches, and uses a converted warehouse as its headquarters. It attracts low-maintenance customers, and its operations are very efficient.

Profits are growing, and it is now the largest online bank. Customers get what they want—high interest—so they stay, and customer retention is twice that of other banks. However, competitors are moving into the market, and ING Direct is looking at expanding its product mix to keep growing. A mortgage business is being added. This will increase the product mix; but it will still be small, and ING Direct will remain focused.

drug discovery and marketing.[17] Take the situation at J. Crew as another example. When Mickey Drexler took over, the company was growing slowly. His first task was to make changes in the product mix. All trend-driven clothes were dumped, even product lines that were selling well. This allowed J. Crew to focus on and even expand its lines of luxury products. These luxury lines have higher margins and have helped the company increase profit growth significantly.[18]

Jack Kennard, Senior Vice President, Executive Director of Global Brand Development, Brown-Forman Beverages Worldwide, emphasizes the value of adding new product lines: "Adding new product lines can provide an ongoing source of novelty, create excitement, and help capture new customers. Jack Daniel's Country Cocktails is one example. This new product line helped Brown-Forman enter the premium low-alcohol beverage market. Jack Daniel's Country Cocktails expanded the Jack Daniel's brand into new consumer markets, particularly females. By attracting new customers, Brown-Forman increased sales and enhanced the Jack Daniel's brand."

Branding Strategies

Our discussion of branding in Chapter 8 focused on branding decisions for a single product. As firms expand product mixes and extend product lines, brand decisions become more complicated. Companies marketing multiple products and services need a strategy to guide branding decisions. The basic options are presented in Exhibit 10–8.

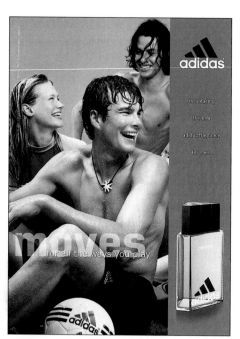

Many companies market a diverse product mix. Adidas emphasizes a product mix to meet different customer needs.

One option is to use an **individual brand name strategy;** that is, the firm establishes specific brand names for each individual product in a product line. This approach allows a firm to choose what seems like an effective brand name for a particular product. The drawback is that because individual brand names are unrelated, products stand alone. Brand equity from one brand cannot benefit another. Procter & Gamble is probably the most famous user of individual brand names. P&G's objective is for all products to compete on their merits, so each product has its own brand name. For instance, P&G's detergent products have well-known individual brand names such as Tide, Cheer, Bold, Dash, and Oxydol.

The other basic option is to adopt a **family brand name strategy;** in this case, all brand names are associated with some type of family brand name. One approach is to brand all product items in the product mix with the company name, as Heinz and General Electric do. Another choice is to use different family brands for different product lines, with all items in a given product line bearing that same family brand name. Sears does this by using the Craftsman brand for tools, the Kenmore brand for appliances, and the Die Hard brand for batteries. A final alternative is to use both a family and an individual brand name for each product—for example, Kellogg's Rice Krispies and Kellogg's Raisin Bran.

Exhibit 10–8   *Branding strategies*

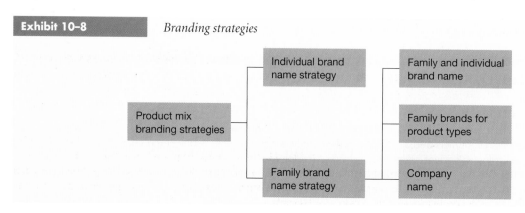

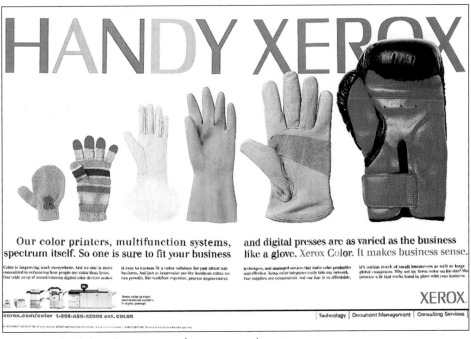

Xerox uses a family brand name strategy for its entire product mix.

Family brand name strategies can help firms increase product lines or add product lines. New products that build on the brand equity of an established brand are called *brand extensions.* Research indicates that the positive associations consumers have with a brand can be transferred to new products in the same category (increasing product lines) as well as to new products in different product lines (adding product lines). If successful, these extensions build additional brand equity.[19] There is some risk to using a family brand name strategy, however, because unsuccessful new products could weaken the brand equity of the established brand.

Ethical Issues in Product and Service Strategies   Marketers

should ensure that products are safe and not harmful; consumers receive relevant product information; there are meaningful differences among products in a product line; and if something goes wrong, there is a mechanism for redress. It is important to continuously assess performance and safety issues from the new product development process through production and marketing. Any identified problems should be corrected as soon as possible. Failure to do so can lead to dissatisfied customers, product recalls, and expensive lawsuits.

Product recalls mean the marketer must allow customers to return the product to get the performance or safety defect corrected. This can be very expensive and harmful to a company's image. Companies can limit expenses and harmful effects by establishing a procedure to recall the product voluntarily. Without an established procedure, the process is likely to be inefficient and costly. If marketers do not proactively recall the product, they can be coerced to do so by various government agencies.

Potential harmful effects from products is a difficult issue. Should firms market products that consumers want but that are harmful to them? Some observers argue consumers should be allowed to decide through their purchasing practices; others think companies should not market products with harmful effects. The current battle over the marketing of cigarettes is an example of this issue. Another example is movie theater popcorn. Most movie theaters prepare popcorn with coconut oil, which raises blood cholesterol more than any other fat or oil. Movie theaters could change to a more healthful way of preparing their popcorn, but consumers like the smell and taste of coconut oil–popped popcorn better. This issue will continue to receive attention because it is being pushed by the Center for Science in the Public Interest.[20]

Product counterfeiting is an increasing problem for many products. A U.S. Customs agent drives a steamroller over 17,000 counterfeit designer watches smuggled into the country. These watches were worth $620,000.

The issue of harmful effects goes beyond individual consumers to society at large. Products that are not harmful to consumers may create environmental problems for society as a whole, such as emissions from automobiles, nonbiodegradable packaging, and polluting chemicals. Marketers should act in a socially responsible manner by addressing the potential environmental problems associated with product use and disposal.

An increasingly important ethical and legal issue from a global perspective is product counterfeiting. *Product counterfeiting* occurs when a company copies another firm's trademark, copyright, or patent. Although this sometimes happens with U.S. firms, product counterfeiting by foreign companies is a major problem. The World Customs Organization estimates counterfeiting worldwide represents lost sales of as much as $512 billion a year. Seizures of fakes by U.S. Customs jumped 46 percent last year. Unilever Group estimates counterfeits of its shampoos, soaps, and teas are growing 30 percent annually. The counterfeit trade is growing rapidly, and counterfeiters are becoming more sophisticated.[21]

To ensure they are operating in an ethical manner, marketers need to answer the following questions appropriately:[22]

- Is the product safe when used as intended?
- Is the product safe when misused in a way that is foreseeable?
- Have any competitors' patents or copyrights been violated?
- Is the product compatible with the physical environment?
- Is the product environmentally compatible when disposed of?
- Do any organizational stakeholders object to the product?

Conclusions

As this chapter clearly shows, product and service strategies are extremely important. These decisions must be integrated at different levels of the organization, and they provide direction for the other areas of the marketing mix. Pricing, distribution, and marketing communications decisions are all influenced by the product and service strategies of a firm.

Summary

1. **Understand the different characteristics of a product mix.** A product mix is the assortment of products marketed by a firm. It consists of individual products organized into product lines. The basic characteristics of a product mix are its width, length, and consistency. *Product mix width* refers to the number of different product lines in the mix; *product line length* to the number of different products in a product line; and *product mix consistency* to how related the product lines are.

2. **Recognize the stages and characteristics of the product life cycle.** Products go through a life cycle similar to a biological life cycle. The basic stages of the product life cycle are introduction, growth, maturity, and decline. Sales and profits change over the life cycle as competitors enter the industry and markets become saturated.

3. **Identify appropriate marketing strategies for products in different life cycle stages.** Marketing strategies differ for products as they move through different life cycle stages. In the introduction stage, the firm emphasizes generating consumer awareness and stimulating trial of the product. During the growth stage, it focuses on building consumer brand preference to secure a strong market position. The

maturity stage calls for a variety of strategies to maintain market share and extend the life cycle. During the decline stage, the firm must consider options to maintain, harvest, or drop the product.

4. **Describe the limitations of the product life cycle concept.** The product life cycle concept applies mainly to product forms rather than to specific brands. If, because of the concept, a marketer thinks a product has a predetermined life, it could adopt a marketing strategy that limits the product's life. The product life cycle concept is descriptive, not predictive.

5. **Discuss different product-mix and product-line strategies.** The basic product-mix strategic alternatives are to add to or drop product lines from the mix. The similarity between product lines and the use of a firm's strengths are key considerations in making these strategic decisions. Branding strategies are also important as firms add products to a product mix.

   The basic product-line strategies are to increase or decrease the length of a line. Downward-stretch, upward-stretch, two-way-stretch, and line-filling strategies can be used to increase product line length. Product line contraction will decrease product line length.

Understanding Marketing Terms and Concepts

Thinking about Marketing

1. What are the major differences between the growth and maturity stages of the product life cycle?

2. What alternative marketing strategies might firms use for products in the maturity stage?

3. What are the major differences between style, fashion, and fad?

4. How do shortened product life cycles affect marketers?

5. Look at "Being Entrepreneurial: Developing an Effective Product Mix." Why has Skechers been so successful?

6. How would you define the product mix for any firm?

7. Reread "Creating Customer Value: A Simple Product Mix." Why has ING Direct been so successful with only one basic product?

8. Why is product line contraction so difficult?

9. What is meant by the term *cannibalization*?

10. What risks are associated with adding new product lines that differ greatly from a firm's existing product lines?

Applying Marketing Skills

1. Go to a local supermarket, drugstore, or discount store. Walk through the packaged goods aisles, consider promotional and packaging information, and identify at least five examples of marketing strategies for mature products. Evaluate each marketing strategy example.
2. Obtain the annual report for any firm. Draw a chart that illustrates the product mix for this firm. Evaluate the firm's product mix.
3. Assume you have just invented a new-to-the-world product. Describe the product, and develop the marketing strategies you would use in the introduction and growth stages of the product life cycle.

Using the www in Marketing

Activity One Go to the Starbucks Web site (*http://www.starbucks.com*).

1. Discuss the product mix offered by Starbucks.
2. How does Starbucks use this Web site to expand relationships with customers?
3. What recommendations can you offer to improve the Starbucks Web site?

Activity Two Fender Musical Instruments is one of the largest and most famous guitar manufacturers in the world. The Guitar Center retail chain is the largest reseller of Fender products. Go to the following Web sites:
Fender (*http://www.fender.com*)
Guitar Center (*http://www.guitarcenter.com*)

1. Describe the product mixes offered by each company.
2. Describe the product lines offered by each company.
3. Discuss the reasons for the similarities and differences in the product mixes and product lines offered by the two companies.

Making Marketing Decisions

Case 10–1 *American Express: Expanding Electronically*

American Express has developed a trusted brand name in its 155-year history. The company is posting record profits and expects continuous profit growth in the future based on recent changes in its product mix.

Current sales are about $29 billion annually. Most of these sales are from credit cards (60 percent), the financial advisory business (25 percent), and travel services (6 percent). The financial advisory business has not been doing well. Investors withdrew more than $5 billion from its equity funds last year. There have also been some problems with regulators. CEO Kenneth Chenault wants American Express to "focus on businesses that have terrific growth opportunities and terrific returns." Therefore, he plans to spin off the financial advisory business to shareholders. It will become a stand-alone asset management firm. Although this move will remove financial advisory services from the American Express product mix and lower revenues, it will improve profits.

Several things will be done to increase the credit card business. American Express currently has about 21 percent of the U.S. credit card business compared to 43 percent for Visa and 30 percent for MasterCard. It has fewer customers, but these customers tend to charge over four times more than Visa or MasterCard customers. The plan is to continue to focus on the customers that charge the most and offer them more products and services. Reward programs and promotions for its green, gold, platinum, black, blue, and Optima cards have been expanded. There has also been a successful effort to expand in the corporate credit card business by signing up small and medium-sized businesses.

A court ruling that banks can issue American Express credit cards is a positive development. The company has capitalized on this opportunity by signing up MBNA and Citigroup to issue American Express credit cards. These banks are among the largest issuers of Visa and MasterCard credit cards. But American Express has made it very attractive for them to issue its credit cards. The banks have responded by switching many good customers from Visa and MasterCard to American Express.

Another strategy is to sign up unconventional merchants. For example, American Express has made deals with luxury apartment buildings in New York City and elsewhere that allow customers to charge their monthly rent. American Express is also exploring ways to make it possible to charge payments for insurance, college tuition, health care, and mortgages to its cards. The ultimate objective is for customers to be able "to use American Express for everything they buy."

Finally, the company is rolling out a system called ExpressPay. This system uses radio frequency identification technology that allows a customer to pass a credit card across a reader and walk away without having to sign a receipt. The charges appear on the next monthly statement. This will make it easier for customers to charge more items at more places and will add significantly to sales and profits at American Express.

Questions

1. Why would American Express eliminate its financial advisory business when it generated about 25 percent of company sales?

2. What are the key elements of the American Express strategy to increase its credit card business?

3. What is your assessment of the changes American Express is making to its product mix?

4. What ideas do you have to improve the product mix at American Express?

Case 10–2 *Hewlett-Packard and Compaq: The Right Product Mix*

After a long and hard fight, the merger between Hewlett-Packard (HP) and Compaq was finally completed in May 2002. Many meetings were conducted to make sure the merger worked. However, a number of issues were unresolved. One of the toughest issues was determining the right product mix. There was clear overlap in some product lines, so dropping some product lines eliminated costs, but it also reduced sales and hurt some customer relationships.

The first step was to compare competing HP and Compaq products side-by-side and kill the weaker ones. This resulted in eliminating a number of products and product lines, notably HP's branded servers, business PCs, and its Jornada handheld computer, and Compaq's Tru64 Unix operating system. The companies started with 85,000 products, and this process reduced the total number to 62,000.

One surprising decision was to continue selling both HP and Compaq PCs in stores. The combined brands represented 60 percent retail market share. Keeping both brands gave the merged company more retail shelf space. This helped keep competitors off the shelves and led to increased sales. In addition, the brands were targeted at different market segments. Compaq is focused on consumers who want to set up home offices and connect wirelessly to the Internet. HP PCs, in contrast, are positioned as home entertainment devices and as digital imaging machines for photography enthusiasts. The critical question is if this strategy will lead to more PC sales and more sales of add-ons, such as printers and digital cameras, that have high profit margins.

The new strategy did not work as well as desired, and Carly Fiorina was replaced as chairman and CEO by Mark Hurd in February 2005. Industry and company personal computer sales have been growing slowly since 2002. Concern at HP has now moved to the printer business. HP's printer business accounts for about 30 percent of company sales but over 70 percent of profits. HP is still the market leader in printers; but market share fell 6 points, profit margins are being squeezed, and competitors such as Dell are going after HP customers.

HP is responding with a new effort called "Operation Lead Dog." The plan is to cut expenses and head count in the printing division by more than 10 percent, prune the HP product mix, develop new printer products, and move into fast-growing market segments like printers for digital entertainment and photography. It is too early to tell if this transformation will be successful for HP.

Questions

1. What were the critical product mix decisions for the HP and Compaq merger?

2. What process would you suggest for determining which products to eliminate?

3. Do you think both the HP and Compaq PC brands should have been kept? Why or why not?

4. What recommendations do you have for increasing the performance of HP after the merger with Compaq?

Chapter Eleven

PRICING CONCEPTS

11

After studying this chapter, you should be able to

1 Realize the importance of price and understand its role in the marketing mix.

2 Understand the characteristics of the different pricing objectives that companies can adopt.

3 Identify many of the influences on marketers' pricing decisions.

4 Explain how consumers form perceptions of quality and value.

5 Understand price–quality relationships and internal and external reference prices.

Wal-Mart

Wal-Mart stores are known for their size, assortment of brands and product categories, and low prices. In the fiscal year ending January 31, 2005, Wal-Mart Stores, Inc., the world's largest retailer, had $285.2 billion in sales with more than 3,600 stores in the United States and more than 1,500 stores outside the United States. The company has four divisions: supercenters, discount stores, neighborhood markets, and Sam's Clubs. The retailer emphasizes providing "everyday low prices" to consumers.

How is the company able to successfully pursue this low-priced focus, when low prices often mean minimal profit margins? First, Wal-Mart puts relentless pressure on its suppliers. However, and in spite of bad press, Wal-Mart is fair with its suppliers but strives for the very best prices for its consumers. Wal-Mart does not ask suppliers for slotting fees or request unreasonable funds for promotion. Second, Wal-Mart makes every effort to take costs out of the system and to introduce efficiencies in the supply chain. As such, expectations from Wal-Mart act as incentives for suppliers to improve their systems and to constantly search for ways to reduce costs. Third, Wal-Mart seeks improved technology to assist its suppliers and customers. For example, Wal-Mart's Retail Link system gives its suppliers daily point-of-sale data and helps track inventories at regional warehouses.

Last, Wal-Mart is innovative in the development of brand offerings. For example, Nike has made an exclusive distribution deal to sell its Starter line of running and basketball shoes, but without the signature swoosh symbol. Likewise, some analysts argue that one motivation for Procter & Gamble's purchase of Gillette was Wal-Mart's willingness to sell private labels. In a way, the added influence of the Gillette brand may help P&G lessen pressures on the manufacturer to assume greater costs in dealing with large retailers like Wal-Mart.

Many factors influence price, which in turn influences sales and profits. Companies can charge premium prices because they offer high-quality products that consumers value. The premium prices enable distributors of the products to maintain sizable margins (the difference between price and cost of goods sold) and gain healthy profits. Perceptions of value at the consumer level allow higher prices, which can be used to maintain high quality in production and gain enthusiastic support by distributors and retailers.

Determining prices for complex product lines is an important task. Prices set too high will discourage sales; prices set too low may result in unprofitable business and a revenue stream that does not cover costs and expenses. Buyers in business-to-business markets, as well as individual consumers, often evaluate other factors, but price remains a primary choice determinant. And the interaction of prices with promotional activities often affects the firm's image. Downward pressures on prices are evident from the increased purchasing power of retailers like Wal-Mart, the Internet (which increases the ability to compare prices), and the role of China and other developing areas, where low labor costs have driven down the prices for many manufactured goods.[1]

In this chapter we discuss the role of price and the major influences on pricing decisions. We explore the various pricing objectives governing marketers' decisions. Finally, we discuss how advertised prices affect consumer perceptions of value and decision making.

The Role of Price

Price is the amount of money a buyer pays to a seller in exchange for products and services. It reflects the economic sacrifice a buyer must make to acquire something. This is the traditional economic concept of price, called the **objective price.** Where barter and exchanges pass for currency, prices may be nonmonetary. Much trade between developed and less developed countries involves barter. This practice, called *countertrade* by economists, holds particular promise as a means of helping Eastern European economies. For instance, Germany has traded Mercedes-Benz trucks to Ecuador for bananas, and Russia has traded passenger aircraft to China for some consumer goods. An additional method of payment is *equity.* This method was frequently used in the technology sector in 2000, when the customers were small businesses buying hardware. West End Resources, a New-York–based consultant to small businesses, regularly receives payment partly in cash and partly in customer equity.[2]

Prices frequently have other labels. The price of a university or college education is called *tuition.* The prices charged by professionals such as doctors and lawyers are referred to as *fees.* Loans are paid for by *interest payments;* charges for meter violations and overdue books are paid as *fines;* apartment charges are called *rents.* Other terms used to describe prices include *premiums, taxes,* and *wages.* In nonprofit situations, *donations* and *time* represent prices to support charities and political candidates. In all cases, however, these terms reflect prices associated with the receipt of something of value.

Speaking from Experience

Mack Turner
Managing Director
Bank of America

"In financial services today, we hear that our products have become or are becoming 'commodities.' This assumption means undifferentiated from substitute and competitor-offered products and, therefore, unable to support higher-than-average prices. As marketers, I believe it is our role to continue to create opportunities for our product and service development teams to build products that can support differentiated pricing. I also believe that the application of statistical tools frequently found in the toolkit of marketing researchers can help develop target costs that support or increase rather than shrink margins."

Turner joined Bank of America in 1981 after completing his MBA at the University of South Carolina. Previously, he managed marketing research and the bank's service quality and incentive plan management divisions. Turner stresses the importance of relationships and the value of services. If the banker does a good job understanding the customer's business strategy and truly finds creative solutions to his or her client's business needs, he or she will be rewarded with additional business and less price sensitivity. Research has consistently shown that customers do have relationships with banks and within that small set of relationship banks they have "lead" banks. The lead bank receives the majority of the revenue the customer awards his or her banks.

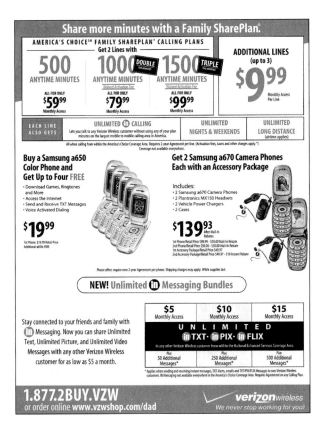

Telephones and telephone services have become quite price competitive, and frequent dealing is used to attract price-sensitive customers.

List prices, set before any discounts or reductions, may differ from the actual market price or price paid. Price discounts, allowances, and rebates may make the market price different from the list price. Also, a product's price may differ for particular uses or segments. In pharmaceuticals, for example, a drug might have a prescription price, a hospital price, and a Medicare price[3] *Partitioned prices* involve services for which different prices are listed separately, and customers of all types need to examine their bills carefully. For example, package carriers, such as FedEx and UPS, include a growing list of fees that do not fall under normal delivery pricing.[4]

Basic Price Mix versus Price Promotion Mix

A recent view of the marketing mix (price, product, marketing communications, distribution) makes a distinction between the firm's basic price mix and the price promotion mix,[5] described in Exhibit 11–1. The **basic price mix** includes those components that define the size and means of payment exchanged for goods or services. Examples include the list price, usual terms of payment, and terms of credit. The **price promotion mix** includes supplemental components of price, which aim at encouraging purchase behavior by strengthening the basic price mix during relatively short periods. These include sale prices, end-of-season sales, coupons, temporary discounts, and favorable terms of payment and credit. For business-to-business marketers, a number of factors may reduce the invoice price to a final transaction price. The most common include prompt payment discounts, volume buying incentives, and cooperative advertising incentives.[6]

Price promotions are designed to attract nonusers of products and services, as well as product users of competing brands. Price promotions may also be intended to increase the quantity and/or frequency of consumption among current brand users. Marketers must be careful, however, that price promotions do not detract from perceptions of quality, which eventually lowers overall perceived value and intentions to buy. Some argue that consumers who buy only because of the promotion will cease to buy once the price reduction is retracted. For these reasons, nonmonetary promotions such as premiums and extra quantity may be as effective in generating loyal behavior in the long term.

Often retail grocery and discount store prices are described as being either EDLP ("everyday low price") or HiLo ("high–low"). The latter strategy involves offering temporary but deep discounts in a small group of product categories. EDLP assumes constant

Exhibit 11–1	*The basic price and price promotion mixes*

The Mix	Components	Examples
Basic price mix	Fixed prices and terms of exchange	List price, usual terms of payment, terms of credit
Price promotion mix	Additional price reductions in various forms for short periods to tempt people to buy	Exceptionally favorable price, end-of-season sales, exceptionally favorable terms

Thinking Critically

Manufacturers may charge different prices for the same product in different markets. The pharmaceutical industry has come under criticism for charging high prices for certain drugs, such as AIDS medicines, in the United States, while providing the same medicines at substantially reduced prices in less developed countries. Is this practice justifiable from a consumer and a business perspective?

low prices across a wide assortment of product categories. In practice, retailers do not adopt a single position, but customize their pricing strategies and tactics to market conditions, to categories, and to brands. In fact, price strategies can vary on at least four dimensions. *Price consistency* reflects the EDLP/HiLo continuum. *Price promotion intensity* represents the frequency, depth, and duration of price discounts. *Price/promotion coordination* represents the extent to which price discounts occur with supporting in-store displays and/or advertising. Last, the brand price level relative to the cost of other brands in a category is important. For example, higher-priced national brands are often effectively price discounted.[7] The practice of offering price promotions remains entrenched in the minds of consumers and many retailers. Price promotions can increase store traffic, clear time-sensitive inventory, communicate a low-price image, and attract customers who will buy other high-margin products.[8]

The Importance of Price and Pricing Decisions

Price is the one aspect of the marketing mix that is most easily changed. Setting a price does not require the investment involved with advertising, developing products, or establishing distribution channels. Price changes are certainly more easily implemented than distribution and product changes. Consequently, the fastest and most effective way for a company to realize its maximum profit is to get its pricing right.[9]

Price also affects customer demand. **Price elasticity of demand,** or the responsiveness of demand to changes in price, is more than 10 times higher than advertising elasticity. That is, a certain percentage change in price can lead to 10 to 20 times stronger effects on sales than the same percentage change in advertising expenditures.[10] For these reasons pricing decisions are among the most important decisions that marketers regularly confront.

Price promotions or price reductions have become so common in some consumer product categories that sale prices represent the norm. Price reductions provide many benefits to consumers, manufacturers, wholesalers, and retailers. The primary benefits are listed in Exhibit 11–2. Importantly, price elasticity varies across brands. For example, one study revealed that a 1 percent increase in prices at Barnes & Noble decreased sales by 4 percent. In contrast, the same increase in prices at Amazon reduced sales by only 0.5 percent—a net revenue gain.[11]

Both the importance and difficulty of pricing decisions have increased in recent years. These changes have arisen because of several environmental phenomena:[12]

- Introduction of look-alike products increases sensitivity to small price differences.

- Internet access to price and competitive information has made price comparisons easier and has increased pressures on prices.

- Demand for services, which are labor-intensive, hard to price, and sensitive to inflation, has increased.

- Increased foreign competition, particularly from economies with low labor costs like China, has placed added pressure on firms' pricing decisions.

Exhibit 11–2	*Benefits of price promotions*

- Stimulate retailer sales and store traffic.
- Enable manufacturers to adjust to variations in supply and demand without changing list prices.
- Enable regional businesses to compete against brands with large advertising budgets.
- Reduce retailer's risk in stocking new brands by encouraging consumer trial and clearing retail inventories of obsolete or unsold merchandise.
- Satisfy trade agreements between retailers and manufacturers.
- Stimulate demand for both promoted products and complementary (nonpromoted) products.
- Give consumers the satisfaction of being smart shoppers who are taking advantage of price specials.

- Changes within the legal environment and economic uncertainty have made pricing decisions more complex.

- Shifts in the relative power within distribution channels from manufacturers to retailers, who are more price-oriented, also has increased the importance of price decisions.

- A bottom-line emphasis places more pressure on performance. Price reductions boost short-term earnings more effectively than does advertising.

- Technology that has reduced the time from new product idea generation to production also shortens the average life span of products.

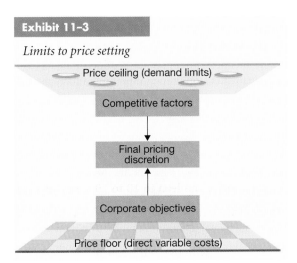

Exhibit 11–3

Limits to price setting

The downward price pressure from a business slowdown requires careful pricing execution. Lowering prices may help cover fixed costs and enhance short-term performance. Managerial pricing decisions should attempt to stabilize prices and limit industry price erosion in economic downturns and to maintain price margins for select customers and markets. Companies with low-cost structure, such as Dell, Southwest Airlines, and Wal-Mart, may be able to cut costs, lower prices, and build market share in weak economic situations. However, for many firms, pricing decisions during an economic downturn should not necessarily involve distinctively cutting prices. Instead of sales goals, firms often set profit contribution goals for individual products, market segments, and individual customers.[13]

The general limits on prices are depicted graphically in Exhibit 11–3. Prices are limited on the high side by what the market will accept and by competitive prices. On the low side, prices must cover costs plus some return on investment. Corporate objectives generally increase pressure toward higher prices to cover overhead and fixed costs and generate an adequate return or profit level. The exhibit depicts the limited latitude that managers may actually have in setting prices.

Internet Pricing Effects

Interactive shopping on the Internet continues to improve consumer access to price and quality information. And across-store and across-source comparisons are facilitated. These phenomena hold for both individual consumers and business-to-business buyers. Questions remain, however, as to whether price sensitivity will increase from this easier access to information or whether easier access to other information that differentiates products will offset these pressures toward price sensitivity.[14]

For goods that are common across stores or business-to-business sellers, price sensitivity will undoubtedly increase. Prices for many products sold on the Internet are being pulled downward by cost-conscious consumers who comparison shop. Auctioneers, such as *eBay.com* and *icollector.com,* offer competitive prices for even hard-to-locate items and are particularly well suited to marketing smaller items that can be scanned for viewing and easily shipped.[15] During the dot-com period of rapid growth, online retailers used giveaway prices to attract consumers. Unfortunately, these buyers were the types of consumers firms needed to avoid. Also, the prevalence of fixed prices may diminish due to the Internet in that the public arena, in which consumers decide to buy based on the manufacturer's suggested price, is less used. Auctions, in which supply and demand set prices, reach new customers and free selling efforts to focus on brand benefits. However, the drawbacks of online auctions include the growing realization that some customers will resent paying more than someone else for the same item and that auctionlike mechanisms focus on price comparisons that may erode brand loyalty.[16]

For sellers, savings come from lower real estate and rental costs and reduced outlays for advertising, inventory, and transportation. However, price is not the only avenue to success for marketing on the Internet. Customer satisfaction and customer service are paramount.

Customers lured online with low prices, no search costs, and easy ordering are demanding service like traditional customers. Increasingly, companies are making available service reps, offering the ability to track orders, and responding more quickly to e-mail. Recently Compaq Computer Corporation had to offer $250 gift certificates to appease customers who were dissatisfied with its Internet shopping service.

Of particular importance, marketers who begin to sell online face problems in balancing their online efforts with their traditional outlets. This balance has been particularly difficult for computer companies like Dell and Gateway that sell to both individual consumers and businesses. Dell sells direct to consumers and uses the Internet to sell and support corporate buyers. Online sellers must consider the effects of both their Internet efforts and the prices they are charging on their own dealers and outlets.[17]

New Product Pricing Decisions

Marketers of both business-to-business and business-to-consumer products and services often realize a substantial percentage of their profits from new product introductions. Effective pricing of innovative products involves the consideration of a series of critical market and product factors. The answers to the following questions enhance the ability of firms to make final new product pricing decisions:

1. What new benefits can prospective customers acquire from the innovation?
2. Which market segments will benefit from these new benefits the most?
3. What current problem-solutions will be replaced?
4. What range of prices will be possible in the segments that will benefit the most?
5. Given this range of prices, what costs can be afforded?
6. What complementary products are associated with use of the new introduction?
7. How can the innovation's benefits and price be communicated?[18]

Global Pricing Considerations

Pricing in international markets is particularly difficult. Firms pursuing global opportunities find that prices for the same item can be extraordinarily different across countries, even within countries; prices seem to be driven by different dynamics in each situation. For example, Coca-Cola has encountered severe price pressures in Germany from discount chains, and profit margins have been adversely affected. Coke's hesitancy to reduce prices initially limited its distribution as well.[19]

The changes caused by the introduction of the euro currency in Europe are currently evolving. With the introduction of the euro, consumers should be able to more easily compare prices, which should lower prices for some goods. Clothing items are still often bought regionally, but mass-produced autos—Volkswagen, Fiat, Renault, and Peugeot—should be negatively affected by greater transparency in price differences. On the practical side, currency changes have made operations initially more difficult for retailers, banks, and vending machine companies.[20]

International pricing is also made difficult by exchange rate differences and the need to present prices in foreign currency values. The **exchange rate** is the price of one country's currency in terms of another country's currency. Changes in exchange rates can affect the prices consumers in different countries have to pay for imported goods. Also, prices of goods are often driven up by taxes, tariffs, and transportation costs. *Protective tariffs* are taxes levied on imported products to raise the prices of those products in efforts to keep local prices competitive.

With the transition in Europe to the euro monetary system, marketers now encounter a market system that rivals that of the United States. The use of a single currency is forcing marketers to restructure their pricing decisions. This adoption of a single currency weakens what has been a powerful marketing tool—price differentiation by country. Price differences between countries that were hidden by currency differences have become apparent and are forcing companies to differentiate their products in other ways.[21]

Pricing Objectives

Pricing decisions are made to achieve certain objectives consistent with a firm's overall mission and marketing strategy. Five objectives commonly guide pricing decisions: ensuring market survival; enhancing sales growth; maximizing company profits; deterring competition from entering a company's niche or market position; and establishing or maintaining a particular product quality image.[22]

Firms may pursue a combination of these objectives. The objective at Texas Instruments in pricing calculators is to achieve a cost advantage by virtue of growth in sales and dominant market share.[23] For Texas Instruments, large market share translates into competitive advantage through economies of scale from high-volume production and marketing operations. Kmart emphasizes low prices in efforts to generate sales growth and volume. Such objectives provide long-term direction to a company's pricing and promotion decisions.

Market Survival

In some instances, a firm must set prices to ensure its short-term survival. That is, the firm adjusts prices so it can stay in business. Excess production capacity, for example, may require a firm to lower prices so it can keep plants open and maintain operations. In some instances, a firm may adjust prices upward if increased revenues are required.

Several years ago the cruise industry's top two carriers, Carnival Cruise Line and Royal Caribbean Cruise Line, for example, broke all reservation records. To fill their rooms, however, they had to resort to deep price discounts. Increasing price consciousness and worries about the economy had led consumers to postpone trips, to trade down to less expensive accommodations, and to demand lower prices.[24]

Frequent end-of-season deals by retailers represent efforts to move inventory and thereby recoup cash for investment in continuing operations and for purchasing new merchandise. Similarly, manufacturers may reduce prices as new products are introduced in place of existing models. In some cases, even very successful companies like Procter & Gamble have lowered prices to lessen erosion in sales.[25] Pricing for survival is a short-term objective, however. At some point, profitability and return on investment must be satisfactory to ensure long-term success.

Banks in recent years have seen their market share erode significantly and have begun to price aggressively. In efforts to combat this erosion of interest income, banks have resorted to charging extra fees for some services, such as ATM machines and credit cards. These fee increases represent higher prices to consumers. However, many feel these charges are unethical and reflect unnecessary gouging of customers in efforts to earn extraordinary profits.[26]

Sales Growth

Often companies set prices to stimulate sales growth, realizing that price and sales volume are inversely related (lower prices will normally increase volume). The benefits from higher volume are based on the assumption that increased sales lower unit production costs, increase total revenues, and enhance profits at lower unit prices. **Penetration pricing** is often the strategy used to accomplish this objective. Firms set penetration prices low to encourage initial product trial and generate sales growth, often as part of market entry strategies. The assumption is that the market is sensitive to price differences and that low prices will drive up sales. In this case, short-term profits are sacrificed for future growth. Penetration pricing is also useful for deterring new competitors and reducing short-term costs through high-volume production runs. The main ingredients for successful penetration strategies are a large segment of customers for whom low price is the primary purchase motivation, benefits in cost reductions as costs per unit drop with increased sales, and a fixed cost structure that benefits from increased sales.[27]

For international market entry, particularly for unknown companies or companies entering developing countries, a penetration approach is often useful. Penetration pricing can be effective for limited periods and in the right competitive situation. However, firms can overuse this approach and end up creating a market situation where everyone is forced

the EURO.
OUR money

On 1 January 300 million Europeans in 12 countries woke up to a new currency: the euro. The euro is not new: it's been used in electronic transactions and by banks and international businesses since January 1999. Now, following the launch of euro banknotes and coins, everyone living, doing business or travelling in any of the 12 countries is benefiting from dealing in just one currency.

There are seven euro banknote denominations, which can be recognised easily by their look and feel: the larger the banknote, the higher the value. On one side, the banknotes show windows and gateways, symbolising a spirit of openness. On the other they feature bridges, signifying co-operation between the nations of Europe and the rest of the world.

The eight euro coins have a common side and a national side. The common side shows the value of the coin. The national side differs from country to country, but you can use all the coins in each of the euro area countries. The launch of euro banknotes and coins has, however, had a profound impact way beyond the participating countries.

Indeed, for businesses and individuals alike, 1 January 2002 marked the beginning of a brand new era as, for the first time in the history of Europe, 12 national currencies made way for just one: the euro. www.euro.ecb.int

EUROPEAN CENTRAL BANK

Banks compete on the basis of different charges and fees associated with their line of services.

to lower prices continually, driving some competitors from the market but limiting the return on investment for all firms in a market.[28]

Often firms set a high list price but then use a low introductory offer to generate initial sales. This approach is advantageous in that the high list price can signal product quality; otherwise, some buyers may question the quality if a low introductory price is used alone.[29]

Market share describes the firm's portion, or percentage, of the total market or total industry sales. Price setting to maximize market share is similar to price setting in pursuit of sales growth. Greater market share increases a firm's market power, which enables it to extract more favorable channel arrangements (price and distribution advantages with suppliers) and, in turn, to maintain higher margins.[30]

Mack Turner, Managing Director, Bank of America, discusses the short-term effects of price reductions and the attraction of new business: "When interest rates are high, many banks offer high promotional rates in hopes of attracting new customers. However, some of these offers attract only short-term investors that quickly leave the bank for even more attractive deals elsewhere. Relatedly, some banks give away free checking hoping the new customers will purchase other loans and credit cards. Yet banks that follow this strategy but do not have specific sales strategies in place to cross-sell additional services to these new customers frequently find this tactic to be unprofitable."

Market share and firm profitability are often related. As in the case of Texas Instruments, greater market share leads to economies of scale. Economies of scale produce competitive advantages because of increased experience and efficiency; that is, companies learn to produce more efficiently with experience, and per-unit costs decline as volume increases.

Even companies with high market shares can be affected by price competition. Gerber, for example, held 72 percent of the $1.1 billion baby food market. When it raised prices by 5.5 percent, however, competitors Beech-Nut and Heinz began discounting their prices. Monthly sales for Gerber fell quickly by 16 percent.[31] Similarly, price competition between Kellogg Company, the number one marketer of cereals, and Post has forced Kellogg to reduce prices on some of its most popular brands, like Rice Krispies and Fruit Loops, to fight declining market share.[32]

An increase in market share is a reasonable pricing objective, but not when competitors have lower unit costs. In such instances, it may be impossible to build market share by lowering prices. Similarly, it is foolish for a company to use pricing strategies to increase market share when customers are not price sensitive.[33] In this case, a firm may be better served by targeting particular market segments in which new products have a competitive advantage other than price.

For many companies, the immediate emphasis will be growth in volume, irrespective of market share. This may occur when there are many firms in a market and all have low share. In addition, growth in sales may be derived from generating new customers or getting current customers to buy more per occasion or to buy more frequently, beyond increased growth from attracting competitors' customers.

Profitability

Maximization of profits is a frequently stated objective for many companies. Yet this objective is difficult to implement. Profit maximization requires complete understanding of cost and demand relationships; and estimates of cost and demand for different price alternatives are difficult to obtain. As Exhibit 11–4 demonstrates, if prices are set too low, marketers' profits are insufficient; if set too high, no one will buy. If price is set too high, the product will not sell. However, these problems can be addressed by lowering price. Charging too little is even more dangerous. Prices set too low cause the company to forgo profits but also set the product's market value position at a low level.[34] Clearly, however, adequate profits are required, and companies are sensitive to changes in profits over time as indications of performance. Pricing indifference bands can range from 17 percent for branded consumer health products to as little as 0.2 percent for some financial products. The location of a product within these indifference amounts can dramatically affect the profits of companies.[35]

Increased prices can affect profitability three to four times more than increases in sales volume at constant prices. One consumer durable products company increased operating profits by nearly 30 percent with only a 2.5 percent increase in average prices. An industrial equipment manufacturer boosted operating profits by 35 percent by raising prices only 3 percent.[36]

Price skimming is a strategy often associated with profit maximization. It includes setting prices high initially to appeal to consumers who are not price sensitive. In sequential skimming, the firm subsequently lowers prices to appeal to the next most lucrative segments.[37] This strategy allows companies to maximize profits across segments. Besides improving short-term profitability, price skimming lessens demand on production capacity, recoups R&D expenditures, and obtains profits before competitors enter the market. Moreover, consumers may associate product prestige and quality with the high introductory prices prevalent in a skimming approach. Du Pont and IBM are well known for using high introductory prices and skimming practices in marketing new products.[38]

Exhibit 11-4   *Optimal pricing decisions*

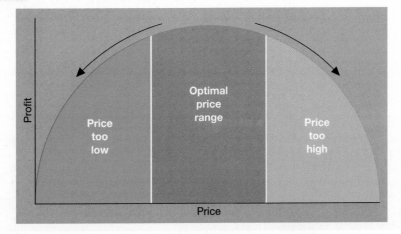

Profitability is often related to **return on investment (ROI).** ROI is the ratio of income before taxes to total operating assets associated with the product, such as plant and equipment and inventory. As for profitability objectives, the evaluation of the effects of alternative prices on ROI requires realistic estimates of cost and demand for a product or service at different prices. Firms attempting to obtain a desired ROI must take a longer-term, visionary view.

Competitive Pricing

Prices may also be set in reaction to competition. As in penetration pricing, a firm may keep prices low to inhibit competition from entering. Or it may set prices close to those of lower-priced competitors to avoid losing sales. **Price competition** occurs most often when the competing brands are very similar, or when differences between brands are not apparent to prospective buyers.

ITT Sheraton's simplified pricing system, modeled on the airlines' pricing approach, has been criticized by competitors as "rate cutting." The Sheraton pricing structure involves one room rate for business travelers, another for 14-day advance reservations, and a third for weekend rates. Sheraton also lowered its standard price. Not surprisingly, Hilton and Hyatt spokespeople warned that price competition would hurt the industry.[39]

Price competition may result in price wars, with prices spiraling downward in succeeding rounds of price cuts. They may lead to such low prices that all competitors operate at a loss in the short run. Price wars are frequent in the airline and computer software industries. Recent price wars over software in Europe may reduce the sizable margins U.S. companies once obtained for their products, margins once justified by the costs of translation.

In **nonprice competition,** the firm attempts to develop buyer interest in benefits such as quality, specific product features, or service. For this to work, customers must view the distinguishing attributes as desirable. Finally, focusing on unserved target markets in which competition is minimal may allow a firm to charge higher prices. For example, Charles Schwab uses its technological communications advantages to offer low competitive prices for financial services.

Competitive strategies have been described as being arrayed on a continuum labeled the **competitive strategy-positioning continuum.** This continuum is anchored by "low-cost leadership" on one end and "differentiation" on the other. For example, one furniture store may emphasize low costs of overhead and operation—a "no frills" warehouse positioning. Alternatively, a competing store may emphasize a more luxurious atmosphere

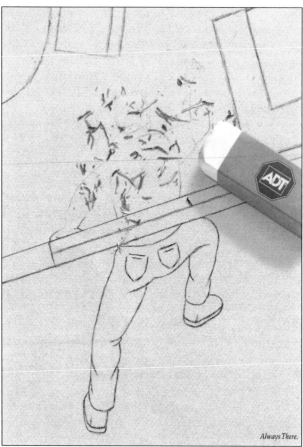

Prices charged for products must cover the entire bundle of product attributes. These prices also apply to complex offerings such as security services.

USING TECHNOLOGY

eBay and small business marketing

In an effort to increase appeal and growth, eBay has begun to target small businesses, particularly firms with fewer than 10 employees. Using advertising in industry trade magazines, eBay employed a series of testimonials from satisfied small business customers. Direct mail advertisements also helped generate awareness that eBay is an effective means of buying and selling. The use of eBay to purchase equipment and to sell products by small businesses allows wide market coverage and enables control of prices paid and received. As a result of this growth and recent international success in Europe and China, the firm's earnings are excellent, and the company has matured to achieve status as a mainstream retailer with the credibility of Dell and other major corporations.

with extensive decorations that appeals to more sophisticated customers. This latter store is more likely to compete on attributes other than price, while the former retail outlet attempts to attract consumers largely by low prices.[40]

Quality and Image Enhancement

Firms often keep prices at a premium to maintain an image of product quality leadership. **Prestige pricing** is based on the premise that some buyers associate price with quality and avoid products or services for which they perceive prices as too low. The American Express Gold Card and Lexus are examples of products that have images of exclusivity generated through premium prices. Professionals such as lawyers, doctors, and consultants often charge high fees for similar reasons. In these instances, low prices might imply lower-quality service or expertise; the reputations of these service providers allow the higher prices to be charged. The prestige associated with high-price/high-quality products and services is particularly important in gift-giving situations.

Economic events affect the purchase of luxury goods for all classes, not just the very upscale. During the boom cycle of the 1990s, the percentage of Americans buying image products, including $50,000 autos and $50 socks, was quite high. As the economy weakened, pressures became even more acute on companies that market luxury goods. Firms from car manufacturers to jewelers are marketing their luxury goods to broader audiences using mass-marketing campaigns. As the spread of small luxury BMWs and Mercedes suggests, previously upscale image brands are now readily available. Questions remain regarding the long-term effects of these new lower-priced entries on quality image perceptions.[41]

When the costs of malfunction are high, business buyers often purchase the highest-quality product available, regardless of price. They believe the risk of nonperformance—say, shutting down an entire production line or process—outweighs the risk of paying too much. Likewise, critical component parts that form the core of manufactured goods, such as electronic circuit boards, are likely to carry high prices.

Influences on Pricing Decisions: The Five Cs of Pricing

To ensure that pricing decisions are effective and consistent with the firm's objectives, marketers should consider the **five Cs of pricing** shown in Exhibit 11–5: costs, customers, channels of distribution, competition, and compatibility.[42] These five elements represent the critical influences on pricing decisions.

Costs

Costs associated with producing, distributing, and promoting a product or service are instrumental in establishing the minimum price or floor for pricing decisions. Prices must cover, at least over the long term, the investment and support behind the product, as well as provide enough income and profit to the company. In some instances, costs must be reduced to maintain price competitiveness. This phenomenon is evident in the airline industry. Low-cost providers such as Southwest Airlines have forced full-service airlines, such as American, United, and Delta, to control costs in efforts to maintain

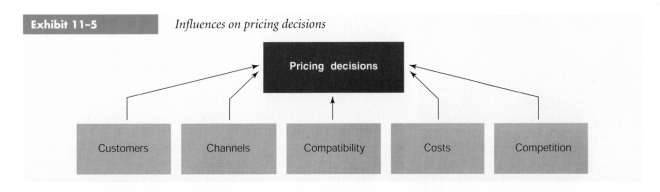

Exhibit 11–5   *Influences on pricing decisions*

| Exhibit 11-6 | *Product prices as the mix of costs and profit* |

Retailers pay record companies $7 to $11 and more for the CDs they sell for $11 to $17. Who gets that money depends on contracts and market forces. Big-name artists may get 20 percent or more royalties; when a CD goes gold (500,000 copies) or platinum (1 million), marketing costs drop, and the record company's profits rise. Here's how the take on a typical $15 CD—one that's gone gold—is split:

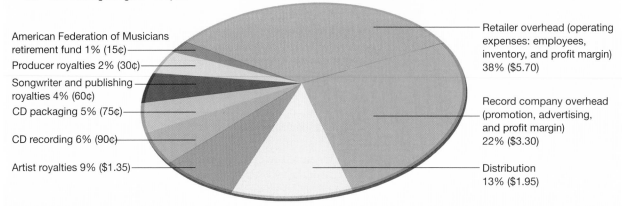

American Federation of Musicians retirement fund 1% (15¢)

Producer royalties 2% (30¢)

Songwriter and publishing royalties 4% (60¢)

CD packaging 5% (75¢)

CD recording 6% (90¢)

Artist royalties 9% ($1.35)

Retailer overhead (operating expenses: employees, inventory, and profit margin) 38% ($5.70)

Record company overhead (promotion, advertising, and profit margin) 22% ($3.30)

Distribution 13% ($1.95)

competitive prices. These cost reductions have been forced by consumers who are willing to accept fewer extras in service for lower fares.[43]

Exhibit 11–6 details the various costs that must be covered by a $15 price for a CD. The largest of these costs are marketing related: retailer overhead, including operating expenses and profit margin, is 38 percent of the total price; record company overhead, including promotion, advertising, and profit, is 22 percent; and distribution is 13 percent. For this product, nonproduction costs far exceed the other sources of costs that must be covered by price.

Timex also bases its pricing and production decisions on cost considerations. Timex used to make most of its parts itself. Today the company outsources its components (buys the parts from other manufacturers) so it can make production changes quickly. It is able to use its position as a dominant buyer of watch components to keep costs competitive and get faster payback on watches with shorter life cycles.[44] Old Navy maintains low prices by keeping the design of its products simple and by using less costly fabrics. Through clever packaging and color design, Old Navy successfully offers products, unlikely to go out of style, at cut-rate prices. Procter & Gamble has reduced costs by standardizing product formulas and packaging, reducing reliance on consumer promotion as well as trade promotions, and limiting costly new product launches. Due in part to competition from Unilever and Colgate, P&G has begun to offer lower-cost value brands targeted for the poor both overseas and in the United States. These consumer markets are huge and seldom can afford to buy high-priced premium brands.[45] Intel Corporation has instituted a cost reduction program aimed at limiting costs of materials through purchasing from its suppliers. The emphasis is on the entire supply chain and on programs that regularly identify low-cost alternatives that maximize value to Intel.[46]

Customers

Customer expectations and willingness to pay are important influences on pricing decisions. Buyer reactions are primary determinants of demand. In some instances, customers may be willing to trade off increased prices for more benefits or enhanced product features.

The customer interest in value has not gone unnoticed. Many firms now emphasize value by offering lower prices and higher quality. JCPenney has returned to its original position as a moderately priced merchant. General Motors has seen substantial customer approval of its value-pricing approach that reduces the prices of its cars, including models with attractive options.[47]

Pricing strategies, product image, and distribution exclusivity must be coordinated. For example, higher-priced and upscale products are associated with a unique image and limited distribution.

Service companies occasionally use **value-in-use pricing** to factor customer input directly into pricing decisions. They base prices on customer estimates of the costs if the service could not be obtained. Such firms are responding to consumer perceptions of value. Computer repair services, for example, might be based on some percentage of the savings to the company from limiting computer downtime. This approach, while requiring some market research, satisfies customer needs and requirements for service at the price the customer defines as reasonable value.[48]

Target costing, a concept developed in Japan, combines both cost and customer input into price decisions. The process results in a market-driven cost estimation procedure to determine for a product what the manufacturing costs must be to achieve (1) the profit margin the company desires, (2) the features sought by customers, and (3) the prices that will be attractive to potential buyers. The result is the development of a product geared toward the needs of buyers at prices they are willing to pay.[49]

The effects of technology on prices paid by individual consumers are still evolving. Amazon was caught pricing the same DVD differently for different customers on the same day. This behavior caused a substantial uproar that alarmed pricing managers. Faster computers, more sophisticated analyses, and large amounts of data that retailers are collecting allow grocers, drugstores, mortgage lenders, and computer makers, plus other merchants, to charge consumers "special prices." Of course, airlines have perfected the practice of pricing the same seat and trip differently for business travelers versus vacation travelers who book tickets in advance. Grocers post one price but charge another to their cardholders and another to customers redeeming coupons.[50]

Consumers vary in their reactions to price. For example, one study found that more educated consumers and those with fewer income constraints were less price sensitive. In addition, the effects of price promotions on consumers are often described as being asymmetric. First, reactions to price reductions vary by brand type, with price reductions for premium brands drawing consumers from segments who regularly buy competing brands and consumers who usually buy moderate or private-label brands. Price reductions for lower-priced brands are less effective at generating incremental sales. Second, and as will be explained in Chapter 12, consumers react more strongly to price increases than decreases. Hence consumer effects of price increases should be carefully considered.[51]

Channels of Distribution

Prices must be set so that other members of the channel of distribution earn adequate returns on sales of the firm's products. Marketers must consider the margins that others in the channel can make. If channel intermediaries cannot realize a sufficient margin, they will not market the products adequately. Moreover, the product's image must be consistent with the channels of distribution. For a product that attracts buyers with a low price, the goal would be low-cost distribution. For a product that attracts buyers with its superior attributes despite a high price, distribution must complement those attributes.[52] Blockbuster changed its relationship with suppliers by agreeing to give movie studios a share of rental fees in return for lower up-front prices on DVDs. These arrangements in the channel of distribution increased the availability of hit movies, making customers happy as well as increasing profits for both Blockbuster and its suppliers.[53]

Marketers give special sales promotion allowances and support to channel members to encourage purchase. These trade sales promotions now represent the largest of all marketing communication expenditures. Channel arrangements also involve restrictions on resale price, although manufacturers cannot require independent wholesalers and retailers to charge certain prices. Price guarantees stating that prices are the lowest available are also often given to retailers and wholesalers to encourage their patronage.

Competition

Prices charged by competing firms and the reaction of competitors to price changes also influence pricing decisions. Haggar cotton pants and Levi's Dockers are but one example of products that actively compete on price. As a rule, pricing decisions should not be made

Prices charged by manufacturers to their distribution partners should be set so that members of the channel of distribution can profit as well. Distributors and retailers must be able to establish sufficient margins to profit from their purchase and resale of manufacturers' goods.

simply to make the next sale or to meet some short-term pricing objective. Companies that price successfully in competitive markets know that the goal is not just winning sales; they want to maintain those sales in the future.

American products are experiencing increasing competition in Eastern Europe as shoppers become hesitant about higher-priced brands from Western companies. For example, given the still-small average monthly salary in Poland, consumers are returning to cheaper homegrown merchandise. In response, Western companies are introducing low-cost, low-priced alternatives to compete with the cheaper Polish products. For example, Germany's Benckiser compensated for its expensive laundry detergent, Lanza, by introducing a much cheaper brand, Dosia. This strategy enabled the German firm to still compete with lower-priced Polish products without damaging the reputation of its higher-priced Lanza brand.[54]

Competitive effects on prices are complex and can vary due to technological influences, the market position of the brands involved, and regulatory changes affecting some industries. For example, competitive pressures from the Internet and the ability of consumers to make price comparisons across outlets are helping pull prices downward. One study noted that, even after accounting for shipping costs, prices for prescription drugs and apparel were over 20 percent less than those in traditional retail outlets.[55] Blockbuster is facing increased price pressures from cheaper DVDs at Target and Wal-Mart.

For many consumer packaged goods, competition among products of different quality is asymmetric. Price promotions by higher-quality brands draw disproportionately more market share from lower-quality brands. Firms in previously regulated industries, such as utilities, are finding much more intense competition and must manage pricing decisions carefully.[56]

Compatibility

Finally, the price of a product must be compatible with the overall objectives of the firm. Again, a firm's long-term image considerations will influence the prices it establishes. High brand equity enables a firm to launch brand extensions, to extract better arrangements from distributors and retailers, and to charge higher prices.[57] Dial soap, after 40 years, is still the category leader; Chips Ahoy, a 25-year-old brand, is still the leading chocolate chip

Thinking Critically

Consider Wal-Mart and Macy's department stores. Although both companies are large retailers that offer a variety of products to consumers, they differ dramatically in their approaches. Discuss how the five Cs of pricing affect how these two companies operate. Point out both the similarities and differences for each influence on price. Which firm's overall pricing decisions seem to be more effective?

cookie. These brands have strong brand equity and hence high prices and excellent margins. In both cases, the prices charged are compatible with the overall marketing strategy for the brand.

In pricing a product, a firm must also consider the prices of other products within its product line. The price of one product or brand should not cannibalize sales—that is, shift sales from other brands within the same line of products. If a top-of-the-line model in a line of running shoes is priced at $150, a low-end model targeted to the novice runner should be priced so as not to steal sales from the higher-end model. Likewise, Boeing prices its line of commercial airlines so that low-end models do not detract from the larger, top-of-the-line airplanes.

Ethical and Legal Restraints on Pricing   Marketers must consider more than

the influences of the five Cs in price decisions. Pricing practices must also conform to laws and regulations and ethical expectations of customers and society in general. A variety of legislation affects the pricing decisions of firms. The objectives of this legislation are largely twofold: to protect competition among companies within markets and to protect the rights of consumers. The most important of these laws, summarized in chronological order of enactment in Exhibit 11–7, influence the ethical aspects of pricing decisions.

The Sherman Act (1890) inhibited price fixing and restraint of trade among competitors. Pricing practices designed to drive competitors from the market and conspiracy among competitors are limited by the case law established following this legislation. The act represents one of the government's first attempts to establish antitrust policies. A recent case involved allegations that 55 private educational institutions engaged in price-fixing agreements that resulted in overly high student fees. The Sherman Act was also used by the American Football League in its suit against the National Football League.

The Federal Trade Commission Act (1914) established the FTC as the administrative organization for monitoring unfair and anticompetitive business practices. The FTC is charged with limiting deceptive pricing and advertising practices.

The Clayton Act (1914) restricted price discrimination and purchase agreements between buyers and sellers and strengthened the antitrust limits on mergers and competitor arrangements of the Sherman Act. The act also limited requirements that a purchaser of one product must buy other products from the seller.

The Robinson-Patman Act (1936) placed more stringent restrictions on **price discrimination** practices—selling the same product to different customers at different prices. Price discrimination can inhibit competition, particularly among resellers. It is legal to charge final consumers different prices (senior citizen discounts, student rates) because this does not impair competition. A manufacturer, however, may violate the law by charging different prices to different retailers. Quantity discounts are not an issue as long as all buyers can take advantage of uniform discount policies.

Exhibit 11-7   *Significant U.S. legislation influencing price decisions*

- Sherman Act, 1890: Establishes illegality of restraint of trade and price fixing. First antitrust policy instituted by U.S. government. Predatory pricing to drive competitors from market is also restricted.
- Federal Trade Commission Act, 1914: Establishes Federal Trade Commission, which is charged with limiting unfair and anticompetitive practices of business.
- Clayton Act, 1914: Restricts price discrimination and purchase agreements between buyers and sellers; strengthens antitrust limits on mergers.
- Robinson-Patman Act, 1936: Limits the ability of firms to sell the same product at different prices to different customers. Price differentials can lessen or harm competition, particularly among resellers.
- Wheeler-Lea Act, 1938: Allows the Federal Trade Commission to investigate deceptive practices and to regulate advertising. Also ensures that pricing practices do not deceive customers.
- Consumer Goods Pricing Act, 1975: Eliminates some control over retail pricing by wholesalers and manufacturers and allows retailers to establish final retail prices in most instances. Places limits on resale price maintenance agreements among manufacturers, wholesalers, and retailers.

Not all price discrimination is illegal, however. Under certain conditions, price discrimination may be permissible if the buyers are not competitors; the prices charged do not limit competition; the price differentials reflect differences in costs of serving the different customers; or the price differences occur because of efforts to meet competitor prices.

Acceptable price discrimination may reflect price differences based on time, place, customer, and product distinctions. For example, different prices are charged for telephone use and movies depending on the time of the day. Place differences account for differences in prices at hotels and entertainment events. Even individual customers may be charged different prices based on negotiations or differences in need.

Charges of price discrimination do occur in the marketplace. For example, many pharmacists claim that they pay more for prescription drugs than managed care providers that command discounts for large purchase quantities. In past years, drug manufacturers have pledged to limit price increases to inflation rates or less. However, recent price increases in prescription drugs have risen above those rates as health care reform pressures subsided. Now many pharmacists claim that they are unfairly burdened and at a competitive disadvantage to hospitals and HMOs that pay lower prices for drugs.[58]

To reduce consumer anger, the car rental industry and online travel agencies have begun to roll out a program described as "total pricing," intended to quote prices that include all taxes, fees, and surcharges. Previously, research found that car rental purchasers paid an average of 24 percent in taxes and surcharges over the base rate at major airports.[59]

Dumping—selling a product in a foreign country at a price lower than its price in the domestic country, and lower than its marginal cost of production—is a form of price discrimination. Most governments have antidumping regulations that protect their own industries against unfair foreign pricing practices. Typically, appeals for government assistance are based on the argument that offending firms are practicing **predatory dumping**—pricing intended to drive rivals out of business. A successful predator firm raises prices once the rival is driven from the market. One famous case involved Sony Corporation of Japan. Sony was selling TV sets for $180 in the United States while charging $333 in Japan for the same Japanese-made product. Threats of increased tariffs on Japanese TVs eventually forced increases in the prices of those exported to the United States. Fuji and Kodak have engaged in litigation regarding claims of product dumping.

The Wheeler-Lea Act (1938) expanded the FTC's role to monitor deceptive and misleading pricing and advertising practices. More recently, the Consumer Goods Pricing Act (1975) supported the right of retailers to determine final prices. The effect of the legislation is to limit the ability of manufacturers to control prices in their channels of distribution.

Implications for Pricing Decisions

Primary implications of legislation and case law for pricing include the following:

- Horizontal price fixing among companies at the same level of a distribution channel is illegal.

- In most cases, retailers are free to establish their own final selling prices. Prices charged by manufacturer- or wholesaler-owned retailers may still be restricted by the owner.

CREATING CUSTOMER VALUE

Best Buy's customer-centric focus

Best Buy, the nation's largest electronics retailer with over 800 stores in North America, continues to evolve as customer preferences change. As music sales decline and video demand increases, the company will shift space from CDs to DVDs. DVDs, digital TVs, MP3 players, and laptops have become the fastest-growing categories. To avoid price discounting and to maintain price margins, Best Buy works to tailor stores to local conditions. The electronics chain determines if local customers tend to fall into key categories, including "busy suburban mom" and "affluent professional." Stores serving the wealthy emphasize home entertainment, while stores patronized by young families focus on digital cameras.

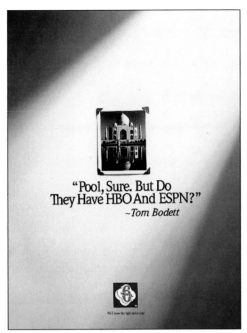

"Pool, Sure. But Do
They Have HBO And ESPN?"
~Tom Bodett

Even ads that do not promote prices should be consistent with the overall pricing strategy of the firm. This nonprice communication subtly reinforces the low-price positioning of Motel 6.

- Some states have enacted minimum price laws that prevent retailers from selling merchandise for less than cost.
- Prices must not be presented in a way that deceives customers.
- Discrimination that reflects extremely low prices to eliminate competition, or that does not reflect cost differentials, may be illegal.
- In industries with a few large firms, it is generally acceptable for the pricing behavior of smaller firms to parallel that of larger firms.

International Agreements and Organizations

The prices charged for products and services are also affected by a number of international agreements or organizations. Among the more important agreements are the General Agreement on Tariffs and Trade (GATT); the Organization of Petroleum Exporting Countries (OPEC); the European Union (EU); and the North American Free Trade Agreement (NAFTA). All have wide-ranging effects on the prices charged in global markets.

For example, OPEC is a loose federation of many of the oil-producing countries. This cooperative arrangement is designed to influence market prices and short-term profits for crude oil. The cartel has been affected by acts of cheating on production among its own members as well as nonmembers' independent pricing actions. OPEC's effectiveness at controlling prices has been uneven in recent years.

Coffee cartels in South America actually enhanced the competitive positions of high-priced marketers of coffee—companies like Starbucks. Restrictions placed on production of coffee, similar to those of OPEC on oil production, have hurt moderately and lower-priced national brands by raising their costs and squeezing their already low margins. Starbucks and other high-priced sellers have greater margins to absorb the rising costs.

Customer Price Evaluations

We have talked so far about pricing from the perspective of the marketer or the seller. But how does the buyer judge prices? What determines a customer's evaluation of a product or brand?

The key to learning how prices influence purchase decisions lies in understanding how buyers perceive prices.[60] This **perceived monetary price** is the consumer's reaction that the price is high or low, fair or unfair. Further, consumers do not always remember prices, even within the store, and often encode or process them in personally meaningful ways.[61]

The effects of price framing and how prices are presented can dramatically impact price evaluations. A provider of term life insurance tried three separate headlines in separate communications for a policy that cost $360 per year and was paid in two separate payments of $180. The three headlines read as follows: $360 per year, $30 per month, and $1 per day. Buyers were 3 times more likely to buy when the headline read $30 per month and 10 times more likely to buy when the promotion suggested $1 per day, in comparison to the annual basis.[62]

Judgments of Perceived Value

Perceived value describes the buyer's overall assessment of a product's utility based on what is received and what is given. It represents a trade-off between the "give" and the "get" components of a purchase transaction and plays a critical role in purchase decisions.[63] Some observers describe perceived value as "quality per dollar."[64]

The give is mainly the product's price. Increasingly, consumers base brand decisions on their notions of a "reasonable price" and compare prices regularly.[65] Exhibit 11–8 summarizes the effects of price on buyer judgments of value. Perceived value ultimately determines willingness to buy. Perceived value in turn is determined by a combination of the perceived

Exhibit 11-8 *Relationships among price, perceived value, and willingness to buy*

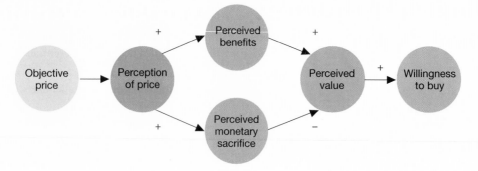

benefits, or quality received, and the monetary sacrifice made. Higher benefits enhance value; higher monetary sacrifice detracts from it. These offsetting effects reflect the trade-off of the give and get components inherent in consumer perceptions of value.

The power of consumer perceptions of value has not gone unnoticed by marketers. Well-known consumer companies whose stated primary emphasis is on consumer value include McDonald's, Wal-Mart, Sara Lee, Toyota, and Taco Bell. Business-to-business marketers now focusing on value through lower prices and enhanced quality include Emerson Electric, Electronic Data Systems (EDS), and 3M.

The determinants of value for services are even more critical to understand. As one noted expert in services marketing emphasizes, the lack of differentiation among many competing services encourages managers to overuse price as a marketing tool; the mistake is thus made that price and value are equivalent. In truth, value represents the benefits received for burdens endured. These burdens include not only price but also slow service, busy telephone lines, and rude boundary employees who interact directly with the customers of service providers.[66] The role of the marketer is to identify perceived value associated with the firm's products and services across the different target market segments and then to set prices accordingly. Offerings then should be sold on the basis of value, not just price.[67]

Price–Quality Relationships

Consumers trade off prices paid for benefits received, or product or service quality. The **price–quality relationship** describes the extent to which the consumer associates the product's price with higher quality. Higher prices do not always signal higher quality, however. Evidence suggests that, if there is a positive relationship, it is not very strong.[68] Sometimes uninformed consumers mistakenly use price to make quality judgments. When price and quality are not related, buying a higher-priced brand is a poor decision.

One study of *Consumer Reports* ratings revealed some interesting findings regarding the existence of actual price–quality relationships.[69] In tests across brands within nine product classes, prices and objective quality ratings were found to be positively related, negatively related, and not related, depending on the products investigated. For example, positive relationships between price and quality existed for bicycles, washing machines, and frozen pizza. Negative relationships were observed for stereo speakers, blenders, and spray cleaners. Thus consistently assuming higher prices mean higher quality does not always result in wise decisions.

Consumer Use of Price Information

The effect of prices on consumers varies across people and situations.[70] Uncertainty about prices and quality can make purchase decisions difficult. The importance of quality and a buyer's previous experience determine the role of price in consumer evaluations. Ideally, consumers should use a **best-value strategy,** picking the lowest-cost brand available with the desired level of quality. In a **price-seeking strategy,** some consumers

AT $79 IT'S SEXY.
AT $320 IT'S OBSCENE.

Designer clothing 40-75% off, every day. A Daffy's will open in early December at 17th and Chestnut.
DAFFY'S
CLOTHES THAT WILL MAKE YOU, NOT BREAK YOU.™

Consumer expectations about market prices affect decisions to buy. Prices noticeably above and below expectations can lead to unfavorable reactions to product offerings.

make a price–quality assumption and choose the highest-priced brand to maximize expected quality. Other consumers follow a **price-aversion strategy,** buying the lowest-priced brand simply to minimize risks of having spent more than necessary.

Mack Turner comments on pricing strategy: "In the past several years, commercial banks and investment banks have attempted to maintain their profit margins by offering superior levels of advice and maintaining long-term commitments to client relationships. This strategy, coupled with a strong brand image, has allowed us to sustain superior pricing advantages, as well as maintain share of the market. The perceived higher-level service, which includes the banker demonstrating a greater strategic knowledge of the client's business and business sector, is believed to lead to pricing advantages. In investment banking, this phenomenon is especially true when the bank is able to leverage a strong brand image built from a successful track record of major deals. Banks support this image through matter-of-record advertising that highlights the major deals they have won and the significance of the bank's role in the deal."

Recognition that consumers use different purchase approaches can influence the firm's marketing strategies. If product quality is not obvious to the consumer but has high importance (imported wines, for example), firms often use a *price signaling strategy:* They set prices higher to imply higher quality. Where quality information is more readily available and the importance of quality is high (appliances, perhaps), firms often pursue a value-based strategy and use informative advertising. In this case, the firm keeps prices competitive and focuses marketing communications on the benefits and quality of the product. Firms market generic brands and brands that compete largely on low price in recognition that some consumers are price-averse. Interestingly, low prices or heavy advertising expenditures can signal high quality in some instances. When quality is not observable and can be assessed only through consumption (experience goods), "wasteful" expenditures by the firm via low introductory prices or an expensive ad campaign may signal high quality for products dependent on repeat business.[71]

How Are Price Judgments Made?

How do people judge whether prices are too low, too high, or fair? Consumers compare product prices with internal and, in some cases, external reference prices. **External reference prices** include those charged by other retailers or comparison prices that a retailer provides to enhance perceptions of the published price.

Internal reference prices are comparison standards that consumers remember and use to make their judgments. There are several internal reference prices. One is the expected price, a primary determinant of whether a buyer perceives a price as fair and reasonable. Another is the **reservation price,** an economic term for the highest price a person is willing to pay. Expectation of future prices is also a key internal reference, as the forward-looking consumer evaluates the costs and benefits of buying now versus buying at some future time.[72] Other internal reference prices include "the price last paid, the average retail price, and the price I would like to pay."[73] Consumers sometimes infer motives for prices, particularly unexpected high prices, and these motives affect perceptions of price fairness. When high prices are assumed to reflect marketer "greed," fair-price perceptions generate negative inferences to the seller. As such, fair price is an important internal reference price in certain circumstances.[74]

A model of consumer evaluations of prices is presented in Exhibit 11–9.[75] It assumes that consumers have price information through past experiences with purchases of the same product or similar products.[76] Most people may be uncertain about specific prices but have some general expectations about market prices and a range of acceptable prices. They evaluate how the price of a product fits these expectations. They may interpret prices judged as too low as indicating suspect product quality; prices judged as too high are dismissed as out of the question or associated with a different product category. Buyers typically have lower

Exhibit 11–9   *Consumer evaluations of prices*

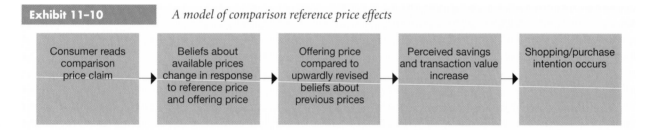

Exhibit 11–10   *A model of comparison reference price effects*

and upper price thresholds, or a range of acceptable prices for a purchase. These limits are not constant and shift as buyers obtain information regarding the actual range of prices in a product category, line, or market. The upper limit reflects prices perceived as too high or unfair; prices below the low limit raise concerns about product quality.[77]

Individual price evaluations may be influenced by external factors such as budget constraints, time pressure, anticipated use situations, or the cost of further search for lower-priced items. Consumers are generally less willing to pay higher prices for brands they perceive to have frequent price promotions.[78]

Advertised Comparison Prices

Advertisers often provide comparison prices (external reference prices) to persuade shoppers to buy. Comparison prices generally take one of three forms: prices previously charged by the retailer, prices charged by other retailers in the area, or manufacturer-suggested prices. Exhibit 11–10 summarizes the effect of comparison prices.[79] Comparison pricing increases the perceived **transaction value** of the purchase (the perceived merits of the deal) by raising the shopper's internal price standard, which makes the advertised price appear more attractive.[80] Increased transaction value then enhances overall acquisition value, which increases the likelihood of purchase. Such price-induced incentives are particularly effective for positioning products that are relatively undifferentiated from those of competitors. These transaction value-enhancing strategies are prevalent for jewelry, luggage, and some electronic products. In fact, retailers such as Best Buy and Circuit City often present sale prices coupled with either "previously offered prices" or manufacturers' suggested prices.[81]

Comparison prices are used to "frame" offerings as a good deal or high value. Many retailers present both MSRP and sale prices.

Summary

1. **Realize the importance of price and understand its role in the marketing mix.** For every good or service sold, the determination of price is critically important to the level of demand and the profits earned. A price set too high will discourage demand; a price set too low will result in less revenue; both lead to lower total profits. Determining an optimal price is becoming more difficult with changing marketplace trends, including faster technological progress, the proliferation of new products, increased demand for services, and growing global competition.

   Relationships between the determined price and the other marketing mix variables affect sales of the product and others the company offers. Price is only one aspect of the firm's marketing mix; other aspects, such as product and distribution, must be considered in pricing decisions. Further, price offers the selling firm a basis for competing whenever other differences among competing brands are not apparent to buyers.

2. **Understand the characteristics of the different pricing objectives that companies can adopt.** Common objectives that guide company pricing decisions include ensuring market survival, enhancing sales growth, increasing market share, maximizing profits, realizing a certain return on investment, deterring competition, and establishing or maintaining a particular quality image. Firms often pursue profitability objectives by a price-skimming strategy and growth and competitive deterrence by a penetration pricing strategy. Prestige pricing is consistent with quality and image-enhancement objectives.

3. **Identify many of the influences on marketers' pricing decisions.** Pricing decisions are influenced by the five Cs of pricing: costs, customers, channels of distribution, competition, and compatibility. Costs determine the minimum level of prices. Prices must at least cover costs in the long term, or insufficient profits and income result. Customer expectations, as well as perceptions of value and fairness, determine price acceptability.

   Price determination must also take into account other members of the channel of distribution. Intermediaries in the channel must be able to earn sufficient margins. Competitive factors also influence prices. When products are similar and price differences are important to consumers, prices will tend to move toward the going price.

   Pricing decisions must also be compatible with the overall marketing and communications objectives of the firm. Finally, national and international laws and agreements also influence price decisions.

4. **Explain how consumers form perceptions of quality and value.** Potential buyers, including individuals and business buyers, form perceptions of value that influence their willingness to buy (purchase behavior). Perceived value is the overall assessment of the utility of a product, depending on what is received and what is given or paid. Price influences perceived value in terms of perceived benefits and perceived monetary sacrifice. Consumers vary in their reactions to price, but they typically adopt one of three strategies: a best-value strategy, a price-seeking strategy, or a price-aversion strategy.

5. **Understand price–quality relationships and internal and external reference prices.** Consumers frequently infer quality from prices. This reaction describes the price–quality relationship. These opinions, regardless of their accuracy, influence the buyer's decision; customers are more likely to pay a higher price if they believe a product to be of higher quality.

   Many consumers compare advertised prices with expected prices, a frequently used internal reference price. If prices are above expectations, perceived value of a product declines; lower-than-expected prices may cause perceived value to rise. Companies often provide external reference prices by pairing an offered price with a higher comparison price designed to make the lower price more attractive. These comparison prices may be previously charged prices, manufacturer-suggested prices, or competitive prices.

Understanding Marketing Terms and Concepts

Thinking about Marketing

1. What is the meaning of *price*? Contrast the basic price mix with the price promotion mix.

2. Why are pricing decisions so important? What are the effects of setting prices too low? Too high?

3. What environmental conditions make pricing decisions so difficult? How might these effects influence estimation of costs and revenues?

4. How do these pricing objectives differ: quality enhancement versus market survival? Sales growth versus profitability?

5. Describe briefly how information on the Internet affects price sensitivity. How might these effects differ for well-known versus less familiar brands?

6. How does Charles Schwab compete with other brokerage houses such as Merrill Lynch? What influences Schwab's pricing strategy?

7. What are some of the primary legal restrictions on marketers' pricing decisions?

8. Contrast external reference prices with internal reference prices. Give several examples of each. How do reference prices affect consumer reactions to prices?

9. Define consumer perceived value and explain what determines it. How do price and perceived quality affect perceptions of value? Explain the relationship between price and quality.

10. Explain these purchase strategies that consumers use to evaluate prices: best value, price seeking, price aversion.

11. Describe both EDLP and HiLo pricing strategies. How do these strategies differ based on the various dimensions of pricing strategies?

12. What are some important considerations about pricing that are associated with international markets?

13. What impact does competition have on prices? How do some pricing strategies specifically focus on a company's competitors?

Applying Marketing Skills

1. Interview a small retailer. Ask how prices are determined and how products put on sale are selected. Does support from the manufacturer influence the initial price of goods? What role does consumer demand play?

2. Find in your local newspaper reference price advertisements from two different retailers. What are the original prices and the sale prices? What are the percentage reductions? With whom or with what is the sale price compared? What wording is used to make the reference price claim?

3. Interview a close friend or relative. Ask this question: "What comes to mind when you consider the purchase of a personal computer?" At what point does the person mention price? To what extent does the order of the attributes mentioned reflect their importance in determining the purchase?

4. How are frequent price fluctuations (sales promotions, discounts, couponing, or inflation) likely to affect consumers' reference prices? If it is assumed that frequent price promotions lower consumers' reference prices and create some resistance to returning to higher "normal" prices, is an EDLP strategy superior to a price promotion strategy?

Using the www in Marketing

Activity One As you know, more and more consumers are using the Internet to shop and gather information. This phenomenon is particularly prevalent in the sports industry. Consider the price information for two brands of tennis racquets. Wilson and Prince offer a variety of models:

1. How is the price information presented? Can consumers make easy price comparisons within lines?

2. Why are the dealer companies unable to present discounted price information for the most recent models?

3. Why have price discounters for sports equipment been so successful? Is it ethical for consumers to shop at local retail stores—and even borrow equipment from the store for trial use—but then purchase from a price discounter using a magazine advertisement or the Internet?

Activity Two Consider the Web site *www.bizrate.com*.

1. To what extent do the prices for DVD players vary?

2. How do the high- and low-end prices affect quality perceptions?

3. To what extent does the Web price information correspond to information offered within large electronics stores?

Making Marketing Decisions

Case 11–1 *Hummer's Bummer*

Through the first nine months of 2004, Hummer sold 20,284 vehicles, mostly H2s, in the United States. However, sales were down over 20 percent from the same period in 2003. The car is very high-priced, has modest interior appeal, and is very inefficient. Competing luxury SUVs, like the Land Rover and Lincoln Navigator, are nicer inside and have more room. With the addition of the H3, GM and Hummer hope to become more approachable and sell over 50,000 units in 2005. The H3, designed to be more energy efficient than the 10–13 mpg H2, will be priced from $35,000 to $45,000. Future offerings include a small pickup, large pickup, diesel derivatives, and a small SUV. In addition, Hummer hopes to derive sales further by introductions in foreign markets. The H2 SUV pickup was priced at $48,000; the H3 is priced from $28,000 to $35,000.

Other efforts are being made to revive the high-priced automobiles. Starting in 2006, warranties are being extended to four years/50,000 miles. These limits are similar to Mercedes, Lexus, and BMW. It is hoped that the smaller H3 will attract a new class of buyers, including those under 40, for whom the brand has a special appeal. The objective will be to market a lower-priced, smaller, more efficient line of autos without losing the rugged appeal.

Questions

1. How can Hummer justify the auto's pricing structure?

2. What market segments does Hummer target?

3. How does the future look in terms of product and price alternatives for the company?

4. What competitive and environmental effects impact price elasticity for Hummer vehicles?

Case 11–2 *Priceline.com: Price Search and Competition*

Priceline.com has pioneered a unique type of e-commerce known as a "demand collection system" that enables consumers to use the Internet to save money on a wide range of products and services, while enabling sellers to generate incremental revenue. Priceline.com has generated substantial success in the sales of airline tickets and hotel rooms. The firm now offers the ability to buy cars, long-distance telephone services, and grocery products for home delivery, while other purchase opportunities are available or under development. Home loans can even be arranged using priceline.com.

Priceline.com makes money on the spread between what a customer is willing to pay and the price offered by the vendor. Priceline.com collects information regarding the numbers of customers, their product and service preferences, and the amount they are willing to pay. Partnerships between priceline.com and other companies provide the opportunity to generate incremental demand for the partnering firms, without disturbing partner-firm normal pricing structures. Consumers must guarantee their offer by credit card, must agree to keep their offer open for a certain period, and must be flexible regarding brand selection.

Competition for priceline.com on the Internet in terms of price services and auctions is evolving at a very fast rate, and online haggling is now among the hottest phenomena in e-commerce. As examples, Amazon.com has begun an auction service, and America Online now offers eBay as one of its features. Potentially, cyberauctions could push aside normal sticker prices and begin an era of dynamic pricing. The no-cost aspects of using the Internet make price bargaining an easy means of shopping.

The company is now more focused on name-your-own prices for hotels, airlines, rental cars, home finance, and new cars. The company remains, however, essentially an online travel agency for leisure travelers. After failures in gasoline and grocery offerings, the company now recognizes that consumers desire convenience and fast service as much as cost savings. Currently priceline faces a troublesome future. It has lost customer loyalty, and a new competitor, Hotwire, has signed deals with eight major airlines.

Recently priceline acquired Travelweb, the Internet hotel distributor launched by a group of hotel chains. Priceline plans to offer Travelweb inventory. Currently priceline's revenues and growth are fine, and travel bookings are expected to continue to climb. Costs associated with the new Travelweb acquisition and increased advertising have raised concerns about costs.

Questions

1. What effects will priceline.com have on brand integrity for the companies with which it is involved? Will sites like priceline.com undermine brand loyalty?

2. What other industries represent potential opportunities for priceline.com?

3. What effects, if any, will Internet offerings like priceline.com have on both consumer search behavior and sensitivity to prices?

4. As competitive alternatives expand on the Internet, what will priceline.com have to do to maintain its competitive advantage?

Chapter Twelve

PRICE DETERMINATION AND PRICING STRATEGIES

12

After studying this chapter, you should be able to

1 Discuss the interrelationships among price, demand, demand elasticity, and revenue.

2 Understand methods for determining price.

3 Recognize the different pricing strategies and the conditions that best suit the choice of a strategy.

4 Recognize the importance of adapting prices under shifting economic and competitive situations.

5 Understand the ethical considerations involved in setting and communicating prices.

eBay

Founded in 1995, eBay continues to be among the most consistently profitable Internet companies; it is used by millions of consumers worldwide. The site offers online trading opportunities in which consumers can bid on products and sellers can auction items for sale. Of particular importance, and unlike traditional exchange relationships in the marketplace, buyers have significant input into the determination of prices.

As one of the few dot-com companies to have made a profit from the beginning, the site tries to establish a sense of community by drawing together people with similar perspectives and interests. eBay enables consumers to pursue their individuality and offers sellers financial opportunities. eBay enables one-to-one transactions across divisions caused by geography and class. Trust among individuals is critical to the success of relationships, and fraud on the site has been remarkably infrequent. eBay offers free insurance in case transactions go bad, as well as escrow accounts that, for a fee, hold funds until deals are complete. Trust is engendered by the site's feedback forum, in which auction winners are encouraged to describe their experiences and transactions. Sellers on eBay with positive comments are subsequently sought out by others and command better prices.

Meg Whitman, eBay's CEO, now has a firm understanding of what technology means to her company and is determined to develop the kind

of e-commerce system previously believed impossible. Continued development of eBay should enable the company to continue to prosper, as growth projections suggest significant potential market demand.

Satisfying the millions of daily visitors and eBay member buyers and sellers is an ongoing endeavor. eBay's international operations include presence in 22 markets worldwide, with a particularly strong brand in Europe. Retailers are now opening sites on eBay to move goods that previously were not selling in brick-and-mortar operations. eBay is a unique outcome of the Internet: Outside of the Web, the company could not operate. Without buying, selling, or stocking any inventory whatsoever, eBay has managed to not only survive but actually grow throughout the fall of many dot-coms.

Recently many small businesses have become upset with increased prices charged for use of eBay. The price hikes have most affected high-volume sellers who have set up what are called eBay stores. eBay is trying new growth initiatives, as in its Chinese site and PayPal payment processing service. Of note, however, is the presence of a growing number of competitors. These competitors include Amazon's fast-growing Marketplace and search site Google, which lets merchants narrowly target potential buyers searching for specific products. As such, the prices associated with the use of eBay are a concern.

Internet influences on consumer prices and the prices charged for products have been profound. The eBay situation underscores the importance of price when products can be reasonably evaluated and when consumers have some idea of their needs and the kinds of products and services that can satisfy those needs. This example illustrates only one approach to pricing, however. In this chapter we examine the processes companies use to select a specific pricing strategy. Additionally, we discuss some theoretical and practical issues affecting the determination of prices. Some of these issues involve ethical considerations. Price determination and evaluation of appropriate pricing strategies are a continual managerial challenge.

As many now believe, electronic commerce is leading to fundamental changes in the way companies relate to their customers and, in the case of auctions, the way consumers relate to one another. The effects are being felt as much as anywhere in the area of pricing. For example, comparing insurance rates from hundreds of companies used to require hundreds of calls. Now price comparisons are possible with the click of a mouse. Allstate has already reduced its labor force and begun selling on the Internet. Sites such as eCoverage and Quotesmith.com make comparisons readily available.

This chapter describes many procedures and strategies for setting and changing prices. Developing pricing capabilities allows firms to respond more effectively to competitor actions and to match prices more closely to what consumers are willing to pay. Such pricing capabilities become an important source of competitive advantage.[1] For example, for a company with sales of $100 million, even a small improvement in price performance can translate into hundreds of thousands of dollars annually on the bottom line.[2]

Price Determination: An Overview

The step-by-step procedure diagrammed in Exhibit 12–1 presents a logical approach for setting prices.[3] Execution of this process requires an understanding of the concepts described in Chapter 11. First, the firm must set

Exhibit 12–1   *The price-setting decision process*

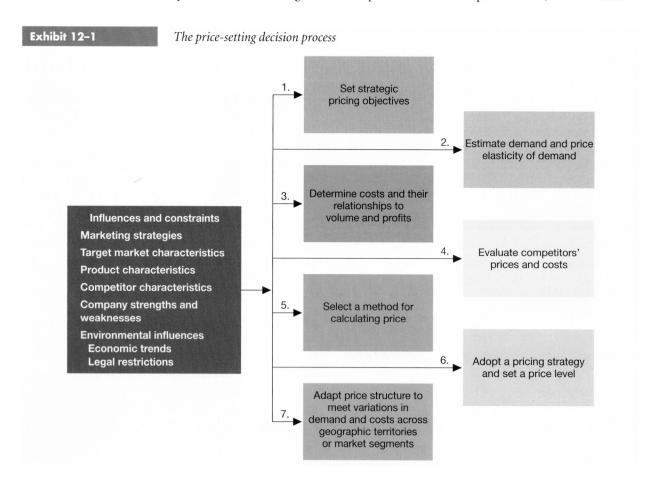

pricing objectives consistent with its overall marketing and strategic efforts and with the product's image and quality. Common pricing objectives are to maximize profits or sales growth. Second, the firm must consider market demand and the responsiveness of demand to different prices. What will the level of sales be at different prices? How do sales change as prices vary? As such, the design of an appropriate pricing strategy is a challenging task, in part because the process involves the complex dynamics associated with the diffusion of the product in a given market.[4]

Next, the firm determines the costs to manufacture products or provide services and the relationship of costs to volume. The company evaluates competitor prices and costs. If prices are set well above market prices, consumers will not purchase. If prices are too low, revenues and profits may be lost. Then the firm may use one of various methods for determining prices, including markup pricing, break-even analysis, and target-return pricing methods.

Finally, the firm must set specific prices, often using one of the common pricing strategies. After setting prices, the firm monitors and adjusts them to adapt to differences in demand and costs across market segments or to meet competitive reactions.

As Exhibit 12–1 shows, the stages in this pricing process are subject to several influences and constraints. These include product characteristics, company strengths and weaknesses, and legal constraints. Moreover, both costs and demand are difficult to estimate. Sometimes price determination involves setting a price first, then revising in response to market performance. Ultimately, prices must reflect customers' willingness to pay. To optimize long-term profitability, price setting must reflect good value that customers recognize. Therefore, improving pricing strategy and price-setting processes can quickly increase both margins and sales volume.[5]

Price and Demand

Exhibit 12–2

Demand curve representing relationship between price and quantity demanded

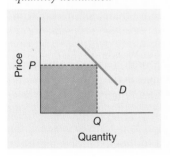

Demand Curves

The relationship between price and demand is expressed in the traditional market **demand curve** labeled D in Exhibit 12–2. Under normal conditions, customers buy more as prices drop; they buy less when prices rise. If price is set artificially low, excess demand will occur, as for the $325 typical price for a 2002 Super Bowl ticket that failed to balance supply and demand. Moreover, artificially low prices may result in secondary markets such as online auctions.[6] Price is only one determinant of demand, however. Others include household income, tastes and preferences, population growth, and prices of related products. For many business-to-business situations, demand is driven by general economic conditions and consumer demand, as well as by the preferences and needs of the firm's buyers. New software technologies are greatly enhancing retailers' ability to merchandise their products through the analysis of historical price sales data, as well as consumers' responses to the determinants of demand, such as price, inventory levels, promotion, and seasonality.[7]

Price Elasticity of Demand

Price elasticity of demand is a basic business concept. The relationship between price and quantity demanded varies; as one increases, the other decreases. Price elasticity of demand is computed as follows:

$$\text{Price elasticity of demand} = \frac{\text{Percentage change in quantity demanded}}{\text{Percentage change in price}}$$

Computational procedures and an example are shown in Appendix B.

Elastic demand exists when small price changes result in large changes in demand. When demand is elastic, a small decrease in price increases total revenues. Elastic demand prevails in the motor vehicles, engineering products, furniture, and professional services industries.

Speaking from Experience

"IBM's approach of helping customers solve their business issues or problems (versus our just trying to sell them the products we have in our product line) has led us to a strategic focus on selling solutions. The proposed solution, which can include hardware (servers, storage, printers, and OEM equipment), software (operating systems, middleware, and applications), and services (ranging from traditional IT services to consulting), is priced as a bundled or bottom-line price. This solution approach and related solution pricing allows the customer to more easily determine the value of a given project to their business. In addition, the single, total-solution price is lower than if they purchased the solution elements separately."

Dennis Hurley
Financial Offerings Executive
International Business Machines

Dennis Hurley has a bachelor of science degree in business from the University of North Carolina and an MBA in finance from Wake

Forest University. He is Financial Offerings Executive for International Business Machines, Atlanta, GA.

Exhibit 12–3

Elastic and inelastic demand

A. Elastic demand

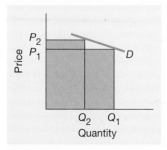

B. Inelastic demand

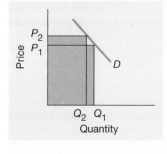

Inelastic demand exists when price changes do not result in significant changes in demand. Inelastic demand often occurs for books, magazines, newspapers, and clothing, as well as in the banking and insurance, beverage, and utility industries.[8] Exhibit 12–3 depicts elastic and inelastic demand situations. Overall, demand is likely to be inelastic to price changes when there are few or no product substitutes; when buyers do not readily notice the higher price and are slow to change their buying habits or to search for lower prices, or when they think higher prices are justified by product improvements or inflation; and when the product or service represents a small portion of their household income.[9]

Where demand is price-elastic, marketers must carefully evaluate any proposed increases in price. Price changes may cause significant change in quantity demanded. Long-term elasticities may differ from short-term ones as customers become aware of changing prices and have time to search for alternative products or services.

One managerial implication from research is that price elasticities are strongest in the growth stage of product categories, both for durables and for packaged goods. These results suggest that when managers introduce a new category, a penetration strategy (low to high) is more effective than a skimming strategy (high to low).[10]

Cross elasticity of demand relates the percentage change in quantity demanded for one product to percentage price changes for other products. For example, products are often part of a line of similar products; and changes in the price of one brand may affect the demand for other items in the product line. When products are close *substitutes,* such as cola beverages, a rise in the price of one will increase the demand for the other. For businesses, a sharp increase in prices of steel fasteners used in the construction of trucks would cause increased demand for less expensive plastic or aluminum fasteners.

Alternatively, when products are *complements,* a price increase of one may decrease the demand for the other. For example, large price increases for personal

---

ACTING ETHICALLY

"Weight-Out"

Some consumer products makers have been increasingly using the "weight-out" option, or slimming the size of products without proportionally reducing the price of the slimmed-down products. Some industry sources suggest that consumers react more favorably to less quantity than higher prices. Others argue that these changes are deceptive and go unnoticed. But if

consumers feel duped, marketers run the risk of undermining their trust. Kellogg went against the weight-out trend recently by maintaining its package weights and simply announcing a 2 percent price increase for many cereal brands, such as Frosted Flakes and Special K.

computers would cause a decrease in the demand for printers. And price reductions of taco shells may increase sales of taco sauce.[11]

Some marketers believe that a primary objective is to create inelasticity for their products. This requires a thorough understanding of demand, allowing the firm to offer brands with attributes that customers find irresistible regardless of price. That is, brands are designed to offer benefits that entice consumers to pay prices high enough to be profitable to the firm. Relatedly, efforts to retain customers through loyalty programs and specialized services are designed to inhibit shifts in demand resulting from changing prices of the firm's products or competing products.

Costs, Volume, and Profits

Price plays a critical role in competition among firms for some industries. Here Norwegian Cruise Line promotes price to attract travelers.

Low-priced autos can use warranties and other information to provide assurances about quality.

We have seen the trade-offs between prices and quantity demanded. Yet price determination must also consider the costs incurred in the production and sale of goods. **Fixed costs** (*FC*) such as plant and large equipment investments, interest paid on loans, and the costs of production facilities, cannot be changed in the short run and do not vary with the quantity produced. These costs would occur even if the quantity produced were zero. Many advertising costs are viewed as fixed costs, at least over a predetermined period.[12]

Variable costs (*VC*) such as wages and raw materials change with the level of output. Marketing variable costs include packaging and promotional costs tied to each unit produced.

Total costs (*TC*) are the sum of variable costs (*VC*) and fixed costs (*FC*). Variable costs are made up of the variable cost per unit times the number or quantity of units manufactured (*Q*):

$$TC = (VC \times Q) + FC$$

Marginal costs (*MC*) are incurred in producing one additional unit of output. They typically decline early over some level of production because of economies of scale, but eventually begin to increase as the firm approaches capacity and returns diminish.

Marginal revenue (*MR*) is the additional revenue the firm will receive if one more unit of product is sold. This amount typically represents the price of the product. **Total revenue** (*TR*) is total sales, or price times the quantity sold:

$$\text{Total revenue} = \text{Price} \times \text{Quantity}$$

To determine the price that maximizes profits, the firm combines cost information with demand or revenue information:

$$\text{Profits} = \text{Total revenue } (TR) - \text{Total costs } (TC)$$

This difference is greatest at the point where profits are maximized, where the firm's marginal revenue (*MR*) equals marginal cost (*MC*). When marginal revenue exceeds marginal cost, additional profits can be made by producing and selling more product. An example of these computations is presented in Appendix B.

Price Determination Methods

A firm may choose from several methods of determining price. It may subjectively determine a price based on what management feels is appropriate at the time. Or it may use a combination of methods or procedures. It is important to note that firms should stress both demand and cost considerations in determining prices. Following initial price setting, firms can adjust prices according to trial-and-error experiences and fluctuations in demand. Some basic approaches are markup pricing, break-even analysis, target-return pricing, and price sensitivity measurement.

Markup Pricing

Retailers typically use some form of **markup pricing**, where markup is the difference between the cost of an item and the retail price, expressed as a percentage. A product's price is determined by adding a set percentage to the cost of the product. These percentages are often standardized across product categories. Formally,

$$\text{Price} = \text{Unit cost} + \text{Markup, or}$$
$$\text{Price} = \text{Unit cost}/(1 - k)$$

where k = desired percentage of markup.

Assume, for example, that a retailer purchases a popular branded tennis racket at $80 and adds $40 to the cost, for a retail price of $120.

$$\text{Markup as a percentage of selling price} = \frac{\text{Markup}}{\text{Selling price}}$$
$$= \frac{\$40}{\$120} = 33\%$$
$$\text{Markup as a percentage of cost} = \frac{\text{Markup}}{\text{Cost}}$$
$$= \frac{\$40}{\$80} = 50\%$$

In some cases the retailer may wish to know the markup charged for a product given the price and the original cost. This markup percentage can be computed simply:

$$\text{Markup (\%)} = [(\text{Price} - \text{Unit cost})/\text{Price}] \times 100\%$$

Other procedures and examples for determining retail prices and markups are summarized in Appendix B.

Break-Even Analysis

Break-even analysis is a useful guide for pricing decisions. It involves calculating the number of units that must be sold at a certain price for the firm to cover costs and, hence, break even. The approach is shown graphically in Exhibit 12–4. The *break-even point* (*BEP*) is determined by the intersection of the total revenue line ($TR = P \times Q$) and the total cost line ($TC = FC + VC \times Q$). The area between the two lines and to the right of the intersection represents profits. To make a profit, the quantity sold must exceed the *BEP*.

Exhibit 12–4

Break-even analysis

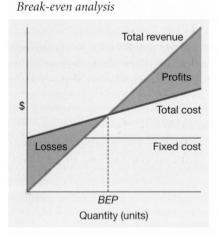

Thinking Critically

Break-even analysis is useful for evaluating how alternative cost and price combinations affect the quantity required to break even.

- The break-even point can be lowered by raising the price. However, what if similar products in the marketplace are offered at prices below the higher price under consideration?
- Likewise, the break-even point can be lowered by reducing variable costs. However, what if reducing variable costs hurts product quality?

The slope of the total revenue line is determined by the price charged. A higher price would make the total revenue line steeper, and the *BEP* would be lower. Lower costs would also reduce the *BEP*.

Washburn Guitars provides an excellent example of the relationships between total revenues, total costs, contribution margin, and break-even quantity. The instruments Washburn sells to first-time buyers are mass-produced items; thus they have much lower variable costs in terms of labor and materials per unit than the guitars designed individually for rock stars. In addition, the lower prices appeal to the more price-sensitive entry-level buyer. Consequently, lower variable costs per unit enable Washburn to price its mass-produced items competitively and to sell beyond needed break-even quantity levels at modest market prices.

The *BEP* in units is

$$Q(BEP) = FC/(P - VC)$$

where P = unit price and $Q(BEP)$ = break-even quantity. The quantity $(P - VC)$ is typically referred to as the product's **contribution margin**.

Consider a case of plastic medical gloves priced at $7.25 and entailing $2.25 in variable costs. At total fixed costs of $200,000, the required break-even quantity would be 40,000 units. That is,

$$40,000 = \$200,000/(\$7.25 - \$2.25)$$

If the price were raised to $12.25, and assuming sufficient demand existed, the *BEP* would drop to 20,000 units.

The *BEP* can also be expressed in dollars:

$$Q(BEP\$) = FC/(1 - VC/P)$$

Using the previous medical gloves example, the *BEP* in dollars would be

$$\$289,855 = \$200,000/(1 - \$2.25/\$7.25)$$

Break-even analysis is useful for evaluating the effects of various price and cost structures on needed demand levels. And by adding a desired profit amount to the fixed-cost portion of the equation, a firm can calculate the number of units that must be sold at a certain price to achieve a certain profit level.

Break-even analysis can be expanded to consider different price and quantity combinations. This modified break-even analysis (described in Appendix B) recognizes that the *BEP* can vary depending on the price chosen. Profits do not necessarily increase as quantity increases because lower prices may be needed to generate the increased demand.

Target-Return Pricing

Target-return pricing is a cost-oriented approach that sets prices to achieve some desired rate of return. Cost and profit estimates are based on some expected volume or sales level. The price is determined using this equation:

$$\text{Price} = \text{Unit cost} + \frac{(\text{Desired return} \times \text{Invested capital})}{\text{Expected unit sales}}$$

Assume a national manufacturer of office supplies sells a computer-paper organizer. Average variable costs for the product are $8; total assets employed in the business are $4,500,000. The firm desires a 15 percent return and expects to sell 200,000 units. Therefore, the target-return price is

$$\text{Price} = \text{Unit cost} + \frac{\text{Desired return} \times \text{Invested capital}}{\text{Unit sales}}$$
$$= \$8 + (0.15 \times \$4,500,000)/200,000 = \$11.38$$

The firm would price the product at $11.38. Again, the success of the approach assumes the supplier can reach the expected sales volume of 200,000 units.

Target-return pricing forecasts a fair or needed rate of return. However, the effects of other variables in the marketing mix and competitive factors are not considered directly; and target-return pricing, like break-even analysis, is best combined with consideration of other determinants of demand.

Exhibit 12–5

The role of cost in Japanese pricing

```
        ┌─────────────────────────┐
        │          JAPAN          │
        └─────────────────────────┘
                    ▼
        ┌─────────────────────────┐
        │   Marketing research    │
        └─────────────────────────┘
                    ▼
        ┌─────────────────────────┐
        │  Product characteristics │
        └─────────────────────────┘
                    ▼
        ┌─────────────────────────┐
        │   Planned selling price │
        │    less desired profit  │
        └─────────────────────────┘
                    ▼
        ┌─────────────────────────┐
        │       Target cost       │
        └─────────────────────────┘
                    ▼
   Design       Engineering    Supplier pricing
```

Target costs for each component force marketers, designers, and engineers from all departments and suppliers to struggle and negotiate trade-offs.

```
        ┌─────────────────────────┐
        │      Manufacturing      │
        └─────────────────────────┘
                    ▼
        ┌─────────────────────────┐
        │ Continuous cost reduction │
        └─────────────────────────┘
```

Some Japanese firms use an approach to pricing that recognizes the effects of price on demand and the role of costs in determining demand. As Exhibit 12–5 shows, the Japanese specify a target cost based on the price they believe the market is most likely to accept. Designers and engineers then meet target costs. This approach emphasizes the product's ability to achieve market acceptance by considering more directly the interface between the prices buyers are likely to accept and the costs necessary to create products at those prices. As such, the Japanese recognize the effects of both demand and cost considerations in determining their prices. Nissan, Sharp, and Toyota use this approach.

Some U.S. and European companies design a new product first, and then calculate the cost. If the cost is too high, the product must be redesigned or the company must settle for a lower profit level.[13] Generally, the Japanese worry less than American and European manufacturers about cost accounting. They work backward from a price and make sure the product can be produced with the quality demanded at that price.

A related concept is **target-cost pricing**, in which new products are developed based on what the market wants and the price it will accept. Briefly, a six-step process is involved:

1. Define the market segments that will be targeted for the sale of the new product.
2. Base the design of the new product on an analysis of competitive advantages and disadvantages.
3. View the positioning of the new product within the context of the company's overall strategy.
4. Fine-tune the product design and pricing based on customers' preferences, perceived value of individual features, and willingness to pay.
5. Use market simulations to estimate price responses for various combinations of specific features via marketing research techniques such as conjoint analysis.
6. Estimate target costs as the difference between the optimal price, given demand effects, and the desired target margin.[14]

Income-Based Pricing

One important and common pricing approach sets price based on the income to be generated by the product under consideration. **Income-based pricing** is frequently used for pricing real estate, marketable securities, and businesses. For example, consider a business that is for sale that has annual net income (income after salaries and so forth are paid) of $600,000. The typical return on investment for similar companies in this industry is 18 percent. A beginning purchase price would be $3.33 million ($600,000/.18). This selling price for the business might be adjusted for unique competitive strengths or the likelihood of improved revenue streams in the future.[15]

Prices and Customer Value

Effective value creation is based on a thorough understanding of target customers, including an exploration of how value is created. Determining price is a critical aspect of this valuation creation. Prices set too high result in limited trial, whereas prices set too low result in poor positioning and missed opportunities. For example, Neiman Marcus relies on heavy product innovation as defined by the uniqueness of its products. The firm typically uses high everyday pricing to reinforce exclusivity and does not depend on frequent price promotions likely to detract from its intended upscale marketplace positioning.[16]

One approach for setting realistic consumer prices is the *BDM*, named for the three researchers who developed the technique. BDM enables the estimation of how much consumers are willing to pay (WTP) at the point of purchase under desired marketing mix

Exhibit 12–6   *Flow chart of BDM procedure*

conditions. Briefly, and as summarized in Exhibit 12–6, the process operates as follows. Target consumers are told that they have a chance to buy the product without spending more money on the purchase than they want. They are told that the price has not been set and will be determined randomly. Respondents are asked to offer a price for the product, which should equal the highest price they are willing to pay. A price is then drawn randomly from a distribution of prices. If the drawn price is less than or equal to their offer, they are required to buy the product at the drawn price. If the drawn price exceeds their offer, they are not allowed to buy the product. This process has been shown to result in a fair estimate of consumers' WTP because understating one's true WTP reduces the chance of buying at a gain and overstating WTP increases the chance of buying at a loss.[17]

Value in use (VIU) analysis is a useful approach for determining the economic value that a product has relative to an existing competitive offering. This approach is useful for determining what price to charge and what arguments suppliers can use to justify higher prices. An example is shown in Exhibit 12–7. In this case the analysis reveals the new product has

Exhibit 12–7   *Value in use (VIU) pricing*

Example

A chemical plant uses 200 O-rings to seal valves carrying corrosive materials. The O-rings cost $5.00 each and must be changed during regular maintenance every two months. Suppose the equipment must be shut down each time the O-rings are changed and the cost of a shutdown is $5,000.

A new product has 2 times the corrosive resisting power of the incumbent O-rings. What is the VIU of the new product?

Incumbent product							New product				
200	×	6	×	$5	+	$5,000 × 6	=	200 × 3 × VIU	+	$5,000 × 3	

$$\underset{\text{Equipment cost}}{\bullet} \qquad \underset{\text{Shutdown cost}}{\bullet} \qquad \underset{\text{Equipment cost}}{\bullet} \qquad \underset{\text{Shutdown cost}}{\bullet}$$

$$(\$6,000) \quad + \quad (\$30,000) \quad = \quad \boxed{\begin{array}{c}(600 \times VIU)\\ \text{Solve for VIU}\end{array}} \quad + \quad (\$15,000)$$

$$\boxed{VIU = \$35} \qquad \text{The VIU is seven times that of the incumbent product!}$$

seven times the value of an existing product and that a price for the new product well above the $5 being charged already would be appropriate. If the product cost $10 and the price were set at $25, the purchasing company would be $10 better off ($25 versus $35 VIU) if the switch were made to the new product.[18]

Pricing Strategies

Setting prices to achieve the firm's objectives requires the selection of a specific pricing strategy or a combination of strategies.[19] The 11 pricing strategies shown in Exhibit 12–8 fall into four categories: differential pricing, where the same brand is sold to consumers under different prices; competitive pricing, where prices are set to take advantage of competitive market conditions; product-line pricing, where related brands are sold at prices that take advantage of interdependencies among brands; and psychological pricing, where prices are based on consumer perceptions or expectations.

The appropriateness of a particular pricing strategy depends on several circumstances: the variability of demand (the presence of different market segments), the competitive situation, the characteristics of consumers in the market, and the expectations or perceptions of consumers.

Several commonsense assumptions about buyers underlie all pricing strategies. First, some buyers have search costs in taking time and effort to obtain information about which firms sell what products and at what prices. Second, some buyers have low reservation prices, the highest prices they are willing to pay. That is, some price-sensitive buyers do not need a product enough to pay the high price others pay.

Differential Pricing

Prices are often varied across segments. Reduced prices for senior consumers are a frequently and effectively used form of price discrimination.

Differential pricing involves selling the same product to different buyers under a variety of prices. This is price discrimination, or the practice of charging different buyers different prices for the same quantity and quality of products or services.[20] Differential pricing works because the market is heterogeneous; or more simply, differences in reactions to price exist among consumers or consumer segments in the market.

The ability to engage in differential pricing has been facilitated greatly by the ever-growing number of online auction sites, such as priceline.com, and shopbots that search the Web for low prices. If a business sells a product or service that rapidly depreciates in value, such as computers, or that becomes worthless in a moment, such as airline seats, then online auctions with their ability to differentiate prices are viable sales channels. Moreover, one additional benefit from consigning products to online auction houses is that the auction site sells to end consumers and sellers avoid the perception of undercutting their own prices.[21]

SECOND-MARKET DISCOUNTING   The most common form of differential pricing, **second-market discounting**, occurs when different prices are charged in different market segments. (Recall that this practice may be legal in retail, but illegal in wholesale if it harms competition.) Second-market discounting is useful when the firm has excess capacity and different market segments exist. Generic brands and some foreign

Exhibit 12-8	*Example pricing strategies*		
Differential Pricing	**Competitive Pricing**	**Product-Line Pricing**	**Psychological Pricing**
Second-market discounting	Penetration pricing	Bundling	Odd–even pricing
Periodic discounting	Price signaling	Premium pricing	Customary pricing
	Going-rate pricing	Partitioned pricing	One-sided claims

markets often provide opportunities for second-market discounting. For example, if a firm can sell its product cost-effectively in a foreign market, it may be profitable to export at a price even below local prices. The exporting firm must have excess production capacity (so no new fixed costs are required), and the markets must be sufficiently separated so that transaction costs prevent interaction between markets.

Second-market discounting also occurs when the company sells a portion of its output as generic brands at lower prices to price-sensitive segments. Other examples include differences in student and senior citizen discounts for entertainment ticket prices.

For price discrimination to be successful, some rather restrictive conditions must be satisfied:

- The market must have segments that respond differently to price variations.
- Members of the market paying the lower price must not be able to resell the product to the people paying the higher price.
- Competitors should not be able to undercut the prices charged to the higher-price segment.
- The cost of segmenting and policing the market should not exceed the extra revenue derived from charging the higher prices.
- The practice should not cause consumer resentment.
- The form of price discrimination used should be legal.[22]

PERIODIC DISCOUNTING   In some cases it is advantageous for a firm to offer periodic or occasional discounts. **Periodic discounting** enables a firm to take advantage of the presence of consumer segments that differ in price sensitivity. This approach includes **price skimming**, where an initial high price is determined for new products to skim the market. Price skimming allows product development costs to be recovered when introductory sales are growing. People willing to pay the high price purchase first, and then the firm lowers prices as sales slow to attract the next-highest level of price-sensitive buyer. Du Pont, a well-known innovator of industrial products, frequently uses a price-skimming strategy.

Competitive Pricing

Competitive pricing strategies, based on the firm's position in relation to its competition, include penetration pricing, limit pricing, price signaling, and going-rate pricing.

Penetration pricing calls for a low initial price to generate sales volume and take advantage of economies of scale (larger production runs at lower unit costs). It is often used when the marketer wants to maximize sales growth or market share. Penetration pricing may be particularly beneficial when there are a significant number of price-sensitive consumers in the market (demand is price-elastic) or the firm fears early entry of a competitor if prices are set high and margins appear attractive. **Limit pricing**, another term

Many retailers use introductory low prices to stimulate initial product sales and to build sales volume.

for low penetration pricing, also entails setting prices low to discourage new competition. In situations in which competitive reaction is unlikely, firms may engage in price skimming, described earlier.

Price signaling puts high prices on low-quality products. This approach, while clearly not beneficial to buyers, may reflect unethical behavior; but firms can pursue it successfully if several conditions are satisfied. First, there must be a segment of buyers whose experience is consistent with a price–quality relationship, who believe firms spend more to provide higher quality, or who trust the market and assume a positive relationship between price and quality exists.[23] Second, information on the level of quality should be hard for buyers to obtain.[24] *Consumer Reports* regularly reports examples of successful brands that have high prices and suspect quality.

Going-rate pricing reflects the tendency of firms to price at or near industry averages. This approach is frequently used when products compete on the basis of attributes or benefits other than price. Going-rate pricing has the additional advantage of lessening the threat of aggressive price wars, which may be unprofitable to all competitors.

Competitive pricing strategies also determine the positioning of many retail organizations. Value retailers, like Family Dollar and Dollar General, are becoming the newest high-growth concept. These low-overhead, low-price general merchandisers compete with large retailers—Wal-Mart, Kmart, and Target—by offering lower prices to the growing segment of households earning $25,000 or less. Both Family Dollar and Dollar General target lower-income and fixed-income families, often in neglected geographical markets.[25]

Product-Line Pricing

Firms often offer a line of multiple versions of the same product, such as Radio Shack stereo speakers priced from $59.99 to $149.99. Low- and high-end prices may influence buyer perceptions of quality and set standards for comparing items within the product line.

Low-end prices frequently influence doubtful or price-conscious buyers to purchase and are often used as traffic builders. The high-end price has considerable influence on the quality image of the entire product line. Marketers must be sensitive to price changes in the product line. A price change in one product can detract from sales of other products in the line because they are often substitutes for one another.[26]

BUNDLING   Increasingly, companies are realizing the value of combining separate products into bundles. **Bundling** is marketing two or more products or services in a single "package." The practice is seen frequently in the marketing of ski packages, hotel services, restaurant meals, and stereo and computer systems. Bundling also occurs in the purchase of health care equipment by hospitals. In these cases the bundle price is typically less than if each item in the package is bought separately. Interestingly, bundling of season tickets for performances or games can actually decrease consumption. For bundled season tickets, consumers are less likely to link sunk costs associated with the initial purchase with benefits, so they treat later performances or games in the bundled package as almost free goods. With less pressure associated with purchases, consumers are less likely to use tickets previously paid for.[27]

Bundling terms are used interchangeably and can cause some confusion. Two marketing scholars, Stefan Stemersch and Gerard Tellis, have recently provided term definitions that are both simple and consistent with legal interpretations:

1. *Bundling*—sale of two or more separate products (and/or services) in one package (such as opera tickets).

2. *Price bundling*—the sale of two or more separate products as a package at a discount, without any integration of the products (variety pack of cereals).

3. *Product bundling*—the integration and sale of two or more separate products at any price (sound systems).

4. *Pure bundling*—a strategy in which a firm sells only the bundle and not (all) the products separately (IBM's bundling of tabulating machines and cards).

5. *Mixed bundling*—a strategy in which a firm sells both the bundle and (all) the products separately (telecom bundles).[28]

Product-line pricing decisions pose a common dilemma for marketers. Price ranges associated with items in a line affect the perceived levels of quality for the line, while individual prices must be set so that sales are increased for the line without negatively affecting the sales of items within the line.

Monsanto has maintained its market position for the herbicide Roundup by dropping its price before patent expiration but tying the purchase of Roundup to the firm's patented and genetically modified seeds. This combination may make Monsanto the world's most profitable agriculture company, commanding 80-plus percent of its two primary agricultural-related markets.[29]

In addition to often selling at lower prices than if unbundled, bundling reduces consumer search costs and the cost to sellers from individual transactions. New computers come bundled with software, the shopping for which most consumers desire to avoid. Many cable providers are bundling telephone service with cable TV service. Bundling has other benefits to the seller as well: Price bundling can increase frequency of purchase and profitability. This conclusion is based on recent findings that suggest consumers allocate lower cost to each bundled unit following purchase.

PREMIUM PRICING   When a firm offers several alternative models, it often uses a premium-pricing strategy. **Premium pricing** sets higher (premium) prices on more deluxe product versions. The various models are designed to appeal to different price-sensitive segments or to segments wanting different combinations of features. Typically the firm (the manufacturer or the retailer) makes most of its profits on the expensive models and less on lower-priced models in a product line. Premium pricing occurs often for beer, clothing, appliances, and automobiles. As another example, Hewlett-Packard successfully competed with IBM for corporate data-center business by aggressively promoting its top-line models in its HP9000 series.[30]

Two-thirds of China's population earns very little income per month. In recognition of this economic environment, Procter & Gamble developed a tiered pricing initiative to help compete against local brands while protecting the value of its premium global brands. The effects have been dramatic. For example, Tide Clean White detergent is priced much lower than the premium Tide Triple Action brand, but it outperforms every other brand at that low price level.[31]

PARTITIONED PRICING   Many firms divide the prices they charge into parts in lieu of charging a single price. These "part" prices are often termed the *base price* and the *surcharge*. This practice is called **partitioned pricing**. Examples include catalog or Internet prices for items, plus the shipping and handling charges associated with delivery. A Sony telephone from a mail catalog for $69.95, plus $12.95 for shipping and handling, is one specific combination used in a well-designed study of partitioned prices. Recent research suggests that this practice is common in the marketplace because consumers do not process the base price and surcharges completely and accurately; the total cost remembered is less, and therefore demand is increased.[32]

Psychological Pricing

Psychological pricing recognizes that buyer perceptions and beliefs affect their price evaluations. Prestige or premium pricing and comparing competitors' prices with a firm's lower sale prices deal with the psychological aspects of consumer reactions to prices. Odd–even pricing and customary pricing are other applications of psychological pricing.

ODD–EVEN PRICING   **Odd–even pricing** presents prices at values just below an even amount, a common practice. Instead of pricing contact lenses at $200, for example, the price is set at $199.95. The marketer intends for consumers to associate the price with the

$100 to $200 range, assuming that demand for the contacts will be less at $200 than at $199.95. In addition, the precision associated with the $199.95 price implies a bargain. For instance, J. Crew and Ralph Lauren generally use 00-cent endings on regularly priced merchandise and 99-cent endings on discounted items. Another explanation is that 9 endings act the same way as a sale sign, implying that customers are getting a good deal.[33]

Odd–even pricing, or *just-below pricing* as it is sometimes called, may be beneficial for other reasons as well. First, evidence suggests that when low price is important to the consumer, the just-below price is more effective at getting consumers' attention. Second, just-below prices may have memory effects; that is, the leftmost digits of a price represent the greater amounts of money and are therefore the most important. Some studies have revealed that people recall the just-below endings as underestimates from memory. Odd prices created from round-number prices have been shown to be the most effective. For example, a price such as $199.95 would likely lead to a substantially lower average recalled price than $249.95.[34]

CUSTOMARY PRICING   In the past, consumers associated a **customary price** with a product, but frequent price promotions and price increases have made this practice less prevalent today. The classic example of customary price is the much-dated 5-cent candy bar; today's customary price might be 50 cents. Customary price beliefs represent consumers' strongly held expectations. Pricing strategies that set customary prices typically modify the quality, feature, or service of a product without adjusting the price.

"Package shrink" has become a common strategy for increasing margins in recent years for coffee, candy bars, diapers, and more recently, some snacks. For example, Frito-Lay passed along silent price hikes to its customers by shrinking Lay's regular 13.25-ounce bags to 12.25 ounces. New versions of Ivory and Joy, handwashing dish detergents offered by P&G, come in smaller bottles at the same price. However, the taller containers are designed to look bigger and pour faster, adding up to an effective 12 percent price increase.[35]

ONE-SIDED PRICE CLAIMS   Concerns arise regarding the implications of one-sided price claims in which superiority in price for one attribute or offering is made. However, what happens when the prices of firms' other offerings are actually higher? One study of prices for mail delivery services found that consumers overgeneralize one-sided price claims to the prices for other but omitted services. Specifically, a significant number of subjects in a recent study erroneously concluded that a well-known mail carrier had the lowest overall prices just because the firm promoted its low price for guaranteed morning delivery, when in fact its prices were higher for package pickup and delivery by 5 P.M. the next day. These issues are important to those concerned with consumer welfare to the extent that such practices lead to deception and inaccurate decision making.[36]

B2B Pricing Strategies

One view of industrial and B2B pricing strategies organizes the various pricing practices used by firms marketing to other firms into four major categories: (1) new product pricing situations, (2) competitive pricing situations, (3) product-line pricing situations, and (4) cost-based pricing situations. This organization is shown in Exhibit 12–9. The specific strategies within each category overlap many of the strategies and definitions associated with consumer goods pricing. For example, new product pricing approaches include price skimming, penetration pricing, and experience curve pricing. The definitions of these pricing strategies are given in Exhibit 12–9, along with related strategy terms.

A sample of 270 industrial firms revealed that cost-plus pricing is the most frequently employed pricing strategy. However, most firms employ multiple strategies, depending on the situation. For example, price skimming is used most often in markets with a great deal of product differentiation and when firms are at a cost disadvantage due to limited economies of scale. Cost-based pricing is used when demand is difficult to estimate. Customer value pricing involves the offer of a stripped-down version of a current product to appeal to more price-sensitive segments and to take advantage of new distribution channels.[37] Cost-plus pricing should be augmented with consideration of value provided. B2B pricing approaches should consider the value provided, not simply focus on the costs involved plus some add-on for profit. That is, the focus should be on the total market and how differences in value added can be delivered to different segments of customers.[38]

Exhibit 12–9	*Industrial pricing strategies*	
Strategy	**Description**	**Related Strategies**
New Product Pricing Situation		
Price skimming	We set the initial price high and then systematically reduce it over time. Customers expect prices to eventually fall.	Premium pricing, value-in-use pricing
Penetration pricing	We initially set the price low to accelerate product adoption.	Low introductory prices
Experience curve pricing	We set the price low to build volume and reduce costs through accumulated experience.	Learning curve pricing
Competitive Pricing Situation		
Leader pricing	We initiate a price change and expect the other firms to follow.	Umbrella pricing, cooperative pricing, signaling
Parity pricing	We match the price set by the overall market or the price leader.	Neutral pricing, follower pricing
Low-price supplier	We always strive to have the low price in the market.	Parallel pricing, adaptive pricing, opportunistic pricing
Product-Line Pricing Situation		
Complementary product pricing	We price the core product low when complementary items such as accessories, supplies, spare parts, services, and the like can be priced with a higher premium.	Razor-and-blade pricing
Price bundling	We offer this product as part of a bundle of several products, usually at a total price that gives our customers an attractive savings over the sum of individual prices.	System pricing
Customer value pricing	We price one version of our product at very competitive levels, offering fewer features than are available on other versions.	Economy pricing
Cost-Based Pricing Situation		
Cost-plus pricing	We establish the price of the product at a point that gives us a specified percentage profit margin over our costs.	Contribution pricing, rate-of-return pricing, target-return pricing, contingency pricing, markup pricing

Adapting Prices

Determining a pricing strategy and setting prices are only the beginning. Prices change as competition occurs and as the firm's marketing and production expertise improves. The firm must react to competitive price changes as well, constantly considering how often and how much to change prices. Price discounts and geographic pricing decisions also require marketers to adapt their prices.

Price Decreases and Increases

Over the last few years, many companies have tried unsuccessfully to raise their prices, losing volume as customers (consumers or businesses) shifted to lower-priced competitors or found substitute products. In many instances, raised prices were forced down again in efforts to recoup lost market share.[39] Sometimes lowering price improves profits through higher sales. When market share is declining or excess production capacity exists, the firm can lower prices. This may stimulate demand and allow greater use of production or plant investments. Depressed economic conditions may also necessitate price reductions. The lack of pricing power and discretion, and in many cases pressures to cut prices, is affecting business across manufacturing and services. One reason the economy is weak and corporate profits are minimal is the pricing pressures that often face companies. In addition, weak corporate earnings limit subsequent investment and economic growth.[40]

Price reductions, however, are risky. Competitive retaliation to price decreases is particularly important. Firms may encounter three traps in reducing prices:[41]

- *Low-quality trap*—Buyers may question the quality of low-priced products.
- *Fragile market share trap*—Price-sensitive buyers may switch to the next lower-priced product that comes along.

• *Shallow pockets trap*—Higher-priced competitors that reduce prices also may have longer staying power due to higher margins.

Price decreases may be implemented in several ways, with direct reductions from the original price most common. Firms may also reduce prices by offering quantity discounts or rebates. Bundling additional products or services with the basic product, while maintaining the current price, is another tactic. In retail clothing, recent analyses suggest that reduced prices should be offered sooner but with smaller discounts. To improve effectiveness, Saks has begun using software to determine the timing and extent of price decreases. This approach helps avoid deep markdowns at the end of seasons.[42]

Price promotions by manufacturers affect the strategies engaged in by resellers of grocery and other packaged goods. In fact, many grocery retailers and wholesalers depend on the purchase of products at reduced manufacturer prices. In these instances, reseller firms become dependent on *forward buying,* a practice in which large quantities of products are bought on sale, giving the wholesalers and retailers larger margins when the products are sold to consumers. These practices then lead to consumers' spending heavily for products that are on sale. For example, almost 71 percent of total supermarket sales for carbonated beverages in one 52-week period occurred when the products were being price promoted.[43]

Price increases are also common. A primary reason is inflationary pressure: increases in the costs of inputs and production force prices upward. In Central and South America, price increases from inflationary pressures are common, often requiring high increases over very short periods. Also, when demand is great, firms often raise prices. Moreover, they may do so indirectly by reducing or eliminating quantity discounts, cash discounts for prompt payment, and trade allowances. Services once included with a product may be unbundled so the buyer actually receives less for the same price. In effect, these tactics enable firms to adjust real prices upward without raising list prices. Even consumer products manufacturers are considering add-ons as a means of increasing prices. For example, Procter & Gamble has launched a number of products that include mechanical or electrical gadgets. These include Scentsories, an electric air freshener, and the Tide StainBrush, a battery-powered brush.[44]

Both price increases and decreases must be noticeable to affect purchase decisions. For example, a reduction from $5.75 to $5.45 may not influence demand, whereas a reduction to $5.15 might be meaningful. Buyers have **price thresholds** for products, and they notice when prices go under or above those limits. Thresholds depend on the average price of the product. A 10-cent reduction on a $10 product, for example, differs from the same reduction on a 50-cent product.

Ranges of acceptable prices also exist. The **acceptable price range** includes prices buyers are willing to pay. Airwalks, for example, demonstrates the role of price as part of a product's marketing mix. With its low-cost structure, due largely to outsourced foreign manufacturing and corresponding low price, the Airwalks shoe offers an acceptable and generally low price range to a segment of young consumers. Buyers may react negatively when prices move outside the acceptable range, above or below. Prices raised too high may exceed buyer budgets or be judged as unfair. Marketers that gouge buyers by charging excessively high prices are often publicly criticized. Prices reduced below the acceptable range generate concerns about product or service quality: the low-quality trap.[45]

Buyers (both consumers and organizational buyers) often resist price increases and are particularly hesitant to pay prices perceived as unfair. Price changes that result in undue profits for the firm are perceived as unfair, while price increases that just maintain firm profit levels are judged as fair. This notion is referred to as the "principle of dual entitlement." Relatedly, there is growing irritation among many business travelers with increasing airline fares and rules that guarantee that executive travelers are charged the highest prices.[46]

Reacting to Competitive Price Changes

Competitive pressures affect pricing decisions of retailers and companies that sell to other businesses. Price competition among retail marketers is particularly acute with the advent of Wal-Mart, grocery superstores, and club warehouses. Past Target ads have accused Wal-Mart of using misleading pricing tactics. Price comparisons by large retailers are likely to intensify as Wal-Mart, Target, and others run out of territories to conquer.[47]

John Deere, the farm equipment company, took advantage of a recent merger among competitors that created GNH Global. Deere offered owners of the competing firms' equipment large price reductions, reduced interest, and cash to trade in their equipment for Deere products. Deere then slashed prices on the trade-ins, affecting sales of new products and generating concerns among buyers about the subsequent trade-in value of the newly formed company's offerings.[48]

Brand managers should react to competitive price changes case by case. If price decreases among competitors do not increase total market demand, then price competition can hurt all competitors. The firm must try to determine the purpose of its competitive price change, its likely duration, and the reaction of other competitors in the market.

If buyers make decisions on nonprice characteristics, a reactive price decrease to meet the competition may not be necessary. Competitors instead might try to compete on service, quality, and features. When competition is based largely on price, however, a price decrease to match the competition may be required.

Examples of competitive price reactions are easy to find even among the most well-known companies. Pressures to reduce prices have been particularly strong in the computer software market, where competitors have undercut rivals by as much as six times. IBM reacted to the success of Toshiba and Compaq in the PC notebook market by aggressively promoting the capabilities of its line and offering competitive prices. In a similar move, Apple reduced its base price by more than $1,000 to stimulate sales of notebook computers.[49] Hertz cut its car rental rates to match competition from Alamo Rent-A-Car and Budget. Hershey Foods was forced to match price reductions by M&M Mars.[50]

Price reductions are often implemented to give the impression of low costs and to enhance the firm's ability to compete. However, and as has occurred in the telecommunication and airline industries, price reductions can result in unprofitable price wars. Kmart's unsuccessful attempt at EDLP pricing resulted in price reductions by Wal-Mart. In these instances, competitive actions based on price and countermeasures are typically retaliatory price cuts. But nonprice strategic alternatives may prevent a price war. For example, firms may offer to match all competitor prices, promote everyday low prices, and emphasize their cost advantages in marketing communications. Marketers may also increase product quality and differentiation by adding features and building awareness of unique benefits. Advertising can also emphasize the performance risk associated with low-priced alternatives.[51]

Generalizations about Price Changes

Considerable research has been conducted regarding the effects of price changes. These studies have involved experiments in which price levels were systematically varied and analyses of scanner data were collected in-store. A review of these studies yielded the following conclusions:

- Temporary retail price reductions substantially increase store traffic and sales.
- Large-market-share brands are hurt less by price changes from smaller competitors.
- Frequent price dealing lowers consumers' reference prices, which may hurt brand equity.
- Price changes for high-quality brands affect weaker brands and private-label brands disproportionately.[52]

Dennis Hurley of IBM talks about relationship pricing: "In many cases, customers want to have some assurance on future pricing, particularly in project rollouts that call for installation of our products or services in their business over an extended time. In these cases we use relationship pricing, also known as index pricing. In relationship pricing we offer a fixed discount off the list price or Web price, or a third-party index for selected products (when sold through that channel). So the prices the customer pays change automatically as the market moves prices up or down. This way the customer can feel comfortable the pricing will stay current and competitive (particularly important in technology, where price–performance often is improving year-to-year), and also we, as the vendor, eliminate the need to continually renegotiate prices for a given project."

Marketing policies and practices that continually allocate large percentages of budgets to price-related promotions serve only to reduce baseline revenues from higher-margin

Price discounts and trade allowances are used by manufacturers to encourage retailers to carry their products. In this General Mills trade ad to retail buyers, the message emphasizes advertising support and price discounts to retailers.

and unpromoted sales. As such, many brand managers worry that funds are being taken away from image advertising designed to nurture brands for the long haul and that constant price promotion activity will only damage brand equity that enables firms to charge more profitable premium prices.[53]

Price Discounts and Allowances

The actual price a customer pays may differ from the market or list price, perhaps because of discounts from the original price. Discounts, which take many forms, occur in consumer and reseller transactions. They include cash discounts, trade promotion allowances, and quantity discounts.

Marketers often offer *cash discounts* for prompt payment by retailers. For example, terms of payment may be "3/10, net 30," indicating that the full amount of purchase is due in 30 days with a 3 percent discount available if the customer pays the bill in 10 days.

Trade sales promotion allowances are concessions a manufacturer pays or allocates to wholesalers or retailers to promote its products. The manufacturer or wholesaler may reduce prices on certain items so retailers can offer sale prices. Or the manufacturer may give additional marketing communications incentives to help the retailer pay for advertising. In fact, much of the newspaper advertising for grocery stores is supported by manufacturers' cooperative advertising payments.

Marketers give *quantity discounts* when the customer buys large quantities of a product. For example, full price might be charged for 500 or fewer reams of computer paper. For purchasing 501 to 1,000 reams, the customer receives a 3 percent discount per ream. For purchases over 1,000 reams, a 5 percent reduction off list price would be offered. A cumulative quantity discount entitles the purchaser to a larger discount as the sum of purchases within a specified period, usually a year, exceeds a certain amount. Noncumulative quantity discounts apply to each purchase and are based on the size of the order.

Geographic Pricing

Companies with geographically dispersed customers sometimes adjust prices because of costs resulting from distance. Shipping costs may be substantial and detract from profit if they are not included in the price. Marketers use geographic pricing approaches to address these issues.

One of the more commonly used methods is **FOB origin pricing**. *FOB* stands for "free on board," meaning the goods are placed on a carrier (truck, train, barge) and shipped to the customer. FOB pricing requires customers to pay the unit cost of the goods plus shipping costs, which differ with location or market. An opposite strategy is to charge the same price and transportation cost to all customers. Using a **uniform delivered price**, the company charges each customer an average freight amount. A principal advantage of this method is ease of administration.

Zone pricing is an approach between FOB pricing and uniform delivered pricing. Customers within an area (say, the Northeast) are charged a common price. More distant zones or areas are charged higher freight amounts.

Freight absorption pricing is another form of geographic pricing. Here the seller absorbs freight costs—offers free or reduced costs of delivery—to attract more business. This practice occurs when competition among sellers is heavy.

Competitive Bidding and Negotiated Pricing
In the United States, retail prices for most consumer goods normally are not negotiable. However, outside the United States, price negotiations for consumer goods occur regularly. Likewise, almost all business-to-business purchases are negotiated to some extent. In fact, many organizational

Exhibit 12–10		*Alternative bid prices and expected values (in $000)*		
Submitted Price (Bid)	**Costs**	**Contribution to Profit**	**Probability of Selection**	**Expected Value**
$250	$170	$ 80	.75	$60.00
275	170	105	.70	73.50
300	170	130	.65	84.50
325	170	155	.50	77.50
350	170	180	.45	81.00

Note: Expected value = Contribution to profit × Probability of selection.

buyers now view every aspect of their purchase transactions as negotiable. Negotiated pricing is the norm in marketing to the federal government, the largest purchaser of goods and services.

Sealed-bid pricing is unique in that the buyer determines the pricing approach and the eventual price. The buyer encourages sellers to submit sealed bids, or prices, for providing their products or services;[54] the sellers set prices on the basis of cost considerations and expectations about what competitors will bid.

Sealed-bid pricing may be difficult for the seller. First the seller must determine the costs involved in providing the product or service. The seller must then set a price according to the prices it expects competing firms to submit. The price must cover costs, provide a reasonable return, and be low enough to be selected by the purchaser. Overall, the bidding company must be able to evaluate the chances of winning a particular contract at different prices, determine the profit potential under various bidding outcomes, and identify projects for which the expense of preparing and submitting a bid is economically justified.[55]

An example bidding situation is shown in Exhibit 12–10. This framework allows the seller to evaluate alternative bids in terms of the costs of the project, the contribution of each alternative to profits, and the probability of winning the job at each bid price. As the price or submitted bid increases, the probability of winning decreases.

Negotiated pricing is common for large investments, such as buildings or other installations, and for consulting arrangements, many professional services, or governmental work. Negotiation between vendor and supplier replaces evaluation of multiple bids. If these are long-term arrangements, or agreements likely to involve future negotiations, concern for developing and maintaining relationships is critical. In some smaller deals, sales reps may negotiate prices and margins for the company in the field on a transaction-by-transaction basis. Field salespeople can help identify situations when price quotes need to be more competitive to avoid losing profitable business.[56]

Reverse auctions, in which sellers bid instead of buyers and prices fall instead of rise, enable buyers to negotiate lower prices from multiple suppliers. That is, the competition is from the sellers' side. In one B2B example for plastic automobile parts, with 25 suppliers bidding, the starting price was $745,000, the most recently paid price. After 20-plus minutes into the auction, the bidding was concluded at $518,000, saving 31 percent for the customer.[57]

Pricing Services

The unique characteristics of services—intangible, perishable, inseparable, and nonstandardized—make their pricing difficult. Price determination is influenced by the nature of the service involved. For professional services, such as those provided by attorneys and accountants, prices vary according to the complexity of the service and the amount of work or services provided. However, pricing decisions for services, as for tangible products, should consider expenses or costs involved with service delivery, price expectations of customers, management objectives of a reasonable return, and pricing for similar services by competitors.[58] Generally, the larger the share of the market held by a service provider, the higher the price it can charge relative to competition.

One difficulty in pricing services is the need to manage off-peak periods of demand. Movies, airlines, and car rental firms, for example, price services to shift demand to periods

Pricing services and utilities can be difficult. As deregulation spreads, utility companies face increasing pressures to price competitively.

of excess capacity. The perishable nature of these services makes creative pricing and demand management an important aspect of service pricing. That is, once a movie starts, an airline flight takes off, or a rental car remains unused over a weekend, the potential income from these unpurchased intangibles is lost.

In some industries, pricing of services is extremely competitive. The airline industry has wide differences in prices across markets, time periods, and competitors. The entry of competitive firms can influence prices dramatically. The keys to pricing services effectively are profiling the competition in terms of the factors that drive competition and understanding the economic impact that the service offering has on customers' costs and revenue streams.[59]

Bundling of services into a single package and price is a common strategy. Hotels (lodging, meals), banks (large deposits yield free travelers' checks), physicians (exams, diagnostic tests), and airlines (travel, rental cars), for example, provide services for a single bundle price.[60] Bundling increases demand by providing increased savings and convenience to the consumer.

After-sales services associated with products are also important. For many manufacturers, service plans can be a valuable source of revenues if properly designed and priced. In fact, manufacturers of everything from elevators to freezers to security systems and transportation equipment—products built to last—find that revenues from after-sales product installation, maintenance, and repairs are 30 percent or more of revenues.[61]

Ethical Issues and Deceptive Practices

Ethical problems associated with business pricing are common and are often the focus of much public scrutiny. A recent congressional investigation into the pricing practices of a national hospital company revealed significant bill padding. Patients were charged $44 for saline solutions (salt water) costing 81 cents and $103 for crutches costing $8.[62] Pharmaceutical companies have been cited for overpricing life-saving drugs, as in the case of AIDS medications.[63] Claims of price gouging have also been leveled against major airlines for their pricing during peak travel times or in geographic areas where a major carrier dominates. Following Hurricane Andrew, Florida's attorney general subpoenaed top plywood manufacturers for records justifying soaring prices. Evidence of profiteering and consumer gouging was found among sellers of batteries, chain saws, and flashlights. Similar accusations arose after the 1994 Los Angeles earthquake. In contrast, Home Depot, a national retailer of home-building supplies, sold its products at cost immediately following Andrew.[64] Undoubtedly, Home Depot's positive response earned the company much goodwill.

FTC Guidelines and Deceptive Pricing

Many advertised prices include comparison prices. These can enhance the attractiveness of the offer by making the price reduction appear lower than merely stating it alone. Comparison price advertising typically pairs the sale price with prices formerly charged by the retailer, competing retailer prices, or manufacturer-suggested prices.

Comparison price advertising is effective, and it provides useful information to buyers. Unfortunately, the ease with which claims can be made and their influence on buyers increase the likelihood of deceptive pricing practices. Federal Trade Commission (FTC) guidelines provide specific procedures for avoiding deceptive price advertising. The most common practices addressed by the guidelines include these:[65]

- *Comparisons with former prices*—Prices claimed as former prices charged by the retailer ("Regularly $XX, Now Only $YY") must have been offered to the public on a regular basis for a "reasonable" period. Although sales are not required at the higher price, the former price must have been a genuine offer.

- *Comparisons with other retailer prices*—When prices are said to be lower than those being charged by other retailers for the same merchandise in the advertiser's trade area, the advertised higher prices must be based on fact.

- *Comparisons with prices suggested by manufacturers or other nonretail distributors*—If prices are said to be reductions from the manufacturer's list price or suggested retail price, these comparison prices must correspond to the prices at which a substantial proportion of the product's sales are made.

Several years ago May Department Stores in Denver was cited by the attorney general of Colorado for "engaging in continuous and repeated patterns of deceptive price advertising and sales practices." Examples included houseware products "on sale" at the same sale prices for two years and luggage advertised as discounted from "regular" prices that never were May's prevailing prices and that were double the luggage prices for the same items charged by other local retailers.[66]

The context under which consumers make decisions can affect the ethics of marketing practices as well. For example, in cases where individuals are suffering from extreme grief, such as following the death of a loved one, decisions regarding funeral arrangements are difficult. Retailing experts have learned that presenting only corners of caskets in a product line arrangement, instead of using large showrooms displaying numbers of whole caskets, makes decisions easier for the buyer. However, the practice raises the average price paid as consumers avoid lower-end models. The ethics and fairness of this product-line pricing strategy certainly warrant evaluation.[67]

Bait and Switch

Grocery stores and department stores advertise some brands at cost or near cost to attract consumers. These marketers hope that low-priced items or *loss leaders* will generate traffic and sales of other items in the store. A **bait and switch** occurs when the retailer advertises but does not actually offer a reasonable amount of the promoted product. If the product is not, or was not, actually available, consumers may trade up and buy a more expensive version of the advertised loss leader. This bait-and-switch practice is illegal and unethical.

Predatory Pricing

In some instances, companies charge very low prices to drive competition from the market. Any losses incurred can be recouped later by charging higher monopoly prices once competition has been discouraged. This practice is called **predatory pricing**. A company that claims predatory pricing by a competitor must demonstrate that the low-priced firm, typically a larger firm, charges prices below its average total costs with the *intent* to harm competitors.

Predatory pricing is difficult to prove in the courts because juries are skeptical of these claims.[68] The company that sues must show not only that a rival firm prices below cost but also that it does so intending to raise prices later. Wal-Mart was once accused of predatory pricing by pharmacy chains because of its aggressive drug pricing practices. The Justice Department charged American Airlines of illegally forcing smaller competitors out of its Dallas hub. After the smaller carriers left, prices to consumers were raised. Predatory pricing has also been discussed in the government's case against Microsoft, which often gives away software to build market share.[69]

Unit Pricing

The number of products, brands, and package sizes in the marketplace presents a bewildering array of choices. The potential to be misled or at least confused is likewise great. Many states have passed unit pricing legislation to help consumers process in-store price information. **Unit pricing** presents price information on a per-unit weight or volume basis to facilitate price comparisons across brands and across package sizes within brands. Unit pricing is intended to help low-income consumers and price-vigilant shoppers.[70] Although not an ethical issue per se, unit pricing is designed to improve consumer decision making and to reduce the potential for being misled or misinformed by the vast amount of in-store information.

Summary

1. **Discuss the interrelationships among price, demand, demand elasticity, and revenue.** Marketplace conditions influence prices. The higher the price of most goods or services, the lower the demand. These relationships are depicted in the familiar economic demand curve. The extent to which demand changes as price changes is the price elasticity of demand. Inelastic demand exists when a seller increases price and sees little decrease in sales. Demand is elastic when small changes in price cause large changes in the quantity demanded.

   The profit-maximizing price level is the point where total revenues minus total costs is highest. This point occurs at the price where marginal revenue equals marginal cost. This expression of profit maximization does not consider factors such as the seller's ability to influence demand through promotional activities.

2. **Understand methods for determining price.** Cost-oriented methods for determining price include markup pricing, where the price is set as a certain percentage increase above its cost; break-even analysis, which calculates the number of units required to be sold to cover costs at a certain price; and target-return pricing, where the price is set to provide some specific desired rate of return on investment. A competition orientation to determining price suggests firms charge prices similar to competitors' prices.

3. **Recognize the different pricing strategies and the conditions that best suit the choice of a strategy.** Four broad categories of pricing strategies are differential pricing, competitive pricing, product-line pricing, and psychological pricing.

   When differences exist across consumer segments, differential pricing is effective. Examples include second-market discounting, where different prices are charged to different segments, and periodic discounting.

   Competitive pricing includes penetration pricing, where a firm sets an initial low price to stimulate demand or deter competition, and price signaling, or offering a high price for a low-quality brand in hopes consumers will infer high quality.

   Product-line strategies are important for firms that sell a variety of brands of the same product, as the price set for one of the brands often affects sales of the entire product line. Some firms use bundling strategies, where separate products or services in a line are sold as a single bundle. Premium pricing, when the firm charges higher prices for deluxe brands within a product line, is most successful when market segments want different combinations of features. Psychological pricing includes the practice of odd–even pricing and customary pricing.

4. **Recognize the importance of adapting prices under shifting economic and competitive situations.** Prices are reduced under several circumstances: declining market share, changing customer preferences, or lower competitive prices. If competitors can easily detect price reductions and are willing to retaliate, price reductions are risky. Lowering prices may also affect consumer perceptions of quality, may work only until an even lower-priced product is available, and may be difficult to maintain in the presence of larger and stronger competitors.

   When products compete on attributes other than price (service, features), price changes in the face of competitive price shifts may not be required. In homogeneous markets, however, where products are similar and compete largely on price, price reductions by competitors will probably have to be matched. Inflation or excessive demand sometimes leads to price increases.

   For a price change to affect demand, the increase or decrease must exceed some minimal threshold so as to be noticeable. Buyers also have a range of acceptable prices. Prices reduced below the lowest acceptable price may generate perceptions of inferior quality; prices above the highest acceptable price will be rejected.

5. **Understand the ethical considerations involved in setting and communicating prices.** Ethical considerations are an issue in pricing decisions. Prices must not potentially mislead or take advantage of customers. The FTC offers guidelines that govern advertised price specials and comparison pricing. The most common aspects of comparison pricing governed by the FTC include comparisons with former prices, comparisons with other retail prices, and comparisons with prices suggested by manufacturers or distributors.

   Another unethical practice involves predatory pricing: pricing below average cost until competitors are forced out of the market. After driving out competitors, the firm raises its prices. Unit pricing is required in some states to provide price information on a per-unit or volume basis to enhance consumer decision making.

Understanding Marketing Terms and Concepts

Thinking about Marketing

1. Define *price elasticity*, and explain its relationship to demand.

2. Briefly explain the steps that should be considered in determination of a price.

3. Why are pricing decisions so important, and why are these decisions becoming more difficult?

4. Why may pricing decisions involving international marketing be so problematic?

5. Contrast break-even analysis pricing with markup pricing. What are the shortcomings of each approach?

6. How might the pricing strategies for a line of low-calorie Chinese grocery items vary over time?

7. Contrast penetration pricing with price skimming.

8. Identify two examples of both pure price bundling and product bundling.

9. Consider the pricing of services. What will determine the prices charged by firms that provide accounting services to small businesses?

10. How does the Federal Trade Commission view reference claims for advertisements involving (a) former price comparisons and (b) comparisons with competing retailers?

11. Discuss the relationships among costs, volume, and profits. Be sure to explain the role of price within these relationships.

12. Compare and contrast differential pricing and competitive pricing.

13. What are some of the psychological aspects of pricing, and why are these important?

Applying Marketing Skills

1. Identify a new brand entry in two different product categories. How do their prices compare to competing brands in each category? What factors might account for differences between prices within the categories?

2. Are the following practices ethical? Explain.
   a. John Doe is a retailer of brand X fountain pens, which cost him $5 each. His usual markup is 50 percent over cost, or $7.50. Doe first offers the pens for $10, realizing he will be able to sell very few, if any. This offer lasts for only a few days. He then reduces the price to $7.50 and promotes as follows: "Terrific bargain: X Pens, Were $10, Now Only $7.50!"
   b. Retailer Doe advertises brand X pens as having "Retail Value $15, My Price $7.50," when only a few distant suburban outlets charge $15.

3. Explain why long-distance telephone suppliers charge different prices at different times of the day.

Using the www in Marketing

Activity One The eBay Web site discussed in the introduction of this chapter has been influential in affecting how consumers search for low prices. Consider the following questions as they relate to price search using eBay:

1. What activities are required for an individual consumer to offer products for sale on eBay?

2. What are the characteristics of products that are most consistent with selling on sites such as eBay?

3. What advantages does eBay offer traditional retailers?

4. For what kinds of pricing situations are online auctions likely to be most effective?

Activity Two Identify and describe the pricing strategies for the following products. Explain why these pricing objectives are appropriate for the respective environments in which the organization operates:

1. Florida Power and Light: *http://www.fpl.com.*

2. Boeing: *http://www.boeing.com.*

3. L'Eggs: *http://www.leggs.com.*

4. Goodyear: *http://www.goodyear.com.*

Making Marketing Decisions

Case 12–1 *Saturn's Upscale New Cars and Prices*

General Motors Corporation's Saturn Division began as a low-cost, basic transportation carmaker. Saturn has now introduced a sporty roadster, the Sky, and a midsized Aura sedan concept. A midsized sport wagon will follow next. The 2006 Sky starting prices will be just under $25,000. The company is trying to move Saturn slightly upscale with more expensive cars to compete with import brands such as Volkswagen and Honda. As such, Saturn will have a broader range of prices to coincide with a significantly expanded product portfolio. Some analysts believe that it could be a stretch trying to introduce that much new product into a dealer network that has been accustomed to handling a limited number of models in the past.

Sales of the 15-year-old division were down 22 percent in 2004, and the division is losing as much as $1 billion per year. The new cars will be steel-based instead of plastic. The styling and interiors of the new vehicles will be heavily influenced by European styles. The goal is to sell enough cars at premium prices for the division to break even in 2008. Transforming Saturn from a unit that sells cheap small cars to one that sells more fashionable vehicles will be a difficult task.

Questions

1. How will the new prices interact with the five Cs of pricing?

2. Will prior price expectations for Saturn affect the range of acceptable prices for the new vehicles?

3. What is the role of the dealership network in determining final consumer prices?

Case 12–2 *Starbucks: Brewing High-Priced Beverages*

 Starbucks is opening stores at a rapid pace and has over 6,000 company-operated stores in the United States. Seventy-eight percent of revenues come from coffee and other beverages. If master plans succeed, there will be 10,000 Starbucks stores worldwide by 2005. Its largest U.S. competitor, Diedrich Coffee, Inc., based in Irvine, California, has only 380 stores. The strategy in New York is interesting and somewhat mixed. The strategy of serving as a "third place" appears to have worked in the city in which the first place is a cramped apartment and the second place is a cubicle. The coffee shops provide a place for doing homework, holding business meetings, and socializing or reading the newspaper. However, attempts to sell lunch and housewares have not been as well received.

The marketing mix for Starbucks includes minimal advertising, but the brand has remarkable recognition fueled significantly by word of mouth. One restaurant consultant asserts that "the stores are the marketing for Starbucks." Prices are high, and the premium coffee outlets are supported by distribution through their ever-expanding network of stores and in-grocery store sales. Starbucks concentrates its efforts on key neighborhoods, even at the expense of possibly hurting existing stores. The success of the high-priced beverage sold so easily by Starbucks has led some small restaurant chains to offer profitably high-priced sandwiches instead of burgers and fries. Some of these premium sandwich chains, like Cosi, Panera, and Briazz, have names designed to convey European sophistication.

Criticism predicted that the Starbucks venture into Japan would fail in a country strong on tea consumption. Japan now has 300 successful stores, and 30 percent of the business is takeout. Will the strategy in Europe be successful? The Starbucks model, with long on-site consumption or paper-cup takeout, is foreign to European patterns of coffee drinking. The experience in Vienna has been profitable so far. The company expects more resistance in Italy and France but anticipates that younger consumers will endorse the Starbucks concept.

About 30 million customers visit Starbucks worldwide each week. Somehow Starbucks has made it seem normal to spend $4.02 for a grande Frappuccino, the chain's signature creamy coffee. In late 2004 the Seattle-based company planned to boost prices above the average $2–2.50 per drink. College professors often use Starbucks as an example of inelastic demand. If demand is inelastic, why does the company not raise prices more often and boost revenue?

Questions

1. What role does price play in the purchase of Starbucks coffee? Is the demand elastic or inelastic? Why?

2. How does the price menu detract or enhance the image of Starbucks?

3. What competition does Starbucks face?

4. How does the role of price in the United States compare with the role of price in European markets?

5. What are the implications of price elasticity for Starbucks?

Chapter Thirteen

MARKETING CHANNELS

13

After studying this chapter, you should be able to

1 Explain the functions and key activities of marketing channels.

2 Discuss the role of intermediaries in marketing channels.

3 Distinguish between direct and indirect marketing channels.

4 Illustrate how some firms use multiple channels successfully.

5 See how marketing channel decisions are related to other key marketing decision variables.

6 Understand how power, conflict, and cooperation affect the operation of a marketing channel.

7 Give examples of ethical and legal issues encountered in the operations of marketing channels.

Timbuk2

Timbuk2, a San Francisco–based manufacturer of urban shoulder bags, iPod holsters, tote bags, and yoga mat carriers, has learned that having the right channels for distributing its products is every bit as important for success as having cutting-edge products. When CompUSA agreed to carry Timbuk2 bags, CEO Mark Dwight thought his company had hit the jackpot. Four months later, Timbuk2 was hard-pressed to keep up with the high-volume demand and remain profitable given its low selling price to CompUSA. CompUSA's aggressive retail pricing meant that Timbuk2 had to bundle extra accessories with each computer bag sold to avoid undercutting other retailers selling Timbuk2 bags. Dwight decided to pull his bags from CompUSA and reformulate his go-to-market strategy.

In rethinking his distribution strategy, Dwight decided that specialty retailers such as REI, Apple, EMS, Urban Outfitters, and

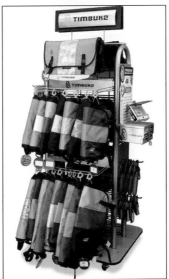

the Discovery Channel Store would be superior to large discount chains such as CompUSA and Office Depot. Specialty chains attract customers who value quality and brand, rather than low price. The shopping environment is more personalized in specialty stores, with a knowledgeable sales staff to explain the unique features of niche products.

Having the right channel has boosted Timbuk2, not only by a dramatic increase in sales, but also by spawning new products. With the popularity explosion of the Apple iPod, Timbuk2 has introduced a line of iPod accessories, and other new products are opening doors to new retailers. Timbuk2 is now sold in 1,200 specialty retailers, the largest of which feature elaborate point-of-purchase Timbuk2 displays. With its brand equity at an all-time high, Timbuk2 is leveraging its specialty retailer channel to keep the momentum moving at a fast pace.

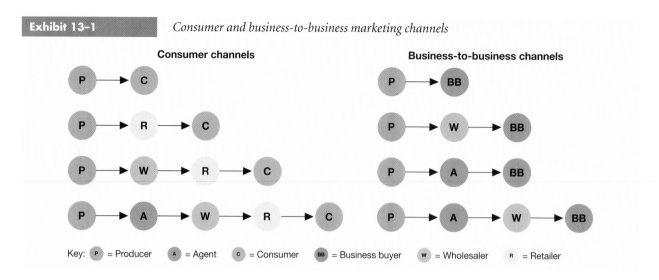

Exhibit 13-1   *Consumer and business-to-business marketing channels*

The Timbuk2 profile introduces several issues of interest in this chapter. First, the right product produced at the right time must be matched with the right means of distributing it to the marketplace. Second, the right means of distribution often changes over time. Third, understanding buyer needs is crucial for success.

In this chapter we explore the **marketing channel,** or channel of distribution, defined as a combination of organizations and individuals (channel members) who perform the required activities to link producers of products to users of those products to accomplish marketing objectives.[1] In thinking about marketing channels, keep in mind that products can be goods, services, or ideas. Producers can be manufacturers, service organizations, or idea-generating groups or companies. Some alternative consumer and business-to-business channels are shown in Exhibit 13–1.

Different types of marketing channels require the services of **intermediaries,** often referred to as *middlemen,* who are directly involved in the purchase or sale of products as they flow from the originator to the user. Intermediaries include retailers, which sell to ultimate consumers, and wholesalers, which sell to retailers, other wholesalers, government buyers, manufacturers, and other business customers. Retailers and wholesalers are discussed in detail in subsequent chapters.

We introduce various types of marketing channels in this chapter. Some companies, such as Burger King, reach their customers through franchising. Personal computer manufacturers use a variety of channels, including electronics stores, computer specialty stores, printed catalogs, membership clubs, and office supply stores. Apple sells through its own retail stores, and many companies sell directly to customers over the Internet or with their own salespeople. Decisions on marketing channels are prime elements in a firm's overall marketing strategy and a factor in pricing, product, and marketing communications considerations.

Importance of Marketing Channels   Because marketing channels determine how and where customers buy, the establishment of and any subsequent change in channels are indeed critical. Other marketing variables can be manipulated frequently, and changes are often easy to make. Marketers can raise and lower prices, vary advertising media and messages, and add and delete products from their market offerings without revolutionizing the way they do business.

Making major changes in marketing channels is not so easy. Marketing channels are harder to change because other parties, such as retailers and wholesalers, may play important roles in the channel. For example, several manufacturers receive a sizable portion of their sales volume from Wal-Mart. Home appliance manufacturer National Presto Industries gets more than a third of its sales volume from Wal-Mart and a sizable percentage from Target.[2] Dial, Del Monte, and Revlon all have more than 20 percent of their sales with

Wal-Mart, and Procter & Gamble sells 18 percent of its volume through Wal-Mart. Approximately 60 percent of all DVDs are sold through Wal-Mart, Best Buy, and Target.[3] Where would these manufacturers make up the lost volume if they decided not to sell through Wal-Mart and Target? It would require a marketing miracle for these companies to sell as much merchandise without giant discounters.

Marketers are sometimes bound to their channels when significant sunk costs are involved. For example, the franchise system of McDonald's and company-owned outlets such as Exxon's convenience stores represent huge dollar investments. Such investments are made only after much forethought, and abandoning them is the last resort. For these reasons, marketing channels take on more of a sense of permanence—change is certainly an option, but one that is not so likely to be frequently exercised as with other marketing variables.

Functions of Marketing Channels

By performing five critical functions, marketing channels play an important role in accomplishing the key marketing activities discussed in Chapter 1 (Exhibit 1–7). These functions, shown in Exhibit 13–2, include the management of marketing communications, inventory, physical distribution, market feedback, and financial risk. It is important to note that none of these functions can be eliminated, but they can be shifted from one channel member to another.

Marketing Communications

Channel members are frequently involved in marketing communications activities, which include advertising and public relations, sales promotion, personal selling, and direct marketing communications. REI, for example, a leading retailer of outdoor sports gear, uses well-placed ads and mailings to reach customers and provides a highly trained sales staff to assist customers. REI also uses in-store displays and workshops to inform customers about mountain climbing, Nordic skiing, white-water rafting, and snowshoeing. TAG Heur, a luxury watchmaker, often uses its print advertising to support dealers by pointing out that the only way to be assured of buying an authentic TAG Heur watch is to buy from an authorized dealer. The ads warn consumers that a watch bought from unauthorized dealers may be counterfeit, damaged, or tampered with or contain inferior parts. The ads also provide a Web site for locating authorized dealers.

Inventory Management

Marketing channel members sometimes provide inventory management functions. For example, auto parts wholesalers must stock thousands of products, many of which sell for under a dollar each, to be competitive suppliers to the independent repair shop market. In

| **Exhibit 13–2** | *Key functions performed in marketing channels* |

Marketing communications
- Advertising the product
- Providing point-of-purchase displays
- Providing a sales force that offers information and service to customers

Market feedback
- Serving on manufacturer advisory boards
- Informing other channel members of competitive activity
- Participating in test market evaluations

Inventory management
- Ordering an appropriate assortment of merchandise
- Maintaining adequate stock to meet customer demand
- Storing merchandise in an appropriate facility

Financial risk
- Offering credit
- Managing risks related to product loss or deterioration
- Managing risks related to product safety and liability

Physical distribution
- Delivering products
- Coordinating delivery schedules to meet customer expectations
- Arranging for the return of defective merchandise

contrast, a Corvette-only parts wholesaler may stock fewer products but offer virtually every part available for repairing Corvettes of all vintages.

Physical Distribution

The actual movement of products and other physical distribution activities are important elements in a marketing channel. For example, it is not unusual for suppliers of raw materials and components to a high-volume, fast-paced manufacturing plant to be given windows of only a few minutes to make deliveries. The coordination of delivery times is thus a major issue in meeting customer expectations, and suppliers who cannot meet such operating demands will lose business.

Marketing Information

Buyer–seller relationships are enhanced when channel members provide valuable information to other channel members, leading to better performance in the channel. One company that provides useful information to intermediaries is Building Materials Distributors (BMD), an international distributor of building materials and construction tools. BMD supports home improvement retailers, one of its key customer groups, with its product knowledge and expertise in retailing and an extensive line of services designed to help retailers improve sales and profitability. Product literature, assistance with desktop publishing, merchandising plans, market research, product catalogs, in-store training, and trade show assistance are among the tools offered by BMD to support its retail customers.[4]

Financial Risk

The last function performed in marketing channels relates to ownership of the products passing through the channel. With ownership, or taking title, come various forms of risk. Perishable products may deteriorate; thefts may occur; or nature may deal out a flood, fire, or some other disaster.

Another risk involves accounts receivable: Who gets stuck if the customer doesn't pay the bill? For example, Kmart's suppliers took a big risk when they continued to ship to the discounter after Kmart declared bankruptcy. One of its largest suppliers, food wholesaler Fleming Companies, declared bankruptcy two months after it lost its supply contract with Kmart, which represented 20 percent of Fleming's business.[5] Fleming had tried unsuccessfully to negotiate an agreement with Kmart to ensure more prompt payment of Kmart's outstanding debt with Fleming.

The assumption of risk is part of the quest to make a profit. It is an essential part of the job for members of any marketing channel.

Contributions of Intermediaries

It can be fashionable to rail about the perverse influence of channel intermediaries, or middlemen. Wholesalers and retailers in the grocery industry are sometimes portrayed as antiheroes, for example, whereas farmers may be seen as economic victims.

Those who take these views typically feel that intermediaries reap unfair profits. It is true that short-term imbalances in the economic system may allow opportunistic retailers and wholesalers to capture largely unearned windfall profits. For example, hotels may inflate prices for rooms, food, and beverages to maximize profits from a captive market, say, fans attending the Super Bowl.

In the long run, however, intermediaries must justify their existence in economic and societal terms to survive. An intermediary must be able to perform some marketing channel activity better than any other channel member. For example, Target Corporation, a major retail intermediary for apparel, home furnishings, and electronics, reaches consumers through more than 1,300 stores in the United States. It also operates a comprehensive Web site where it sells brands such as Wrangler, Apple, RCA, Mattel, and Black &

A retail intermediary, Target performs a wide range of functions, including advertising, selling, managing inventory, delivering merchandise, providing feedback to suppliers, and assuming financial risk.

Decker. Target provides a wide range of channel activities to boost sales, including advertising and sales support, store displays, Web site promotions, inventory ordering, stocking, delivery, and consumer credit. Manufacturers such as Nike, Sony, and Levi Strauss benefit from the channel activities of Target and other retailers. Without retail intermediaries, these manufacturers would have to build their own stores or sell directly to consumers through catalogs or some other means. If they could market more effectively and efficiently without Target, good business sense says they would do so. Obviously, Target is performing some of the marketing channel functions better than the manufacturers could.

Justifying their existence is painfully necessary for intermediaries in the highly competitive grocery products industry. Large supermarket chains continue to move away from independent wholesalers to their own distribution networks in an effort to control costs and improve product availability. As mentioned earlier in the chapter, Fleming, once a major food wholesaler, was forced into bankruptcy in this highly competitive business sector. The influence of Wal-Mart and other large chain stores has been dramatic in shaping the grocery industry. With their buying power, the large chains constantly prod suppliers into improving quality and lowering prices. Increasingly, independent grocers and smaller chains, the key customer segment for food wholesalers, have had a difficult time being price competitive with the large chains, which in turn hurts the overall sales and profit levels for food wholesalers. Some wholesalers have diversified successfully to maintain positive business performance. For example, Minnesota-based SUPERVALU, one of the largest food wholesalers in the world, supplies approximately 2,300 retail grocery stores and also operates 1,550 stores of its own. SUPERVALU also maintains a prominent place in the food marketing channel by offering services such as store design and construction.[6]

In the vast majority of cases, intermediaries are not profiteering parasites; they are simply businesses trying to compete by adding value to the market offering. Given far-flung global markets, intense competition, and specialized support services, intermediaries are likely to remain integral in most marketing channels.

Types of Marketing Channels

The major alternatives available for structuring a marketing channel include direct and indirect channels, single and multiple marketing channels, and vertical marketing systems.

Speaking from Experience

"Manufacturers are constantly trying to improve the productivity of their channels. One way to do this is to use indirect channels rather than a direct sales organization. While direct channels are often necessary for specialized products, they are expensive—as much as 30 cents for each dollar of revenue generated. If manufacturers can decrease the level of specialization necessary to sell their products, indirect channels can boost productivity."

As channels manager in a software division of Hewlett-Packard, Eiron is responsible for improving selling efficiencies and developing new sales channels. Prior to joining HP, Eiron was general manager with Franz Inc., a California software manufacturer. He earned an MBA from U.C. Berkeley and an undergraduate degree from Tel-Aviv University, Israel.

Hanoch Eiron
Channels Manager
Software Engineering Systems Division, Hewlett-Packard

Channel management sometimes requires that existing channels be modified. Avon has begun selling through retail stores in the United States to supplement its traditional direct marketing channel.

Direct and Indirect Marketing Channels

A marketing channel may be direct or indirect. A **direct channel** describes movement of the product from the producer to the user without intermediaries. An **indirect channel** requires intermediaries between the originator and the user to perform some functions related to buying or selling the product to make it available to the final user. A given company might employ both direct and indirect channels.

DIRECT CHANNELS   Direct channels frequently occur in the marketing of medical and professional services, where the use of an intermediary is often impractical. Direct channels are also frequently used in business-to-business markets, where production equipment, component, and subassembly manufacturers sell directly to finished product manufacturers. Exhibit 13–3 gives some examples of direct marketing channels. Increasingly, consumer goods manufacturers are adding direct channels via the Internet for at least some of their products to reach ultimate consumers. For example, Mattel, Polaroid, and Levi Strauss have active Web sites where consumers can bypass traditional retailers and buy directly from the company.

Some of the more spectacular marketing success stories come out of companies using direct channels of distribution. Dell Computer Corporation sells its products directly to customers. Dell has earned many industrywide awards for product quality and customer satisfaction, including a designation as one of *Fortune*'s "most admired" companies. Using a customer-focused approach, Dell sells more than $51 billion worth of computers, software, and accessories worldwide, the majority of which go to demanding large business customers. The first company to offer customers direct, toll-free technical phone support and next-day on-site support, Dell management believes its close relationships with customers are the key to its success.

Exhibit 13–3   *Companies using direct marketing channels*

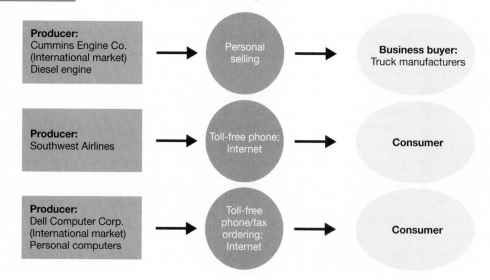

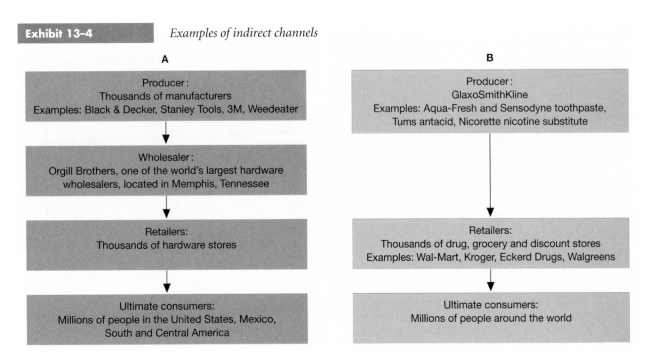

Exhibit 13–4   *Examples of indirect channels*

Direct channels can also be used to market services. Banking, employment services, home mortgages, and insurance providers are well represented on the Internet, with small companies sharing the spotlight with companies such as Bank of America, which offers online banking.

Cummins Engine Company successfully uses direct channels in business-to-business markets. Cummins's salespeople must be knowledgeable about maintenance costs, engine operating costs, and other technical data to effectively sell directly to truck manufacturers such as Chrysler, Navistar, Kenworth, and Volvo-GM.

INDIRECT CHANNELS   Despite the increasing popularity of direct channels, most consumer purchases (homes, automobiles, groceries, appliances, clothing) are still made in an indirect marketing channel, where there is some intermediary between the producer and the end user. Indirect channels are also important in some business-to-business settings.

Two examples of indirect marketing channels are shown in Exhibit 13–4. Orgill Brothers, one of the world's largest hardware wholesalers, is an important intermediary for thousands of manufacturers that want to reach small and medium-sized retail hardware stores. It would not be economically feasible for most manufacturers to provide the sales support to individual hardware stores that Orgill Brothers provides. Example B is GlaxoSmithKline, which uses indirect channels to sell to ultimate consumers through retail intermediaries.

Single and Multiple Marketing Channels

Some companies use a **single-channel strategy** to reach their customers; others rely on a **multiple-channels strategy.** Some companies with multiple products or brands may use a single-channel strategy in one situation and a multiple-channels strategy in another. A single-channel strategy involves the use of only one means of reaching customers. For example, Nexxus shampoo is distributed exclusively through hair care professionals. Prell shampoo, widely available at discount, drug, and grocery stores, is a product distributed through multiple channels. Liz Claiborne uses a multiple-channels strategy to reach different market segments. Its Elisabeth stores serve large-size customers, while Claiborne outlet stores market unsold inventory from past seasons. Liz Claiborne merchandise is also widely distributed in department and specialty stores.

As markets become increasingly fragmented, more firms use a multiple-channels strategy to appeal to as many potential buyers as possible. The basic idea is to allow customers to buy how and where they want to.

Naturally, the finest materials in the business result in the finest warranty in the business.

The Rocky Mountain Warranty. *Each Rocky home is warranted against material defect for a full 10 years. The warranty covers everything Rocky manufactures and provides — logs, the Weather Lock® system, beams, plus all factory milling and joinery.*

® *Weather Lock is a registered trademark of Rocky Mountain Log Homes.*

Rocky Mountain Log Homes uses only the finest grades of dry-standing western pine, spruce, Douglas fir and cedar. Each log is milled to exacting specifications and fitted with our unique Weather Lock® spline and gasket system. This meticulous

approach to material selection and craftsmanship not only makes a better home, it provides the foundation for a better warranty. Naturally.

We invite you to call for our plan book ($14).

ROCKY MOUNTAIN LOG HOMES
Custom Milled, Handcrafted and Log Frame Homes.
1883-HI, Hwy. 93 S., Hamilton, MT 59840
406/363-5680

Most consumers buy houses in an indirect marketing channel with the assistance of a real estate agent. Others may buy in a direct channel from producers such as Rocky Mountain Log Homes.

Hanoch Eiron, channels manager in a software division of Hewlett-Packard, discusses why the popularity of multiple channels is increasing: "The move to multiple channels in many industries is driven by market fragmentation and buyer preferences. For example, in the computer industry, there are significant markets for home computers and business computers. Within these two broad categories, individual buyers have different preferences. Some like to buy in a retail store, some on the Internet or toll-free phone system, some from a local dealer, some directly from the manufacturer sales specialist. A manufacturer that uses only a single channel will most likely miss sale opportunities. Multiple channels let customers buy as they want to."

Exhibit 13–5

Types of vertical marketing systems

Channel systems

Corporate
Forward integration:
Polo, Laura Ashley, Apple Computer
Backward integration:
Winn-Dixie grocery chain
Description
One channel member owns one or more other channel members.

Contractual
Wholesaler-sponsored voluntary groups:
Ace Hardware, Western Auto
Retailer-sponsored cooperative groups:
Affiliated Grocers, True Value Hardware
Franchise systems:
McDonald's, Holiday Inns, H&R Block
Description
Channel members operate according to contractual agreement.

Administered
Abbott Labs, General Electric, Rolex
Description
Channel members operate according to agreed-upon plan.

Vertical Marketing Systems

Emphasis on buyer–seller relationships has contributed to the growth of **vertical marketing systems.** These systems are centrally coordinated, highly integrated operations that work together to serve the ultimate consumer. The word *vertical* refers to the flow of the product from the producer to the customer. This flow is usually thought of as "down the channel" or "downstream," meaning that the product flows down from the producer to the customer.

Vertical marketing systems are now used in a sizable majority of the total sales of consumer goods. Exhibit 13–5 gives examples of the three basic types of vertical marketing systems: corporate, contractual, and administered channel systems.[7]

CORPORATE CHANNEL SYSTEMS   Vertical coordination in a corporate channel system is achieved through ownership of two or more channel members on different levels of distribution. A corporate channel system in which one channel member owns one or more of its buyers downstream is called **forward integration.** Some of the companies that have used forward integration to open their own stores are Polo, Esprit, and Laura Ashley.

Business-to-business marketers also use forward integration. For example, Ashland, a *Fortune* 500 company with operations in 120 countries, began as a regional petroleum refiner. Later the company used a forward integration strategy to found Ashland Distribution, which has become a leading distributor of chemicals and plastics in North America.

Other companies attempt to improve the efficiency and effectiveness of their marketing channels through ownership of one or more of their suppliers, not their buyers. This practice is called **backward integration.** The Winn-Dixie grocery store chain, for example, acquired its own cattle

Cheng Ming Ming used forward integration to sell her own brands of beauty products through an international chain of beauty schools and salons that extends from Southeast Asia and China to the United States.

farms, coffee plantations, and ice cream manufacturing facilities for better control of the price and availability of key food products.

The global integration of marketing channels allows companies to take advantage of the strengths of various countries or regions of the world to maximize marketing efforts. For example, a company might manufacture its products in low-wage countries and use forward integration to establish retail distribution in more lucrative markets. This has been the channel strategy used by ProFlowers, which is the third largest flower retailer in the United States. A significant portion of ProFlowers's products are grown outside the United States in the Southern Hemisphere, where labor costs are lower. The flowers arrive at a distribution center in Miami, where they are shipped in refrigerated trucks to 12 retail markets. By taking advantage of low labor costs outside the United Sates and an efficient distribution system that features forward integration to the retailer level, ProFlowers has been highly successful as a low-cost marketer.[8]

CONTRACTUAL CHANNEL SYSTEMS   Contractual systems may allow some channel members to gain clout in the marketplace and compete effectively with large corporate systems. Coordination between independent firms is achieved through contractual agreements rather than through ownership of channel members upstream or downstream. In this way, contractual channel members try to improve their buying power, gain economies of scale, and realize greater efficiencies through the standardization of operating procedures. The three primary types of contractual channels are wholesaler-sponsored voluntary groups, retailer-owned cooperative groups, and franchise systems.

Wholesaler-sponsored voluntary groups consist of independent retailers that operate under the name of a sponsoring wholesaler. Examples of wholesaler-sponsored voluntary groups are Ace Hardware and Western Auto. The wholesaler (Ace Hardware) buys in quantity, makes deliveries to the individual stores, and offers a variety of services that benefit its retailers. These services may include merchandising, advertising, and pricing support based on quantities purchased. Ace Hardware retailers buy most of their merchandise from the group wholesaler and pool their funds for advertising.

Retailer-owned cooperative groups operate like wholesaler-sponsored voluntary groups, but the retailers actually own the wholesaler. Affiliated Grocers and True Value Company are two well-known examples of this type of system.

The third type of contractual channel system is the **franchise system.** One party, the **franchisor,** grants another party, the **franchisee,** the right to distribute and sell specified goods and services. The franchisee agrees to operate according to marketing guidelines set forth by the franchisor under a recognized trademark or trade name.

Franchise systems have been responsible for the growth of some of the most recognizable names in the business world, such as McDonald's and Holiday Inn. Nonretail franchise operations are also prominent, with companies such as Snelling & Snelling and AccounTemps in the personnel placement business and the Coca-Cola bottlers at the wholesale level. Exhibit 13–6 lists some other examples of nonretail franchise organizations. Retail franchising is discussed in more detail in Chapter 14.

ADMINISTERED CHANNEL SYSTEMS   A system designed to control a line or classification of merchandise is called an **administered channel system.** Here channel members agree on a comprehensive noncontractual plan, and no channel member owns another. The parties in an administered system may work closely to reduce joint operating costs for advertising, data processing, inventory control, order entry, or delivery schedules.

One example of an administered channel system is the Kawasaki Motors independent motorcycle dealer network in the United States. Unlike automobile dealers, which typically represent only one brand such as Ford or Toyota, motorcycle dealers typically carry different manufacturers' brands. This requires that the competing manufacturers vie for their

| Exhibit 13-6 | *Nonretail franchise channel systems* |

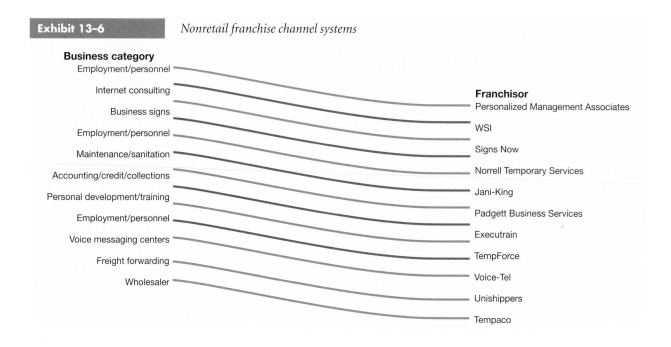

fair share of the dealers' attention to sales and service opportunities. Kawasaki decided to use its dealer Web site as a key sales support tool and means of communicating with its dealers. The dealer Web site, which draws 16,000 hits per month, has allowed dealers to earn commission from additional sales without having to stock extra parts. Most dealers have limited storage space, and the elimination of inventory carrying costs is a big plus to the dealers. In this instance, Kawasaki's savvy use of technology has helped the company administer its marketing channel.[9]

In the retail sector, successful administered marketing channels include General Electric and Rolex. Both companies have reputations for quality products backed by highly effective marketing plans and activities. As a result, retailers are usually quite receptive to suggestions made by General Electric and Rolex for pricing and display practices.

Managing Marketing Channels

The management of marketing channels requires decision making and action in the six areas shown in Exhibit 13–7. First the firm formulates its marketing objectives and strategy. Only then can managers develop marketing channel strategies and objectives. Various channel alternatives are then evaluated to determine capabilities, costs, compatibility with other marketing variables, and their availability to the firm. Next the firm establishes its channel structure and implements the channel strategy. Finally, the firm must constantly evaluate channel performance, which may lead to adjustment in one or more of the other five management areas shown in the exhibit.

Formulate Marketing Objectives and Strategy

Marketing channels often represent a significant dollar investment, and established channels can be difficult to change without risking lost sales volume. As a result, it is imperative that a firm develop marketing channel objectives and strategy only after formulating its overall marketing objectives and strategy.

Lexus by Toyota has become one of the biggest success stories in the luxury car market by positioning the exclusivity of the brand. The Lexus marketing strategy called for extending the marketing channel beyond existing Toyota dealers to a relatively small number of selected Lexus dealerships. With less competition between dealers, maintaining higher prices to support the exclusive image is not as problematic as when a geographic market is flooded with competing dealers. Higher prices mean higher profit margins, which makes it possible for dealers to provide exceptional service to their customers, an

Exhibit 13–7   *Managing marketing channels*

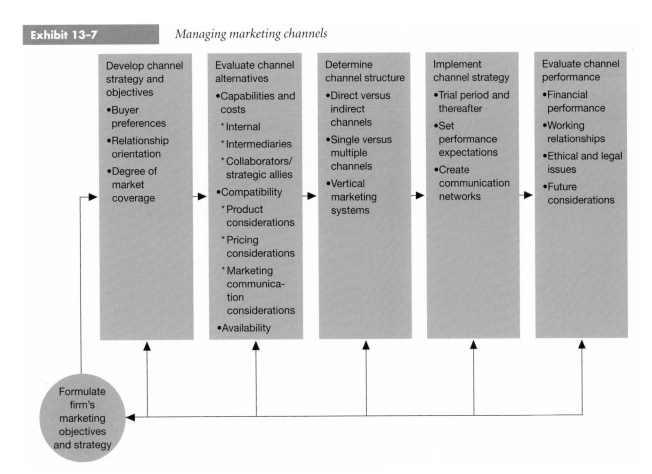

objective that is also compatible with the overall marketing strategy. By ensuring that other marketing mix variables are compatible with the chosen marketing channel and that the entire mix is compatible with the exclusive image of the product, Lexus has become a huge success as the top-selling luxury car line in the United States. It is interesting to note that channel strategy was conceived by Lexus executives as a key ingredient in overall marketing strategy from the very beginning. In a document titled "The Lexus Covenant," the importance of channel strategy is noted: "Lexus will win the race because Lexus will do right from the start. Lexus will have the finest dealer network in the country."[10]

Develop Channel Objectives and Strategy

Channel objectives should be specifically stated, measurable, and consistent with the firm's marketing objectives. Objectives are often stated in terms of sales volume, profitability, market share, costs, number of wholesale or retail outlets, or geographic expansion. **Channel strategy** is an expression of a general action plan and guidelines for allocating resources to achieve the channel objectives.

The development of channel strategy involves decisions in three key areas: buyer preferences, relationship orientation, and the degree of market coverage.

BUYER PREFERENCES   Buyer preferences are important in determining channel strategy. Understanding the logic behind letting customers buy the way they want to is a hallmark of both established marketing leaders and entrepreneurs who beat the odds by breaking into long-established markets. Sellers of thousands of products, most notably books, recorded music, computers, and financial investments, have found that millions of consumers worldwide prefer to buy online. Sellers of these products who did not fully appreciate buyer preferences are now playing catch-up.

Ignoring buyer preferences is contrary to any sort of rational marketing thinking. Nonetheless, industry leaders sometimes have to be prodded into action only after more opportunistic marketers have tapped the market via a new channel. For example, Dell, then Gateway, developed the direct-to-customer market for computers. Reluctantly, IBM, Hewlett-Packard, and others followed years later. E*Trade pioneered online brokerages, a move resisted by Merrill Lynch and other traditional brokerage houses. Amazon.com built the market for online book purchasing, while small independent stores and large chains such as Barnes & Noble were slow to react. If a company does not pay attention to the channels preferred by the customer, the risk of competition from new entries into the market is indeed a real threat.

RELATIONSHIP ORIENTATION Most successful organizations try to establish strong relationships with others in their channel—not only because it is profitable in the long run, but also because they believe that to do otherwise would be risky. Recall from Chapter 5 that a relationship orientation between buyers and sellers is a major trend, and that negotiations between parties often seek an outcome whereby both can win. This is the case with antivirus vendor McAfee, formerly Network Associates. McAfee had been criticized by some of its resellers for selling directly to end users rather than through the reseller channel. McAfee revamped its channels program, pledging to sell only through resellers except on large sales, where a direct sale better serves the end user. The company also set up 10 technical training centers to provide training for resellers and set up a channel partner advisory board to enhance the working relationship between McAfee and its resellers."[11] For an example of how strong relationships in the channel can build value for both buyers and sellers, see "Creating Customer Value: SAP Rolls Out New Channel Support Program."

Hanoch Eiron, channels manager in a software division of Hewlett-Packard, comments on the importance of manufacturers working with others in the channel: "Good working relationships with channel intermediaries are absolutely essential for success. Manufacturers should view their wholesalers and retailers as extensions of their companies, and use a team approach to maximize channel performance. This is sometimes difficult because these intermediaries sell competing manufacturers' brands. It is necessary that a manufacturer's objectives are compatible with those of the intermediary, and that there is a strong commitment to work together toward common objectives."

DEGREE OF MARKET COVERAGE **Market coverage** has to do with the number of outlets used to market a product. Market coverage commonly takes one of three forms: intensive, selective, or exclusive distribution. With **intensive distribution,** the product or service is distributed through every available outlet. For example, PepsiCo has long used intensive distribution with its soft drinks, selling through all sorts of retail stores, vending machines, restaurants, and concessionaires. Pepsi is now competing aggressively with Coke to intensify its sales to restaurants, theaters, sports arenas, and schools in the fountain sales category.

   Selective distribution involves selling a product in only some of the available outlets. This is commonly used when after-the-sale service is necessary, as with home appliances. Maytag, for example, sells appliances via selective distribution, and the company is even more selective in designating certain dealers as authorized service centers. In a metropolitan area of a million residents, Maytag products might be sold through a dozen retail

CREATING CUSTOMER VALUE

SAP rolls out new channel support program

SAP, based in Germany, is one of the leading software firms in the world. With its new channel program, named the SAP Partner-Edge Channel Program, SAP is making an aggressive move to increase sales to midsize customers served by resellers. The program will utilize the latest technology to offer reseller support by telephone and an online network to facilitate collaboration between resellers and SAP. In a move enthusiastically supported by hundreds of resellers, SAP resellers will receive financial incentives for sales transactions, but also for desirable activities that add value over a longer time span. These value-building activities include training technical staff, earning certifications, scoring well on customer satisfaction measures, and completing market studies. This approach is intended to build a bond between SAP and its resellers that transcends making money when something is sold. By working strategically to build value for end users, SAP and its resellers intend to make their offering less of a commodity and more of a complete software solution backed by expertise at the manufacturer and reseller levels.

The benefits of a relationship perspective can extend beyond economic advantage to the promotion of socially desirable results. General Motors is among the leading companies working to develop business relationships with minority-owned suppliers.

stores, only two or three of which are designated as authorized service centers.

Exclusive distribution occurs when only one outlet is used in a geographic marketplace. In contrast to home electronics producers like Sony, which use intensive distribution, high-end audiophile equipment manufacturers typically use exclusive distribution. Such manufacturers include Marantz, McIntosh, NAD, and Manley Labs.

The Internet offers a convenient way to use exclusive distribution for selected products on a limited time basis. IBM and Procter & Gamble have used the Internet in this fashion, and music artists often offer concert tickets and recorded music on an Internet-only basis for limited periods. Consumer goods companies also use exclusive distribution to offer retailers different versions of products, so that each competing retailer has exclusive rights to a particular model or brand. For example, Levi Strauss offers its low-priced Signature line of jeans for men, women, and children exclusively to Wal-Mart.[12]

Evaluate Channel Alternatives

As shown in Exhibit 13–7, the evaluation of channel alternatives requires analysis in three related channel areas: capabilities and costs, channel compatibility with other marketing variables, and availability.

CHANNEL CAPABILITIES AND COSTS Marketers must determine exactly who will perform the various channel activities and at what cost. Establishing marketing channels can be expensive and difficult to reverse, so firms should carefully assess the costs and capabilities of each channel alternative.

The evaluation of channel alternatives often begins with an assessment of how the firm's internal resources might be used to accomplish channel activities. This naturally leads to subsequent examination of how intermediaries could fit in, if at all.

In the travel market, airlines and rental car companies have been through this evaluation in recent years, resulting in widespread elimination of commissions for travel agents. With travel information so widely available through airline and rental car Web sites, the need for travel agents to book routine trips has been greatly reduced. Customers who wish to use travel agents typically pay an additional fee rather than the carrier paying a commission to compensate the travel agent. Among the airlines leading the movement to eliminate travel agent commissions are JetBlue, Southwest, and Independence Air.[13]

The analysis of channel capabilities and costs sometimes leads companies to jointly market a product. For example, PepsiCo distributes Starbucks Frappuccino to grocery stores, and Dreyer's Ice Cream distributes Starbucks ice cream. In a similar arrangement, Coca-Cola Company distributes the French-based Groupe Danone SA's Evian mineral water in the United States.[14]

In the wake of the shakeout among Internet retailers, channel partnerships among Web-based marketers have become commonplace. Some Internet marketers have found it more efficient and effective to partner with Internet marketing specialists rather than approach the online channel on their own. Amazon.com, through its international Amazon.comAssociates program, now serves as a link for 600,000 vendors that sell a huge assortment of goods ranging from toys and games to tools and hardware.[15]

CHANNEL COMPATIBILITY   Channel alternatives need to be compatible with other marketing variables affecting a firm's offering, including product, pricing, and marketing communications factors. For example, product perishability, consumer sensitivity to

Thinking Critically

Rebecca Wetzel has just been appointed to a newly created position, manager of retail dealer development for HomeRight, a major home appliance company. She is responsible for providing training for retail salespeople and advice to dealers in the areas of merchandising, store promotions, and advertising. In the past, the HomeRight sales force had provided these support activities to the retail dealers. In her first few weeks on the job, Rebecca visited several dealers in different markets and found that the retail support provided by the sales force had been inconsistent—good in some cases, bad in others.

- What should Rebecca do within her own company to begin building a solid retail support program?

- To maximize dealer support and increase sales, what suggestions can you make to Rebecca for getting input from HomeRight dealers?

purchase price, and the nature of point-of-sale promotion could affect the compatibility of a particular marketing channel. The point-of-sale environment has been crucial to the success of Ecko Unlimited's Mark Ecko Collection. The core market for Ecko is a younger urban consumer who identifies with skateboarding and hip-hop music. The company's founder, Mark Ecko, recalls that FUBU, his key competitor, began selling to JCPenney and Foot Locker, a move that Ecko thought was incompatible with an urban lifestyle brand. Instead, Ecko wanted more control over the immediate sales environment—10 feet from the customer. Ecko opened some of its own stores and worked with other retailers to create a selling environment that contrasted sharply with the standardized environments of JCPenney and Foot Locker. According to Mark Ecko, "Staying out of those distribution channels was the smartest thing I ever did."[16]

PRODUCT CONSIDERATIONS   A product-related consideration is the product's desired image. Consider the case of OshKosh B'Gosh Inc. Oshkosh, a maker of children's clothing, traditionally relied on expensive department stores and specialty stores for retail distribution, in keeping with its high-quality image. When OshKosh expanded into Sears and JCPenney stores, the company was concerned that such a move would affect its image and, subsequently, sales in upscale department stores where image is important.

OshKosh hoped to avoid problems with the upscale department stores by offering them exclusive, higher-profit items such as a novelty denim line. OshKosh was trying to minimize a possible product/channel incompatibility by differentiating its product offerings to two different types of retail customers.

PRICING CONSIDERATIONS   Which marketing channels are appropriate can also depend on pricing strategies and tactics. The recorded music industry is facing a tough dilemma in matching the price of its number one seller, the compact disk, to its channels. Traditionally, recorded music has been sold through music stores, general discounters such as Wal-Mart, and home electronics and entertainment stores such as Best Buy. The problem is that list prices for CDs are often too high for the average consumer, who increasingly is downloading digital versions of songs, borrowing copies and reproducing them at home, or simply cutting back on purchases. Most music industry analysts believe that music companies must offer lower-priced formats and tap less expensive channels, such as electronic distribution, to avoid a continuing downward sales spiral with younger generations.[17]

MARKETING COMMUNICATION CONSIDERATIONS   Compatibility with marketing communication plans and strategies also determines the suitability of various marketing channels. Sony, in an attempt to showcase its full product line better, supplements its independent dealer network with its own Sony Gallery and Song Style stores in Chicago, New York, and San Francisco. Reebok now sells directly to colleges and high schools while continuing to sell through its traditional retail channel. Reebok took this action to address a lack of representation among American basketball players, a market dominated by Nike.

AVAILABILITY   Another important issue in the evaluation of various channel alternatives is whether the channel is available under reasonable conditions. Quite often, new companies may have a hard time establishing an appropriate marketing channel. The right channel may simply be unavailable, or the desired channel is too expensive.

For large, powerful sellers, channel availability is less of a problem. Indeed, a firm with the financial wherewithal can simply purchase a channel of distribution. Such is the case with AutoNation, the largest automotive retailer in the United States. Republic Industries, a waste management company, diversified into the automobile business, acquiring most of the 370 dealerships now operating as part of AutoNation.[18]

Determine Channel Structure

The fourth phase of managing marketing channels shown in Exhibit 13–7 is to determine channel structure. The major decisions here concern whether to use direct or indirect channels, a single channel or multiple channels, or one of the many forms of vertical marketing systems. Firms often mix direct and indirect channels, and many firms use multiple channels, especially to reach new markets.

Implement Channel Strategy

The first four phases of managing marketing channels concentrate on planning the appropriate channel strategy and structure. The task now is to implement channel strategy. The full-scale implementation of a new channel strategy is often preceded by a trial period. Other important implementation tasks include setting performance expectations and creating communication networks.

Some companies join forces to move products through marketing channels. Coca-Cola distributes Evian mineral water, a product from France, in the United States.

RUN A TRIAL PERIOD   The results of a trial period may indicate that a change is warranted, or just the opposite—that an existing strategy should stay in effect. Trial periods helped convince DVD marketers that additional channels would be beneficial. One additional channel for DVDs emerging successfully from a trial period is McDonald's, where customers can pick up current movies from ATM-like rental vending machines.[19] In other cases, trial periods convince the company to stick with existing channels. For example, Tupperware stopped selling its kitchenware to Target when existing party-plan distributors opposed the move.[20]

SET PERFORMANCE EXPECTATIONS   As marketing channel members have become more interdependent, the setting of performance expectations has evolved into more of a joint decision process, rather than one party's dictating standards to another. Sun Microsystems, in an attempt to clarify performance expectations for its resellers, uses a program called iForce Grow America Tour. The program provides a joint opportunity for Sun sales management executives and resellers to meet in cities across the country so they can devise better ways of collaborating to increase sales. Recent feedback from resellers indicates that Sun needs to do a better job supporting resellers' marketing efforts, especially using Sun's salespeople to bolster the sales efforts of reseller salespeople.[21]

Lack of agreement on performance standards could indicate that some other channel arrangement might be appropriate. If a channel is set up without advance agreement on performance standards, evaluation of channel performance becomes much more difficult.

To supplement the efforts of its independent dealer network, Sony uses its Sony Style stores to showcase new products.

Thinking Critically

For the past three months, Ted Lucas had been trying to set up a business relationship with Williams Supply, an automobile repair parts wholesaler. The owner, Mr. Williams, had been promising Ted that he would begin stocking some of Ted's products, but he would never make a commitment. After another failed attempt to set up Williams as a wholesaler, Ted made several sales calls on Williams's customers to see if he could convince them to buy from one of Ted's current wholesalers. Several of Williams's customers indicated they would be glad to switch their business, especially because Ted was offering a special price deal for new business through his current wholesaler. When Mr. Williams learned what had happened, he angrily told Ted that any chance of their doing business together was lost forever.

- Ted used coercive power in this situation. Was it justified?
- Assuming that Ted wants to resume his efforts to sell through Williams Supply, what should he do next?

CREATE COMMUNICATION NETWORKS Another crucial aspect of channel strategy implementation is to establish communication networks among channel members. Sophisticated computer and communication technologies have greatly enhanced the capabilities of channel members to share important information on a timely basis, maintain goodwill, and solve problems in the mutual interest of channel members. The importance of ensuring adequate communication in the marketing channel is seen in the case of IBM across multiple channels in computer hardware, data storage, consulting services, and software markets. IBM channel partners (resellers) account for a third of the company's sales, and IBM dedicates 6,400 employees and an annual budget of $2.5 billion to its channel programs. As a result of its efforts, IBM has been recognized as the number one "Channel Champion" by *CRN* magazine.[22] IBM's resellers give the company high marks for understanding their needs and providing consistent communication to its resellers.

Evaluate Channel Performance

The evaluation of channel performance, the last area in Exhibit 13–7, can necessitate changes in any of the other decision areas. Evaluating marketing channels requires attention to four key areas: financial performance, working relationships with other channel members, ethical and legal issues, and future plans.

FINANCIAL EVALUATION For the short run, channel members may be willing to operate at low levels of financial performance. Over time, however, financial results must be positive to sustain relationships in the channel.

An interesting example here involves Procter & Gamble. After years of offering significant discounts and costly promotions to retailers in the grocery trade, P&G concluded its marketing channel was too expensive. One step the company took was to drastically reduce discounts and other trade promotions. This angered some of P&G's retailer customers, but some analysts think the company was deliberately shifting some of its distribution from grocery stores to discount stores, where the everyday-low-price policy is more welcome.

EVALUATE WORKING RELATIONSHIPS Three related concepts—power, conflict, and cooperation—are important in evaluation of working relationships among channel members. A firm may gain power in a variety of ways and use it to enhance its position in the marketing channel. Conflict among channel members is natural and sometimes constructive, but it can become destructive if it rages out of control. As power is wielded and conflicts ensue, channel members often find cooperation is essential if they are to flourish and survive.

CHANNEL POWER Channel members may gain **channel power** in many ways.[23] For example, a giant retailer like Home Depot offers vendors the opportunity to sell their products in more than 1,400 stores in the United States. In effect, Home Depot is in a position to use **reward power** when it agrees to buy from a vendor—the reward being widespread distribution and the high probability of large sales volumes. Other examples of reward power might be a manufacturer's granting exclusive distribution rights to a wholesaler, offering special credit terms to deserving customers, or extending lenient returned-goods policies.

Another form of power is **legitimate power,** which lies in ownership or contractual agreements. Holiday Inn has a certain amount of legitimate power over its franchisees through contractual agreements, for example, and Polo controls one of its channels by ownership of its retail stores.

Power developed through the accumulation of expertise and knowledge is called **expert power.** Large retailers have gained a tremendous amount of expert power using point-of-sale scanners to gauge product movements, price sensitivities, and trade promotion effectiveness. In fact, retailers can know more about how manufacturers' products are doing in the marketplace than do the manufacturers. This expertise gives large retailers more power to negotiate favorably with their suppliers.

Some companies have achieved the status of channel leaders because of their expertise in marketing. Foot Locker is a channel leader in the athletic footwear market.

Power based on the desire of one channel member to be associated with another channel member is called **referent power.** For example, a jewelry store may wish to be selected as an exclusive dealer for Rolex watches. The store's desire would put Rolex in a powerful position with such a retailer.

Another form of power sometimes seen in channel relationships is **coercive power.** A manufacturer that threatens to cut off a distributor's credit unless the distributor pays its bills more promptly exemplifies coercive power. The use of coercive power can become abusive and even illegal. For instance, a distributor's coercing a manufacturer into dropping a competing distributor might be ruled a conspiracy in restraint of trade, a violation of federal antitrust legislation. Another example involves Coca-Cola and its bottlers in Mexico, where the antitrust commission found they had abused their market power. Coke was ordered to suspend certain marketing and sales practices, including illegally preventing small independent retailers from selling rival products.[24]

All channel members must develop some sort of power to survive. Some may build enough power to act as a **channel leader**—that is, a channel member with enough power to control others in the channel. Current channel leaders include Wal-Mart, Kroger, General Electric, and Foot Locker. Foot Locker has 3,600 stores with plans to open another 1,000 in the coming years. Foot Locker uses its size to its advantage, negotiating to get the hottest products from Nike and Reebok earlier and at lower costs than its competitors. Large, successful organizations can gain buying power and selling power by controlling economic assets and resources, but smaller companies can also build power, especially by developing knowledge and expertise to gain expert power. Before it became a huge company, Foot Locker built its power base by becoming adept at mixing athletic shoes with clothing, something it does better than its competitors.

CHANNEL CONFLICT   It is inevitable that channel members experience conflict with one another. **Channel conflict** may result from poor communications, a struggle over power in the channel, or incompatible objectives. For example, some apparel manufacturers and department stores are involved in a major conflict over pricing and markdown practices. For years, some suppliers have guaranteed retailers specified profit margins on clothing during the markdown periods. These suppliers are now fighting back, saying they were forced to guarantee profit margins or lose the business. Certain suppliers, including Nicole Miller, have refused to do business with retailers who make such demands. Other suppliers have claimed that meeting the retailers' demands could threaten their ability to stay in business. The conflict has escalated into a legal battle, and

Exhibit 13–8			*Examples of channel conflict*
Who Is Upset?	**With Whom?**	**Why?**	**Consequences**
Tommy Hilfiger	Wal-Mart	Wal-Mart's sale of imitation Hilfiger clothing	Wal-Mart is fined and ordered (by federal court) to cease
Bayer	Rite Aid drugstores	Unauthorized deductions from invoices	Reduced profits for Bayer
Auto dealers	General Motors	Use of dealer money for national advertising	Lawsuit against GM
Music distributors	Music retailers	Sale of used CDs cuts sales of new CDs, deprives artists of royalties	Sony, Warner Music, and others halted co-op advertising allowances to retailers that sell used CDs

the Securities and Exchange Commission is looking into how markdown practices have impacted retailers' stated earnings.[25] Exhibit 13–8 provides several examples of routine channel conflict.

Channel conflict is commonplace in a competitive market where profitability is a requirement for survival, pointing up the importance of cooperation in resolving conflict to avoid senseless disagreements that can drain channel members' resources.

CHANNEL COOPERATION   **Channel cooperation** can help reduce the amount of conflict and resolve conflicts once they occur.

The incentive to cooperate with other channel members is clearly strongest if all parties agree on their functional roles, and if agreement on performance standards has been reached prior to or early in the business relationship. When channel members do not agree on these matters, conflicts may be settled according to where the power lies. But conflicts settled only by the exercise of power often resurface, especially if the loser in the prior conflict gains an edge in the power dimension. As we suggest frequently in this book, more and more companies are embracing cooperation and building relationships as a superior way to ensure lasting market strength.

ETHICAL AND LEGAL ISSUES   The management of marketing channels calls attention to a number of ethical and legal issues, some of which are illustrated in Exhibit 13–9. Certainly, some channel conflicts have ethical and legal implications. And strange as it might sound, cooperation taken to the extreme may also present problems, especially if agreements between channel members violate the key laws affecting marketing dis-

Exhibit 13–9	*Examples of ethical and legal problems in marketing channels*
Situation	**Ethical/Legal Problem**
Large retailer threatens to stop buying unless supplier grants unreasonably low prices.	Unfair use of coercive power (unethical).
Powerful producer of consumer goods dictates how its products will be displayed without regard for space constraints in smaller stores.	Unfair use of coercive power (unethical).
Large wholesaler demands that the supplier replace its male sales rep with a female because the purchasing agent does not like to deal with men.	Unfair use of coercive power (unethical, potentially illegal).
Desperate to sign up new franchises, franchisor's sales rep downplays financial risk of owning franchise.	Deceptive communications (unethical, potentially illegal).
Wholesaler requests that supplier stop selling to competing wholesaler; supplier grants request.	Excessive cooperation among channel members (illegal).
Two manufacturing companies agree not to sell to a particular wholesaler in an effort to damage the wholesaler's business.	Excessive cooperation among channel members (illegal).
Salesperson agrees to give retailer a lower price than competing retailers, based solely on friendship.	Excessive cooperation among channel members (illegal).

cussed in Chapter 2. There are opportunities for channel members to work together on programs for the benefit of society and further their businesses at the same time. For an example of such a program, see "Acting Ethically: Tom's of Maine Melds Idealistic Values with Mass Marketing."

Because of the range of marketing activities that occur within any marketing channel, the potentially relevant legal issues for channels are numerous. Laws about pricing, product liability, and truth in advertising are a few examples of thousands of international, federal, state, and local regulations that might pertain to a given channel situation. Our discussion here focuses on the legal environment as it affects channel structure and selected buyer–seller interactions.

Producers may want to set up channel arrangements to ensure their products are given substantial market support by either wholesalers or retailers. One producer might wish to set up **exclusive territories** so that no other reseller in a given geographic area sells a particular brand of a product. Another might enact **exclusive dealing agreements,** which would restrict a reseller from carrying a competing product line.

Another possibility is **tying contracts,** which require a reseller to buy products besides the one it really wants to buy. For example, a copier manufacturer may also require a customer to buy ink cartridges on the grounds that the printer can reach acceptable performance standards only if the specified cartridge is used.

Exclusive territories, exclusive dealing agreements, and tying contracts are legally acceptable unless they have anticompetitive effects or tend to create monopolies. A substantial reduction in competition through such arrangements is a violation of federal or state antitrust laws.

FUTURE CONSIDERATIONS   The final requirement in the evaluation of channel performance is to cast an eye to the future. Essentially, the firm should ask itself one key question: How well can this channel be expected to perform in the future? The answers can have far-reaching implications as marketers make necessary changes in pursuit of their long-term goals.

Sometimes customers drive changes in channels, as we have seen with e-commerce in both consumer and business markets. In other cases, working relationships between channel members or a company's financial situation may suggest that a change is in order. For example, candymaker Hershey Foods was not satisfied with the return on some of its brands. Hershey was getting 35 percent of its sales from its top three brands, while key competitor Mars was getting 67 percent of its sales from its top three brands. This led Hershey to reevaluate all aspects of its marketing, and eventually the company began marketing aggressively through convenience stores, previously a minor channel.[26]

Changing marketing channels is a major undertaking, and companies do not change if they are convinced the tried-and-true channel will get the job done. In the current environment characterized by changing consumer preferences, intense competition, and information technology innovation, expect more companies to alter their channels.

ACTING ETHICALLY

Tom's of Maine melds idealistic values with mass marketing

Tom's of Maine, a manufacturer of all-natural toothpaste and other natural products, is successful at retailing in both small chains such as Wild Oats and huge chains like Wal-Mart and Rite Aid. Throughout its history, Tom's has been recognized not only for savvy marketing, but also for its ethical business approach. The company donates 10 percent of its pretax profits to charity and pays its Maine manufacturing employees approximately 15 percent higher than the local wage rate for comparable work.

Tom's of Maine sponsors a program called Common Good Partnerships, which builds promotional programs with retailers to support social and environmental causes. For example, one partnership with Brooks Pharmacy, a chain in New England, sought to improve children's oral health through grants to dental clinics. Tom's achieved its community-focused objectives while more than doubling its sales through Brooks Pharmacy. Tom's of Maine clearly demonstrates that an ethical approach can definitely be good for your business—and your customer's business.

Summary

1. **Explain the functions and key activities of marketing channels.** A marketing channel, sometimes referred to as a *channel of distribution,* is a combination of organizations that perform the activities required to link producers to users to accomplish particular marketing objectives.

   The primary goal of a marketing channel is to allow companies to reach their customers with the right product at the right time, to meet customer expectations, and to stimulate profitable sales volume. The key functions of marketing channels are marketing communications, inventory management, physical distribution, market feedback, and the assumption of financial risk.

2. **Discuss the role of intermediaries in marketing channels.** Intermediaries, often called *middlemen,* provide key marketing channel functions. To survive in the economic system, an intermediary must perform its particular functions more efficiently than any other channel member.

3. **Distinguish between direct and indirect marketing channels.** Direct marketing channels use no intermediaries to move products from producers to end users. Indirect marketing channels use at least one intermediary before the product reaches its final destination. Despite the dramatic growth of direct marketing channels, most products reach ultimate consumers through indirect marketing channels.

4. **Illustrate how some firms use multiple channels successfully.** As markets become increasingly specialized and companies seek to globalize their marketing efforts, the use of multiple channels is growing. Several examples of companies using multiple channels were presented in the chapter.

5. **See how marketing channel decisions are related to other key marketing decision variables.** Marketing channel strategies and objectives must be based on a firm's overall marketing strategies and objectives. After a channel strategy has been developed, different channel alternatives can be evaluated for capabilities, costs, and availability. Channel alternatives can also be evaluated for compatibility with product, pricing, and marketing communication variables.

6. **Understand how power, conflict, and cooperation affect the operation of a marketing channel.** Channel members develop power based on such factors as economic strength or market knowledge. In some instances, this power may be abused, leading to conflict between channel members.

   Conflict can also result from poor communication or incompatible goals among channel members. It is becoming increasingly necessary that channel members cooperate to resolve conflict and pursue mutually beneficial goals.

7. **Give examples of ethical and legal issues encountered in the operations of marketing channels.** The unfair use of power can raise ethical concerns. For example, a large buyer might try to force a small supplier to grant unreasonably low prices as a condition for continuing to be a supplier.

   If taken to the extreme, cooperation between channel members can be a violation of the law, as competition may be unfairly constrained. Certain arrangements between channel members may violate antitrust laws if they reduce competition. Exclusive territories, exclusive dealing agreements, and tying contracts are examples of potentially illegal channel arrangements.

Understanding Marketing Terms and Concepts

Thinking about Marketing

1. What are the key activities performed in a marketing channel?

2. How do indirect marketing channels differ from direct marketing channels? How do intermediaries contribute to marketing channels?

3. Explain the concepts of forward and backward integration.

4. How do franchisees and franchisors work together in a franchise system?

5. Review "Creating Customer Value: SAP Rolls Out New Channel Support Program." Citing specific points in the boxed insert to support your answer, what type or types of power did SAP use to support its dealers?

6. Describe the varying degrees of market coverage—intensive distribution, exclusive distribu-

tion, and selective distribution—and give examples of each.

7. Channels must be compatible with the other elements of the marketing mix. Give examples that reflect compatibility between channels and product, pricing, and marketing communication considerations.

8. How might channel members build their power bases relative to other members of the channel?

9. Review "Acting Ethically: Tom's of Maine Melds Idealistic Values with Mass Marketing." How can socially responsible programs between channel members be good for business?

10. How can poor communication, abuse of power, and too much cooperation in marketing channels create ethical and legal problems?

Applying Marketing Skills

1. Discuss the advantages and disadvantages to the consumer of buying these products in alternative channels as opposed to grocery stores:

Product	Alternative Channel
Citrus fruit	Farmers' market
Rib-eye steaks	Specialty meat market
Milk	Home delivery
Popcorn	Movie theater
Bottled soft drink	Vending machine

2. Assume you own the concession rights for the New York Yankees's home baseball games. What factors should you consider and what specific information would you need in deciding whether to buy soft

drink cups from a local distributor, who buys the cups from a Taiwanese manufacturer, or directly from the manufacturer?

3. Beth Norman is a sales rep for a leading manufacturer of commercial air-conditioning systems. She currently sells to three distributors in Dallas, who in turn sell exclusively to building contractors. One of Beth's distributors, Maverick Supply Company, has produced disappointing sales results for Beth during the past six months. Upon investigation, Beth discovered that Maverick bought heavily from one of her chief competitors. How might Beth use the five power bases discussed in this chapter to regain her lost position with Maverick?

Using the www in Marketing

Activity One As explained in the chapter opener, Timbuk2 sells primarily through specialty retailers such as Apple retail stores and Eastern Mountain Sports (EMS). Timbuk2 also sells through online retailers such as ebags (www.ebags.com) and onlineshoes (www.onlineshoes.com). Examine these online retailers and the Timbuk2 Web site at www.timbuk2.com and answer these questions:

1. Do you think the images and operations of the online retailers are compatible with the brand image of Timbuk2? Why or why not?

2. Compare the two online retailers' Web sites. Which offers a better shopping experience for Timbuk2

customers? How could both sites be improved to better feature Timbuk2?

3. After reviewing the Timbuk2 home page, cite examples of how the company supports its marketing channel through marketing communications, specifically by sponsoring events that generate favorable publicity for the Timbuk2 brand. You should click on the press and events links on the home page to answer this question.

Activity Two Visit the Rite Aid Web site at www.riteaid.com. As a major drugstore chain, Rite Aid depends on hundreds of suppliers. From the site map, locate the Our Company link, then explore the supplier-related links such as How to Become a Supplier and EDI/EC. Now answer the following questions:

1. What evidence can you find that Rite Aid might be a channel leader? Which types of channel power (reward, legitimate, expert, referent, and coercive) does Rite Aid use in dealing with its suppliers?

2. What criteria does Rite Aid use in selecting suppliers? How do these criteria relate to improving value for Rite Aid's retail customers?

3. How important is it for Rite Aid's suppliers to be technologically competent in managing the flow of products to Rite Aid?

Making Marketing Decisions

Case 13–1 Will CarMax Revolutionize Used Car Channels?

Consumer dissatisfaction is the driving force behind a revolution in the automobile industry. Consumers enjoy having a new automobile, but they hate the buying experience. This is especially true in the used car market, where sales practices are so bad that jokes and even movies ridicule dealers. Enter CarMax, a creation of electronics giant Circuit City.

In direct contrast to most used car dealers, CarMax offers a huge inventory, a pleasant showroom, a food court, a children's play area, low-pressure salespeople, and no-haggle pricing. Customers can use computer kiosks to search for the right vehicle, and CarMax backs its vehicles with a five-day, 500-mile money-back guarantee.

Increasingly, consumers are turning to the Internet for both new and used car purchases. While state franchise laws make it practically impossible for manufacturers to sell directly to consumers, the major manufacturers have set up Web sites to facilitate sales through their dealers. Third-party online car companies, including MSN Autos, have become a much larger factor in the market.

Used car sellers are also feeling the competitive pressure from new car dealers. Generous lease deals are attracting some customers who might typically buy used cars. These lease deals also keep a huge number of late-model autos in the market, which helps keep prices down.

CarMax was one of the first companies to see the opportunity for a new marketing channel in the used car market. The company realized that consumers had gotten used to better shopping experiences—on the Internet and through other venues—for most products and services

that exist in superstores, shopping malls, and catalogs. In recent years, mass-market distribution for everything from home electronics to vacation packages had brought prices down. Consumers are more demanding that prices be as low as possible, but they expect great selection and service. In short, they have discovered that they can get what they want at a reasonable price, with retailers such as Nordstrom and online bookseller Amazon.com becoming the new standard. Auto industry analysts believe that these same consumers will shape the future of used car marketing channels.

CarMax has attracted a lot of attention, some of which translates into competitive activity. Local used car dealers have responded by improving service and taking advantage of CarMax's no-haggle policy to undercut prices. Analysts predict more CarMax outlets in the future, and they expect the company to become even more price competitive with other dealers. Poised for more growth, CarMax executives like to point out that 93 percent of the company's customers say they would recommend its stores to friends.

Questions

1. What marketplace conditions led to the emergence of CarMax?

2. What are the biggest threats facing CarMax as it attempts to become the preferred outlet for used automobiles? How can the company address these threats?

3. How can independent, local used car dealers respond to CarMax and other used car chains?

Case 13–2 Caterpillar's Channels Span the Globe

 Caterpillar is well positioned to further strengthen its reputation as a worldwide leader in the construction and mining equipment industry. The company has more than held its own against Japanese rivals Hitachi and Komatsu in recent years. Sales volume is strong,

primarily due to close relationships with its dealers in 200 countries. This is consistent with Caterpillar's Code of Worldwide Business Conduct, which identifies close, long-lasting relationships with dealers as a key priority.

Having parts and service readily available is important to Caterpillar customers, and the dealers play an important role in adding value after the sale. The typical Caterpillar dealer stocks 40,000 to 50,000 parts and has a huge investment in warehouses, fleets of trucks, service bays, highly trained technicians, and service equipment. Many provide around-the-clock service.

Caterpillar supports its dealers in several ways. Caterpillar rejects the notion of selling directly to end users with three exceptions: newly opened markets of formerly socialist countries, original equipment manufacturers, and the U.S. government. Even in these cases, dealers provide most of the after-sales service and support.

Caterpillar also supports its dealers by providing financing on equipment purchased and offering programs on inventory control, equipment management, and maintenance programs. Additional support is available to dealers in quality management and continuous improvement, training on a wide variety of topics, and localized marketing programs.

Cat is also encouraging its dealers to open Cat-branded rental stores and reduce the amount of inventory held at the dealer level. Though both of these moves will hurt Cat's short-run profits, it will strengthen the dealers' competitiveness. In the long run Cat should benefit from these tactics. Caterpillar dealers operate more than 1,400 branch locations and in excess of 600 Cat rental stores. Cat features a worldwide dealer locator service on its Web site and introduces visitors to rental stores via Web storefronts.

Another important element in the management of Caterpillar's marketing channel is a comprehensive communication program. To communicate effectively, it is imperative that mutual trust exist between Caterpillar and its dealers. Trust is essential because of the sensitive nature of some of the information that is exchanged, including financial data and strategic plans. Technology plays an important role in communications: dealer employees have real-time access to continually updated databases of service information, sales forecasts, and customer satisfaction surveys.

Communications are further enhanced by personal visits and other routine contacts between people at dealerships and all levels of Caterpillar. Top Caterpillar executives meet annually with key dealers at regional conferences to discuss sales goals for each product line and the activities necessary to achieve the goals.

Caterpillar management is candid in pointing out that relationships with dealers are not perfect. For example, problems arise over pricing policies and dealer service-territory boundaries. When conflicts do arise, the chances of a mutually agreeable resolution are high because Caterpillar and its dealers respect one another. By making its dealers its partners, Caterpillar has strengthened its position as a world leader in its industry and has positioned itself well for future success. Cat's dealer network is twice the size of those of its four major competitors, and it continues to widen the market share gap with Komatsu, its chief competitor. In a tough time for capital investment, Cat and its dealer network are setting the pace in heavy equipment.

Questions

1. What are the advantages to Caterpillar of using its dealer network rather than selling directly to equipment users?

2. Caterpillar sells directly to end users in just three cases: newly opened markets in formerly socialist countries, original equipment manufacturers, and the U.S. government. Why would Caterpillar sell direct in these situations? Some dealers might resent Caterpillar's selling direct in these situations; how might Caterpillar minimize any conflict?

3. How does Caterpillar contribute to its partnership with dealers? How do the dealers contribute?

Chapter Fourteen

RETAILING

14

After studying this chapter, you should be able to

1 Understand the economic importance of retailing and its role in the marketing channel.

2 Cite evidence of the globalization of retailing.

3 Discuss some of the advances in retailing technology.

4 Explain the reasons behind the growth of nonstore retailing.

5 Describe key factors in the retail marketing environment, and understand how they relate to retail strategy.

6 Cite important ethical and legal issues facing retailers.

Best Buy

Best Buy, the nation's largest seller of electronics, is doing what many retail analysts believe all retailers should do: Focus on certain types of customers and ignore the rest. For the chosen customers, Best Buy is creating more value by concentrating on their needs and preferences. For those not chosen, Best Buy would be happy if those customers took their business elsewhere.

Following this logic, Best Buy has implemented a customer-centric strategy that distinguishes customers as either "angels" or "devils." The angels account for the majority of Best Buy's profits and typically buy high-margin items at full price. The devils are bargain hunters, frequently return merchandise, and take up a high portion of customer service representatives' time. They are not profitable to Best Buy, and the company tries to discourage them from shopping at Best Buy by reducing price promotions and strictly enforcing its return policy.

Among the desirable angels set, Best Buy identifies five groups: upper-income men, small business owners, suburban mothers, technology

enthusiasts, and young family men. The strategy is for each store to analyze its local market, then focus on two of these groups. In the 85 stores where this has been tried, average sales per store gained 8 percent over the prior year, compared to an overall gain of 2 percent in the "nonsegmented" stores. Best Buy is now totally committed to the new strategy and expects that all of its stores will adopt the customer-centric strategy by 2008.

Encouraged by the results of its new customer-centric strategy, Best Buy has announced an ambitious growth plan. It plans to increase from 673 stores in the United States to 1,000 and to increase its Future Shop stores in Canada from 145 to 200. It will also open additional Geek Squad stores, with plans to develop a national chain. In China, Best Buy will open "lab stores" with an eye toward future expansion. By putting the customer at the focus of its efforts, Best Buy is outperforming other electronics retailers and also giving retailers in all sectors something to contemplate as the competition heats up.

Retailing, an important part of many marketing channels, includes all the activities involved in selling products and services to the ultimate, or final, consumer. This chapter explains the importance of retailing in the U.S. economy, discusses the functions retailers perform within the channel, and illustrates different types of retailers. Several trends in retailing are discussed: globalization, advances in technology, the focus on customer service, and nonstore retailing. We explore factors in the retail environment—both controllable and uncontrollable—that a firm must constantly monitor and coordinate to ensure a successful retail strategy. Finally, we examine some important ethical and legal issues in retailing.

The Role of Retailing

The role of retailing is to supply products and services directly to the final consumer. Retailers are differentiated from wholesalers according to the primary source of sales. **Retail sales** are sales to final consumers; **wholesale sales** are those to other businesses that in turn resell the product or service, or use it in running their own businesses. To be classified as a retailer, a firm's retail sales must equal or exceed 50 percent of its total revenues. Firms with less than 50 percent retail sales are classified as wholesalers. Wal-Mart was reminded of the distinction when its Sam's Wholesale Club was forced to change its name to Sam's Club in states in which its retail sales exceeded the 50 percent benchmark. Ultimately, the word *wholesale* was dropped from all Sam's Club store names.

Economic Importance

Retailing is a major force in the economy. Approximately 3 million retailers in operation in the United States employ 14 million people, about 10 percent of the total U.S. labor force. Retailers generate an astonishing $2.5 trillion in annual revenues. This translates into a $9,100 retail expenditure for every man, woman, and child in the United States.[1] Leading retailers are shown in Exhibit 14–1.

Retailing also includes a diverse range of **service retailers.** Service retailers include dry cleaners, photo developers, shoe repair shops, banks, fitness clubs, movie theaters, game arcades, rental businesses (automobiles, furniture, appliances, videos), tourist attractions, hotels and restaurants, automotive repair shops, and some providers of health care services. Spending for services has fueled increasing consumer spending growth rates, exceeding expenditures on products for quite some time.

Retailers' Uniqueness in the Channel

Retailers differ from other marketing channel members in that they handle smaller but more frequent customer transactions; they also provide assortments of products. A pleasant shopping environment is also more important in most forms of retailing than at other levels in the channel. Creation of a pleasant shopping atmosphere entails additional expense, which contributes to higher prices.

SELL SMALLER QUANTITIES MORE FREQUENTLY Retailers offer products in the sizes suitable and convenient for household consumption. Besides buying smaller sizes, most consumers buy products frequently because they lack sufficient storage space and funds to maintain large inventories of products. The average convenience store transaction is for only a few dollars, for example, but the average convenience store handles thousands of transactions per week.

PROVIDE ASSORTMENTS Retailers assemble assortments of products and services to sell. If retailers did not do so, shoppers would have to go to the bakery for bread, the butcher shop for meat, the dairy for milk, and the hardware store for light-

Exhibit 14–1	*Leading retailers*		
Company	Sales ($ millions)	Profits ($ millions)	Employees
1. Wal-Mart	288,189	10,267	1,600,000
2. Home Depot	73,094	5,001	325,000
3. Kroger	56,434	(128)	290,000
4. Target	49,934	3,198	300,000
5. Costco	48,107	882	82,150
6. Albertson's	40,052	444	241,000
7. Walgreens	37,508	1,360	140,000
8. Lowe's	36,464	2,176	139,678
9. Sears	36,099	(507)	247,000
10. Safeway	35,823	560	191,000

bulbs; a simple shopping trip could take hours to complete. By providing assortments, retailers offer the convenience of one-stop shopping for a variety of products and services. The typical supermarket carries 20,000 to 30,000 different items made by more than 500 different manufacturers.

An assortment of items seen by the customer as reasonable substitutes for each other is defined as a **category.** Discount retailers that offer a complete assortment and thus dominate a category from the customer's perspective are called **category killers.** These include Toys "R" Us, Home Depot, and Circuit City. Because category killers dominate a category of merchandise, they can negotiate excellent prices from suppliers and be assured of dependable sources of supply.

Today's retailing environment finds numerous retailers experimenting with the assortments they offer, attempting to get the right combination to entice consumers. Target and Kohl's, for example, have moved into designer apparel, attempting to lure shoppers away from department and apparel stores. Target has added Mossimo clothing, while Kohl's moved into the designer niche with Nine West and Liz Claiborne. Target and Kohl's are exploiting consumers' lack of excitement with department store assortments, as many of these traditional stores are focusing on selling their own private labels along with the lines of leading designers such as Polo and Tommy Hilfiger.[2] In the durable goods category, Wal-Mart and Home Depot now sell major home appliances, while Circuit City has dropped them from their assortment. Wal-Mart is further expanding its assortment by selling and leasing automobiles at select locations.[3]

EMPHASIZE ATMOSPHERICS   **Atmospherics** refer to a retailer's combination of architecture, layout, color scheme, sound and temperature monitoring, special events, prices, displays, and other factors that attract and stimulate consumers. Retailers spend millions of dollars to create the retail atmospheres that enhance their respective images and the products and services they offer for sale. NikeTown, Planet Hollywood, F. A.O. Schwartz, and Express are pioneers in the use of atmospherics in retailing. As NikeTown and Planet Hollywood have learned, however, changing the atmosphere is important to keep customers coming back. Declining numbers of customers at Planet Hollywood suggest that no matter how interesting consumers find the environment on the first visit, they may treat it like a museum—"Great! I really enjoyed it and may come back someday. Now where are we going?"

In response to an increasingly hard-to-impress consumer, retailers are seeking active involvement of shoppers; that is, they are trying to give the shopper a memorable experience, or "shoppertainment." For example, Whole Foods, the all-natural grocery chain, is trying to make shopping for food a fun, interactive experience. Its stores are arranged by food groupings, many of which invite customer participation. In the company's flagship store in Austin, Texas, shoppers can dip fresh fruit in a flowing fountain of chocolate at Candy Island for an instant treat. At the Fifth Street Seafood section, customers can have any of 150 fresh seafood items prepared several ways while they chat with the chefs. In Whole Foods stores, customers will increasingly shop where the music, lighting, and smells are carefully orchestrated to encourage customers to linger and spend money while doing so.[4] Dick's Sporting Goods and REI create interesting atmospheres with rock climbing walls near the front of some of their stores. For many retailers, there is no doubt that the consumer has become an important role player in creating the right atmospherics and shopping experience.

Atmospherics are an important part of retailing. The Mall of America near Minneapolis uses a variety of dramatic atmospheric factors to attract and stimulate consumers.

The best-known retail operation to gain headlines for its atmospherics is the Mall of America, located in suburban Minneapolis. The Mall of America has a two-story miniature golf course, a 300-foot walk-through aquarium, Camp Snoopy (an amusement park with more than 30 attractions), and a Lego Imagination Center, complete with dinosaurs 20 feet tall. These features create an exciting atmosphere for shoppers who roam the 4.2-million-square-foot facility (2.5 million square feet of retail shopping space). Mall of America draws more than 42 million people per year, more than Walt Disney World and the Grand Canyon combined.[5]

Atmospherics, though expensive to create, can generate considerable benefits for retailers. Atmospherics can boost the number of consumers who visit a retail location. Indeed, some retailers are trying to make their stores a "destination" for shoppers, a place a shopper will make a special effort to reach. Atmospherics can also boost the average time a shopper spends at the location and the average amount spent on each shopping trip. Atmospherics often allow retailers to charge higher prices. Compare the atmosphere of a discount store to that of a full-line traditional department store or an exclusive specialty shop, for example.

Types of Retailers

Powell's City of Books, an independent retailer in Portland, Oregon, competes effectively against large chains by offering a broad range of titles, including used books.

Many leading franchisors are expanding their international operations. A 7-Eleven subsidiary operates this popular franchise in Japan.

Retailers can be classified according to the type of merchandise and services sold, location, various strategic differences, and method of ownership. Here we examine different ownership categories to provide an overview of several types of retailers.

Some significant retail enterprises, such as military exchange stores and public utility appliance stores, operate outside the realm of private enterprise. Within the private sector, there are several major retail ownership categories, including independent retailers, chains, franchising, leased departments, and cooperatives.

Independent Retailers

Independent retailers own and operate only one retail outlet. Independent retailers account for more than three-fourths of all retail establishments, a testament to Americans' desires to own and operate their own businesses and a relative lack of barriers to entry. There are no formal education requirements, no specific training requirements, and few legal requirements to owning a retail business. This ease of entry likely accounts for the unpreparedness and the high failure rate experienced by new retailers.

Chains

A **retail chain** owns and operates multiple retail outlets. Examples are Nordstrom, Mervyn's, Best Buy, Pappagallo, Gap Inc., and JCPenney. By far, chain stores sell more merchandise than any other category of retailers. Their major advantage is the ability to service large, widespread target markets by selling a large assortment of products and services. For an illustration of how a successful chain operates, see "Creating Customer Value: Wegman's Sets the Standard."

Franchising

Retail franchising is a form of chain ownership in which a franchisee pays the franchisor (parent company) fees or royalties and agrees to run the franchise by prescribed norms, in exchange for use of the franchisor's name. Well-known franchisors include McDonald's, Holiday Inn, Avis, Mrs. Fields, and Jiffy Lube. According to the International Franchise Association, about 3,000 franchise companies operate in the United States. Franchising operations employ 8.5 million workers at approximately 558,000 separate establishments. Franchises generate approximately a trillion dollars per year in sales.[6]

Franchising is also a major retailing force outside the United States. McDonald's decided to go international in 1967, and now has almost 12,000 units in 113 countries outside the United States.[7] The largest market for franchising outside the United States is Europe, with franchising popular in France, Germany, and the United Kingdom. Japan is the most active franchising market in the Asia–Pacific region; there is a significant amount of franchising in Australia, Hong Kong, Singapore, Indonesia, Malaysia, and India; and franchising is also well established in Canada and Mexico.[8]

Although many successful international franchised retailers are U.S.-based, an increasing number of expansion-minded franchisors outside the United States view the world as their market. For example, Canada's Tim Horton's bakery/coffee restaurants and Taiwan's Kumon Math and Reading Centers are well established international franchised retailers.[9]

Under the best of circumstances, the arrangements between franchisors and franchisees offer considerable benefits to both parties. In return for fees or royalties, the franchisee may receive management training, participation in cooperative buying and advertising, and assistance in selecting an appropriate location. The franchisor benefits in turn from a constant stream of income, fast payment for goods and services, and strict control over franchised operations that encourages consistency among outlets.

Franchising systems are popular because they offer the franchisee a proven business and the franchisors the ability to establish a national presence with the funds provided by the sale of franchises. Although risk is a factor in any business, franchising has a better track record than most start-ups. Approximately half of new U.S. businesses fail during the first five years, whereas almost 90 percent of franchises survive.[10]

Exhibit 14–2 presents some of the best-known franchise operations. These franchise companies were selected by *Entrepreneur* magazine based on financial strength and stability, size, growth rate, years in business and in franchising, and start-up costs.

Exhibit 14–2	*Leading international retail franchise companies*

1. Subway	11. ServiceMaster Clean
2. Curves	12. Century 21 Real Estate
3. Quizno's	13. Dunkin' Donuts
4. Kumon Math & Reading Centers	14. McDonald's
5. Kentucky Fried Chicken	15. Snap-On Tools
6. The UPS Store	16. Coldwell Banker Real Estate
7. RE/MAX International	17. Sonic Drive-In Restaurants
8. Domino's Pizza	18. Jan-Pro Franchising
9. Jani-King	19. InterContinental Hotels
10. GNC Franchising	20. Jazzercize Inc.

CREATING CUSTOMER VALUE

Wegman's sets the standard

Wegman's, a privately owned grocery chain based in New York, has cultivated a loyal customer base that is unmatched in the grocery industry. While most grocery chains have been losing ground to nontraditional grocers such as Wal-Mart, Wegman's keeps getting stronger, with sales per square foot estimated as 50 percent higher than the industry average. Wegman's does it with superior merchandising, knowledgeable, enthusiastic employees, and what the company calls "telepathic" customer service.

In an industry where labor costs are a big concern, Wegman's pays higher-than-average wages, but its employee turnover rate is far lower than its competitors. The employees take pride in their work, and Wegman's is adept at turning employee knowledge into an enhanced shopping experience for customers. Customers can get advice on how to prepare food or how to match food with wine; and in a pinch, they can count on Wegman's to go the extra mile to keep them happy. In one case, Wegman's chefs cooked a customer's Thanksgiving turkey in the store because the one she bought was too big for her oven.

Building customer value has helped insulate Wegman's from the competitive heat of discount grocers. According to a company executive, Wegman's takes customers where they have not been before. Apparently they enjoy the trip, because they keep coming back, eager to spend their money not only for the food, but for the experience.

Global retailing can be quite sophisticated, as is the case with this superstore in Poland, which offers a wide variety of food and nonfood items. In contrast, retailing can be quite simple, as is the case for this Chinese consumer who is buying Head & Shoulders shampoo in a small sidewalk store.

Leased Departments

Leased departments are sections in a retail store that the owner rents to a second party. Typically department stores rent their jewelry, shoe, hairstyling, and cosmetic departments. For example, Mothers Work Inc. sells maternity clothing in leased spaces in 225 department stores such as Macy's and Sears; travel agencies and hair salons often lease space in department stores; and cosmetics such as Estée Lauder and Clinique are sold through leased space in department stores.

As with franchising agreements, a leased-department arrangement benefits both lessor (the department store) and lessee. The lessor receives rental fees, can reduce inventory investment and subsequent risk, gains expertise in a specialized area, and enjoys the benefits derived from the store traffic generated by the leased department. Lessees benefit by operating in an established location with the assurance of store traffic and advertising.

Cooperatives

Responding to competitive pressures exerted by the buying power of chain stores, independent retailers sometimes band together to form **retail cooperatives.** Although each store remains independently owned, the retail cooperative generally adopts a common name and storefront. The stores participate in joint purchasing, shipping, and advertising, which allows cost savings normally enjoyed by chain outlets. Retail cooperatives include Associated Grocers and Ace Hardware.

Trends in Retailing

We have seen dramatic examples of change in retailing, such as Kmart declaring bankruptcy, then merging with Sears. Hundreds of Internet-based retailers have come and gone since the turn of the century. Wal-Mart has increased its dominance as a general-line discount store and become a major player in the grocery sector. Among the most noteworthy retail sectors when it comes to dealing with change is the department store sector. JCPenney was struggling just a few years ago with its private labels such as Arizona jeans, losing out to designer labels such as Polo and Hilfiger in the more upscale department stores and to less expensive clothing at Target and Wal-Mart. But now JCPenney has gained momentum with improvements in cost cutting, store layout and checkout upgrades, and finding the right combination of private label and national labels such as Levi, Mudd, and l.e.i.[11]

Meanwhile, other department stores have evidently failed to connect with shoppers. Kohl's, a hybrid discounter/department store, is performing well, but most others are stalled, with no major plans for expansion. Consumers say department stores are boring, with too much of the same merchandise featured at competing stores. Decades of consolidation continue in the department store sector with the recent Federated proposal to buy

LaneHawk provides retailers with patented scanner technology that detects merchandise in the bottom of shopping carts and then enters the merchandise price in the cash register. This special scanner speeds up the checkout process and prevents lost sales to the retailer.

May department stores. Federated owns Bloomingdales's and Macy's, while May owns Marshall Field's, Lord & Taylor, and several regional chains such as Kaufmann's and Hecht's.[12] For struggling retail sectors like the department store sector, as well as growing sectors such as discount stores and upscale automobile dealers, future success is likely to hinge on how well they seize on important trends in retailing. Notable current trends in the retailing environment include global retailing, the increasing use of technology, a renewed emphasis on customer service, and the rapid expansion of nonstore retailing.

Global Retailing

With domestic markets becoming saturated and sales growth slowing, many retailers are exhibiting a global perspective. U.S.-based retailers have long been the leaders in global expansion, with, for example, McDonald's, Kentucky Fried Chicken, Radio Shack, and Wal-Mart being among the more progressive companies and L. L. Bean, Eddie Bauer, and Gap Inc. expanding in Japan with great success.

Retailers from other countries are becoming more active in global retailing. In recent years, retailers based outside the United States have become more aggressive in global marketing. A fine example is Europe's largest retailer, France's Carrefour. Carrefour, through company-owned stores and those generated by franchisees and partners, operates 11,300 stores in 31 countries. Poised to fight Wal-Mart around the world, Carrefour has been a pioneer in store design, softening the look of its gigantic stores with wood floors and softer lighting. Carrefour is known for selling groceries, clothing, and other merchandise under one roof. This format, which combines a discount store with an oversized supermarket, is called a **hypermarket.** The format, now becoming popular in America, was begun in France. Carrefour operates approximately 870 hypermarkets around the world. Many of its stores also offer myriad services, such as watch repair services, cell phone service, and travel services. Although Carrefour is not expected to challenge Wal-Mart in sales volume, the company has already proved a formidable competitor against Wal-Mart in several markets, including those of Brazil and Argentina. In addition to the markets in these two countries, Carrefour is the leading retailer in France, Taiwan, Spain, Portugal, Greece, and Belgium.[13]

Technological Advances

Retailers have embraced the technological perspective, and advances in retail technology have developed at a phenomenal pace. A familiar example is the scanner linked to computerized inventory systems that greatly improve a retailer's efficiency level. Scanners speed the checkout process, reduce computational errors, and instantaneously input the transaction into the inventory system. This allows retailers to precisely track sales on a per-item basis, minimize out-of-stock problems, and judge the effectiveness of various pricing and marketing communications tactics. Other technological advances that directly influence customers include automated cash registers that can issue temporary charge cards and gift certificates, provide customer information, and process customer payments, as well as passenger computer terminals and aircraft satellite systems that make in-flight shopping possible.

Wireless computer technology is finding many applications in retailing. Electronics Boutique uses wireless registers to check customers out during peak times; Gap uses wireless technology to check product availability in the stockroom and in surrounding stores; ski resorts are using wireless scanners so skiers can go directly to the lift rather than stand in a separate line to buy a lift ticket. Retailers have long tried to find ways to reduce the

Speaking from Experience

Kelly Seibels
Owner
Seibels

"We try to provide excellent customer service for both new and returning customers by focusing on four key principles. First, we hire conscientious employees who clearly understand the importance of giving good service. Second, we model our customer service according to how we would like to be treated if we were customers. In cases involving home delivery, we follow up after the delivery to ensure that we have met or exceeded all customer expectations. Finally, we constantly search for suppliers who will work with us not only to meet our expectations, but also to help us provide our retail customers with excellent service."

Kelly Seibels is the owner of Seibels, a specialty retailer based in Homewood, Alabama. Seibels sells home furnishings and accessories to the camp and cottage market through its retail store, a print catalog, and an online catalog. Before founding Seibels, Kelly worked as a professional writer. He earned a B.A. degree in English from the University of Alabama.

amount of time customers must wait in line to pay, and wireless technology is helping to achieve this objective.

Retailers are also using wireless technology to contribute to shoppers' enjoyment in other ways. In Seattle and San Francisco, coffee shops offer Wireless Fidelity networking, commonly referred to as Wi-Fi, so customers can surf the Web while having a cup of coffee. The idea is that if customers enjoy the experience, they will stay longer and spend more. With a thousand cities in the United States alone planning to become huge "hot spots" for wireless access, the availability of wireless connections in retail settings is on the verge of becoming commonplace.[14]

Technology, most notably the Internet, has also affected nonstore retailing, to be discussed shortly. For an example of how technology can affect retailers and its shoppers, see "Using Technology: Will Smart Carts Boost Retail Sales?"

Customer Service in Retailing

Customer service refers to the activities that increase the quality and value customers receive when they shop and purchase merchandise. Retailers rush to give lip service to the importance of customer service, but many still fall woefully short of providing it. Today's consumers are tougher, more informed, and so sensitive to poor service they often walk away and never come back to a store rather than point out the service problem to the retailer. Worse yet, the average consumer with a service problem tells several other people about the problem. Retailers offer a variety of customer services as shown in Exhibit 14–3.

Store loyalty is the major reward for customer service, a benefit that builds on itself, because customers well served are customers retained. One company that has built a solid business based on customer service is The Container Store, a Dallas-based chain of 33 stores with $425 million in annual sales. The Container Store sells shelving systems, boxes, buckets, bolts, jars, trunks, baskets, hangers, drawer dividers, and more to help customers get organized in their garages, home offices, closets, hobby rooms, and kitchens. The retail philosophy of The Container Store is to equip its sales personnel to solve customer problems and to work together as a team to get the job done. Container Store personnel receive 235 hours of training in their first year and 162 hours in each following year. The average training time in retailing is just 10 hours a year. By emphasizing customer service, The Container Store has been growing in excess of 20 percent annually, a rate that most retailers will never experience.[15]

Thinking Critically

- If everyone agrees that customer service is important to retail success, why is good service still an exception to the rule?
- What can retailers do to ensure good service?

Exhibit 14–3

Customer services offered by retailers

Acceptance of credit cards
Alterations of merchandise
Assembly of merchandise
ATM terminals
Bridal registry
Check cashing
Delivery
Dressing rooms
Layaway plans
Gift wrapping
Parking

Personal assistance in selecting merchandise
Personal shoppers
Play areas for children
Presentations on product use
Provisions for customers with special needs (wheelchairs, translators)
Return privileges
Special orders
Store warranties

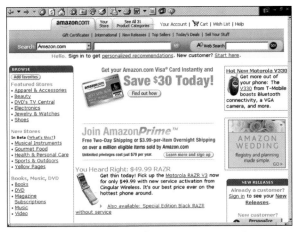

Consumers can buy almost anything via nonstore retailing. Amazon.com, which began as an online bookseller, now offers thousands of products ranging from home electronics to baby toys.

Retailers can provide good service without necessarily providing personal service. Automated teller machines, credit card–processing gas pumps, and point-of-sale audiovisual materials in home improvement stores are examples of how technology can assist in providing customer service.

Nonstore Retailing

Traditional retailing is generally thought of as the selling of products and services in stores or some other physical structure. In contrast, **nonstore retailing** refers to sales outside a physical structure. Although stores account for almost 90 percent of all retail sales, the growth rate of nonstore retailing has far surpassed that of store-based retailing in the past few years.

Nonstore retailing offers consumers the convenience of selecting and purchasing merchandise according to their own schedules. Merchandise is delivered directly to consumers or shipped to convenient vending locations, methods that particularly appeal to consumers with few store choices, busy people who care little for shopping, those who are bored or dissatisfied with store shopping, and consumers with limitations on movement, such as some nondrivers or disabled people. There are disadvantages of nonstore retailing. Customers cannot try on merchandise, test it out, or have it altered before delivery. In addition, some nonstore retailers offer limited assortments. The three most common forms of nonstore retailing are direct retailing, direct selling, and vending machine sales.

DIRECT RETAILING   **Direct retailing** is the portion of direct marketing in which ultimate consumers, not business customers, do the buying. **Direct marketing** can be defined as "the distribution of goods, services, information, or promotional benefits to targeted consumers through interactive communication while tracking response, sales, interests, or desires through a computer database."[16] The consumer is exposed to the merchandise through a nonpersonal medium (catalogs, TV shopping programs, interactive electronic networks) and then purchases the merchandise by computer, mail, or telephone. Familiar direct retailers include Amazon.com, L. L. Bean, Spiegel, Fingerhut, Lands' End, and Lillian Vernon. More recently, TV home shopping has become a legitimate form of retailing; major retailers Spiegel, Nordstrom, Bloomingdale's, and The Sharper Image are involved in TV home-shopping programs.

Direct retailing sales growth has been steadily outpacing growth for total retail sales for several years. It is estimated that direct retailing will top $1.3 trillion in sales in 2005, up almost 50 percent from direct retail sales in 2000.[17] More than half of the U.S. adult population buys from at least one direct retailer·each year, with clothing being the most popular item. Direct mail, including catalogs, remains the most popular direct retailing method, followed by telephone, newspaper, and television.

USING TECHNOLOGY

Will smart carts boost retail sales?

Touch-screen computers mounted on shopping carts are being touted as a new way to build customer value through the use of technology. IBM's version, the Shopping Buddy, and the Concierge from Springboard Retail Networks are the early entries into this market. Both models let manufacturers advertise a shopper's favorite products, a process enabled when shoppers scan their preferred shopper cards into the computer. The smart carts also have a localized version of a global positioning system (GPS), which helps shoppers find specific items or organize an entire shopping trip.

Perhaps the biggest value for the customer comes with the smart cart's built-in scanner, which allows customers to scan items as they drop them into the cart. This produces the final bill without waiting for a checker to scan each item and a faster getaway because only bagging remains when the shopping is finished. In the end, grocers hope that the added convenience from the new technology will help build value and thus customer loyalty.

Without question, the most attention-getting sector of direct retailing in recent years is that conducted over the Internet. While retail sales over the Internet, often referred to as **e-retailing,** presently account for less than 4 percent of total retail sales, their growth rate indicates that this is becoming an important form of direct retailing. In a period of slow growth rates for retailing in general, e-retailing is growing rapidly. In 2005 retail sales were expected to grow approximately 4 percent, while e-retailing was expected to grow 19 percent to $80 billion.[18] For some product categories, such as books and computer hardware and software, e-retailing has already become an important form of retailing. Other popular categories include travel, flowers, event tickets, recorded music and video products, consumer electronics, and home furnishings.

The e-retailing industry has been extremely competitive in recent years, with numerous business failures in the sector. Notables include EToys, Fogdog.com, MotherNature.com, Pets.com, PlanetRX., and Value America. Nonetheless, e-retailing has a bright future, as indicated by several industry developments and shopper behaviors. First, retail shoppers like having online buying as an alternative. Approximately a third of all retail shoppers buy in all three of these retail channels: store, catalog, and online.[19] A high percentage of online shoppers also shop in retail stores, and a similar percentage use the Web to research products they are buying. Thus retailers who ignore e-retailing run a big risk of missing out on a significant portion of the market.[20] Second, major retailers now dominate the e-retailing industry. In the early days of e-retailing, Internet-only companies such as Amazon.com and CDNOW were key players, but the bulk of business is now accounted for by multichannel retailers. Established retailers like Barnes & Noble, Best Buy, and L. L. Bean are among these multichannel marketers driving the growth of e-retailing. Third, the e-retailing industry is now profitable. Profits from successful companies have overcome the losses of marginal performers, and the overall outlook is that e-retailing can be profitable. The previously mentioned high growth rate also bodes well for the future of e-retailing. Nonetheless, online retailers can expect that while growth will occur in this sector, the growth rate will slow down as it has in recent years. The novelty of online e-retailing has disappeared, and online retailers will now face many of the same challenges as traditional retailers as they vie for customers in a highly competitive environment.

Retailers may use **portals,** or virtual shopping malls, to generate more traffic for their individual store Web sites. For example, Yahoo! Shopping links thousands of large and small retailers in its portal. Companies pay a monthly hosting fee ranging from $39.95 to $299.95. In addition, merchants pay Yahoo! transaction fees ranging from three-quarters of a percentage point up to one and a half percentage points on every dollar in sales depending on which level of participation and service the merchant chooses. Well-known retailers using the Yahoo! portal include Nordstrom, Old Navy, Brooks Brothers, and Office Max.[21]

E-retailing offers several advantages compared with shopping in a store. Consumers can order from stores around the world 24 hours a day from home or from any location with Internet access. There is no waiting in line to check out, nor the hassle of transporting purchases home. On the other hand, there is not the instant gratification that comes with a store purchase, and some consumers are worried about credit card security when buying online. Others find navigation around e-retail Web sites cumbersome and slow. On balance, a growing number of consumers enjoy shopping online, and growth will likely be dramatic in the coming years.

DIRECT SELLING   **Direct selling** involves the sale of a consumer product or service, person-to-person, away from a fixed retail location.[22] In approximately three-quarters of all direct selling transactions, the salesperson interacts with

Several direct selling companies are expanding their efforts in international markets. One of the leaders, Avon, is enjoying spectacular growth in Taiwan.

the customer or group of customers in a face-to-face encounter. The most popular setting for face-to-face direct selling is the home, with such encounters also taking place in the workplace, exhibition halls, theme parks, fairs, and shopping malls. Person-to-person direct selling is also conducted over the phone and the Internet. There are 13 million direct sellers in the United States, almost all of whom are part-time independent contractors. Eighty percent are females who primarily sell products in the home/family care, personal care, services, wellness, and leisure/educational categories.[23] Mary Kay, Avon, Cutco Cutlery, and Tupperware are familiar examples of companies that use direct selling.

VENDING MACHINE SALES   Vending machines allow customers to purchase and receive merchandise from a machine. Estimates of industry size range from $19 billion to $28 billion annually, with offerings of predominantly beverages, food, and candy.[24] Vending machines are frequently located at work sites, hospitals, schools, tourist destinations, and travel facilities.

Developing Retailing Strategy

The scope of retail products and services and the demands of consumers combine to produce a constantly changing business environment. A successful retailer must effectively manipulate the factors it can control to survive in a largely uncontrollable environment. A few uncontrollable and controllable factors of interest to retailers are listed in Exhibit 14–4.

Uncontrollable Factors

A number of constantly changing factors in the retail environment are beyond the retailer's control. To survive, retailers must constantly monitor and adapt to changing, uncontrollable factors in the marketing environment such as legal restrictions, discussed later in the chapter, and advances in technology. The important uncontrollable factors we describe here are consumers, competition, economic conditions, and seasonality.

CONSUMERS   Consumer demographics and lifestyles undergo constant changes, which retailers must recognize to satisfy the needs of their customers. For example, clothing retailer J. Crew has changed its merchandise mix based on two related consumer trends. First, consumers like low prices, but the upper-income portion of the consumer market likes luxury at a lower price. Second, consumers are tired of the sameness found in many apparel selections in department stores. Accordingly, J. Crew revamped its supply chain and sought low-cost providers for luxury materials such as cashmere and certain grades of leather. This allows J. Crew to offer Italian-made women's shoes and men's cashmere blazers at prices significantly lower than comparable designer merchandise. J. Crew also began following a principle of scarcity with limited production runs of luxury items, so that consumers would feel a sense of exclusivity when they made a purchase, rather than a sense that they were purchasing a product routinely found in

---

Exhibit 14–4   *Understanding retail strategy: Important controllable and uncontrollable factors*

most department stores. By following consumer preferences, J. Crew has dramatically improved its sales per store and overall profitability.[25]

Kelly Seibels, owner of Seibels, comments on the importance of adapting to consumer trends, specifically the fact that consumers are busier than ever: "We know that people are generally rushed when they are shopping, and we try to offer a relaxing, inviting shopping experience that will encourage shoppers to spend enough time in our store to get the feeling of being at home in their camp or cottage. Rather than departmentalize by product types, we group lifestyle settings complete with accessories to help shoppers visualize just how unique and comfortable our furnishings can be. Barney, my chocolate Lab, is always around the store, and he adds to the relaxed setting, which customers find enjoyable. There is no question that people are busier than ever, and that success in retail depends on offering a shopping environment in the store and, in our case, in our print catalog and on our Web site, that encourages shoppers to slow down and shop."

COMPETITION   Whether from new entries into the marketplace or from existing marketers, retail competition is fierce. One indicator of competition intensity is retail bankruptcies. Kmart, the largest retailer in history to declare bankruptcy, joins a long list of retail bankruptcies in recent years. Other well-known retailers filing for bankruptcy were Service Merchandise, Montgomery Ward, Filene's Basement, Caldor, Bradlee's, Tower Records, Party America, and grocery retailers Winn Dixie and Eagle Food Centers. And small independent retailers, especially bookstores, have been hit especially hard by competition. Independent booksellers saw their market share drop by 50 percent in the past decade. Some independents tried to form regional chains to compete with the larger national chains, but none of these regional chains survived. Competitive pressure from large chains such as Borders and Barnes & Noble, warehouse clubs, and online booksellers such as Amazon.com is intensifying even further, and the outlook for independent bookstores is grim.

Although the major chains have hurt smaller chains and independents, they, too, are feeling the effects of increased competition. Retailers are finding that many markets are overbuilt; that is, there are more retail stores than needed to meet consumer demand. As a result, Staples, OfficeMax, and Pep Boys are but a few of many national chains to close stores. Of course there are success stories amidst the reports of failing chain retailers. Wal-Mart and Target are doing well in the discount sector, Best Buy continues to perform well in consumer electronics, and both Home Depot and Lowe's are succeeding in the home improvement area. With overall store retailing sales growth averaging 4 percent annually, success for these companies usually comes at the expense of their competitors.

To survive, retailers try to improve the productivity of their operations, attract new customers, and get existing customers to buy more. This sometimes requires redefining the business, as has occurred with Radio Shack. Radio Shack was having a hard time getting brand-name products into its stores. Management was also unhappy with the lower operating margins on the sale of electronics equipment caused by price competition from Best Buy and other discounters. Noting that manufacturers were not satisfied with their lack of dedicated selling space in larger retail stores, Radio Shack felt that manufacturers would respond to a well-trained sales staff, something not found in the discount stores. Radio Shack refurbished its stores and partnered with Compaq, RCA, Verizon, and Sprint to better diversify its product sales mix. As a result, audio and video equipment has been displaced by telephones and electronic parts, accessories, and batteries as the top sellers. Other key elements in Radio Shack's revamped strategy are increasing its online sales and operating hundreds of kiosks in Sam's Clubs, where it will sell Sprint's wireless phone equipment and calling plans.[26] The Radio Shack experience serves as a reminder that retailers must sometimes undergo substantial changes to remain competitive.

In a broad sense, there are two major types of competition: intratype and intertype. **Intratype competition** describes competition among retailers that use the same type of business format. McDonald's, Wendy's, and Burger King are intratype competitors, for example; they are all fast-food restaurants. **Intertype competition** prevails among retailers using different types of business to sell the same products and services. The intertype competitors of McDonald's would include all other food retailers, ranging from vending

Thinking Critically

Consider the case of Ann Saxton, an artist who specializes in watercolors of wildlife and landscapes of the Pacific Northwest. Ann is contemplating opening a shop across the street from a major state university in Oregon. She has no retailing experience but believes that her works would be popular with faculty, staff, and students.

- What factors should Ann consider before making a final decision?

machines to fine restaurants. Retail businesses that appreciate both types of competition tend to be better prepared to face challenges and avoid the pitfalls of marketing myopia—that is, too narrowly defining the scope of their business.

ECONOMIC CONDITIONS   Economic conditions are another factor beyond the retailer's control. For several years, the overall world economy has been relatively stable, more flat than booming. In certain sectors, especially those involving travel and tourism, retailing has been operating under tough conditions. As a result, restaurants, hotels, airlines, resorts, and car rental companies have generally not prospered in recent years. In these sectors, price competition has been intense as companies hope to maintain their market shares until profit opportunities increase. With the increased cost of motor fuel, automakers have continued to use rebates and other promotions heavily despite their negative impact on profitability.

The state of the economy also significantly affects retail growth strategy. For example, the three largest dollar store chains—Dollar Tree, Family Dollar, and Dollar General—plan to capitalize on price sensitivity by doubling the number of their stores by 2010. In a similar move, Target has opened dollar areas in more than 1,000 of its stores.[27] Wireless Toyz, a specialty retailer for cell phones and satellite television, has taken advantage of poor economic conditions in some markets to acquire real estate at high-traffic corner locations. Wireless Toyz purchases dilapidated buildings and eyesores at low prices, then converts them into attractive retail environments. The strategy has helped enable spectacular growth for the company, which plans to have a nationwide presence by 2010.[28]

SEASONALITY   **Seasonality** refers to demand fluctuations related to the time of the year, which may be moderated or exacerbated by unpredictable changes in weather and in consumer preferences. Retailers specializing in clothing, sporting equipment, amusement parks, fresh food, hotels, and car rentals are particularly affected by seasonality. A retailer may minimize the effects of seasonality by adjusting some controllable variables within its retail strategy mix. For example, some retailers initiate special promotions to encourage consumers to buy during the off season. Other retailers, like sporting goods stores, alter their product mix by focusing on different products for different seasons. Ski resorts have redefined their businesses to become year-round attractions, adding summer festivals, mountain biking, water slides, golf, and other activities to their product assortment.

Controllable Factors

The four categories of controllable factors we discuss are location, the goods and services the retailer offers, the prices the retailer charges for products and services, and the marketing communications consumers receive.

LOCATION   The old saying—and experts confirm it—is that the three most important factors in retailing are location, location, and location. To most retailers, location *is* the most crucial factor and the least flexible element of retail strategy. A retailer can modify prices, products and services, and marketing communications relatively easily, but a poor location is difficult for even the best merchant to overcome. Moving is complicated by lease agreements, the transfer of inventory from one location to another, and perhaps even the sale of the building if the retailer owns it.

Retail locations can be found in practically every nook and cranny of the world, ranging from street vendors and mall kiosk operators to familiar superstore operators. With the growth of nonstore retailing, cyberspace is an increasingly important location. Mixed-use spaces that include retail, office, and housing are becoming more popular in urban and suburban locations. Themed shopping areas such as River Walk in New Orleans and Ghirardelli Square in San Francisco are popular tourist destinations. These newer developments in retail location strategy are exciting, but four retail location alternatives remain most important in terms of total sales generated: the central business district (CBD); strip centers; shopping malls; and freestanding locations.

The **central business district (CBD),** commonly known as downtown areas, remains an important part of the retail scene in the United States and many major cities around the world. These districts are designed to meet the day-to-day shopping needs

Retailers, especially those operating in large urban areas, are concerned that shoppers may shop less frequently or shop only during certain hours of the day because they fear crime. This shopping mall in Miami uses additional security measures to ensure shopper safety.

of the surrounding neighborhood. **Strip centers** feature parking in front of all stores and are not enclosed under one roof. This form of retail location may be found in small neighborhoods within a community, may draw from the entire community, or may even have more of a regional draw depending on the size and mix of retailers that locate in the strip. **Shopping malls,** unlike strip centers, are designed more for pedestrian flow under an enclosed roof. **Freestanding sites** are not adjoined to other retail structures but are often located adjacent to other retail locations. For example, Home Depot, Circuit City, Best Buy, Sam's Club, and P. F. Chang's restaurants often utilize freestanding locations near large strip centers or shopping malls. Freestanding locations are also popular at exits along interstate highways and busy city streets where car dealers may congregate. In recent years, the popularity of shopping malls has waned somewhat, and there has been a resurgence in the popularity of strip centers. Another popular strategy for retail developers has been to combine a mall with surrounding strip centers and freestanding locations, as has been done with great success at Flatirons Crossing near Denver. The advantages and disadvantages of the major types of retail locations are shown in Exhibit 14–5.

GOODS AND SERVICES   Another controllable factor in the retail strategy is the goods and services offered for sale. Retailers must decide on the number of product lines to carry, referred to as *width* or *variety*. They must also decide on the assortment of each product line, called *length* or *depth*. These decisions require several considerations. Major product considerations include compatibility (how well the product fits in with existing inventory), attributes (such as bulk, required service, selling levels), and profitability. Market considerations include stage in the product life cycle, market appropriateness (a product's appeal to the store's current target market), and competitive conditions. Finally, supply considerations such as product availability and supplier reliability need to be explored.

   Retailers must be alert to the effects of changes in their product mix and open to a redefinition of competitors. For example, the practice of adding unrelated product categories to existing product lines is referred to as **scrambled merchandising.** In the not-too-distant past, grocery stores predominantly sold food items. Today consumers can buy motor oil or rent movies at grocery stores. Scrambled merchandising allows grocery

Exhibit 14–5   *Selected criteria to consider when evaluating retail locations*

Location Issues	CBD	Strip Center	Shopping Mall	Freestanding
Large size draws people to area	+	−	+	−
People working/living in area provide source of customers	+	+	−	−
Source of entertainment/recreation	?	−	+	−
Protection against weather	−	−	+	−
Security	−	−	+	−
Long, uniform hours of operation	−	+	+	+
Planned shopping area/balanced tenant mix	−	−	+	−
Parking	−	+	?	+
Occupancy costs (e.g., rent)	?	+	−	+
Pedestrian traffic	+	−	+	−
Landlord control	+	+	−	+
Strong competition	+	+	−	+
Tax incentives	?	?	?	?

Exhibit 14–6

Scrambled merchandising

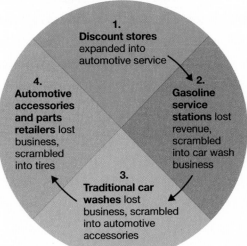

1. **Discount stores** expanded into automotive service

2. **Gasoline service stations** lost revenue, scrambled into car wash business

3. **Traditional car washes** lost business, scrambled into automotive accessories

4. **Automotive accessories and parts retailers** lost business, scrambled into tires

stores to obtain higher profit margins than the traditional 1 to 2 percent made on food items. Consumers, in turn, enjoy the extra convenience of one-stop shopping provided by a wide array of merchandise; in effect, they have received improved quality and value in their overall shopping experience.

Scrambled merchandising has had a chain-reaction effect something like that shown in Exhibit 14–6. When discount stores aggressively expanded into automotive service, traditional gasoline service stations lost revenue and scrambled into the car wash business. Traditional car wash operations then expanded their sale of automotive accessories, causing lost volume for traditional automotive accessory and parts retailers. These retailers responded by scrambling into tires to supplement their lost sales on accessories.

Amazon.com provides an example of scrambled merchandising in e-retailing. Originally a bookseller, Amazon expanded into music and videos, then followed with a wide range of products, including electronics, computers, sports equipment, tools, software, and other offerings on its way to becoming the world's largest online retailer, serving customers in 220 countries. Amazon is making these products available through its zShops concept, where independent vendors pay a small monthly fee to link with Amazon. As Amazon scrambles its merchandise to the extreme, it excludes only items it considers to be unethical or illegal, including stolen and counterfeit goods, promotional media, unauthorized and unlicensed merchandise, and recopied media.[29]

PRICING   Retailers also control the final prices they charge consumers for their products and services. Retail prices are ultimately based on the store's target market, the desired store image, and the congruence between price and other elements of the retail mix (location, quality of products and services, marketing communications). Although price-conscious consumers may appear to dominate in many markets, successful retailers are found at all price ranges, from high to low.

Everyday-low-pricing (EDLP) strategies, pioneered by Wal-Mart, are now used by many retailers. With EDLP, retailers demand low prices from their suppliers, minimize costly advertising and promotions, and keep their retail prices consistently low to lure consumers. Now many retailers are adopting "low-price leader" or "value pricing" programs. These programs feature low competitive prices across the board and a continual mix of special offers to keep consumers coming back.

MARKETING COMMUNICATIONS   Decisions about the mix of marketing communications are also controllable. These decisions specify how the retailer allocates resources among personal selling, advertising, public relations, direct marketing, and sales promotion. Retailers such as The Limited emphasize personal in-store selling and do little advertising; convenience stores promote sales by placing signs in their windows; others promote "a sale a week."

Giant Food Incorporated uses extensive advertising as part of its marketing communications program. It also gains favorable publicity from outdoor advertising, as seen at Baltimore Oriole's Park at Camden Yards.

Marketing communications influence **store image,** the picture shoppers conjure up of a store's identity. This image is a composite of shoppers' perceptions of the store's location, goods and services sold, and atmospherics. Essentially, store image is a reflection of consumers' feelings about a store. It affects consumer perceptions of the quality of products and services offered, prices, and the store's fashionability.

Types of Strategy Mix

Retailers differentiate themselves from one another according to the **strategy mix** they pursue. The elements of the retail strategy mix are the controllable variables we have

Exhibit 14–7		*Examples of retail strategy mixes*			
Type of Retailer	**Location**	**Merchandise**	**Prices**	**Atmosphere and Services**	**Marketing Communications**
Convenience store	Neighborhood	Medium width and low depth of assortment; average quality	Average to above average	Average	Moderate
Superstore	Community shopping center or isolated site	Full assortment of supermarket items, plus health and beauty aids and general merchandise	Competitive	Average	Heavy use of newspapers and flyers; self-service
Warehouse store	Secondary site, often in industrial area	Moderate width and low depth; emphasis on national brands purchased at discounts	Very low	Low	Little or none
Specialty store	Business district or shopping center	Very narrow width of assortment; extensive depth of assortment; average to good quality	Competitive to above average	Average to excellent	Heavy use of displays; extensive sales force
Department store	Business district, shopping center, or isolated store	Extensive width and depth of assortment; average to good quality	Average to above average	Good to excellent	Heavy use of ads; catalogs; direct mail; personal selling
Full-line discount store	Business district, shopping center, or isolated store	Extensive width and depth of assortment; average to good quality	Competitive	Slightly below average to average	Heavy use of newspapers; price-oriented; moderate sales force
Factory outlet	Out-of-the-way site or discount mall	Moderate width, but very poor depth of assortment; some irregular merchandise; low continuity	Very low	Very low	Little; self-service

discussed: location, products and services, pricing, and marketing communications. Exhibit 14–7 describes a range of retailers and their strategy mixes. Although a multitude of combinations exist, specialty stores, department stores, and convenience stores are the more obvious examples of retailers that combine the strategy mix variables in different ways to achieve their desired positions in the marketplace.

SPECIALTY STORES   Specialty stores sell a narrow variety of products but offer a deep assortment of product choices. Typical examples of specialty stores are The Limited, Radio Shack, and The Sharper Image.

Because many specialty stores are not large enough to generate sufficient customer traffic on their own, most are commonly located in shopping clusters (malls, shopping centers) where their product selections complement goods provided by neighboring retailers. The marketing communications mix of a specialty store generally includes personal selling along with advertising that emphasizes the uniqueness of offerings and the depth of assortment. Specialty stores are also known for their medium to high prices.

Hot Topic is a specialty clothing and accessories chain that caters to the teen market. By thoroughly understanding its customers, Hot Topic competes quite effectively against other more established retail chains. Abercrombie & Fitch is another example of a successful retailer who appeals to young consumers.

DEPARTMENT STORES   Department stores are characterized by a wide variety of merchandise and extensive depth of assortment, and they offer customers one-stop convenience for multiple shopping needs. Operations are typically organized around sales departments such as apparel, home furnishings, cosmetics, and housewares. Employees also work within centralized functional departments such as buying, merchandising, and advertising. Some of the more well-known department stores are Bloomingdale's, Dillard's, and Macy's.

Department stores generally occupy **anchor positions** in shopping centers, shopping malls, or downtown areas; that is, they are strategically placed at different ends of the shopping cluster. Because department stores generate a lot of customer traffic, this placement creates a traffic flow throughout the entire shopping facility.

Marketing communications for department stores focus on product selection and quality; services offered, such as alterations, gift wrapping, and credit; shopping atmosphere; and store image. Department stores are heavy users of newspaper advertising, catalogs, direct mail, and personal selling. As do specialty stores, department stores commonly charge at or above competitive prices.

CONVENIENCE STORES   Convenience stores have developed their own unique marketing mix. They carry a modest variety and shallow assortment of products. Prices are high, which consumers tolerate because of the ease of shopping offered by such retailers. Convenience stores often occupy **interceptor locations** between residential areas and the closest supermarket. Marketing communications are predominantly limited to the store's sign and banners displayed in the front windows.

Two convenience stores, Circle K and 7-Eleven, have been in bankruptcy, and the entire industry faces a predicted decline in new store growth over the next decade. The industry's problems can be traced to three main sources. First, the industry is overbuilt, with the proliferation of convenience stores constructed by major oil companies such as Shell, Texaco, and BP. Second, as drugstores and supermarkets extend their hours of operation, convenience stores have increasing difficulty differentiating themselves on convenience. Moreover, increases in the minimum wage, store rents, and other general expenses have dramatically increased operating costs. Even though sales through convenience stores are increasing, profit margins are declining.[30] Profit margins on merchandise are increasing, but this increase is more than offset by declining profit margins on motor fuel. Convenience stores have had difficulty passing on wholesale price increases for motor fuel to the ultimate consumer.

To survive, many convenience stores have repositioned themselves as quick-service eateries specializing in "one-handed" food—items you can eat with one hand while driving with the other, such as hot dogs, corn dogs, pizza, burritos, and egg rolls. Compared to past sales patterns, convenience stores are increasing their sales of general merchandise, including items such as scooters and electronics, coffee, publications, and health and beauty items. These shifting patterns indicate that convenience stores may be moving slightly away from meeting shoppers' fill-in needs to becoming more general retailers that have some characteristics of general stores, drugstores, newsstands, and health food stores.[31]

MARGIN AND TURNOVER STRATEGY MIXES   Besides type of store, another distinction between retailers is gross margin and inventory turnover. **Gross margin** refers to sales revenue less the retailer's cost of goods sold. A retailer with higher margins makes more from each dollar of sales. **Inventory turnover** refers to how quickly merchandise is sold; it describes the number of times the retailer sells its average inventory during the year. Margin and turnover concepts are illustrated in Appendix A at the end of the text.

There are three strategic combinations of gross margin and inventory turnover among successful retailers. Jewelry stores exemplify a high-margin/low-turnover strategy. They realize high profits per sale but make fewer sales. Such retailers are also noted for their attention to personal service and attractive atmospheres that help support the merchandise.

Grocery stores use a low-margin/high-turnover strategy. They typically have a net profit margin of 1 to 2 percent but turn merchandise over very quickly. The third option is high-margin/high-turnover, demonstrated by convenience stores.

Kelly Seibels, owner of Seibels, points out that teamwork can be an important part of a successful retail strategy: "At Seibels, all employees are equal partners in serving the customer. We all have different areas of particular expertise, so the right person can step up and help when the situation calls for it. We keep files on all of our customers' purchase history, including pending orders for delivery. All employees have instant access to these files, so no matter who is on the floor, they can follow up on customer inquiries in short order. By working together to serve the customer, Seibels enjoys a high level of customer satisfaction, which brings loyal shoppers back to us time after time."

Ethical and Legal Issues in Retailing
Retailers engage in highly visible activities, and their marketing communications are similarly visible and thus subject to a fair amount of scrutiny. Ethical or legal violations that retailers have been accused of include deceptive advertising, dishonest sales practices, charging unreasonably high prices to disadvantaged consumers, selling potentially harmful products without adequate control, and selling prohibited products to underage consumers.

Additional factors pose special concerns for retailers: consumer fraud, supplier labor practices, shoplifting, slotting allowances, the use of personal customer information, and ecological considerations.

Consumer Fraud
Retailers that adopted the customer-is-always-right concept are having second thoughts when it comes to liberal return policies. Known in the industry as return churn or boomerang buying, return fraud is a growing problem for retailers. Fraudulent returns cost retailers more than a billion dollars annually. L. L. Bean notices more requests for returns in the spring, when yard sales pick up and old boots and camping equipment are bought cheap and then returned with a request for a full refund. And some customers take merchandise off the shelf, then proceed to customer service for a refund, claiming that the receipt has been lost. Others use retailers as free rental centers for big-screen TV sets, snow blowers, and formal apparel. Retailers are fighting back, cutting down on the time during which returns are accepted and being more insistent that the customer has a receipt. Among those cracking down on returns are Home Depot, Best Buy, The Sports Authority, Express, and The Limited. Some retailers remain lax in their return policy, saying that most

consumers are honest and that strict policies would punish the majority because of the actions of a small minority. Nordstrom is the best known retailer that follows this policy. Interestingly, Circuit City abandoned its no-penalty return policy after it found that customer returns increased without its 15 percent restocking fee on big-ticket items.[32] Fraudulent consumers drive up the cost of retailing, which ultimately translates into higher prices for honest consumers.

Supplier Labor Practices

Many retailers, including Wal-Mart, JCPenney, Talbots, and Macy's, have been part of a controversy involving the working conditions in their supplier manufacturing facilities. Referred to as *sweatshops,* these facilities are located primarily in low-wage countries in Asia, Latin America, and Eastern Europe. Sweatshop workers, many of whom are underage, are subjected to adverse working conditions and extremely low wages.

A storm of bad publicity began in the mid-1990s and continues today, with retailers, manufacturers, and celebrity spokespersons receiving unwanted exposure. Since then, many retailers have strengthened existing policies and adopted new procedures to address the sweatshop issue. The U.S. Department of Labor has commended several retailers for their active role in eliminating sweatshops, including Express, Nordstrom, The Limited, Patagonia, Nicole Miller, Lane Bryant, and Liz Claiborne.

More than 300 leading retailers have signed the National Retail Federation's Statement on Supplier's Legal Compliance, which pledges that retailers will not buy from vendors who violate labor laws of the United States and other countries. Even so, antisweatshop groups feel that enforcement is insufficient and that retailers should do more to pressure their suppliers in the area of humane labor practices. In 2005 Nike, Gap, Patagonia, and five other companies joined with six antisweatshop groups to devise a set of uniform labor standards with a common factory inspection system. This coalition is conducting a 30-month trial in the hopes that commonly accepted global standards will be developed.[33] Only through the combined efforts of suppliers, retailers, and humanitarian groups can lasting progress be made to eliminate sweatshops. The issues surrounding sweatshop-produced merchandise are likely to remain key ethical issues for retailers well into the future.

Retail Theft

Retailers lose approximately $10 billion a year to shoplifting by customers and an additional $15 billion to employee theft.[34] Nationwide, the incidence of shoplifting has increased sharply in recent years. Experts claim the primary contributors to increased shoplifting are fewer clerks per store and new floor layout arrangements that divide stores into separate boutiques. This type of layout creates barriers between departments, which makes it easier for shoplifters to conceal their activities. Specialty clothing stores, drugstores, convenience stores, and department stores are hit hardest by shoplifting. Items most frequently stolen are fashion accessories, costume jewelry, fine jewelry, recorded music, health and beauty aids, sporting goods, radios, and television sets. Some methods for deterring shoplifting are detailed in Exhibit 14–8.

Exhibit 14–8   *Shoplifting deterrents*

- Use electronic tags on vulnerable merchandise.
- Install surveillance cameras in plain view.
- Install convex mirrors to observe corners and aisles.
- Use locked cases for expensive and frequently stolen goods.
- Closely supervise the selling floor.
- Instruct personnel to make eye contact with customers.
- Make it easy for employees to contact security.
- Publicize that shoplifters will be prosecuted.
- Monitor entrances and exits from the store.
- Lower displays that could limit visibility of the sales floor.
- Monitor fitting areas.

Slotting Allowances

Another retailing issue that has legal or ethical implications is the use of slotting allowances. **Slotting allowances** are fees manufacturers pay to retailers or wholesalers to obtain shelf or warehouse space for their products. In other words, retailers and wholesalers receive money from manufacturers in exchange for allocation of shelf space.

Slotting allowances, a common practice in grocery retailing, are controversial. They were first instituted to keep manufacturers from introducing not-so-new brands or bogus product line extensions. Colorado State University professor Joseph P. Cannon notes that "the reason slotting fees came about was the number of new products, making it more difficult to evaluate them. Test marketing fell by the wayside because of the [importance of] speed to market and also because if you test your product, your competitors can see it before you go national."[35] Even though test marketing is less popular than in the past, slotting fees are more established than ever. Large manufacturers resist paying these questionable fees, but large wholesalers and retailers insist slotting fees be paid as a condition of doing business. In effect, slotting allowances place manufacturers in direct opposition to their customers: wholesalers and retailers.

Overall, slotting allowances are predominantly associated with negative consequences. They may increase conflict between channel members and reduce competitiveness at some levels. Large channel members can demand slotting allowances that increase their profit margins, while the smaller members must fend for themselves.

Slotting allowances may also reduce customer service by forcing fewer brand choices, higher retail prices, and less prepurchase information. This could ultimately threaten the quality of product provided to the consumer. The costs of slotting allowances incurred by vendors is typically a well-guarded secret. Neither vendors nor retailers are required to disclose slotting allowance payments. In a quirky one-year exception to the rule, the U.S. Financial Accounting Standards Board required that companies restate their 2001 accounts by subtracting slotting allowances from their sales revenue. The amounts paid by food and beverage companies to gain shelf space were astounding. For example, Campbell Soup, Kellogg, Coca-Cola, PepsiCo, and Kraft averaged about 13 percent of sales in slotting allowances. Kraft, for example, spent $4.6 billion on slotting allowances. Such large numbers and the secrecy of the practice have attracted government attention, so it is plausible that we may know more about the scope and impact of slotting allowances as time passes. A prime concern of regulators is the overall impact on competition, and thus consumer prices. Small manufacturers claim that slotting allowances may drive them out of business, thus creating a less competitive marketplace.[36]

Use of Customer Information

Advances in database technology provide retailers greater access to and storage of consumer information and purchase histories. For example, when a customer calls Spiegel to check a catalog order, the service rep has instant access, via an order number, to the customer's previous sales and service transactions. This information can be used to sell other products and service warranties and to process orders more efficiently.

Are retailers free to use such information for any purpose, or is the customer's right to privacy being violated? Although this question is the subject of much debate, public sentiment favors the protection of consumer privacy. Some of the major videotape rental firms no longer maintain records of customers' past rentals. Other companies that fear adverse publicity will quite likely take a right-to-privacy stance.

Ecological Considerations

Retailers are paying more attention to how their operations affect the environment. Recreational Equipment Inc. (REI), for example, won an award for its energy conservation and environmental sensitivity in its 37,500-square-foot store in Portland, Oregon. In constructing the store, REI diverted 96 percent of the waste from landfills into recycling processes, used photo cells to minimize electrical lighting when natural light is sufficient, reduced water consumption by a third with low-water bathroom fixtures, and utilized recycled building materials extensively throughout the store.[37] Home Depot also shows its awareness of ecological issues by refusing to sell wood from environmentally endangered areas. Home Depot sells more lumber than any other company in the world, and its move was influential in getting other retailers to be more supportive of environmental issues.[38]

Another indication that retailers are becoming more concerned with environmental issues is a move to ban smoking in shopping malls. Since the Environmental Protection Agency released a report on the dangers of secondhand smoke, shopping centers across the country have not waited for legal prompting; instead, they have taken the initiative to ban smoking.

Like all marketing institutions, retailers are finding that following an ethical perspective can be good for business. They are also acutely aware that questionable ethical practices can lead to consumer protest, tarnished images, and lost sales. Consumers must also take some responsibility for correcting some of the ethical problems in retailing. Shoplifting and consumer fraud hurt retailer profits. They also hurt honest consumers in the form of higher prices and inconvenient security measures.

Summary

1. **Understand the economic importance of retailing and its role in the marketing channel.** The role of retailing in the marketing channel is to provide products and services to the ultimate, or final, consumer. Retailing is an important economic activity in that (1) there are approximately 3 million retailers in the United States; (2) nearly 14 million people, 10 percent of the U.S. labor force, are employed in retail or retail-related activities; and (3) retailers generate approximately $2.5 trillion in sales. Retailers differ from other channel members in that they sell smaller quantities more frequently, offer assortments of products, and emphasize atmospherics in their selling.

2. **Cite evidence of the globalization of retailing.** McDonald's, Wal-Mart, Gap, Radio Shack, France's Carrefour, and L. L. Bean are but a few companies expanding retail operations around the globe. Markets in countries with highly developed economies such as the United States are somewhat saturated; thus retailers are increasingly eager to expand to less competitive markets.

3. **Discuss some of the advances in retailing technology.** Retailing has benefited from various technologies in recent years. Automated cash registers, electronic kiosks, universal product code scanners, computerized shopping carts, and wireless networks are some examples of technology put to good use in retailing. The explosive growth in nonstore retailing is fueled in part by computer and communications technology.

4. **Explain the reasons behind the growth of nonstore retailing.** Busy people like to shop at their preferred times in the convenience of their own homes. Successful catalog retailing has encouraged consumers to try other forms of nonstore retailing such as TV shopping and online shopping. The growth of nonstore retailing is probably also the result of consumer boredom and dissatisfaction with some traditional retail stores.

5. **Describe key factors in the retail marketing environment, and understand how they relate to retail strategy.** Controllable factors include location, products and services, pricing, and marketing communications. Uncontrollable factors are consumers, competition, economic conditions, and seasonality. To be successful, retailers must effectively manipulate the controllable factors to manage the environment created by always-changing uncontrollable factors.

6. **Cite important ethical and legal issues facing retailers.** Routine legal restrictions govern practically every aspect of retailing. Contemporary ethical and legal issues of special concern are consumer fraud, supplier labor practices, retail theft, the use of slotting allowances, the use of customer information, and ecological considerations. Consumer fraud in the form of unwarranted return of merchandise costs retailers more than a billion dollars a year, which ultimately is passed on to consumers. Some progressive retailers began monitoring the labor practices of their suppliers after sweatshop practices made the headlines, resulting in negative publicity for retailers and suppliers. Employee, consumer, and supplier theft are costly to retailers, resulting in higher prices for consumers. Slotting allowances are fees manufacturers pay to retailers or wholesalers to obtain shelf or warehouse space for their products. It's an ethically questionable practice and may be illegal. Other concerns are the retailer's use of customer information versus the individual's right to privacy, and the ecological impact of retail operations.

Understanding Marketing Terms and Concepts

Thinking about Marketing

1. What evidence can you cite supporting the economic importance of retailing?

2. How do retailers differ from other members in the channel of distribution?

3. How can retailers improve customer service by using technology?

4. Review "Creating Customer Value: Wegman's Sets the Standard." How do Wegman's employees build customer value? How would Wegman's customers differ from Wal-Mart grocery customers in what they expect from a grocer?

5. Review "Using Technology: "Will Smart Carts Boost Retail Sales?" How does this concept create value for consumers? For retailers and their suppliers?

6. What uncontrollable factors affect the retail environment? What can retailers do to minimize the impact of these factors on sales?

7. What types of locations are possible alternatives for retailers? Briefly define each type of location.

8. List and describe the three types of nonstore retailing. What are the advantages and disadvantages of nonstore retail operations?

9. Discuss the benefits of retail franchising from both the franchisor's and franchisee's point of view.

10. Discuss some of the key ethical and legal issues in retailing.

Applying Marketing Skills

1. Retailers that sell secondhand merchandise, such as flea markets or Salvation Army stores, have been doing relatively well in recent years. Can you explain their success in terms of economic conditions and consumer preferences discussed in this chapter?

2. Tune in to a television shopping program once a week for a month, and analyze the products sold and the sales methods used. In particular, assess the following issues:
   - What is the primary pricing strategy?
   - What role do celebrities play in the programming?
   - Can you generalize about the size and colors offered in apparel sales?
   - Is it important to have merchandise with easy-to-demonstrate features?

3. For each of the following types of retail operations, suggest complementary products, either goods or services, that could logically be added to the merchandise mix:
   - A small coffee shop that features light desserts, pastries, espresso, cappuccino, and gourmet coffees.
   - A small independent bookstore located near a retirement community.
   - A large parking garage adjacent to a downtown office building.
   - A hairstyling salon.
   - A pet supplies store.

Using the www in Marketing

Activity One L. L. Bean is a successful retailer in both store and nonstore formats. One reason for L. L. Bean's success is excellent customer service. Visit the Web site at *http://www.llbean.com* and identify customer services not typically available from retail stores (refer to Exhibit 14–3 for services typically offered by retail stores). How do these services build stronger customer relationships?

Activity Two Compare online retailers at Yahoo!com, *www.yahoo.com*. From the home page, select the "shopping" link. Select any two of the retailers listed and answer these questions:

1. How would you describe the target market for each retailer? This will require some speculation on your part, but describe the likely demographics and lifestyle characteristics of the intended target markets for each retailer.

2. Which of the two retailers has done the best job in appealing to its target market with its online offerings? Please support your answer.

Making Marketing Decisions

Case 14–1   Chico's Sales Are Booming

The women's retail apparel market is an interesting scene these days—that is, if you like mysteries. One of the big mysteries in women's apparel is why more retailers are not paying attention to the desires of an important segment in the market. Baby boomer women, those aged from the mid-30s to the mid-50s, comprise 43 percent of the U.S. population, and they account for 40 percent of sales. Retailers, however, are focused on GenX and GenY shoppers in their early teens to their mid-20s who contribute only 17 percent of the women's apparel dollars. As a result, middle-aged women have gone beyond complaining about ill-fitting clothes in styles they do not like—they have slowed down their purchases. Retailers have begun to notice and say they are adjusting their product assortments. But they will have a long way to go to catch Chico's, a Florida-based company with 691 stores operating under the names Chico's, WhiteHouse/Black Market, and Soma by Chico's, most of which are located in upscale malls. Chico's sells clothing, shoes, and fashion accessories, targeting mid- to higher-income women aged 25 to 55.

Chico's was named after the bilingual parrot of a friend of the founders, Marvin and Helene Gralnick. The Gralnicks moved to Florida from Mexico and opened their first store in Sannibel Island, Florida, in 1983. Since then, their success has been built on understanding the female baby boomer market and giving them an alternative between the extremes of young, sometimes too casual for the office attire and the more tailored look as typified by Talbot's.

Middle-aged women have grown tired of trying to fit into fashions designed for a younger demographic. Shoppers openly complain at Gap, Banana Republic, Old Navy, Urban Outfitters, and even department stores such as Macy's. Many are dismayed when they have to increase their sizes, even though they have not gained weight in recent years. Store buyers say that middle-aged women are generally in much better shape than previous generations, and that they are not heavier. Yet today's fashions often make them feel as if they are. Chico's offers a simplified sizing scheme ranging from 0 to 3, where 0 is equivalent to sizes 4–6; 1 equals 8–10; 2 is 12–16; and 3 equals 16–18. The clothes are generously cut and comfortable. Granted, not all women like the roomier styles. But Chico's is on target with most women in the boomer demographic. Sales have grown at a double-digit rate annually since 1997. In 2005, sales are up 27 percent over 2004 figures, and gross margins remain above 60 percent. This comes at a time when apparel sales to the boomer demographic are up less than 5 percent across the United States.

With results like these, Chico's can expect increased competition. Nordstrom is finding success with Cambio, a German manufacturer that offers more fashions such as midrise jeans for middle-aged customers. Gap is swinging back toward more traditional clothing, and Neiman Marcus is signaling its designers to get more in tune with the boomer market. Eileen Fisher and J. Jill are courting the same market targeted by Chico's and will turn up the competitive heat. Gymboree Corporation has introduced a new chain, Janeville, aimed at the 35-plus female. Target is doing well with its Linden Hill fashion label, and Gap is opening new stores for female boomers under the Forth & Towne banner. Another new competitor is the private label show, where women meet in friends' homes, sort of like a Tupperware party, to shop for lesser known, more conservative labels.

Chico's management is confident that they can handle the competition, and the chain continues to expand aggressively. Chico's executives think they have figured out how to give women a comfortable fit without making them look foolish. The large number of women in their target market and a healthy $85,000 average annual household income give Chico's the opportunity to offer more upscale merchandise than some of the mass retailers it competes with. To hedge its bets, Chico's also sells via the Internet and through its catalog. Combined sales in these two channels are growing steadily, and Chico's reports that both the Web site and the catalog are also driving more traffic into its stores. A loyalty program called Passport rewards customers who spend $500 with a lifetime 5 percent discount. Among the first to see the opportunity in serving the most lucrative niche in the women's apparel industry, Chico's will be a tough act to beat.

Questions

1. Why have so few retailers successfully targeted and met the needs of the middle-aged women's apparel market?

2. How does Chico's sizing method add customer value?

3. How can Chico's stay ahead of the pack in serving its market?

Case 14–2 *Home Depot and Lowe's Go Head-to-Head*

Recent market conditions have been favorable for home improvement retailers. Mortgage rates for new homes have been favorably low the past few years, keeping the market for new houses strong despite a slow economy. The resale home market has been strong as well, as some consumers find more value for their dollar in resales. As Americans spend more time at home, a trend called "cocooning," the remodeling market has also been strong. Even the weather has been cooperating, with milder winters extending the busy season for home improvement retailers. Industry leaders Home Depot and Lowe's have benefited from these favorable conditions and are now more than ever locked in a head-to-head battle to lead this retail sector.

Based on size, Home Depot is winning the battle. The company has grown from four stores in Atlanta in 1979 to almost 1,900 in four countries in 2005. It is the nation's second largest retailer behind Wal-Mart, having passed Sears several years ago. Lowe's, by comparison, has 1,100 stores. Home Depot sells twice as much merchandise as Lowe's, with an expected 2005 revenue of $73 billion. Home Depot earns about 6.8 percent of sales in profits, while Lowe's earnings are about 6 percent of sales.

Both Lowe's and Home Depot recognize the importance of the female shopper in the home improvement market. Half of Lowe's clientele is female, and the chain is attracting more and more nonprofessional home improvement shoppers. Bolstered by higher-margin items such as Laura Ashley paints and high-end bathroom fixtures, Lowe's has recently shown steady increases in its gross margins.

Home Depot CEO Bob Nardelli says that customer service is a priority at Home Depot. He ordered stores to restock at night so forklifts in the aisles would not detract from shopping during the day. Salespeople now spend 70 percent of their time with customers, where in the past they spent only 30 percent of their time with customers. Nardelli put Home Depot on a cost-cutting program and reengineered basic processes such as accounting, purchasing, and logistics. In effect, he overhauled the company's supply chain, tightening up inventory controls and customer return policies.

Home Depot, like Lowe's, also recognizes the importance of the female customer. Both chains are cleaning up their stores to reduce the clutter and warehouse feel. Better signage directs shoppers to the various departments, and better lighting improves the ambience of the stores. Lowe's is sticking with its singular format, while Home Depot also has 39 Expo Design Centers featuring upscale design concepts for new homes and major renovation projects. Home Depot is also instituting a program called At-Home Service to set up and install everything it sells to tap into the convenience-seeking portion of the home improvement market. Among its other innovations is a Web site to provide services to contractors that facilitates job planning, product selection, order pickup and delivery, and online payment.

Both Lowe's and Home Depot plan to add new stores as they fight for market share. Interestingly, Home Depot is downsizing many of its new stores so they can fit into densely populated areas. At the same time, Lowe's is moving away from its focus on small towns into Home Depot's backyard, opening larger stores in metro areas. In terms of their emphasis on the female consumer and in their plans for expansion, it certainly appears that Home Depot and Lowe's are going head-to-head in a fierce competitive battle.

Questions

1. Critics claim that Home Depot is doing too much too fast with its new Expo Design Center chain and its continuation of expanding through new stores. Is this a better strategy than Lowe's emphasis on a single store format?

2. How can Home Depot and Lowe's go beyond what they have done to attract the female shopper without losing ground with male shoppers?

3. How would the marketing strategy differ for the building contractor as compared to the nonprofessional home improvement shopper at Home Depot?

Chapter Fifteen

WHOLESALING AND LOGISTICS MANAGEMENT

15

After studying this chapter, you should be able to

1 Understand wholesaling and describe the three basic categories of wholesalers.

2 Identify and discuss the roles of different types of full-service and limited-function wholesalers.

3 Explain differences among the functions of agents, brokers, and commission merchants.

4 Understand the differences between manufacturers' sales branches and offices.

5 Appreciate how slow growth rates and globalization will affect wholesaling in the future.

6 Define logistics management and explain its key role in marketing.

7 Understand logistics activities, including warehousing, materials handling, inventory control, order processing, and transporting.

8 Discuss how some of the key ethical and legal issues affect logistics.

Grainger

W. W. Grainger, Inc., was founded in 1927 to meet the needs of customers who required products faster than manufacturers could deliver. Today Grainger is a leading business-to-business wholesaler, providing over 400,000 supply products and 5 million repair parts to more than 1.3 million commercial, industrial, contractor, and institutional customers around the world. Grainger represents some of the top suppliers in the world, including companies such as Fuji, Champion, Nutone, Briggs & Stratton, General Electric, and John Deere. The company's vision statement provides direction for its business: "To be a primary source through the breadth of our offering and a focus on the lowest total cost solution for each of our customers."

Grainger serves its customers from 600 branches with 15,500 employees, 1,900 of whom are customer sales representatives. A satellite network links all of the branches and nine distribution centers. Grainger truly covers the market, with 70 percent of all U.S. businesses located within 20 minutes of a Grainger branch.

A key part of Grainger's marketing communications effort is its catalog, which lists 220,000 products. E-commerce is also important to Grainger; online sales grew 25 percent in 2004. The company also has an online auction site and another site featuring six different companies offering thousands of products not stocked by Grainger.

Grainger clearly listens to its customers. The company uses surveys and focus groups to get feedback about product availability and service quality. Grainger's "No Excuses" policy empowers its employees to solve problems and ensure customer satisfaction. It has earned the trust of its customers, being named a preferred, distinguished, or select supplier for organizations such as Abbott Laboratories, Campbell Soup Company, 3M, Motorola, Masco, Tyson Foods, and Yale University.

Respect for the environment is another noteworthy aspect of Grainger's approach to business. Its catalog is printed with soy-based, nonpetroleum ink, and the color section and index are printed on recycled paper. Grainger also works with its paper suppliers to replenish natural resources; two trees are planted for every one that must be cut to print the catalog. The catalog also features many energy-saving products, identified with the "Energy Right" symbol.

The world of wholesaling, in contrast to retailing, does not often feature glamorous products. Nor are wholesaling companies part of our daily lives. Rather, it is from behind the scenes that Grainger and other leading wholesalers build value for their customers and keep the wheels of commerce rolling.

Ingram Micro is the largest global wholesaler of technology products, offering 280,000 products from 1,700 technology manufacturers.

In this chapter we discuss two key areas related to the marketing channel and the other marketing mix elements: wholesaling and logistics management. Briefly, **wholesalers** are intermediaries in the marketing channel that sell to customers other than individual or household consumers. **Logistics management** is the planning, implementation, and movement of goods, services, and related information from point of origin to point of consumption. Increasingly, logistics management involves supply chain management and the broader term supply management, discussed in Chapter 5.

Wholesalers are often involved in all five key functions of the marketing channel: marketing communications, inventory management, physical distribution, provision of market feedback, and assumption of financial risk. Logistics management also has some relevance to those functions, but it normally relates more specifically to inventory management and physical distribution activities. Logistics is an important function for wholesalers, especially if they handle the products they are reselling.

Wholesaling

Wholesaling is an important aspect of the marketing channel strategy for many firms. It refers to the marketing activities associated with selling products to purchasers that resell the products, use them to make another product, or use them to conduct business activities. Wholesaling does not include transactions with household and individual consumers, nor does it include the small purchases businesses occasionally make from retail stores. Essentially, wholesalers sell to manufacturers and industrial customers, retailers, government agencies, other wholesalers, and institutional customers such as schools and hospitals.

We mentioned in Chapter 13 that all intermediaries in a marketing channel, including wholesalers, must justify their existence by performing at least one function better than any other channel member. For wholesalers, this often means adding value to goods and services as they pass through the channel. For example, Computer Associates, a leading software company, uses **value-added resellers (VARs)** to sell to small and medium-sized business customers. Many of these customers do not have their own computer departments to design, implement, and maintain management information systems, so they need VARs to do it for them. Computer Associates VARs add value in many ways, including showing customers how to integrate existing systems with new technology, training customer employees, and providing technical support.

Types of Wholesalers

According to the U.S. Department of Commerce, the three basic categories of wholesalers are merchant wholesalers; agents, brokers, and commission merchants; and manufacturers' sales branches and offices. Exhibit 15–1 shows the three categories and the main types of wholesalers within each. Independent wholesalers that take title to the products they sell are called **merchant wholesalers**. Wholesalers in the second category, agents, brokers, and commission merchants, do not take title to the products bought or sold. They are sometimes referred to as *functional middlemen*. Those in the third category, manufacturers' sales branches and offices, are owned by producers or manufacturing firms.

Speaking from Experience

Don Becker
Owner
Becker Marketing Services, Inc.

"We have to add value to the products we buy from manufacturers in order to justify our position in the channel. How? By being the absolute product specialist in our custom polyethylene packaging niche—the go-to-guy for our customers; by providing the largest line of custom products available in the marketplace (perhaps 20–30 times what any one single manufacturer could provide); by buying with such clout that we are competitive even when we have to compete with other manufacturers; and by servicing our customers better than our competition."

Before founding his packaging wholesaling company, Don Becker worked in sales, product management, and sales management with Procter & Gamble and Mobil Corporation. He is a graduate of Drury College in Springfield, Missouri. Don is well aware of the need for wholesalers to constantly justify their position in the marketing channel.

Exhibit 15–1	*Categories and types of wholesalers*

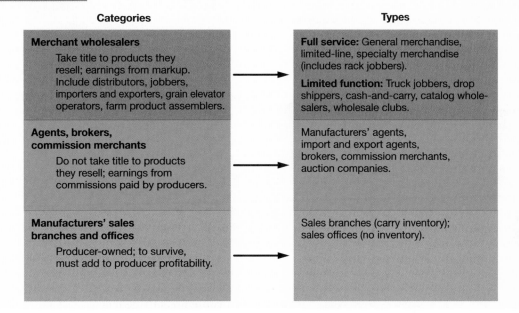

Categories

Merchant wholesalers
Take title to products they resell; earnings from markup. Include distributors, jobbers, importers and exporters, grain elevator operators, farm product assemblers.

Agents, brokers, commission merchants
Do not take title to products they resell; earnings from commissions paid by producers.

Manufacturers' sales branches and offices
Producer-owned; to survive, must add to producer profitability.

Types

Full service: General merchandise, limited-line, specialty merchandise (includes rack jobbers).

Limited function: Truck jobbers, drop shippers, cash-and-carry, catalog wholesalers, wholesale clubs.

Manufacturers' agents, import and export agents, brokers, commission merchants, auction companies.

Sales branches (carry inventory); sales offices (no inventory).

MERCHANT WHOLESALERS   According to the *Census of the Wholesale Trade*, published by the Department of Commerce, there are more than 375,000 merchant wholesalers based in the United States, accounting for 83 percent of the wholesale establishments in the country.[1] Merchant wholesalers, often called *distributors*, are categorized as either full-service wholesalers or limited-function wholesalers.

FULL-SERVICE WHOLESALERS   **Full-service wholesalers** by definition perform a wide range of services for their customers and the parties from which they purchase. These wholesalers might perform all key activities in an entire marketing channel (as in Exhibit 15–2), whereas limited-function wholesalers are likely to specialize in only a few activities.

Full-service wholesalers include general merchandise, limited-line, and specialty-line wholesalers. For a better idea of services available from full-service wholesalers, see Exhibit 15–3. **General merchandise wholesalers** carry a wide variety of products and provide extensive services for their customers. A typical example is Alabama Paper Company, which serves retail, industrial, and business customers throughout Alabama from its Birmingham warehouse. Its diverse product line, in excess of 5,000 items, includes consumer electronics, fishing and hunting merchandise, industrial adhesives and packaging materials, office supplies, and home improvement items. As a full-service wholesaler, Alabama Paper

| Exhibit 15–2 | Functions performed by wholesalers | | | | |

Type of Wholesaler	Marketing Communications*	Inventory Mgmt. and Storage	Physical Distribution	Market Feedback/ Advisory Board	Financial Risk/ Offer Credit†
Full-service merchant wholesalers	Yes	Yes	Yes	Yes	Yes
Truck jobbers	Yes	Yes	Yes	Sometimes	Sometimes
Drop shippers	No	No	Yes	Yes	Yes
Cash and carry	No	Yes	No	Sometimes	No
Catalog wholesalers	Yes	Yes	Yes	Sometimes	Sometimes
Wholesale clubs	Sometimes	Yes	No	Sometimes	No
Mfrs.' agents	Sometimes	Sometimes	Sometimes	Yes	No
Auction companies	Yes	Sometimes	No	No	No
Import and export agents	Sometimes	Sometimes	Sometimes	Yes	No
Brokers	No	No	No	Yes	No
Commission merchants	Yes	Yes	Sometimes	Yes	Sometimes
Mfrs.' sales branches	Sometimes	Yes	Yes	Yes	Yes
Mfrs.' sales offices	Sometimes	No	No	Yes	Yes

Note: Refer to Exhibit 13–2 for multiple examples of each functional area.

*By definition, all wholesalers are involved in at least one form of marketing communications (selling).

†All wholesalers not classified as agents, brokers, or commission merchants incur financial risk when they assume ownership, or take title, to the products they subsequently resell. This exhibit refers to the financial risk taken by wholesalers that offer credit to their customers.

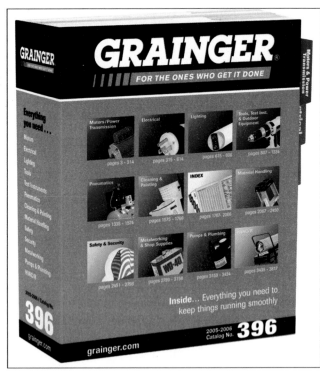

W. W. Grainger, featured in the chapter opener, is experiencing impressive sales growth through its electronic catalog.

performs many marketing channel functions and provides services for its customers and their suppliers.

Limited-line wholesalers do not stock as many products as general merchandise wholesalers, but they offer more depth in their products. Among merchant wholesalers, **specialty-line wholesalers** carry the most narrow product assortment—usually a single product line or part of one. To justify their existence, specialty-line wholesalers must be experts on the products they sell.

Rack jobbers, a category of specialty-line wholesalers, sell to retail stores. They set up and maintain attractive store displays and stock them with goods sold on consignment (the retailer pays for the goods only when sold). Rack jobbers are also called *service merchandisers,* a term that better captures the service-oriented aspects of their roles. Retailers depend on rack jobbers particularly in the provision of health and beauty aids, hosiery, and books and magazines. Some rack jobbers might be considered limited-function wholesalers if they carry very small inventories or fail to provide other services listed in Exhibit 15–2.

LIMITED-FUNCTION WHOLESALERS Exhibit 15–1 shows five primary types of **limited-function wholesalers**: truck jobbers, drop shippers, cash-and-carry wholesalers, catalog wholesalers, and wholesale clubs. As Exhibit 15–2 shows, these wholesalers do not offer the comprehensive services of full-service wholesalers.

Producers of fast-moving or perishable goods that require frequent replenishment often use **truck jobbers**. These limited-service wholesalers deliver within a particular geographic area to ensure freshness of certain goods (bakery, meat, dairy). Marketers often choose truck jobbers, with their quick delivery and frequent store visits, to wholesale miscellaneous high-margin items such as candy, chewing gum, cigarettes, novelty items, and

Exhibit 15-3	*Services provided by full-service wholesalers/distributors*	
Distributor Services	**To Manufacturer**	**To Retailer**
Sensible buying	• Market feedback improves production planning, reducing costs of raw materials, components.	• Distributor buying clout passed on through low prices. • Dealing with only one or two wholesalers cuts purchasing costs, leads to one-stop shopping.
Distribution flow	• Reduces storage needs, moves products faster, cuts inventory costs. • Products stored closer to retailer for faster delivery; may cut need for costly distribution centers.	• Weekly deliveries reduce need for product storage, increase selling space. • Faster turnover increases profits.
Timely delivery	• Large orders, retail delivery fleets, and coordinated back-haul programs reduce transportation costs, keeping product prices competitive.	• Regular deliveries permit better planning, cut receiving costs. • Fast restocking of high-demand products for immediate display.
Traffic-building promotion	• Centralized co-op programs maximize ad dollar at local level. • Increases consumer awareness, establishes products, builds market share.	• Direct-mail circulars, ads, and the like build retail traffic, increase store capabilities, save administrative effort. • Co-op programs save time, money.
Marketing	• Reduces selling costs, frees executive time as distributors serve many retail accounts; products receive wider representation.	• Retail sales training, merchandising, display, layout improve with distributor aid. • Computer systems provide price stickers and program margin requirements, optimize profits. • Hundreds of mfrs' products in one retail location.
Distributor Manages Assets	**Manufacturer Benefits**	**Retailer Benefits**
Product inventory	• Storage and delivery costs reduced to minimum. • Feedback on item movement improves production planning and use of assets.	• Turnover improved, promotional impact maximized, cash flow/return on investment increased. • In stock, good prices, superior service.
Physical plant	• Majority of plant used for production, not storage. • Need for regional redistribution facilities reduced or eliminated.	• More productive use of square footage ensured by lower inventory requirements, distributor printouts on product movement and margin management. • Market impact from merchandising assistance, in-store displays, signing, customer traffic flow.
Cash flow and credit	• Receivables minimized, credit risks reduced. • Administrative workload reduced.	• Cash flow accelerated through more frequent small purchases, less cash tied up in inventory. • Best credit terms, extended dating, less paperwork.
People	• Can concentrate on manufacturing and marketing; distributors take product to market. • Concentrating on distributor customers enhances strong relationships with fewer customers.	• Selling techniques, product knowledge enhanced through distributor training, sales aids. • One-on-one contact with distributor management to seize market opportunities.

inexpensive toys sold in retail stores. Retailers hate to be out of these items, for consumers will usually buy them at the next most convenient store instead.

Drop shippers arrange for shipments directly from the factory to the customer. Although they do not physically handle the product, drop shippers take title and all associated risks while the product is in transit. They also provide the necessary sales support. Drop shippers operate in a wide variety of industries, including industrial packaging, lumber, chemicals, and petroleum and heating products.

As the term implies, **cash-and-carry wholesalers** do not deliver the products they sell, nor do they extend credit. Small retailers and other businesses whose limited sales make them unprofitable customers for larger wholesalers are the primary customers for cash-and-carry wholesalers. For example, cash-and-carry wholesalers are common in coastal towns, serving restaurant and grocery customers who make daily trips to the wholesaler to purchase fresh seafood.

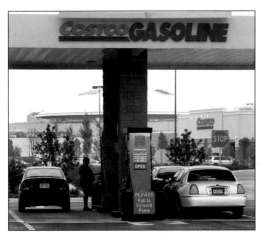

Costco Wholesale Corporation is an international operator of wholesale clubs with stores in North America, Asia, and the United Kingdom. Its clubs are larger than the average discount store and sell a variety of perishable and packaged food, clothing, automotive supplies, electronics, and other products.

Catalog wholesalers serve both major population centers and remote geographic locations and offer an alternative to cash-and-carry wholesalers. Most catalog wholesalers use delivery services such as UPS and require prepayment by check, money order, or credit card. Catalog wholesalers such as BrownCor International have established a large customer base by offering a wide range of competitively priced products, including office furniture, equipment, and supplies; directional signs; packaging materials; and shelf and storage systems. These products can be conveniently ordered using toll-free telephone or fax systems.

Wholesale clubs are a growing phenomenon. These enterprises, which also serve retail customers under the same roof, are especially popular with small business customers, civic and social organizations, and church groups. Wholesale club members pay an annual fee that entitles them to make tax-free purchases at lower-than-retail prices. As leaders such as Costco, BJ's Wholesale Club, and Sam's Club enjoy steady expansion, wholesale clubs are making major inroads into markets once dominated by older forms of wholesaling, such as office supply and institutional food wholesalers. They are also taking business away from certain types of retailers, such as supermarkets and tire dealers.

AGENTS, BROKERS, AND COMMISSION MERCHANTS Almost 48,000 agent, broker, and commission merchant organizations operate at the wholesale level, making up approximately 11 percent of all wholesale establishments. As Exhibit 15–1 indicates, these wholesalers do not take title to the products they resell. They perform a limited number of marketing channel activities, emphasizing sales or purchases (see Exhibit 15–2). Because these wholesalers perform so few marketing channel functions, they must be very knowledgeable and build strong relationships with their customers and suppliers to generate income through commissions.

AGENTS **Manufacturers' agents**, also called manufacturers' representatives or reps, constitute the largest group in this wholesale merchant category. There are more than 29,000 manufacturers' agents in the country, all of which sell related but noncompeting product lines for manufacturers. For example, Ruddell and Associates, a San Francisco firm, sells Christmas ornaments, greeting cards, candles, books, calendars, and novelty items to gift stores, all furnished by different manufacturers. Manufacturers' agents frequently work by contract with the companies they represent; they usually have exclusive rights to represent each manufacturer within a specified geographic area.

Another type of agent is the auction company, of which there are approximately 1,300 in the United States. Auction companies, also called **auction houses**, sell merchandise at a given time and place to the highest bidder. They typically promote the sale of the merchandise through advertising that specifies the time, date, and location of the auction, along with a description of the merchandise to be sold and the auction rules.

Auction houses are a popular way to sell livestock, tobacco, used automobiles, and art and antiques. Famous art auctioneers are Sotheby's, and Christie's, where works by noted artists sometimes fetch millions of dollars. Both the London-based Christie's and the New York–based Sotheby's are expanding into new international markets and searching for ways to further use the Internet for live auctions. An **online auction company** uses a computer network, typically the Internet, to bring buyers and sellers together. Online auction companies usually charge a nominal listing fee and collect a 5–8 percent commission on goods sold.

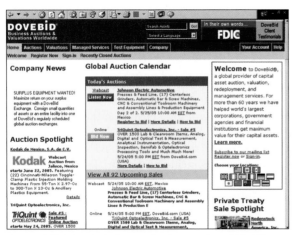

Agent wholesalers, including auction houses, do not take title to the products they sell. DoveBid is an online auction house specializing in business-to-business auctions.

The explosive growth of online auction sites is having a significant impact on wholesaling. Previously, online auction sites were dominated by person-to-person and business-to-person transactions. However, the business-to-business sector, including wholesaling, is showing signs of rapid growth. The leading online auction company, eBay, offers thousands of products at wholesale in large quantities. Books, computers, clothing, jewelry, tools, office supplies, toys, and electronics are just a few of the categories available at wholesale on eBay. To better service large-volume transactions, eBay provides sellers with value-added services, including sales strategy development, enhanced customer service, and improved logistical support.[2] The growth of eBay has been astonishing, reaching $3 billion in annual revenue faster than Microsoft and Dell Computer. eBay now operates in 31 countries and is expected to generate $6 billion in revenue by 2006.[3]

Online auction houses have established a strong presence in the sale of surplus equipment and other capital assets. DoveBid, a leading auction company in this sector, has handled the disposition of surplus goods for major corporations around the world, including Bank of America, IBM, Motorola, General Electric, and Xerox.[4] Both buyers and sellers like the large market reach of online auctions, and buyers especially like the idea of getting a bargain through the auction process. For sellers, the prospect of getting a fair market price for merchandise no longer needed or wanted is appealing. Further, online auctions are frequently a faster alternative for buyers compared to researching the market and finding a vendor. With technology constantly improving and easy access becoming more commonplace, expect online auctions to continue to grow in popularity.

Two other types of agents, import and export, specialize in international trade. **Import agents**—approximately 600 in the United States—find products in foreign countries to sell in their home countries. For example, cut flowers, available at lower cost outside the United States, are flown into the country daily. On a typical day, import agents arrange air cargo shipments from the Netherlands and South America to bring tulips, carnations, and roses to the United States. In many countries it is extremely difficult (or even illegal) to try to sell products from another country without going through an import agent or similar intermediary.

On the other hand, **export agents** locate and develop markets abroad for products manufactured in their home countries. Basically, they function as manufacturers' agents in the home country and are paid commissions by the companies they represent. There are more than 1,200 export agents in the United States. Export agents offer several advantages for companies seeking new markets, especially smaller companies. They offer exporters an opportunity to increase market exposure and sales volume with little financial investment or risk.

BROKERS Brokers are intermediaries that bring buyers and sellers together. They are paid a commission by either the buyer or the seller, depending on which party they represent in a given transaction. Unlike manufacturers' agents, brokers do not enter into contracts for extended periods with the parties they represent. Instead, they work on a transaction-by-transaction basis. There are approximately 8,600 wholesale broker firms in the United States, many of them in food and agricultural businesses.

COMMISSION MERCHANTS Commission merchants provide a wider range of services than agents or brokers, often engaging in inventory management, physical distribution, and promotional activities, and offering credit and market feedback to the companies they represent. More than 6,700 commission merchants operate in the United States, primarily working to sell agricultural products for farmers.

MANUFACTURERS' SALES BRANCHES AND OFFICES More than 29,000 manufacturer-owned wholesalers operate in the United States. Approximately 58 percent of these, or 17,000, are **manufacturers' sales branches**, which maintain inventory and perform a wide range of functions for the parent company. Manufacturers' sales branches handle delivery and act as an extension of the manufacturer to provide credit, market feedback, and promotional assistance.

Manufacturers' sales offices are the other significant type of producer-owned wholesaler, with more than 12,000 outlets in the United States. Sales offices do not maintain inventory, but they perform a limited range of functions, including assisting with sales and service, providing market feedback, and handling billing and collection for products sold.

Developments in Wholesaling

Three developments in wholesaling deserve special attention: the continuing struggle to grow, the globalization of wholesaling, and the increasing emphasis on developing relationships with others in the marketing channel.

WHOLESALERS FACE SLOW GROWTH   Wholesalers play an important role in the world economy, but growth is difficult to achieve. As power retailers such as Kroger, Office Depot, and Wal-Mart take over a larger share of the retail market, there has been an associated increase in retailers' buying directly from manufacturers, thus eliminating wholesalers. Wholesalers' positions in markets served by retailers could grow even more precarious. Industry observers see power in the channel continuing to shift toward retailers.

Other circumstances have threatened wholesalers, including a move to reduce overall health care costs. This puts pressure on a wide variety of wholesalers to reduce their costs; in addition, sales growth is decreasing as hospitals and other health care facilities are trying to reduce their usage of supplies and delaying major purchases, more so than in the past. Travel agents have also felt the pressure, with airlines and rental car companies cutting their commissions. Further, traditional wholesalers are facing more competition from transportation and distribution companies that are expanding the scope of their operations by offering services traditionally performed by wholesalers.

Wholesalers have taken several steps to combat tough market conditions. Some have grown through acquisition of other wholesalers, and others have expanded into retailing. Supervalu, the largest food and grocery wholesaler, has done both with its acquisition of another large wholesaler, Wetterau, and by operating its own stores under various names, including Cub Foods, bigg's, Farm Fresh, Scott's, and Shop'n Save.

GLOBALIZATION OF WHOLESALING   In response to tougher conditions in domestic markets, many American wholesalers have moved into international markets. Office Depot, which serves both retail and wholesale customers, has aggressively expanded its wholesale operations in international markets. It acquired Viking Office Products, a catalog and Internet wholesaler, to gain more coverage in seven European countries, Japan, and Australia. Office Depot is further expanding its international reach through its Business Services Group. In a dozen European countries it has established its own sales force to develop new business on a contract basis with large corporate accounts.[5] The Business Services Group can work more on an individual basis with major customers, offering them customized pricing and tailored logistics programs rather than the standard offerings available in the store, on the Internet, or from a catalog.

As U.S. wholesalers become more prominent in international trade, they are following a pattern of development shown in Exhibit 15–4. This pattern suggests that international wholesalers play an important role in servicing the needs of a country with a simple economy. As the country's economy reaches the advanced stage, however, the role of conventional wholesalers becomes less important. Finally, when the country becomes part of a global economy, international wholesalers reemerge as an important element in the economic system. The United States, along with its primary trading partners, is part of a growing global economy, a factor that may help wholesalers maintain or expand their base of business.

RELATIONSHIPS IN WHOLESALING   Many wholesalers are turning to partnerships with suppliers and customers to strengthen their market positions. Exemplifying the partnership approach is the highly successful Ingram Micro Inc., a large wholesale distributor of computer products. Ingram has designed storefront Web sites for the value-added resellers in its national distribution network that buy through Ingram. These Web sites feature the VARs' own brands. Customers who access the VAR sites see Ingram's enormous

Thinking Critically

Brothers Office Supply is a traditional office supply company, operating in a midwestern college town of 100,000. In addition to office supplies, Brothers sells high-quality office furniture. The company also sells calculators and electronic organizers, but it does not sell computers. Brothers's primary target market has been small and medium-sized companies. Business was good until Sam's Club opened a store nearby last year. Rumor has it that Office Depot will open within the coming year.

• How can Brothers Office Supply compete with these lower-priced competitors?

Exhibit 15–4   *Cyclical wholesaling patterns by stages of economic development*

Stages of Economic Development	Wholesaling Patterns
Simple economy	Dominance of international wholesalers (channels controlled by all-purpose wholesale merchants)
Expanding economy	Emergence of interregional wholesalers (regional specialization)
Maturing economy	Growth of specialized wholesalers (product-line and functional specialization)
Advanced economy	Decline of conventional wholesalers and regrouping by wholesalers (channels controlled by large-scale retailers and manufacturers)
Global economy	Reemergence of international wholesalers

inventory, wide range of services, and 24-hour delivery system. To the customer, the full scope of the local VAR's offering, as supplemented by Ingram, is readily apparent. The local VAR gets the credibility of a major corporation without the high overhead.[6]

Manufacturers are also finding that partnering with wholesalers can pay off. Kansas City–based Associated Wholesale Grocers (AWG) has partnered with manufacturers to service 478 grocery stores, winning special recognition from Procter & Gamble, the leading consumer goods manufacturer for nonfood items sold to the grocery industry.[7] AWG is credited with literally keeping many of its retail customers in business during an intense competitive battle with larger chains. Both manufacturers and retailers benefit from AWG's expertise in merchandise and display planning, market research, site selection, retail training, procurement and billing, and construction management support. Primarily due to AWG's support, its retail accounts hold 60 percent market share in Kansas City—running contrary to the national trend, where larger chains dominate.

Don Becker, owner of Becker Marketing Services, Inc., fully understands the importance of strong relationships with suppliers and customers: "It's only natural that there will be some friction and conflict in a marketing channel. As a wholesaler, my company is often caught in the middle, with the supplier pushing me in one direction and the customer pulling me in another. Our people have been able to establish strong relationships with most of our customers and suppliers. When it looks like we're heading for a major disagreement, I remind customers and suppliers that we are in this together, and that everybody has to benefit. Sometimes I'll sacrifice, sometimes the customer compromises, and sometimes the supplier has to pitch in something extra—all for the good of the long-term relationship."

Logistics Management

Logistics management, as defined at the beginning of the chapter, deals with the movement of goods, services, and related information from point of origin to point of consumption. The importance of logistics management has increased in today's environment, marked by the use of speed as a competitive edge (to deliver customers' orders, for example), development of exciting new computer technologies, and increased realization that overall operating costs are extremely sensitive to the various costs of handling and holding inventory.

In progressive companies, logistics management has moved far beyond shipping and receiving to become a differentiating factor in marketing strategy. Logistics is instrumental in meeting such challenges as increasing responsiveness to customers, maintaining market position, stemming price erosion, and maintaining competitiveness in domestic and international markets. Consumers and business buyers are increasingly saying "I want it now!" More and more marketers are providing quality products at competitive prices. But that is not enough unless the product is available at the right time in the right place. As electronic commerce becomes more prevalent, marketers face the challenge of developing new logistics systems to deal directly with customers rather than always relying on wholesalers and traditional retail stores for distribution.

Logistics management relies on a variety of methods for moving products and materials, including cargo planes and oceangoing supertankers. In some cases, simple means of transportation are used, such as with these UPS motorcycles in Brussels and this dogsled for newspaper delivery in North Dakota.

Importance of Logistics to Marketing

The drive to enhance customer satisfaction while simultaneously improving productivity and profitability has put logistics in the spotlight in the marketing efforts of many successful firms. For example, Star Furniture Company, a subsidiary of Berkshire Hathaway and the largest furniture retailer in Texas, revamped its logistics system to gain considerable clout with its customers. As it became more important to buy furniture manufactured in Asia, Star partnered with three other Berkshire Hathaway retailers to negotiate favorable freight rates and arranged to use all-water transportation from Asia to Houston. Retail customers benefited in several ways. First, product costs were reduced, and retail prices reflected these lower costs. Second, customers got the quality they were seeking. Finally, the information technology in the system allowed Star to make firm, reliable delivery commitments to its customers. According to Star's vice president of logistics, "Being flexible and giving your customers extra service while keeping prices competitive is how you stay in business."[8] For another example of how logistics can be critical to successful marketing, see "Creating Customer Value: VF Uses Logistics to Fuel Growth."

The logistics system should be as economical as possible while achieving an acceptable level of customer satisfaction. To keep customers satisfied, a logistics system should be easy to use and dependable and offer timely information. These attributes are detailed in Exhibit 15–5.

CREATING CUSTOMER VALUE

VF uses logistics to fuel growth

VF, the largest apparel company in the world, is the parent company to Chic, Gitano, Wrangler, The North Face, Nautica, Van's, and Jansport. Not only does VF understand how to stay ahead of the curve with product design and advertising, but the company also knows how to build value for its retailer customers through logistics management. Take the case of The North Face, acquired by VF in 2000. When purchased by VF, The North Face had become notorious for shipping its orders late or incomplete. The company was operating at a loss despite its reputation for outstanding product quality and a fanatical following by the most demanding outdoor enthusiasts.

After the VF takeover, North Face benefited from VF's understanding that superior logistics can give a company a competitive advantage. According to VF CEO Mackey McDonald, "A lot of clothing companies lack the discipline to deliver the right product at the right time. That's an opportunity for us." After integrating The North Face into VF's supply chain systems, VF saw its investment pay off almost immediately. North Face turned a profit within a year and is now VF's fastest-growing brand. There is no doubt that VF and The North Face understand that in fast-moving retail markets, it is not enough to have the best product—the best product has to be on the shelf when the customer is ready to buy to ensure success.

Exhibit 15-5	*Customer expectations of suppliers' logistics systems*

- Timely pickups for outgoing orders
- On-time delivery
- Prompt settlement of claims for damaged or lost merchandise
- Accurate invoicing
- Interactive Web site for tracking and customer service
- Well-trained drivers and customer support staff
- Process for analyzing and correcting service failures
- Centralized, accessible customer service
- Good communication with customers
- Responsiveness from all supplier departments

Key Activities in Logistics

Logistics includes five key functions: warehousing, materials handling, inventory control, order processing, and transporting raw materials and finished products from origin to destination. In the best logistics systems, these areas are carefully coordinated to gain customer satisfaction at an affordable cost.

WAREHOUSING   Companies can choose private or public warehouses or distribution centers. *Private warehouses* are operated by the company using the warehouse. *Public warehouses* are for-hire facilities available to any business requiring storage or handling of goods. Public warehouses charge fees for storage and handling (receiving and moving goods out of storage).[9]

Distribution centers are superwarehouses that serve a large geographic area. These automated warehouses do more than store products; they receive, process, and ship customer orders. Technological advances have allowed companies to save money and provide better service through distribution centers. Among the many companies using distribution centers are manufacturers such as Nike, Komatsu Dresser (heavy equipment), and Troll Associates (children's books); retailers such as 50-Off Stores, Athlete's Foot, Williams-Sonoma, Wal-Mart, McCrory Stores, and General Motors; and online merchant Amazon.com.

With the increased volume of online buying, many companies are utilizing distribution centers that specialize in e-commerce. Warehouses designed for e-commerce differ from those designed for distributing consumer goods to retail stores. E-commerce warehouses are designed to pick and ship individual items to customers in a wide geographic area, whereas traditional warehousing for retail stores typically distributes large quantities of a given item in palletized truckload or railcar shipments. The demise of many e-retailers in the early part of this decade opened up a lot of available warehousing capacity, but prospective users had to consider whether the storage, stock picking, and conveyor systems would be compatible with their needs. In some cases, the fit matched, and companies were able to add warehousing at bargain prices. Such was the case with KB Toy Stores, which acquired a 440,000-square-foot distribution center from the bankrupt eToys.com. KB uses the center to supplement its distribution system for its online division.[10]

MATERIALS HANDLING   Materials-handling activities include receiving, identifying, sorting, and storing products, and retrieving the goods for shipment. The use of technology is extremely important in this area of logistics. Bar coding is among the most noteworthy of the technological advances in materials handling, particularly in distribution centers. **Bar coding**, which allows a product to be identified by its computer-coded bar pattern, is used in a variety of logistics functions. Big Dog Logistics uses bar coding as an integral part of its systems for servicing a wide range of clients, including publishing companies, pharmaceutical companies, retailers, and transportation companies. Bar codes facilitate warehousing, sorting, and

Logistics includes warehousing, materials handling, inventory control, order processing, and transporting products to customers. This Unilever facility conducts all of the major logistical functions for retail customers in Nigeria.

shipping functions in a mobile network of cell phones, personal data appliances such as the Palm Pilot, and two-way radios. The bar codes allow accurate tracking of shipments and inventory assessment as products move through the supply chain.[11]

A **radio frequency identification (RFID)** may eventually replace bar codes. RFID allows the printing of radio antennas that can be affixed to products in place of a bar code. The advantage is that an entire container of diverse items could be scanned instantly at a distance, rather than up close and one item at a time, as is the case with bar codes. The application of RFID to warehousing, order processing, and shipping seems inevitable now that costs for producing the radio tags are declining. Wal-Mart and Home Depot are among the most enthusiastic backers of RFID, with Wal-Mart already using the technology to track Coca-Cola, Bounty paper towels, and Gillette's Mach 3 razors through Sam's Club.[12] For more on RFID, see "Using Technology: RFID—Ready for Immediate Distribution?"

INVENTORY CONTROL   Another key area of logistics is inventory control, which attempts to ensure adequate inventory to meet customer needs without incurring additional costs for carrying excess stock. Two such inventory control systems are in place in many industries: just-in-time and quick-response systems. Rarely used before 1990, these systems are now commonplace.

Just-in-time (JIT) inventory control systems apply primarily to the materials-handling side of logistics. These systems deliver raw materials, subassemblies, and component parts to manufacturers shortly before the scheduled manufacturing run that will consume the incoming shipment—thus the JIT label. Automobile manufacturers are among the most enthusiastic users of JIT systems, and suppliers often locate manufacturing or distribution facilities near automobile plants to provide prompt service at a reasonable cost.

Don Becker, owner of Becker Marketing Services, Inc., comments on the JIT process: "In the years I have had my own company, as a middleman (broker) selling to other middlemen (stocking wholesale distributors), it has been very important for us to select and sell our products to wholesale distributors that believe in buying in large quantities (of custom-produced product) and providing JIT to their customers, the end users. By JIT, I mean the end user customer calling for an order and the wholesale distributor delivering the order in one hour, if necessary. By linking ourselves to the right distributor, we have been able to build a large business satisfying hundreds of end user customers."

Quick-response (QR) inventory control systems are used by companies that provide retailers with finished goods. Quick-response systems are based on frequent but small orders because inventory is restocked according to what has just been sold—yesterday or even today in some systems. By melding strategy and technology, retailers such as Wal-Mart, Kmart, and Dillard's have matched up with vendors like Procter & Gamble, Gitano, and baby clothes manufacturer Warren Featherstone to improve both responsiveness to the marketplace and productivity. Exhibit 15–6 describes the key steps required to implement a QR system.

USING TECHNOLOGY

RFID—Ready for immediate distribution?

Radio frequency identification (RFID) has been on the launching pad for several years, and analysts think it will reach full lift-off any day now. In 2003 Wal-Mart decreed that its top 100 suppliers would implement RFID by January 1, 2005. When the deadline arrived, only 57 of the top 100 were in compliance, and Wal-Mart did not fire any of the noncomplying vendors. Despite a lack of full compliance by Wal-Mart's suppliers, most industry observers say that RFID will in fact be the next big thing in logistics and supply chain management.

The benefits of knowing where each item is at any time can extend from the point of production all the way through the channel. When benefits to retail customers help drive increased sales, the costs of implementing RFID will be less of an issue. For example, retail customers equipped with handheld scanners and computers could check their home inventory before heading out to shop or have a frozen dinner transmit cooking instructions to the microwave. Another driver of RFID technology is concern for security during shipment. The Departments of Defense and Homeland Security are interested in RFID to determine the contents of shipping containers and to know if the contents are changed during transit.

Key activities in quick-response systems

- Retailers track sales and inventory for each item (stock-keeping unit).
- Automatic replenishment systems monitor stock to support smaller, more frequent shipments.
- Retailers assume responsibility for inventory carrying costs.
- Vendors commit to high level of service, stressing shipping accuracy and on-time delivery.
- Retailers share data with vendors to help plan production and commit to specific volume of purchases.
- Vendors mark shipping containers to speed delivery through distribution center to stores.

Thinking Critically

Jean Robbins is a sales representative for Cribben Paper and Plastics Supply Company, a wholesaler to the garment manufacturing industry. One of Jean's customers is a large Arrow shirt manufacturing plant. The plant buys preprinted bags in which the shirts will be displayed and sold in retail stores. Cribben maintains a stock of the bags in its warehouse and ships to Arrow on a JIT basis. Recently, the plant manager has threatened to buy directly from the bag manufacturer in truckload quantities, approximately 1,000 cases, or a month's supply. He claims he can get the bags at a 20 percent discount by buying direct.

- What should Jean do to keep her business with Arrow?

Participants in quick-response systems must join together in a logistics partnership. A true partnership is necessary because buyers and sellers share sensitive information and must maintain constant communication. In fact, QR systems require so much information exchange that they take massive investments to implement. Bar coding and point-of-retail-sale scanning devices are needed. **Shipping container marking (SCM)** systems must be installed so tracking information can be fed into a computerized information system. This system is referred to as an **electronic data interchange (EDI)**.

EDIs are becoming increasingly popular for firms operating in global markets. For example, Xicor, Inc., a California-based computer circuit manufacturer with about 60 percent of its sales outside the United States, developed an EDI system to better meet the needs of its customers, including IBM, Samsung, Motorola, and Alcatel. Around the world, Xicor uses independent salespeople and distributors who need real-time information about product availability and shipping status. Xicor's EDI system bypasses regional and local offices in favor of a centralized location for all data utilized in the system. The system allows trading partners, salespeople, and end-user customers to coordinate production and shipping, saving Xicor time and money and virtually eliminating the possibility of inventory management mistakes.[13]

As EDI becomes more popular, progressive companies are trying to move beyond linked systems to those that can run on the Internet. Cost savings can be substantial, and access is available with a PC and an Internet connection. Home Depot, Office Depot, and Barnes & Noble are among those making extensive use of Web-based EDI. Barnes & Noble, for example, uses Web-based EDI for about 1,200 of its 30,000 suppliers. Those using the Web-based version of EDI tend to be Barnes & Noble's largest suppliers, while smaller publishers use traditional EDI.[14] The growth of Web-based EDI is promising, yet traditional EDI with direct communication between companies' computers is expected to remain a significant means of conducting business for years to come.[15]

With a true partnership agreement, technology such as electronic data interchanges, and other resources such as personnel and training, QR systems offer the potential benefits shown in Exhibit 15–7.

Although JIT and QR systems offer impressive advantages, they can present drawbacks as well. Heightened security on shipments, particularly those coming from foreign countries, has slowed shipments and jeopardized production schedules of manufacturers that use JIT. Most major U.S. automakers have been affected, causing them to scale back production and even close plants. Ford, for example, closed five factories and cut production 13 percent in response to slower shipments from Mexico, Japan, and Europe.

Potential benefits of quick-response inventory control

- Reduced negotiating costs for both buyer and seller.
- Increased responsiveness to marketplace needs.
- Stability of supply to the buyer and demand to the seller.
- Smoothing of production runs (fewer peaks and valleys).
- Decreased investment in inventory and storage space.
- Fewer out-of-stock occurrences.
- Higher levels of customer satisfaction.

This distribution center in St. Louis, Missouri, features bar-code scanners for routing orders through an automated system that selects the items to be shipped, prints the customer invoice, and sends the products to the shipping docks.

Creating and continuously enhancing customer value is a key focus of logistics companies. In this add, TRANSFLO stresses its understanding of customer needs, including managing the supply chain.

With no extra inventory on hand for key parts, Ford had little choice but to close plants once the delays set in. To ensure a steady, timely flow of parts, Ford eventually spent over a billion dollars to bail out Viseton, a former subsidiary and its largest parts supplier.[16] Ford's ordeal serves as a reminder that marketers are never completely insulated from inventory control problems, whatever the technological advances. Cautious marketers may shun quick-response systems in favor of carrying extra inventory, at a cost.

ORDER PROCESSING   Order-processing activities are critical to ensure that customers get what they order, when they want it, properly billed, and with appropriate service to support its use or installation. Accuracy and timeliness are key goals of order entry processes. QR and JIT systems automatically handle order-processing activities. In other situations, order processing includes order entry, order handling, and scheduling for delivery. The term *order* here refers either to a customer's purchase order or to an order transmitted by a salesperson. Order handling entails procedures such as communicating the order to the shipping department or warehouse, clearing the order for shipping, or scheduling it for production. Eventually the order is selected from stock, packaged, and scheduled for delivery. The order documentation becomes part of the customer's file of transactions with the seller. See Appendix B for mathematical calculations related to the determination of order quantities.

TRANSPORTING   The final logistics activity we consider in this chapter is transporting, which starts with selecting modes of transportation for delivery of products or materials. Shippers have five basic ways to move products and materials from one point to another—rail, truck, air, pipeline, and water transport—and each has advantages and disadvantages. Logistics managers must assess each mode for costs, reliability, capacity, ability to deliver to customer receiving facilities, transit time, and special handling requirements such as refrigeration and temperature control, safety controls, and the capacity to deliver undamaged goods.

RAILROADS   Railroads carry approximately 40 percent of all U.S. freight, most of which is heavyweight, bulk cargoes. Railcars are the major shipping mode for coal, grain, chemicals, metallic ores, stone, sand, and gravel. Two-thirds of the automobiles manufactured in the United States move at least part of the way to dealerships on railroads.[17]

Rail transport is fairly reliable but subject to interruption due to periodic labor disputes. These interruptions are usually short, and the federal government has often intervened to prevent massive shutdowns of rail service.

TRUCKS   Trucks can deliver almost anywhere, which is particularly important for customers that lack a rail siding. Their fairly fast transit time makes trucks extremely effective and efficient for delivery to destinations within 500 miles. Trucking companies face more competition, primarily from railroads, on long-haul trips than on short-haul trips. Although generally reliable, trucks can be negatively affected by inclement weather. Trucking has also been hampered at times by labor strikes, more so than have railroads.

Technology, especially in mobile communications and tracking equipment, plays an important role for successful trucking companies such as Roadway Express, J. B. Hunt, and M. S. Carriers. The human factor is important too. From a marketing point of view, the top priority for most trucking firms is recruiting, training, and retaining drivers. Considering the role that logistics can play in increasing customer satisfaction and profitability, trucking firms should emphasize hiring dependable drivers who can enhance customer relationships. With the increasing need for home delivery from e-retailers, and the expectation that the world economy will grow at least moderately in coming years, there is little doubt that a shortage of qualified truck drivers will continue to be a major concern for trucking firms. The American Trucking Association estimates that the current shortage of 20,000 truck drivers could grow to 110,000 by 2014.[18] According to an ATA spokesperson, the driver shortage is at an all-time high and significantly limits the amount of freight that can be moved by truck.

AIR FREIGHT   Air freight is tops in speed but highest in transportation cost. Sometimes air freight is an integral part of a company's operations, as with catalog businesses or firms marketing perishable items from faraway destinations, such as Maine lobster delivered to seafood restaurants in California. The air freight business is experiencing little growth, with the average air freight volume of FedEx and UPS, the dominant air shippers, dropping for more than a year. Interestingly, FedEx and UPS are partly responsible for their own decline in air shipping, as both companies have made significant upgrades to their ground shipping alternatives. With improved delivery from their trucks, FedEx and UPS are finding that many customers simply do not see the value in paying more for air shipments. Another factor working against air shippers is increased airport security, especially if shipments are going into the cargo hold of a commercial flight. As global trade increases, air shipping will benefit. For domestic deliveries, however, overnight shipping, the key service offered by FedEx, UPS, and DHL, is not expected to return to its days as a growth business.

PIPELINES   Pipelines, such as the Alaska Pipeline, transport chemicals, gases, liquefied fossil fuels, and petroleum products. They offer fairly low-cost, reliable transportation to a limited number of destinations. Although the operation of a pipeline uses little energy, pipeline construction arouses environmental concerns about the land under which the line must travel.

WATER   Water transport is a good, low-cost alternative for large quantities of bulky products that must be shipped long distances. This includes bulk shipments of agricultural products, automobiles to and from foreign countries, and petroleum from distant oil-producing nations.

In the United States, water transport is available primarily in the eastern part of the country. The Mississippi River carries a large proportion of the country's water transport, and other rivers serve Cincinnati and Chicago. Rivers are also shipping routes for large amounts of cargo along the Gulf Coast between New Orleans and Houston, and between the Pacific Ocean and Portland, Oregon.

In the Great Lakes region, freighters carry huge shipments of raw materials—such as iron ore to Detroit—to service the automobile manufacturing industry. Other destinations served via the Great Lakes include

Both the relationship and global perspectives are illustrated with YFM Direct, a strategic alliance between Yellow Freight System and Royal Mass Group of The Netherlands. YFM provides truck delivery of trans-Atlantic shipments throughout North America and Western Europe.

Milwaukee, Buffalo, Chicago, and Toronto. The St. Lawrence Seaway, stretching from Lake Ontario to Montreal, can handle both barge traffic and oceangoing vessels. This project was jointly financed by the United States and Canada, with Canada providing approximately three-fourths of the necessary funds.

INTERMODAL Although one mode of transportation may get the job done for a given shipper, **intermodal shipping** is often the choice. This involves the use of two or more modes of transportation. Loaded trailers, for example, may travel piggyback on railcars or in "stack trains."

Large retailers, including Home Depot, JCPenney, Gart Sporting Goods, and Target, receive goods that are shipped by intermodal means. This method is particularly well suited for shipments that originate in distant locations. For example, U.S. retailers receiving goods from Asia might be best served by a combination of water, rail, and truck delivery to move the product from point of origin to in-store locations.

The outlook for intermodal shipping is fairly positive because the right combination of transportation modes can optimize costs versus speed and other service considerations. Over the past decade, intermodal shipping involving railways has been the fastest-growing segment in the rail industry. Intermodal shipping is now the number one revenue generator for railroads, surpassing coal for the first time in 2003.[19]

Ethical and Legal Issues in Logistics

The legal environment for logistics is shaped by thousands of local, state, national, and international laws, tax codes, and tariff regulations that govern the movement of materials and products. The Interstate Commerce Commission, Federal Maritime Commission, and Department of Transportation are the major U.S. regulatory agencies.

The **deregulation** of transportation industries that began in the 1970s sought to promote free competition among carriers. Over the past three decades, many marginal transportation providers that engaged in unethical and/or inefficient practices have disappeared from the scene. Generally speaking, deregulation helped to reward companies that strive for high levels of customer satisfaction, facilitated the move to expand internationally, and encouraged the development of solid business relationships based on both economics and trust between parties.

An emphasis on ethical considerations remains an important aspect of logistics management. This is readily apparent with safety issues. Recent events have led to more vigilance over products as they move through the supply chain, and there is an important need for cooperation between government agencies, shippers, receivers, and law enforcement agencies to minimize the risk to employees and the general public. FedEx has taken a lead position in the fight against terrorism, urging its 250,000 employees to be spotters of potential terrorists. The company has a unit called the FedEx Police, a detective unit that works with the FBI to deter terrorism and uses detectors to sniff for explosives in overseas facilities.[20] In addition to the concerns over what may happen to cargo while in transit, other safety issues include the use of oversized truck trains (trucking rigs pulling two 28-foot trailers) and working conditions for operators. In the trucking and water transportation industries, operator fatigue has been a long-standing safety issue. As the trucking industry grows faster than the highway infrastructure, traffic congestion is a growing concern for safety and air quality reasons. Such issues raise ethical and legal questions.

Shippers have a responsibility to protect their employees and the general public from unsafe practices and materials. It is obvious that some materials such as explosives or corrosive chemicals require special handling; but other less obvious products might also pose dangers. Ignorance or negligence can be costly, as in the deadly 1996 Value Jet airlines crash, which was caused by improper shipping of oxygen tanks.

Shippers are being held more accountable for their impact on the environment. With stricter emission standards being placed in effect by the Environmental Protection Agency in 2007, the trucking industry is testing new technology, including low-sulfur diesel engines, hybrid engines, and tires that can improve fuel efficiency.[21] Along with the trucking industry, the rail industry has joined the EPA's SmartWay transport program to reduce locomotive fuel consumption and emissions.[22]

As logistics managers and wholesalers face the future, they must surely see the exciting prospect of playing an ever-increasing critical role in marketing. Change and adaptation will be necessary for the survival of individual firms, and the management of information will play a key role for survivors. But wholesalers and logistics managers have tremendous technology at their disposal and can remain strong links in the chain that ultimately delivers customer satisfaction, profitability, and success.

Summary

1. **Understand wholesaling and describe the three basic categories of wholesalers.** An important part of marketing, *wholesaling* refers to the activities associated with selling products to purchasers that resell the products, use them to make another product, or use them to conduct business activities.

   The three basic categories of wholesalers are merchant wholesalers; agents, brokers, and commission merchants; and manufacturers' sales branches and offices. Some of these wholesalers provide a wide range of services, while others offer a narrow range of specialized services.

2. **Identify and discuss the roles of different types of full-service and limited-function wholesalers.** There are three main types of full-service wholesalers: general merchandise, limited-line, and specialty-line wholesalers. Of these, general merchandise wholesalers carry the broadest assortment of products and provide extensive services to their customers. These services may involve promotional assistance, inventory management and storage, physical distribution, market feedback, assumption of financial risk, and offering of credit.

   The two others carry progressively smaller and more specialized assortments and provide different levels of service. Limited-function wholesalers include truck jobbers, drop shippers, cash-and-carry wholesalers, catalog wholesalers, and wholesale clubs. Of these, catalog wholesalers and wholesale clubs showed the most growth in recent years.

3. **Explain differences among the functions of agents, brokers, and commission merchants.** Agents, brokers, and commission merchants concentrate on making sales or purchases. They do not take title to the products they resell. These types of wholesalers must be quite knowledgeable to develop strong relationships with their customers and suppliers. They are paid a commission, a percentage of the value of each completed sale or purchase.

4. **Understand the differences between manufacturers' sales branches and offices.** Manufacturers' sales branches maintain inventory, handle delivery, and act as an extension of the manufacturer for a wide variety of services. Manufacturers' sales offices offer a narrower range of services, primarily because they do not maintain inventory.

5. **Appreciate how slow growth rates and globalization will affect wholesaling in the future.** Slow growth rates in most developed economies are putting a significant amount of pressure on wholesalers, which often face declining profit margins. As large retail chains gain more power and increase direct purchases from manufacturers, wholesalers can expect tough operating conditions to continue.

To cope with slow growth, wholesalers often enter into relationships with manufacturers, customers, and in some cases, other wholesalers. Global markets offer more growth potential for some wholesalers. As trade between nations becomes easier, wholesalers will have opportunities that have been difficult to realize in the past. Further, as developing economies grow, wholesalers that have the capability to conduct business outside the domestic marketplace can benefit by supplying them.

6. **Define logistics management and explain its key role in marketing.** Logistics management describes the planning, implementing, and controlling of the movement of goods, services, and related information from point of origin to point of consumption. In recent years, logistics management has grown more important in overall marketing strategies, because customer satisfaction is greatly affected by factors such as responsiveness to special shipping requirements and condition of delivered merchandise.

7. **Understand logistics activities, including warehousing, materials handling, inventory control, order processing, and transporting.** Some firms use independently owned public warehouses; others operate their own private warehouses or distribution centers. Materials-handling activities include receiving, identifying, sorting, storing, and retrieving goods for shipment. Inventory control is used to meet customer stock requirements without incurring excessive costs of carrying inventory. Just-in-time and quick-response systems are examples of inventory control programs used in a wide variety of industries.

   Order processing, triggered by the customer's purchase order, includes order entry, order handling, and delivery scheduling. The final part of logistics is transporting, which requires decisions about how to ship the product. Shippers may choose among rail, truck, air, pipeline, and water transport, or some combination of these modes.

8. **Discuss how some of the key ethical and legal issues affect logistics.** The deregulation of the freight delivery industry over the past three decades has generally produced positive results. Shippers are more competitive, and there is more emphasis on customer satisfaction, partnerships between shippers and clients, and ethical business behavior. Safety issues are more important than ever in the shipping industry. Protection of in-transit cargo, working conditions for vehicle operators, and the use of oversized trucking trains are among the safety issues with ethical and legal implications. Increasingly, shippers are taking an active role in improving the environment through gains in fuel efficiency and reduction of harmful emissions.

Understanding Marketing Terms and Concepts

Thinking about Marketing

1. What is wholesaling? What are the three basic categories of wholesalers?

2. Which category of wholesalers does not take title to products they resell? What types of wholesalers fall into this category?

3. How do manufacturers' agents differ from manufacturers' branch offices?

4. In the grocery industry, are wholesalers becoming more or less powerful in the marketing channel?

5. Why has logistics management become more important in marketing during recent years?

6. Review "Creating Customer Value: VF Uses Logistics to Fuel Growth." How important is it for suppliers to deliver complete orders on time to retail accounts?

7. What are the key activities in logistics management?

8. What are the benefits of a quick-response inventory control system?

9. What are the five basic ways to move products and materials from one point to another? What are the key factors to be considered when choosing among these modes of transport?

10. Review "Using Technology: RFID—Ready for Immediate Distribution?" How does this concept create value for manufacturers and retailers?

Applying Marketing Skills

1. Assume you are the traffic manager for a large manufacturer of consumer goods. Your company is designing a quick-response delivery system for several large retail accounts. The system includes railcar delivery to distribution centers, direct-to-store truck delivery in a few isolated locations, and emergency service by air freight. What can you do to get feedback from your customers to aid in the design and implementation of the system?

2. Periodically, floods in the midwestern United States disrupt shipments of grain by barge on the Mississippi River. Which other modes would be logical for shipping grain? How would massive flooding affect these modes?

3. An established rock group is thinking about firing its agent of five years. The agent gets 10 percent of all concert revenues and 1 percent of all other band-related profits, including those from merchandising agreements, commercial work, and paid TV appearances. The band members basically feel the agent is not really earning his seven-figure annual income. How would you advise the band? What factors should be considered before hiring another agent or, alternatively, eliminating the agent in favor of a less expensive salaried manager? [*Hint: This exercise pertains to the wholesaling portion of the chapter.*]

Using the www in Marketing

Activity One Grainger, described in the chapter opener, is a leading business-to-business wholesaler. Review the Grainger Web site at *http://www.grainger.com* and answer these questions.

1. In which category of wholesalers does Grainger fit? Within the chosen category, which type is Grainger? (Refer to Exhibit 15–1.)

2. What services does Grainger offer its international customers? Do these services add value to the tangible products sold by Grainger?

Activity Two Many countries are signing onto the Internet to facilitate trade with other countries. Check the Trade Commission of Mexico Web site at *http://www.mexico-trade.com.* This site lists selected Mexican exporters classified by industry sector. There is also a comprehensive resource guide covering Mexico's economic, legal, and political systems.

1. Select three exporters that you think would be promising for national distribution in the United States, and give your reasoning. To complete this portion of the exercise, click on the "Services" link, then the "Trade Leads in Mexico" link.

2. Compare business practices for exporters to Mexico to business practices in your home country. To complete this portion of the assignment, examine the information from the "Doing Business in Mexico" link. List a minimum of five business practices that are different from those in your home country, and explain the differences.

Making Marketing Decisions

Case 15–1 Gallo: Distributor Support a Key to Success

E & J Gallo Winery, based in Modesto, California, is a world sales leader in a wide variety of categories. In the United States, Gallo sells about 25 percent of all wine. Among its most important corporate priorities is to expand and strengthen its distribution network, comprising 630 distributors that sell Gallo's 3,000 products to 300,000 retail accounts in 120 countries.

To support its wholesale distribution network, Gallo coordinates its marketing, sales, supply chain management, and information systems activities. Gallo's supply chain management is responsible for synchronizing the receipt of raw materials, glass manufacturing, wine processing, and logistics management of its regional distribution centers. By managing the supply chain from the flow of raw materials from their points of origin all the way to the retailer or distributor, Gallo gives its distributors the quick, dependable delivery with minimal back orders that drives maximum sales in the field. Tight controls minimize the opportunities that competitors may have from Gallo out-of-stock occurrences at the retail level.

Gallo's marketing personnel provide distributors with consumer research, media planning and advertising support, and videos to support distributor training and promotional activities. Marketing personnel work with Gallo's information systems personnel to keep distributors up-to-date on changes in the marketplace and detailed shopping information that can be used to tailor promotions for individual retail stores. For example, when Gallo introduced Turning Leaf wines in a 1.5-liter bottle, having specific retailer-level information helped distributors decide which stores would be best for point-of-purchase displays and other in-store promotions. The information system, called the Sales Management Information System (SMIS), is updated monthly, an important activity because competitive activity varies widely and an estimated 6,000 retail stores open, close, or change ownership every month.

Prior to implementing SMIS, Gallo lacked a complete view of what was happening once its product entered the distributors' stock. Losing sight of shipments once they got to the distributor made it difficult to plan, execute, and measure the success of various retailer-aimed marketing efforts. Now distributors give Gallo high marks for supplying them with relevant information. Impressed with how much Gallo knows about its retail customers, distributor customer satisfaction with Gallo is on the increase.

Gallo's salespeople work directly with their distributors to build sales volume and market share. They are responsible for distributor support in shelf, cold box, and special display merchandising; facilitating advertising and promotion; keeping the distributor competitive in the pricing area; assisting in restaurant merchandising; and making sales calls with distributor salespeople.

Throughout its 70-year history, Gallo has depended on its wholesale distribution network to reach its market. Through systematic market research and analysis, along with on-site support from Gallo sales-people and marketing campaigns designed for local retailers, Gallo continues to pursue its stated corporate priority of strengthening its wholesaler network.

Questions

1. Getting the product "on the shelf" is only half the task when selling through retailers and wholesalers. Explain how Gallo helps distributors and retailers get the product "off the shelf."

2. Why does Gallo choose to sell through wholesalers rather than directly to retailers? In other words, what value do Gallo's distributors provide to both Gallo and to the retail customers?

3. Other than making money from one another's efforts, how can Gallo and its distributors work together to build long-term beneficial relationships between the two parties?

Case 15–2 *Columbia Sportswear: A Logistics Leader*

 Founded in 1938, Columbia Sportswear is one of the world's largest marketers of outdoor clothing and skiwear. The chairman of the board, 78-year-old Gert Boyle, is often featured in Columbia's offbeat, humorous TV ads. These ads typically show Ms. Boyle putting her son and company president through outdoor ordeals to test the durability of Columbia's products. Headquartered in Portland, Oregon, Columbia owns and operates sales offices in North America, Europe, and Asia. Columbia also owns and operates retail stores in the United States, Japan, and Australia.

When Columbia's retail customer base reached 10,000 retailers around the globe, its distribution system was in need of an overhaul. The market for outdoor clothing was attracting new competitors, some of whom are among the leading marketers of brand-name clothing. Both Polo and Tommy Hilfiger had expanded their lines beyond dress and casual dress clothing to include parkas, windbreakers, and fleece products. Large retail chains were also gaining market-place clout and demanding fast, accurate delivery from their suppliers. In response, Columbia enhanced and expanded its distribution center in Portland's Rivergate Industrial District.

Double the size of the previous center, the new facility utilized the latest technology to speed up incoming and outgoing shipments and to improve order accuracy and meet retailers' demands for the fulfillment of specialized orders. As a second major step, Columbia opened another new distribution facility in Kentucky in late 2004. The Kentucky center specializes in footwear distribution but can handle orders for a wide variety of products if needed.

These improvements have led to improved customer satisfaction and contributed to impressive sales growth. Deciding where to locate distribution centers is part science, part common sense. Dave Carlson, vice president of global distribution for Columbia, points out that transportation costs are always a key consideration, but that nothing is more important than how quickly orders can reach customers.

In the planning stages, Columbia considered outsourcing its distribution function to logistics specialists. By keeping the distribution center in-house, Columbia is able to provide specialized service for retail accounts. Some retailers want price tags added, and some want product shipped on hangers ready for display on retail racks. By owning its facility, Columbia can control the process and provide customized services—a definite advantage in a highly competitive market.

Questions

1. What are the advantages of Columbia's distribution centers for retailers? For Columbia?

2. In this situation, Columbia spent $75 million for its new distribution centers. What factors should be considered to determine whether the system is a good investment?

3. As technology evolves, what factors should Columbia consider before changing its current system?

Chapter Sixteen

AN OVERVIEW OF MARKETING COMMUNICATIONS

16

After studying this chapter, you should be able to

1 Discuss the objectives of marketing communications.

2 Understand the marketing communications mix and its role.

3 Explain the key elements of the marketing communications process.

4 Discuss the seven steps in the marketing communications planning process.

5 Demonstrate awareness of some of the key ethical and legal issues related to marketing communications.

FedEx

FedEx is a household name in the overnight shipping business, thanks in large part to its 50,000 delivery vehicles, or rolling billboards as one company executive describes them. So when the company pays millions to sponsor sports events and for naming rights to stadiums, it is not as interested in increasing exposure for its brand as it is in cultivating long-term relationships with key customers and contributing to a positive corporate image over time. Analysts estimate that for its role in sponsoring the FedEx Orange Bowl the company receives about $32 million in television exposure, a figure that FedEx officials discount deeply. The company regards such television exposure as a plus, but not nearly as important as the other benefits that come with sponsoring the Orange Bowl and holding naming rights to the National Football League Washington Redskins' stadium and the Memphis Grizzlies' National Basketball Association arena. FedEx also has numerous sponsorship arrangements with NASCAR and professional golf.

So what does FedEx get for its sponsorship money? In a given year, the company will entertain 45,000 customers at sports events, which typically include hospitality tents and recreation as part of a multiple-day event. According to T. Michael Glenn, CEO of FedEx corporate services, "We know exactly how much revenue an existing customer has been giving us in the last 12 months. Then we will track that after their participation . . . I can take every one of these events and tell you what the return on investment is. Sports marketing can be a lot of fun for people, but our board of directors expects to see ROI on every event."

In addition, FedEx uses sponsorship to reward its employees, approximately 20,000 of whom attend sponsored sports events each year. The company also realizes some public relations benefits from its sponsorship activities. For example, in Washington, D.C., the company's name on the NFL football stadium helps give FedEx a presence as a good corporate citizen. This is important because FedEx has to deal with a constant flow of legislative issues in the nation's capital. In a similar vein, naming the NBA Memphis Grizzlies' arena in its headquarters city and sponsoring the FedEx St. Jude golf tournament remind local residents and government officials that FedEx helps support the local economy and charitable causes.

Sponsorships work extremely well for FedEx. According to one executive, "A lot of companies would look at it and say it's a nontraditional lever for communicating with customers. But we feel like we've cracked the code, and we've got a little secret going on."

Marketing communications, sometimes referred to as *promotion,* involve marketer-initiated techniques directed to target audiences in an attempt to influence attitudes and behaviors. The FedEx example illustrates several relevant points for the planning and implementation of marketing communications. First, marketers utilize activities such as event-based personal interaction to connect with their customers. Second, sponsoring sports events and naming sports facilities is another alternative for companies that wish to supplement traditional marketing communications such as advertising. Third, marketing communications can involve considerable expenditures, and increasingly, companies are attempting to determine the return on investment for those expenditures. To determine those returns, it is important to set objectives and carefully plan the execution of marketing communications before commencing communications. Finally, a given set of activities may support multiple company objectives. In the FedEx example, sports sponsorship helps enhance customer relationships, reward employees, and build a positive image for the company.

Marketers may use one or all of several marketing communications methods. There are five major categories: advertising, public relations, sales promotion, personal selling, and direct marketing communications. Together they constitute the **marketing communications mix**, sometimes referred to as the *promotional mix.*

This chapter explores these five major categories, as well as the major objectives of marketing communications and how the communications process works and is implemented. We discuss how the marketing environment, including ethical and legal concerns, can influence the marketing communications effort.

The Role of Marketing Communications

The ultimate goal of marketing communications is to reach some audience to affect its behavior. There may be intermediate steps on the path to that goal, such as developing favorable consumer attitudes. Exhibit 16–1 lays out the three major objectives of marketing communications: to inform, to persuade, or to remind the marketer's audience.

Informing

Informing present or potential customers about a product is an important marketing communications function. Any time a new product is launched and promoted, marketing communications inform audience members (the target market) about it. For example, Toyota used a clever campaign to introduce its three-vehicle Scion line to young consumers. When early attempts based on traditional advertising failed to build awareness, Toyota reexamined its target market of consumers in their twenties. Finding potential buyers to be highly individualistic, Web-savvy, and with a fair amount of discretionary spending power, Toyota moved to events and the Web as primary marketing communications tools. To tie in with an urban, multicultural image for the Scion line, Toyota used a traveling art show, an interactive Web site, and test drive events at popular restaurants, music stores, and clubs to inform the target audience about the vehicles. The low-profile campaign worked, with Scion selling briskly and moving from thirtieth to ninth among potential targeted buyers when asked which car they would buy next.[1]

Marketing communications also serve an important role when new companies are founded and are seeking to build brand awareness. San Diego–based Leap Wireless broke into the highly competitive cell phone market with its Cricket Comfortable Wireless service thanks to a

Exhibit 16–1

The marketing communications mix

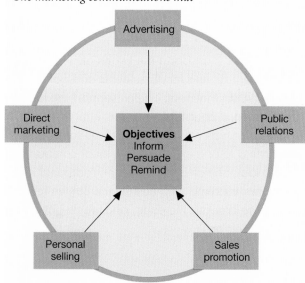

One major objective of marketing communications is to inform both customers and potential customers. Benjamin Moore used this ad to announce the availability of paint in sample-size containers that make it easier for consumers to select the right colors.

Marketing communications are also used to remind consumers and reinforce positive perceptions. This ad reminds consumers that Wisconsin Cheese has been producing high-quality products for more than 150 years.

clever integrated campaign featuring advertising, public relations, personal selling, and sponsorship of high-profile events. In its first major market, Denver, Cricket became a presence with its overstuffed, yet comfortable, bright green couch serving as a promotional tool to draw traffic. In some cases, couches were given away in consumer contests held at Denver Broncos games and concerts at the nearby Red Rocks outdoor amphitheater. Cricket was aiming for virtually 100 percent brand awareness within 90 days, which it achieved. In a one-year period, Cricket's subscriber base increased tenfold, to 1.1 million.[2]

Informing the public can be an important objective, even for goods, services, or ideas that have been around for a while. For example, the European Union countries are attacking the dangers of smoking with an awareness-building campaign utilizing shocking photographs of rotten teeth, wrinkled skin, and blackened lungs. All 25 EU countries are running television ads to deglamorize the use of tobacco, and some countries plan to use the attention-grabbing photos on cigarette packages.[3]

Speaking from Experience

"Competitive leadership has never been more challenging than in today's marketplace. Those who succeed in leading their respective fields will win the battle by directly linking the message (the objective), medium (all marketing communications components), and the target (minds of the intended consumers who must be receptive to the message), all at a cost compatible with bottom-line objectives."

Dorothy Brazil Clark, Director, Market Research and Strategic Planning, at Ralston Purina in St. Louis is well aware of the need to maintain close relationships with customers at a reasonable cost. Her previous experience includes business development and sales with Norden Laboratories, a subsidiary of SmithKline Beecham. Dorothy earned her B.A. degree from the University of Iowa and an MBA from the University of Missouri.

Dorothy Brazil Clark
Director, Market Research
and Strategic Planning
Ralston Purina

Please join Samsung, Sears and Boomer to help the children.

Marketing communications can be used to persuade others to take action. This ad encourages people to make financial contributions to fight cystic fibrosis.

Persuading

Marketing communications may concentrate on persuading customers to purchase a firm's market offering. For instance, when Cingular Wireless announced that it was purchasing AT&T Wireless, rival Verizon Wireless undertook a persuasion-focused campaign to get AT&T users to switch to Verizon. The advertising campaign posed this question in newspaper, magazine, and television ads: "Attention AT&T Wireless Customers: As long as your wireless carrier is changing, why not change to the best?"[4] In this hotly contested market, Verizon plans to continue with highly persuasive ads, anticipating that the Cingular/AT&T merger will create service problems for the newly joined companies.

Persuasive advertising is also used by nonprofit and government organizations. For example, the Office of National Drug Control Policy, with its Partnership for a Drug-Free America, frequently uses persuasive advertising aimed directly at young people, encouraging them to call a toll-free number or visit a partnership Web site for advice if they have no one at home to talk with about drugs. The same organization runs ads directed at parents who need guidance in how to talk with their children about drugs.[5]

Reminding

When consumers are aware of a firm's brand and have positive attitudes toward it, a reminding objective may be appropriate. Although consumers may be sold on the product, they are still vulnerable to competitors' appeals. Marketing communications can remind consumers of a product's benefits and reassure them they are making the right choice. Telarc, a record label, uses **permission marketing** to remind its online customers of new music releases and special promotions. Permission marketing occurs when the customer grants the marketer permission to send regular updates of interest to the consumer. E-mail is typically used for permission marketing, but regular mail or a fax could also be employed for this purpose.

Personal selling is another way to remind buyers of the value of continuing the relationship and making repeat purchases. Among the best at using personal selling for all three objectives of marketing communications, including reminding, are Dell Computer, Charles Schwab, Cisco Systems, Northwestern Mutual, and General Mills.

The Marketing Communications Mix

To inform, persuade, and remind targeted consumers effectively, marketers rely on one or more of the five major elements of the marketing communications mix. We discuss these briefly here and in more detail in subsequent chapters.

Advertising

Advertising is nonpersonal, paid for by an identified sponsor, and disseminated through mass channels of communication to promote the adoption of goods, services, persons, or ideas. Marketers use media such as television, radio, outdoor signage, magazines, newspapers, cell phones, and the Internet to advertise. Its ability to reach a mass audience often makes advertising an efficient method for communicating with a large target market.

Traditionally, advertising has been the most recognized form of marketing communications largely because of its high visibility. We cannot escape the advertising that surrounds

EXCLUSIVE SAVINGS ON WNBA MERCHANDISE BELOW!

This ad illustrates the combination of sales promotion and advertising. The sales promotion message (temporary price discount) is part of a print ad for the WNBA professional basketball league.

us in our daily lives. This high visibility is achieved through enormous expenditures. For example, General Motors spends more than $3.5 billion annually on advertising, and Time Warner, Procter & Gamble, Pfizer, Ford, and DaimlerChrysler all spend in excess of $2 billion per year on advertising. Procter & Gamble spends more than any other company advertising outside the United Sates, leading all companies in China, Germany, and the United Kingdom. The U.S. government is among the top 25 advertisers in the United States, spending a billion dollars a year on ads, well ahead of Target, Wal-Mart, Dell, Nissan, IBM, and McDonald's.[6]

The global advertising industry has been fairly stable in recent years, with modest increases in expenditures typically occurring from year to year. In general, advertising expenditures outpace the economy in good years and lag behind in down times. As marketers experiment more with new and emerging advertising media, most forecasters predict that online and cell phone advertising will grow faster than other media in the coming years.

Public Relations

The **public relations** function seeks to positively influence feelings, opinions, and beliefs about a company and its market offering to a variety of publics or stakeholders. Employees, customers, stockholders, community members, and the government are examples of various publics for many firms.

A key aspect of public relations is publicity. **Publicity** refers to non-paid-for communications about the company or product that appear in some media form, often the news media. Because the firm cannot completely control the message being disseminated, publicity may generate more believable messages than paid-for communications such as advertising. Many firms hire outside agencies to handle their public relations and publicity requirements.

Sales Promotion

Sales promotion includes communications activities that provide extra value or incentives to ultimate consumers, wholesalers, retailers, or other organizational customers and that can stimulate immediate sales.[7] Sales promotion attempts to stimulate product interest, trial, or purchase. Coupons, samples, premiums, point-of-purchase displays, sweepstakes, contests, rebates, and trade show exhibits are all examples of sales promotion.

Consumer sales promotion is directed at ultimate users of the product or service; *trade sales promotion* is directed at retailers, wholesalers, or other business buyers. Marketers spend comparable amounts of money for consumer and trade sales promotion. Although comprehensive estimates of consumer and trade sales promotion expenditures are not available, trade sources estimate that the two forms of sales promotion, when combined, account for more expenditures than the total spent on advertising.[8] One reason that it is difficult to get a good estimate on trade promotions is that trade promotions are not readily observable outside a given industry. For example, slotting allowances (discussed in Chapter 14) are not clearly identified as an expense item in most cases. Nonetheless, we can safely conclude that expenditures on both consumer and trade promotions are significant, particularly for consumer goods.

Dorothy Brazil Clark, Director, Market Research and Strategic Planning at Ralston Purina, points out the need to understand marketing communications as an integrated process focused on targeted consumers: "The requisite for good marketing

Professional salespeople play an important role in the marketing communications effort for complex products. Shown is a marketing representative for Health Images, Inc., who educates physicians on the use of MRI (magnetic resonance imaging) equipment.

communications in a world that demands end-to-end service is a total understanding of both the communicator and the organizations involved as well as the place each occupies during all phases of the process. Successful management of the communication process then demands complete mastery of the process and its components, synchronization between existing components, and a dismantling of the 'mass market' concept in favor of one emphasizing a family of segmented consumer groups."

Marketers typically use sales promotion in conjunction with other marketing communications elements. For example, sales promotion programs such as sweepstakes or contests may use advertising to spread the word to mass consumer markets. Marketers also frequently link sales promotion with many forms of direct marketing, especially direct mail, or include it as part of a trade show (product giveaways, merchandise imprinted with ad messages or logos).

Unlike some other forms of marketing communications, sales promotion is usually intended to produce immediate results. This probably explains why marketers have increasingly turned to sales promotion to improve sales volume and market share in a wide variety of highly competitive markets.

Personal Selling

Personal selling involves interpersonal communications between a seller and a buyer to satisfy buyer needs to the mutual benefit of both parties. The personal nature of this method distinguishes it from nonpersonal forms of marketing communication. Personal selling allows immediate feedback, enabling a message to be tailored to fit the buyer's individual needs. Its dynamic nature and flexibility make personal selling an excellent communications medium for establishing and nurturing customer relationships.

Personal selling is an important element of marketing communications when the product is complex. The sale of medical equipment to hospitals and physicians would be practically impossible without well-informed salespeople who can provide the necessary details to prospective buyers.

Direct Marketing Communications

Direct marketing communications are a process of communicating directly with target customers to encourage response by telephone, mail, electronic means, or personal visit. Popular methods of direct marketing communications include direct mail, telemarketing, direct-response broadcast advertising, online computer shopping services, cable television shopping networks, infomercials, and in some instances, outdoor advertising.

Direct marketing communications are used by all types of marketers, including retailers, wholesalers, manufacturers, and service providers. A fast-growing segment of the marketing communications field, direct marketing often uses precise means of identifying members of a target audience and compiling customer/prospect databases with postal addresses, telephone numbers, account numbers, e-mail addresses, or fax numbers to allow access to the buyers.

Integrated Marketing Communications

Today's highly competitive business environment puts considerable pressure on marketing communications to reach and spur busy, value-conscious consumers to buy. As a result, marketers are increasingly turning to **integrated marketing communications (IMC)**, which are the strategic integration of multiple means of communicating with target markets to form a comprehensive, consistent message. According to an expert in the field, this involves using new media along with more established forms of marketing communications: ". . . My cry is to integrate, not isolate. Yes, we need to explore and develop the new

Thinking Critically

Advertising, personal selling, sales promotion, public relations, and direct marketing can be used singularly or in combination to achieve marketing communications objectives. For each of the following situations, specify which marketing communications tools would be most appropriate:

- Attempting to sell a foreign government a dozen cargo planes.
- Raising money to support academic programs at your college or university.
- Informing an existing set of customers about a product modification.
- Trying to convince a local Chevrolet dealer to donate a vehicle to be used as the grand prize in a drawing to benefit United Way.
- Informing the general public of a product recall.

media and new approaches, but we need to do that within the context of what exists and what is likely to evolve."[9] For a look at an emerging technology of interest to marketers, see "Using Technology: Television Right at Home on the Internet."

In one sense, marketing communications are integrated horizontally, or across various methods of communications. For example, the advertising message must be consistent with the personal selling message. But a campaign can also be integrated vertically, extending from the marketer down through the marketing channel. For example, salespeople are often dispatched to retailers to arrange for adequate inventory levels and to assist in setting up in-store displays.

Another aspect of integrated marketing communications is that they consider any contact with a brand, product, or company to be part of marketing communications. As a result of integrated marketing communications, consumers could see a product in a movie, a commercial message or brand name on a T-shirt, and a company name prominently displayed on a hot-air balloon. Television viewers often see branded products become part of the show, as was the case with Reebok on *Survivor.* Pro golfers and tennis players frequently become live billboards, with logos on their clothing featuring everything from consulting companies to airlines. Though none of the major U.S.-based sports leagues have advertising on their team uniforms, the commissioner of the National Basketball Association has proclaimed, "I don't doubt it will eventually happen, but at a price that recognizes that value."[10] Some companies, including Microsoft, use Web-based video games to promote their products. A Web site hosting a video game promoting Halo 2, Microsoft's sequel to the Xbox video game, drew 80 million hits before Halo 2's market debut.[11] The game generated $125 million in sales during its first 24 hours on the market—the biggest debut in the history of console video games.

These sorts of marketing communications are sometimes called **stealth marketing** because their intent is not as blatant as some forms of marketing communications such as advertising. Such efforts are actually publicity generators and thus part of the marketing communications mix as we define it. These activities are increasing as marketers try to find new ways to reach audiences that may have become jaded by too much advertising, sales promotion, and other traditional methods of communicating with a target audience. It will be interesting to see how long it takes for consumers to tire of marketing communications in these alternative venues. On popular beaches, Hawaiian Tropic's swimsuit-wearing employees supply free sunscreen, and Panama Jack logos adorn concession stands, rental equipment, and lifeguard clothing. Planes circle overhead with promotional messages, and beach vehicles are often lent from manufacturers to earn the "official vehicle" designation. Ads are now appearing routinely in parking garages, restrooms, and department store windows. Television screens run ads in taxicabs in Boston, Chicago, Las Vegas, and San Francisco. Twentieth Century Fox is promoting forthcoming movies in shopping mall restaurants and shopping garages, and

USING TECHNOLOGY

Television right at home on the Internet

As marketers explore new avenues for reaching consumers, one hot approach is to combine old media with new media. For example, television is increasingly finding a home on the Internet, either by duplication of existing shows or programming that informs consumers about their favorite TV shows and stars. The Pepsico *Pepsi Smash* concert series has been extended from Time Warner's WB network to Yahoo's Web portal, where it will offer on-demand performances, interviews, and lifestyle feature stories. Major music acts such as Coldplay, Kanye West, and Gwen Stefani will perform. As more consumers get broadband connections to the Internet, such programming offers marketers a way to advertise in a new medium that can be integrated with other marketing communications. In the case of *Pepsi Smash* concerts, Pepsico will use print, TV, and radio advertising along with offline events in an integrated effort to draw viewers to the concerts.

Another Web venue for television fans is CNET.com, which offers online content such as plot summaries, video clips, and discussion forums. CNET, like Yahoo, is enjoying a surge in revenue as online ads grow rapidly in the wake of the dot-com bust in the early 2000s. With consumers increasingly using the Internet in their daily activities, it is a logical move for television programming, along with some of its advertising revenue, to extend its reach to the Internet.

Sponsorship programs can be an important element of integrated marketing communications. In this ad, Chicago Marathon sponsor LaSalle Bank encourages donations and participation in the race against cancer.

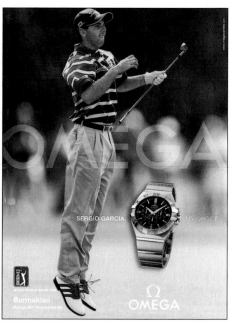

Credibility is critical in marketing communications. Sergio Garcia, a popular professional golfer with an international following, effectively represents the durability, dependability, and high quality of Omega watches.

advertisers can buy tattoo space on human beings at www.humanadspace.com. A Wyoming man is selling advertising on truck mud flaps.[12] With ads and other marketing communications becoming omnipresent, marketers will eventually have an even harder time getting consumers' attention.

Sponsorship programs, an investment in causes and events to support overall corporate objectives and marketing objectives,[13] may be an important part of an integrated marketing communications strategy. Sponsors may back a single event, such as the Olympics or the World Cup, or multiple events, as State Farm Insurance does with golf tournaments on the LPGA tour. As noted in the opening vignette for this chapter, organizations may also sponsor places, such as sports stadiums. For example, Invesco is paying $60 million over 20 years to sponsor the Denver Broncos NFL playing field, while American Airlines is paying $195 million over 30 years for the American Airlines center in Dallas. Even areas in and around stadiums are up for sponsorship. In Miami's NFL stadium, the parking lot is divided into sponsored zones, each bearing the name of a Toyota model, including Camry, Tundra, and Sequoia. Sponsorship of places has spread to school gyms, convention centers, hospitals, performing arts centers, museums, and other places where people congregate.[14]

Expenditures on sponsorships are growing faster than those for advertising and sales promotion.[15] They offer a good opportunity to match with particular lifestyles, to gain exposure beyond traditional avenues, and in some cases, to be associated with worthwhile causes. Sponsorships also allow small organizations to compete locally against larger rivals that have extensive communications budgets.

Most sponsorships have multiple objectives for the marketer and utilize multiple means of communicating with target audiences. For example, Ford Motor Company began a three-year sponsorship of the Ironman Triathlon in 2005 to reinforce its "Built Ford Tough" advertising theme and the rugged image of its SUVs, and to attract shoppers to its showrooms. The company is promoting the Ironman sponsorship in various advertising media and is conducting extensive onsite marketing activities at Ironman events, including an opportunity for visitors to test their own biking, running, and swimming skills while interacting with Ford SUVs.[16]

Coca-Cola and Procter & Gamble are masters at integrating their marketing communications efforts. Both are well known for consumer advertising. Their sales promotion efforts in the form of coupons, sweepstakes, and contests are also familiar to millions of consumers. The average consumer, however, does not see their highly trained salespeople who call on wholesalers and retailers. Both P&G and Coke have used direct marketing effectively. Like many others, Coca-Cola and P&G also manage sophisticated public relations and publicity efforts to support their marketing communications campaigns. Coke underscored its commitment to sponsorship as a major piece of its integrated marketing communications strategy by paying $500 million to become the sponsor for the National Collegiate Athletics Association for the 2003–2014 period. Under the agreement Coke will have beverage marketing and media rights to NCAA championship events and will support the events through advertising, sales promotion, and other marketing initiatives.[17]

The Marketing Communications Process

Communication is the process of establishing shared meaning, exchanging ideas, or passing information between a source and a receiver. Exhibit 16–2 shows how the marketing communications process works. Note that the intended target for any basic communication is the **receiver**. This could be a purchasing agent listening to a sales presentation, a consumer reading a magazine ad, or another of the various publics served by the marketer, such as stockholders or government officials.

Sources of Marketing Communications

The marketer is the **source**, or message sender, of marketing communications. Two types of sources normally play a role in marketing communications: the message sponsor and the message presenter. The **message sponsor** is typically the organization attempting to market its goods, services, or ideas. The **message presenter**, perhaps a salesperson, actor, or television personality, actually delivers the message. For instance, Nike is a message sponsor, whereas Tiger Woods is one of Nike's message presenters.

Exhibit 16–2   *The marketing communications process*

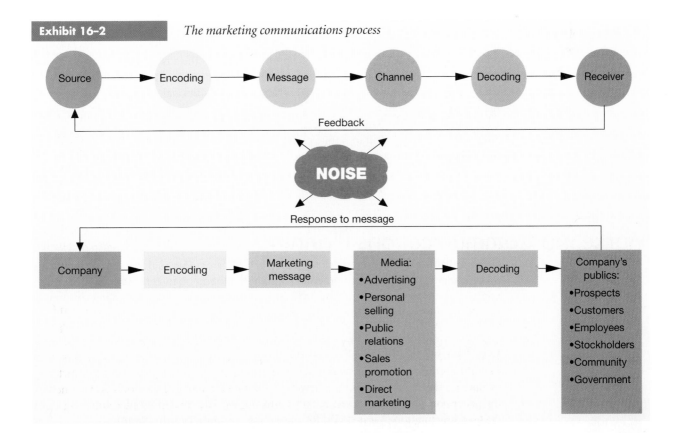

Communications Messages

The source sends a message through a channel to a receiver. The **marketing communications message** represents what the company is trying to convey about its products. A **message channel** is the means by which the message is conveyed. In advertising, message channels are often referred to as *media*, a reference to advertising vehicles such as newspapers, television, magazines, outdoor billboards, and radio. Mail, telephones, audio- and videocassettes, salespeople, and computer networks and disks are also examples of message channels.

Encoding and Decoding

The source does the **encoding** by choosing the words, pictures, and other symbols used to transmit the intended message. **Decoding** is the process by which the receiver deciphers the meaning of the words, pictures, and other symbols used in the message. When the message is not decoded as the source intended, a lack of communication results. For example, a consumer may find the copy in a magazine ad too technical and thus not understand the message.

Feedback

Feedback is the part of the receiver's response that is communicated to the sender. Depending on the nature of the communication, the sender can assess feedback to judge the effectiveness of the communication. Personal selling and many forms of sales promotion offer relatively quick feedback. Feedback is not so immediate for mass advertising and public relations, and only subsequent sales figures or marketing research will indicate the effectiveness of the message.

Noise

Noise is any distraction or distortion during the communication process that prevents the message from being effectively communicated. Competing messages and interruptions, such as a telephone call during a salesperson's presentation, constitute noise. Noise can even come from within the message itself, sometimes at quite an expense. For example, Nike often seeks a controversial edge that may reduce the effectiveness of some its ads. In China, its ads featuring pro basketball star Lebron James caused an uproar and were banned by the government. The ads showed James slaying a kung fu master, a pair of dragons, and two women dressed in traditional Chinese attire. The problem was that the ads offended consumers and violated a Chinese mandate prohibiting ads that ridicule national practices and culture. In China, dragons are considered a sacred symbol in the traditional culture, and martial arts masters are a source of national pride.[18] Similar ads also touched off protests in Singapore, a key market for Nike. The offensive Singapore ads were posters that resembled graffiti. In Singapore, creating graffiti in public places is a crime punishable by flogging.[19] Some argue that Nike's ads connect with their intended audiences, but such tactics may complicate the communications task. The obvious lesson here is that noise should be eliminated or at least minimized, lest the communications task become more difficult.

Marketing Communications Planning

There are seven key tasks in **marketing communications planning**: marketing plan review; situation analysis; communications process analysis; budget development; program development; integration and implementation of the plan; and monitoring, evaluating, and controlling the marketing communications program. These are diagrammed in Exhibit 16–3.

Marketing Plan Review

Marketing communications planning draws heavily on the firm's overall marketing strategy and marketing objectives. A review of the marketing plan is thus a logical place to start the process of planning marketing communications. The marketing plan often contains detailed information that is useful for marketing communications planning.

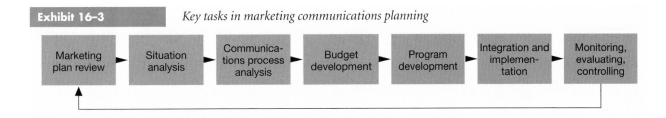

Exhibit 16–3   *Key tasks in marketing communications planning*

Situation Analysis

An analysis of the marketing communications situation considers how internal factors, such as the firm's capabilities and constraints, and other marketing mix variables will affect marketing communications. The situation analysis is also concerned with the marketing environment now and in the future. For example, competitive, economic, and social factors affect marketing communications. The political and legal environments, discussed later in this chapter, are also addressed in the situation analysis.

THE COMPETITIVE ENVIRONMENT   Marketing communications are often used to foil the actions of competitors. For example, fast-food chain Wendy's completely revamped its marketing communications after losing ground to its key competitors, Burger King and McDonald's. After founder Dave Thomas passed away, Wendy's had a difficult time with its advertising because Thomas had been the chain's likable and effective ad spokesperson for many years. Using a new theme, "Do What Tastes Right," Wendy's moved from one message broadly aimed at the masses to more targeted messages focused on three market segments: baby boomers, young adults, and teens. Wendy's also increased its advertising budget and added Internet advertising and product placement to its marketing communications mix.[20] Although results of the changes are not yet known, there is no doubt that Wendy's sees marketing communications as a key dimension in remaining competitive in an extremely competitive industry.

THE ECONOMIC ENVIRONMENT   Budgets for marketing communications often decline in hard economic times, yet savvy marketers resist large reductions in their communications spending. They know that brand awareness, image, and equity are hard to achieve, and drastic reductions in communications budgets can endanger hard-won marketplace victories. Most companies, rather than cutting their budgets significantly, have been searching for the most productive means of communicating with customers. This has meant that an increased portion of the communications budget is being spent on highly measurable communications activities or in new vehicles. For example, a lot of companies integrated the Web into their communications mix in recent years, while others increased the proportion of direct mail, e-mail campaigns, sponsorships, and various forms of stealth marketing. At the same time, expenditures have decreased for newspaper and other print advertising. Cable television, with its highly targeted audiences, is typically gaining ground at the expense of the traditional major networks such as ABC, NBC, and CBS.

To properly budget marketing communications, companies should decide if expenditures are an investment in the future of their brands or if expenditures represent an expense for which an immediate return is expected. In reality, most companies view their communications expenditures as part investment and part current expense. When economic times are tough, there is an undeniable pressure to make every dollar spent pay off—often in the short run. But the best marketers know that some money has to be dedicated to preserving what has already been achieved and for building brands of the future. Immediate payoff is not likely the best indicator of communications success in these cases.

The economic environment may cause firms to reconsider which components of the marketing communications mix to emphasize. One significant change in the economic environment is that electronic commerce has become a much more important part of the U.S. economy in recent years. As a result, major marketing organizations such as Procter & Gamble, Walt Disney, Philip Morris, AT&T, and Johnson & Johnson are increasing their proportion of spending on Internet advertising.

We have dozens of less painful ways to show your Mom you care.

She owns a special place in your heart. And perhaps there's no better way to show her than with roses from Bailey's Nursery. Why not get Mom a potted rose plant. It's the permanent way to show your mom how much you care. There, that didn't hurt a bit. Phone orders, call 348-6351, or stop by 5415 Boggy Creek Road. **Bailey's Nursery**

Marketers recognize that women are buying products traditionally bought by men and vice versa. This ad uses a humorous approach to encourage male patronage of a florist shop.

THE SOCIAL ENVIRONMENT   Communications messages often reflect social trends. For instance, many marketers communicate supposed environmental benefits of their products. Although shoppers indicate that they are concerned about the environmental impact of the products they purchase, companies have typically had difficulty translating this concern into a competitive advantage in the marketplace. It seems that the desire for convenience is actually a much stronger social trend, with plastic disposables replacing glass containers for baby food, water, and food service items. Another social trend of note is that personal wellness and safety are prime concerns. Seventh Generation, a brand of natural household products, changed its slogan from "Products for a healthy planet" to "Safer for you and the environment."[21]

Perhaps the most important social trend is the changing composition of the population in many countries of the world. As discussed in Chapters 2 and 7, multiculturalism in the United States is a far more important trend than in the past because of the emergence of some ethnic groups as prime markets for a wide range of products. It is estimated that U.S. marketers spend more than $2 billion annually to target the Latino market, $1.5 billion on the African American market, and $250 million on Asian American initiatives.[22] Further, it is estimated that diverse markets will grow faster and outspend the so-called mainstream market by the year 2020.[23]

The concept of multicultural marketing communications and specific campaigns targeting one or more ethnic or alternative lifestyle groups is becoming far more commonplace than just a few years ago. Gateway, H&R Block, and Lincoln-Mercury have all successfully launched multicultural campaigns. These three companies, along with many others, realize that they must successfully communicate with emerging markets of importance in order to succeed. At Gateway, the term *growth* is largely synonymous with multicultural markets, and the company has appointed a director of growth markets to head up multicultural marketing communications.[24]

Dorothy Brazil Clark, Director of Market Research and Strategic Planning at Ralston Purina, is mindful of the importance of approaching diverse markets with appropriately tailored marketing communications: "Those aspiring to be market leaders must successfully forge new communication pathways focused on and mirroring the diversity and pluralism reflected in the collective social, economic, political, and technological impact on both domestic and international environments. These customized pathways can serve as the integrating forces that connect the organization with its intended audiences."

MARKETING MIX CONSIDERATIONS   Compatibility of product, price, and channel characteristics with marketing communications is essential. The physical characteristics of a product or product package (color, size, shape, texture, ingredients) and its brand name communicate a lot to consumers. For instance, the bright colors on the Cheer detergent package imply it is powerful enough to get clothes bright and clean without fading them. Brand names such as Arrid Extra Dry, Finesse, Ivory, Total, Huggies, Sheer Energy, and Angel Soft convey certain messages about the products.

The product's price also conveys a message. Consumers often use price as an indicator of product quality. The $20,550 price tag on a Rolex President watch indicates more than the cost of the watch; it also conveys a message of quality and prestige. Although both Rolex and Timex watches keep good time, each conveys a different message with its pricing strategy, and each has built an image consistent with its price.

The chosen marketing channel also communicates to the consumer. For instance, Wal-Mart and Neiman-Marcus convey different messages. Wal-Mart stands for everyday low prices—products that are very expensive and of the finest quality are typically not found there. Consumers generally assume items sold at Neiman-Marcus are of high quality because of the store's well-established image. The prices of products at Neiman-Marcus help convey that message.

Communications Process Analysis

In this step, marketers analyze the various elements of the basic communications model shown in Exhibit 16–3. Objectives for marketing communications are also set in this part of the planning process.

APPLYING THE BASIC COMMUNICATIONS MODEL   Marketers try to understand the decoding processes of potential receivers of marketing communications to create effective messages and select appropriate message channels. For example, will the consumer need detailed information from a well-trained salesperson to make a favorable decision? Or can simple point-of-sale displays achieve the desired results?

SETTING MARKETING COMMUNICATIONS OBJECTIVES   Exhibit 16–4 lists several general marketing communications objectives. Like all business objectives, a marketing communications objective should be stated as specifically as possible to help gauge the effectiveness of marketing communications efforts. It is also necessary to set objectives for each marketing communications effort, assuming separate programs are developed for individual products, product lines, geographic areas, customer groups, or time periods. For example, greeting card marketer Hallmark might run separate sales promotion programs to correspond with major occasions such as Christmas, Mother's Day, and Halloween.

Budget Development

Determining the optimal amount to spend on marketing communications involves considerable subjective judgment. Further, it is hard to measure precise results achieved by most forms of marketing communications. For example, corporations pay $6 million to sponsor a golf tournament on the Professional Golf Association tour.[25] Pinpointing the exact value of advertising exposure, new business generated, and goodwill gained is not typically feasible. Rather, subjective judgments are often used to gauge the impact of such expenditures. Likewise, it is difficult to tie concrete dollar results to most advertising and public relations expenditures.

Exhibit 16–4	*Examples of marketing communications objectives*

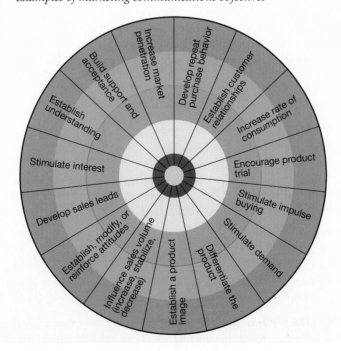

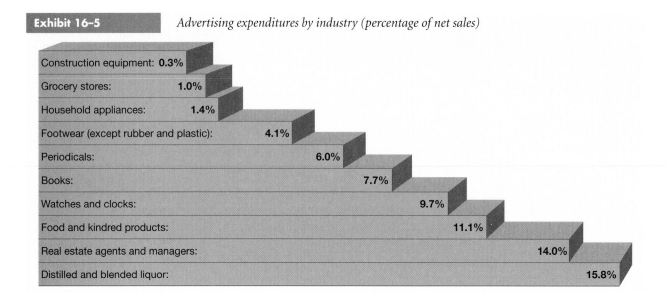

| Exhibit 16–5 | Advertising expenditures by industry (percentage of net sales) |

Construction equipment: **0.3%**
Grocery stores: **1.0%**
Household appliances: **1.4%**
Footwear (except rubber and plastic): **4.1%**
Periodicals: **6.0%**
Books: **7.7%**
Watches and clocks: **9.7%**
Food and kindred products: **11.1%**
Real estate agents and managers: **14.0%**
Distilled and blended liquor: **15.8%**

INFLUENCES ON BUDGETING   The budget depends on the size of the company, its financial resources, the type of business, the market dispersion, the industry growth rate, and the firm's position in the marketplace. As shown in Exhibit 16–5, marketing communications expenditures also vary by industry.

The marketing communications budgets for business marketers are generally quite different than budgets for consumer products and service companies. For example, business marketers spend a majority of their marketing communications dollars on personal selling, whereas consumer marketers spend more on other forms of communications, with various forms of advertising leading the way.

BUDGETING METHODS   Firms typically use any of four methods to determine the marketing communications budget: **percentage of sales, competitive parity, all-you-can-afford,** and **objective-task.**

PERCENTAGE OF SALES   Using the preceding year (or even a longer period) as a basis, a company can set its marketing communications budget as a percentage of sales. A drawback is that the assumed causal sequence of effects is reversed; that is, expenditures for marketing communications should partially determine sales levels, rather than past sales levels determining marketing communications expenditures.

Firms can also budget according to percentage of forecast sales. When doing so, they often use industry standards such as those shown in Exhibit 16–5 as guidelines for determining a percentage. Percentage of sales approaches ensure some stability in planning, but they fail to consider competitive and economic pressures.

COMPETITIVE PARITY   Some firms set marketing communications budgets to equal the percentage allocated by other companies in the industry. This approach at least acknowledges competitive actions. The disadvantage is it assumes that the competition is correct, that marketing communications dollars are spent with equal effectiveness across companies, and that other firms have similar objectives and resources. These assumptions may be dangerous oversimplifications of actual conditions.

ALL-YOU-CAN-AFFORD   Sometimes firms spend what they can afford, or some amount left over after covering other costs. Such a budgeting technique fails to consider a firm's objectives and to commit expenditures necessary to achieve them. This is a questionable approach for the firm struggling to make a profit because reduction of marketing communications expenditures may prevent any improvement and actually speed a downturn.

OBJECTIVE-TASK   More detailed than the other budgeting methods, this approach sets the budget at the level necessary to achieve stipulated marketing communications

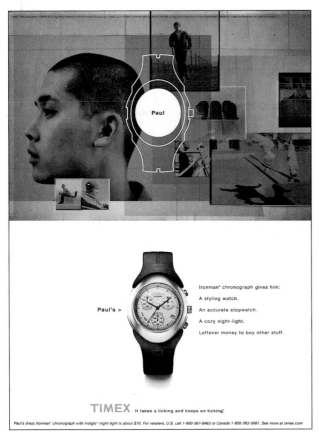

Paul

Paul's >

Ironman* chronograph gives him:

A styling watch.

An accurate stopwatch.

A cozy night-light.

Leftover money to buy other stuff.

TIMEX It takes a licking and keeps on ticking.

Paul's dress Ironman* chronograph with Indiglo* night-light is about $70. For retailers, U.S. call 1-800-367-8463 or Canada 1-800-263-0981. See more at timex.com

This ad illustrates how both explicit and implicit marketing communications can be part of the same message. Just like the watch, this Ironman competitor can "take a licking and keep on ticking."

objectives. The objective-task method forces identification of tasks that must be achieved to meet established objectives and provides a way to evaluate results. It has the advantage of requiring management to spell out its assumptions about the relationships among dollars spent, exposure levels, product trial, and continuing consumer purchases.

Research indicates that marketing managers rely heavily on historical data—for example, last year's sales results—in allocating dollars to various marketing communications tools. This may be an acceptable practice in stable business environments; in many marketing environments, however, there is significant variation from year to year in consumer tastes, economic conditions, and competitive activity. When managers are operating in such unstable environments, they will likely be more successful if they rely more on objective-task, or zero-based, budgeting.[26]

Marketing Communications Program Development

Developing a marketing communications program involves developing general marketing communications strategies and allocating budgets to specific programs. A firm must decide the proper uses of explicit and implicit communications. And it must decide whether to adopt a push strategy, a pull strategy, or a combination strategy.

EXPLICIT AND IMPLICIT COMMUNICATIONS

Marketing communications may be either explicit or implicit. **Explicit communications** convey a distinct, clearly stated message through personal selling, advertising, public relations, sales promotion, direct marketing, or some combination of these methods. **Implicit communications** are messages connoted by the product itself, its price, or the places it is sold. Candymaker Mars, for example, wanted to appear more local in various European markets rather than as a U.S. brand. Departing from its regular advertising strategy, the company paid far more attention to local detail than ever before in a major campaign featuring 10 television ads and 20 print ads. In the United Kingdom, the theme for the ads was "Pleasure You Can't Measure"; in Germany it became "It is Mars—das hat was" ("That's it") and in France the theme was "Mars—Quede bonheur" ("Mars—What happiness"). In England the ads were associated with World Cup soccer; in France, the month of August, the popular time for vacations; and in other countries, adaptations were made specifically for each country. For Mars, the campaign marked a departure from featuring the physical attributes of the brand toward more of an emotional appeal. The implicit part of the communication was that Mars, an old, established brand in Europe, was now more a part of local tastes and traditions.[27]

PUSH, PULL, AND COMBINATION STRATEGIES

A **push strategy** involves convincing intermediary channel members to "push" the product through the channel to the ultimate consumer. The company directs its marketing communications efforts toward promoting and selling the product to a reseller, which then does the same to another reseller or to the ultimate consumer. Personal selling is a primary tool in this method. Sales promotion and advertising directed at channel members may also be used. For example, manufacturers may provide sales incentives to retailers or place ads in retailer-oriented trade magazines.

A **pull strategy** attempts to get consumers to "pull" the product from the manufacturing company through the marketing channel. The company concentrates its marketing communications efforts on the consumer; that is, it hopes to stimulate interest and demand for the product at the end-user level. If consumers want and ask for the product, resellers are more likely to carry and distribute it. A firm with a new, unproved product might find a pull strategy useful if distributors are reluctant to carry the product. The firm could use advertising and sales promotion tools such as coupons to get many consumers to go to the retail store and request the product, thus pulling it through the channel.

Many firms practice a **combination strategy**, aiming marketing communications at both resellers and ultimate consumers. Nabisco, for example, uses personal selling and trade promotions to sell its products to grocery retailers. At the same time it makes extensive use of advertising and sales promotion directed at ultimate consumers. Strict reliance on either a push or a pull strategy does not take full advantage of the power of marketing communications. A firm with limited resources, however, may not be able to follow both strategies and may emphasize one over the other.

Integration and Implementation

Implementation is setting the marketing communications plan into action. Depending on which tools the firm uses, it creates ads, purchases media time and space, and begins its sales promotion programs. If appropriate, the firm's personal selling, public relations, and direct marketing components also direct its efforts toward achieving the marketing communications objectives. The key aspect of implementation is coordination.

Monitoring, Evaluating, and Controlling

Firms can use a variety of methods to monitor, evaluate, and control marketing communications. For example, a firm might monitor sales promotion by the number of coupons redeemed or measure the effectiveness of a new personal selling strategy by looking at the number of new accounts opened by the sales force. After an advertising campaign, a firm might run tests to see if consumers noticed the ad. Researchers could ask how many of those who noticed the ad linked the company name to it or actually read it. They might also ask consumers about their attitude toward the company and the product both before and after a marketing communications program to see what effect, if any, the program had.

Marketers often rely on surveys and tests to evaluate marketing communications. Sometimes they look at sales results and attribute fluctuations in sales volume to the marketing communications, while largely ignoring the effects of other factors. Unfortunately, this narrow view prevails in many business settings.

Even though it may be difficult to measure the absolute effectiveness of most marketing communications, marketers have certainly not given up on the task. Quite the opposite is true, in fact, as marketers are increasingly under pressure to justify money spent on communications. In some cases, the effectiveness of marketing communications cannot be accurately assessed until a significant amount of time has passed. For example, a five-year antidrug campaign by the U.S. government was declared a failure when ads apparently had little effect on actual or intended drug use. In seeking a continuation of the $180 million annual budget for the program, the U.S drug czar pledged that all ads would be tested for effectiveness before they were released, compared to only a third that were tested during the previous campaign. In this case pretesting could have saved a lot of money, and the effectiveness of the ads could have been assessed without waiting five years to declare the program a failure.[28]

The effectiveness of marketing communications designed to elicit a straightforward consumer response in a fairly short time period are easier to measure than those having to do with lifestyle or attitude modification. For example, British Airways ran ads in *The New York Times* Web edition to lure new members for its frequent flyer program. The cost of the online campaign was $300,000, and it exceeded its goal by 40 percent, signing up 12,000 new members. The cost of acquiring a new customer was $25, or three-fourths of the average acquisition costs in previous online campaigns. Additional revenue will more than pay for the costs of the campaign.[29] Results like these are what all marketers aspire to.

Ethical and Legal Considerations

Exhibit 16–6 notes the ways the five areas of marketing communications may be subject to criticism from an ethical and legal viewpoint. Much to the dismay of upright professional marketers, ethical problems and legal violations in marketing communications continue. The good news is that an *ethical perspective* is also evident in marketing communications. In fact, marketing communications are frequently used to encourage responsible behavior such as contributing to charitable causes, practicing safe driving, and supporting community action programs. Marketing communications are also used to inform buyers about legal issues with reminders like "Buckle up, it's the law" or "You must be 21 years old to purchase this product."

An example of marketing communications contributing to society is the Target stores' "Take Charge of Education" program, whereby a percentage of sales is returned to participating schools in local communities. Target generates a considerable amount of favorable publicity with this program and promotes the program on its Web site, with in-store signage, and in some of its advertising. The program has returned more than $138 million to deserving schools, students, and teachers.[30] Such programs remind us that marketing communications are essential not only to profit-seeking marketers but also to groups that support the improvement of our society. In some instances, the two constituencies overlap.

Legal—But Ethical?

Some marketing communications may be technically legal but raise significant ethical questions. For example, after four decades of self-imposed restrictions, the liquor industry now advertises on cable and local television stations. Critics, citing problems arising from excessive consumption of alcohol, are outraged. Citing lost market share to beer and wine manufacturers, liquor companies argue that they are legally entitled to use advertising to promote their businesses. Although the major national television networks (ABC, CBS, NBC) do not currently accept liquor ads, the growth in advertising for liquor on local broadcast stations has increased dramatically in recent years. In 2002 only 60 local stations accepted liquor ads; in 2004 the number had increased to more than 600.[31] Further, the ban on liquor sponsorships by NASCAR, the stock car racing organization, was lifted in late 2004, and several racing teams are expected to strike sponsorship deals by the end of 2005.[32] The American Medical Association strongly opposes the NASCAR sponsorships and television ads for liquor, nothing that one of the fastest-growing audiences for NASCAR is 12- to-18-year-olds. According to the AMA president, "Advertising liquor on the actual race cars that youth idolize sends the wrong message."[33]

Another apparently legal but ethically questionable practice is the extensive promotion of higher-cost drugs when health care costs are spiraling out of control. The Federal Trade

| Exhibit 16–6 | *Ethical and legal concerns in marketing communications* |

Marketing Communications Element	Ethical/Legal Concerns
Advertising	• Using deceptive advertising • Reinforcing unfavorable ethnic/racial/sex stereotypes • Encouraging materialism and excessive consumption
Public relations	• Lack of sincerity (paying lip service to worthwhile causes) • Using economic power unfairly to gain favorable publicity • Orchestrating news events to give false appearance of widespread support for corporate position
Sales promotion	• Offering misleading consumer promotions • Paying slotting allowances to gain retail shelf space • Using unauthorized mailing lists to reach consumers
Personal selling	• Using high-pressure selling • Failing to disclose product limitations/safety concerns • Misrepresenting product benefits
Direct marketing communications	• Invading privacy by telemarketing • Using consumer database information without authorization of consumers • Creating economic waste with unwanted direct mail

Hindsight is easy.

It's thinking ahead that's hard. But that's how Liberty Mutual serves our customers and why we're one of the world's leading groups of insurance companies, with over $19.6 billion in revenue. Over the last 93 years, we've introduced innovative products and services and helped to develop hundreds of groundbreaking safety initiatives through the Liberty Mutual Research Institute for Safety. Along the way, we've learned that helping people reduce risk and prevent accidents is just good business. **IT'S MORE THAN INSURANCE. IT'S INSURANCE in ACTION.**

libertymutual.com   © 2005 Liberty Mutual Group

Liberty Mutual.

Marketing communications can be used to communicate a corporation's role in socially responsible activities. Liberty Mutual used this ad to inform readers about its role in introducing hundreds of new safety initiatives aimed at preventing accidents.

Commission is considering a probe into prescription drug pricing, as complaints have arisen that pharmaceutical firms have been marketing directly to patients who are using drugs for which patents are about to expire. Such drugs would then face intense price competition from generic drugs. There are also questions about the drug firms' use of heavy promotional allowances to pharmacies in return for pharmacies' agreements to push proprietary instead of generic drugs.[34]

Additional concerns about how prescription drugs are advertised have been raised by the Food and Drug Administration. In the 1997–2005 period, the makers of the painkiller Celebrex have been cited seven times for questionable marketing communications practices, including the use of misleading television ads and lack of proof for some performance claims made for the drug.[35] The FDA has also cited the producers of Lipitor, the best-selling cholesterol drug, and Claritin allergy medication multiple times between 1997 and 2005. There have been calls for reform in how prescription drugs are advertised and promoted, and the negative publicity arising from these numerous violations by major drugmakers leads some analysts to believe that future marketing appeals will be more straightforward.[36]

Deception in Marketing Communications

Exhibit 16–6 indicates that many problems relate to deception of consumers. Although this may happen in any area of the promotion mix, deceptive advertising is a prime concern. **Deceptive advertising**, communications intended to mislead consumers by making false claims or failing to disclose important information, is a major focus of the Federal Trade Commission (FTC), the government agency responsible for overseeing American business practices.

Deceptive advertising often involves false pricing offers and performance claims that cannot be substantiated. A particularly problematic category is weight loss products, where the FTC has found a pervasive pattern of deceptive advertising. Under a program called "Operation Big Fat Lie," the FTC has cracked down on several deceptive marketing programs, including those conducted by Selfworx.com, which was fined $100,000 and barred from making false or unsubstantiated claims.[37] In other health-related cases, the FTC's "Project AbSurd" gained a $2 million settlement against the marketers of AB Energizer and forced the Canadian marketer of defective HIV test kits to cease Internet sales in the United States.[38] For more on the subject of misleading advertising, see "Acting Ethically: FTC and Courts Crack Down on Deceptive Ads."

Visits to the Better Business Bureau Web site at *www.bbb.org* and the FTC site at *www.ftc.gov* can be educational for those who wish to learn more about deceptive advertising. These sites offer tips for consumers on how to avoid scams and guidelines for ethical and legal marketing communications.[39]

Additional Regulatory Concerns

Additional FTC guidelines can affect marketing communications. Although the FTC provides for **comparative advertising** (which compares one product with other products), it also requires that comparative claims be supported. If Pontiac wants to claim that its Bonneville costs thousands of dollars less than, but performs as well as, Lexus or BMW, it must make the basis for comparison clear to the consumer.

Product endorsers must be qualified to make judgments and must actually use the product being endorsed. Moreover, any demonstrations used in advertisements must be accurate representations and not images that are misleading.

Marketers who use comparative advertising must be able to substantiate their claims. In this instance, Whitehall Laboratories uses comparative advertising to claim that Advil is gentler on the stomach than aspirin and that it works better on headache pain than Extra Strength Tylenol.

Packaging and labeling practices of food and drug marketers are heavily scrutinized by consumers and regulatory agencies. At the national level, the Food and Drug Administration (FDA) keeps a watchful eye on health-related messages. In 1991 the FDA's regulatory power was extended by legislation that required manufacturers to disclose dietary and nutritional information on product labels about the amounts of fat, sugar, cholesterol, additives, and certain other elements in the product. The National Advertising Review Council (NARC) is also active in monitoring health and nutritional claims. In one case NARC found that print advertising by Campbell Soup Company for its V8 juice, claiming that five or more servings per week greatly reduced the risk of prostate cancer, overstated the proved scientific relationship between consumption of tomato products and cancer prevention.[40] As a result, Campbell's modified its claim to be more consistent with scientific evidence.

Effects of Globalization

The increasing globalization of marketing often requires adjustment of the communications mix from country to country to avoid legal and ethical problems. Differences in language, culture, legal and ethical norms, and availability of various media are usually significant. Telemarketing laws, for example, in some European countries are far more stringent than are those in the United States. The use of humor and sex in marketing communications across countries and cultures can be a high-risk tactic due to the potential of misunderstandings. Sales promotion techniques that involve contests and giveaways are regulated quite differently in various countries. And of particular importance, effective advertising messages in one country may be offensive to residents of other countries, and what constitutes acceptable personal selling behavior also varies significantly across countries and cultures. For example, in many Latin and Far Eastern countries, establishing a personal relationship prior to developing a business relationship is crucial.

Recall that the global perspective also includes a recognition of multiculturalism within a given market or country. In a growing number of countries around the world, including the United States, marketing communications are addressing multicultural aspects of the market. Marketers must take special precautions not to perpetuate unfavorable stereotypes of ethnic and racial groups; often these precautions include hiring ad agencies, research firms, and other specialists to guide their marketing communications efforts. Even so, consumers may be offended, which reinforces the importance of paying careful attention to cultural differences in marketing communications.

Acting Ethically

FTC and courts crack down on deceptive ads

Advertisers have long been aware that specific performance claims for their products must be substantiated; yet the Federal Trade Commission, local and state regulators, and the court system have a steady stream of cases where substantiation has not been documented. In 2005 the FTC ruled that Tropicana Products Inc. made false performance claims related to its orange juice's ability to lower blood pressure and improve cholesterol. In settling the case with Tropicana, the FTC prohibited Tropicana from making similar health-related claims in the future unless they can be substantiated by valid scientific studies.

In another case involving alleged deceptive advertising, a U.S. district court in Connecticut ruled that Gillette misled consumers with ads claiming that the M3Power razor raises up hair away from the skin to give the "world's best shave." The court found no support for the claims. Energizer Holdings, parent company of key competitor Schick, announced plans to sue Gillette, seeking punitive damages when the lawsuit goes to trial. Some advertisers feel that the FTC and other regulators are overly strict in dictating the rules of advertising. Other industry practitioners feel the relatively light penalties for misleading advertising encourage unethical and sometimes illegal behavior. Meanwhile consumers are increasingly skeptical of advertising claims, which makes the job of legitimate advertisers more challenging.

Summary

1. **Discuss the objectives of marketing communications.** The primary objective of marketing communications is to reach an audience to affect its behavior. In general, the three major objectives of marketing communications are to inform, to persuade, and to remind. The emphasis placed on one of the five primary communications methods to achieve these objectives depends on the company's marketing and communications strategy.

2. **Understand the marketing communications mix and its role.** Marketing communications allow marketers to reach current and potential customers. Advertising, public relations, sales promotion, personal selling, and direct marketing are the primary categories of marketing communications. Each of these tools has unique advantages, providing a variety of techniques for reaching consumers. It is important that marketing communications be consistent with a firm's overall corporate and marketing strategy. Marketing communications must be coordinated with product, price, and channel factors to reach the desired target audience effectively.

3. **Explain the key elements of the marketing communications process.** Communication occurs when there is shared meaning between source and receiver. Communication is considered effective to the extent that the source gets a desired response from the receiver. From a marketing communications perspective, a firm as the source sends a marketing communications message through any of several message channels to its target audience, the receiver. The firm encodes the message by putting it into words, pictures, or symbols that best convey the message. Target audience members then decode the message by determining the meaning of the words, pictures, and symbols. Sometimes the intended message is not received if there is noise in the communication process.

4. **Discuss the seven steps in the marketing communications planning process.** The key tasks of marketing communications planning include marketing plan review; situation analysis; communications process analysis; budget development; program development; integration and implementation of the plan; and monitoring, evaluating, and controlling the marketing communications process.

5. **Demonstrate awareness of some of the key ethical and legal issues related to marketing communications.** All areas of marketing communications have come under criticism for unethical and illegal activities. Some of the more frequently publicized problems include deceptive advertising; inability to substantiate comparative claims; unfair reinforcement of ethnic, racial, and sex stereotypes; and encouragement of materialistic values.

Understanding Marketing Terms and Concepts

Thinking about Marketing

1. Briefly define *marketing communications* and describe the elements of the marketing communications mix.

2. What is sponsorship? What are some of its advantages and disadvantages? Give an example of sponsorship, and comment on its effectiveness.

3. What is the goal of marketing communications? Name three major objectives of marketing communications. For each objective, give an example of how an actual firm uses marketing communications to reach it.

4. Refer to "Using Technology: Television Right at Home on the Internet." With traditional television advertising declining in popularity, are advertisers being overly optimistic to think that online TV programming will be a viable alternative?

5. What factors could cause a marketing communications message to be decoded differently from the way the source intended?

6. Briefly describe the steps in marketing communications planning.

7. How can other aspects of the marketing mix affect the marketing communications mix?

8. What influences the amount of money a company might spend on marketing communications?

9. Refer to "Acting Ethically: FTC and Courts Crack Down on Deceptive Ads." Other than having to modify future ads and possibly pay a fine for deceptive ads, what other negative consequences are there for companies that engage in misleading advertising?

10. Give several examples of ethical or legal issues related to marketing communications.

Applying Marketing Skills

1. Select a major marketer of consumer goods that has advertised on national television within the past month. Try to identify approaches other than television advertising that have been part of this company's recent marketing communications mix.

2. Identify several specific examples of marketing communications that you feel are either ethically or legally questionable. What elements in each communication cause the problem? How could each communication be improved to remove any doubt about its ethical or legal acceptability?

3. Choose a product you are familiar with, and illustrate how product, pricing, and marketing channel factors influence the marketing communications activities for the product.

Using the www in Marketing

Activity One The FedEx Web site at *www.fedex.com* offers opportunities to learn more about the company's integrated marketing communications efforts. From the home page, explore the "In the United States" link where you can look further at the "advertising" link.

1. What is the theme of the TV ads? Can you describe the target market for FedEx based on its TV ads? Do you think the TV ads would be effective for the apparent target market?

2. What is the theme of the print ads? Can you describe the target market for FedEx based on its print ads? Do you think the print ads would be effective for the apparent target market?

3. Explore the "Sports" link to learn more about FedEx's sponsorship activities. How do the sponsorships reinforce the print and TV ads?

Activity Two Part of being a professional is keeping up with your field. In today's environment, this increasingly means staying abreast of international developments. Trade publications are useful for this purpose. For example, *Advertising Age* is one of the most widely read trade sources for all forms of marketing communications. Access the Web site *http://www.adage.com* and click on menu items of interest.

1. Locate and summarize three examples of marketing to various demographic, lifestyle, or ethnic market segments.

2. Find and summarize two good examples of integrated marketing communications campaigns, identifying the target market, the goals of the campaign, and the media used to reach the target market. If available, note how results of the campaign are measured.

Making Marketing Decisions

Case 16–1 *Liquor Companies Increase TV and NASCAR Advertising*

Major liquor companies have been rethinking the industry's self-imposed ban on television advertising. Since the mid-1990s, Seagram's and other major distillers have dabbled with cable television advertising, a move that raised the eyebrows of consumer watchdogs and government regulators. In 2002 it appeared that the major liquor companies were ready to expand their advertising efforts to the national television networks. NBC had signaled a willingness to accept liquor ads and began running a spot featuring the Smirnoff brand that urged the use of designated drivers. NBC intended to run such public service ads for four months, then begin mainstream ads emphasizing liquor, not safety. The network backed off when the public and political backlash grew too strong. Many industry analysts think it is only a matter of time before liquor companies advertise on national TV because the liquor industry is losing market share to wine and beer purveyors. Meanwhile, liquor advertising on local and cable television has increased tenfold since 2001.

The controversial aspects of liquor ads on TV revolve primarily around social questions. Opponents argue that drinking alcohol leads to increased social costs as a result of alcoholism, more automobile accidents, acts of violence, and employee absenteeism, and that alcohol, when consumed in excessive amounts, contributes to physical and mental disorders. Particularly troublesome to critics is that they feel that liquor companies target young and, in some cases, underage consumers.

In late 2004, automobile racing circuit NASCAR gave its approval for liquor companies to sponsor stock car racing teams. As with television advertising, critics contend that many underage consumers are subjected to liquor ads and that consumption of liquor may be glamorized by its ties to NASCAR. NASCAR teams that are sponsored by liquor companies typically offer anti–underage drinking messages as part of their agreements.

There are some risks to liquor companies if they persist with sports sponsorships such as NASCAR and television advertising. The federal government has increased its scrutiny of liquor marketing. The FTC reviewed ad content and media placement of eight major advertisers of beer, liquor, and wine. The FTC recommended improvements in self-regulatory codes and will undoubtedly investigate further the age profiles of television programs and print media where alcoholic beverages are advertised. Because there is bipartisan political support against advertising liquor on television, an increase may bring countermeasures such as increased taxes on alcohol, point-of-sale restraints, and restrictions on ad content. It appears that the liquor companies are willing to take these risks.

Questions

1. The U.S. government may enact regulations to prohibit liquor advertisements on television. How would liquor companies argue against such regulation?

2. Should liquor companies withhold sponsorship of sports events and advertising on television in an attempt to be more socially responsible?

3. How could liquor companies convince the public and government officials that their ads are not targeted toward consumers under the age of 21?

Case 16–2 *Vans and Nike Go Toe-to-Toe*

 Vans, a Southern California company and subsidiary of VF Corporation, is the largest and oldest company in the skate-shoe business. Not known for being particularly innovative, the company has succeeded by relying heavily on its checkerboard-print slip-on with "grippy" soles and a constant dedication to promoting the sport of skateboarding. Vans sells more than $350 million a year in the skate-shoe market, while its chief competitors such as Quicksilver, DC Shoes USA, and Volcom rarely exceed $100 million in annual sales.

Nike, through its purchase of Savier, a Portland, Oregon, skate-shoe company, represents a significant new competitive threat for Vans. Further, Nike has purchased Hurley's, an Orange County, California, clothing competitor of Vans. Hurley's does not yet make shoes, but industry observers expect Nike will use Hurley's to broaden its push into the fast-growing skateboarding market.

Nike tried unsuccessfully in the 1990s to break into the skate-shoe market. Its reputation as a corporate giant did not sit well with independent-minded teens and preteens, the prime demographic in the skateboarding market. Historically, Nike has been viewed as a supporter of team sports and conformity by skateboarders, while skateboard retailers see the company as arrogant and unwilling to support the industry in the committed fashion demonstrated by Vans throughout its 38-year history.

Some of these perceptions are changing. For one thing, Vans has gotten to be quite a corporate entity itself. Its products are distributed well beyond the skateboard specialty shops, where image is of paramount importance. Vans can be found in Foot Locker and other mainstream retail stores. Vans also has a music label, produces sports television shows for two networks, and has produced a movie called *Dogtown*, which it hopes will become a skateboarding cult classic just as *Endless Summer* was for surfing. *Dogtown* is backed by a $5 million marketing communications campaign from Sony Pictures, and Vans is selling *Dogtown*-licensed merchandise in conjunction with the film's release. Working with Sony Pictures and selling to Foot Locker may seem just as "corporate" to members of the young target market as some of Nike's main-stream moves.

Meanwhile, Nike is keeping its ownership of Savier as quiet as possible. The emphasis has been on how Savier shoes fit, and Nike is going toe-to-toe with Vans in a fight for market share. One of its prime marketing communications tools is the "Trade'Em Up" tour, which features a van (a coincidence?) that visits skate-board parks in an attempt to get Vans wearers to trade up to a pair of Saviers. Kids like the comfort of the Saviers, and they now seem less concerned about Nike's association with the company. There are 1,000 skateboard parks in the United States, with 200 of them built since early 2001. Nike first concentrated on 47 parks in California because California skate-boarders tend to be the trendsetters. The tour then moved on across the country into key markets. Feedback and sales have been good, with durability joining comfort as key product attributes that skate-boarders like.

Vans marketing personnel are worried about Nike's presence in the market, noting that Nike does not give up easily when faced with a marketing challenge. The antiestablishment sentiment that dogged Nike in the past does not seem as strident now, and Vans must face the fact that it too is part of the same establishment that Nike belongs to. Nike is redoubling its efforts to reach suburban white males, and the skateboard market may be a profitable avenue for doing just that. Industry analysts think that skateboarding is becoming a main-stream sport, and that sports like Little League baseball may be considered alternative in a few years. Tradition-ally, Nike has built its brand image on advertising using celebrity sports figures. A survey of preteen boys found that retired skateboarder Tony Hawk has more status than Michael Jordan. The sneaker market, following a big surge in the late 1990s for basketball shoes, has essentially leveled off. Nike, ever the hungry giant, may make it rough for Vans in the coming years. But no one expects Vans to give up easily either.

Questions

1. What directions can you suggest for Vans as it plans its marketing communications strategy in the near future? How much attention should be paid specifically to the Savier/Nike threat?

2. How should Nike proceed with its marketing communications in the near future to reach the skateboarding market? Can you make specific recommendations for reaching a preteen and teen male market?

3. How could both companies use multiple marketing communications tools (advertising, public relations, personal selling, sales promotion, and direct marketing) in an integrated marketing communications program?

Chapter Seventeen

ADVERTISING AND PUBLIC RELATIONS

17

After studying this chapter, you should be able to

1 Understand the characteristics, functions, and types of advertising.

2 Realize how people process advertising information and how it affects buyer behavior.

3 Discuss approaches to developing advertising campaigns.

4 Describe different advertising objectives and the message strategies used to achieve them.

5 Understand the decisions involved in selecting media and scheduling advertising.

6 Explain how marketers assess advertising effectiveness.

7 Appreciate the roles of public relations and publicity in marketing.

British Airways

After several turbulent years, British Airways is shrinking its capacity by going to smaller planes and fewer routes. The efforts are designed to increase profitability by recasting British Airlines as the preferred choice for business and corporate travelers. As long as the airline dominates British airports, it will be able to charge premium prices for a large portion of transatlantic travel. In addition, the firm is determined to return to its tradition of innovation. These changes include seats that can turn into beds and face the rear of the plane and that are connected with multichannel entertainment centers. New television advertisements concentrate on customer service and benefits. The challenge is to maintain the airline's premium positioning in the marketplace while still being concerned with the sale of unsold seats through Internet auctions and price-search avenues. This is a difficult task because the airline's primary target audience is busy, watches little TV, and is overexposed to advertising.

British Airways has used its advertising in a variety of efforts. For example, the company's "Future and Shape" strategy includes a marketing

blitz to combat its damaging reputation as an expensive airline. BA, which has seen its market share eroded by budget carriers, invests heavily in tactical advertising to promote competitive fares to Europe. Recent plans also include heavy use of public relations to introduce its lower fares and to fight against budget airlines such as easyJet. The company realizes the need to compete more on price. One aspect of this effort is the attempt to get more customers to buy tickets online. The company has not fared well lately, but hopes to improve its profits by reducing costs and appealing still to premium business travelers on transatlantic flights, who provide most of the company's profitable routes.

BA has been aggressively cutting costs, and competition on key long-haul routes has increased. Recently the carrier has placed renewed emphasis on building its brand and improving customer service. Moreover, the airline now recognizes the influence of the Internet and price competition on short-haul flights. As one spokesperson implied, the advertising message to convey is "getting the customers from A to B with all their luggage, and at a reasonable price."

The British Airways marketing program is a good example of how marketers use different advertising media and communications approaches to reach their desired target segments. To handle its Internet presence, BA has selected an advertising agency that specializes in designing interactive Web sites. The airline promotes its services through both traditional advertising and other marketing communications, such as public relations and sales promotions, along with the interactive aspects of its Web site.

In this chapter we explore issues associated with advertising, the most visible marketing activity. We discuss the related topic of public relations as well.

The Nature of Advertising

Advertising Defined

Advertising is the activity consumers most associate with the term *marketing*. **Advertising** is defined as a marketing communications element that is persuasive, nonpersonal, paid for by an identified sponsor, and disseminated through mass channels of communication to promote the adoption of goods, services, persons, or ideas.[1]

Effective advertising can present information about new or existing products, demonstrate meaningful uses of a product, and establish or refresh a brand's image.[2] It can reach a diverse or wide audience with repeated communications and gives a company the opportunity to dramatize its products and services in a colorful way.

Advertising stimulates demand, helps build brand success, develops and shapes buyer behavior, and gives the seller a measure of certainty about the level of sales. In addition, it informs buyers about product characteristics and availability and makes markets more competitive.[3]

In many markets, first-time purchasers are rare. Here advertising is critically important in affecting brand shares by inducing switching or retaining customers who otherwise might switch. Brand switching is generated from advertising through building brand awareness or altering consumer beliefs about brands.[4]

Advertising performs other functions as well. Some advertising supports personal selling efforts. For example, many companies advertise to increase consumer awareness of products, making later personal selling efforts easier. Such advertising, if executed effectively, generates sales leads and communicates product advantages to prospective buyers. In addition, one study of three computer companies found that advertising spending increased investor responses beyond the expected direct effects of advertising on increased sales and profits.[5]

Advertising and the Marketing Concept

It is important to remember that advertising is expensive and must be targeted effectively to achieve a firm's objectives. Firms do not have unlimited budgets; thus these funds must be allocated with a clear view of target markets and, hence, the audience for the organization's advertising. Further, conceiving product offerings on the basis of consumer needs and benefits is not sufficient without some form of communication, frequently advertising. That is, communication (advertising) *and* desired product attributes are both integral aspects of the marketing concept.

Mass media and advertising are playing a critical role in the creation of global consumption symbols. The direct influence of MTV and similar channels is evidenced by teens who watch these channels being more likely to display the signs of global teen culture and a global culture of consumption. Recent scholars have proposed that advertising can be used to position brands by a strategy referred to as *global consumer culture positioning*. This approach, not entirely the same concept as standardization discussed in Chapter 7 on market segmentation, can be contrasted with strategies in which the brand is associated with local cultures (such as Budweiser's small-town American culture in its U.S. advertising) and foreign consumer culture positioning in which the brand is positioned with a specific foreign culture (such as Singapore Airline's use of the "Singapore Girl" in its global media advertising).[6]

The Advertising Industry

Advertising is a huge industry, with annual global expenditures close to $300 billion worldwide. General Motors, Procter & Gamble, and DaimlerChrysler each spend more than $1 billion on media advertising.[7] Exhibit 17–1 presents the amount advertisers spend in the United States on each medium.

Two of the fastest-growing media are magazines and cable TV networks. In fact, their growth has caused average nightly audience shares of the major networks (ABC, NBC, CBS) to drop to under 50 percent; hence network advertising revenues have dropped by more than 10 percent.[8]

Ad Agencies

Many advertisers hire **advertising agencies** to create ad campaigns and to purchase media time and space. Exhibit 17–2 lists the world's top five advertising organizations as measured by gross income. All of them employ many people in organizations worldwide, and two have their central offices in New York.

Ad agencies employ creative people who develop unique advertising messages and media specialists who provide media planning and scheduling. Creative strategies and a proven track record clearly are good reasons to hire an ad agency. To limit costs and save on commissions, however, some large companies such as Benetton have in-house advertising functions to handle everything from creative design to media decisions. Other companies, such

---

Exhibit 17–1   *Total national advertising spending by type of medium for 2004*

Medium	Expenditures ($ millions)
Network TV	$ 22,500
Newspapers	24,600
Spot TV*	17,300
Magazines	21,300
Cable TV networks	14,200
Syndicated TV	3,900
National newspapers	3,300
National spot radio	2,600
Outdoor	3,200
Internet	7,400

*Spot TV refers to purchased time on selected television stations affiliated with one of the major networks.

Exhibit 17–2   *World's top five advertising organizations*

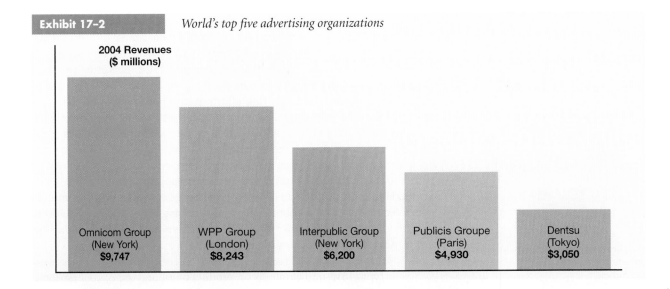

2004 Revenues ($ millions)

Omnicom Group (New York) $9,747
WPP Group (London) $8,243
Interpublic Group (New York) $6,200
Publicis Groupe (Paris) $4,930
Dentsu (Tokyo) $3,050

as Procter & Gamble, now buy their own media space and time instead of relying entirely on ad agencies. Some firms, such as IBM, Bayer, 3M, and Campbell Soup, have pared down the number of agencies used globally. This consolidation further enhances the "single voice" aspects of integrated marketing communications.

The choice of a competent ad agency is especially important for firms targeting new global markets. One U.S. soap manufacturer, for example, simply dubbed its commercials—showing people singing in the shower—into Polish TV ads. Poles laughed heartily at the advertiser's naïveté: There are very few showers in Polish homes, and because hot water is so limited, no Pole would take a leisurely shower. Marketers can avoid such gaffes by establishing close partnerships with a capable advertising agency.[9] Coca-Cola has shifted its $1.6 billion worldwide account to the Leo Burnett and the McCann-Erickson agencies. Interestingly, since China opened its markets in 1979, virtually every major ad agency has opened offices in this soon to be the world's third largest advertising market.[10]

Historically, agencies have been able to charge a 15 percent commission of their gross billings for time and space purchased for their clients. More recently, accountability and economic pressures have led to alternative compensation plans. First, many firms now charge rates below 15 percent. Second, some agencies use a labor-based system based on the number of hours worked. Third, in some instances, advertisers pay their agencies under an incentive program based on the extent to which the advertiser's objectives are met. Driver's Mart, which owns a network of used car dealerships and spends $40 million on advertising, pays its agency a commission for every car sold.[11] The U.S. Army also has shifted to a pay-for-performance plan in which its advertising agency will be paid based on recruitment success.

P&G has also decided to pay its agencies according to increases and decreases in sales, instead of paying labor-based fees or commissions based on media spending. The sheer size of the company's ad budget has resulted in significant attention to this shift toward pay for performance. In contrast, advertising executives worry about the other factors that affect sales and factors that are not under ad agency control. For instance, if an agency does great work, but the company fails to run the ads frequently enough, should the agency suffer? Conversely, if a company designs a great product that would sell without a lot of advertising, should the ad agency benefit?[12]

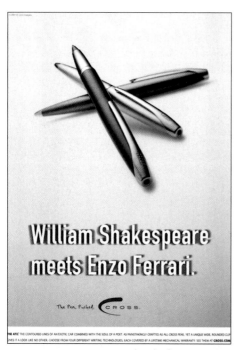

A. T. Cross Co. recognizes cultural influences in its advertising, which promotes the distinctiveness of its products.

An Industry in Transition

Today marketers increasingly question each advertising expenditure. Targeting mass markets with advertising alone no longer makes sense for many companies. Simply buying airtime during a specific TV program or buying a certain page in a specific magazine is not enough to reach targeted audiences. For example, companies like Unilever and its ad agencies are downgrading the importance of the 30-second TV spot advertisement and shifting more effort to Net entertainment and game venues.[13] Advertisers often must use multimedia campaigns, combining television, print ads, videos, billboards, trade shows, direct mail, and activities such as event sponsorship into an integrated marketing communications program.[14]

Globalization of marketing efforts is another example of changing times. In many instances, both product and advertising must meet local market needs and fit in with cultural practices. Strongly religious areas such as Saudi Arabia and Iran, areas with multiple cultural influences such as Japan and Korea, and more homogeneous areas such as Sweden and Australia each require different advertising communications.[15] For example, Kraft advertised its processed cheese slices using a common theme (milk content) but different advertising styles and presentations to match the consumer preferences and uniqueness in Canada, the United Kingdom, Australia, and Spain.[16]

Japanese advertisers favor "soft selling" and often use indirect messages. The typical Western emphasis on product merit and use of spokespeople directly stating brand advantages are missing in much Japanese advertising.[17] And surprisingly, given the Japanese attraction to Western culture, the appearance of American images and settings has increased only modestly in Japanese advertising. Foreign advertisers in Japan should recognize these differences.

Technological changes keep the advertising industry in transition as well. The extension of cable TV, the widespread penetration of VCRs, the introduction of TiVo, and remote control capability all suggest some loss of effectiveness of TV commercials. Remote control use, in particular, has given rise to **commercial zapping,** or changing the channels during commercials.[18] One study revealed that ads aired during competing sports events encountered audience losses of up to 50 percent. Zapping is heaviest during news and late-night programming.[19] In addition, younger viewers and members of higher-income households are more likely to get up and do something else during TV commercial breaks.[20] As TiVo and like competitors grow, the advertising industry will have to accept that it is operating in an environment in which viewers have control.[21] Prerecorded shows that allow skipping forward through ads and these other technological advances have advertisers and media executives very concerned. Television as a free service enjoyed by consumers depends on effective exposure to advertising. Otherwise, advertisers will not purchase the time, and the economics of advertising as a means of supporting television will not work.[22]

What then does this transition mean for advertising? The future looks brightest for media that reach target audiences more efficiently than broad-based ones like network TV. The winners are expected to be radio stations, specialized cable networks, new kinds of in-store advertising, online advertising, and weekly newspapers, all of which appeal to specific rather than to broad audiences.[23]

Internet Advertising

Online advertising is predicted to reach $15.5 billion, or over 5 percent of total media expenditures, by 2007.[24] The evolution of the Internet as a meaningful channel of commercial communications is profoundly affecting the way firms do business. For example, advertising designed to establish consumer brand images will no longer focus only on the 30-second commercial complemented by some print advertising. Advertisers and agencies alike are now required to consider all contacts with consumers in efforts

The increasing number of specialized cable channels enables marketers to more effectively reach target markets with unique characteristics and specific interests.

Speaking from Experience

Pat Garner
Vice President and Chief
Marketing Officer
Intersections, Inc.

"In my experience, the term 'integrated marketing' is perhaps the single most overused (but underdelivered) phrase in the marketing lexicon. Marketers typically confuse integration with what they do (versus what occurs in the mind of the consumer). True 'marketing integration' is not just about one sight, one sound, one smell. Real marketing integration results from the sum total of everything the consumer observes, reads, hears, or learns through word of mouth (buzz) about a product or service. I believe that 'everything communicates'; therefore, the marketer must constantly place himself/herself in the role of the consumer and ask, Does everything add up to a single clear compelling message? Or as a consumer, do I sense conflicting signals?"

Pat Garner is currently Vice President and Chief Marketing Officer for Intersections, Inc., which provides credit management and identity theft protection products and services to over 5 million customers of the nation's leading financial institutions. He worked previously as senior vice president for Nextel Corporation and the Coca-Cola Company. During his 20 years with Coca-Cola, Pat held a number of positions, including president of the Southeast and West Asia Divisions, as well as vice president and director of strategic marketing. Garner has a B.S. degree from Tulane University and an M.B.A. from the University of South Carolina, plus advanced training from the Harvard Business School and the University of Pennsylvania Wharton School.

to develop strong brands and brands that can be effective across borders. The media mix is shifting in favor of Internet-based contextual advertising, through which ads are served up online to an individual viewer based on the content the reviewer is reading.[25] In addition to the fact that Internet advertising growth is exceeding other forms of media advertising, blogging sites are also expected to eventually attract large numbers of advertisers. The nature of blogging site advertising and the eventual effects of this new media source remain uncertain.[26] Overall, with consumers harder to reach, ad spending on targeted and easily measured media is increasing. The largest projected growth rates are for Internet advertising (25 percent), direct mail (9.5 percent), magazines (7.3 percent), and cable TV (7 percent).[27]

Three factors have hit the online industry—failing dot-coms that were heavy Internet advertisers, low click-through rates for most banner ads, and a general recession for all types of media. Other concerns include ads that obscure site editorial content, ads that promise one thing and deliver another, and multiple ads on a page competing for attention. In response to poor performance, new advertising formats have been introduced that include oblong ads on the side of a page and rectangle boxes much larger than banners, as

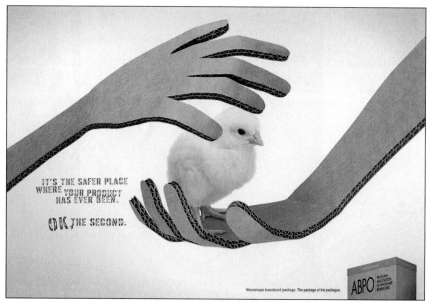

ABPO packaging promotes its packaging benefits in this B2B advertisement.

well as miniwindows that open independently and will not disappear until closed by the viewer. Advergames, such as Dodge Speedway, represent a new genre of computer games that market everything from dandruff shampoo to movies. In fact, consumer advertisers are adopting online advertising programs used by B2B marketers, such as creating extranets and building microsites with their marketing partners.

Many well-known brands, like Pepsi, Volvo, Frito-Lay, and others, have begun to view online advertising as an interactive supplement to their traditional advertising. Online advertising is more than click-through rates. Branding advantages are important as well. The manner in which online advertising should be evaluated depends on the situation. If the firm is Lands' End or L. L. Bean, click-through conversion is important. If the firm is focused on branding, then awareness, recall, and attitudes are important. The New York–based Interactive Advertising Bureau has proposed a series of guidelines that are designed to improve the accuracy of Internet audience measurement.[28]

Classification of Advertising

Advertising can be classified by target audience, geographic area, medium, and purpose, as shown in Exhibit 17–3.[29] The special types discussed here are corporate image advertising, corporate advocacy advertising, public service advertising, classified advertising, direct-response advertising, business-to-business advertising, and cooperative advertising.

Corporate image advertising, directed toward the general public or investors and stockholders, promotes an organization's image and role in the community as a corporate citizen, independent of any product or service. **Corporate advocacy advertising** announces a stand on some issue related to the firm's operation, often one threatening the company's well-being. For example, Exxon addressed environmental issues in advocacy advertising following its Alaska oil spill.

| **Exhibit 17–3** | *Classification of advertising* |

By Target Audience	By Geographic Area	By Medium	By Purpose
Consumer advertising: Aimed at people who buy the product for their own or someone else's personal use.	**Local (retail) advertising:** Advertising by businesses whose customers come from only one city or local trading area.	**Print advertising:** Newspaper, magazine.	**Product advertising:** Intended to promote goods and services.
Business advertising: Aimed at people who buy or specify goods and services for use in business:	**Regional advertising:** Advertising for products sold in one area or region, but not the whole country.	**Broadcast (electronic) advertising:** Radio, TV.	**Nonproduct (corporate or institutional) advertising:** Intended to promote firm's mission or philosophy rather than a product.
• **industrial:** Aimed at people who buy or influence the purchase of industrial products.	**National advertising:** Advertising aimed at customers in several regions of the country.	**Out-of-home advertising:** Outdoor, transit.	**Commercial advertising:** Intended to promote goods, services, or ideas with the expectancy of making a profit.
• **Trade:** Aimed at wholesalers and retailers who buy for resale to their customers.	**International advertising:** Advertising directed at foreign markets.	**Direct-mail advertising:** Advertising sent through the mail.	**Noncommercial advertising:** Sponsored by or for a charitable institution, civic group, or religious or political organization.
• **Professional:** Aimed at people licensed to practice under a code of ethics or set of professional standards.			**Action advertising:** Intended to bring about immediate action on the part of the reader.
• **Agricultural (farm):** Aimed at people in the farming or agricultural business.			**Awareness advertising:** Intended to build the image of a product or familiarity with the product's name and package.

Public service advertising is donated by the advertising industry to promote activities for some social good. For example, the World Wildlife Fund presents environmental public service advertisements. Frequently, marketers donate advertising time to drug and alcohol abuse prevention efforts, such as the "Just Say No" program and Mothers Against Drunk Driving (MADD). The Ad Council has been instrumental in supporting public service advertising for over 60 years as a means for generating positive social change. The issues addressed include supporting higher education, advancing diversity, encouraging volunteerism, and promoting health and safety issues.[30]

Direct-response advertising (discussed in more detail in Chapter 20) is intended to elicit immediate action, often a purchase. Direct-response ads on TV typically request immediate calls to telephone numbers shown on the TV screen. Direct-response ads also appear in magazines and direct mail. **Classified advertising,** mainly in newspapers, typically promotes transactions for a single item or service.

Firms use **business-to-business advertising** to promote their products or services directly to other firms. The largest B-to-B advertising buyers are Verizon, Microsoft, IBM, and Sprint. Most business advertising involves print ads in trade periodicals or direct mail sent to targeted buyers. In trade or business-to-business advertising, just as in consumer advertising, product benefits must be highlighted and a solution offered to prospects' problems. A significant portion of business-to-business advertising should also be devoted to building and nurturing the brand images for the company as well as promoting/developing/enriching its key products and services."[31] Just like consumers, B2B customers buy the brands they trust; so building brand reputation and equity is as important as promoting product benefits. Buyers' attitudes and expectations about business products are just as important as the products themselves.[32] Some business marketers, such as Ricoh Copiers, IBM, and Fed Ex, advertise on TV in time slots likely to reach sophisticated adult audiences. Like business-to-consumer advertisers, B2B advertisers must coordinate trade magazine advertising, trade show activity, and online database efforts in an integrated marketing communications program. B2B trade advertising must also have a strong visual to attract attention and a clear selling proposition. Too often advertising of all types, including B2B appeals, is so clever that the message is not processed.[33]

Cooperative advertising often entails manufacturers contributing to a local dealer or retailer's advertising expense. The marketer typically runs manufacturer-developed advertising that includes the outlet's name and logo. In many cases, cooperative advertising simply means several businesses pooling their funds to buy print or broadcast advertising on a regular basis in efforts to obtain better deals and to increase exposure.[34]

Consumer Ad Processing
How then does advertising actually influence consumers? In this section we explain how consumers process advertisements and how ads affect consumer attitudes and decisions.

Hierarchy of Effects
Advertising's influence on consumers is often explained by using the **hierarchy of effects,** or information-processing, model. This sequence of effects—exposure, attention, comprehension, acceptance, retention—is shown in Exhibit 17–4. Of course, not every consumer consciously, or even subconsciously, goes through a sequence of steps for all ads. Yet each stage of this hierarchy represents a specific goal for advertisers to pursue.

A marketer achieves *message exposure* by placing ads in appropriate media, such as magazines, TV programs, or newspapers, which gives the consumer the opportunity to process

Exhibit 17–4   *Advertising hierarchy of effects*

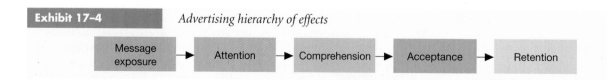

the message. According to the "mere exposure" hypothesis, positive evaluation of a brand can occur simply from repeated exposure to an advertisement.

Consumer *attention* is the next step. The ad must stimulate the consumer to direct mental effort toward it. The attention-getting properties of an ad are its physical characteristics. For print ads, these include size, number of colors, and brightness. Motion, attention-getting models, and novelty also help grab attention.[35] One recent large study of magazine ads revealed, surprisingly, that advertisers aiming to maximize attention to the entire advertisement should consider devoting more space to the text and that prominent placement of brand symbols and visual identity in print advertisements increase attention.[36]

Attention does not necessarily mean the consumer will process a message further. *Message comprehension,* the next stage, means the consumer understands the ad's meaning. Comprehension includes categorization of the stimulus or advertised brand based on prior information stored in memory. Elaboration of the information included in the ad furthers comprehension. Comprehension is enhanced to the extent the individual is motivated at the time of exposure and has some prior product category knowledge. Ad information that appears first (primacy effects) or last (recency effects) is often most comprehended.

Then *message acceptance* must occur for the consumer to develop favorable attitudes about the advertised product or service and its subsequent purchase. Message acceptance includes cognitive thoughts or responses related to the information in the ad as well as feelings, or affective responses, that occur because of the advertisement.

Message retention occurs when the consumer stores ad information in long-term memory, which is critical for affecting later purchase decisions and behavior.

A related view of how advertising works, and one developed recently by two advertising scholars from the London Business School, can be summarized partially as follows. First, advertising from the target brand and competing brands serves as input to the consumer. Strategic variables, including the scheduling of media, message content, and repetition, are components of this input. The individual's motivation and ability (consumer involvement) filter this input. Initial consumer responses include thoughts and thinking (cognition) and feelings and affect (attitudes). These consumer outcomes then lead to choice behavior, consumption, loyalty, and habit formation.[37]

Selective perception can occur at any stage. Exposure varies when consumers change channels during commercial breaks on television. *Selective attention* occurs when consumers notice certain ads but not others. Advertisers and advertising creative personnel expend considerable effort in developing ads that generate attention. Color, sexual images, attractive celebrity endorsers, and humor are frequently employed to garner attention.

Selective comprehension involves consumer interpretation of information provided in ads. Persuasion researchers have documented the tendency of individuals to perceive incoming information consistent with their own opinions and preferences. For example, an ad that disparages a consumer's favorite brand may be seen as biased or untruthful and its claims not accepted. *Selective retention* relates to what parts of the advertised information consumers actually remember. Given the low-involvement nature of ad encounters, messages are often kept simple and advertisers frequently use mnemonics, such as symbols, rhymes, and unique images, that assist the learning and remembering of brand information.

Influences on Ad Processing

Buyers' needs influence their processing of advertising messages. For example, a firm with a pressing need for waste removal would pay more attention to ads for this service than to aesthetic ads from a plant service to beautify the corporate office.

In addition, the buyer's motivation, ability, and opportunity to process brand information come into play. These concepts serve as important filters between advertising input (message content, media scheduling, and repetition) and the consumer. Consumer responses include thoughts or cognitions, affective feelings, and experiences.[38] First, *motivation* is related to the concept of consumer involvement, or the personal relevance or importance of the marketing communications message. Motivation is the desire to process the information. When motivation is low, potential customers pay little attention and remember minimal information, if any. *Ability* implies the buyer knows enough about the product category to understand the advertised message.[39] *Opportunity* is the extent to which distractions or limited exposure time affect the buyer's attention to brand information in an ad.

The opportunity for processing any single brand advertisement is diminished to the extent that the ad is surrounded by ads for competing brands. Consequently, advertisers attempt to avoid competitors' ads when buying advertising time and space. Competitive interference effects are particularly likely to occur for new brands. Because consumers' stored memory is limited, it is much more difficult for them to remember product information from ads for new brands in heavily advertised product categories. In contrast, well-known brands are less affected by competitive brand advertising; hence they have important advantages in maintaining market share in the face of competing new brands.[40]

Product involvement may also affect the extent to which advertising is processed. Highly involved consumers are more likely to process the information in advertising and to notice differences in product attributes as advertised. In addition, extended problem solving is more likely; hence complex advertisements may be more effective because thoughtful processing of information is common in high-involvement situations.[41]

One well-known theory of persuasion, the **elaboration likelihood model,** includes individual motivation and ability to elaborate information in advertisements as determinants of two different "routes" to persuasion. Specifically, when consumer motivation and ability are high, persuasive message arguments are more thoroughly processed and the strength of the arguments influences persuasion in what is termed the "central route" to persuasion. However, when motivation and ability are low, peripheral cues become important in enhancing persuasion. In these cases, aspects of advertisements such as pictures and the use of celebrity and/or attractive models are important. In these latter cases, persuasion occurs through what is labeled the "peripheral route" to persuasion.[42]

Developing an Advertising Campaign

An ad campaign requires an analysis of the marketing situation, the target market involved, and the firm's overall communication objectives. As Exhibit 17–5 shows, once the firm has selected its target market, it must determine advertising objectives, determine the advertising budget, design the creative strategy, select and schedule media, and evaluate advertising effectiveness.

Selecting Target Markets

The development of an effective advertising campaign is dependent upon the selection of target markets that the company can effectively serve. As explained in both Chapter 3 and Chapter 7, the selection of which target markets to serve is based on a number of factors related to the marketplace and the advertiser. The most important of these determining

Exhibit 17–5   *Advertising development and evaluation*

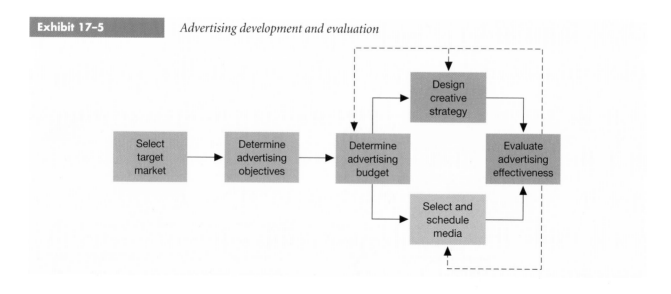

factors include the firm's core competencies, its overall vision, and the potential of the intended targets in terms of long-term sales and profits. Targeting the right consumers often involves appealing to those consumers who are already loyal, rather than attempting to attract new users. For example, the successful "Got Milk" ad campaign targeted those consumers who already had favorable attitudes toward milk.[43] For the placement of advertising during TV programs, the shows are selected for their ability to deliver exposure to intended target markets. Segments that advertisers are trying to reach are traditionally identified by age, income, gender, education, and ethnicity. The youth are often the focus for their ability to establish what is trendy, while the older baby boomers offer attractive markets because of their substantial disposable incomes.

Determining Advertising Objectives

Advertising objectives should be realistic, precise, measurable, and consistent with the firm's overall marketing and communications objectives. One objective might be to increase brand awareness from 10 to 35 percent of all consumers within a particular market—say, cereal eaters between the ages of 18 and 55. Another might be to increase sales or market share, such as achieving sales growth of 2 percent in the next quarter. Setting objectives enhances the firm's ability to evaluate the effectiveness of its advertising expenditures.

In some cases, advertising objectives may be tied to other variables, such as market awareness, that are indirectly tied to sales objectives. In the face of low share for some of its products, Minolta used advertising to increase awareness of its entire line of products. Likewise, IBM recently spent $75 million on a global print campaign developed by Ogilvy & Mather just to improve the awareness of its technology services and consulting.[44]

Determining Advertising Budget

The size of the advertising budget depends on the size of the company, its financial resources, the industry growth rate, market dispersion, and the firm's position in the marketplace. Smaller firms usually spend less; dominant firms may spend a disproportionately large amount to maintain market share and discourage competition. And a growing industry may warrant higher advertising budgets to build awareness, sales, and market share. Frito-Lay increased spending by 50 percent on Cheetos, Doritos, and Lay's in a budget shift associated with a "pull" marketing strategy designed to increase consumer demand.[45]

As explained in Chapter 16, budgets are often based on percentage of sales, competitive parity, all the firm can afford, or allocation by objectives, the recommended approach. Advertising budgets are more important in today's business environment, which more and more views marketing communications as a profit center. Advertising generates income, but expenses must be controlled; and advertising, as well as all marketing communications, should show a net profit.[46]

Designing Creative Strategy

Creative strategy combines the "what is said" with the "how it is said." Typically the advertiser specifies the general content or theme of the message, and the ad agency works with the company to develop the presentation.

Usually the theme is the product's primary benefit or competitive advantage, presented in an attention-getting message the target audience can comprehend and remember. As competition for audience attention increases, highly creative and entertaining commercials become commonplace.[47] iPod used a starkly simple ad campaign in its successful marketing approach, in which silhouettes emphasize the enjoyment of music while in motion.[48]

On occasion, failures in creative execution occur. Chrysler botched the introduction of its Intrepid by the use of very high-tech

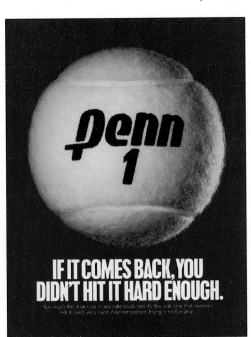

Advertisements often make use of novel pictorial displays to get attention and generate brand awareness. These ads are effective at encouraging information processing after initial exposure.

advertisements that only briefly showed the car at the end of the commercial. Sometimes questionable advertising is unintentionally humorous. For example, one sleep aid promoted the cautionary message "may cause drowsiness," while one snack brand advertised its contest as "You could be a winner! No purchase necessary. Details inside."[49] Levi's has returned to emphasizing its authentic heritage, instead of chasing after street fashion and transient "cool."[50]

MESSAGE STRATEGY ALTERNATIVES

Advertising messages can make objective or subjective claims. **Objective claims** describe product features or performance in measurable terms, such as "Chevy mid-sized vans are available with V-6 or V-8 engines." Objective claims often promote the benefits customers receive from the price paid. For example, Reebok advertises the custom fit from its pump technology. AT&T advertises service reliability for its monthly charges.

Subjective claims are not measurable, often stress image enhancement, and may include *puffery,* which is simply some level of acceptable exaggeration, such as Budweiser's "the king of beers" or Del Monte's "super natural" advertising phrases.[51]

Some advertising for brands with high awareness and high penetration is designed to increase usage by current customers. This type of advertising is termed **expansion advertising** and is intended to encourage "substitution in use." Advertising messages such as "Use A-1 to grill burgers" or "Consume Special K as an afternoon snack" have been found effective for encouraging expanded usage.[52]

Another strategy used by advertisers emphasizes the product's relative competitive value in the marketplace. Such value-based advertising is now prevalent in many consumer goods categories. The danger in heavy reliance on advertising messages that focus predominantly on value or price claims is that these strategies increase consumer sensitivity to price and make price differences more salient to buyers.[53]

Pat Garner, Vice President and Chief Marketing Officer for Intersections, Inc., comments on the role of consumer insights and the development of an ad campaign: "The biggest shortfall of many marketers is that they process great quantities of information, too few relevant and meaningful consumer insights, and even fewer actionable marketing implications. In dialogue with fellow marketers, I often ask three questions: 'what,' 'so what,' and 'now what?' Marketers should be ever mindful that their job is to translate significant consumer insights and marketing implications into value-creating 'actions' for their enterprise. Value-creating actions increase shareowner value over time. Value-creating actions build long-term brand equity, as well as drive sales in the short term. Value-creating actions lead to sustainable growth in volume, share, and profit. The key indicator of a vibrant consumer marketing culture is an organization's heightened capacity for value-producing actions."

Message strategies frequently attempt to convey a distinct product image or quality appeal. Timex ads, for example, consistently focus on product quality; Lexus ads appeal to buyers' self-images. Some messages appeal to the hedonistic, or pleasure-seeking, side of consumers.

Comparative advertising relates a sponsored brand to a competitive brand on at least one product attribute. Objective attribute comparisons seem to be most effective at enhancing consumer attitudes about the sponsoring brand. Well-known comparisons include MCI against AT&T; Subaru against Volvo; Toshiba computers against Compaq; Maxwell House coffee against Folgers; American Express credit cards against Visa; Pizza Hut versus Domino's; and Weight Watchers diet meals against Lean Cuisine.[54] Gillette's Duracell brand has raised its market share relative to Energizer from the use of a series of indirect comparative ads.[55] In some countries, like Greece and Argentina, comparative advertising is restricted to brand X comparisons. In Japan comparative advertising is not used at all.

Thinking Critically

Typically it is branded product manufacturers that undertake heavy advertising and promotion to increase awareness about not only a specific brand but also an entire product category. Generic or store brands may also reap the benefits of increased category awareness without having incurred substantial advertising costs, and are therefore able to offer the same product at a lower price. What can brand advertisers do to limit this "free-rider" effect?

Fear appeals are often used to encourage support for social programs, in this case related to the use of cell phones while driving.

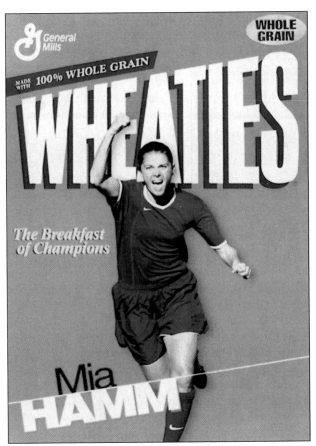

Celebrity endorsers are a frequent means of getting attention and generating positive attitudes toward sponsored brands.

Typically, the advertiser claims superiority of its product on the most important features being compared. By not claiming superiority on a less important attribute, the advertiser implies admission of a slight shortcoming, which may actually enhance the credibility of the other claims. An advertiser may also enhance a lesser-known product by comparing it with a well-known product. Comparative claims may represent either direct or indirect comparative advertising. In direct comparative advertisements, the advertised brand is compared overtly with a named competitor or competitors. Indirect claims involve no mention of competing brand names but assert generally that the advertised brand is superior or better.

Message strategies with *emotional appeals* attempt to evoke feelings, moods, and memories. Diet Pepsi and Dr. Pepper commercials, for example, associate warm feelings with their brands. Marketers of insurance, tires, and automobiles may use *fear appeals* related to safety. The "baby in a tire" theme, produced by DDB Needham Advertising Agency of New York for Michelin Tires, recognizes the value of such advertising. The Club, an automobile antitheft device, stresses fear in its advertisements. And deodorant, shampoo, and toothpaste ads frequently play on the consumer's desire to be liked or to avoid disapproval.

A *celebrity endorsement* may be an element of the creative message strategy. Well-known spokespersons, such as Mike Piazza, Shaquille O'Neal, Britney Spears, and Tiger Woods, can enhance the persuasive impact of a message. The Williams sisters' endorsement deals have made them the most highly paid females, promoting such brands as Reebok, Avon, and Nortel Networks.[56] George Foreman's personal appeal, based on his transformation from a boxer to an admired spokesperson, has been the stimulus for his endorsement success across a large number of product categories.[57]

The milk-mustache appeals have been very effective at encouraging attitude change among consumers toward the use of milk and its nutritional benefits. These ads have included models, actors, and athletes as celebrity endorsers. This strategy is not without some risk, however, as evidenced by problems encountered by former frequent endorsers Michael Jackson, Madonna, Burt Reynolds, and O. J. Simpson.

Humor appeals can increase consumer attention and recall. The Energizer Bunny campaign created by TBWA Chiat Day agency has been rated as the most effective by consumers.[58] The most traditional of Super Bowl advertisers, Anheuser-Busch, relies heavily on humor and has been particularly successful when animals are used in its ads to generate humorous situations. Miller Lite has used humor successfully in its claims of being the "president of beers" in competition with Anheuser's Bud Light as the "king of beers." These ads underscore the fact that humor is one of the most popular advertising techniques

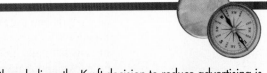

ACTING ETHICALLY

Kraft reduces ads to kids

Kraft has decided to stop advertising for junk foods targeted to kids under 12. The decision should improve the company's image among parents and public policy officials worried about obesity among children. The reduction in this form of advertising will also hurt television network advertising even further. Rival food executives worry that the move is an admission of guilt. Others believe the Kraft decision to reduce advertising is a shrewd public relations strategy. However, Kraft's decision to pull kids' ads for unhealthful snacks and promote more nutritious fare reflects ethical decision making in the face of legitimate concerns about childhood obesity.

Happy Halloween.

Oral-B

Humor also generates interest and attitude change as an advertising message strategy.

around the world. Interestingly, recent advertising research reveals that effective humor campaigns are driven by an initial "surprise" response on the part of the viewer, which precedes the humor recognition and humorous response.[59]

One strategy alternative that is controversial in terms of both the ethical issues involved and practical effectiveness is **subliminal advertising.** Although initially related to ad messages presented at a rate or level below thresholds of conscious awareness, this practice today most often involves the embedding of hidden symbols, such as sexual images or brand information, in advertisements. A number of books have been written on the dangers of subliminal advertising, but evidence supporting its practical effectiveness is virtually nonexistent. Most important, the very fact that such messages are embedded or concealed make the subliminal information extremely weak relative to more vivid stimuli.[60]

A growing phenomenon is the **advertorial,** a special advertising section with some nonadvertising content included in magazines. Advertorials are typically sold as special deals to advertisers that would not normally advertise in the magazine. An example is the "Guide to Entertainment" presented in *The New Yorker,* paid for by Chrysler. Advertorials offer advertisers a way to stand out in a cluttered media environment.[61] Television's counterpart is the **infomercial,** a 30-minute ad that resembles a talk show or news program. This form of direct marketing is now frequently seen on both network and cable TV.

A new form of advertising, **product placement advertising,** combines the efforts of marketers with moviemakers. Noteworthy examples include Apple in *Forrest Gump* and Dr. Pepper in *101 Dalmations.* Cingular Wireless was placed in the megahit *Spiderman.* Recently, however, marketers have been reluctant to participate in Hollywood deals due to increasing prices and questionable increases in sales.[62] A related phenomenon is the use of joint advertising efforts to promote movies and products. Milk producers used *The Phantom* for a milk-mustache ad. PepsiCo and *Star Wars* have been featured in joint advertising, much like the long-term agreement between McDonald's and Disney.[63]

Selecting and Scheduling Media

Traditionally, ad agencies have started with creative design and then sought ways to deliver those messages. In other instances, the process is reversed in that planning begins with how to reach and influence consumers, followed by the development of creative themes. Whatever the process, selecting and scheduling media are critical aspects of successful advertising campaigns.[64] Media planning involves decisions on *media class* (television, magazines) and *media vehicles* (specific television programs, specific magazines). Marketers must then decide on *media schedules* (frequency, timing of ads).

MEDIA CLASSES   There are seven classes of advertising media: television, magazines, newspapers, radio, outdoor, transit, and direct mail. There are advantages and disadvantages of these, and the effectiveness of each approach depends on its unique capabilities.

Television, magazines, and radio are useful in building brand awareness. TV, in particular, can reach mass markets. And with the advent of cable and specialized networks, TV can target specific markets at a relatively cheap cost per individual exposure. Television commercials, however, are expensive in total. Moreover, because TV ads typically last 15 to 30 seconds and are surrounded by other messages, consumers can easily tune them out. Broadcast TV viewership has been on the decline for the past 10 years, and getting brand messages to take hold is increasingly difficult. Consumers simply do not use traditional broadcast and major network TV as in the past.[65]

Magazines can present complex and factual information. Messages can be read leisurely, have a long life, have pass-along exposure, and can be targeted to specific audiences. One study that compared magazine and TV ratings found that the top 25 women's magazines command larger audiences among women age 18 to 49 than the top female-targeted TV shows.[66] But magazine ads are subject to interference from competing ads and take a substantial time to develop and introduce. The largest spenders on magazine advertising are Philip Morris, General Motors, and Procter & Gamble. The magazines that produce the most advertising revenue are *People, US Weekly, Time,* and *Sports Illustrated.*

Newspaper advertising is excellent for local retail sales promotions. It can be developed quickly and can effectively target particular locations. But newspapers contain many ads and do not typically generate much audience involvement. The production quality of newspaper advertising is fairly low, though newspaper inserts do enable higher quality. For retailers, however, newspaper advertising is an effective communications medium.

Radio advertising can be quite cost-effective, the commercials can be targeted to specific audiences, and repetition of messages is possible. However, radio messages are subject to channel zapping and of course have no visual impact. Further, radio messages have a short life and typically generate only minimal involvement.

Outdoor advertising consists mainly of billboards constructed on leased property and rented to advertising companies. Billboards reach large numbers of consumers effectively and inexpensively. Billboard advertising is useful in supporting TV and radio campaigns and is particularly effective for building awareness of new brands. The average American now spends more time driving than eating meals, and two-thirds of that time is spent driving alone. U.S. outdoor advertising includes more than 400,000 billboards, plus billboard-sized ads placed on 37,000 buses. The costs for billboards are based on traffic counts and the average number of daily impressions.[67] However, billboards present only limited message content, the span of exposure is brief, and messages must be viewed at a distance. One of the most popular features in outdoor technology is the digital projector-based technology in which video messages can be shown and changed electronically.[68]

Transit advertisements—signs and messages on or in public buses and trains—are billboards on wheels. Transit ads inside vehicles are low in cost and provide frequent and lengthy exposure to riders. But message space is limited and typically reaches a restricted audience. The vehicle environment may detract from the prestige of the advertiser or message, and crowded conditions during rush hours may limit the opportunity to process the messages.

Direct mail, among the fastest-growing means of advertising today, has several significant advantages. It can reach narrow markets and enable the advertiser to elaborate on ad claims. Direct mail is also important in support of business-to-business marketing communications programs and is available to small and large companies. When coupled with toll-free numbers or return envelopes, direct mail can generate direct-response sales. But the frequency of direct-mail advertising can limit its effectiveness. Many consumers perceive such ads as junk mail and don't pay much attention to them. The success of direct-mail campaigns depends on the quality of the mailing lists used to target customers. In addition, printing, mailing, and development costs can make direct-mail marketing expensive. Wal-Mart has an extensive in-store television system that reaches 130 million viewers every four weeks in many store locations. The in-store network shows a stream of consumer product ads purchased by companies like Kraft, Unilever, Hallmark, and PepsiCo. According to Wal-Mart's rate card, advertisers pay $137,000 to $292,000 for running commercials over a four-week period.[69]

MEDIA VEHICLES   Once the marketer has selected the media class, it must choose the specific advertising vehicles (specific magazines, radio stations, or TV shows). The selection depends on the cost-effectiveness of a particular outlet for reaching desired market audiences. Factors include audience size and composition and the cost of running the ad. Advertisers seek audiences that contain high proportions of target customers. It is in making these decisions that demographics (characteristics of audiences) are often so important. Firms such as Simmons Research Bureau can help here. For example, an advertiser can request data exposure or magazine readership for women with incomes over $30,000 who regularly purchase tennis equipment. Similar sources for TV and newspaper audiences are provided by Arbitron, ACNielsen, and MediaMark.

A common method to evaluate vehicles within a specific medium is by **cost per thousand (CPM).** For magazines, the formula is

$$CPM = [(\text{Magazine page cost} \times 1,000)/\text{Circulation}]$$

"Drive":30

1.) Title card: "I Can Be Better" With Tiger Woods. Brought to you by the new Air Zoom TW.
Anncr. (VO): I can be better with Tiger Woods, Brought to you by the new Air Zoom TW.

2.) (Cut to Tiger)
Tiger: Today's topic . . . tee height.

3.) (Cut to close-up of golf ball on tee)
Tiger (VO): I like to tee off my ball just above the club head.

4.) (Cut to Tiger watching to see where his golf ball lands)
SFX: Sprinkler comes on.

5.) (He keeps watching . . .)
SFX: Lawn mower.
(. . . and watching)

6.) Tiger: Experiment and you'll find the tee height that's right for you.
Title card: Nike and Tiger Woods logo.

TV storyboards are used to display the sequence and content of advertisements. Here a humorous theme is employed using Tiger Woods as the spokesperson for Nike.

Using data from *www.mediastart.com,* assume *Sports Illustrated* charges an insertion cost of $215,000 for a full-page, four-color advertisement and has a paid circulation of 3,150,000. The CPM for *SI* would be

$$[(\$215{,}000 \times 1{,}000)/3{,}150{,}000] = \$68.25$$

Marketers can calculate this value for other magazines in that class and make comparisons for the decision. Rate and circulation statistics can be obtained from *Standard Rate & Data Services: Consumer Magazines.* Although this is a useful decision tool, CPM figures cannot be used to make comparisons across media and do not account for the quality of the audience, pass-along readership, the appropriateness of the media vehicle for the product category, or the nature of the editorial content.

An alternative to the CPM concept is CPM-TM, or the cost per thousand to reach a desired target market segment. Consider again the *SI* example and assume that Cadillac, a

Thinking Critically

The objectives of many consumer ads for individual brands seen on national network and cable programs are to build brand recognition, attitudes, and sales. Hence the effectiveness of these ads will eventually be considered in light of brand performance (sales, market share).

• What criteria or outcomes might be used to evaluate the effectiveness of corporate image campaigns? Of corporate advocacy advertising?

• How might a business-to-business company evaluate its own trade advertising when personal selling is the business's primary means of promotion?

frequent sponsor of golf events, wishes to reach men with incomes over $50,000. This group makes up 40 percent of *Sports Illustrated* readership. The effective circulation then is only 1,260,000, and the CPM-TM increases to $170.63. This figure reflects more closely the cost-efficiency of reaching an important target segment for Cadillac.

MEDIA SCHEDULES   The most basic concepts in media scheduling are reach and frequency. **Reach** refers to the number of different people or households exposed to an ad or campaign over a specified period (usually four weeks). **Frequency** refers to the number of times a person or household is exposed to a communications vehicle. Advertisers must address a basic question: Emphasize reach or frequency? When advertising is for a new brand, reach may be the paramount objective. Messages presenting detailed information or vying with heavily advertised competitors need greater frequency or repetition.

Increased repetition relative to competing brands has been shown effective at increasing top-of-mind awareness and brand preference. Advertising works cumulatively, and messages are stronger when repeated. As such, advertising expenditures and brand equity are related in many mature product categories, such as cereal, soft drinks, and beer. Because advertising is often directed at consumers with existing knowledge and preferences, increased repetition helps maintain the ready accessibility of brand associations in the minds of consumers.[70] In addition, research has shown that higher levels of repetition for even incongruent or surprising brand extensions enhance new product brand attitudes when the message focuses on primary product benefits.[71]

One rule of thumb has been that three exposures are required for impact; that is, three exposures on average per individual are thought necessary to generate adequate message processing. More recently, practitioners have begun to realize that for large, well-known consumer brands, two repetitions within a purchase cycle may be sufficient. In truth, a large number of variables affect advertising frequency, including how old the brand is and how well-known it is among its target audiences.[72] In summary, new or unfamiliar brands may require more ad frequency to break through the clutter of competing ads in the marketplace. Complex ads, including emotional appeals, may be able to benefit from higher exposure. All advertisements are subject to wearout, and new campaigns warrant consideration.[73]

For TV advertising, several conclusions regarding media schedules and the amount of advertising were recently offered in a summary of a large number of tests of the effectiveness of split-cable advertising:

1. Brands in categories in a growth mode are more likely to benefit from increased TV advertising.

2. Increased advertising added to either the front end or back end of a media plan is more likely to result in higher sales than is increased advertising distributed throughout the plan.

3. Increased spending is generally effective only when coupled with changes in creative executions.

4. Increased spending for new brands or line extensions is more effective than similar increases for established brands.[74]

Interestingly, the findings from a series of additional split-cable studies conducted by Frito-Lay confirmed these conclusions. Moreover, its results showed a significant increase in sales within the first three months for the effective campaigns (those campaigns resulting in significant increases in sales compared with control areas in which the campaigns were not run).[75]

Evaluating Advertising Effectiveness

The evaluation of advertising typically includes pretesting or copytesting, posttesting, and sales effectiveness research. Given today's bottom-line emphasis, firms are making the evaluation of advertising effectiveness a much more important task. Often the objective has been to maximize efficiency of advertising budget expenditures in terms of prices paid for media exposure. Ultimately, however, the marketer's effectiveness is judged by sales, profits, and return on investment. Likewise, the contributions of advertising and media are increasingly being judged for their effectiveness using similar criteria.[76] Companies in every segment of business have become focused on the ability to measure marketing performance by linking advertising and other aspects of marketing investments to sales and brand awareness. For example, Home Depot has a proprietary computer model that correlates marketing investments with product sales and regional variations that have led the retailer to push paint using radio spots in some markets and newspaper inserts in others.[77]

PRETESTING   In general, **pretesting** proposed print and broadcast ads is done by evaluating consumer reactions through direct questioning and focus groups. Marketers evaluate the ads for overall likability, consumer recall of information, message communication, and their effects on purchase intentions and brand attitudes.

Pat Garner, Vice President and Chief Marketing Officer for Intersections, Inc., discusses the importance of evaluating advertising effectiveness:

"During my many years at the Coca-Cola Company, I definitely had a predisposition toward and comfort level with traditional consumer brand and advertising awareness tracking studies. In 1982 I was a part of the core team that created and launched Diet Coke. In July, in a star-studded evening at Radio City Music Hall in New York City, we introduced Diet Coke to the U.S. market as the one and only 'diet drink' that you were going to drink 'Just For the Taste of It!' Our consumer brand awareness tracking studies began a few days later to establish the 'baseline' measures for monitoring the progress of our advertising campaign, which was scheduled to start the following week on all major networks. To our surprise and pleasure, our baseline tracking study revealed that Diet Coke 'unaided' advertising awareness had reached 36 percent, propelled by the tremendous news value of our introduction. One must understand that Diet Coke was the first ever 'extension' of the world's most well-known brand in its close to 100-year history. Fortunately, we read these results of our consumer awareness study and actually delayed the start of commercial television for two to three weeks while we leveraged the 'free publicity' that our introductory fanfare had created. The resulting savings was a few million media dollars, which was reinvested to extend our introductory advertising campaign for several weeks longer than originally planned."

Research Systems Corporation (RSC) evaluates advertising for marketers and ad agencies.[78] From 500 to 600 randomly chosen consumers view TV pilot programs and a number of commercials, including the ones being evaluated. Before the screening, participants are shown various consumer products and are asked to indicate which they would like to receive. After the screening, a second questionnaire is administered. A persuasion score is computed for each commercial, which indicates the differences in percentages of consumers selecting the advertised product before and after the screening. Respondents are also called 48 hours later to explore estimates of recall. These viewer reactions are used to predict sales effectiveness of the ads.

BEING ENTREPRENEURIAL

Nonprofits going commercial

Nonprofit organization budgets have tightened in the wake of declining endowments, reduced funding, and rising competition as contributors limit the number of causes they support. Given these environmental phenomena, marketing efforts of nonprofit organizations are changing. These changes include greater emphasis on organization–supporter relationships, the use of online communications, and less reliance on donated free advertising. Like marketers of all types, nonprofits and advocacy groups are finding it more difficult to reach their target audiences. In recognition of these problems, the American Heart Association, the American Cancer Society, and other nonprofit organizations have gone commercial. For example, with ads in *Parade* and other media outlets, the American Heart Association is in the midst of a three-year $36 million innovative advertising campaign to raise awareness of heart disease. These efforts reflect a marked change from traditional reliance on donated time and space public service announcements.

POSTTESTING   Marketers use **posttesting** through recall and attitude tests and inquiry evaluations to assess the effectiveness of an ad campaign. In **unaided recall tests** for print ads, respondents are questioned with no prompting about ads included in magazines. In **aided recall tests,** subjects are given lists of ads and asked which they remembered and read. An **inquiry evaluation** comes from the number of consumers responding to requests in an ad, such as using coupons or asking for samples or more product information.

Starch Message Report Services provides awareness and readership data about ads carried in consumer and business magazines. Burke Market Research administers a day-after-recall program (DAR) for TV commercials. DAR is the percentage of individuals in an audience who recall something specific about the ad being posttested. High levels of recall do not necessarily result in increased sales, however.

SALES EFFECTIVENESS EVALUATIONS   Sales effectiveness evaluations are the most stringent tests of advertising efficiency. They assess whether the advertising resulted in increased sales. Given the many factors that affect sales and the number of competing messages, sales effectiveness evaluations are difficult, and marketers and ad agencies can differ on measures of results. Increasingly, however, evaluations of advertising effectiveness based on brand awareness will no longer be sufficient. Advertising evaluations instead will be based on contributions to sales growth.

Some newer programs combine awareness and sales data to evaluate advertising effectiveness. For example, ASI Monitor combines three data sets: (1) traditional ad awareness and attitude telephone surveys, (2) Nielsen household panel purchase data, and (3) Nielsen Monitor Plus data that include gross rating point (GRP) measures. The GRP measures incorporate both reach and frequency information. This tracking program allows advertisers to determine if advertising messages are getting through to consumers as schedules are run over time and the effects of that advertising on sales.[79]

Recognizing the need to provide quality advertising that improves company performance, DDB Needham rebates a substantial portion of its fee if sales for an advertised product do not improve. If ad campaigns are successful, DDB Needham receives a bonus in addition to its fee.[80] ACNielsen has been a leader in studying the effects of advertising on sales. In one Nielsen study using matched samples of 4,000 households, results showed that for 9 of 10 packaged goods investigated, households exposed to magazine ads were more likely to purchase the advertised product than were those who had not seen the magazine ads. ACNielsen is also developing measurement procedures for assessing the global effectiveness of Internet ads and audiences via a service called Nielsen/NetRatings.[81]

An understanding of the effectiveness of direct TV advertising on purchase behavior is emerging as advertisers study the results of their practices as part of direct-response television messages. For example, the effects of 1-800 direct-response advertising mostly disappear within eight hours. Response to daytime advertising is highest in the hour in which the ad is run. It is important to note that sales effects differ substantially by station and creative design.[82]

Some Important Research Findings

In the *Journal of Marketing,* two advertising scholars from the London Business School, Demetrios Vakratsas and Tim Ambler, provided a series of summary findings in their review of a large number of studies regarding "how advertising works." Their summary included the following noteworthy results:

1. Advertising elasticities are higher for durables than nondurables.

2. Price promotion elasticities are up to 20 times greater than advertising elasticities.

3. Advertising elasticities are greater early in the product life cycle and for established brands.

4. The first exposures to advertising are most important to short-term sales.

5. Price advertising increases price sensitivity, whereas nonprice advertising decreases price sensitivity.[83]

Ethical and Legal Issues in Advertising

Advertising provides many useful functions for buyers, advertisers, and society. For buyers, benefits include comparative information about the availability and the characteristics of products and brands. For advertisers, advertising builds long-term brand recognition, introduces new products, and enhances corporate images. For society, advertising increases economic efficiency by enabling products to be sold in mass markets at lower unit costs and to be distributed over wide geographic areas.

Advertising does have its critics, however, and abuses do occur. In some instances, advertising malpractice has received considerable notoriety. Several years ago, Volvo Cars of North America altered cars in its "monster truck crushing" ads, for example. Other ethical issues related to advertising are more subtle. We discuss them here.

Is Advertising Manipulative?

Some critics charge that advertising stimulates needs and wants by creating unrealistic ideals about appearance and social identity. And indeed, students of marketing agree that advertising is intended to influence buyer behavior. Are ads that are designed to emphasize the idea that happiness and well-being depend on physical attractiveness ethical? Hair-loss remedies and surgical "lift" procedures are frequently advertised with their messages and themes tied to enhanced self-esteem.[84] But if it's so easy to manipulate people into buying, why do so many products fail? It would seem more likely that instead of being manipulated by advertising, the reverse is true, and buyers exercise control over the marketplace by the choices they make with their discretionary income.

Thinking Critically

Consider each of the legal/ethical issues discussed in this section. Evaluate the arguments presented, and determine your personal view regarding whether each issue is indeed unethical. What is the support for your opinions?

Is Advertising Deceptive or Misleading?

The Federal Trade Commission (FTC), which monitors marketplace abuses, prohibits advertising messages that deceive consumers by presenting false claims, by omitting relevant information, or by giving misleading impressions that result in faulty decisions.

In some instances the FTC requires **corrective advertising** to remedy misleading impressions or information in an ad. The offending advertiser or marketer must develop and pay for advertising that counters the misperceptions. Corrective advertising is required most often when there have been outright misrepresentations of fact, rather than presentation of half-truths.

In one of the earliest cases, Warner-Lambert was required in 1975 to spend $10 million in advertising to correct misleading claims about the ability of Listerine mouthwash to combat colds. Volvo was instructed to run corrective ads in local newspapers, *USA Today*, and *The Wall Street Journal* to explain its withdrawal of ads misrepresenting the effect of the "monster truck crushing" demonstration just discussed.[85] The FTC required Volkswagen (and Audi) to run a series of full-page national magazine ads to inform consumers about product performance problems. The magazine advertising was required to reach a nonduplicated audience of at least 75 million adults. The FTC has also become very involved with the deception that can occur from "implied claims" included in the advertising of dietary supplement products. H&R Block was ordered to stop advertising "rapid refunds" of taxes. The court found that H&R Block concealed that its clients were actually receiving high-interest loans just to get their refunds a few days early.[86] The FTC forced Wonder Bread to not use unsubstantiated ads claiming that the bread can improve brain power and memory.[87]

How Does Advertising Affect Children?

The youth market offers tremendous potential to business, and much advertising is directed toward children. Advertisers know young consumers influence parental decisions and exert significant buying power themselves. Concerns about advertising to children center largely on three important issues:

- Children's ability to understand advertising's intent to persuade.
- The nutritional value of food and candy products marketed to children.
- The influence of advertising on children's demands to parents for advertised products.

On the other hand, some opponents of limits on advertising to children argue as follows:

- Parents are better able than the FTC to help children interpret information and make decisions.
- Children know that fruits and vegetables are more nutritious than sugared foods.
- Banning TV advertising to children limits free speech.[88]

In response to criticism about questionable program content that carries advertising designed to appeal to children, Procter & Gamble and other major advertisers, such as IBM, GM, Sears, and Johnson & Johnson, are paying the Time-Warner WB network to develop and air shows with less sex and violence. Many parents are opposed to exclusive marketing deals, signed by such companies as Coca-Cola and PepsiCo, that pay schools for the right to sell their products in the classroom. Schools obtain money, supplies, and programming in exchange for the right to beam ads to students on classroom TVs.[89] Concerns about advertising and marketing to children relate to the Internet as well. In fact, online marketer deception has increased calls for legislation to protect both children's privacy as well as the future of e-commerce.[90]

Is Advertising Intrusive?

Many people are irritated by unwelcome advertising messages that threaten their right to privacy. Most observers agree the marketplace is cluttered with advertising messages and that any one ad has limited ability to influence consumers. Yet recognition of this limitation only reinforces pressures to increase ad repetition.

Related questions have to do with methods of ad communications delivery. Is it ethical for infomercials to package commercial messages as regular programming? What about the practice of allowing TV advertisers into school classrooms? Intrusiveness concerns about technology also extend to junk faxes and "spam advertising." Specifically, the same laws that require telemarketers to maintain "do-not-call" lists—the Telephone Consumer Protection Act—also prohibit marketers from sending unsolicited advertisements to facsimile machines. Recipients of faxed coupons from a Hooters restaurant won a $12 million judgment in a class action lawsuit. Complaints can be filed with the Federal Communications Commission, the recipient's state attorney general, or the sender's state attorney general.[91] Several state legislatures have passed laws, and federal legislation has been drafted governing unsolicited e-mail, or "spam advertising."[92]

Cause-Related Advertising

An extension of corporate advocacy advertising is the concept of **cause-related marketing (CRM)**, or social advertising. Cause-related marketing is the increasingly common phenomenon of companies' aligning themselves with causes, such as AIDS research, drug-abuse prevention, gay rights, racial harmony, and conservation. The real objectives of these campaigns vary from solely economic (the cause affiliation is entirely strategic) to solely social, where there is extraordinary commitment to the cause. One well-known example is the campaign of Benetton shock ads that combine both economic and social objectives. The ads, which highlight issues such as AIDS, the Bosnia conflict, and the plight of refugees, are designed to both get attention and position Benetton as a cutting-edge social marketer. Sears stopped selling Benetton clothes for a period in reaction to Benetton's campaign tied to capital punishment. For these programs to work, the objectives for the campaign should be long-term, the cause should fit the company, and the employees should believe the issues are important.[93] While most cause-related marketing is designed to enhance corporate image perceptions, P&G is tying CRM to individual brands, such as Ariel and Daz, in efforts to build trust among consumers by linking individual brands to environmental causes. Also, in Europe, P&G linked New Covent Garden Soup with a homeless charity to raise funds through sales of its soup to help refurbish the charity's kitchens.[94]

Advertising Harmful Products

The use of advertising to market harmful products, such as cigarettes and alcohol, is frequently criticized. Regulations, both legislated and self-imposed, exist but critics often argue for further restrictions on such advertising. In markets without restrictions, tobacco advertisers frequently connect smoking with glamour, excitement, and the great outdoors.

The Joe Camel campaign was quite successful in raising brand recognition, particularly among children and adolescents. In response to much criticism of the ads, however, Camel recently agreed to discontinue the use of the well-recognized cartoon character. Substantial opposition has arisen also to previously announced plans to advertise liquor products on TV.[95]

Public Relations

Public relations (PR) is often used as a complement to support advertising, personal selling, and sales promotions for disseminating marketing communications. The most recent edition of the advertising text by George Belch and Michael Belch offers the following *Public Relations News* definition of public relations:

> The management function which evaluates public attitudes, identifies the policies and procedures of an organization with the public interest, and executes a program of action and communication to earn public understanding and acceptance.[96]

Public relations has evolved from a discretionary part of the marketing mix to a critical component of most company communications programs, serving to enhance other aspects of the marketing mix, as well as working on media relations and public opinion.[97] PR communications are not overtly sponsored in the typical advertising sense and are a useful support to other forms of marketing communications. PR is an attempt to improve a company's relationship with its publics. Public relations may focus on customers, employees, stockholders, community members, news media, or the government. Most large corporations operate central PR departments to carry out coordinated public relations programs, and smaller companies with limited resources must also deal with PR issues. For example, AT&T and other companies support scientific studies to reduce fears about links between the use of cellular phones and cancer.[98] PR is considered today to be more of a strategic management function and, like other forms of communication, involves communicating specific messages to specific audiences that result in specific responses. As such, firms are considering the returns on investment in public relations and the need to add value.[99]

As advertising becomes less effective, companies of all sizes try to build public awareness and loyalty by supporting customer interests. The general public increasingly demands that companies behave responsibly toward society as a whole and that they have obligations to more than their customers and stockholders. Profit maximization and social responsibility need not be incompatible, however. Today companies show greater concern for employee welfare, minority advancement, community improvement, environmental protection, and other causes. A PR department plays a critical role in planning, coordinating, and promoting these visionary activities for an organization.[100] Some companies have effectively embodied public relations principles into their overall marketing communications program. For example, Members Only fashion company funded over $100 million worth of social consciousness–raising advertising about drug abuse and voter registration. More recent advertising promotes care for the homeless.

Public Relations Functions

Most frequently, PR functions support a firm's products and services. Often, however, public relations activity addresses corporate image and social responsibility. Exxon Corporation's varied program to maintain and improve its corporate image is a good example. Its PR activity ranges from an ongoing campaign about environmental damage from the Alaskan oil spill targeted toward the scientific community to charitable support of the Special Olympics.[101] The remarkable turnaround of Sears is attributed in part to its effective use of PR communications in rebuilding relationships with the financial community and the media.

Public relations functions include press relations; product promotions; internal and external corporate communications; lobbying to promote, defeat, or circumvent legislation and regulations; advising management about public issues and company positions and image; and overall, responding to a variety of occurrences in the marketplace.[102]

Public relations functions designed to support marketing activities are termed **marketing public relations.** These activities are as follows:

1. Building marketplace excitement before media advertising breaks.
2. Creating advertising news where there is no product news.
3. Introducing a product with little or no advertising.
4. Providing a value-added customer service.
5. Building brand-to-customer bonds.
6. Influencing the influentials (opinion leaders).
7. Defending products at risk and giving consumers a reason to buy.[103]

Driven by the Internet, the thrust of public relations firms is moving more from influencing the press to influencing companies. PR firms and PR departments within companies are acquiring new skills as they work to build business strategies and to establish marketplace presence and positioning. These companies often start with PR work, even before advertising, in efforts to generate word-of-mouth communications. Gaining positive exposure among investors and analysts is crucial to young high-tech companies' survival.[104]

Public relations can be **proactive** or **reactive,** as shown in Exhibit 17–6. For reactive PR efforts, crisis managers need to move faster and use communications vehicles such as Web sites and chat rooms that reach consumers in real time. Consumers have become more accustomed to bad news, and the time available for effective firm reaction is diminishing due to the frequency of corporate misdeeds and poor management, investigative 24-hour TV shows, and a proliferation of class action lawsuits.[105]

Publicity

Publicity, the generation of information by a company to the news media, has a narrower focus than public relations. The primary publicity techniques are news releases, press conferences, and feature articles, often presented in the business press.

One advantage of publicity is its relatively high credibility, because the messages are not paid for by a commercial sponsor. Information about a company presumably must be newsworthy to be published by an objective source. However, publicity messages may be revised by the media, then released at times most convenient to the broadcaster or publisher. Unfortunately, some publicity may be negative news stories beyond the firm's control, as when product tampering occurred for Tylenol and Diet Pepsi. A firm's PR department must be prepared to react constructively and without delay when unfortunate events occur.

As companies such as Intel and Polaris Software, which saw flaws in their products exposed to the world via the Internet, have learned, negative publicity can spread extremely

Exhibit 17–6	*Proactive and reactive marketing public relations*
Proactive Marketing PR	**Reactive Marketing PR**
• Product release announcements, statements by a firm's spokespeople, event sponsorship, articles in business press.	• A firm's response to negative events and damaging publicity.
• Corporate image enhancement and development of goodwill; corporate advocacy advertising support of a certain position on a given social issue.	• Negative information comes from news media, consumer advocacy groups, government agencies; usually related to product defects or problematic company practices.
• Cause-related marketing in which the firm contributes a specified amount to a designated cause when customers buy the firm's products.	• Success depends on the firm's ability to align its interests with the public's interests so both are served.

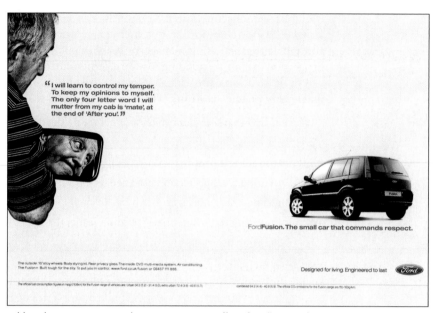

Public relations can support the communications efforts for all types of organizations. Large firms, such as Ford Motor Company, should have proactive plans in place to use if negative events occur.

fast. Ameritech Corp., Quaker Oats Co., and Allstate Corp. have gone so far as to monitor Internet discussion groups or chat rooms in efforts to learn of negative comments about their products and services.[106]

Proactive PR requires that the firm formulate a crisis plan for communications in the event of an emergency. Such a plan should try to determine what unfortunate events might occur and specify who will speak for the company and who will be the audience. In times of emergency, one primary audience likely will be the news media. In instances of product recall, an important audience will be retailers.[107]

Summary

1. **Understand the characteristics, functions, and types of advertising.** Advertising, like other promotional elements, plays an important role in the total marketing communications program. Advertising is impersonal, paid for by an identified sponsor, and disseminated through mass channels of communication to promote the adoption of goods, services, persons, or ideas.

   Advertising can serve a number of functions, including heightening consumer awareness, disseminating information about a product's attributes or social value, shaping product images or emotional responses, persuading buyers to purchase, or reminding consumers about products, brands, or firms.

   Advertisements can be classified according to the target audience, geographic area, medium, and purpose. Corporate image advertising promotes an organization's image and role in the community as a corporate citizen. Other types are corporate advocacy, public service, classified, direct-response, business-to-business, and cooperative advertising.

2. **Realize how people process advertising information and how it affects buyer behavior.** Advertisements rely on successive stages of processing by a targeted individual: exposure (presenting the information to a receiver), attention (the conscious direction of a receiver's mental effort toward the advertising stimulus), comprehension (the degree to which the receiver correctly understands the intended message), acceptance (the degree to which the receiver accepts or yields to the message), and retention (the extent to which the receiver can recall or recognize the message at a later time).

   The relationships between these stages, and therefore the effectiveness of the advertising itself, may be affected by consumer needs as well as consumer motivations, opportunities, and abilities to process the information.

3. **Discuss approaches to developing advertising campaigns.** The steps in developing an ad campaign are (1) determining advertising objectives, (2) determining advertising budget, (3) designing appropriate creative strategies, (4) selecting and scheduling media, and (5) evaluating ad effectiveness.

4. **Describe different advertising objectives and the message strategies used to achieve them.** Advertising objectives should be consistent with the organization's overall marketing objectives and be realistic, precise, and measurable. Advertising objectives may be to inform, to persuade, or to remind.

   Many different message strategies can be used to achieve the advertising objective. One strategy is to compare the advertised brand to another. Celebrity endorsements, humor, and fear appeals are other tactics used to enhance the persuasive impact of advertisements.

5. **Understand the decisions involved in selecting media and scheduling advertising.** Decisions on media class involve choosing the most appropriate media channels, such as television, magazines, or radio. This choice depends on both the size and characteristics of the firm's target markets and the characteristics of the message itself.

   Decisions on media vehicles refer to the selection of the specific outlets within the chosen media class. These decisions usually depend on factors such as cost and the size and characteristics of the audience. Reach and frequency are important considerations in making these decisions.

6. **Explain how marketers assess advertising effectiveness.** Effectiveness evaluations involve some combination of pretesting, posttesting, and sales response research. Pretesting usually involves evaluating consumer reactions to proposed advertisements. Posttesting is used to measure the effectiveness of the chosen strategy during or after the ad campaign. Posttesting may include aided or unaided recall measurements, attitude evaluations, and sales impact effects.

7. **Appreciate the roles of public relations and publicity in marketing.** Public relations functions include the dissemination of press releases, product promotion efforts, and corporate communications, as well as lobbying and advising corporate executives about public issues affecting the firm. Publicity refers to the dissemination of nonpaid communication in news outlets and represents only a part of the larger activity of public relations.

   Marketing-oriented public relations can be proactive or reactive. Proactive marketing public relations refers to the initiation of positive public relations; it may take the form of corporate image advertising, advocacy advertising, or cause-related marketing. Reactive marketing public relations refers to defending an organization from negative and potentially damaging information, including negative events and adverse publicity.

Understanding Marketing Terms and Concepts

Thinking about Marketing

1. What different functions can advertising perform?

2. What are advertising agencies, and what services do they provide?

3. Explain why advertising expenditures have declined during recent years.

4. Define the following: business-to-business advertising; corporate image advertising; corporate advocacy advertising; direct-response advertising; and corrective advertising.

5. What steps are involved in a consumer's processing of advertisements? Why is understanding the sequence of these stages important to advertisers?

6. What can advertisers do to increase exposure, attention, and retention? How does audience involvement influence these processes?

7. Identify the steps involved in the development of an advertising campaign.

8. What are media class decisions, and how do they differ from media vehicle decisions?

9. Contrast pretesting with posttesting in the evaluation of advertising effectiveness. Explain the problem with using sales results as a measure of advertising effectiveness.

10. Explain the differences between advertising and public relations.

11. How should advertising strategy relate to the marketing concept?

12. What is the elaboration likelihood model? How do motivation, opportunity, and ability influence the various routes to persuasion?

13. What are the different types of message strategy alternatives? How might a marketer determine which strategy is most appropriate?

14. What are the primary legal/ethical concerns associated with network TV advertising?

Applying Marketing Skills

1. Collect two examples each of (*a*) corporate image advertising; (*b*) corporate advocacy advertising; (*c*) public service advertising; (*d*) comparative advertising; (*e*) classified advertising; (*f*) direct-response advertising; and (*g*) business-to-business advertising.

2. Consider the differences across magazine, radio, television, and outdoor advertising. Describe how each works to get consumers' attention and ensure retention.

3. Assume the average issue circulation for *People* magazine is 3,350,000. The cost for a one-page ad in a regular issue is $128,500. Estimate the CPM for that magazine. Compare it with similar data for *Time*: page cost, $202,000; circulation, 4,000,000. What might you advise a potential advertiser of personal computers? Of cosmetics?

4. Critics contend that advertising induces consumers to buy products that they don't really need. For example,

direct-to-consumer (DTC) advertising of prescription drugs has been shown to increase patient demand for pharmaceuticals that are often not medically necessary (for hair growth, weight loss, wrinkle removal, and so on). Is DTC advertising creating better-informed consumers or an overmedicated population?

Using the www in Marketing

Activity One Consider the current Web site of British Airways, the company featured in this chapter's opening vignette.

1. How would you characterize the company's image based on its Web site? Using examples, what elements of British Airways's communication mix are mentioned?
2. Examine the site of one of British Airways's competitors. How do the advertising strategies differ?

Activity Two The Federal Trade Commission is the regulatory body that governs advertising at the federal level and rules on a case-by-case basis regarding deceptive advertising. Consider the information available on the Internet regarding the ongoing activities of the FTC.

1. What guidelines are available that define or describe what constitutes deceptive advertising?

2. Refer to a recent cease-and-desist order in which a company was prevented from further deceptive practices. In this case, what circumstances led the FTC to find the company's advertising deceptive?

3. What guidelines are offered regarding advertising substantiation (test results or data that support ad claims)? Consider the May Department Stores (of Denver) case. What was deceptive about that firm's price advertising?

4. Telemarketing critics refer to this practice as a nuisance and intrusive. Some states have already passed legislation, and federal legislation is being considered, to regulate unsolicited telemarketing calls. If government regulation is warranted for telemarketing, is it also warranted for other types of advertising that may be considered intrusive—such as Internet ads, television commercials, and radio spots?

Making Marketing Decisions

Case 17–1 *Google and Internet Advertising*

Unlike conventional advertising, in which a lot of creative effort is devoted to the development of advertising messages and media strategy, an Internet search engine like Google already has access to consumers searching for something in particular. Companies can reach buyers actively interested with tailored messages. The fact that companies like Eli Lilly, Napster, Novartis, and Staples are among advertisers of the Super Bowl, as well as regulars on Google, underscores the prevalence of Google advertising. In 2004, keyword search represented more than 40 percent of the $8.7 billion in U.S. Internet ad spending. Importantly, the more consumers come to Google, the more advertisers are participating.

Founded by Stanford University students Larry Page and Sergy Brin, Google is based on technological innovation. Google's approach to advertising is not entirely driven by straightforward payments for ads such as banners or payments for click-throughs to an adver-

tiser's site. Advertisers pay to be listed alongside search results as "Sponsored Links." The revenues and net earnings for Google are huge. On February 1, 2005, the net earnings for fiscal year 2004 were $400 million on revenues of $3.2 billion.

Yet concerns about the use of Google as a source of advertising presentation are emerging. First, the prices for keywords are increasing dramatically, and companies like eBay are seeking ways to lessen increasing media costs associated with Google advertising. One approach is to buy a larger array of more specific keywords, as broad generic keywords have become very pricey. Second, competition is evident. Companies like Yahoo, Microsoft, and Ask Jeeves are enhancing their presence in the marketplace. For example, MSN Search of Microsoft has launched a $150 million advertising campaign to promote its strengths as a search engine. The MSN approach includes showing advertisers aggregate audience profiles for keywords to aid in search planning. This audience approach is likely to be much more comfortable to brand managers. A third concern stems from the unwanted results from search. Large companies like Kraft are worried that Google lacks the controls to ensure that their links or ads appear consistent with company values. As a result, Google plans to give advertisers more control about where and how their ads are shown.

Questions

1. What environmental factors are likely to impact Google's advertising income?

2. How does Google generate revenues? Compare its click-through capabilities with keyword revenue generation.

3. What new products and extensions is Google pursuing to maintain its current strong position?

Case 17–2 *Toyota: Advertising Drives to Success in Europe*

More and more international companies are moving away from global standardized advertising—that is, presenting the same advertising campaign in every country in which the company conducts business. A standardized strategy often fails to provide the most effective advertising for a given geographical area because each area has its own distinctive political, legal, and cultural characteristics. The use of advertising suited to the particular characteristics of a country may be more effective.

Toyota has always taken an unstandardized approach, tailoring its advertising country by country. It lets local marketers handle all the aspects of advertising for their particular area on the theory that they know the market best. Toyota simply supplies the local advertisers with the necessary raw materials (information pertinent for promoting Toyota vehicles) to develop effective advertisements for their area. This system has been effective for Toyota, which enjoys a significant market share in countries in North America, Asia, and Europe.

Eased trade conditions within Europe could allow Toyota to reevaluate just how integrated (if at all) it wants to make its advertising. Today Toyota uses an integrative European approach to its advertising for only one brand, the Lexus luxury automobile, which has met with some success. The company might also find it profitable to reduce the number of advertising agencies it works with in Europe. Becoming more standardized in its advertising could offer Toyota certain economies of scale.

Additional growth will occur in Europe as barriers limiting imports from Japan fall away. Under export restraint conditions so far, Japanese car dealers have been forced to promote largely their most expensive brands. Now dealers are learning how to sell higher volumes of lower-margin models. Two other phenomena are occurring in the advertising and marketing strategy for Toyota in Europe. First, Toyota Europe has contracted with Saatchi & Saatchi Advertising to handle strategic brand issues for all of Europe. This change suggests a move toward a consolidation of advertising support for Toyota in Europe. Second, the number of dealers receiving new cars has been reduced substantially, with the affected smaller dealers serving as partners providing only service and taking new orders. With these changes, the time could be right for Toyota to implement a more standardized advertising program across Europe.

Toyota, a Japanese firm, faces a number of unexpected global obstacles. In Japan, concerns have been expressed that Toyota's American strategy has become the company's lifeline. The United Kingdom offers Toyota a particular global challenge. Having long suffered from a reliable but dowdy image, Corolla, the best-selling car in the world, has performed poorly in the U.K. The objective for Saatchi & Saatchi is very much one of changing consumers' perceptions of the car. As part of its European campaign, Toyota has engaged in the U.K.'s largest railway poster campaign in an effort to reach busy commuters with advertising promoting Corolla. In addition, Toyota is sponsoring programming on satellite channels to reach a younger demographic segment. The "pride" campaign depicts people who do not own a Corolla, but would like to give the impression that they do.

Questions

1. Enumerate and explain the advantages and disadvantages to Toyota of using an integrative, standardized approach versus maintaining its current approach to advertising in Europe.

2. What would you recommend Toyota do regarding its advertising in the U.K.? Elsewhere in Europe?

3. Explain the impact that differing cultural values, legal considerations, and economic considerations have on international advertising.

4. Why is Toyota more successful in the United States than Japan, assuming that this situation holds?

Chapter Eighteen

CONSUMER AND TRADE SALES PROMOTION

18

After studying this chapter, you should be able to

1 Explain the role and significance of sales promotion in the marketing communications mix.

2 Understand why sales promotion expenditures account for a significant portion of many firms' marketing communications budgets.

3 Discuss the objectives and techniques of consumer sales promotion.

4 Discuss the objectives and techniques of trade sales promotion.

5 Explain the limitations of sales promotion.

6 Realize how deceptive and fraudulent sales promotion victimizes both consumers and marketers.

McDonald's

McDonald's, long a leading user of special promotions to attract consumers to its stores, made industry headlines with its Monopoly game promotion in 2004. McDonald's teamed with WildTangent, a major manufacturer of online games, which produced online demo games modified to include McDonald's product placements. McDonald's then used the games as prizes in its Monopoly contest, and promotion partner WildTangent benefited from the introduction of its games to millions of prospective game customers. In the process, McDonald's became one of the largest distributors for WildTangent's games. The hugely successful promotion was one reason McDonald's was named Marketer of the Year by *Advertising Age* and served 1.6 million customers more per day than in the previous year.

When McDonald's in-store customers made purchases, they received a number on a Monopoly game piece peeled from food or beverage packaging. The number provided access to a special Web site where they could choose prizes from WildTangent, SonyConnect, Netflix, and other digital sponsors. From the 800 million game pieces distributed, there were 6 million winners.

The four online games created for McDonald's by WildTangent are easy to play, and judging from the number of repeat visitors, ultimately addictive. The most popular of the four is Polar Bowler, in which a polar bear rides a block of ice down a hill, striking bowling pins marked with McDonald's golden arches logo. During the month of the promotion, 300,000 unique visitors spent an average of 40 minutes playing the game.

The Monopoly campaign is credited with boosting overall McDonald's same-store sales by 7 percent over the previous year. Larry Light, McDonald's chief marketing officer, says that creative new approaches to consumer promotions are needed, and that the joint online game effort with WildTangent was among McDonald's first major steps to be more relevant and of immediate interest to consumers. For WildTangent, which has created successful online games featuring the products of clients such as Nike, Toyota, and Sony, it was a clear demonstration that innovative promotional efforts can indeed pay off.

As the Mc Donald's WildTangent example illustrates, sales promotion is designed to boost sales. **Sales promotion** consists of media and nonmedia marketing communications employed for a predetermined, limited time to stimulate trial, increase consumer demand, or improve product availability.[1] Common sales promotion tools are coupons, samples, displays, contests, and sweepstakes. Sales promotion may be directed at ultimate consumers, retailers, or wholesalers. **Consumer sales promotion** is directed at consumers, and **trade sales promotion** is directed at resellers.

This chapter examines the growing role of sales promotion in marketing communications. The objectives, techniques, and limitations of consumer and trade sales promotion are explored. The chapter also looks at ethical and legal issues related to sales promotion.

The Role of Sales Promotion

A unique characteristic of sales promotion is that it offers an incentive for action. A consumer might receive a rebate for making a purchase, for instance, or a retailer may be offered an allowance for purchasing a specific quantity of a product within a specified period. In contrast to many forms of advertising, sales promotion is oriented toward achieving short-term results. Sales promotion activities rarely stand alone, however; they are typically combined with other forms of marketing communications to create an integrated program.

Effective sales promotion, like all forms of marketing communications, should result from adequate planning as discussed in Chapter 16. Because sales promotion seeks results in the near future, it is possible to set specific, measurable objectives and to accurately monitor results. It should also be understood, however, that because sales promotion often works in conjunction with other communications, coordination of messages and timing is crucial for success. Exhibit 18–1 presents the primary considerations in sales promotion planning.

Sales promotion can be used to encourage action by ultimate consumers, retailers, or wholesalers. In this promotion, consumers are offered free services when they switch from cable to DIRECTV.

The Significance of Sales Promotion

As discussed in Chapter 16, the expenditures for most forms of marketing communications have not increased significantly in recent years. Expenditures for sales promotion have remained fairly stable, suggesting that marketers see sales promotion as an important marketing communications tool in both strong and weak economic times. Given an ongoing need to stimulate sales for most product categories, expenditures for sales promotion are expected to remain at significant levels in the coming years.

Sales Promotion Expenditures

The combined expenditures on consumer and trade sales promotion are estimated to exceed the expenditures on advertising. What has motivated the significant expenditures on sales promotion in recent years? Changes in the marketing environment—consumer attitudes, demographic shifts, and lifestyle changes—are favorable for sales promotion, as are emerging technology and changes in retailing. Also, marketers are under pressure to perform well in the short term and are increasingly accountable for achieving measurable results.

| **Exhibit 18–1** | *The 10 commandments of creative sales promotion* |

1. **Set specific objectives.** Undisciplined, undirected creative work is a waste of time and resources.
2. **Know how basic promotion techniques work.** A sweepstakes shouldn't be used to encourage multiple purchases or a refund to get new customers. A price-off deal can't reverse a brand's downward sales trend.
3. **Use simple, attention-getting copy.** Most promotions are built around a simple idea: "Save 75 cents." Emphasize the idea, and don't try to be cute.
4. **Use contemporary, easy-to-track graphics.** Don't expect to fit 500 words and 20 illustrations into a quarter-page, freestanding insert.
5. **Clearly communicate the concept.** Words and graphics must work together to get the message across.
6. **Reinforce the brand's advertising message.** Tie promotions to the brand's ad campaign.
7. **Support the brand's positioning and image.** This is especially important for image-sensitive brands and categories, like family-oriented Kraft.
8. **Coordinate promotional efforts with other marketing plans.** Be sure to coordinate schedules and plans. A consumer promotion should occur simultaneously with a trade promotion; a free-sample promotion should be timed in conjunction with the introduction of a new line.
9. **Know the media you work through.** Determine which media will work best. Should samples be distributed in stores, door-to-door, or through direct mail? Does the promotion need newspaper or magazine support?
10. **Involve the trade.** Build relationships with key resellers.

CONSUMER FACTORS   With the U.S. population growing at less than 1 percent annually, most mature products see only modest growth in per capita consumption. The natural result is increased competition for market share. Sales promotion techniques, particularly price breaks, are therefore key.

Today's busy consumer cares less about shopping. If two spouses work outside the home, shopping time is limited. This makes consumers inevitably more responsive to sales promotion deals that encourage multiple purchases and to in-store displays.

Another factor in favor of sales promotion is simply that consumers like it. Shoppers get a lot of satisfaction from getting a good deal, and they are accustomed to special sales, rebates, and other forms of sales promotion. One comprehensive study found that consumers derive six unique benefits from sales promotions. First, monetary savings can be realized with some promotions. Second, consumers may be able to buy higher-quality products as a result of some promotions. Next, promotions can be a convenience to shoppers by helping them find the product they are looking for or reminding them of the product they wish to buy. For some consumers, promotions offer the opportunity to express or enhance their self-concept and personal values, such as being a responsible buyer. A fifth benefit is that promotions can fulfill consumers' needs for stimulation and variety as they explore products and services featured in new promotions. Finally, consumers find some forms of promotions, such as sweepstakes and games, to be fun and entertaining.[2] With such a wide range of consumer benefits, it is understandable that businesses will engage in consumer and trade promotion to build consumer traffic, sales, and satisfaction. In today's competitive environment, promotions are often necessary simply to maintain, much less increase, consumer purchases.

IMPACT OF TECHNOLOGY   There is ample evidence that technology has stimulated sales promotion. Computerized scanning devices let retailers know what is and what is not selling every day. They also provide quick input on which brands are most profitable. In the case of trade sales, portable computers in the hands of field salespeople let vendors track product movement practically instantaneously. As a result, both retailers and manufacturers can measure the effectiveness of various sales promotion programs very quickly. Manufacturers can thus adjust or eliminate unproductive programs, freeing up investment for more productive ones. Practically all major consumer goods manufacturers, including PepsiCo, H.J. Heinz, and Procter & Gamble, use scanner-tracked promotional programs.

INCREASED RETAIL POWER   Huge retailers such as Wal-Mart, Home Depot, and Target wield tremendous clout by virtue of their immense purchasing power. Sales promotions directed at both retailers and consumers make the manufacturer's product more appealing.

As retailers gain more power, they have tried to increase sales of their own private label products. Although retailers can tout their private labels while limiting in-store promotions for national brands, they cannot do much about sales promotion efforts such as couponing. No doubt the struggle of national brand marketers against private labels has contributed to the growth of sales promotion.

The private label trend is also occurring in European markets, where a lingering recession has compelled consumers to seek more value for their money. Private label products are increasing in France, Switzerland, and Italy. To combat private label sales, multinationals such as Unilever and Nestlé are promoting both their traditional brands and "Eurobrands," products designed for the entire European market.

Consumer Sales Promotion

Consumer sales promotion, with techniques such as coupons and rebates, helps pull a product through the channel of distribution. Both small and large companies can effectively use it with either new or existing products. Sometimes sales promotion may increase interest in mature or mundane products by imparting a sense of urgency to buy before the promotion ends.

Sales promotion can play an important role in stimulating consumers to try the product. In this ad, the reduced price offer will stimulate consumer trials of the new flavors of Crest toothpaste.

Objectives of Consumer Promotions

Sales promotion may accomplish a variety of objectives, all related to affecting present or prospective consumers' behavior. As Exhibit 18–2 shows, objectives may be to stimulate trial; increase consumer inventory and consumption; encourage repurchase; neutralize competitive promotions; increase the sales of complementary products; stimulate impulse purchasing; and allow flexible pricing.

STIMULATE TRIAL   Marketers commonly use sales promotion to stimulate product trial—to get consumers to try a product. This is particularly so for newly introduced or improved products. The decision to buy a new product entails risk, which may prompt buyer resistance. Sales promotion techniques that reduce consumer cost, such as coupons, rebates, or samples, help alleviate this risk. When Bristol-Myers Squibb wanted to encourage trial of its cholesterol-reducing medication Pravachol, it offered a free 30-day trial supply. In the minds of most people, no cost means no risk.

INCREASE CONSUMER INVENTORY AND CONSUMPTION
Sales promotion sometimes encourages consumers to increase their inventory or consumption of a product by enticing them to buy more than they would in the absence of a special incentive. The idea is that people tend to consume greater quantities of a product if it is on hand. For instance, a buy-one-get-one-free special on potato chips may

Exhibit 18–2	*Objectives of consumer sales promotion*

- Stimulate trial.
- Increase consumer inventory and consumption.
- Encourage repurchase.
- Neutralize competitors.
- Increase sales of complementary products.
- Stimulate impulse purchasing.
- Allow flexible pricing.

Sales promotion can help to stimulate impulse buying in retail stores. This ad from Duraflame encourages retailers to use the company's special display to stimulate impulse buying.

stimulate consumers to buy more than normal. Because chips can get stale if not eaten within a certain time, if they are around the house, people are likely to eat more than they normally would. Also, the more inventory of a given brand that consumers have, the less interest they have in stocking up on a competitor's brand.

ENCOURAGE REPURCHASE   Sales promotion offers a variety of ways to help establish repeat-purchase patterns, on which the product's survival ultimately depends. Vail Resorts, operators of Vail, Keystone, and Breckenridge resorts in Colorado, uses a program whereby skiers and snowboarders earn points toward free lift tickets, meals, and clothing when they make purchases. BMG Music Club awards bonus points redeemable for free CDs when members make a regular-price purchase. Office supply wholesalers offer free merchandise and other rewards based on total purchases, and most airlines offer frequent flier programs designed to stimulate repurchase. Other examples of repeat-purchase promotions are the special price incentives magazines use to gain subscription renewals and the on-the-package coupons for future discounts that companies such as Domino's and Pizza Hut feature.

NEUTRALIZE COMPETITIVE PROMOTIONS   Sometimes marketers use sales promotions to combat competitive promotions. Consider the perennial battle between Coca-Cola and Pepsi, for example. Both firms constantly use promotions to attract consumers. As a result, the two firms often compete on price. Promotions to neutralize other retailers are also commonplace in the fast-food and cellular telephone markets.

INCREASE SALES OF COMPLEMENTARY PRODUCTS   Using sales promotion to attract buyers to one product can increase sales of a complementary product. A rebate Gillette offered for its Mach 3 Turbo razor, for example, allowed consumers to get the product for practically nothing. Gillette hoped to cash in on sales of its Mach 3 razor blades, a complementary product the consumer must buy on a recurring basis. The promotion worked as planned, and the Mach 3 Turbo is now a leading brand.

STIMULATE IMPULSE PURCHASING   Many people do not take the time to develop shopping lists. This tends to increase impulse purchasing. As the term implies, an impulse purchase is unplanned. It satisfies a strong desire to acquire a product quickly, without a lot of forethought. Retailers use special feature displays to generate impulse purchases.

ALLOW PRICE FLEXIBILITY   Sales promotion facilitates tailored price changes, which allow marketers to pursue opportunities as they arise. Suppose a manufacturer has set relatively high list prices, intending to appeal to the least price-sensitive segment of the

Speaking from Experience

Kevin Marie Nuss
Vice President of Marketing
Churchill Downs

"Consumer sales promotions can be used to achieve several objectives. We use some promotions to encourage casual race fans to come to Churchill Downs. These promotions are intended to generate new customers by providing other activities for customers in addition to horse racing. For example, the Kentucky Microbrew and Barbecue Festival is a promotion during which customers can sample different microbrewery and barbecue products from Kentucky in the Churchill Downs Infield during the race day. Other promotions are directed to increase frequency of attendance. This year we gave away Churchill Downs T-shirts on Mother's Day. Customers wearing these T-shirts receive free admission to Churchill Downs during the remainder of the meet."

Kevin Marie Nuss is Vice President of Marketing for Churchill Downs, the home of the Kentucky Derby. Her responsibilities include advertising, promotions, group sales, sponsorships, licensing, and merchandising for the Churchill Downs and Sports Spectrum facilities. She earned a B.A. in English from the University of Louisville.

market. Later the manufacturer can appeal to price-sensitive segments of the market through sales promotions. Automobile manufacturers follow this strategy despite the advent of no-haggle pricing.

Consumer Sales Promotion Techniques

Most people recognize the familiar consumer sales promotion techniques and have probably participated in some. Exhibit 18–3 lists some popular ones.

PRICE DEALS   A **price deal** is a temporary reduction in the price of a product. Marketers may use price deals to introduce a new or improved brand, to convince current users to purchase more, or to encourage new users to try an established brand. There are two primary types of price deals: cents-off deals and price-pack deals. **Cents-off deals** offer a brand at less than the regular price. Sometimes the manufacturer's package itself specifies a price reduction in dollars or cents or by a certain percentage, say 25 percent off. Such deals are often promoted in the store in some manner and may also be advertised.

Price-pack deals offer consumers something extra through the packaging itself. Perhaps they can buy a package of Martha White brownie mix that is 20 percent bigger than usual or a box of Double-Chex with 40 percent more cereal for the price of the normal size.

Marketers would be smart not to overuse price deals, however. If a brand is frequently offered on a price deal, consumers come to expect it. They hold off purchasing the product until the company offers another deal. Frequent deals on the same product eventually erode its normal retail selling price and may diminish its brand value.

Price deals are also common with nonpackaged goods such as consumer durables and services. They are used extensively by online retailers in an attempt to attract customers and build market share. For example, Overstocks.com lists daily bargains in numerous categories, including books, electronics, apparel, jewelry, and sporting goods. It also features a "Clearance Bins" section where shoppers can buy even further discounted products.[3] Better-informed consumers know when a price deal is really a deal, and comparing prices is becoming easier thanks to comparison shopping sites on the Web. For price-sensitive consumers, a deal featuring some form of discount is indeed a popular sales promotion tactic. Research, however, suggests that monetary-based promotions can have detrimental effects on market share when used to promote certain brands with high customer equity against low-priced brands. The use of monetary promotions with high-equity brands that offer consumer benefits related to self-esteem, fun, and stimulation may not be as effective as nonmonetary promotions that offer gifts, prizes, or a fun experience for the consumer.[4]

COUPONS   A **coupon** is typically a printed certificate giving the bearer a stated price reduction or special value on a specific product, generally for a specific period. Coupons allow the manufacturer to reduce the product's price at any time. They are particularly useful in encouraging new product trials.

Couponing is a popular consumer sales promotion tool in the U.S. packaged goods industry; it is also a significant factor in Canada, Italy, and the United Kingdom. The most popular product categories for coupon use are personal care items, pet food and treats, household cleaning products, rug and room deodorizers, and snacks.[5] However, coupons have lost some ground in recent years. For example, in 2000, a third of brand marketers

---

Exhibit 18–3	*Consumer sales promotion techniques*

- Price deals
- Coupons
- Rebates
- Cross-promotions
- Contests, sweepstakes, games
- Premiums
- Sampling
- Advertising specialties

Issuing coupons to consumers during checkout at the grocery store is growing in popularity. Catalina Marketing's Checkout Direct dispenser compiles customer profiles using check-cashing card data and issues coupons to match predicted future purchases.

cited coupons as one of the three most important marketing tactics. By April 2005 that figure had dropped to 16.7 percent.[6] Retailers, never fond of manufacturers' coupons, have increased their handling fees, especially for coupons that cannot be scanned. Some manufacturers, most recently Unilever and Kraft Foods, have cut their expenditures for coupons, apparently favoring other means of promoting their products.[7]

The number of coupons distributed has increased in recent years, but the percentage redeemed by consumers has declined. Of the 258 billion coupons distributed in 2003, only 3.6 billion, or 1.4 percent, were redeemed by consumers.[8] Analysts point out that couponing has been negatively affected by manufacturers' use of shorter expiration periods on coupons and their attempts to get consumers to make multiple purchases to take advantage of coupons. Electronic promotions have also contributed to a decline in the use of coupons. Nonetheless, coupons are expected to be a primary consumer sales promotion tool well into the future. One reason for this is that some major companies have introduced couponing into their sales promotions. For example, both Linens 'n Things and Bed Bath and Beyond have added significant coupons for up to 20 percent off to their promotional mix, and Procter & Gamble increased its coupon distribution by 16 percent in 2004 to support its BrandSaver program.[9] These retailers are seeking value-conscious consumers to build sales, and coupons remain an important avenue to reach these customers.

Coupons may be distributed in several ways. The most popular method is through the **freestanding insert (FSI),** a preprinted coupon (sometimes contained in an ad) placed into a separate publication, such as a newspaper. FSIs represent more than 80 percent of the coupons distributed in the United States annually. In-store handouts deliver about 5 percent of all coupons; coupons in or on the package also make up approximately 5 percent. The remainder of coupons are distributed by direct mail, magazine, newspaper, and miscellaneous methods such as distribution at special events and via the Internet.

One technique to distribute in-store coupons, **on-shelf couponing,** uses a dispenser mounted near the manufacturer's particular product. Retailers also use in-store **checkout dispensers.** Catalina Marketing, the leading dispenser company, operates checkout dispensers in supermarkets around the world. Although coupons dispensed through Catalina are more expensive to manufacture than those in newspapers, consumers redeem in-store coupons at a much higher rate. Using checkout scanner data about the consumer's purchases, the Catalina system dispenses coupons for similar products or beyond-the-store promotions. For example, a consumer who buys baby food might receive a coupon for Sears Portrait Studios.

Online couponing, the distribution of coupons on the Internet, is a growing phenomenon. Catalina is also in this business, as are companies such as Val-Pak and other entrepreneurial ventures. To celebrate its tenth year in business, Yahoo! provided its Web visitors with in-store coupons for a free scoop of Baskin Robbins ice cream.[10]

Distribution of coupons by e-mail is also on the increase. For example, book and music retailers Barnes & Noble and Borders send coupons by e-mail for discounts on in-store purchases. Circuit City also uses e-mail to distribute in-store coupons.

Distributing paperless coupons by cell phone is another emerging marketing technique. For years, consumers in Asia and Europe have received paperless coupons on their cell phones. McDonald's and Dunkin' Donuts are among the U.S. companies experimenting with the distribution of paperless coupons by cell phone.[11]

REBATES   A **rebate** is a cash reimbursement to a buyer for purchasing a product. The consumer typically must mail a rebate form, the purchase receipt, and some proof of purchase (often the universal product code) to the manufacturer within a certain time frame. Although consumers often purchase as a direct result of a rebate offer, many forget to send for the reimbursement or run out of time. Incentives such as coupons are easier to use, and rebates may not offer consumers the instant gratification that makes other incentives attractive.

Rebates are a popular consumer sales promotion tool. In this case, FISKARS uses a rebate as part of a seasonal sales promotion program.

Rebates serve several functions. They act as an economic appeal to attract customers, particularly price-conscious buyers. They have a deadline, so consumers are encouraged to act by a certain time. They also offer a good way to reduce the perceived risk in trying a new brand: A lower price represents less risk to most consumers.

Rebates also encourage increased consumption. The Quaker Oats Company, for instance, may offer a rebate on the purchase of two or more packages of instant oatmeal when the typical purchase is for only one package. Offering a rebate also allows the manufacturer to maintain a brand's original price while enjoying the benefits of a temporary price reduction. Manufacturers are also assured that the savings go directly to the consumer, rather than to the retailer. This is an advantage to the manufacturer that wishes to build brand loyalty with the ultimate consumer.

Some manufacturers are extending the use of rebates to Internet sites that specialize in promoting products with rebates. For example, Rebate Place features rebates on products made by well-known manufacturers of computer hardware, software, and consumer electronics.[12] Promising products free to consumers after rebates has produced some questionable business practices and misleading sales promotion. CyberRebate.com declared bankruptcy, leaving many consumers awaiting approximately $80 million in unpaid rebates.[13] Some "free-after-rebate" sites, including CyberRebate.com, offered nonrebate merchandise for sale, often at higher-than-market prices. Consumers should be skeptical of deals that sound too good to be true and engage in comparison shopping for significant purchases.

CROSS-PROMOTIONS   A **cross-promotion,** sometimes called a *tie-in,* is the collaboration of two or more firms in a sales promotion. Cross-promotions enhance the communications effort of all the participating firms. For example, grocery retailer Kroger teamed with Masterfoods USA Snack Food's M&M's chocolate candy brand to increase sales for both parties. The cross-promotion was designed to sell more candy and more products from Kroger's floral departments. M&M bouquets were created for exclusive sale at Kroger's, and consumers were offered an opportunity to get a free bouquet with the purchase of three bags of M&M's candy. The cross-promotion worked as intended, with a combined M&M's and floral products sales increase of 146 percent during the two-week program.[14]

Cross-promotions have been particularly popular with online retailers that link with well-known brand marketers to get more exposure for their own names. Amazon.com, for example, has run cross-promotions with Target, Toys R Us, and Hamilton Beach.

Kevin Marie Nuss, Vice President of Marketing, Churchill Downs, discusses the value of cross-promotions: "Cross-promotions can be beneficial to all participating companies. We partner with different companies in a variety of cross-promotions. One example is a cross-promotion with a local dry cleaner and pizza restaurant. These partners sold reduced-price admission to our Festival in the Field promotion. This increased their business and gave our event exposure in their advertising efforts. Both partners sold all of their tickets, so we knew we would have a big crowd for the event. Another example is with Tricon Global Restaurants. Tricon sponsors the Junior Jockey Club for children. Participating families receive coupons for Taco Bell, KFC, and Pizza Hut products. This cross-promotion increases the attendance at Churchill Downs and also increases business at Tricon's different restaurants."

Cross-promotions offer several advantages. Relationships forged between strong brands reinforce the image of each. The image of a new product, or one with low market share, may be enhanced through association with a leading brand. Also, the resources pooled in a cross-promotion enable larger incentives to be offered and generate more fanfare in introducing the promotion to consumers. For more on cross-promotions, see "Creating Customer Value: Big Idea's Cross-Promotions with Applebee's and Tyson Foods."

CONTESTS, SWEEPSTAKES, AND GAMES   A **contest** offers prizes based on the skill of contestants. Participants must use a skill or some ability to address a specified problem to qualify for a prize. Kodak has used photo contests successfully for decades,

This ad from CNN/Sports Illustrated directs readers to a Web site where they can play a sports trivia game and possibly win a trip to a Maui resort. Sales promotion games help marketers build an emotional bond between the consumer and the brand.

and contests are popular in association with major sporting events such as the Olympics and the Super Bowl. Internet-based contests, sweepstakes, and games are becoming more popular, as are those conducted with camera cell phones. For example, Pontiac promoted its G6 model with a photo contest, and Toyota promoted its Scion in the same manner. Kodak, Qwest, and *Jane* magazine have also used cell phone photo contests in their promotions.[15]

A **sweepstakes** offers prizes based on a chance drawing of participants' names. Sweepstakes have strong appeal because they are easier to enter and take less time than contests and games. LA Gear promoted its new track shoe line with a sweepstakes to build brand awareness and clarify its image. Consumers entered the sweepstakes online, where they viewed short films and learned about new styles and colors. Sweepstakes winners received a home gym, gift certificates for spa treatments, workout suits and shoes, and sessions with a personal trainer.[16] By law, purchase cannot be a requirement to enter a sweepstakes.

Games are similar to sweepstakes, but they cover a longer period. They encourage consumers to continue playing in order to win. Fast-food chain Jack in the Box used an instant winner game to reward loyal customers and increase the sale of combo meals in its 2,000 restaurants. By teaming up with Southwest Airlines, Nintendo, American Express, and Musicmatch, the game offered prizes such as free airfare, music downloads, an American Express branded gift card, the Nintendo DS gaming system, and more than 10 million Jack in the Box food prizes.[17]

Contests, sweepstakes, and games can create interest and motivate consumption by encouraging consumer involvement. They are often used in integrated marketing communications programs along with in-store displays (part of trade promotion) and advertising. Although marketers ranked contests, games, and sweepstakes as a lower priority in a recent survey than in the past, the future for these types of promotions is promising.[18] Consumers seem to enjoy the friendly competition, and technology is lending a hand. Contests and games frequently appear on the Internet, where marketers are trying to get consumers to spend more time, thus increasing involvement and interest in the product or service. Automobile and truck manufacturers have been active in this area, including Jeep and Ford. Jeep used an Internet-based photo contest in which consumers submitted photos to address the contest theme, "What the Jeep Brand Means to You." The grand prize was modest, a Jeep boombox, yet the contest drew 250 entries and gave Jeep valuable insights into brand image among some of its most enthusiastic owners. Jeep also has used the Internet to conduct virtual off-road driving contests leading to a final competition at its annual Camp Jeep, held in mountainous venues around the country.[19]

CREATING CUSTOMER VALUE

Big Idea's cross-promotions with Applebee's and Tyson Foods

Big Idea, a subsidiary of Classic Media LLC, uses cross-promotions with other companies to increase sales of its *Veggie Tales* videos aimed at the children's market. Applebee's 1,500 participating restaurants handed out 5 million kids' meal activity books and cups, which included a $2 coupon for the purchase of a *Duke and the Great Pie War* DVD or VHS tape. The activity books entertain the kids, and the coupon builds value with the parents who choose to buy the video. The cross-promotion also includes a contest with 500 prize winners and a trip to tour the Big Idea studio.

Big Idea has also partnered with Tyson Foods to promote the *Veggie Tales* video release. In this promotion, Tyson labeled a million of its Fun Nuggets chicken snack food packages with a special mail-in rebate offer worth $3 with a purchase of two specially marked products. A free mug was included with the video purchase. Cross-promotions such as Big Idea's pairing with Applebee's and Tyson Foods are good business for the companies, and consumers receive extra value from the fun elements of the promotions and the financial incentives offered by the companies.

Thinking Critically

Assume you are a brand manager for a specialty manufacturer with only one product, a high-priced toothpaste with extraordinary whitening power. The product has been highly successful in Europe, and now you are planning national distribution in the United States. If you could use only one consumer sales promotion technique of those shown in Exhibit 18–3, which one would you use? Support your reasoning.

PREMIUMS   An item given free or at a bargain price to encourage the consumer to buy is called a **premium.** Prepaid phone cards, for example, are often used as premiums. These cards, one of the most popular premiums in recent years, are imprinted with the company or brand logo, thus reminding the consumer of the sponsor every time the card is used. In addition, callers will often hear a short promotional message when they dial the free access number to use the card. Other popular premiums include consumer electronics, gift certificates (especially if they are redeemable online), and items that are related to popular entertainment such as television programs and movies. For example, Columbia Pictures and Kellogg joined forces in a global promotion surrounding the release of the *Spider-Man 2* movie. Spider-Man items, including the Spidey water squirter, trading cards, and collectible photos, were offered as premiums in Kellogg's cereal brands sold around the world. The premiums played a major role in helping both Kellogg and Columbia achieve their objectives. With an objective of maximizing movie revenue, *Spider-Man 2* opened number one at the box office in all 70 countries where the promotion ran. The objective of increasing sales of participating brands by 50 percent was successful, with Corn Pops leading the way with a 63 percent increase in global sales.[20]

Premiums are intended to improve the product's image, gain goodwill, broaden the customer base, and produce quick sales. Premiums that require saving in-pack coupons, proofs of purchase to be redeemed, or multiple purchases to complete a set can create consumer loyalty. For instance, McDonald's offers young female consumers especially attractive premiums compared to premiums targeted to young boys. This is because young men grow up to become the most loyal McDonald's customers, whereas many young women lose interest in eating at McDonald's. In one promotion, Matchbox toy cars with a retail value of $1.29 were the premium included in a Happy Meal oriented toward boys, while the female-oriented premium was a miniature Madame Alexander doll, worth several times the value of the Matchbox car. According to McDonald's personnel, the more expensive female-oriented premiums are succeeding in building more enduring brand loyalty in the female segment.[21] In the promotions to both boys and girls, McDonald's increased consumer loyalty by offering a series of toy cars and dolls.

Research comparing the effectiveness of premiums with that of price discounts suggests that marketers might want to experiment with premiums, especially if their competitors are heavy users of price promotions. For example, a free spatula worth $3.99 at retail generated more consumer interest than a $2 price discount on pizza; and an offer of $2,500 worth of camping gear had a higher impact on consumer interest in buying a $28,500 utility vehicle than did a $2,000 discount on the vehicle. Because these premiums can be acquired by marketers at wholesale prices, the return on investment in these promotions can be highly attractive. Further, there is less danger of eroding brand image, which sometimes occurs with price-based promotions.[22]

SAMPLING   A **sample** is a small size of a product made available to prospective purchasers, usually free of charge. Marketers use samples to demonstrate a product's value or use and encourage future purchase. Sampling reduces the consumer's perception of risk by allowing product trial before purchase of a full-size version.

Marketers find sampling particularly useful for new brands with features that are difficult to describe adequately through advertising. Samples also draw heightened attention to a brand. For instance, parent company Just Born Inc. used sampling in an 18-city tour to promote its Marshmallow Peeps brand, the top-selling nonchocolate candy during the Easter season. The program sought to increase brand awareness for Marshmallow Peeps, raise donations for Easter Seals, and drive traffic to CVS Pharmacy stores. The program succeeded in accomplishing all objectives, distributing 31,000 samples along the tour.[23] For Just Born Inc. and many other companies, sampling is a versatile promotion tool that can be used for many purposes, from introducing a new product to reinforcing already established customer relationships.

Although usually mailed to prospective customers, samples may be distributed door-to-door; at trade shows, movies, and special events; or in-store. They sometimes accompany the purchase of a related product, such as a free sample of laundry detergent with the purchase of a washing machine.

Sampling can be expensive; thus marketers must determine the most cost-effective manner of distribution. This depends on the target audience and the size of the sample. Although larger samples cost more, the sample should be big enough for consumers to make an adequate evaluation. Some companies have found unusual ways to get their samples into consumers' hands. In Brazil, most home cooking stoves run on small tanks of compressed gas that are delivered door-to-door. The delivery personnel know their customers personally and have built trust-based relationships over the years. Sara Lee, Johnson floor wax, Procter & Gamble, Unilever, and Nestlé are among the brands that have used the home gas delivery system to distribute samples. Ultragaz, a subsidiary of Royal Dutch/Shell Group, charges five cents for each sample distributed, which marketers consider a very reasonable fee compared to other methods of sampling.[24]

ADVERTISING SPECIALTIES   An **advertising specialty,** also called a *promotional product,* is an item of useful or interesting merchandise given away free of charge and typically carrying an imprinted name or message. These items are typically low in cost, although some can be expensive. According to the Promotional Products Association, the most popular advertising specialty products categories are clothing, writing instruments, desk accessories, calendars, bags, and glassware.[25]

Specialty advertising has several common uses. It can reinforce other advertising media to strengthen a message. It can also produce or foster high levels of brand recognition when the item has a relatively long life. A unique specialty advertising item can attract interest among target audience members and perhaps stimulate action. In addition, a useful specialty item can create a positive attitude toward the provider. Poor-quality merchandise, however, may detract from the marketer's image. For an illustration of how advertising specialties can be used to promote a social cause, see "Being Entrepreneurial: Success of *Accidental Magic* No Accident."

Trade Sales Promotion

Trade sales promotion at the wholesale and retail level helps push products through the marketing channel. Unlike consumer sales promotion, trade promotion is not easily observed by ultimate consumers. Although consumer sales promotions are very visible, in fact they are dwarfed by the magnitude of trade sales promotion. Marketers spend approximately twice as much money on trade promotion.

Objectives of Trade Promotions

Sales promotions aimed at the trade have many varied objectives. As listed in Exhibit 18–4, common trade promotion objectives are to gain or maintain distribution; influence resellers to promote a product; influence resellers to offer a price discount; increase reseller inventory; defend a brand against competitors; and avoid reduction of normal prices.[26] Trade promotions may be conducted by manufacturers, service providers, or wholesalers, all directing their efforts toward other channel members, most notably retailers.

Exhibit 18–4

Objectives of trade sales promotion

- Gain/maintain distribution.
- Influence resellers to promote product.
- Influence resellers to offer price discount.
- Increase reseller inventory.
- Defend against competitors.
- Avoid reduction of normal prices.

GAIN OR MAINTAIN DISTRIBUTION   Sales promotion influences resellers to carry a product. Manufacturers selling directly to retailers may strike special introductory deals to get established with the retailer. Later, sales promotion may help maintain distribution in the face of competition or a flat sales period. Such is the case in the soft drink market, in which Coke and Pepsi use sales promotion on a regular basis. Other incentives, such as providing free in-store displays, may encourage retailers to purchase by reducing their perceived risk. A trade show is another example of sales promotion that may provide a way to introduce the product to potential distributors and gain their business.

INFLUENCE RESELLERS TO PROMOTE THE PRODUCT   Getting a product into a reseller's inventory is not always enough to realize sales objectives. In other words, it's not enough to get the product on the shelf; it may take sales promotion to move it off the shelf. Ways manufacturers can influence retailers to promote a product include offering incentives to the retail sales force, splitting advertising costs with the retailer, furnishing free display materials, or various other techniques. Quaker State, for example, could encourage service station attendants to promote the sale of motor oil by paying them 25 cents per can sold during a contest period. At the end of the contest, the attendant with the most sales would receive two free tickets to a NASCAR race. The basic idea is for additional sales volume to offset expenses involved in running the promotion or for sales to clear the dealers' inventory to make way for more profitable sales in the future.

INFLUENCE RESELLERS TO OFFER A PRICE DISCOUNT   Sometimes the manufacturer gives wholesalers and retailers allowances or discounts so that its product will be offered at a reduced price. The manufacturer hopes the lower price will lead to increased sales. This often occurs with end-of-season merchandise. For example, fishing equipment manufacturer Zebco might offer sporting goods stores a clearance price on factory-premarked rods and reels and a special display barrel with promotional signs indicating "Rod & Reel Riot! $12.99 While They Last!"

INCREASE RESELLER INVENTORY   Suppliers do not want channel members to run out of stock. A product being out of stock results in more than lost sales; it creates dissatisfaction among customers seeking to make a purchase. Sometimes a manufacturer may want to shift products to wholesalers or retailers because of the costs involved in holding inventory. The other channel members, of course, are well aware of the cost and risks of holding excess inventory, and the supplier may grant them special deals in exchange for doing so. Such an approach is common in the greeting card industry, in which suppliers offer retailers special pricing and deferred payment in exchange for their booking orders well in advance.

DEFEND AGAINST COMPETITORS   Just as at the consumer level, sales promotion can stave off competitors at the trade level. An incentive may prompt channel members to choose one firm's brand over a competing one.

Kevin Marie Nuss, Vice President of Marketing, Churchill Downs, talks about the use of trade sales promotions: "Many companies use their sponsorship of the Kentucky Derby as basis for various trade sales promotions. Companies such as PepsiCo establish contests for their retailers. The winning retailers are provided tickets to the Kentucky Derby and entertained at the Marquee Village at Churchill Downs. The equine division of Bayer takes a different approach. The company set up a tent at the Churchill Downs backstretch stable area for the two weeks before the Kentucky Derby. The tent contained displays and information about Bayer equine pharmaceutical products. This mini-trade show was visited by many veterinarians and horsemen during the two-week period."

AVOID PRICE REDUCTIONS   Rather than reduce the price of a product permanently, marketers may use some form of trade promotion to offer channel members a temporary price reduction. If there is a momentary oversupply of product on the market, for example, a manufacturer might elect to maintain sales volume by offering a "1 free with 10" program of short duration. In effect, the customer gets a discount in the form of free goods, but the manufacturer avoids a permanent price reduction.

BEING ENTREPRENEURIAL

Success of *Accidental Magic* no accident

Roy H. Williams is president of Williams Marketing, Inc., an ad agency that teaches creative thinking, strategic planning, and human persuasion to its clients. Williams, also an author, applied some of his entrepreneurial thinking to the publication and marketing of one of his books on creative writing. The proceeds for the book were donated to needy citizens in Guatemala.

To promote the book, titled *Accidental Magic*, Williams used promotional products in a special mailing to hundreds of media contacts, university professors, business associates, and other people he knew who shared an interest in Guatemala. To spur interest in the country, Williams included a small hand-made product from Guatemala in each mailing. One item was a cloth bracelet with the message "We Guatemalans invite you to wear a goodwill bracelet as a token of our friendship."

Roy Williams showed the creativity of a true entrepreneur with his promotional products mailing. Not only did *Accidental Magic* become a successful book, but good sales promotion helped raise money for deserving people.

Lamb Weston used a rebate and the chance to win a dream vacation—a Hawaii cruise for two—as extra incentives for restaurant operators to try Twister Fries. This promotion was designed to simultaneously maintain and build distribution through Lamb Weston distributors.

Exhibit 18–5

Trade sales promotion techniques

- Trade allowances
- Dealer loaders
- Trade contests
- Point-of-purchase displays
- Trade shows
- Training programs
- Push money

Trade Sales Promotion Techniques

Trade sales promotion techniques can be applied independently or in combinations. And firms often link trade sales promotion with consumer sales promotion and other elements of the communications mix. Some frequently used trade sales promotion techniques are shown in Exhibit 18–5.

TRADE ALLOWANCES **Trade allowances** are short-term special allowances, discounts, or deals granted to resellers as an incentive to stock, feature, or in some way participate in the cooperative promotion of a product. There are several kinds of allowances, including slotting allowances, which we discussed in Chapter 14. Another type, the *buying allowance,* is payment of a specified amount of money to a reseller for purchasing a certain amount of a product during a particular period. The payment may be by check or as a credit against an invoice. A manufacturer usually offers a buying allowance to increase the size of the reseller's order.

A *display allowance* is money or a product provided to a retailer for featuring the manufacturer's brand in an agreed-upon in-store display. An *advertising allowance* is money paid a reseller for including the manufacturer's product, along with other products, in the reseller's advertising efforts. Somewhat similar to this, *cooperative advertising* occurs when the manufacturer helps finance the reseller's advertising efforts featuring only the manufacturer's product. For example, Pioneer may help a local electronics store pay for a newspaper ad featuring Pioneer products.

DEALER LOADERS A **dealer loader** is a premium given to a reseller to encourage development of a special display or product offering. Loader techniques help ensure proper stock and display of the item, of particular interest to many manufacturers at certain seasons or holidays.

There are two common types of loaders. A *buying loader* is a gift, such as a free trip, for buying, displaying, and selling a certain amount of a product within a specified time. A *display loader* allows the reseller to keep some or all of the display when the promotion

Point-of-purchase displays call attention to featured products. Duracell uses this eye-catching display to boost sales for several different sizes of batteries.

Thinking Critically

Assume you are a sales representative for a consumer packaged goods company that sells through grocery wholesalers. Your company is offering a limited-time buying allowance. One of your customers requests a higher allowance, which you deny. The customer then suggests that he will buy a huge additional order if you will allow him to claim $200 off the next invoice for "damaged goods" on his last order, even though the goods arrived unharmed. It is within your authority to allow customers to claim deductions for damaged goods up to $250 per claim. What would you do and what would be the implications of your decision?

ends. A tennis racket manufacturer, for example, might allow qualifying retailers to keep an expensive, custom-produced lighted display featuring action photos of top players to help promote sales.

TRADE CONTESTS   A **trade contest** typically associates prizes with sales of the sponsor's product. As do consumer contests, trade contests generate interest, which makes them useful for motivating resellers. Effective trade contests should be held periodically rather than all the time—otherwise they lose some of their motivating potential. Effective contests can boost short-term sales and improve relations between manufacturer and reseller. Dinosaur Adventure, an educational software company, used a trade contest to increase sales and build better relationships with 1,500 dealers. As part of the promotion, dealers competed for a $2,000 prize for the best in-store display for a software package called the Gargantuan Dinosaur Adventure. When the two-month-long promotion began, the software package was the 25th best-selling educational software title. At the conclusion of the promotion, the package had become the number one selling title.[27]

POINT-OF-PURCHASE DISPLAYS   **Point-of-purchase displays** are generally used at the retail level to call customer attention to a featured product. Point-of-purchase displays are popular in grocery, drug, and discount stores and in the restaurant, food service, and tavern industry. Typically provided free or at low cost by the manufacturer to the reseller, point-of-purchase displays attract consumers while they shop, encouraging purchase of the particular product. With much of retailing self-service today, point-of-purchase displays support the retail sales effort by highlighting the product and offering information. Given that consumers make many purchase decisions in the store rather than before entering it, these displays can be important selling tools.

A disadvantage of displays is that manufacturers must assemble and place them. Retailers are busy, and they are deluged with point-of-purchase materials, many of which never make it to the sales floor. Displays often become unused throwaways, an unnecessary waste in marketing communications. Displays come in many varieties, including special racks, display cartons, banners, signs, price cards, video and computer monitors, mechanical dispensers, and robots. The names given to several popular point-of-purchase displays by retailers are shown in Exhibit 18–6, along with their descriptions.

TRADE SHOWS   A **trade show** is a periodic, semipublic event sponsored by trade, professional, and industrial associations at which suppliers rent booths to display products and provide information to potential buyers. Trade shows are big business in the United States, Europe, the Middle East, Africa, Asia, and Latin America. In many of these markets, trade shows are a more influential part of the marketing process than in the United States.

Marketers can use trade shows to accomplish any number of objectives, including demonstrating products, acquiring new prospect leads, making sales, providing information, comparing competing brands, introducing new products, enhancing the corporate image, and strengthening relationships with existing customers.

Some shows are simply too large for customers to effectively visit each exhibit. Many companies use preshow mailings or phone calls to boost exhibit traffic. Companion promotional products are also effective for generating traffic and creating a memorable exhibit. For example, a surgical glove manufacturer wanted to draw traffic and increase sales leads at the trade show held in conjunction with the Association of Operating Room Nurses convention. Prior to the trade show, the company mailed surgical gloves, pictured on track and field athletes on trading cards, to 5,000 nurses. The cards featured a theme of "A glove for every event." On the back of the cards were short quizzes. Nurses were invited to bring their quiz answers to the company's display booth to claim a prize. Daily grand prize winners received valuable merchandise from a gift catalog. Traffic increased significantly, and customer leads increased 30 percent over previous shows.[28]

Exhibit 18-6	*Types of point-of-purchase displays*

Type of Display	**Sign Language**
Aisle interrupter	Cardboard sign that juts into the middle of the aisle.
Dangler	Sign hanging down from a shelf that sways when shoppers pass.
Dump bin	Box-shaped display holding products loosely dumped inside.
Glorifier	Small plastic "stage" that elevates one product above the rest.
Wobbler	A jiggling sign.
Lipstick board	Plastic surface on which messages are written with crayons.
Necker	Coupon hanging on a bottle neck.
Y.E.S. unit	"Your Extra Salesperson," a fact sheet that pulls down like a shade.

Trade shows allow marketers to accomplish several objectives as they gain exposure with interested prospects and strengthen relationships with existing customers. This photo is from the annual Comdex trade show, one of the world's largest, which brings computer-industry buyers and sellers together.

Trade sales promotion sometimes includes reseller training. In this photo, Hewlett-Packard dealers receive training at the company's facility in Mexico City.

Passing out T-shirts or other specialty advertising items carrying the company's name and logo or constructing an unusual, eye-catching display can also generate booth traffic. It is important for companies to have well-trained salespeople available at a trade show. In addition, follow-up after the show is critical.

Major trade shows are held in large cities; thus lodging and associated expenses for company personnel can be expensive. To hold travel expenses to a minimum, many companies prefer regional trade shows. Even in Chicago, home to several major international trade shows, most conventioneers are attending smaller events, with 1,000 or fewer participants, and most are traveling less than 400 miles to attend.

TRAINING PROGRAMS   Some manufacturers sponsor or pay for training programs for customer employees. Armstrong Tile, for example, a manufacturer of floor tile, provides sales training to teach some of its key dealer personnel how to sell or use its products.

Marketers may also provide training on a number of other topics, including retail and wholesale management procedures, safety issues, or current technical developments in an industrial field. Training programs are expensive, and results are often hard to measure. To be effective, training should be continual, or at least periodically reinforced, thus adding to the expense. Even though it is expensive, training can build productive relationships with customers.

PUSH MONEY   **Push money,** also called **spiffs** (for special promotional products incentive funds), is what a manufacturer pays retail salespeople to encourage them to promote its products over competitive brands. This payment may be in the form of money, merchandise, or other incentives with monetary value such as a gift certificate.[29] Push money may also be used to encourage the retail sale of specific products in the manufacturer's line. This extra incentive helps to get the manufacturer's brand special representation or favored treatment. The disadvantage is that the retail salesperson's extra enthusiasm for the manufacturer's product may wane once the spiff is eliminated, especially if another manufacturer offers a new spiff.

Limitations of Sales Promotion

Although sales promotion can accomplish a variety of objectives, there are certain things it cannot do. Sales promotion can help boost sales, but it typically cannot reverse a genuine declining sales trend. If sales are slipping, marketers should evaluate and perhaps change the product's marketing strategy. Attempting to use sales promotion as a quick fix may temporarily postpone worsening of the problem, but it cannot eliminate it.

In a similar vein, marketers cannot reasonably expect sales promotion to convert rejection of an inferior product into acceptance. Consumers judge a product on whether it satisfies their needs. Products that do not meet consumer needs naturally fade from the market over the course of time.

Beyond its inability to improve a brand's image, sales promotion may even weaken the brand image. As a sales promotion develops a life of its own, perceived product differentiation can be blurred; consumers may come to see the deal as more important than any other real or perceived brand difference. In essence, buyers reach a point at which they fail to see any differences among brands, and the marketer has unwittingly created short-run price-oriented behavior. In the soft drink market, for instance, many consumers see Coca-Cola and Pepsi as interchangeable and decide which of the two they will purchase primarily on the basis of price.

Sales promotion, far more than any other marketing activity, has also been blamed for encouraging competitive retaliation. Promotions can be developed quickly, and one company can respond to a competitor's sales promotion with its own. Quick response may stave off the potential of sales lost to the competitor's promotion. Although a promotion battle benefits consumers, two firms that compete head-to-head often both lose profits. Other forms of marketing communications are less likely to evoke such quick retaliatory efforts.

Sales promotion can result in manufacturers' gaining short-term volume but sacrificing profit. Special incentives and deals promote **forward buying** among both distributors and consumers. That is, people buy more than they need at the deal price. They purchase enough to carry them to the next deal, when once again they can stock up at low prices. Thus the manufacturer may sell more at the expense of less profit.

To overcome this problem, manufacturers are increasingly using **pay-for-performance trade promotions,** through which retailers are rewarded for making sales to consumers rather than making purchases from manufacturers. Scanner data can be used to measure results, and the incentive to overload warehouses to take advantage of lower prices during deal periods is reduced.

Ethical and Legal Issues in Sales Promotion

The American Marketing Association Code of Ethics stipulates the "avoidance of sales promotion that uses deception or manipulation." Sales promotion provides an environment ripe for exploitation, and many of the ethical and legal problems in marketing communications are related to questionable promotions. Deception and fraud are the primary issues. Global marketing poses added ethical concerns because of requirements specific to different cultures. Deceptive sales promotion costs consumers millions of dollars annually, not to mention the time spent pursuing worthless "free" offers of unethical businesses. Partners in promotions must also take care to ensure that all parties are meeting their obligations as specified in the promotional program. For an example of how a partner can cause harm to another partner, see "Acting Ethically: FTC Holds Retailers Responsible for Supplier Promises."

The use of push money is drawing increasing attention, as consumers often depend on salespeoples' recommendations in making purchasing decisions. Obviously, push money can bias these recommendations. In some industries, including music for radio air play and pharmaceuticals, promotional dollars are adding significantly to the cost of gaining distribution to the point where the ethics of the practice are the subject of hot debate.[30]

A popular consumer sales promotion tool, the sweepstakes, is often used deceptively. As a result, a variety of regulatory agencies, including the U.S. Postal Service and the Federal Trade Commission, actively police sweepstakes. In addition, all 50 states have various combinations of gambling, lottery, and consumer protection laws that regulate sweepstakes. At

| Exhibit 18–7 | *Examples of coupon and rebate fraud* |

The Fake Storefront

A scam artist rents space cheap, sets up a store, then starts sending in coupons to manufacturers for payment. Pretty soon the store's shelves are bare, but the "owner" is still sending in coupons obtained illegally.

Stuffing the Ballot Box

A retailer legitimately obtains cash from clearinghouses and manufacturers for coupons handed in by shoppers, but boosts the take illegally by sending in extra coupons purchased at steep discounts from various sources, such as unscrupulous printers.

Playing the Middleman

An ambitious operator makes money supplying other operators—collecting coupons by the pound and selling them to retailers, buying and selling proofs of purchase, or counterfeiting coupons and proofs of purchase.

The Redemption Scam

Manufacturers offer big cash rebates on large items to shoppers who mail in forms, together with proofs of purchase—receipts, labels, or box tops. A con artist uses the rebate forms and proofs of purchase, real or counterfeit, to illicitly collect refunds without buying products.

least nine states regulate the use of simulated checks, and separate restrictions exist for sweepstakes promoting tobacco, liquor, milk, and time-share lodging.

The increased scrutiny of sweepstakes by lawmakers has somewhat simplified consumers' participation in sweepstakes but makes them more difficult to use as a promotional tool. One industry executive says, "I'm doing a project now that, if I didn't know it was a sweepstakes, I would swear that I was building an airplane."[31] With consumer privacy a key issue, regulators will likely be more interested in how marketers use and store data that are collected through sweepstakes, contests, and games. With a history of deceptive practices, sweepstakes users can expect little tolerance for deception with future sweepstakes.

Caution is the best policy when designing a sweepstakes program. In fact, the same could be said for any sales promotion—to ensure that manufacturers, wholesalers, and retailers steer clear of unethical or illegal activity. Basically, marketers must tell consumers the truth and clearly spell out the action necessary to enter the sweepstakes. In addition, marketers must take responsibility for the fair and equitable treatment of buyers and nonbuyers during a promotion, taking care not to make it significantly more difficult for nonbuyers to enter. Finally, a legitimate sweepstakes program entails honest distribution of prizes, which may require the services of a sweepstakes management company to avoid insider rigging.

Fraud

Another significant problem involves coupon and rebate fraud, with manufacturers the intended victims. Exhibit 18–7 points out some of the ways cheaters can profit from coupons and mail-in offers. Industry analysts say that unethical retailers are responsible for a majority of fraudulent coupon claims.

ACTING ETHICALLY

FTC holds retailers responsible for supplier promises

The Federal Trade Commission held CompUSA, Inc., a computer superstore chain, responsible for paying hundreds of thousands of dollars in rebates that were promised to consumers who bought products supplied by QPS, Inc. The rebates ranged in value from $15 to $100. Lydia Barnes, acting director of the FTC's Bureau of Consumer Protection, says, "When it comes to rebates, retailers must deliver on their promise. The message to retailers is clear—the FTC is on the beat and will take action if you advertise manufacturers' rebates when you know they aren't honoring their promises."

The FTC also required CompUSA to revamp its rebate procedures. The chain is prohibited from advertising rebates unless it can prove that the manufacturer pays rebates promptly. If no such proof is available from a past or existing business relationship with the supplier, CompUSA must conclude from a financial analysis that the manufacturer can pay the offered rebate. The FTC also prohibited the owners of QPS from using rebates in the future. With complaints about rebates on the increase, the FTC is taking a tougher position on deceptive rebate practices. The settlement with CompUSA marked the first time a retailer was charged over its advertising of rebates.

Manufacturers have resorted to high-tech methods to combat coupon fraud. To circumvent coupon counterfeiting, special inks produce the word *void* on coupons exposed to the light used in copying machines. New checkout scanner technology now polices misredemption at the store level. Even low-tech methods, such as shortening the redemption period, are used.

The most widespread effect of fraud and deceptive sales promotions is that, in the long run, consumers pay more for products than they would otherwise. Consumers also pay through taxes for the considerable government regulation needed to combat fraud and deception.

Diverting

Consumers are not the only victims of unethical and illegal sales promotion. Manufacturers can also be the targets of fraud. A controversial, yet commonplace, activity is **diverting** (also called *arbitraging*), or secretly purchasing a product where it is less expensive, usually as a result of a trade promotion, and reselling in areas where prices are higher.

Diverters use up-to-the-minute computerized information to find out where the deals are, purchase merchandise for shipment to a buyer authorized by the manufacturer to receive the deal, then divert all or part of the shipment to an unauthorized location while the goods are in transit. Diverters include both intermediaries and chain stores. Intermediaries are fairly tight-lipped about diverting, and some even maintain secret operations in the offices of legitimate wholesalers and supermarket chains.

Diverting can distort supply and demand and cause marketing strategies to backfire on manufacturers. Industry analysts believe diverting is inevitable if manufacturers offer the same products at different prices in different geographic markets. Some manufacturers, most notably Procter & Gamble, have instituted a one-price nationwide policy to reduce diverting.

Global Concerns

Marketers must make an extra effort to become familiar with local laws and customs when operating in other countries. In Spain, for example, it is legal to require the purchase of a product for entry in sales promotion contests, whereas such a requirement is illegal in most other European countries. Further, according to an expert on sales promotion in Spain, the Spanish people are generally keen on gambling and participate heavily in promotional games of chance. Logically, sales promotion in Spain is extremely popular, more so than in other European countries with stricter regulations. As a result, it is impossible to design a sales promotion campaign for the entire European market—marketers must adapt programs to the appropriate legal framework.

In Canada a variety of laws affect sales promotion. For example, if entry into a contest requires that the consumer send in a UPC label, entrants are also allowed to submit a handwritten facsimile of the label. In Quebec, language laws require that most marketing communications be in French. Also, most contests must be structured to require that entrants answer a skill-testing question to be eligible for a prize.

These examples from Spain and Canada are reminders that marketing activities should be conducted to meet varying applicable local requirements, often a composite of national, state (or province), and local laws. Because most sales promotion tools involve mass distribution of written documents, extreme caution should be used to ensure compliance with relevant laws.

Summary

1. **Explain the role and significance of sales promotion in the marketing communications mix.** Sales promotion is one way firms may communicate with intended target audiences. Sales promotion uses media and nonmedia marketing communications for a predetermined, limited time at consumer, retailer, or wholesaler levels to stimulate trial, increase consumer demand, or improve product availability. Sales promotion is unique in that it offers an extra incentive for action. Its importance is evidenced by the considerable amount of money firms invest in it.

2. **Understand why sales promotion expenditures account for a significant portion of many firms' marketing communications budgets.** Expenditures in sales promotion have been fueled by changes in consumer demographics, lifestyles and attitudes, technological advances, a shift of power to retailers, a focus of firms on the short term, and an increasing emphasis on accountability for results.

   Many shoppers today are busy and price-conscious, making sales promotion attractive. Scanning technology allows both retailers and manufacturers to gauge the effectiveness of promotions quickly and accurately, thus reinforcing the use of sales promotion. Retailers have gained considerable power in the marketing channel in recent years, and manufacturers are virtually required to engage in sales promotion to increase or maintain distribution. Because sales promotion is generally short term, it fits with the time horizon most favored today in business. Finally, the results of sales promotion are easier to assess than the results of advertising, prompting its use in an era of accountability.

3. **Discuss the objectives and techniques of consumer sales promotion.** Consumer sales promotion attempts to stimulate trial, increase consumer inventory and consumption, encourage repurchase, neutralize competitive promotions, increase sales of complementary products, stimulate impulse purchasing, and allow flexible pricing policies. Consumer sales promotion techniques include price deals, coupons, rebates, cross-promotions, contests, sweepstakes, games, premiums, sampling, and advertising specialties.

4. **Discuss the objectives and techniques of trade sales promotion.** Trade sales promotion can help gain or maintain distribution, influence retailers to promote a product or to offer a price discount, increase reseller inventory, defend against competitors, and avoid price reductions. Popular trade sales promotion techniques involve trade allowances, dealer loaders, trade contests, point-of-purchase displays, trade shows, training programs, and push money.

5. **Explain the limitations of sales promotion.** Sales promotion cannot permanently reverse a genuine decline in sales, nor can it capture enduring acceptance of an inferior product. Overused sales promotion may actually weaken a brand image rather than strengthen it. Because it is short term and often highly visible, sales promotion can spur retaliation from competitors, which tends to diminish its effectiveness. In addition, consumers and resellers may engage in forward buying to take advantage of sales promotions, possibly causing the manufacturer to gain volume at the expense of declining profitability.

6. **Realize how deceptive and fraudulent sales promotion victimizes both consumers and marketers.** Deceptive sales promotion costs consumers millions of dollars annually. Moreover, manufacturers pay consumers and resellers hundreds of millions a year for fraudulently submitted rebates and coupons. The average consumer eventually pays a higher price for products to cover the cost of fraud in sales promotion. In addition, taxpayers have a heavier burden due to the increased costs of regulation at the federal, state, and local levels.

Understanding Marketing Terms and Concepts

Thinking about Marketing

1. What factors have contributed to significant expenditures in sales promotion?

2. What are the objectives of consumer sales promotion?

3. Define and briefly discuss these consumer sales promotion techniques: price deals, coupons, rebates, cross-promotions, contests, sweepstakes, games, premiums, sampling, and advertising specialties.

4. How do the objectives of trade sales promotion differ from those of consumer sales promotion?

5. Define and briefly discuss these trade sales promotion techniques: trade allowances, dealer loaders, trade contests, point-of-purchase displays, trade shows, training programs, and push money.

6. How would these parties be affected if consumer and trade sales promotions on grocery products were banned by law? (*a*) consumers; (*b*) retailers; (*c*) manufacturers with their own brands.

7. Discuss the issue of deception in sales promotion, and give examples of deceptive sales promotion.

8. Discuss the problem of coupon and rebate fraud, and identify several ways unscrupulous operators could exploit manufacturers through fraud.

9. Refer to "Creating Customer Value: Big Idea's Cross-Promotions with Applebee's and Tyson Foods." What factors should a company consider before joining with another company to promote its brand?

10. Refer to "Acting Ethically: FTC Holds Retailers Responsible for Supplier Promises." How can a retailer protect its image and reputation when promoting manufacturers' rebates?

Applying Marketing Skills

1. Consult the Sunday edition of a local newspaper. Identify examples of as many consumer trade promotion techniques as possible. You may find examples of price deals, coupons, rebates, cross-promotions, contests, sweepstakes, games, premiums, and even sampling. Select one example from each category of consumer sales promotion techniques that you have identified, and try to determine the main objective of the promotion: stimulating trial, increasing consumer inventory and consumption, encouraging repurchase, neutralizing competitive promotions, or increasing the sale of complementary products.

2. Look again at the Sunday newspaper. Collect a minimum of 10 coupons or other sales promotion materials intended to stimulate trial of a new product. You may need to review the paper for a couple of weeks to collect 10 examples. Visit local retailers to determine whether the new products are in stock. If the product is in stock, note any other point-of-purchase materials that encourage a purchase. If the product is not in stock, see if you can find out why.

3. Assume you own a small independent bookstore in a large metropolitan area. You face heavy competition from Amazon.com and large national chains such as Walden Books and Barnes & Noble. Your clientele is more upscale, educated, and intellectual than that of your competition. You are attempting to develop a sales promotion program to encourage your clientele to become loyal customers. Explain how you would choose one or more consumer sales promotion techniques to accomplish this objective.

Using the www in Marketing

Activity One   Val-Pak is best known for mailing coupons to consumers. Access the company's Web site at *http://www.valpak.com*, then answer these questions:

1. Coupons are available on the Val-Pak Web site. What are the advantages and disadvantages of distributing coupons online as compared with traditional methods such as distributing them in the newspaper, via direct mail, or in a store?

2. Other than coupons, do you see any evidence that Val-Pak uses sales promotion at its Web site? If not, how could Val-Pak use sales promotion to build awareness and usage of its services?

Activity Two   Go to the *PROMO Magazine* Web site at *www.promo.com*. Explore the site, especially the "Campaigns" link. In the most recent two-week period, see how many concepts from this chapter are mentioned in current news stories from the world of sales promotion.

1. List the chapter concepts you identify, and note how specific companies are using the concepts in their promotional programs.

2. Also, write a brief description of the best promotional program in the most recent two weeks. What led you to choose this particular program as "best"?

Making Marketing Decisions

Case 18-1 Women on Their Way by Wyndham

Headquartered in Dallas, Texas, Wyndham International, Inc., is one of the world's largest hotel operators. Wyndham owns, leases, manages, and franchises properties in the United States, Caribbean, Europe, and Canada. The company has 25,000 employees. Wyndham serves both business and leisure travelers and has become particularly well-known for catering to female business travelers, a fast-growing segment of the business travel market.

Wyndham began intensifying its efforts to develop the female business traveler market in 1995, when it held its first annual "Women on Their Way Contest." Contest entrants were asked to describe how they would improve business travel for women. Over the years, many suggestions from customers have been implemented at Wyndham properties. Women indicated they would like to have a comfortable, private place for conversation, not the hotel bar or lobby. Wyndham responded with its signature library in its Garden Hotel properties, a location convenient to the lobby and bar, but distinctly separate from these facilities. Guest suggestions led to an option of receiving prenotification by phone before room-service delivery, a safety and courtesy measure.

Over the years, the theme for the annual contest has changed. In 2005 the contest had entrants make a short video describing how they or someone they knew overcame a major obstacle in life to become a successful business traveler. Entrants were encouraged to portray how they turned potential trials and tribulations into joy and success on the road. Such information is valuable input into an ongoing relationship marketing program between Wyndham and its female customers. As part of the relationship marketing program, Women on Their Way members (membership also open to males) receive an e-mail newsletter featuring travel news and special promotional offers.

In addition to its annual contest, Wyndham uses other sales promotion tools to provide incentives and add value for its customers. Price deals such as two nights for one and special weekend rates help Wyndham boost sales volume, and cross-promotions with major airlines are also popular.

When Wyndham registers a guest for the Women on Their Way program, the company learns how often the person travels, how much travel is business or leisure, whether children accompany the guest, and with which airlines the guest flies. Prospective members also indicate if they are members of the National Association of Business Owners or the National Association of Female Executives.

There are signs that Wyndham's Women on Their Way program is helping position the company as a specialist in meeting the needs of traveling women. The program has been featured on international television via Cable News Network (CNN). Overall bookings are up for the Wyndham chain, though it is hard to tie booking results directly to the program. It is also difficult to tie specific results of the program to increased sales volume because Wyndham has grown rapidly since it began the program in 1995, causing an overall increase in bookings. Inquiries to Wyndham's Web site are increasing, and feedback from guests and the female executive advisory board continues to be positive. Fred Leisner, Wyndham's CEO, says, "Our women's advisory board has a 10-year history with Wyndham now. Our top executives meet with the board twice yearly. The dialogues with women that visit the Web site, along with the advisory board input, are responsible for motivating us to make major changes to our brand that benefit not only women, but all travelers."

Questions

1. Explain how Wyndham uses a sales promotion tool, the annual contest, to better define and meet the needs of its female guests.

2. Wyndham often engages in cross-promotions with airlines and other travel-related companies. What other cross-promotion opportunities do you see for Wyndham?

3. What other sales promotion objectives and tools could you recommend for Wyndham?

4. The results of sales promotion should be measurable. What can Wyndham do to better measure the sales promotion aspects of its Women on Their Way program?

Case 18–2 *GlaxoSmithKline's Sales Promotion in India*

GlaxoSmithKline (GSK) is a leading worldwide pharmaceutical company based in the United Kingdom. GSK puts a lot of emphasis on research and development of new pharmaceuticals, and it also invests heavily in the marketing area. Of GSK's 100,000 employees, 40,000 are in sales and marketing. The company has the largest global sales force in the pharmaceutical industry.

The practice of using special incentives to encourage physicians to prescribe specific branded drugs, not generics or competitors' brands, has been part of the pharmaceutical industry for decades. So has the practice of offering incentives to pharmacists to honor these prescriptions rather than switching to a generic or competitive brand when the patient fills the prescription. Recently, these practices have become more controversial for two primary reasons. First, the overall cost of health care has risen around the world. Some believe that promotional costs incurred by pharmaceutical companies ultimately result in higher costs to consumers. In some cases, higher costs mean lack of access to consumers with low incomes or those not insured. The second reason that pharmaceutical promotional spending has become more controversial is that some companies have expanded the use of incentives, raising ethical questions about the practice.

A case in point is how GSK and other companies promote their pharmaceutical products in India. Pharmacy owner Ranjit Ranawat surprised his wife by bringing home a new 29-inch television set he received for ordering 600 vials of Fortum, an antibiotic, and 100 boxes of Ceftum, a drug for urinary tract and respiratory infections. Ranawat ordered these products from GSK in quantities approximately 10 times his normal quantity in order to receive the television set. Such incentives have become commonplace in India, where many consumers are too poor to see a doctor and rely on medical advice from the pharmacist. There are approximately half a million pharmacists in India, and they have quite a bit of clout in determining which drugs will be best sellers.

The widespread use of special incentives to pharmacists in India troubles health care professionals for several reasons. First, special incentives based on high-volume purchases require that the pharmacist push the product hard when it may not be appropriate for all patients. Second, if pharmacists get extra profits instead of dropping the retail price, consumers are paying more for needed drugs. Third, about half the highly promoted drugs are antibiotics, which experts say are overused and abused in India.

GSK and other drug companies defend the use of promotional incentives, saying they are intended not to increase total industry sales but to persuade pharmacists to substitute their drugs when prescriptions are written for a competitive drug. According to GSK's director of pharmaceuticals, for every two GSK prescriptions that are written, only one is actually filled because druggists make a switch. GSK thus justifies the use of incentives as simply defending its market share.

The role of sales incentives in India in the future is unclear. Current law allows easy duplication of patented drugs, which means there are thousands of drug manufacturers there. With so many companies, self-regulation of the industry would be difficult: Some competitors would undoubtedly rely on incentives to build their business. India's patent law is due for an overhaul in 2005, but the results of the new law remain to be seen. Pharmacists are powerful, and it is customary for their trade associations to demand special allowances. Some pharmacists claim they need the additional profit that promotional incentives bring because some of their customers are poor and do not pay their bills. When pharmaceutical companies have resisted paying promotional incentives, some pharmacies immediately reduced the amount of their purchase orders.

The international pharmaceutical industry is interested in what happens in India, but offers little advice. For example, the Pharmaceutical Research and Manufacturers of America (PRMA), a major trade group, notes a "disturbing" trend toward shifting the responsibility for prescribing drugs away from doctors toward other health care professionals, including pharmacists. While noting that price controls do not work, the PRMA does not take an explicit stand on incentives granted to pharmacists.

It is not clear what GSK and other industry leaders will do with their promotional allowances in the future. For now, none have spoken out against the practice. GSK says its expenditures on promotional allowances in India represent less than 1 percent of sales. At such a small percentage, there is little incentive to reduce the allowances from a cost-cutting perspective.

Questions

1. Is the payment of promotional allowances to pharmacists in India justified from an economic point of view? From a societal point of view?

2. What other types of sales promotion could GSK engage in that would not be so controversial?

3. Are industry leaders such as GSK under any obligation to set the standards for ethical sales promotion practices?

Chapter Nineteen

PERSONAL SELLING AND SALES MANAGEMENT

19

After studying this chapter, you should be able to

1 Understand the role and importance of personal selling in the marketing communications mix.

2 See how the key steps in personal selling depend on a relationship perspective.

3 Identify the similarities and differences in the job responsibilities of salespeople and sales managers.

4 Describe the key activities in sales management.

5 Appreciate important ethical issues faced by salespeople and sales managers.

Pfizer

Started in 1849, Pfizer has grown to be a worldwide pharmaceutical company. Much of this success came under the leadership of CEO William Steere. Steere started as a Pfizer sales representative in San Francisco over 40 years ago. He was then promoted to district sales manager and, after 12 other promotions, was named CEO in 1991. During his tenure as CEO, Pfizer advanced from thirteenth in worldwide prescription drug sales to second.

Pfizer's success is due to many factors. Steere divested unrelated businesses so the company could focus on pharmaceuticals. Pfizer also spends heavily on research and development, the efforts of which have produced a number of new drugs that have been successful in the marketplace.

Developing new drugs is one thing; making them successful in the marketplace is another. This is largely the role of Pfizer's award-winning sales force. The Pfizer sales force is the largest in the industry, with 11,000 sales representatives in the United States and more than 38,000 worldwide. A survey of U.S. physicians ranked Pfizer's sales force first overall in terms of their disease and product knowledge, credibility, and service. This was the ninth straight year Pfizer was ranked first, which is a record for the pharmaceutical industry.

The basic role of Pfizer salespeople is to provide physicians with reliable information about drugs so they can confidently prescribe them to their patients. As described by Steere, "The sales representatives are the ultimate technology transfer between our laboratories and the practicing physician. Doctors get a lot of information from our representatives, ranging from technical information on new products to new information on older drugs." The Pfizer sales force is so good that other pharmaceutical companies have partnered with Pfizer to bring new products to market. For example, Pfizer salespeople helped launch Warner-Lambert's cholesterol-lowering drug Lipitor and G. D. Searle's arthritis drug Celebrex.

Steere retired as CEO in January 2001, but not before he directed the acquisition of Warner-Lambert. Hank McKinnell took over as CEO and shortly thereafter announced the $60 billion acquisition of Pharmacia.

Pfizer is the leading pharmaceutical company in the world, with annual sales in excess of $52 billion. Effective personal selling is one of the keys to Pfizer's success.

The Pfizer example highlights the important role that personal selling can play in a firm's marketing strategy. Continuously introducing new drugs is critical to success in the pharmaceutical industry and requires both a concerted R&D effort and a strong marketing effort. Although Pfizer does advertise to physicians and consumers and informs them about diseases and new drug products, the Pfizer sales force is critical to the success of new product launches. Pfizer salespeople develop close relationships with physicians, and physicians rely on them as an important source of information about new drug products. It is also interesting to note that the company's previous CEO—William Steere—started his career as a Pfizer salesperson and that his first promotion was to district sales manager.

Personal selling is another element of the marketing communications mix: the face-to-face interaction between a seller and a buyer for the purpose of satisfying buyer needs to the benefit of both. This chapter describes the roles of professional salespeople and illustrates various types of sales jobs. We look at the key personal selling activities, especially the way salespeople work with customers to establish mutually beneficial relationships.

The remainder of the chapter discusses sales management. In simple terms, **sales management** provides leadership and supervision of an organization's personal selling function. Besides managing sales personnel, sales managers develop and implement sales strategy. As in other areas of marketing, personal selling and sales management roles are being redefined to meet the challenges of today's competitive, customer-driven marketplace. For example, the new definition of marketing presented in Chapter 1 emphasizes creating, communicating, and delivering value and managing relationships. Salespeople in many firms, such as Pfizer, play a key role in value creation and relationship development.

We also discuss ethical issues in personal selling and sales management. Salespeople are among the most visible representatives of an organization's marketing effort, and they operate under considerable pressure to generate sales revenue. Because of these factors, it is extremely important for salespeople and sales managers to be aware of their ethical and legal responsibilities.

The Multiple Roles of Salespeople

Salespeople fulfill multiple roles that contribute to the overall success of a business. We look at these roles in two ways: as contributions to the marketing effort, and as functional roles (the different types of personal selling jobs).

Contributions of Personal Selling to Marketing

Personal selling contributes to a firm's marketing efforts by producing sales revenue, meeting buyer expectations, and providing marketplace information. The key to successful marketing lies in understanding customer requirements and then matching a firm's offerings to those requirements. Because salespeople are often the most direct link between a firm and its customers, they can heavily influence whether the firm succeeds.

Personal selling is an important element of a firm's marketing strategy. A sales representative helps a retail store manager improve the display of clothing.

PRODUCING SALES REVENUE Salespeople make perhaps their most important contribution to the marketing function as revenue producers. Businesses scrambling for survival in a highly competitive world have become more profit-oriented in recent years. To produce an adequate bottom-line profit, it is imperative to achieve a suitable top-line, or sales revenue, figure. And salespeople are on the front line, supported of course by marketing research, product development, distribution, and other areas of the business. Sales personnel, along with management, are the prime bearers of the burden of contributing to profit by producing revenue.

Speaking from Experience

Gerald J. Bauer
Sales Competency Leader and
Field Marketing Manager (ret.)
Du Pont Company

"We have come to realize at Du Pont that sales are not just an individual effort by salespeople. Anyone involved at the customer interface or in support of the customer plays a key role in overall sales success. The actions of a customer service representative, a technical representative, a truck driver, or a CEO can make or break the sale. Processes and systems need to be made customer-friendly to give our customer team efficient and effective support. Roles need to be clear, and redundancy eliminated. At Du Pont, we realize that our competitive advantage comes from our organizational capacity and capability. The combined capability of people is hard to duplicate, and the people of Du Pont are our strength."

Gerald Bauer recently retired from Du Pont where he held a variety of positions, including sales, sales management, product management, industry management, customer service management, purchasing management, and sales training. He continues to work for Du Pont as a consultant and trainer. Jerry earned a BBA and MBA in marketing from the University of Toledo.

MEETING BUYER EXPECTATIONS   To succeed in a competitive marketplace, salespeople must—at a minimum—meet buyer expectations. Salespeople are at the heart of building customer relationships. There is no question that the competitive environment has given buyers more clout in dealing with salespeople. According to the Institute for Supply Management, buyers are less likely to tolerate salespeople who waste their time with poorly prepared sales presentations or who will not address their concerns.[1] Dennis Ferguson, a buyer for California-based Rayley's supermarkets, advises salespeople, "I'm busier than ever. Don't tell me what I already know. Tell me why and how your product . . . will disappear off the shelf."[2]

Exhibit 19–1 presents a number of dos and don'ts for salespeople. As suggested by the exhibit, many buyers today take a no-nonsense attitude when dealing with salespeople. They expect straightforward, honest communication. In short, they expect salespeople to live up to high professional standards.

PROVIDING MARKETPLACE INFORMATION   Because personal selling involves face-to-face interaction with buyers, salespeople can get immediate feedback from customers. Just as marketplace feedback can help in a firm's development of future products

Exhibit 19–1	*What buyers expect from salespeople*

Dos	Don'ts
• Know your product and its competition better than the buyer does.	• Use industry buzzwords without knowing what you're talking about.
• Be a tough, but open, negotiator.	• Portray your company as quality-conscious if it's not.
• Have the backing of your company to make strategic partnerships.	• Focus exclusively on short-term sales goals.
• Understand the customer's future plans and offer ideas about how your company can help further them.	• Talk about strategic alliances without having the support of your company.
• Be willing to change your processes and products.	• Say, "We want your business, and we'll make it up later."
• Offer something unique—a technological change, a new way of delivering, or a large price concession.	• Try to persuade purchasers to buy something that doesn't meet their needs.
• Get to know all the people interested in the product, from purchasing managers to engineers.	• Simply talk pricing.
• Keep on top of potential product problems.	• Give a canned presentation.
• Be able to explain how your company plans to improve the quality and reliability of its products.	• Come without ideas.
	• Know nothing about the competition.
	• Fly by the seat of your pants.
	• Offer products today that you're not likely to have tomorrow.
	• Roll over dead in negotiations.

and promotional programs, direct customer feedback adds value to the personal selling function. Feedback to the company can include information on competition and analysis of existing and potential customers and markets, which is useful in sales forecasting. Administaff is one company that realizes the value of information provided by its salespeople. The company has established an internal advisory board consisting of top salespeople. This team provides management with input about the marketplace and changes in the company's sales organization.[3]

Although the basic job of salespeople is to sell, most sales positions require a variety of different activities. Studies indicate that salespeople may spend only about 10 percent of their time in front of customers selling. Other activities and typical percentages of time are administrative duties (31 percent), traveling (18 percent), phone calls and e-mail (17 percent), solving problems for customers (14 percent), and prospecting for new customers (10 percent). These percentages differ across sales jobs, but many sales organizations are trying to decrease the amount of time salespeople spend on administrative activities and increase the time spent in selling or more sales-related activities, such as solving customer problems and prospecting for new customers.[4]

Job Roles of Salespeople

Although all personal selling involves face-to-face interactions with customers, there are distinct differences in the nature of these interactions. Salespeople's contributions to the overall company effort may be made in a variety of job roles. Exhibit 19–2 classifies personal selling jobs into two major categories: business-to-business and direct-to-consumer.

BUSINESS-TO-BUSINESS SALES   Business-to-business selling involves the sale of products and services that are resold by the customer, used as part of the customer's manufacturing process, or used to facilitate the operation of the customer's business. Business selling involves three major types of salespeople: sales support, new business, and existing business.

Sales support salespeople are not directly involved in concluding customer purchases. Rather, they support the personal selling function by promoting a product or providing technical support. Sales support salespeople may work in coordination with other salespeople who actually solicit customer purchases, and their activities can be modified to meet the needs of individual customers.

New technologies can help salespeople perform their job roles more productively. The use of laptop computers turns a car into a virtual office for a salesperson.

Exhibit 19–2	*Types of personal selling jobs*

	Business-to-Business
Sales support:	Promote the product or provide technical service. Includes missionaries and detailers.
New business:	Focus on sales growth by selling new products or selling to new customers. Some salespeople are trade show specialists, and some work in the field (out of the office).
Existing business:	Maintain and enhance relationships with an established customer base. Includes salespeople who follow an established route, writing up routine orders.
	Direct-to-Consumer
	Represent the seller in transactions with ultimate consumers. Includes retail salespeople, representatives of direct selling firms, and most real estate and financial services.

Retail salespeople help consumers satisfy needs and solve problems.

One primary type of sales support job is that of the *missionary.* Missionary salespeople, like religious missionaries, work at the grassroots level to spread the "gospel"—that is, help promote their company's products. In this instance, the grassroots level means with product users or with a channel intermediary such as a retail store. Broker organizations often use sales support personnel to visit individual grocery stores, assisting in merchandising and providing point-of-purchase sales information, thereby providing support to build sales volume for the broker's products. Textbook salespeople, such as those from McGraw-Hill/Irwin, are a type of missionary salespeople.

In the pharmaceutical industry, highly specialized missionaries, or *detailers,* work for most major drug firms. Detailers call on medical professionals and provide them with technical information and product samples to encourage doctors to write prescriptions for the company's drugs. Pfizer salespeople represent a good example of detailers.

Technical support salespeople are an important element of the sales support function. They have expertise in areas such as design and installation of complex equipment and may provide specialized training to customer employees. Technical support salespeople are especially effective in sales teams formed to address customer needs.

Members of the sales force who concentrate on selling new products or selling to new customers are called **new-business salespeople.** These people are extremely important to companies focusing on sales growth. Suppose a newly established franchising firm depends on the sale of new franchises to achieve its growth objectives. Salespeople representing the franchising company may then travel the country in search of new franchisees.

Many salespeople are assigned to work with established customers to produce a steady stream of sales revenue. **Existing-business salespeople,** sometimes called *order takers,* include wholesaler reps who follow an established route, writing up fairly routine orders from their customers.

Business-to-business salespeople often represent some combination of the sales support, new-business, and existing-business roles. For example, salespeople from General Mills serve all three functions. They seek new business when new grocery retailers enter the market or when General Mills introduces a new product; they work with existing grocery chains and co-ops to maximize sales of existing and new products; and they provide sales support as they visit individual grocery stores to maximize the General Mills presence at the point of sale.

DIRECT-TO-CONSUMER SALES   **Direct-to-consumer salespeople** sell to individuals who personally use the products and services. This category includes over 4.5 million retail salespeople and over a million others who sell residential real estate and financial securities to ultimate consumers. Several additional million direct-to-consumer salespeople represent firms such as Avon, Mary Kay, Tupperware, Creative Memories, Amway, and other direct-selling companies.

The job market for salespeople is expected to grow in the future with many new sales positions and career opportunities available. Industries with especially good opportunities for sales jobs, compensation, and professional development include health care and pharmaceuticals, office products, business services, insurance, and technology.[5] An interesting trend is the outsourcing of the sales function. Instead of having a company sales force, some companies are outsourcing the sales function. Outsourcing companies, such as Fusion Sales Partnerships, provide full-time salespeople on a contract basis to firms such as IBM, Agilent, and GE. For example, GE Medical Systems contracted with Fusion for a sales team experienced in capital equipment sales. These salespeople were Fusion employees, but sold only GE products to smaller hospitals. The results of this arrangement were good for Fusion and GE, so the contract has been renewed. This trend provides sales job opportunities selling outsourcing services or becoming part of an outsourced sales force.[6]

The Sales Process: A Relationship Approach

Whatever their role, salespeople try to maximize their effectiveness in the **sales process,** which involves initiating, developing, and enhancing long-term, mutually satisfying relationships with customers. This view of selling—called **relationship selling**—is a departure from the old approach that focused more on a salesperson's ability to make a compelling, and often manipulative, sales presentation than on customer needs. Exhibit 19–3 describes its components.

Exhibiting Trust-Building Attributes

To succeed in relationship selling, salespeople must have certain attributes. Although specific attributes vary depending on the sales context, the ability to build trust is basic. Research has shown that five attributes help to build relationships with customers. Salespeople must be customer-oriented, honest, dependable, competent, and likable.[7] Each of these elements is important in building trust with customers, as indicated by Blake Conrad, a medical supplies salesperson for Centurion Specialty Care:

> You simply cannot have productive relationships with your customers unless they trust you. I work really hard to show customers that I care about their bottom line, and I would never sell them anything they don't really need. If I don't have an answer for them on the spot, I make every effort to get the answer and get back to them on the same day. Customers appreciate the fact that I do what I say and follow up on all details. To me, being customer-oriented and dependable is just part of my job. It makes selling a lot more fun when your customers trust you, and—guess what—I sell more to customers who trust me.[8]

Developing a Selling Strategy

It is not enough for salespeople to exhibit the right attributes; they must also develop a selling strategy, an overall plan for a course of action. As part of integrated marketing communications programs, selling strategies should be developed at three levels: sales territory, customer, and individual sales call.

A sales territory, usually defined geographically, consists of specific customers and prospects assigned to a specific salesperson. Salespeople need an overall territory strategy regarding the amount of time to spend working with current customers versus trying to generate new customers. Salespeople should also have a territory strategy focusing on specific customer needs they can satisfy. For example, Carol Super sells local

Salespeople should develop selling strategies for each customer and for each sales call. Successfully executing these strategies often requires salespeople to perform a variety of activities.

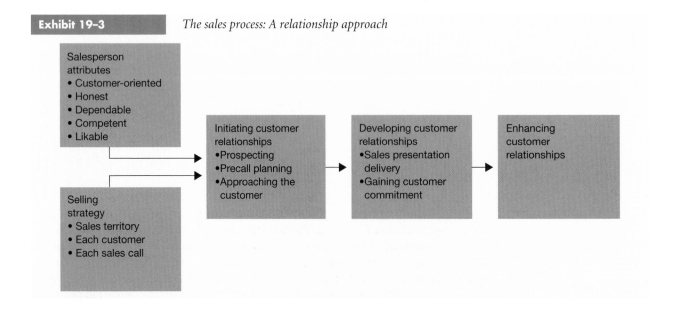

Exhibit 19–3   *The sales process: A relationship approach*

Salesperson attributes
- Customer-oriented
- Honest
- Dependable
- Competent
- Likable

Selling strategy
- Sales territory
- Each customer
- Each sales call

Initiating customer relationships
- Prospecting
- Precall planning
- Approaching the customer

Developing customer relationships
- Sales presentation delivery
- Gaining customer commitment

Enhancing customer relationships

Salespeople play an important role in the pharmaceutical industry. Different strategies are used for different customers.

ads to national magazines as an account manager for Media Networks. Her selling strategy has been very effective, especially during tough times in New York after September 11. She makes cold calls early in the morning before gatekeepers are in the office. Special promotions and PowerPoint presentations are made once a month to individual advertising agencies. She focuses on hotels and the entertainment industry because they have not been advertising much in the past few years. This selling strategy has helped her be the top salesperson in her company. About half of her sales come from new customers and half from existing customers.[9]

Selling strategy should next be developed for each customer within a given sales territory. Carol Super uses specific strategies for her customers. After September 11, the travel and entertainment industries in New York were hit hard. Her selling strategy for hotels was targeted ads to get people in nearby areas to stay in New York hotels. For movie theater customers, the strategy was to capitalize on the tough times because that was when people really wanted to see a movie. As the situation in New York has improved, Super has adapted her selling strategy to meet the changing needs of each customer.[10]

Finally, each sales call, or every meeting with the customer, should be guided by a strategy compatible with customer needs. By developing a specific plan of action for each sales call, the salesperson capitalizes on a major advantage of personal selling as a marketing communications tool. The purpose of each sales call should be to move the sales process along until a commitment from the customer is achieved. Then future sales calls are used to ensure customer satisfaction and expand the relationship with the customer.

Initiating Customer Relationships

Exhibit 19–3 breaks initiating customer relationships into three primary activities: prospecting, precall planning, and approaching the customer. These activities, like the other parts of the sales process, are highly interrelated. They are not necessarily separately distinguishable actions.

PROSPECTING   **Prospecting** is defined as the seller's search for and identification of qualified buyers. Potential prospects come from a variety of sources, including existing customers, personal contacts, directories, computerized databases, trade publications, and trade shows. Prospects may respond to advertising by placing a telephone call or writing for more information. Such responses, called *inquiries,* are often assigned to salespeople for follow-up.

One interesting prospecting approach is to use educational seminars. Gartner, a research and consulting firm, uses its 400-person sales force to invite clients and prospects

Thinking Critically

Select a familiar product
and identify a potential
customer for this
product. Assume that
you are planning a
sales presentation to sell
this product to this
customer.

- Identify three
  questions you would
  plan to ask the
  potential customer,
  and indicate why
  each question is
  important.
- Identify three
  concerns the
  potential customer
  might have, and
  suggest how you
  would address each
  concern.
- Describe the strategy
  you would use to
  gain commitment
  from the potential
  customer, and
  discuss the advan-
  tages and disadvan-
  tages of this
  approach.

to over 300 seminars each year. Each seminar addresses a specific content area. Participants are charged to attend the seminars, but this fee is refunded if an attendee purchases Gartner services within 30 days of an event. These educational seminars have helped Gartner get new customers and also sell additional services to existing clients.[11] New technology developments are also helping salespeople prospect more effectively. Several examples are presented in "Using Technology: Identifying the Best Prospects."

A qualified buyer must be reasonably accessible to the seller, able to afford the purchase, and at least willing to consider making it. To define qualified prospects, salespeople or companies may establish additional criteria involving elements such as geographic proximity marketplace function (sales only to wholesalers, for example), or minimum sales volume levels.

PRECALL PLANNING In **precall planning,** the salesperson focuses on learning more about the customer's situation. Salespeople might visit prospects' places of business to learn more about their needs. BellSouth, a major telecommunications company headquartered in Atlanta, instructs its salespeople to follow up a qualifying call with an information-gathering meeting with the prospect. After the proper information is gathered, the Bell-South account rep plans a sales presentation to be delivered at a later date.

A sales rep must consider a multitude of factors in planning a specific sales presentation. A good idea is to formulate a measurable *sales call objective* to guide the planning process. This should specify the desired customer action resulting from the call; for instance, "the customer will place an order of 400 units for immediate shipment."

Planning involves selecting a format for the sales presentation. In most cases a two-way dialogue between the buyer and the seller may be facilitated by an *organized sales presentation,* a mental or written outline developed by the salesperson. The outline should be flexible enough to allow **adaptive selling;** that is, the salesperson must be able to adjust her or his behavior to respond appropriately to the situation and to address the issues that are most important to the customer.[12]

A format at the other extreme from adaptive selling is a *canned sales presentation.* In effect, this is a fully scripted presentation that the sales rep memorizes; it could even be an automated presentation using audiovisual media. Although generally ineffective in business-to-business personal selling, canned presentations have worked well in consumer settings such as the sale of encyclopedias to families. Although they may be complete and logical, the relative inflexibility of canned presentations limits their usefulness.

Word processing supported by graphics facilitates another presentation format, the *written sales proposal.* Long used in major sales, written sales proposals can now easily be tailored to individual customers with diverse needs. Sales proposals are usually accompanied by face-to-face meetings between the buying and selling parties to define product specifications and negotiate details.

During precall planning, salespeople also decide how to use sales tools such as brochures, audiovisual support material, and computer technology. As an example, Dun's

USING TECHNOLOGY

Identifying the best prospects

Consider the following ways that technology is being used to help salespeople prospect better:

- Pro Premium, One Source, SalesWorks, and Companies and Executives are online databases that allow salespeople to identify prospects by searching the databases using various criteria.
- Salespeople can join InnerSell.com for free. If a salesperson has a customer that needs a product not sold by the salesperson, he/she can find a vendor for the desired product from the site. If the customer buys from

this vendor, the salesperson gets a commission of about 10 percent. More than 1,000 salespeople have joined the site.

- Jigsaw Data is another online prospecting site. Each month a salesperson pays $25 for access to 25 contacts. Alternatively, the salesperson can contribute 25 contacts to the site instead of paying the $25. Even though Jigsaw is very new, it has about 5,000 users and a database of over 440,000 contacts. The database is growing by nearly 3,000 contacts per day.

Exhibit 19–4

Approaching the customer: Violations of ethics and etiquette

A survey of 250 secretaries, administrative assistants, and other "gatekeepers" responsible for scheduling appointments for visiting salespeople revealed these violations of sales etiquette and sales ethics:

- Arriving unannounced to make a sales call.
- Pretending to know the decision maker.
- Treating secretaries disrespectfully.
- Being reluctant to state the purpose of the proposed visit.
- Arriving late for appointments.
- Being overly persistent in attempts to get an appointment.
- Wasting time with unnecessary conversation.
- Failing to cancel appointments that cannot be met.

Marketing Services, a subsidiary of Dun & Bradstreet, greatly improved the effectiveness of its sales presentations by using a computer to demonstrate how its BusinessLine product works.

Precall planning requires a salesperson to think about communicating to customers how various product or service features translate into explicit benefits. A **feature** is merely a statement of fact about some aspect of a product or service. A **benefit** describes what the feature can do for the customer. For example, one feature of a Mitsubishi portable fax machine is a built-in speakerphone. The benefit of the speakerphone is that it allows hands-free conversation. Effective salespeople communicate more about benefits than features, focusing on those of particular interest to each customer.

APPROACHING THE CUSTOMER The final phase of initiating the relationship is approaching the customer. This involves arranging the sales call, usually by making an appointment, and extends into the first sales call when introductions are made and the salesperson attempts to develop the basis for further sales activity. Common courtesy and business etiquette can help make a good initial impression. Improper behavior, on the other hand, can diminish the salesperson's opportunity to proceed in the sales process. Examples of behaviors to avoid are shown in Exhibit 19–4.

Developing Customer Relationships

After successfully approaching the customer, the salesperson can begin to develop the customer relationship. To do this, he or she must deliver an effective sales presentation or, more likely, multiple sales presentations. The relationship is established when the customer makes a commitment to take an action such as making a purchase.

SALES PRESENTATION DELIVERY To make a successful sales presentation, the salesperson must achieve **source credibility**—that is, the customer must perceive its needs being satisfied by the combination of the salesperson, the product or service, and the salesperson's company. The salesperson's personal characteristics such as dress, appearance, and manner may be important in achieving source credibility.

Certain sales approaches can also help achieve source credibility. Prospect-oriented questioning and active listening, as illustrated in Exhibit 19–5, are very important. The salesperson should be careful not to overstate any claims about the product or service and should be prepared to substantiate any that are made. Using third-party evidence such as letters from satisfied customers, called *testimonials,* can enhance source credibility. Finally, pointing out guarantees and warranties that reduce the buyer's risk can assist in establishing source credibility.

Jerry Bauer, Sales Competency Leader and Field Marketing Manager (ret.), Du Pont Company, talks about the importance of questioning and listening during a sales presentation: "Many people think that the key to a successful sales presentation is for a salesperson to be a good talker. At Du Pont, we think the key to sales success is to be a good listener. We emphasize this point in our sales training by saying that salespeople should talk about 20 percent of the time and listen 80 percent of the time. This might be a little stretch, but it encourages salespeople

Exhibit 19–5	*Questioning and listening in sales*

- Remember that you cannot possibly suggest solutions for your clients if you have not listened to what they have said.
- When you are a good listener, you have less chance of dominating the conversation and losing the client's attention.
- You will always learn something valuable from listening. In building customer relationships, this learning process never stops.
- Listening provides feedback on how your sales presentation is going. React to what the prospect is telling you. Clarify the prospect's message when necessary.
- Plan and organize your presentation so you know which questions to ask. Make your questions clear and concise to avoid confusing the client.
- During the presentation, take notes to ensure appropriate follow-up activities or to plan for the next call.

Exhibit 19–6	*Dealing with unreasonable customer concerns and objections*

When a customer lodges a completely unjustified objection, one that is knowingly untrue or unreasonable, salespeople can follow these guidelines for responding.

- Allow customers to retain their dignity. State your position politely.

- Do not argue with a customer. Winning an argument can have detrimental effects on the relationship.

- Appeal to the customer's sense of fair play. Tell the customer you want to do what is right, and try to reach agreement on a course of action to be taken.

- Stand firm if your position is based on facts.

- Do not use company policy as a reason for your position. This tends to invite criticism of the policy.

- If absolutely necessary, be prepared to say no to an unreasonable demand. Agreeing to an unreasonable demand can open the door for more of the same, which will ultimately endanger or ruin the relationship.

to focus on the listening aspect of the job. A parallel skill is the ability to ask good questions. Questioning and listening skills are a focal point of our sales training at Du Pont."

During the sales presentation, the sales rep should expect to resolve buyer concerns before the customer makes a commitment to buy. Buyer concerns, called *objections,* come in many forms ("Your price is too high"; "I don't like the color"; "I am happy with my current supplier") and must be dealt with successfully to make a sale. Objections are a form of *sales resistance,* which also includes unspoken customer concerns. To the extent possible, the salesperson should anticipate these concerns and formulate appropriate customer-oriented responses prior to the sales presentation. Salespeople must understand that questions and concerns are part of the buyer's attempt to make a sound purchase decision; addressing these concerns is an integral element in the sales process.

Many buyer concerns arise when a sales rep has not taken enough time to qualify a buyer and thus calls on a marginal prospect, perhaps one who cannot afford the product or will derive only limited benefits from a purchase. Under any set of circumstances, salespeople should treat buyer questions with patience and respect. Exhibit 19–6 details some ideas on how to deal with customers' unreasonable concerns and objections.

GAINING CUSTOMER COMMITMENT   In most cases, a buyer can choose from among a number of potential sellers; hence sales reps are responsible for gaining customer commitment. This remains true even when the seller is the only available alternative, for a customer may elect to make no purchase at all.

A successful relationship between buyer and seller requires a firm commitment from both parties. Essentially, customer commitment involves an economic transaction between the buyer and the seller (customer buys when salesperson closes a sale) or an agreement between the two parties that moves them toward such a transaction. Some customer commitments take the form of a purchase order. Other examples are agreeing to continue sales negotiations, signing a long-term distribution contract, or accepting the seller's suggestion to maintain specified inventory levels to meet local demand.

To gain a commitment, a professional salesperson must be willing to spend the time necessary to give the customer all the pertinent information. Further, professional salespeople understand that when buyers do not want to make a commitment, it is because they see a commitment as simply not in their best interest at that time.

Relationship-oriented salespeople must walk a fine line between being persuasive and being overly persistent or pushy in an attempt to gain commitment. Buyers do not like being pressured into making decisions they feel are premature, and salespeople must realize that decisions made under pressure are likely to create postpurchase doubts. This can jeopardize the relationship and even lead to its termination.

Enhancing Customer Relationships

The final phase of the sales process shown in Exhibit 19–3 is enhancing customer relationships. The purpose of this step is to ensure that customer expectations are met or exceeded, so that an ongoing, mutually satisfying relationship between the buyer and seller may continue. This stage involves postsale follow-up activities such as entering and expediting customer orders, providing training for the customer's employees, assisting in merchandising and installation activities, and solving customer problems.

Salespeople can enhance the relationship by continuing to provide timely information, alerting the customer to forthcoming product improvements, monitoring customer satisfaction, showing the customer additional ways to use the product, and acting as a consultant to the prospect's business. It is not unusual for salespeople to become confidants of customers, offering opinions when asked on a wide range of topics, some of which are unrelated to the sales offering.

Salespeople should seek feedback from customers rather than waiting for problems to surface. Asking questions such as "How are we doing as your supplier?" is important, as well as follow-up action to continually build value for the customer. Salespeople must never take existing customers' business for granted. The added value to customers can be reinforced through periodic business reviews, where salespeople and perhaps their management meet with customers to analyze sales and profit performance and identify areas for future emphasis.

Sales Management Activities

Sales managers must focus on improving sales operations. Typically, successful sales managers were successful salespeople before being promoted. They usually continue some form of personal selling after becoming managers, perhaps selling to their own set of customers, accompanying salespeople on sales calls, or serving as a member of a selling team. Exhibit 19–7 presents management activities, including developing a sales strategy, designing the sales organization, developing and directing the sales force, and evaluating effectiveness and performance.

These activities require more of sales managers than is expected of salespeople. Whereas salespeople concentrate mainly on relationships with customers, sales managers must work well with customers, salespeople, and many other people in the company to do a good job. Many sales organizations operate with a hierarchy of sales managers in different positions and emphasize different administrative tasks at different sales management levels. Some sales

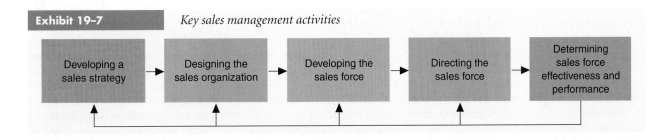

Exhibit 19–7   *Key sales management activities*

Developing a sales strategy → Designing the sales organization → Developing the sales force → Directing the sales force → Determining sales force effectiveness and performance organizations are moving from an administrative to an entrepreneurial sales management approach. An interesting example is presented in "Being Entrepreneurial: An Entrepreneurial Sales Organization."

Developing a Sales Strategy

The starting point for sales management is developing a sales strategy to execute the firm's marketing strategy. A marketing strategy emphasizes the development of a marketing mix to appeal to defined target markets. A sales strategy focuses on how to sell to specific customers within those target markets.[13] Two key elements of a sales strategy are a relationship strategy and a sales channel strategy.

DEVELOPING A RELATIONSHIP STRATEGY
Although there is a clear trend toward relationships, especially in business-to-business selling, different types of relationships are possible. Buyers have different needs and desire to purchase in different ways for different products. Therefore, it is important that the selling firm develop specific **relationship strategies** for specific customer groups. Most firms will need to develop relationship strategies for three to five different customer groups. Exhibit 19–8 presents four basic relationship strategies.

The relationship strategies range from a transaction relationship to a collaborative relationship, with a solutions relationship and partnership relationship in between. As a company moves from transaction to collaborative relationships, the focus changes from just selling products to adding more value; the time frame of the relationship becomes longer; the products become more customized; and the number of customers becomes fewer. Also, the cost to serve customers becomes higher, and there is a greater need for commitment between the buying and selling organization.

DEVELOPING A SALES CHANNEL STRATEGY
A **sales channel strategy** addresses how the company initiates and maintains contact with customers. It may involve the use of a company field sales force, telemarketing, independent sales reps, distributors, the Internet, and/or trade shows.[14] Such a strategy should ensure that customers receive the necessary attention from the sales force. A sales channel strategy must be both effective (get the job done) and efficient (at a reasonable cost).

Exhibit 19–8	*Relationship selling strategies*			
	Transaction Relationship	**Solutions Relationship**	**Partnership Relationship**	**Collaborative Relationship**
Goal	Sell products		⟶	Add value
Time frame	Short		⟶	Long
Offering	Standardized		⟶	Customized
Number of customers	Many		⟶	Few
Cost to serve	Low		⟶	High
Commitment	Low		⟶	High

BEING ENTREPRENEURIAL

An entrepreneurial sales organization

W. L. Gore & Associates makes and sells the key plastic in everything from surgical tubes to guitar strings to winter jackets. No one in the company holds an official title beyond associate, and no one is technically anyone else's boss. All work gets done by teams. Each division generates its own ideas and strategies within this team dynamic. Sales leaders emerge by earning followers. These sales leaders function more as coaches than bosses and spend most of their time guiding, directing, and encouraging salespeople through face-to-face interactions. Sales associates develop their own territories and sales forecasts, and then discuss them with their sales leaders. Salespeople are compensated for customer retention and long-term success, not individual sales in the short term. This entrepreneurial perspective has helped Gore to grow to over $1 billion in annual sales.

Team selling is being used by more firms to better meet the needs of large and important customers. Some firms employ multifunctional sales teams as part of their sales channel strategy.

The key strategic decision is to balance the customer's preference with the cost to serve the customer. In general, lower-cost methods are used in transaction relationships and the highest-cost methods in collaborative relationships. For example, allowing customers to purchase directly from the Internet can be a cost-effective way to serve customers in a transaction relationship. At the other extreme, many companies such as IBM use expensive multifunctional global account teams to serve collaborative relationship customers. Different approaches are typically used for the intermediate solutions and partnership relationship strategies. Thus relationship and sales channel strategies are closely related.

The traditional sales strategy is to have a field salesperson perform all selling activities to all customers. This can be an effective approach, but is typically very costly. Therefore, many sales organizations are looking for ways to replace expensive field selling with less costly sales channels such as telemarketing or the Internet. The potential benefits from this approach are clear. Let's assume the cost of a personal sales call is $250 and the cost of a telephone sales call is $25; each time a personal sales call is replaced by a telephone sales call, the company saves $225. The savings are even greater if the personal sales call is replaced by an electronic interaction over the Internet.

For small customers and many transaction relationships, field selling can be totally replaced by using telemarketing, the Internet, or other sales channels. In other cases, field selling might be integrated with telephone selling or the Internet. For example, prospecting might be performed over the phone or the Internet. Once good prospects are identified, a salesperson makes personal sales calls to establish solutions, partnership, or collaborative relationships. Then various service and reordering activities are performed over the telephone or the Internet. A couple of examples illustrate how companies are doing this:

- Applied Industrial Technologies distributes 1.5 million different industrial products through 380 branch offices with 900 field salespeople and 1,400 inside salespeople. Annual sales are over $1.5 billion. The field salespeople work with customers to determine their needs in order to negotiate pricing agreements. Each customer is then provided a private extranet that can be used to purchase products, check on the status of orders, and get various types of information. Customers can also order or receive information over the phone from the inside salespeople. This approach allows customers to select the sales channel they want for each interaction. And as customers interact more over the telephone and—especially—the Internet, Applied's costs to serve these customers go down.[15]

- Xerox is integrating the Internet into a complicated sales channel strategy that includes retail stores, distributors, and field salespeople. Smaller transaction-type customers typically purchase supplies and smaller systems from retail stores. These customers can now purchase online from the Xerox Web site. If they have questions, the site provides toll-free numbers to reach Xerox service people. Field salespeople establish different types of relationships with larger customers; however, once the relationship is established, many of the customer service functions are performed electronically through private extranets developed for each customer.[16]

These examples represent the types of sales channel strategies being implemented by many companies. The trend is to use different sales channels for different types of customer relationships and to replace more expensive with less expensive sales channels whenever possible.

Although these trends apply to most customers, many companies use various types of **team selling** for their very best customers. These sales teams are typically multifunctional and can include people from different management levels. Normally used in partnership or collaborative relationships with key customers, these approaches are often called *national account, major account,* or *global account* programs. Team selling is an expensive sales channel, but can produce significant sales and profit growth in some situations. The approach used at

Thinking Critically

Select a familiar product that is sold through personal selling by a field sales force:

- What other sales channels might be used in conjunction with personal selling by a field sales force?

- What are the advantages and disadvantages of each sales channel?

- What key challenges face sales managers when multiple sales channels are used?

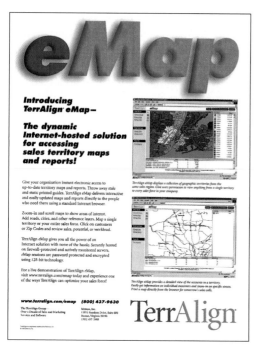

Sales managers can use new technologies to help make better sales organization design decisions. Mapping software such as TerrAlign is useful in designing effective sales territories.

Kele & Associates, a manufacturer of building automation peripherals, is illustrative. The company developed a national account program. Sales teams consisting of members from marketing, sales, accounting, and information technology plan and execute customized strategies to serve the company's best customers. The sales team analyzes each customer's business to identify ways Kele can add more value to the relationship. The strategy has been successful in growing business with these customers.[17]

Designing the Sales Organization

To implement a successful selling strategy, the company must design an appropriate sales organization and adjust it according to subsequent strategic changes. Some key questions to address in designing the sales organization include these:

- Should the sales force be generalists (salespeople who sell the entire product line) or specialists (sell only specific products or only to specific customers)?

- If specialists are used, should they be product specialists, market or customer specialists, or functional (new-business or existing-business) specialists?

- Should tight control be maintained with a centralized sales force, or should sales activities and decision making be moved closer to the customer with a decentralized sales force?

- How much total selling effort is needed to provide adequate sales coverage? How large should the sales force be?

- How should specific customers and geographic areas be assigned to salespeople to form sales territories?

- How should *sales force turnover* (the proportion of salespeople who leave their jobs) be factored into sales organization design decisions?

Companies often use different approaches to address similar situations. For example, Microsoft is responding to the slowdown in corporate technology spending by adding 450 salespeople to develop teams that will focus on securing multiyear software contracts from big customers in 12 industries.[18] Carbis, in contrast, decided to reduce its sales force by 25 percent as a response to reduced capital equipment purchases by oil refineries and chemical companies. The remaining salespeople spend their time only with customers interested in buying immediately.[19]

Developing the Sales Force

There are three main activities in developing the sales force: recruiting, selecting, and training salespeople.

RECRUITING AND SELECTING *Recruiting* is the process of finding prospective job candidates; *selecting* involves choosing the candidates to be hired. Recruiting and selecting salespeople are challenging tasks. Hiring the best sales talent is critical to sales organization success, and the cost of making "bad hires" is high. Although difficult to quantify, general estimates suggest that it costs from 50 to 150 percent of a salesperson's compensation to replace him or her. To increase the likelihood of hiring success, many sales organizations follow a rigorous recruiting and selecting process. This process typically includes planning for recruiting and selection (analyzing the sales job, identifying the key qualifications for the sales job, and developing a job description), locating prospective job candidates, evaluating the candidates (screening applications and résumés, multiple interviews, testing, reference checks, and background investigations), and making a selection decision and job offer.[20]

Information Graphics Group uses a comprehensive recruiting and selection process. It recently made some changes to improve its hiring success. During the interview process,

Sales training is conducted in a variety of ways. A salesperson from a suit manufacturer trains a retail sales staff so they can deliver greater value to customers.

prospective sales job applicants are presented with various scenarios and asked what they would do in the given situation. Those that make it through the interview process spend a full day with two of the company's top salespeople. The job candidates also participate in sales presentation role plays and are taken to lunch to see how they perform in social situations. At the end of this process, the vice president of sales and top salespeople review the performance of each candidate and make the selection decision. These changes have helped Information Graphics improve its hiring of salespeople.[21]

TRAINING   There are two categories of sales training: initial and continual. Newly hired salespeople receive *initial training,* which typically focuses on product knowledge and sales techniques. *Continual training* for all salespeople is becoming more standard as firms attempt to stay current and competitive in an ever-changing environment.

A study of 300 sales executives found that almost 80 percent considered sales training to be very valuable to both new and current salespeople. The topics covered most in sales training programs were product knowledge (88 percent), sales skills (79 percent), computer skills (61 percent), and communication skills (52 percent). Most sales training was performed by in-house trainers using classroom instruction (77 percent), workbooks/manuals (54 percent), public seminars (46 percent), role plays (44 percent), CD-ROM (39 percent), audiocassettes (34 percent), and the Internet (32 percent). Over 40 percent of the sales executives indicated they were considering using some type of online sales training in the near future.[22]

The value of an effective sales training program is illustrated by Aramark Uniform Services. The company has about 300 salespeople, 38 sales managers, and 98 general managers in 212 offices around the country. The sales training manager created a multiphased approach. Phase One is an in-house program for all new hires that covers all aspects of Aramark's business. Phase Two is a consultative selling skills program delivered by a sales training firm. This program builds on Phase One and focuses on six critical selling skills. Phase Three is a Web-based training program that reinforces everything learned in the earlier phases. The effectiveness of the training was evaluated with interesting results. Salespeople who participated in all three phases sold an average of 60 percent more than salespeople participating in only part of the program.[23]

Directing the Sales Force

Directing salespeople to meet goals and objectives consumes much of the typical sales manager's time. These activities include motivation, supervision, and leadership of the sales force.

Many sales organizations offer salespeople a variety of different rewards as incentives. Panasonic promotes its products as rewards for salespeople who work effectively as team players.

MOTIVATION   Sales force motivation involves maximizing the effort salespeople direct toward specific objectives and helping them persist in the face of adversity. Most sales companies offer a variety of financial and nonfinancial rewards in their sales force motivation programs.

Money remains the most sought-after reward among salespeople; but opportunities for promotion, a sense of accomplishment, personal growth opportunities, recognition, and job security are also important. Most companies pay salespeople a combination of salary plus incentives. Incentive pay could include commission, bonuses, or both. Salesperson compensation has been increasing in recent years. Total salesperson compensation levels (salary plus commission plus bonuses) for 2004 were $153,417 for top performers, $92,337 for mid-level performers, and $63,775 for low-level performers. The average for all salespeople was $111,135. This represents a 10–20 percent increase across the different levels from 2001.[24]

Most companies also use sales contests and formal recognition programs to motivate their sales forces. One study found that the most important incentive programs were cash, plaques or awards, recognition dinners, leisure trips or travel, and merchandise or gifts.[25]

SUPERVISION AND LEADERSHIP   Supervision of a sales force deals with direction of day-to-day operations. Computerized **sales automation systems** are one way to assist sales managers in routine supervisory chores such as processing salespeople's call reports, itineraries, and expense reports.

Leadership activities, on the other hand, use more subtle communication to influence salespeople to achieve the company's overall objectives. One leadership function is *coaching*, or providing guidance and feedback on a regular basis to direct salespeople's activities. Another important leadership activity is conducting sales meetings that unite a sales force in an effort to meet common goals.

Many companies use mentoring programs to help develop salespeople. For example, Sealed Air Corporation selects top sales performers to coach new and underperforming salespeople for three-year periods. The mentors spend as much as 20 percent of their time working directly with mentees to help them improve in desired areas. One useful approach is to coach a mentee salesperson throughout the entire sales call process with a difficult customer. Serving as a mentor also helps prepare top salespeople for sales management positions. Over 90 percent of Sealed Air's management has participated in the mentoring program.[26]

The supervision and leadership of salespeople is very much a human endeavor, despite the help of technology. Sales managers routinely deal with human relations problems such as drug and alcohol abuse, sexual harassment, employee job stress, expense-account fraud, and any number of other people problems. Salespeople are no different from any other group of employees when it comes to problem areas.

Jerry Bauer, Sales Competency Leader and Field Marketing Manager, Du Pont Company (ret.), discusses the importance of leadership within the sales function:
"With a constant eye on achieving profitable growth, we are having to change the way we manage our sales forces at Du Pont. Downsizing has led to larger spans of control and more self-managed teams. Mentoring and networking are becoming more and more important. We are looking for leaders who can provide a compelling vision. We want sales leaders who can build self-esteem, emotional involvement, and the knowledge, skills, and abilities of their team, and also instill a sense of excitement. You might say we are moving from 'sales management' to 'strategic leadership.' "

Evaluating Performance and Effectiveness

Sales managers must establish standards by which performance and effectiveness are measured, evaluate performance and effectiveness against these standards, and then take appropriate follow-up action. *Salesperson performance* refers to how well individual sales people meet job expectations. An evaluation of *sales force effectiveness* is in fact an assessment of the entire sales organization. Factors within and outside the sales organization, such as product quality or competitors, can also influence sales force effectiveness.

SETTING STANDARDS   Standards by which performance and effectiveness are assessed usually relate to quantitative outcomes, or *quotas,* such as total sales volume, gross margin, market share, number of new accounts added, and accounts retained. These quotas typically are based on a forecast developed at least in part by the sales manager.

Sales managers must also get the job done within a specified budget. Given the high costs of personal selling, achieving objectives within budget constraints is a constant challenge. Travel-related costs, such as lodging and meals, continue to climb, along with salespeople's pay levels.

It is becoming increasingly difficult to raise selling price only because of increasing sales costs. Thus, to maintain favorable sales-expense-to-sales-revenue ratios, most salespeople are asked to sell more each year, whether economic conditions are favorable or not.

EVALUATING PERFORMANCE   To evaluate individual salesperson performance, sales managers may take a behavior-based perspective, an outcome-based perspective, or a combination of the two. A *behavior-based perspective* defines the sales behaviors expected, such as how many sales calls to make or which sales presentation tactics to use. The salesperson is then evaluated on how well he or she executes the behaviors. An *outcome-based perspective* focuses on the results of sales behavior, such as total sales volume. As relationship selling spreads, the behavior-based perspective is gaining more acceptance.

ANALYZING EFFECTIVENESS   Managers may analyze sales, costs, profitability, and productivity to evaluate the effectiveness of the sales organization. They compare figures of one year with those of the previous year to gauge progress. Managers also compare their own sales force effectiveness with that of competitors, if possible. For example, in the packaged-grocery business, market share data by brand are readily available, and comparisons with key competitors are commonplace.

A simple example of sales force productivity analysis is shown in Exhibit 19–9. Note that District 2 is tied for the lead with District 4 in total sales volume. Also, the sales per salesperson and expenses per salesperson figures in District 2 compare favorably with the other districts. Yet the number of sales calls made per salesperson is low. This may explain why expenses are low, but it may also suggest that salespeople in District 2 may not be providing adequate contact with their customers.

Exhibit 19–9   *Example of a sales force effectiveness evaluation*

	District 1	District 2	District 3	District 4
Sales	$10,000,000	$12,000,000	$10,000,000	$12,000,000
Selling expenses	$ 1,000,000	$ 1,200,000	$ 1,500,000	$ 1,500,000
Sales calls	5,000	4,500	4,500	6,000
Proposals	100	105	120	120
Number of salespeople	10	15	10	15
Sales per salesperson	$ 1,000,000	$ 800,000	$ 1,000,000	$ 800,000
Expenses per salesperson	$ 100,000	$ 80,000	$ 150,000	$ 100,000
Calls per salesperson	500	300	450	400

Numbers, then, do not tell the whole story; analysis of the numbers can, however, suggest areas worth further investigation by the sales manager. By combining quantitative analysis with personal observation, information from customers, and review with salespeople, sales managers can evaluate the effectiveness of their sales forces.

Ethical and Legal Issues in Personal Selling

Because personal selling activities are highly visible, ethical and legal issues are extremely important for salespeople and sales managers. In building trust-based customer relationships, ethical behavior is even more critical. Major professional groups such as Sales and Marketing Executives International, the American Marketing Association, and the Direct Selling Association have adopted strict codes of ethics for salespeople, as have many companies. An example is shown in Exhibit 19–10.

Sales managers must take responsibility for the proper behavior of their salespeople, and they must also lead by example. They must know the laws related to buyer–seller interactions, the gathering of competitive information, and the management of personnel.

To be on the safe side, salespeople should be honest in their dealings with customers and be informed of relevant laws governing their business situation. All salespeople are subject to some form of contract law, which regulates transactions. Purchase orders are binding contracts, as are oral commitments made by a salesperson. An extensive review of 50 years of legal cases revealed that salespeople can, by inappropriate oral statements, create undesirable legal obligations for their firms. Problems include creation of unintended warranties, understatement of warning messages, disparagement of competitors' offerings without substantiation, misrepresentation of company offerings, and illegal interference with business relationships.[27]

Exhibit 19–11 presents some specific sales behaviors deemed unethical by buyers. Salespeople interested in developing lasting relationships with their customers should refrain from those behaviors; research suggests that buyers will go out of their way to avoid doing business with salespeople they see as unethical.[28]

There are also numerous ethical and legal issues relevant to relationships between sales managers and salespeople. For example, the Civil Rights Act of 1964 prohibits discrimination based on age, race, color, religion, sex, or national origin. The act has implications for recruiting and selecting salespeople and evaluating and rewarding their performance. The Americans with Disabilities Act of 1992 also affects recruiting and other sales management functions, as do guidelines for minimizing sexual harassment issued by the Equal Employment Opportunity Commission.

This is only a brief discussion of the ethical and legal consequences of marketers' actions. Given the pressure on the sales function to generate revenue, it is particularly im-

---

| **Exhibit 19–10** | *Code of ethics for professional salespeople* |

As a Certified Professional Salesperson, I pledge to the following people and organizations:

The Customer. In all customer relationships, I pledge to

- Maintain honesty and integrity in my relationships with customers and prospective customers.
- Accurately represent my product or service in order to place the customer or prospective customer in a position to make a decision consistent with the principle of mutuality of benefit and profit to the buyer and seller.
- Keep abreast of all pertinent information that would assist my customers in achieving their goals as they relate to my product(s) or service(s).

The Company. In relationships with my employer, coworkers, and other parties whom I represent, I will

- Use their resources that are at my disposal for legitimate business purposes only.
- Respect and protect proprietary and confidential information entrusted to me by my company.

The Competition. Regarding those with whom I compete in the marketplace, I promise

- To obtain competitive information only through legal and ethical methods.
- To portray my competitors and their products and services only in a manner that is honest, that is truthful, and that reflects accurate information that can be or has been substantiated.

| **Exhibit 19-11** | *Unethical sales behaviors* |

Research indicates sales behaviors that are unethical in the eyes of customers:

- Exaggerates the features and benefits of his/her products/services.
- Lies about availability to make a sale.
- Lies about the competition to make a sale.
- Sells products/services people don't need.
- Is interested only in own interests, not the clients'.
- Gives answers when doesn't really know the answers.
- Falsifies product testimonials.
- Passes the blame for something he/she did onto someone else.

- Poses as a market researcher when conducting telephone sales.
- Misrepresents guarantees/warranties.
- Makes oral promises that are not legally binding.
- Does not offer information about an upcoming sale that will include merchandise the customer is planning to buy.
- Accepts favors from customers so the seller will feel obliged to bend the rules/policies of the seller's company.
- Sells dangerous or hazardous products.

portant for sales managers to know and adhere to the laws of the marketplace and the workplace. They should be models, provide adequate training, and monitor, reinforce, and direct sales personnel. In developing trust-based relationships with customers, marketers should follow these guidelines not just because of laws or because it's the right thing to do—but because it is also a sound business practice.

Personal Selling and Sales Management in the Future

Changes in the business environment are having an important effect on personal selling and sales management. Salespeople and sales managers will need different skills to be successful in the future. Two studies by MOHR Development suggest the competencies needed by salespeople and sales managers in the future.[29] Salesperson competencies involve the ability to

1. Align customers' strategic objectives with your company's so both gain.
2. Go beyond product needs to assess business potential and add value to the relationship.
3. Understand the financial impact of the decisions made by your company and the client's organization.
4. Organize company resources to build customer-focused relationships.
5. Develop consultative problem solving and a willingness to change.
6. Establish a vision of a committed customer–supplier relationship.
7. Utilize self-appraisal and continuous learning by requesting feedback from customers, colleagues, and managers.

Sales manager competencies involve the ability to

1. Provide strategic vision.
2. Organize company resources by leveraging relationships.
3. Influence company strategy.
4. Coach effectively.
5. Diagnose performance.
6. Select high-potential salespeople.
7. Leverage technology.
8. Demonstrate personal selling effectiveness.

These competencies indicate what it will take to succeed in the future. Notice the focus on developing relationships with customers by salespeople and developing relationships with salespeople by sales managers. Both salespeople and sales managers must possess communication and "people" skills as well as understand the strategic and financial aspects of business. And the need to understand and be able to use technology effectively will be extremely important.

Summary

1. **Understand the role and importance of personal selling in the marketing communications mix.** Personal selling is a valuable part of the promotion mix and the overall marketing effort of many companies. Salespeople fulfill the extremely important role of generating revenue. In today's competitive environment, paying close attention to customer needs and expectations is necessary, and personal selling can help in this endeavor. Salespeople provide crucial marketplace information to their companies, which may further improve the marketing effort.

2. **See how the key steps in personal selling depend on a relationship perspective.** The sales process involves three steps: initiating, developing, and enhancing customer relationships. To initiate customer relationships, salespeople must first locate qualified potential customers through prospecting. They must then plan the initial sales call and the way to approach the customer.

   In developing customer relationships, salespeople must be able to deliver effective sales presentations. During a sales call, it is extremely important that the salesperson use questioning and listening skills to attend to all of the customer's requirements and to gain a commitment from the customer.

   To enhance relationships with customers, salespeople must be customer-oriented and continue to meet or exceed customer expectations. Relationship selling also requires that salespeople formulate and implement different strategies for different customers and that they minimize wasted time in each sales call.

   To be successful in relationship selling, salespeople gain the trust of their customers. To build trust, salespeople should be customer-oriented, honest, dependable, competent, and likable.

3. **Identify the similarities and differences in the job responsibilities of salespeople and sales managers.** Along with their other job duties, sales managers are usually involved in personal selling to some degree. Using an athletic team analogy, the salespeople are the players, and the sales manager is the coach. The sales manager must do everything necessary to field a competitive sales team year after year, including developing the team strategy. Salespeople concentrate on taking care of their customers; sales managers must work not only with customers, but also with others in the company to ensure success.

4. **Describe the key activities in sales management.** The key job activities of sales managers are developing a sales strategy, designing the sales organization, developing the sales force, directing the sales force, and evaluating performance and effectiveness. Sales managers must recruit and select salespeople and provide them with sufficient resources to be effective. Most sales managers play an active role in training their salespeople. They must also help motivate salespeople to reach their full potential and evaluate their performance. Sales managers must accomplish all these activities in a rapidly changing environment, which means they may need to adapt sales strategies to remain competitive.

5. **Appreciate important ethical issues faced by salespeople and sales managers.** Salespeople can develop trust with their customers by avoiding a range of unethical sales behaviors. Examples are lying, selling customers products they do not need, withholding information, and selling dangerous products.

   Sales managers lead by example. They must not abuse the power of their position in dealing with their employees. Sales managers must also be prepared to deal with human relations issues such as drug abuse, sexual harassment, and employee job stress. Ignoring such issues would be less than ethical.

Understanding Marketing Terms and Concepts

Thinking about Marketing

1. Discuss the three major roles salespeople play in the overall marketing effort.

2. How are the roles of sales support salespeople different from those of new-business salespeople?

3. Give several examples of different types of direct-to-consumer salespeople.

4. To practice relationship selling, salespeople must be able to cultivate the trust of their customers. What attributes should salespeople have to cultivate the trust of their customers?

5. The first step in the sales process is to initiate customer relationships. Discuss the three primary activities during this initial step.

6. Review "Using Technology: Identifying the Best Prospects." What ideas do you have to use technology to improve prospecting by salespeople?

7. How important is ethical behavior by salespeople in dealing with customers? Think about trust-building salesperson attributes, and consult Exhibits 19–3 and 19–10 before completing your answer.

8. Consult "Being Entrepreneurial: An Entrepreneurial Sales Organization." What are the most entrepreneurial aspects of the W. L. Gore sales organization?

9. Describe the key responsibilities of sales managers in each of the five activity areas shown in Exhibit 19–7.

10. How are the recruitment and selection of salespeople related to designing the sales force?

Applying Marketing Skills

1. Review the unethical sales behaviors in Exhibit 19–11. Can you recall from your own experiences as a consumer examples of any of those behaviors? In those instances, did you eventually come to trust the salesperson? Did you make purchases? What kind of sales behavior could you suggest for salespeople who wish to earn the trust of their customers?

2. When a commitment is not readily forthcoming from a prospect, some salespeople might use a "buy now" method to get the sale, which gives the buyer a good reason to make an immediate purchase. For example, the salesperson might suggest that the buyer can avoid a planned price increase by placing an immediate order. If no such price increase is actually planned, has the salesperson acted unethically? What if the buyer has been promising to place an order for months, but never has, and now seems to be stalling?

3. Visit a retail store with the aim of getting some details about a product you plan to buy at some future date. Evaluate the listening skills of the salesperson you encounter. Is the salesperson a good listener or not? How was the salesperson's credibility affected by his or her listening skills?

Using the www in Marketing

Activity One Visit the Pfizer Web site (*http://www.pfizer.com*):

1. What are the requirements to become a sales representative for Pfizer?

2. What mergers have been completed by Pfizer? How do these mergers impact personal selling and sales management at Pfizer?

3. How is Pfizer involved in e-commerce? Who can purchase what products from this site?

Activity Two Review the Web site *www.sales force.com*. You can browse the site to get basic information or get a demonstration of the product.

1. What sales tools are available to help salespeople develop relationships with customers?

2. How could sales managers use this site to help them in training salespeople?

3. How could this site be improved?

Making Marketing Decisions

Case 19-1 *Saturn: Taking a STEP to Equip Its Sales Force*

In the late 1980s, the American automobile industry was struggling. Consumers were unhappy with product quality, pricing, advertising, and inane industry sales practices. Foreign automakers were continuing to build market share at the expense of domestic manufacturers. In this environment, General Motors departed from tradition and offered a "different kind of car from a different kind of company." The Saturn success story had begun.

By 1993 Saturn had become a force to be reckoned with. Sales were soaring. Industry analysts cited several reasons for Saturn's rise to prominence: no-haggle pricing, customer-oriented selling, elimination of confusing rebates, and basically, a good car for a reasonable price. Saturn continuously ranks high, and often number one, in the J. D. Power Sales Satisfaction (SSI) and Customer Service Satisfaction (CSI) evaluations in the automobile industry.

In the face of intensified competition, Saturn's sales force has helped to sustain the company's edge in the marketplace. A key element in equipping the sales force is the Saturn Training and Education Partnership, or STEP, a comprehensive program designed to develop job skills.

The STEP program reinforces five key values Saturn wants to instill in all facets of its operations: customer enthusiasm, excellence, teamwork, trust and respect, and constant improvement.

To reinforce these values in sales training, Saturn established the objectives for STEP long before its first dealership opened. Sales managers refined the program with salespeople from dealers who were interested in becoming Saturn dealers, and then with salespeople who had been hired to staff the still-unopened Saturn outlets.

The STEP program requires salespeople to abandon the conventional way of selling cars, which often involves high-pressure, manipulative sales techniques. Instead, Saturn's sales philosophy casts the salesperson in a consultative role to build customer enthusiasm with six key elements: listening to the customer; creating an environment of mutual trust; exceeding customer expectations; creating a "win–win" culture; following up to ensure that customer expectations are met; and constantly improving customer perceptions of quality.

The sales training consists of self-study modules and seminars. The self-study portion, which takes about 11 hours to complete, features learning activities based on short reading assignments and video vignettes. The short assignments can easily be completed one at a time, allowing training to be interspersed with other job activities.

Saturn measures the effectiveness of its training in three ways. For each module, trainees provide a written evaluation of materials, methods, and trainers. Each module is followed by a written test. Sixty days later, trainees are evaluated in a performance check that requires demonstration of the skills developed in training.

Questions

1. What is your assessment of the Saturn STEP program?

2. Would previous sales experience be an asset to a Saturn job candidate? If so, what kind of experience?

3. How would Saturn's recruiting, selection, motivation, and evaluation of sales performance likely differ from that of a high-volume, conventional automobile dealer's sales operation?

4. How does the Saturn sales process compare to your experience in buying a car?

Case 19-2 *Edward Jones: Building Customer Relationships*

Edward Jones operates the country's largest network of brokerage offices, over 10,000. John W. Bachmann has been managing partner for over 22 years and is responsible for much of the company's growth. He has done it very differently than other brokerage firms.

Brokers at Edward Jones sell an array of financial products to include mutual funds, life insurance and annuities, credit cards, and home loans. They receive 40 percent of all commissions, and this is made clear to all clients. There are no outlandish salaries or bonuses.

The company only does a little investment banking, so there is little chance for conflicts of interest between the investment banking and brokerage operations. Research analysts are not allowed to own stock in the companies they cover. This removes another potential conflict of interest. There are also no call centers to market financial products aggressively to customers, and there is little emphasis on margin trading.

Bachmann has helped build a company based on strong relationships with employees and customers.

The company started in rural and small towns, but has moved successfully into most of the major metropolitan areas in the United States, as well as into Canada and Great Britain. The business is built on careful planning based on setting clear objectives at the top, then creating a supportive environment where brokers can grow and be successful.

The approach to customers is similar. Investment representatives focus on building one-to-one relationships with clients, offering personalized attention and investment advice. The company believes in a long-term philosophy toward investments and seeks clients that share this philosophy. In contrast to many financial services companies, Edward Jones discourages clients from frequent trading and does not offer online trading. The investment representatives typically meet with clients in an Edward Jones office to develop a personal relationship and plan a long-term investment strategy. This personal approach helps the representatives know their clients and understand their financial needs so they can provide the best investment advice. According to Bachmann: "The market we serve values relationships. We do not want to encourage you to gamble."

Questions

1. Why do you think Edward Jones has been so successful?

2. What could competitors do to take business from Edward Jones?

3. Do you think Edward Jones should offer online trading? Why or why not?

4. What changes would you suggest to increase the growth of Edward Jones in the future?

Chapter Twenty

DIRECT MARKETING COMMUNICATIONS

20

After studying this chapter, you should be able to

1 Understand the objectives of direct marketing communications, and describe their distinguishing characteristics.

2 Discuss the factors driving the growth in direct marketing communications.

3 Understand traditional direct marketing communications techniques such as direct mail, broadcast and print media, and telemarketing.

4 Recall examples of the use of technology such as electronic media in direct marketing communications.

5 Understand some of the ethical and legal issues facing marketers who use direct marketing communications.

Skechers

Skechers USA, Inc., is a global powerhouse in the lifestyle footwear industry, doing business in 100 countries, including Australia, Chile, China, India, and Japan. Skechers has always had popular products, with current offerings in 20 product lines with 200 styles. A multichannel international marketer, Skechers sells through a wide variety of outlets, including department stores, specialty and athletic stores, the Internet, and company-owned stores. In the United States Skechers operates 125 of its own stores. Outside the United States the company goes to market through 30 global distributors and has 22 company-owned stores.

Founded in 1992, Skechers built its reputation with trendy footwear products and cutting-edge print and television advertising. As the company moved into its second decade in business, diversification became a key ingredient in Skechers's success.

Product lines were added to appeal to new demographic segments. From utility-styled boots, Skechers's product lines grew to include dress, casual, dressy casual, and high-fashion footwear. Demographic groups of interest were added as well, with Skechers now appealing to juniors, women of all ages, working men in industrial settings and in white-collar settings, and automobile driving enthusiasts.

With the addition of new products and new customer segments, Skechers was also diversifying its channels of distribution and its marketing communications efforts. In particular, the Internet was becoming a more popular channel for Skechers, and its many consumers in its diversified customer base shared a common interest in buying on the Internet and using e-mail for daily communication. Accordingly, Skechers began experimenting with e-mail marketing campaigns to replace its hard-copy catalog mailings. By 2004 e-mail had become an established means of marketing communications for Skechers.

Before 2004 Skechers did not have the ability to precisely measure the results of e-mail campaigns. After upgrading its information technology infrastructure and applications, Skechers can track its e-mail campaigns, and the results have been impressive. In one e-mail campaign the goal was to increase traffic in the 125 company-owned U.S. stores and to increase sales volume on the company Web e-commerce site. Sales were 25 percent higher than in previous e-mail efforts, and Skechers was off and running with e-mail marketing. Today the Skechers database has 800,000 consumers who registered at the company Web site, at points of sale, or through product registration cards. Skechers contacts these consumers only after they have granted the company the right to do so. Skechers's use of e-mail illustrates that relevant, targeted marketing communications can give a company a competitive advantage and that the proper marketing communications mix may well include database-enabled direct communications with individual consumers.

Avon is best known for direct selling through several hundred thousand sales representatives. The company also uses a variety of direct marketing communications methods, including direct-response magazine ads and telemarketing, as part of its worldwide integrated marketing communications effort.

In Chapter 16 we saw that most marketers use more than one way to communicate with their target markets. These multiple means of reaching target markets are sometimes developed into integrated marketing communications (IMC) programs. At the heart of many of these programs lie direct marketing communications. This chapter discusses the role and characteristics of direct marketing communications and examines the reasons for their growth. Direct marketing communications (DMC) methods are discussed, including a variety of interactive methods such as mail, video, telephone, salesperson, and computer. The chapter concludes with a discussion of ethical and legal issues in direct marketing communications.

The Role of Direct Marketing Communications

Direct marketing communications have two primary objectives. The first is to establish relationships by soliciting a direct and immediate response from prospects or customers. Customer response could be a purchase, a request for additional information from the marketer, or a reply that furnishes data related to the customer's desires and interests. The second, and increasingly important, objective of DMC is to maintain and enhance customer relationships, whether those relationships have been established by direct marketing communications or by some other means.

Direct marketing communications techniques are used to reach both individual consumers and businesses. For example, in the United States, direct marketing generates almost $2.2 trillion in annual sales split roughly 54 percent to consumers and 46 percent to business markets.[1] In business-to-business markets, direct marketing is extensively used for business services, chemicals and allied products, real estate, and wholesaling. The most important tools in business-to-business direct marketing from a sales volume perspective are telephone marketing and direct mail, which account for almost 70 percent of all sales.[2] Newspaper, television, radio, and **interactive marketing** also are used in business-to-business direct marketing. Interactive marketing, also referred to as *online direct marketing*, is that portion of electronic business, such as marketing on the Internet, that meets the definition of direct marketing communications given in Chapter 16: communicating directly with target customers to encourage response. It is important to note that not all electronic marketing involves online direct marketing.

Popular products bought by consumers via direct marketing include software, computers, recorded music, books, personal gift items, home decorating products, and clothing. In consumer markets, the largest sales generators are telephone marketing, direct mail, newspaper, and television.[3] Interactive marketing is still relatively small from a sales volume point of view but is growing more rapidly than most other forms of direct marketing to ultimate consumers.

Direct marketing can be an important ingredient in integrated communications strategies. For example, Chrysler Group used direct marketing communications along with personal selling, advertising, and public relations to promote the introduction of its Charger muscle car in 2005. Chrysler targeted 100,000 "handraisers"—potential customers who had signed up to receive more information about the Charger at auto shows or on the company's Web site.[4] Chrysler, like General Motors, Ford, Lexus, and other carmakers, is increasing its use of direct marketing as an integral part of integrated marketing communications campaigns.

In the business-to-business area, Hewlett-Packard uses direct marketing in conjunction with other forms of marketing communications such as mass media advertising, personal selling, sales promotion (trade shows), and public relations to sell computers. Sales by telephone make up an especially important part of Hewlett-Packard's direct marketing efforts.

Characteristics of Direct Marketing Communications

Several characteristics distinguish direct marketing from other marketing communications methods. First, direct marketing targets a carefully selected audience, as opposed to a mass audience. Second, it typically involves two-way communication; direct responses from customers make it interactive. Finally, direct-response results are quite measurable—marketers can determine what works.

Customer Databases

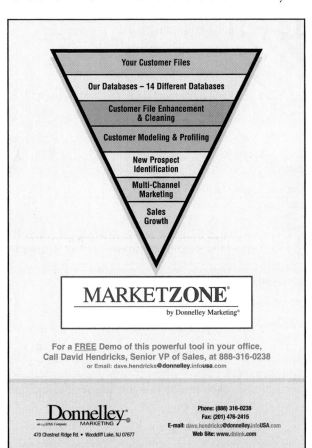

Marketers are increasingly taking advantage of technological advances in their direct marketing programs. Donnelley Marketing fits nicely with this movement by providing computerized databases and related services to facilitate direct marketing.

A key element of direct marketing communications is the use of a list or database of current or potential customers. **Lists** of names and addresses may also provide telephone numbers and data on demographics, lifestyles, brand and media preferences, and consumption patterns. Business-to-business lists may also indicate company characteristics such as annual sales, key decision makers, credit and purchasing history, and current suppliers. Lists can be developed from customer transaction records, newspapers, trade show registration, or other sources that identify specific groups of customers or prospects. Rather than compiling its own lists, a company can purchase (in some cases), rent, reproduce, or use a list on a one-time basis.

Lists, often in the form of sophisticated computerized databases, allow direct marketers to focus on a precisely defined target market, as opposed to using mass-market appeals. **Database marketing,** or the use of computer database technologies to design, create, and manage customer lists, has become commonplace.[5] For an illustration of how databases aid in marketing communications, see Exhibit 20–1.

Customer databases can be quite large. For example, list provider Focus USA offers a database of 19 million small businesses containing e-mail addresses, fax numbers, company type, number of employees, and annual sales information.[6] Consumer databases are often larger than business customer databases. MKTG Services offers a database of 1.5 million consumers who have relocated their residences within the past 90 days. Marketers of a wide variety of products and services ranging from gardening supplies to financial services use this list to reach this market.[7]

Companies use database information to deliver marketing communications tailored to the unique needs of a target audience. Women's clothing retailer J. Crew uses its database to personalize appeals to individual consumers, especially those who visit the company's Web site but do not make a purchase online, from a catalog, or in one of the company's 170 retail stores. According to a J. Crew executive, the company understands the preferences of current buyers and personalizes its marketing appeals accordingly. By tracking nonbuyers' interactions online, the company plans to improve its rate of converting these customers to active buyers.[8] Industry experts consistently point out that personalizing appeals to individual consumers in a database can generate significantly better results for marketers. For more on how databases are used in direct marketing communications, see "Using Technology: Databases Are Not Just for Big Businesses."

Exhibit 20-1 *Customer databases aid communications planning, integration, and execution*

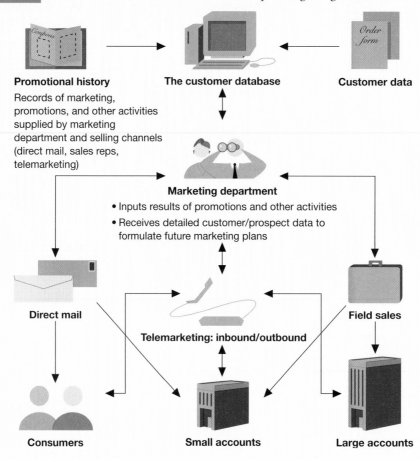

Promotional history
Records of marketing, promotions, and other activities supplied by marketing department and selling channels (direct mail, sales reps, telemarketing)

The customer database

Customer data

Marketing department
• Inputs results of promotions and other activities
• Receives detailed customer/prospect data to formulate future marketing plans

Direct mail

Telemarketing: inbound/outbound

Field sales

Consumers

Small accounts

Large accounts

Immediate-Response Orientation

Direct marketing communications often have deadlines for action and offer special incentives for taking immediate action. An example would be a direct-mail piece from a bank saying, "Call now for superlow 6 percent mortgages. Free property survey. Offer expires June 1." Other marketing communications methods are not typically oriented toward gaining an immediate response from prospects and customers. Publicity, for example, and many forms of advertising are aimed more at achieving results over time. Personal selling seeks a response, but salespeople typically cultivate customers for some time.

USING TECHNOLOGY

Databases Are Not Just for Big Businesses

Small businesses are increasingly reaping the benefits of database-driven marketing efforts. Bob Devaney, owner of three Drycleaning by Dorothy stores in Boston, uses weekly e-mail messages to reach his customers. Before the weekly e-mail, Devaney says he never had time to properly promote his business: "I was running around like a headless chicken, fixing machines and talking to customers." Beginning in 2001, Devaney left newspaper ads with coupons behind and began using e-mail. By 2005 his e-mail list had grown to 3,000, and his list is growing by 25 to 30 names per week. Current customers often forward his e-mail special deals to friends and relatives, and currently registered customers can easily refer a prospective customer via a hot link in the e-mail message.

Devaney uses the e-mail promotions to solidify relationships with existing customers and bring in new customers. His customers look forward to the mailings, and only three have unsubscribed in four years. Devaney is completely sold on e-mail, commenting, "I've been in marketing for 25 years, and e-mail is by far the best thing we've ever done. I can contact up to 5,000 addresses for $50 a month. I can envision someday not doing any other promotion."

Don Condit
President
Condit Communications

"The ability to measure results precisely is always a key advantage of direct marketing communications, particularly when compared to space advertising. For business-to-business clients in intensely competitive markets, another huge advantage is the ability to act covertly. To assess the scope and intent of our campaigns, competitors must rely on reports from field salespeople, a method that can be slow and inaccurate."

Don Condit, President of Condit Communications in Fort Collins, Colorado, specializes in business-to-business marketing communications. Before founding his own company, Don worked with Poppe Tyson Advertising in New York for 10 years as a senior copywriter and as an account supervisor. Don's work has won him honors,

including the American Marketing Association's coveted Gold Effie, for having the year's most successful marketing program. Don, a graduate of Hamilton College in New York, comments here on the advantages of direct marketing communications.

Measurable Action Objectives

Although all marketing communications should try to achieve measurable results, their objectives are generally not as action-specific as those of direct marketing. For instance, an advertising campaign for a new brand may have the goal of achieving brand awareness among 65 percent of its target audience. In DMC, however, marketers usually set much more specific action objectives, such as a purchase or a request for information. Achievement of such objectives can then be measured by calculating the number of purchases or requests for information that result from the campaign.

Action objectives allow the marketer to test several different forms of direct marketing communication. The marketer can then adjust the message and the medium to achieve optimum results. For example, when KinderCare Learning Centers first began using direct marketing, there was no difference in its mailings from one household to the next. By testing several different formats and incentives to entice potential customers into enrolling their children into various child care, reading, and general tutoring programs, KinderCare found an effective combination of appeals to match the desired services of different market segments. Now, when parents visit a KinderCare location, about 90 percent fill out a guest form that allows highly effective postvisit follow-up from KinderCare, with a resulting 4–5 percent increase in new business gained.[9]

The Growth of Direct Marketing Communications   Direct marketing communications have become a larger part of the total marketing communications picture in recent years. From 2002 to 2007, direct marketing is forecast to increase in efficiency with annual sales growing steadily at more than 9 percent.[10]

Total direct marketing expenditures will reach an estimated $255 billion by 2007, split fairly evenly between business and consumer markets. Expenditures on direct marketing are growing at a healthy rate, with the 2002–2007 growth rate expected to be 12 percent.[11] In the remainder of this section we will examine the global growth of DMC and some of the catalysts behind the growth.

Global Direct Marketing Communications

Direct marketing communications are becoming more important in global marketing efforts. This has been true for U.S.-based marketers who have faced a fairly saturated domestic market for several years. It is becoming more commonplace for direct marketers outside the United States to expand their operations, including entry into the U.S. market. Even though the U.S. market may be crowded in some product categories, unique international offerings have a good chance of success in the United States. For example, the British Tourist Authority used a direct mail campaign to target 750,000 senior citizens in

Expansion into global markets is one reason for the growth of direct marketing communications. For more than three decades, Johnson & Hayward, Inc., has been involved in direct marketing communications on a global basis.

the United States, drawing 8,000 direct responses and more than 28,000 Web site hits. The 4 percent response rate was more than double the objective for the campaign and more than paid for itself with increased tourism to the United Kingdom.[12]

Asia has been a particularly attractive region for direct marketing efforts. Neiman Marcus, Patagonia, Eddie Bauer, J. Crew, and Victoria's Secret have been highly successful with their catalogs in Japan, Singapore, and Hong Kong. The forecast growth in direct marketing expenditures in Asia and the Pacific Rim outpaces the expected 12 percent annual growth rate in the United States during the 2002–2007 period by significant margins. Taiwan, South Korea, Hong Kong, Malaysia, and the Philippines are forecasting annual growth rates of 15 percent or higher. Australia and Thailand expect direct marketing to grow at approximately 10 percent per year through 2005. Only Japan shows moderate direct marketing expenditures growth in the region, with a forecast 5 percent per year.[13]

The European nations' annual growth in direct marketing expenditures exceeds that of the United States, led by Ireland at 19 percent. Germany, Italy, the Netherlands, Austria, Spain, and France are growing at approximately 10 percent annually. Latin America is also a growth area. Even Argentina, with its bruised economy, will almost match the United States in annual growth of direct marketing expenditures.[14]

One factor that constrains the growth of direct marketing in Europe is the European Union's strict consumer privacy rules. These rules, discussed in more detail near the end of the chapter, require marketers to get permission in advance for any use of customer financial information in direct marketing campaigns. For example, building a database that includes customer income levels is forbidden without explicit advance consent of all customers in the database. For those engaged in direct marketing in Europe, it is advisable to carefully examine the quality of any database or mailing list before using it, and to buy such lists from in-country providers with established reputations for providing high quality.[15]

Growth Catalysts

The increase in customized products, fragmented markets, and product price sensitivity; shrinking audiences for network television and newspapers; and emphasis on immediate sales all contribute to the expansion of direct marketing communications. Marketers are now forced to identify their target markets more specifically in order to reach them more effectively.

Other forces also contribute to the growth of direct marketing communications. Changes in lifestyles create a need for convenient, time-saving, and dependable ways to shop. Two-worker families have more discretionary income but less time. These conditions make shopping at home, at one's leisure, very appealing. The ease of communication between buyer and seller, combined with the increased use of credit cards and acceptable products, makes direct purchasing an attractive alternative for many consumers.

A major reason for the growth in direct marketing communications has been advancing technology, which allows more precise construction and manipulation of customer databases. **Predictive modeling** on a database allows the marketer to reach a desired target more effectively, thus avoiding waste and enhancing profits. Sophisticated computerized statistical techniques known as *neural networks* can calculate weights for customer characteristics such as age, income, education, or time on the job. Using artificial intelligence, neural networks "learn" which targets are more likely to respond by examining data examples and calculating the relationships between predictor characteristics and known results.

Direct Marketing Communications Techniques

Direct marketing communications include direct mail and some forms of broadcast advertising, such as infomercials and direct-response television and radio advertising. Direct-response advertising appears in newspapers and magazines as well. Other techniques include telemarketing and supplementary electronic media.

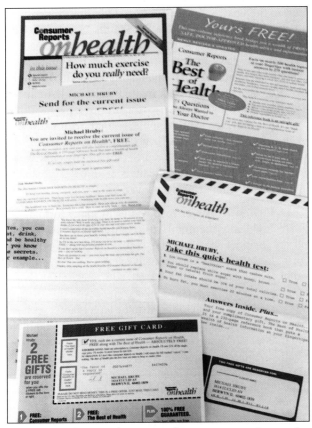

Direct mail can be a simple one-piece flyer or a more sophisticated multiple-piece mailer. In this case, *Consumer Reports* uses a multipiece mailer to sell subscriptions for its magazine.

Direct Mail

Direct mail includes any form of direct-response advertising addressed to prospects through public or private delivery services. It can range in complexity from a simple flyer to a package including a letter, multipage brochure, CD, and response card. The direct-mail response rate per thousand people reached trails only telephone marketing, with both small companies and industry giants such as IBM, General Motors, Lockheed, and American Express using direct mail. Advantages and disadvantages of direct mail are summarized in Exhibit 20–2.

Direct mail has considerable flexibility in its self-contained message and the form used to convey it. A message could be written on a postcard or conveyed by CD. Moreover, direct mail can appeal to a narrow audience and be designed to suit a prospect's specific needs. Midwest Corvette Specialties, for example, can reach Corvette owners through its parts magazine. Working from a list of Corvette owners, the company avoids advertising to consumers who have no interest in its products.

Don Condit, President of Condit Communications, offers these thoughts on what makes effective direct mail: "In direct mail we often search for gimmicks to make a piece of mail resemble a personal letter written for one reader. But the best device of all is copy that truly speaks to each reader personally—about relevant issues with a voice that is direct, honest, and disarming. By splitting copy, we can tailor each piece of mail for each audience segment and achieve the most important direct-mail success of all—readership."

The marketer can achieve nearly 100 percent coverage of the intended target market with direct mail, with fewer distractions than in some other media. For example, television or radio commercials are broadcast along with other ads and the regular programming. And magazine ads are juxtaposed with articles and other ads. A direct-mail piece, however, is typically viewed with less competition.

Exhibit 20–2	*Advantages and disadvantages of direct mail*	
	Advantages	**Disadvantages**
	• Self-contained message.	• High cost per exposure.
	• Flexibility in message content and form of delivery.	• Potential delivery delays.
	• Thorough coverage of target market.	• Lack of support from other media.
	• Fewer distractions from other media.	• "Junk mail" easy to ignore.
	• A large number of consumers like to make mail-order purchases.	• Seen as wasteful, harmful to environment.

Callaway Golf's house organ is a full-color magazine featuring golf tips, interviews with professional players, and new product information mailed to stockholders, retailers, customers, and the sports media.

Perhaps the biggest advantage of direct mail is its potential effectiveness. Purchasing from a catalog or other mailed solicitations is a routine practice in many countries, including the United States and Great Britain. Purchases resulting from direct mail are more frequent among higher-income consumers, prompting upscale businesses not known for using direct mail to do so. For example, upscale retailer Neiman Marcus has used a special Christmas catalog for years, and Nordstrom has increased its catalog mailings to the upscale female shopper. Other prominent upscale direct mail marketers include Robert Redford's Sundance, The Sharper Image, Herrington, and clothing retailer The Territory Ahead.

Direct mail does have its flaws, however. It has one of the highest costs per thousand of any form of advertising. And it suffers potential delivery delays; it may take up to six weeks for bulk mail to reach its destination. In addition, consumers can easily ignore it, tossing the junk mail without ever being exposed to its message. While popular in many countries, it is not yet a significant method of marketing in some countries. For example, catalog and other direct mail appeals are not particularly effective in South Africa, Australia, and Brazil.[16] And finally, consumers increasingly view direct mail as wasteful and harmful to the environment.

TYPES OF DIRECT MAIL   Direct mail comes in many formats, as shown in Exhibit 20–3. The most common form of direct mail is the *sales letter*, which typically includes the recipient's name and may be mailed with brochures, price lists, and reply cards and envelopes. *Postcards* generally offer discounts, announce sales, or generate customer traffic. Postcards may be combined with a larger piece, such as a magazine cover or product information sheet. The idea is to cut through mailbox clutter with the larger piece, yet have an economical, easy way for the consumer to respond. This combination—called Double Postcard Plus, or DPC+—gives marketers a chance to deliver descriptive messages and compelling graphics not possible with an unaccompanied postcard. Even though costs are higher, more favorable response rates make it feasible in some situations.

Some companies produce publications referred to as *house organs* for mailing to particular audiences. These may be newsletters, consumer magazines, stockholder reports, or dealer publications. Increasingly popular are electronic house organs in the form of e-mail newsletters. For example, House of Blues, the nightclub chain, offers subscribers a free weekly electronic newsletter updating performance schedules and other information for live music fans.

Sales from printed *catalogs* will exceed $155 million in 2005.[17] Lands' End, Eddie Bauer, Patagonia, and JCPenney produce well-known catalogs. Catalogs offer a comfortable, convenient alternative to in-store shopping. Consumers enjoy browsing through the pages and using simple, reliable means such as the mail, telephone, or fax to place orders. Most catalog retailers have well-trained staffs and efficient delivery systems, which further en-

---

Exhibit 20–3   *Types of direct mail*

Sales letter: typically includes recipient's name; may be mailed with brochures, price lists, reply cards, and envelopes.

Postcards: generally used to offer discounts, announce sales, or generate customer traffic.

Catalogs: describe and often picture the product sold.

Video catalogs: serve same purpose as print catalog, but are on videocassettes or CDs.

Promotional videocassettes, audiocassettes, and CDs: used to send product information to selected audiences.

Promotional interactive computer disks: allow the recipient to select information of interest.

Leaflets and flyers: typically single pages that can be folded and included with sales letters.

Statement stuffers: ads included in other mail such as bank or credit card statements or shipped with catalog orders.

Catalog sales are on the increase. Consumers like the convenience, simplicity, and reliability of catalog buying.

hance the shopping experience. Catalogs also play a major role in business-to-business direct marketing, particularly in the office supply and furnishings category.

Catalogs, pioneered by general merchandise retailers such as Sears, are more likely to appeal to a niche market today. In the home furnishings market, successful niche catalogers include L. L. Bean Home, Linen Source, Restoration Hardware, Pottery Barn, and Hold Everything.

Promotional videocassettes, DVDs, and *CDs* filled with product information are becoming popular direct-mail pieces. CDs offer several advantages, including more storage space and smaller size, which minimizes postage costs. DVDs offer the additional advantage of playability on both computers and mass-market DVD players. BMW inserted DVDs in a mail campaign to *Vanity Fair* readers to promote its 3-series automobiles. Trying to reach a younger audience than BMW's traditional buyer, the DVDs featured films starring actor Clive Owen and pop singer Madonna as they drove BMWs to complete their daring missions. In this case, the DVD medium was compatible with the younger target market, and BMW achieved its brand awareness and sales objectives.[18]

Leaflets or *flyers* are typically single pages printed on one or both sides of standard-sized paper (8 1/2 by 11 inches) and folded. *Statement stuffers* are ads included in other mail such as bank or credit card statements.

BUSINESS-TO-BUSINESS DIRECT MAIL   All the forms of direct mail just discussed are frequently used in business-to-business marketing. With the increasing costs of sales calls, marketers use direct mail to generate sales leads, solicit sales, and provide after-sale support and service information. For example, Xerox has conducted a direct-mail campaign to business purchasing decision makers titled "Eat Your Competitor's Lunch." The objective of the campaign is to encourage prospective customers to book an appointment with a Xerox sales representative. A mailing to 4,000 prospects yielded an impressive 9.4 percent response rate. The direct-mail effort is coordinated from beginning to end with Xerox salespeople, who provide names for the mailing list and follow up with all responding customers. The solid response to the campaign is boosted by a fun element: the use of a lunchbox as part of the mailer. The lunchbox is filled with picnic-food flash cards that tout the benefits of Xerox digital printers along with an opportunity for respondents to win a gas grill.[19] For an indication of what makes a successful business-to-business direct mail piece, see Exhibit 20–4.

Broadcast Media

Although used mostly for mass advertising, television and radio are also used for direct marketing communications. Infomercials and direct-response advertising on TV and radio are popular DMC formats.

Exhibit 20–4	*Ways to maximize business-to-business direct mail*

- Target all decision makers from the senior level on down.
- Reach decision makers as early as possible in the sales cycle.
- Deliver messages tailored to the purchase responsibility of each job at each stage of the buying process.
- Communicate at the proper technical level for different people who share the buying decision.
- Recognize that CEOs will probably not have much involvement unless the purchase is large enough to warrant their attention.
- Know the length and stages in the sales cycle, and plan accordingly.
- Develop direct messages based on the buyer's needs, objectives, and strategies.
- Be sure that responses to direct communications are promptly followed up.
- When referring customers to your own Web site, ensure that your direct message is compatible with the image and content of your site.

INFOMERCIALS   **Infomercials** are extended (usually 30-minute) commercials cast in a television show format. Mixing information and entertainment, they strive to look more like a regular TV program than a commercial. Infomercials have become well established on cable television, generating well over a billion dollars a year in sales. Popular product categories for infomercials include health and fitness equipment, cosmetics, small kitchen appliances, and hair and personal care items. Familiar infomercial offerings include Bowflex, Soloflex, Proactiv acne cream, Ron Popeil's rotisserie and barbeque cooker, and George Foreman Indoor/Outdoor Grill.

The infomercial format provides an opportunity to stand out in a cluttered environment. A 30-second commercial is more likely to get lost in the shuffle than a 30-minute one. In addition, an infomercial's length makes it possible to explain an advertised product more fully. For instance, Adams Golf introduced its unconventional "Tight Lies" golf club with infomercials. Legendary golf commentator Jack Whitaker and professional golfers Bill Rogers and Hank Haney explained and demonstrated how the club's bottom weighting made hitting the ball easier than it is with traditional fairway woods. The original Tight Lies club was named the International Network of Golf's "Breakthrough Product of the Year," and the company went on to sell millions of units. Adams has since relied on infomercials for other product introductions with great success.

By featuring a direct-response telephone number, an infomercial guarantees a quick means for measuring results. Moreover, information obtained from those ordering can be used to develop a database.

Infomercials also have certain disadvantages. For one thing, airing is confined largely to cable TV and late-night programming on major networks, perhaps making it difficult to reach the target market with the desired message. Although potentially cost-effective, average production costs for infomercials are high. Thus production costs added to airtime costs make infomercials more expensive than most direct marketing communications methods.

Finally, infomercials have a poor image. Many suffer from exaggerated claims, low-quality production standards, and unprofessional presentation. Moreover, there is some concern that they are deceptive by appearing in the guise of programs. Infomercials for some products have drawn fire from the public, as noted on Web sites maintained by the Federal Trade Commission and nongovernment sites such as *www.infomercialscams.com* and *www.infomercialwatch.org*. Infomercial Watch lists misleading infomercials with links to articles and government releases in several categories, including dietary supplements and herbs, exercise products, hair loss products, pain relievers, and weight loss products.[20] Problems such as these may be overcome as the format develops and attracts more credible sponsors. In recent years, major companies such as Pennzoil, Ford Motor Company's Mercury division, and Internet job site Monster.com have used infomercials, which indicates that these extended direct appeals are gaining in credibility. *Fortune* 1000 firms now produce approximately 20 percent of all infomercials.[21] As infomercials move more into the mainstream among marketing communications alternatives, it is interesting to note that the medium began as an entrepreneurial endeavor, as described in "Being Entrepreneurial: Infomercials Born in Iowa Blanket the Nation's Airwaves."

DIRECT-RESPONSE TELEVISION ADVERTISING   **Direct-response television advertising** includes an 800 or 900 telephone number and an address for placing orders in a typical 30-, 60-, or 90-second commercial. Unlike typical mass advertising, direct-response ads attempt to get an immediate answer from the consumer. Music is often featured in direct-response television ads with major advertisers such as Time-Life Music (*AM Gold* and *Ultra Mix*) and Millennium Partners (*Swing Is King*). Other major products advertised for direct response on television include Intuit's Quicken financial software, Mead Johnson's Boost Vanilla Shake, Glaxo Wellcome's Flonase, Sears's tools, and E*Trade's electronic stock-trading site. Print media, most notably magazines and newspapers, also use direct-response TV ads to reach new subscribers. For example, *Time* magazine and *Sports Illustrated* frequently use the method. The *Chicago Tribune* combines direct-response TV ads with direct mail to generate new subscriptions and maintain renewals.[22]

Lincoln Logs International uses telemarketing as part of its communications mix when recruiting new dealers. A toll-free number is featured in print ads and on the company's Web site.

Although sometimes aired on network television, direct-response commercials are more widely broadcast on cable TV. Cable TV allows effective targeting of audiences through special-interest programming. Bass Pro Shops, a Springfield, Missouri, catalog retailer, for example, uses direct-response advertising on popular cable TV fishing programs. As with infomercials, this form of DMC enables database building and immediate assessment of results.

DIRECT-RESPONSE RADIO ADVERTISING   **Direct-response radio advertising** also offers the ability for immediate feedback through a telephone number or address provided with the commercial. In addition, it can be directed toward a very targeted audience and is relatively inexpensive compared with other forms of direct marketing communications. Radio, however, is not a particularly dynamic medium. Radio audiences tend to be too preoccupied with other things to focus on an address or a telephone number. Certainly a listener hearing a radio commercial while driving cannot easily record an address.

Print Media

Although not so tightly targeted as other direct marketing communications media, newspapers and magazines can also provide an opportunity for direct response. Consumers can respond to ads carrying an address, order form, coupon, or telephone number. The response can be either to purchase or to request additional information. One way to use direct-response print advertising is with a freestanding insert (FSI), discussed in Chapter 18.

Magazines may include other forms of direct marketing communications. Some marketers insert reply cards into magazines. **Reader-response cards** are sometimes used in conjunction with ads to allow consumers to request additional information. Readers wanting more information on a product would circle a number on the card corresponding to the product's ad in the magazine and send the card to the magazine's publisher. Another magazine insert is the computer data disk. *Forbes* magazine, for example, included a disk that contained information from such advertisers as American Express, Chevrolet, Embassy Suites, and Merrill Lynch, among others. America Online has used disk inserts extensively to attract new subscribers.

Telemarketing

Telemarketing is an interactive direct marketing communications approach that uses telephone calls to initiate, develop, and enhance relationships with customers. On a cost-per-contact basis, telemarketing is less expensive than personal selling, but much more expensive

BEING ENTREPRENEURIAL

Infomercials Born in Iowa Blanket the Nation's Airwaves

In the small town of Fairfield, Iowa, an industry more suited for Hollywood was founded in 1986. It was here that Timothy Hawthorne founded Hawthorne Direct, the nation's first infomercial production company. Since then, Hawthorne's company has produced more than 500 infomercials for companies such as Apple, Nissan, and Time-Life. His company employs 70 people, bills its clients $120 million a year, and has a 15 percent market share in the infomercial industry.

As is true in all marketing communications, creative, easy-to-understand, compelling messages are needed to cut through the clutter in busy consumers' lives. Hawthorne sees himself not as an advertiser but as an audiovisual communicator, a story-

teller of sorts. His approach embeds the product in a "tale of hope and transformation that entertains, delights, and persuades."

Whereas yesterday's infomercials were often more about hype than substance, today's infomercials are backed by extensive consumer research and product development and are targeted to carefully selected consumers. Message appeals are tested, and the direct response of consumers allows precise tracking of what is working and what is not. With such characteristics, it is no surprise that Hawthorne's entrepreneurial vision has inspired companies such as Disney and Land Rover to produce their own infomercials.

than mass advertising and direct mail. However, its high return often justifies the added expense. According to the Direct Marketing Association, telemarketing sales will exceed a trillion dollars in 2007.[23] In terms of expenditures and sales generated, telemarketing is the leading direct marketing communications technique.

Outbound telemarketing, sometimes called *teleselling,* occurs when the marketer actively solicits customers or prospects. Inbound telemarketing occurs when a customer calls the marketer to obtain information or place an order. Either case offers the advantage of two-way conversation, allowing the respondent to ask questions and give answers and the marketer to tailor a message to the individual needs of the prospect.

Very popular in business-to-business marketing, telemarketing can be effective in expanding international marketing operations. Gateway, the direct supplier of computers, established a telemarketing center in Dublin, Ireland, as a first step toward entry into European markets. Holiday Inn and Radisson have established telemarketing operations in Australia to handle the entire Asia Pacific region, and Apple serves Europe with telemarketing centers in France, the United Kingdom, and Germany.

Technology has made telemarketing very productive. **Predictive dialing systems** save telemarketers as much as 20 minutes an hour by passing over answering machines, busy signals, and no answers. Predictive dialers automatically dial a designated amount of numbers per minute. Completed calls are immediately passed on to a live telemarketer, who simultaneously receives customer information on a computer terminal.

Unfortunately, telemarketing does not have a good image. Consumers generally view telemarketers as uninvited nuisances. Common complaints are that telemarketing is an invasion of privacy, uses misleading tactics, and is a waste of time. Consumer organizations routinely warn consumers to be wary of telemarketing. Some go beyond warnings, urging consumers to take the offensive against telemarketing. For example, Junkbusters offers an antitelemarketing script at its Web site *(www.junkbusters.com)* under the question, "Telemarketers always use a script: why shouldn't you?" Junkbuster's script is recommended as "what to say when they call if you don't want junk calls."[24]

The public's irritation with telemarketers and unethical practices by some telemarketers prompted the Federal Trade Commission (FTC) to enact a national "do not call" list that prohibits telemarketing calls to consumers who register with the FTC. According to the FTC, 92 percent of the people registered on the do not call list are receiving fewer telemarketing calls, and 78 percent say they are receiving far fewer calls or none at all. The FTC action allows certain types of telemarketing calls, including those from political or charitable organizations, opinion researchers, calls from businesses with whom consumers have made a purchase within the past 18 months or placed an inquiry within the past 90 days, and calls from companies to which consumers have given permission to call.[25] In addition to the National Do Not Call Registry maintained by the FTC, 30 states have do not call laws.[26] The message to telemarketers is increasingly clear: To be accepted as a legitimate marketer, don't bother calling those who do not wish to be contacted. From a common-sense perspective, telemarketers should focus on interested prospects, a practice encouraged by the Direct Marketing Association (DMA). Telemarketing can be a mutually beneficial tool for businesses and consumers. In many cases, particularly in business-to-business settings, it is a productive marketing method and a preferred way to stay in touch from the customer's point of view.

Unfortunately for legitimate companies, consumers do have to exercise caution when dealing with telemarketers. The National Consumers League identifies the top telemarketing fraud schemes in Exhibit 20–5. Telemarketers, then, should provide short, compelling messages because most people will not spend more than a few minutes on the phone for an uninvited sales call.

Electronic Media

Several other electronic forms of direct marketing communications are available besides broadcast media. Although not used as often as other methods, interactive computer services, kiosks, and fax machines are growing in popularity.

Thinking Critically

Blake Stanley, director of promotions for a book retailer, is contemplating running a contest for consumers on his company's Web site. Winners would receive free books and merchandise. Currently Blake's company enjoys sales from around the globe on its Web site. Because this is the first time that Blake has considered running a contest, he is wondering if any precautions are appropriate. What advice can you share with Blake?

| **Exhibit 20-5** | *National Consumers League's top 10 telemarketing frauds list* |

1. *Work-at-home schemes*—Kits sold with false promises of profits.
2. *Prizes/sweepstakes*—Phony prize awards requiring payment of fees first.
3. *Credit card offers*—Phony promises of credit cards requiring payment of fees in advance.
4. *Advance fee loans*—Empty promises of loans requiring payment of fees in advance.
5. *Magazine sales*—Fake sales or renewals for magazine subscriptions that are never received.
6. *Telephone slamming*—Consumers' phone service is switched without their knowledge or consent.
7. *Buyers clubs*—Consumers' credit card and bank accounts may be charged with unauthorized purchases.
8. *Credit card loss protection*—Unnecessary insurance sold using scare tactics or misrepresentations.
9. *Nigerian money offers*—Consumers are lured into revealing their bank account numbers, against which fraudulent checks are written.
10. *Telephone pay-per-call services*—Some 900 number and other "pay-per-call" services are not worth the price of the call.

INTERACTIVE COMPUTER SERVICES As illustrated throughout this book, **interactive computer networks** are increasingly used for direct marketing communications. Traditional networks work via modem over telephone lines. Wireless Internet services, which utilize communications satellites, are also available, and simple Web-access appliances, not full-blown computers, are becoming a factor in this form of direct marketing communications. This includes Web-enabled versions of some personal digital assistants (PDAs) from Palm Pilot and Blackberry and Web-enabled cell phones.

As the rapid growth of electronic commerce continues, it is logical to expect more direct marketing communications via the Internet. This is because a key ingredient of DMC, the use of customer databases, is facilitated by electronic commerce. That is, once consumers buy electronically, they become part of that seller's customer database and may be receptive to direct communications. The obvious low cost of transmitting electronic messages when compared with other forms of direct marketing communications and the global reach of this medium provide strong incentives for marketers to use this communications tool.

Some cautionary notes are worth considering. First, although the total number of Internet users is large and growing, not all are relevant for direct marketers. Further, online users are very particular about unsolicited advertising that arrives by e-mail, called *spam*. Consumers receiving spam often react angrily, boycotting the spammer and "flaming" the offender. Flaming involves negative responses to the advertiser, such as deluging them with thousands of reply messages or sending e-mail "bombs" containing huge files that tie up computers for hours.

Another area of concern is that the Internet is suffering from congestion. Users complain that it takes too long to navigate the vast array of sites, and this could diminish the viability of computer networks as a communications vehicle. One additional concern is that computer vandals or "hackers" may interfere with a Web site's operation, even closing it down. Hackers have succeeded in closing down some of the most popular Web sites for several hours, including Amazon.com, Yahoo!, Microsoft, and eBay. The FBI has warned marketers that their Web sites are only as secure as the other Web sites they link to; thus well-protected sites can still be vandalized through less protected linking sites.

Despite the uncertainties, direct marketing communications via interactive computer networks are growing rapidly. They are an ideal medium for computer-equipped consumers who want to stay in touch with retailers and service providers. Companies encourage this link by publicizing their Web addresses in ads and on product packaging.

Don Condit, President of Condit Communications, comments on the growth of the Internet in marketing communications: "The value of promotion over the Internet will grow more slowly for clients selling expensive capital equipment than it will for others. For each client, the rate of growth will also vary from one target audience to another. Pharmaceutical process engineers, for example, are already accustomed to using the Internet to find new equipment choices and alternate vendors, while engineers in the food-processing industry will not rely on the Internet for years to come."

INTERACTIVE COMPUTER KIOSKS   Another electronic marketing medium is the **interactive computer kiosk.** These kiosks typically use touch-screen technology that allows the consumer to access specific information of interest. Some interactive computer kiosks include catalogs (video or paper) featuring items not stocked in the retail store, with a direct toll-free number for placing orders. Cities frequented by tourists sometimes use kiosks to help sightseers find their way around. These kiosks are often used as direct marketing communications vehicles for restaurants, hotels, and other services and attractions of interest to travelers. Catalog retailers are also using computer kiosks to gain additional exposure and sales from mall and airport shoppers. With consumers becoming increasingly comfortable with computer technology, the use of kiosks is increasing. Best Buy, Office Depot, and Staples use kiosks to allow direct purchases of computers and other items from company Web sites. IBM uses kiosks to communicate directly with job seekers at career fairs, and some pharmaceutical companies are using kiosks in doctor's offices to promote their drugs.

FAX MACHINES   Fax machines allow transmission of written documents via telephone lines. Their use as a direct marketing communications tool has been restricted primarily to business-to-business customers. Direct marketers routinely use fax machines to receive customer orders. **Fax-on-demand systems** allow instant response to 800-number requests for information using a fax. In these systems, a fax machine receives the request for information and immediately faxes the information back to the requester. For example, Bryan Texas Utilities uses a fax-on-demand system to supplement its customer service activities. With a touch-tone phone, customers can request their account information and receive the information almost instantly via fax.[27]

One problem with using fax machines in business-to-business marketing communications is that most businesses do not want to tie up their incoming fax lines with unsolicited information. It is now a fairly common practice to send unsolicited marketing communications after normal business hours, a practice made easy by the delayed-dialing capabilities of most fax machines. Some states, including Texas, Oregon, and Florida, prohibit the transmission of unsolicited fax communications.

Many business-to-business marketers, including accounting firms and equipment manufacturers, depend on disseminating information as a means of attracting clients. Some of these marketers find an advantage in transmitting information in written rather than audio or video form. Many prospective customers would rather read a customized report than listen to one because it is easier to access important parts of the written report. Prices, product availability, shipping schedules, and other marketing mix variables can change frequently, and the fax is extremely accommodating when such changes occur. Many fax documents are never in hard copy form, but exist in computer files that can be changed with the flick of a key stroke just before dissemination. These communications are increasingly sent by e-mail; thus conventional fax technology is declining in use.

Ethical and Legal Issues in Direct Marketing Communications

In this section we discuss three key areas of ethical and legal concern in direct marketing communications: invasion of privacy, deceptive practices, and waste of natural resources.

Invasion of Privacy

As consumer databases become more sophisticated, there is growing concern about invasion of privacy. Surveys consistently confirm that consumers do not trust companies to protect their private information, and the majority favors a stronger government role in combating invasion of privacy.[28] Consumer fears are well-founded, with the Federal Trade Commission reporting that 27.3 million Americans were victims of identity theft in the 2000–2005 period.[29]

Consumers are concerned with a loss of control over how their personal information is used by companies, and they do not wish to receive more advertising messages as a result of divulging their personal information. Some are also concerned that detailed profiling of individual consumer behavior could lead to discrimination by marketers. For example, if a company learns that a consumer shops a lot but does not buy much, the company can leave him or her on hold on help lines and not offer the consumer special deals.

Concerns for consumer privacy have spurred a flurry of federal legislation activity, with 19 privacy acts introduced in Congress in 2003–2004. Topics addressed include the use of spyware, use of credit information, sale of personal information, regulation of wireless telephone calls, and further regulation of computer-based communications.[30] How much of this legislation will eventually become law is uncertain, but recent enacted legislation indicates that the government will indeed play a stronger role in regulating privacy in future years. Meanwhile, significant numbers of consumers are reluctant to share personal information with marketers and shop online.

The privacy of teens and younger children is a particularly sensitive issue. Consumer groups point out that online services may surpass television in influencing younger consumers' lives in the future and believe that some marketers manipulate children. For example, companies offer prizes for personal information—such as e-mail addresses and birthdays—that will be used in direct marketing communications. Critics believe that marketers should fully disclose how such information will be used and get parental consent if information will be identifiable by individuals rather than aggregated into group data.[31]

U.S. marketers are leery of legislative attempts to regulate potential threats to consumer privacy. Consumers in other countries, however, are accustomed to strict privacy statutes. European Union (EU) countries guarantee European citizens absolute control over their private information. If a company wants a consumer's personal information, it must get the individual's permission and explain how the information will be used. The European Union is pressuring marketers from other countries to follow the strict laws adopted by the European Union. According to EU law, no company can transmit personal data about EU citizens to countries whose privacy laws are not as strict as those in the European Union. EU law also prohibits data tags, or "cookies," that track customer preferences on the Web and does not allow marketers to use databases obtained from another marketer to solicit business.[32]

To ward off potential legislative action, some direct marketing companies are taking actions to avoid invading consumers' privacy. Fewer firms make their in-house lists available for rental to other companies. McDonald's, Fisher-Price, and Citicorp, for example, no longer rent their customer lists. Many firms allow consumers to choose whether they are included on lists made available to other firms. Others ask consumers how often they would like to receive mail solicitations.

Deceptive Practices

Attempts at telemarketing legislation have increased at least in part to address numerous telemarketing abuses (see Exhibit 20–6). Consumers exhibit high levels of trust in sellers when they order and pay for a product sight unseen. Direct-response marketers rely on this trust. Yet certain direct-marketing activities have damaged that trust.

After 30 years, marketers have finally convinced consumers that 800-number telephone calls are toll-free. But some marketers ask 800-number callers to punch codes into their telephones that, without the caller's knowledge or consent, convert the call to a billable 900 number. Another abuse comes from sweepstakes marketers that promote 900-number calls for prizes worth much less than the cost of the call.

Automatic number identification and **caller ID intrusion** systems pose additional ethical and legal problems. These systems let incoming telephone numbers of respondents to an ad or a promotion be identified at the onset of the call without the caller's consent or knowledge. Not only is this a possible invasion of privacy, but it also presents an opportunity to capture and sell unlisted numbers.

Exhibit 20-6	*Telemarketing sales rule*

All businesses conducting outbound telemarketing must comply with the amended Telemarketing Sales Rule (TSR) of January 29, 2003. The amended rule gives effect to the Telemarketing and Consumer Fraud and Abuse Prevention Act of 1994. Major provisions of the rule include these:

- Telemarketers are prohibited from calling consumers who have registered on the National Do Not Call Registry maintained by the Federal Trade Commission.
- Telemarketers must transmit caller ID information.
- Misrepresentations are prohibited.
- Telemarketers must disclose costs associated with the purchase, limitations, restrictions, and refund/cancellation policies.
- Abusive acts are prohibited, including profane language and calling people who have indicated that they do not wish to be contacted.
- A "do not call" list must be maintained by the company using telemarketing. Telemarketers are restricted from making calls before 8:00 A.M. and after 9:00 P.M. local time.
- Companies must maintain records on transactions for a period of 24 months.
- The Telemarketing Sales Rule is enforced by both the Federal Trade Commission and by a state's attorney general, who can impose penalties of $11,000 per violation.

Internet fraud is another area of concern in direct marketing communications. Many of the scams in telemarketing (see Exhibit 20–5) are also promoted via e-mail. Nigerian money offers, work-at-home schemes, and bogus credit card offers are frequently transmitted by e-mail. In addition, e-mail is frequently used to offer fraudulent business opportunities and franchises.

Concerns over what consumers would call junk e-mail or spam led to federal legislation, the CAN-SPAM Act of 2003 (Controlling the Assault of Non-Solicited Pornography and Marketing Act). The CAN-SPAM Act establishes requirements for senders of commercial e-mail, specifies penalties for spammers and companies that violate the law, and gives consumers the right to request that e-mail senders stop spamming them. Under the act, false or misleading header information is prohibited, as are deceptive subject lines. Commercial messages must be identified as an advertisement, and the sender must furnish a valid physical postal address, not just a box number. Each violation of the CAN-SPAM act is punishable by fines of up to $11,000.[33] In addition to the CAN-SPAM Act, 33 states have laws regulating the commercial use of e-mail.[34]

Wasteful Practices

People are concerned about the environmental consequences of marketing decisions, thus increasing attention to use of natural resources. In the direct-mail industry, consumer complaints and regulatory interest concerning junk mail have motivated discussion about excessive contributions to landfills, impact on timber production and harvesting, and the economic waste associated with rising paper costs.

It is commonly known that consumers do not want to receive all their unsolicited mail. Two alternatives are easily available to marketers that want to cut down on waste by minimizing undeliverable and unwanted direct-mail pieces. First, a marketer can increase the accuracy of a mailing list by running it through the U.S. Postal Service's national file on changes of address. By using this service, mailers can cut down on undeliverable pieces and perhaps qualify for lower postage rates in the process.

In addition, direct marketers can better inform consumers of their right to remove their names from mailing lists. The Direct Marketing Association coordinates a "preference" program that allows consumers to stop mail and telephone solicitation if they so choose. There may be some way marketers can make consumers more aware of this program, which would eventually lead to less unwanted mail and more efficient direct marketing communications.

Another element of waste in direct marketing communications is the time lost at home and in the workplace dealing with unsolicited messages. The widespread occurrence of spam has irked consumers and had an unknown but significant downward effect on workplace productivity. To repeat a familiar refrain, most legitimate marketers are far more interested in targeting consumers who can benefit from their offerings, then communicating with them in a straightforward manner.

Cutting out waste in DMC requires that consumers join with concerned companies to bring about the desired changes. This is true of most ethical and legal problems facing marketing. Whether we are talking about invasion of privacy, deceptive practices, waste of natural resources, or any other significant ethical or legal issue in marketing, the consumer must take an active role in effecting favorable change.

Summary

1. **Understand the objectives of direct marketing communications, and describe their distinguishing characteristics.** Direct marketing communications are directed at target audiences using one or more media. One objective of direct marketing communications is to elicit a response by telephone, mail, or personal visit from a prospect or customer. Another objective, to maintain and enhance customer relationships, is growing in importance.

   Direct marketing is distinguished from other marketing communications methods in several ways. First, it uses customer databases, or lists, to target an audience precisely. Next, it is oriented more toward an immediate response than are most other forms of marketing communications. Finally, its objectives are specific consumer actions, so results are highly measurable.

2. **Discuss the factors driving the growth in direct marketing communications.** Increasingly fragmented markets make the narrowly focused methods of direct marketing quite attractive. Changes in lifestyles have created a need for convenient, time-saving, and dependable ways to shop. Perhaps one of the biggest motivators of growth in direct marketing communications has been the emergence of database marketing, which gives marketers a more in-depth understanding of productive target customers.

3. **Understand traditional direct marketing communications techniques such as direct mail, broadcast and print media, and telemarketing.** Direct mail comes in a variety of forms, from postcards to video catalogs. Print and broadcast media are used for direct-response advertising, and the infomercial has become a significant means of communicating directly with the target market. Inbound and outbound telemarketing have become extremely popular, even though outbound telemarketing is a nuisance to many consumers. Each of these methods has unique capabilities and limitations, which is one reason marketers typically use multiple methods to reach a given audience.

4. **Recall examples of the use of technology such as electronic media in direct marketing communications.** Interactive computer services, interactive computer kiosks, and fax on demand are three examples of relatively new technology now widely used in direct marketing communications. These tools offer immediate information to consumers and business-to-business buyers, and sometimes allow the customer to do business with the seller after normal business hours.

5. **Understand some of the ethical and legal issues facing marketers who use direct marketing communications.** As database lists become more sophisticated, there is increased concern about invasion of privacy. Abuse of consumers' privacy is likely to lead to legislation to curb it. Telemarketing and e-mail have come under the heaviest attacks, as unethical marketers use deceptive methods in dealing with consumers. Actions can and should be taken to avoid unwarranted or abusive intrusion. Junk mail and unsolicited e-mail have been accused of wasting natural resources and customers' time. Concerned marketers, consumers, and associations such as the Direct Marketing Association must work together to curb these problems. Otherwise, it is certain that some consumers will be victimized and that legislation will be enacted to address the issues.

Understanding Marketing Terms and Concepts

Direct marketing communications	470	Infomercials	478
Interactive marketing	470	Direct-response television advertising	478
Lists	471	Direct-response radio advertising	479
Database marketing	471	Reader-response cards	479
Predictive modeling	474	Telemarketing	479
Direct mail	475		
Predictive dialing systems	480		
Interactive computer networks	481		
Interactive computer kiosk	482		
Fax-on-demand systems	482		
Automatic number identification	483		
Caller ID intrusion	483		

Thinking about Marketing

1. Define *direct marketing communications* and describe their distinguishing characteristics.

2. What is database marketing? How has it contributed to the growth of direct marketing communications?

3. Refer to "Using Technology: Databases Are Not Just for Big Businesses." Other than using the weekly e-mail to promote price specials, how else could Drycleaning by Dorothy stores use e-mail to attract and retain customers?

4. Describe advantages and disadvantages of direct mail.

5. What is an infomercial? What types of products do you think would benefit most from using this type of advertising and why?

6. Refer to "Being Entrepreneurial: Infomercials Born in Iowa Blanket the Nation's Airwaves." Why have infomercials moved from the fringe of marketing communications to become more of a mainstream tactic?

7. What is an interactive computer network? How does it differ from an interactive computer kiosk?

8. Database marketing has come under attack from those who believe it is an invasion of privacy. Should marketers be concerned about this? What can be done to address consumers' concerns? Explain.

9. Review the Telephone Sales Rule in Exhibit 20–6. Is it necessary to have federal government intervention to regulate telemarketing?

10. What can direct marketers do to cut down on the waste generated by their communications methods?

Applying Marketing Skills

1. Working in groups of three to five students, analyze two current infomercials to see if they meet the standards of conduct as set forth by the Electronic Retailing Association:

   a. A "paid advertisement" disclosure must appear at the beginning and end of each infomercial and at each ordering opportunity.

   b. The name of the sponsor must be disclosed.

   c. There can be no misrepresentations as to format, no false claims or deception through omission, and no indecent or offensive material.

   To what extent do the members of the group agree on the last point? Summarize your opinions for class discussion.

2. Assume you are the chair of an alumni fund-raising committee for your college or university. The committee is charged with contacting approximately 30,000 alumni to solicit donations for a new library. The goal is to raise $1 million from the alumni within the next 18 months. The first order of business is to determine what form of communication is to be used in the campaign. The alumni are scattered across the United States, and approximately 10 percent live in a variety of foreign countries. Which means of reaching these alumni would you recommend the committee consider? Briefly explain your reasoning.

   a. Direct mail.

   b. Telemarketing.

   c. Personal selling.

   d. Direct-response television advertising.

   e. E-mail.

   f. Fax solicitation.

3. Which types of direct marketing communications would you choose for each task?

   a. Informing your customers of an upcoming sale in your retail store.

   b. Introducing yourself and your company to new prospects in your sales territory.

   c. Inviting current customers to visit your booth at a trade show next month.

   d. Demonstrating a new software program offered by your company.

   e. Familiarizing European construction managers with your latest piece of earth-moving equipment.

   f. Bringing your 1,200 dealers up-to-date on a variety of happenings in your company.

Using the www in Marketing

Activity One Visit the Skechers Web site at *www.skechers.com*. Explore the site, including the link for e-mail.

1. What benefits would a consumer receive by registering on Skechers's e-mail link?

2. What additional steps could Skechers take to add inexpensive but effective incentives to register on its e-mail link?

3. How can Skechers coordinate its e-mail efforts with other marketing communications efforts such as the television and print advertising that is featured on its Web site?

Activity Two Trade associations often use the Internet to provide valuable information to consumers and managers. The Direct Marketing Association maintains a comprehensive Web site at *http://www.the-dma.org*. What evidence can you find that the Direct Marketing Association promotes an ethical perspective in the practice of direct marketing?

Making Marketing Decisions

Case 20–1 *Cisco Hits the Target with E-Mail*

Cisco Systems built its reputation as the world's leading provider of computer networking products that help other companies use the Internet and corporate intranets. Always focused on the bottom line, *Cisco* used its own Web site at *www.cisco.com* to slash customer service costs, moving most of its customer service support online. With strategic partners such as Microsoft, Oracle, IBM, EDS, and Hewlett-Packard, the company has been recognized as belonging to an elite group of technology companies for almost two decades. In 2005 Cisco was one of the winners in *CRN* magazine's Channel Champions competition for supporting resellers in its channels of distribution.

Now Cisco is making industry headlines through its use of direct marketing communications. Complex equipment requires personal selling, including the involvement of upper management, to complete the sales cycle. Increasingly, Cisco uses direct marketing to supplement the selling efforts of its own sales force and that of its field partners. For several years the company has used computer networks to provide direct communications with salespeople and customers. Recently Cisco made a strong move into direct marketing communications by mounting massive e-mail campaigns.

Early e-mail campaigns proved highly effective and profitable. One campaign generated a 55 percent response rate, $2.2 million in additional sales, and a return on investment of 1,200 percent. A later campaign targeted CEOs, technical staffers, and managers of large corporations such as AT&T, Wells Fargo, and Deutsche Bank. In one part of this campaign, 40,000 technical staffers, all of whom had opted in or given their permission to receive information about optical data products, were offered a technical book as a premium. In return, prospects furnished information that Cisco used to determine if they were viable leads for the sales force. Another part of this campaign was a three-part traditional hard-copy mailer sent to CEOs and nontechnical managers, because research indicated that these people preferred traditional approaches over e-mail. While this campaign turned up some viable sales leads, Cisco's management was somewhat concerned about the quality of those leads. There was some thought that the technical book offered as a premium might have produced some less-than-sincere leads. Even so, the company indicated that it was pleased with the overall results of the campaign, with conversion-to-customer ratios in an acceptable range.

In a follow-up e-mail campaign, Cisco e-mailed 124,000 current customers in an attempt to move the customers into a higher-ticket networking system. According to click-throughs on its Web site, the mailing drew a 35 percent response rate. The cost savings with e-mail versus postal mail was approximately 50 percent.

In addition to responses to its e-mail initiative, Cisco received a large number of leads from ads it ran on Hoover's Online, Bloomberg.com, CFO.com, and direct-response ads it placed in such publications as *The New York Times, Fortune,* and *The Wall Street Journal.* The leads were turned over to Cisco's field sales force. Before the sales force received the leads, a public relations firm further qualified the leads, determining when the companies planned to buy and how much they were willing to spend.

Cisco views its direct marketing efforts as a necessary element in stimulating demand for its products. Due to the complexity of the products, networking customers do not always know exactly what they need to buy. To speed up the sales cycle, direct marketing communications in the form of e-mail are becoming a more important strategy for Cisco.

Cisco CEO John Chambers came up through the sales ranks with IBM before joining Cisco. He has always been an advocate of superior customer service and building customer value through technology. In this instance, Cisco is once again demonstrating that it can use technology, even a fairly simple one like e-mail, to reduce its costs and reach customers with a timely message. Customers win too: keeping up their technology network infrastructure is crucial for success.

Questions

1. Other than supplying sales leads, how does Cisco's e-mail direct marketing communications supplement the efforts of its sales force?

2. Other than e-mail marketing, what other forms of direct marketing communications could be effective for Cisco?

3. What are some ways that Cisco can measure the effectiveness of its e-mail marketing? Would these methods be any different for direct-response print or Internet ads?

Case 20–2 *Musicland Builds Relationships with DMC*

Musicland, a former subsidiary of Best Buy Company, Inc., operates 900 music, video, and software stores in the United States, Puerto Rico, and the Virgin Islands under the names Suncoast Motion Picture, Media Play, and Sam Goody. Musicland makes extensive use of direct marketing communications (DMC) in its customer loyalty program, which is designed to encourage repurchase and give regular customers additional value. At one point, however, this program, called Replay, began experiencing serious problems, causing large numbers of customer defections. Inbound telemarketing representatives were overwhelmed with customer complaints. Record-keeping was poor, preventing qualified customers from receiving rebate checks in a timely manner when they made major purchases. As membership in Replay dropped, store managers became reluctant to promote the program. Musicland's loyalty program was quite simply having the opposite-than-hoped-for effect.

Musicland improved its loyalty program with the help of database marketing specialists from Minnesota-based Group 3 Marketing. The basic idea of Replay remained the same: that it is a consumer club offering its members discounts and other promotions, reviews, information about new releases, and related information. In return, members pay $8.99 a year to belong. To improve the program, the frequency of direct-mail contact with members increased, and the content of the mailings became far more customized.

Now bimonthly newsletters and four to five monthly postcards are sent out. The newsletters generate in-store or online responses of 16 to 18 percent, while the postcards typically generate a 5 to 7 percent response. The newsletters are more customized than the postcards, with message content dependent on customer information from the database. In most cases, content is tailored to music and film preferences, birthdays, proximity to retail stores, and recent purchases. Postcards usually focus on new product releases.

Basic demographic data are captured when members join Replay, and purchase information is gathered when the membership card is swiped in the store. These data are transferred electronically every day to Group 3 Marketing; online purchases are automatically recorded into the database.

One page of each newsletter is predominantly tailored to the individual Replay member. Personalized information includes accumulated point balances, gift certificate rewards status, and product information that matches the member's interests. Other customized material is included in free-standing inserts.

Each Musicland store receives a report on the purchasing activity of its 50 top-spending customers. When these customers make purchases, their names appear on the electronic cash register screens. This allows store personnel to greet the key customers by name and to eventually recognize them as they enter the store. In some cases, this leads to personalized in-store service befitting a top customer.

Musicland uses the Replay database to send e-mail promotions and special offers to members, but only after the members have signed up for these notices. When they sign up online, members have an option to receive their newsletters online. This option will save Musicland a significant amount of money in the years to come as more consumers opt for online direct marketing communications.

Store managers give their enthusiastic support to Replay, and promotional signage for Replay is prominent in the stores. Clearly the company wants to generate a fun-oriented image with its online communications. An example is its "Bad-Gift Boycott" campaign, which positioned Sam Goody as the cure for bad gift-giving and drove increased traffic and store sales. In 2005 the campaign won the highest awards from two industry groups: the Public Relations Society of America and the International Association of Business Communicators. Musicland is looking to expand the online aspect of the program. With 1.6 million paying members, a meaningful database, a user-friendly interface, and highly customized direct marketing communications, the future looks good for Replay.

Questions

1. How could Musicland use the information from its database to enhance in-store promotions and personal selling?

2. How could Musicland use its database to improve market segmentation and target marketing?

3. What methods could you recommend to assess the effectiveness of the various direct marketing communications vehicles used in Musicland's Replay program?

Appendix A

Developing a Marketing Plan

A general strategic planning process is presented in Chapter 3. The basic stages include examining the current situation, identifying potential threats and opportunities, setting objectives, and developing strategies. This appendix illustrates the types of information typically appearing in each section of a marketing plan for a company.

Business units within the firm have their own product marketing plans that focus on specific target markets and marketing mixes for each product. As explained in Chapter 3, marketing plans typically include both strategic decisions (or what to do) and execution decisions (or how to do it). Marketing plans may be developed for a single brand, a product line, or a business unit that markets multiple product lines. For a product, a product line, or a business unit, the general strategic planning process includes the following stages: (1) examine the current situation; (2) identify potential threats and opportunities; (3) set objectives; and (4) develop strategies. These stages may overlap in that work is simultaneously under way regarding each stage. The plans themselves will also include projected financial outcomes and procedures for plan performance monitoring and control.

Overall, planning is a process directed toward making decisions with tomorrow in mind. As such, planning is a means of preparing for future decisions so they can be made rapidly, economically, and with as little disruption to the business as possible. Marketing plans may be for new products and services being introduced or for existing products or services. Regardless of the type of plan, all plans will be reviewed at least annually for needed revisions. Properly developed marketing plans can improve a firm's performance by

- Allocating appropriate financial resources to top priorities.
- Facilitating the development of differentiation strategies to guard against becoming just another commodity in the marketplace.
- Identifying emerging growth opportunities for inclusion in longer-term strategic marketing plans.
- Establishing continuity of marketing efforts as key personnel join and depart the organization.
- Addressing organizational strengths and weaknesses, which can lead to improved performance.
- Setting performance standards and expectations for marketing employees.
- Incorporating feedback from customers and nonmarketing company personnel into continuous improvement initiatives.

Due to competitive activity and volatile conditions in many of today's markets, implementing marketing plans is often more difficult than developing them. To maximize the odds of successful implementation of marketing plans, several points should be noted:

- Accurate sales forecasting is crucial, and multiple methods should be used to develop revenue projections.
- Expense budgets should be carefully prepared and resources secured in advance of implementation. Many great ideas have died from lack of funding.
- Marketing plan objectives should be compatible up, down, and across the organization. For example, marketing should not tout high quality if manufacturing is simultaneously reducing product quality to cut production costs.
- Marketing plans should be candid and realistic given the firm's capabilities and competitive strengths. Over time, marketing planning can improve the firm's capabilities and strengths.
- Be wary of assumptions made in marketing planning, and test the validity of assumptions at the earliest opportunity.
- Generate reliable feedback from customers, customer service personnel, salespeople, and others whose opinions can lead to improvements in future offerings.

A sample marketing plan for Willamette Furniture is presented here.[1] This plan was developed by a real company, but the name and some aspects of the plan have been modified or left blank to preserve confidentiality and proprietary information. The chapters in the book that provide the background information for creating each section of the marketing plan are indicated throughout the plan with the use of the boomerang icon. As you can see, what you have learned about marketing from the text gives you the foundation for developing a marketing plan.

Parts of the Marketing Plan

1. Executive summary
2. Situation analysis
3. Marketing strategy
4. Financials
5. Controls

1.0 Executive Summary

Chapter 3

Willamette Furniture has been riding a growth spurt, having discovered the high-end direct mail channel that gave us a push to new potential volumes through channels. Bolstered by appearances in specialty catalogs, we were able to develop another additional channel through distributors of office equipment that sell directly to corporations.

We believe that by targeting the high-end market, we can successfully occupy an emerging niche that other channels of distribution have not been able to target. With the implementation of the new marketing focus outlined in this plan, we will position our product line as the high-quality, elegant alternative to mainstream office furniture found in office supply stores. Our ability to integrate emerging technologies in our design, provide complementary pieces for a complete set, and custom design ergonomic executive-level office furniture will provide strengths and establish a reputation of unmatched quality.

2.0 Situation Analysis

Willamette Furniture's product offerings focus on the executive-level customer who has an appreciation for quality craftsmanship and materials and wishes to integrate technology into the office environment. Our market segments within the office furniture context include the corporate executive, small business owner, and home office. We will target these markets through a variety of media including the Internet, catalog distribution, and word-of-mouth advertising. Because Willamette offers products at a high cost level, we do not wish to mass market. Rather our strategy is to make our product information readily available to those seeking quality office furniture with specific technological needs. Therefore, we will add internal catalog publishing to our existing catalog marketing programs (currently through high-level channels such as Sharper Image). In addition, because our product assumes the use of computer technology, the development of Web sites will increase our company profile by promoting our product line in the media most appropriate to our customers.

Willamette Furniture occupies a specific niche within the office furniture market. Therefore, our competition does not provide comparable products, as they lack the combination of technological integration and quality in materials and craftsmanship. Our nearest competition includes Ethan Allen, Acme Computer Furniture, and ABC Manufacturing. These companies distribute their products through channels such as chain office supply stores or their own retail locations. In contrast, Willamette targets its potential customers based on their search for our type of product.

2.1 Market Summary

Chapter 2

Our product is positioned very carefully: this is high-quality office furniture combining workmanship and ergonomics for the customer who understands quality, is a user of high-technology equipment, and is willing to spend money on the best. Unlike the mainstream products, we do not use laminates or cheap manufacturing technology.

Our marketing strategy is based mainly on making the right information available to the right target customer. We can't afford to sell people on our expensive products because most don't have the budget. What we really do is make sure that those who have the budget and appreciate the product know that it exists and know where to find it.

The marketing has to convey the sense of quality in every picture, every promotion, and every publication. We can't afford to appear in second-rate catalogs with poor illustrations that make the product look less than it is. We also need to leverage our presence using high-quality catalogs and specialty distributors.

Our target market is a person who wants to have very fine furniture with the latest in technology, combined with an old-fashioned sense of fine woods and fine woodworking. This person can be in the corporate towers, small or medium business, or in a home office. The common bond is the appreciation of quality and the lack of price constraints.

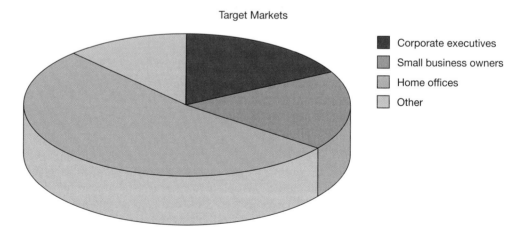
Target Markets

- Corporate executives
- Small business owners
- Home offices
- Other

Chapter 2

2.1.1 MARKET DEMOGRAPHICS   We focus our marketing on three types of target consumers:

1. *Corporate executives:* The Bureau of Labor Statistics (*http://stats.bls.gov*) reports there are 14.4 million executive, administrative, and managerial employees in the United States, and that number is growing at 1.6 percent per year. We estimate the top 1 percent of that number, 144,000, as our market, and we're suggesting the number is growing at the same 1.6 percent annually.

2. *Small business owners and executives:* According to the most recent data available from the Small Business Administration (SBA), there are between 13 and 16 million

Table *Market Analysis*

Potential Customers	Growth	2004	2005	2006	2007	2008	CAGR
Corporate executives	2%	144,000	146,304	148,645	151,023	153,440	1.60%
Small business owners	3%	150,000	153,750	157,594	161,534	165,572	2.50%
Home offices	5%	440,000	462,000	485,100	509,355	534,823	5.00%
Other	5%	100,000	105,000	110,250	115,763	121,551	5.00%
Total	3.99%	834,000	867,054	901,589	937,674	975,385	3.99%

small businesses (500 employees or fewer) in the United States. That includes about 5.5 million employers and 11 million self-employed people. We take the top 1 percent of 15 million to make our potential market of 150,000. We estimate growth at 2.5 percent, a composite of different sources.

3. *Home offices:* According to a story in *Home Office Computing* magazine, there are 36 million home offices in the United States. That means a home office in 27 percent of the households in the country. The U.S. census reports that in 1997 there were 16 million households in this country with incomes of more than $100,000 per year. The 27 percent of those that have home offices are our potential market. That's 4.4 million households (of 132 million total). Our market is the top 10 percent of those, 440,000, which we estimate is growing at 5 percent per year.

4. *Other:* We will also sell to some buyers outside the United States and outside of these targeted market segments. We estimate 100,000 other potential customers, a number that we estimate will be growing at 5 percent per year.

2.1.2 MARKET NEEDS Willamette gives the discriminating personal computer user, who cares about design, quality furniture, and quality of working environment, a combination of the highest-quality furniture and an integration of the latest technology, at a relatively high price. Willamette provides this discriminating customer with more than a piece of furniture. We provide a quality working environment that includes the integration of technological components that generally exist as part of the executive setting. The quality of manufacturing, materials, and ergonomics found in our products enhance the appearance of an executive's office atmosphere, in turn adding to their status and effectiveness as a decision maker, innovator, and leader.

We understand that our target market needs more than just office furniture. This need grew out of the special requirements of personal computing, when combined with office furniture—keyboards at correct height, monitors at correct height, proper channels for cables, and other amenities. Our target customer wants to have all of that, plus fine furniture. There is a need for quality wood and workmanship throughout. We don't just sell office furniture; we sell design, workmanship, fine materials, and a total-quality office environment.

2.1.3 MARKET TRENDS Our market has finally grown to recognize the disparity between most of the standard office furniture sold through channels and our own products.

The development of the high-end office worker, office owners, and the baby-boomer executive is an important trend for us. We now have people who are using computers and also appreciate the old-fashioned workmanship of good furniture.

Today's high integration of technology in the workplace, especially in the multitask-oriented executive environment, sets the stage for growth in the area of high-quality, technologically integrated office environments. Similarly, home offices and small business owners continue to demand more advanced technologies and their integration into the office atmosphere. A sense of craftsmanship and quality of materials, such as oak and cherry, are timeless. The synergy of this desire for the classic cabinetmaker look and use of technology is inherent in Willamette's offerings.

Chapters 4 and 5

Chapter 2

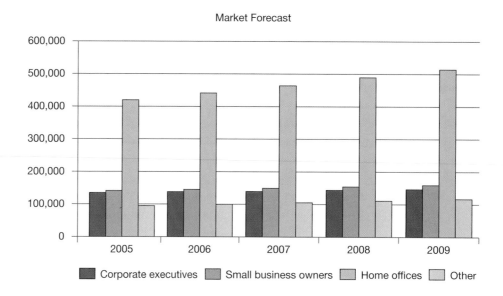

Market Forecast

Chapter 2

2.1.4 MARKET GROWTH
According to [source omitted], the market for office furniture is growing at XX percent per year and is projected to increase. The market for PC-related office furniture is growing even faster, at YY percent per year, and is projected to top $XX billion by the year 2005.

Most important is the growth in home offices with personal computer equipment. As the cost of the computer goes down steadily, the number of home offices goes up. According to [source omitted], this is about 33 million right now, growing at 15 percent per year. Households spent $XX billion last year to equip home offices, and 15 percent of that was spent on furniture.

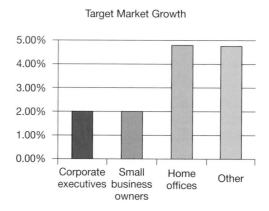

Target Market Growth

2.2 SWOT Analysis

We are on the brink of major opportunity. We have the strength of a combined expertise in high-tech ergonomics and furniture manufacturing, and the opportunity of a growing market and new channels of distribution. We have the weakness of a small company without a lot of experience, and the threat of new competition taking aim at our niche.

2.2.1 STRENGTHS

Chapter 3

- Strategic market segmentation and implementation strategies.
- Combination of skills in ownership: as co-owners, Jim and Susan jointly develop business strategy and long-term plans. Jim is strong on product know-how and technology, and Susan is strong on management and business know-how.

- Diversified market segments: corporate executives, small business owners, home offices.
- Increased capital from successful historical growth in sales.

Chapter 3

2.2.2 WEAKNESSES
- High-end, high-priced product line limits sales volume.
- Addition of in-house catalog design and publishing will add an aspect to Willamette's functions that has not been previously experienced.
- Direct marketing through the development of the catalog creates the need for further research, data gathering, and analysis.
- Establishment on the Internet will produce technological challenges.

Chapter 2

2.2.3 OPPORTUNITIES
- New channels of distribution.
- Internet marketing and sales.
- Specific niche: high-end appreciation for quality materials (cherry and oak), ergonomics, and technology (and integration therein).
- Employee turnover and corporate restructuring are causing increased employee turnover at the highest levels. The new generation of corporate executives, small business owners, and home offices has a far greater appreciation of technology and the needs driven by its implementation, such as office environment quality and integration.

Chapter 2

2.2.4 THREATS
- Growth in the high-end office furniture market invites competition. This competition could emerge from a variety of sources:
  - Established mass-market companies' development of new lines.
  - New start-up companies generated by healthy economic growth nationwide.
  - New marketing strategies for established products and companies.
- Existing competition.

Chapter 2

2.3 Competition

Within our niche we have three significant competitors: Ethan Allen, Acme Computer Furniture, and ABC Manufacturing. Acme is a bigger company, operating mainly in our same niche, whose marketing is better than its product quality. ABC is a subsidiary of Haines Furniture, a major furniture manufacturer, which has recently targeted our niche. Ethan Allen is a furniture manufacturer that produces some office furniture products and markets to the high-level consumer.

In general, however, our competition is not in our niche. We compete against generalized furniture manufacturers, cheaper computer-related furniture, and the mainstream merchandise in the major furniture channels and office supply stores. It is not that people choose our competitors instead of our product; it is that they choose lesser quality, mainstream materials instead of the higher-quality furniture we offer.

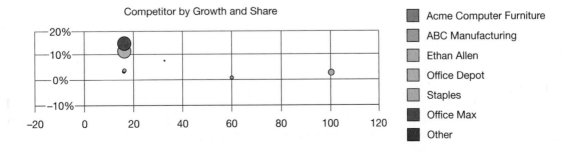

Table	*Growth and Share Analysis*			
Growth and Share Competitor	**Price**	**Growth Rate**	**Market Share**
Acme Computer Furniture	$800	8%	3%
ABC Manufacturing	$1,500	1%	10%
Ethan Allen	$2,500	3%	15%
Office Depot	$400	12%	32%
Staples	$400	4%	10%
Office Max	$400	15%	30%
Other	$0	0%	0%
Average	$857.14	6.14%	14.29%
Total	$6,000.00	43.00%	100.00%

Chapter 8

2.4 Product Offering

Willamette offers very high-quality office furniture designed to effectively incorporate computer machinery into the executive office or home office. The key to the line is an ergonomically effective desk that still looks like an executive desk and looks very good in a high-end office, but is intended to accommodate the personal computer. Each piece is available in either oak or cherry.

1. Our main line is the Willamette computer desk in several versions. This is an elegant piece of office furniture designed to look good in an executive office or a home office, and at the same time be ideal for real use of the computer. The two critical elements of ergonomics—keyboard height and angle, and monitor height and angle—are completely adjustable. Cable runs and shelving add to the utility of the executive desk without sacrificing elegance.

2. We also make complementary pieces to fill out the office suite, including file cabinets, printer stands, and bookcases.

3. In addition, we make custom designs to fit exact measurements.

Further supporting our competitive edge is our assembly strategy, which is based on interlocking wood pieces of such high quality that assembly is not only a pleasure for our customers, it is actually a feature that enhances the sense of quality.

In 2001 we will introduce the new custom option to our executive desk line based on the laptop computer, with a docking station to connect to a network. The new furniture has a different configuration to assume easy access to the docking station, and better use of the space that doesn't have to be dedicated to the CPU case.

We are also going to accommodate larger monitors, the 17″, 19″, and 21″ sizes that are becoming much more common, particularly in our high-end market. We will be watching for technological developments, allowing us to be the first to provide custom furniture for wall-mounted flat screens, liquid crystal displays, and similar technologies.

Chapter 3

2.5 Keys to Success

The keys to Willamette's success have historically been effective market segmentation and implementation strategies. Along these lines of proven success, Willamette will implement direct marketing strategies based on our success in distribution through high-end channels such as the Sharper Image. Our catalog marketing will turn to in-house production for more specific, extensive product descriptions.

- *Uncompromising commitment to the quality of the product:* quality wood, quality workmanship, quality design, quality of end result.

- *Successful niche marketing:* we need to find the quality-conscious customer in the right channels, and we need to make sure that customer can find us.

- *Almost-automatic assembly:* we can't afford to ship fully assembled desks, but assembly must be so easy and automatic that it makes the customer feel better about the quality, not worse.

2.6 Critical Issues

The critical issues emerge from the SWOT analysis and review of the market:

- *The underlying paradox:* How can we sell our high-end customers a packaged kit that requires assembly? Or do we need to find channels to offer delivery of assembled product?
- *Channels versus Internet:* Can we do both? Is there a channel conflict? Are we going to be able to manage our channels well enough to make money with them?

2.7 Historical Results

The following historical results table (page 498) is based on research and some simplifying assumptions:

1. We used the Imarket Inc. Web site at *www.imarketinc.com* to find an estimate for wood office desks. The total market in the United States was estimated at $140 million in 1996.
2. We estimated growth at 2.5 percent per year, using the average growth of the entire office furniture industry as reported by the U.S. Census in Cendata *(http://tier2. census.gov/cgi-win/asm/ASMDATA.EXE).*
3. We estimated an average of $500 per desk to calculate unit numbers from market numbers.
4. We simplified our own financial history somewhat because this makes the analysis more useful for decision making. We rounded some numbers and consolidated so that our numbers are an accurate reflection.

Looking at the table, we can see that we may soon begin to have measurable market share, as our new channels allow us to contemplate future growth. Our present market share is a function of dividing our numbers because we don't show up in any industry surveys—yet.

2.8 Macroenvironment

At a large scale, market research demonstrates that the high-end market that we are catering to is growing and changing to our benefit. Generally, there is a trend toward executive turnover in large companies today. That is, corporate restructuring, increased small business development, and the growth of the home office sector are providing for a younger market in the executive, small business owner, and home office positions. Research indicates that this new generation of executives implements technology to a much higher degree than past trends have indicated. Therefore, with the emergence of this new generation of executives, the appreciation of quality craftsmanship and materials in office furniture that provides for an effective office environment, combined with the utilization of emerging technologies for greater efficiency, dictates that our product line will increase in popularity.

2.9 Channels

Our past marketing strategy assumes that we need to go into specialty channels to address our target customer's needs. The tie-in with the high-end quality catalogs like Sharper Image is perfect because these catalogs cater to our kind of customers. We position our products as the highest-quality, highest-price offering in any channel mix.

By including our products in these high-end catalogs, we were able to successfully target the specific niche that was our marketing milestone. This has provided the foundation for a move to internal catalog production. With a higher degree of information control internally, these catalogs will target the same audience but will include more extensive information in terms of quality, examples, testimonials, and information tailored to past sales experiences.

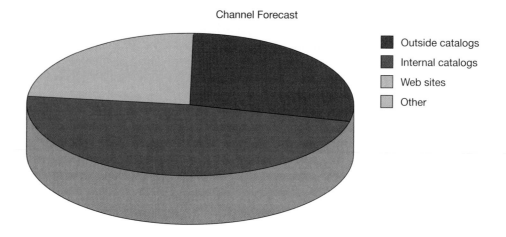

Channel Forecast

- Outside catalogs
- Internal catalogs
- Web sites
- Other

Table *Channel Forecast*

Channel	Growth	2004	2005	2006	2007	2008	CAGR
Outside catalogs	20%	120	144	173	208	250	20.14%
Internal catalogs	40%	200	280	392	549	769	40.03%
Web sites	40%	100	140	196	274	384	39.99%
Other	0%	0	0	0	0	0	0.00%
Total	35.19%	420	564	761	1,031	1,403	35.19%

3.0 Marketing Strategy

Willamette Furniture is moving toward internal marketing control by establishing programs such as an in-house catalog publishing and distribution department, detailed customer service vehicles that will allow us to track the success of our marketing and sales, and further integration with established quality catalog vendors, such as Sharper Image.

Our target markets present great opportunities for company growth, as our niche is not at all saturated at this point. We will dominate the high-end office furniture market by stressing the quality in workmanship and materials of our product lines, keeping up with and integrating technological advances in the personal computing environment, and increasing our market research and customer service to constantly satisfy our markets' needs.

The home office, small business owner, and corporate executive will greatly benefit from our quality products in terms of comfort and appreciation of the office environment. The key to reaching this market is to make them aware that our products are available. We do not need to convince them of anything but the assurance of quality in manufacturing and ergonomic design.

Chapter 3

3.1 Mission

Willamette helps create pleasant, productive office environments with well-designed furniture that incorporates new technology into the classic office model, in which real people can work happily. We are sensitive to the look and feel of good wood and fine furniture, as well as to high-powered personal computing. We always provide the best possible value to our customers who care about quality office environments, and we want every dollar spent with us to be well spent.

We also create and nurture a healthy, creative, respectful, and fun office and workshop environment, in which our employees are fairly compensated and encouraged to respect the customer and the quality of the product we produce. We seek fair and responsible profit, enough to keep the company financially healthy for the long term and to fairly compensate owners and investors for their money and risk.

Chapter 3

3.2 Marketing Objectives

Our marketing strategy assumes that we need to go into specialty channels to address our target customers' needs. The tie-in with high-end quality catalogs like Sharper Image is perfect because these catalogs cater to our kind of customers. We position as the highest quality, offering status and prestige levels of purchase.

Our presence on the World Wide Web will increase the availability of our products to the specific market segments that we wish to target. Because Willamette's product offerings concentrate on the integration of PC technologies, Web presence is a natural objective in reaching appropriate potential customers.

Finally, our movement into internal catalog publishing will provide Willamette's marketing managers with additional control over the content and recipients of our direct marketing. With experience gained through our inclusion in other high-end catalog merchants, and our managers' publishing experience, our internal catalogs will undoubtedly generate great sales increases for Willamette Furniture.

Chapter 3

3.3 Financial Objectives

1. To grow our sales more than three times over during a five-year period, from $450,000 in 2000 to $1.6 million in 2004.

2. To significantly decrease our sales and marketing expenses as a percentage of sales: from 34.5 percent this year to 26 percent by 2004.

3. To increase contribution margin from 40 percent to 48 percent over five years.

Chapter 7

3.4 Target Markets

Our segment definition is itself strategic. We are not intending to satisfy all users of office furniture intended for use with personal computers, but rather only those who are most demanding. We are definitely out to address the needs of the high-end buyer who is willing to pay more for quality.

In our particular market, we also seek the buyer who appreciates two attributes: the quality of furniture workmanship and the excellence of design, with an understanding of technology and ergonomics built in.

- *Corporate executives:* Our market research indicates about 2.5 million potential customers who are managers in corporations of more than 100 employees. The target customer is going to be at a high executive level in most cases because the purchase price is relatively steep compared to standard office furniture.

- *Small business owners:* Our customer surveys indicate a strong market among the owners of businesses with fewer than 100 employees. There are 11 million such businesses in this country, most of them with concentrated ownership that makes the owners potential customers.

- *Home offices:* The home office business has proliferated during the 1990s, and we also have home offices for people employed outside the home. This is a big market—some 36 million home offices—and it is growing faster than other markets.

Chapter 7

3.5 Positioning

Our competitive edge is our dominance of high-technology ergonomics and traditional high-quality furniture workmanship. Although there are many computer furniture manufacturers, and many computer lovers, few have brought the two crafts together as we have.

We focus on a special kind of customer, the person who wants very high-quality office furniture customized to work beautifully with modern technology, including personal computers, scanners, Internet connections, and other high-tech items. Our customer might be in larger corporations, a small or medium business, or in a home office with or without a home-office business. What is important to the customer are elegance, fine workmanship, ease of use, ergonomics, and practicality.

The product strategy is also based on quality, in this case the intersection of technical understanding with very high-quality woodworking, professional materials, and workmanship.

An important competitive edge is our assembly strategy, which is based on interlocking wood pieces of such high quality that assembly is not only a pleasure for our customers, it is actually a feature that enhances the sense of quality.

3.6 Marketing Mix

Chapter 1

Our marketing mix depends mainly on the product and product marketing, but we are also leveraging a lot more in our presence in channels than in our direct national branding. The channels are the key to our recent growth and our prospects for additional growth.

3.6.1 PRODUCT MARKETING

Chapters 8, 9, and 10

Our product marketing has to emphasize the benefits of our unique combination of technological expertise, ergonomics, and fine furniture craftsmanship. We need to sell pride of ownership and workmanship and prestige. That has to come out in our packaging, finishing, shipping, and collaterals.

Product marketing's most important challenge is the problem of assembly and packaging. We know we have the best product when we deliver it locally. That isn't necessarily so when we send it in boxes to be assembled. We have to make sure that the assembly is truly easy.

3.6.2 PROMOTION

Chapters 16, 17, 18, 19, and 20

Our promotion strategy is based mainly on making the right information available to the right target customer. We can't afford to sell people on our expensive products because most don't have the budget. What we really do is make sure that those who have the budget and appreciate the product know that it exists and know where to find it.

The marketing has to convey the sense of quality in every picture, every promotion, and every publication. We can't afford to appear in second-rate catalogs with poor illustrations that make the product look less than it is. We also need to leverage our presence using high-quality catalogs and specialty distributors.

3.6.3 SERVICE

Chapter 8

The service aspect of Willamette's marketing mix is limited in traditional terms. That is, due to our high degree of quality in manufacturing and assembly, our product lines do not require continued maintenance or service. However, we do consider our customer service to be key to the retention of customers. Willamette manufactures many accessories in addition to our main executive desk lines. As a result, we offer a fully integrated office environment, including peripherals such as lamps, cabinets, tables, and chairs. Therefore, a Willamette Furniture customer is not considered to be a one-time buyer. The establishment of a quality office environment can be an ongoing process. Willamette will continue to offer additional pieces to our customers, targeting them based on their previous purchases.

3.6.4 CHANNELS OF DISTRIBUTION

Chapters 13 and 15

The four main manufacturers are selling direct to the office superstores and buying discount clubs. This accounts for the main volume of distribution. The office furniture customer seems to be growing steadily more comfortable with the retail buy in the chain store.

The major corporate purchases are still made directly with manufacturers. Although this is a major channel for some of the more traditional manufacturers, it is essentially closed to new competition. The direct channel is dominated by two manufacturers and two distributors. The distributors will occasionally take on a new line—happily, this has helped Willamette—but the main growth is in retail.

Published research indicates that 51 percent of the total sales volume in the market goes through the retail channel, most of that major national chains. Another 23 percent goes through the direct sales channel, although in this case direct sales include sales by distributors who are buying from multiple manufacturers. Most of the remainder, 18 percent, is sold directly to buyers by catalogs.

In the mainstream business, channels are critical to volume. The manufacturers with impact in the national sales are going to win display space in the store, and most buyers seem content to pick their product off the store floor. Price is critical because the channels take significant margins. Buyers are willing to settle for laminated quality and serviceable design.

In direct sales to corporations, price and volume are critical. The corporate buyer wants trouble-free buying in volume, at a great price. Reliable delivery is as important as reliable quality.

In the high-end specialty market, particularly in our niche, features are very important. Our target customer is not making selections based on price. The ergonomics, design, and accommodation of computer features within the high-quality feel of good wood are much more important than mere price. We are also seeing that assembly is critical to shipping and packing, but our customer doesn't accept any assembly problems. We need to make sure that the piece comes together almost like magic, and as it does, it presents a greater feel of quality than if it hadn't required assembly at all.

Table   *Channel Analysis*

Channel	Reach	Comarketing	Payments	Cost
Outside catalogs	10	8	1	5
Internal catalogs	2	1	8	2
Web sites	4	7	9	2
Other	0	0	0	0

Chapter 6

3.7 Marketing Research

Due to the market segmentation that Willamette Furniture has established, we will require constant updates in terms of the potential sizes, distributions, and purchasing patterns of the quality-conscious, technology-utilizing executive markets. We will use our historical performance to establish a customer database containing this information. This will allow Willamette to target customers more efficiently as a result of actual experience. Furthermore, because our customer service and follow-up are key to establishing retained customers, the marketing database will allow us to divide the potential buying patterns of customers into categories based on future needs.

4.0 Financials

The financial picture is quite encouraging. We have been slow to take on debt, but with our increase in sales we do expect to apply for a credit line with the bank, to a limit of $150,000. The credit line is easily supported by assets.

We do expect to be able to take some money out as dividends. The owners don't take overly generous salaries, so some draw is appropriate.

Appendix B

4.1 Break-Even Analysis

Our break-even analysis is based on running costs, the "burn-rate" costs we incur to keep the business running, not on theoretical fixed costs that would be relevant only if we were closing. Between payroll, rent, utilities, and basic marketing costs, we think $30,000 is a good estimate of fixed costs.

Our assumptions on average unit sales and average per-unit costs depend on averaging. We don't really need to calculate an exact average; this is close enough to help us understand what a real break-even point might be.

The essential insight here is that our sales level seems to be running comfortably above break-even.

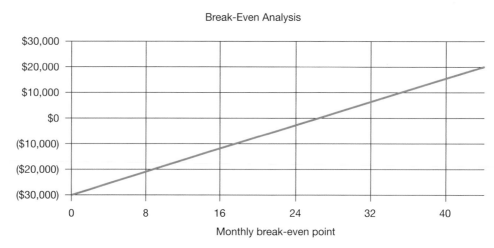

Break-Even Analysis

Monthly break-even point

Break-even point = where line intersects with 0

Table	Break-Even Analysis
Monthly units break-even	26
Monthly revenue break-even	$40,435
Assumptions:	
Average per-unit revenue	$1,550.00
Average per-unit variable cost	$400.00
Estimated monthly fixed cost	$30,000

Chapter 7

4.2 Sales Forecast

Our sales forecast assumes no change in costs or prices, which is a reasonable assumption for the last few years.

We are expecting to increase sales growth from $350,000 last year to $450,000 this year. The growth forecast is in line with our last year and is relatively high for our industry because we are developing new channels. In 2001 and 2002 we expect growth closer to 60 percent per year, to a projected total of more than $1 million in 2002.

For 2000 we plan to internally develop a company catalog, which will include some other products for the same target customers. The focus will be an executive-level office catalog, with furniture, lamps, and other accessories.

Our Oregon location is a distinct advantage for local wood. We can buy higher-quality oak and cherry than either of our competitors (one in California, one in New York). Since our sales increased over the last two years, we have been able to buy at better prices because of higher volumes.

We work with three wood suppliers, all local. Bambridge supplies most of our oak and a bit of cherry and some other specialty woods. Bambridge has been in business for as long as we have, and has given us good service and good prices. This is a good, stable supplier. Duffin Wood Products is a good second source, particularly for cherry and specialty woods. We've used Merlin supplies as well, frequently for filling in when either of our main two suppliers were short.

We also work with a number of specialty manufacturers for furniture fittings, drawer accessories, glass, shelving accessories, and related purchases.

Although we aren't a major player compared to the largest furniture manufacturers, we are one of the biggest buyers of the custom materials we need. Most of our suppliers are selling through channels to hobbyists and carpenters, so they treat us as a major account.

We depend on our dominance of the latest in technology of ergonomics, combined with classic design elements of fine furniture. We must remain on top of new technologies in display, input and output, and communications. For example, our latest models are already assuming the desktop digital scanner as a frequent accessory, and audio for use in creating presentations, e-mail attachments, and so on.

Our assembly patents are an important competitive edge. No competitor can match the way we turn a drawback—having to assemble the product—into a feature. Our customer surveys confirm that customers take the interlocking assembly system as an enhancement to the sense of quality.

In 2000 we will introduce the new line based on the executive laptop computer, with a docking station to connect to a network. The new variation on the executive desk line has a different configuration to assume easy access to the docking station, and better use of the space that doesn't have to be dedicated to the CPU case.

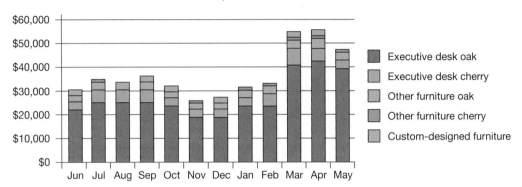

Monthly Sales Forecast

Table   *Sales Forecast*

Unit Sales	2005	2006	2007	2008	2009
Executive desk oak	209	350	600	700	770
Executive desk cherry	31	35	40	45	50
Other furniture oak	45	50	50	55	55
Other furniture cherry	7	10	10	12	12
Custom-designed furniture	6	10	20	30	50
Total unit sales	298	455	720	842	937
Unit Prices	**2005**	**2006**	**2007**	**2008**	**2009**
Executive desk oak	$1,600.00	$1,600.00	$1,600.00	$1,600.00	$1,600.00
Executive desk cherry	$1,750.00	$1,750.00	$1,750.00	$1,750.00	$1,750.00
Other furniture oak	$900.00	$900.00	$900.00	$900.00	$900.00
Other furniture cherry	$1,000.00	$1,000.00	$1,000.00	$1,000.00	$1,000.00
Custom-designed furniture	$2,500.00	$2,500.00	$2,500.00	$2,500.00	$2,500.00
Sales	**2005**	**2006**	**2007**	**2008**	**2009**
Executive desk oak	$334,400	$560,000	$960,000	$1,120,000	$1,232,000
Executive desk cherry	$54,250	$61,250	$70,000	$78,750	$87,500
Other furniture oak	$40,500	$45,000	$45,000	$49,500	$49,500
Other furniture cherry	$7,000	$10,000	$10,000	$12,000	$12,000
Custom-designed furniture	$15,000	$25,000	$50,000	$75,000	$125,000
Total sales	$451,150	$701,250	$1,135,000	$1,335,250	$1,506,000
Direct Unit Costs	**2005**	**2006**	**2007**	**2008**	**2009**
Executive desk oak	$400.00	$400.00	$400.00	$400.00	$400.00
Executive desk cherry	$525.00	$525.00	$525.00	$525.00	$525.00
Other furniture oak	$180.00	$180.00	$180.00	$180.00	$180.00
Other furniture cherry	$300.00	$300.00	$300.00	$300.00	$300.00
Custom-designed furniture	$625.00	$625.00	$625.00	$625.00	$625.00
Direct Cost of Sales	**2005**	**2006**	**2007**	**2008**	**2009**
Executive desk oak	$83,600	$140,000	$240,000	$280,000	$308,000
Executive desk cherry	$16,275	$18,375	$21,000	$23,625	$26,250
Other furniture oak	$8,100	$9,000	$9,000	$9,900	$9,900
Other furniture cherry	$2,100	$3,000	$3,000	$3,600	$3,600
Custom-designed furniture	$3,750	$6,250	$12,500	$18,750	$31,250
Subtotal direct cost of sales	$113,825	$176,625	$285,500	$335,875	$379,000

Chapter 7

4.2.1 SALES BY MANAGER Willamette's sales in terms of our management structure are represented in the following table. Jack and Cassidy are our strongest generators of sales because of their established relationships with past customers and channels. We will bring on two new managers due to our progress on the Internet and through internal catalog publishing. Although the first-year sales projections for Sampson and Bertha are not extremely high, their positions and customer interactions will increase exponentially with the completion of our Web sites and internal catalogs. Willamette has decided to bring them on early because Peggy will be taking a leave of absence during the summer months of 2000. The overlap will also allow Sampson and Bertha to become quite familiar with our product offerings before their respective departments are online.

Chapter 7

4.2.2 SALES BY SEGMENT Willamette's sales by program forecasts are a direct result of past performance stemming from outside catalog marketing and market research. Our expanding markets are, by default, heavy users of the World Wide Web. With our technological integration that is key to Willamette's product offerings, it can be assumed that our target customers will find our products via the Internet (with a relatively aggressive Internet marketing scheme).

Chapter 7

4.2.3 SALES BY PROGRAM Our sales by segment show how strategically we have targeted our market segments in the past and project to continue to do so successfully. With historical experience in targeting these market segments, Willamette will only increase in its market share due to expansions in marketing programs tailored to our past success.

Appendix B

4.3 Expense Forecast

Our expenses occur as the result of both historically successful marketing endeavors and projected marketing programs designed to take advantage of expanding markets and improved product lines. We will be moving into the realm of Internet marketing and sales in the year 2000. The initial costs are high relative to the maintenance costs involved after the Web sites' creation. Similarly, the development of an in-house catalog design and publishing department will incur higher start-up expenses than maintenance costs after the initial publication. We have chosen these two new marketing programs as areas where expenses can initially build up because research indicates that they will cause our market share to increase exponentially over time.

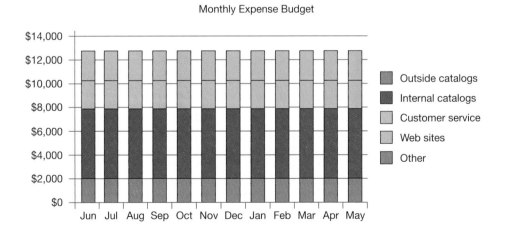

Appendix B

4.3.1 EXPENSES BY MANAGER Willamette Furniture's expenses in terms of manager are directly proportional to the managed program's potential. As our market share increases and capital is generated, we will support further marketing programs and the expansion of current programs, thus increasing our management budgets for these specific departments and projects.

Table   *Marketing Expense Budget*

Marketing Expense Budget	2005	2006	2007	2008	2009
Outside catalogs	$24,000	$50,000	$100,000	$125,000	$150,000
Internal catalogs	$72,000	$104,000	$125,000	$125,000	$125,000
Customer service	$30,000	$40,000	$50,000	$55,000	$60,000
Web sites	$30,000	$30,000	$40,000	$50,000	$60,000
Other	$0	$0	$0	$0	$0
Total sales and marketing expenses	$156,000	$224,000	$315,000	$355,000	$395,000
Percentage of sales	34.58%	31.94%	27.75%	26.59%	26.23%
Contribution margin	$181,325	$300,625	$534,500	$644,375	$732,000
Contribution margin/sales	40.19%	42.87%	47.09%	48.26%	48.61%

Appendix B

4.3.2 EXPENSES BY SEGMENT   Willamette Furniture's expenses in terms of marketing programs are directly proportional to the proposed and historical success of these programs. As our market share increases and capital is generated, we will support further marketing programs and the expansion of current programs.

Appendix B

4.3.3 EXPENSES BY PROGRAM   Willamette Furniture's expenses in terms of market segment are directly proportional to the segment's potential. As our market share increases and capital is generated, we will support further marketing programs and the expansion of current programs.

Chapter 3

4.4 Linking Expenses to Strategy and Tactics

Willamette's growth in sales revenue will happen as a result of the implementation of new marketing programs in accordance with market growth. The expenses generated by these new marketing strategies will be greater in the initial design and implementation stages than in later maintenance stages. For example, it is proven that an Internet presence will increase our sales anywhere from 3 percent to 10 percent. Therefore, it is worth an initial expenditure of $30,000 for design and staffing to maintain the Web sites. Web site expenses increase as Web site importance increases. We will use our increased capital to make wise infrastructure purchases such as internal catalog publishing capabilities and additional design and manufacturing tools.

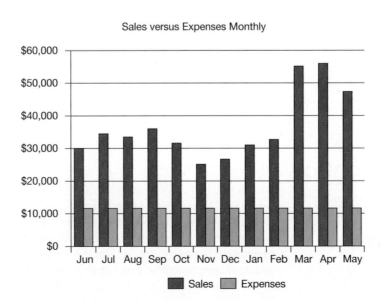

Appendix B
and Chapter 12

4.5 Contribution Margins

Willamette's sales will increase as a result of market growth, market share increase, and Internet presence. Our gross margin will remain steady at approximately 75 percent. The contribution margin will steadily increase as a result of the initial expenses involved with starting marketing programs such as internal catalog publication and Web site development. These second-year expense decreases will offset the increases in retained customer expenses, custom product line development, and outside catalog expansion.

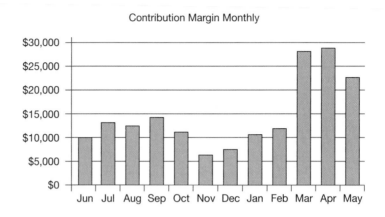

Table   *Contribution Margin*

Contribution Margin	2005	2006	2007	2008	2009
Sales	$451,150	$701,250	$1,135,000	$1,335,250	$1,506,000
Direct costs of goods	$113,825	$176,625	$285,500	$335,875	$379,000
Other variable costs of sales	$0	$0	$0	$0	$0
Cost of goods sold	$113,825	$176,625	$285,500	$335,875	$379,000
Gross margin	$337,325	$524,625	$849,500	$999,375	$1,127,000
Gross margin %	74.77%	74.81%	74.85%	74.85%	74.83%
Marketing Expense Budget	**2005**	**2006**	**2007**	**2008**	**2009**
Outside catalogs	$24,000	$50,000	$100,000	$125,000	$150,000
Internal catalogs	$72,000	$104,000	$125,000	$125,000	$125,000
Customer service	$30,000	$40,000	$50,000	$55,000	$60,000
Web sites	$30,000	$30,000	$40,000	$50,000	$60,000
Other	$0	$0	$0	$0	$0
Total sales and marketing expenses	$156,000	$224,000	$315,000	$355,000	$395,000
Percentage of sales	34.58%	31.94%	27.75%	26.59%	26.23%
Contribution margin	$181,325	$300,625	$534,500	$644,375	$732,000
Contribution margin/sales	40.19%	42.87%	47.09%	48.26%	48.61%

5.0 Controls

The executive furniture market is steadily increasing at an average calculated annual growth rate of 7.75 percent. With this in mind, our marketing programs will expand accordingly. The addition of an internally created catalog will allow Willamette to market to this expanding number of potential customers. Sales will increase accordingly, providing working capital for internal product development, marketing department growth, and Internet development. A presence on the Internet will be a key milestone to expanding sales and marketing potentials through the utilization of new channels.

Chapter 3

5.1 Implementation

Willamette Furniture will begin the year 2000 by continuing to strengthen our alliances with established partners in distribution. We will prepare our catalog placements internally, submitting them by the middle of January 2000. Simultaneously, the internal catalog plan will be polished and submitted by the end of January 2000. This will be possible with the expertise of Rebecca King and James Black, who have brought their industry knowledge to the marketing department of Willamette Furniture. With the completion of this plan, design stages will occur from February 2000 through the middle of March 2000. This time frame is accurate because we have experience in the design stage, as we have historically submitted our own designs to outside catalog vendors. As in past years, spring and fall trade shows will occur at their normal times. These shows will provide test cases for our internal catalog design. Our last milestone category to be implemented will be the expansion of our product distribution through the addition of three new distributors to our current lineup. These distributors will increase our customer base nationwide.

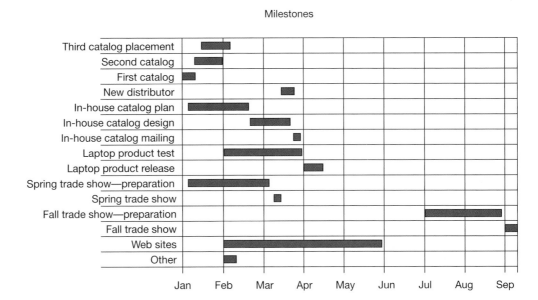

| Table | *Milestones* |

Milestone	Start Date	End Date	Budget	Manager	Department
Third catalog placement	1/15/00	2/5/00	$30,000	Jack	Ads
Second catalog	1/10/00	1/31/00	$40,000	Jack	Ads
First catalog	1/1/00	1/11/00	$50,000	Jack	Ads
New distributor	3/15/00	3/25/00	$5,000	Cassidy	Travel
In-house catalog plan	1/5/00	2/19/00	$3,000	Cassidy	Sales
In-house catalog design	2/21/00	3/22/00	$0	Bertha	Other
In-house catalog mailing	3/25/00	3/30/00	$2,000	Bertha	Other
Laptop product test	2/1/00	4/1/00	$5,000	Terry	Other
Laptop product release	4/1/00	4/16/00	$1,000	Sampson	Other
Spring trade show—preparation	1/5/00	3/5/00	$5,000	Terry	PR
Spring trade show	3/10/00	3/15/00	$15,000	Terry	PR
Fall trade show—preparation	7/1/00	8/30/00	$5,000	Terry	PR
Fall trade show	9/1/00	9/11/00	$15,000	Terry	Travel
Web sites	2/1/00	5/31/00	$20,000	Jack	IT
Other	2/1/00	2/11/00	$0	Jack	IT
Totals			$196,000		

Chapter 3

5.2 Marketing Organization

Susan Graham, president, is responsible for overall business management. Our managers of finance, marketing, and sales report directly to Susan. Susan had a successful career in retail before becoming half owner of Willamette. She was an area manager of Ross Stores, a buyer for Macy's, and merchandising assistant for Sears and Roebuck. She has a degree in literature from the University of Notre Dame.

Jim Graham, designer, is responsible for product design and development, assembly, and manufacturing. Our workshop manager reports directly to him. Jim designed furniture for Haines Manufacturing before becoming half owner of Willamette. He was responsible for one of the first executive desks designed to include customized fittings for personal computers, and was one of the first to design the monitor inside the desk under glass. He has a B.S. and an M.S. in industrial design from Stanford University and the University of Oregon, respectively.

As co-owners, Jim and Susan jointly develop business strategy and long-term plans. Jim is strong on product know-how and technology, and Susan is strong on management and business know-how.

Terry Hatcher, 34, is marketing manager. Terry joined Willamette from the marketing department of the Thomasville Furniture chain, having been in charge of national catalog production and catalog advertising. Terry also managed direct sales at one of the furniture distributors that has since died to industry consolidation. Terry has a B.A. degree in literature from the University of Washington.

Our sales and marketing managers are in the process of revolutionizing the way in which Willamette Furniture reaches its customers. Both of these departments have been integrated with our information technology area in order to sell and market Willamette's product through our own internal Web site. In addition, we have started the publication of our own catalog. Due to the success in marketing with high-end retailers and catalog merchants such as Sharper Image, we have decided to implement this new, internal strategy for future growth and increased market share. If the executive-level employees nationwide are aware of our product offerings, Willamette Furniture will soon become a part of every quality office environment.

Chapter 3

5.3 Contingency Planning

Willamette Furniture is unique in its discovery and utilization of the high-quality, executive-level computer-integrated office furniture niche. Therefore, it is possible that with our success and superior design, other well-established furniture manufacturers may release a competitive product line. However, Willamette focuses specifically on the high-end, technologically integrated aspect of office furniture. With this exclusive concentration, Willamette can continue to focus its resources on producing the best executive-level office furniture available. Another possible challenge would be the emergence of a new company in our niche. This, however, would not be quite as threatening because its initial market share would be minuscule, allowing us to strategize further for continued success. Finally, an established furniture company may choose to begin marketing to our target market. This would not be overly threatening because our products are inherently the best available due to the true craftsmanship involved in their design and manufacture.

Notes to Appendix A

[1]The marketing plan outline included in this appendix is available from Marketing Plan Pro: Palo Alto Software (*http://www.mplans.com/spm/* or *http://www.paloalto.com*).

Appendix B

Applications of Mathematical and Financial Tools to Marketing Decisions

Marketing decisions are often enhanced by the use of mathematical and financial analyses. These computations are helpful in setting prices, evaluating financial aspects of the firm, evaluating suppliers, determining inventory order quantities, and estimating segment potentials. Analysis of the firm's income statement is crucial for control and performance evaluation. This appendix describes and presents example calculations for some of the most frequently used mathematical and financial tools.

Supplier Selection

Business buyers frequently use weighted indexes to evaluate suppliers. As explained in Chapter 5, buyers base decisions regarding selection of suppliers or vendors on the criteria they consider most important. Exhibit B–1 shows a simplified weighted index approach for evaluating two suppliers, A and B. This example is from the experiences of General Electric and its purchases of electrical wiring devices.

In this example, five criteria are used to evaluate two suppliers: quality performance, delivery performance, technical capability, quoted price, and service factors. Price and delivery performance are weighted most heavily. These weights reflect a consensus of managerial judgment and past experiences with purchases of this type of product. Each supplier is evaluated on a 1-to-10 scale for each attribute, with 10 being the best possible rating. The scores are multiplied by an importance weight for each criterion. The "total" columns are summed to produce a score for each supplier. In this case, supplier B, with an overall total score of 867, is selected as the preferred vendor.

Exhibit B–1		Supplier A		Supplier B	
		Simplified weighted decision matrix			
Evaluation Criteria	**Importance Weight**	**Score**	**Total**	**Score**	**Total**
Quality performance	14%	9.7	136	9.4	132
Delivery performance	26	8.2	213	7.7	200
Technical capability	11	10.0	110	8.3	91
Quoted price	42	7.3	307	9.1	382
Service factors	7	6.3	44	8.7	62
Overall total	**100%**	—	**810**	—	**867**

Estimating Segment Potentials

The "Survey of Buying Power" published annually by *Sales & Marketing Management* magazine enables the computation of the *buying power index (BPI)* for individual geographic market segments. Frequently used to evaluate market segment potentials, the BPI is a measure of a particular market's ability to buy. The index converts three basic elements—population, effective buying income (EBI), and retail sales—into a measure of a market's ability to purchase, expressed as a percentage of the total U.S. potential. The three elements are weighted as follows: 0.2, population; 0.3, U.S. retail sales potential; and 0.5, EBI, or effective buying income. The latter weight reflects the importance of income to buying potential. The BPI for a market can be computed as follows:

$$BPI = (0.5)(EBI) + (0.3)(\text{Retail sales }\%) + (0.2)(\text{Population }\%)$$

The computations in Exhibit B–2 provide an example. Specifically, a skiing equipment company in West Virginia is considering expanding its sales operations into one of two neighboring states, Pennsylvania or Kentucky. The company offers premier equipment that it sells at premium prices. Its equipment is targeted toward young adults, aged 25 to 45 years old, with an EBI of at least $35,000.

The figures in Exhibit B–2 suggest that Pennsylvania offers the greatest potential as a market. However, other factors, such as the cost of living, competition, and the legal environment, may differ between these two states as well. Consequently, BPI comparisons should be used in conjunction with other information.

Price Determination

In this section of the appendix, we discuss the break-even formula, elasticities of demand, and methods for computing retail markups. First, we present break-even formulas for quantity (units) and revenue (dollars). Second, we look at examples of other forms of elasticity and discuss profit maximization. Third, we explain markups and markdowns.

Exhibit B-2	*Evaluating geographic target segments*		
	Pennsylvania	**Kentucky**	**United States**
Households aged 25–45	3,746,733	1,295,057	89,860,221
Households with EBI > $35,000	2,688,726	772,092	59,068,857
General merchandise stores' sales ($000)	$109,948,462	$33,332,675	$2,460,886,012

To construct a customized BPI for evaluating each state, the company made the following calculations:

Step 1. The ratio of each state's markets to those of the entire United States:

Pennsylvania	**Kentucky**
% of households aged 25–45:	% of households aged 25–45:
3,746,733/89,860,221 = .041	1,295,057/89,860,221 = .014
% of households with EBI > $35,000:	% of households with EBI > $35,000:
2,688,726/59,068,857 = .045	772,092/59,068,857 = .013
% of general merchandise stores' sales:	% of general merchandise stores' sales:
$109,948,462/$2,460,886,012 = .044	$33,332,675/$2,460,886,012 = .013

Step 2. The company assigns importance weights as follows:

Households aged 25–45	(20%) or .20
Households with EBI > $35,000	(50%) or .50
General merchandise stores' sales	(30%) or .30

Note: These weights sum to 1.0.

Step 3. The BPI is the weighted sum of the three components:

Pennsylvania

$(.20 \times .041) + (.50 \times .045) + (.30 \times .044) = .0439$

Kentucky

$(.20 \times .014) + (.50 \times .013) + (.30 \times .013) = .0132$

Break-Even Analysis

The traditional break-even formula is based on the premise that the break-even point (BEP) in units occurs when total revenues equal total costs. The break-even quantity in units is defined as

$$Q(BE) = \frac{\text{Fixed costs}}{\text{Price} - \text{Variable cost per unit}}$$

The break-even point in dollars is computed as:

$$Q(BE\$) = \frac{\text{Fixed costs}}{1 - (\text{Variable cost}/\text{Price})}$$

The *BEP* in units is derived as follows. Remember that the *BEP* occurs where total costs equal total revenues:

$$TR = TC$$
$$P \times Q = FC + (VC \times Q)$$
$$\text{and } TC = FC + (VC \times Q)$$
$$P \times Q - VC \times Q = FC$$
$$Q(P - VC) = FC$$

Therefore, the BEP in units is $Q(BEP) = FC/(P - VC)$.

This analysis can be extended by considering the effects of different prices and quantity demanded. For example, the data presented in Exhibit B–3 show how the break-even quantity can vary as prices rise and demand declines. Notice the inverse relationship between price and demand. In this example, total fixed cost is $15,000 and variable cost per unit is $7.

This "sensitivity analysis" allows managers to consider alternative assumptions and conditions. It greatly enhances the managerial usefulness and realism of the break-even approach.

Elasticity

Price elasticity represents the change in quantity demanded from a change in price. Elasticities greater than 1 indicate elastic demand; that is, a 1 percent change in price causes a greater percentage change in demand. Inelastic demand occurs when a 1 percent price change results in less than a 1 percent change in demand. A commonly used computational approach for estimating elasticity is to compute the arc elasticity, where the price elasticity of demand is measured over a range using the average price and quantity as the base.

Arc elasticity of demand is computed as follows:

$$E_d = \frac{(Q_2 - Q_1)/[(Q_1 + Q_2)/2]}{(P_2 - P_1)/[(P_1 + P_2)/2]}$$

Exhibit B–3		*Break-even points from different prices and quantities demanded*					
Price	**Quantity Demanded (000s)**	**Total Revenue ($000)**	**Total Fixed Costs ($000)**	**Total Variable Costs ($000)**	**Total Costs ($000)**	**Break-Even Quantity (000s)**	**Profit ($000)**
$10	5.0	$50.0	$15.0	$35.0	$50.0	5.00	$ 0.0
11	4.9	53.9	15.0	34.3	49.3	3.75	4.6
12	4.6	55.2	15.0	32.2	47.2	3.00	8.0
13	4.4	57.2	15.0	30.8	45.8	2.50	11.4
14	4.1	57.4	15.0	28.7	43.7	2.14	13.7
15	3.5	52.5	15.0	24.5	39.5	1.87	13.0

For example, at the price of $8 per ticket, the average moviegoer demands three tickets per month. At a price of $6 per ticket, the average moviegoer purchases five tickets per month. The price elasticity for this example is

$$E_d = \frac{(5-3)/[(3+5)/2]}{(6-8)/[(8+6)/2]} = -1.8$$

Therefore, the price elasticity of demand over this price range is elastic. Remember that price elasticities are normally negative and that typically the negative sign, while shown here, is omitted.

Cross-price elasticity reflects quantity changes in one good or service caused by changing prices of other goods or services. This concept is useful for examining relationships among complementary goods (printers, personal computers) and substitutes (competitive brands, items in a product line, and pure substitutes such as DVD rental charges and movie prices). Conceptually, cross elasticity can be expressed as follows:

$$E_c = \frac{\text{Change in quantity demanded for product A}}{\text{Change in price for product B}}$$

If E_c is positive, products A and B are substitutes. If E_c is negative, the two products are complementary.

Assume the price of a Kodak 35-millimeter camera is $119 and a comparable Minolta is $125. Further, assume the quantities demanded for the Kodak and Minolta cameras at these prices are 50,000 and 100,000 units, respectively. When Kodak lowers its price to $116, the demand increases to 60,000. The Minolta demand, however, declines to 95,000 units. The cross-price elasticity for the Minolta camera is

$$E_c = \frac{-5,000/100,000}{-\$3/\$119} = 2.0$$

In this example, the two cameras are substitutes; hence, decreasing the price of one brand decreases the demand for the other.

Profit Maximization

The traditional economic perspective on price setting is based on the premise that profits are maximized when marginal revenue equals marginal cost. Marginal revenue is the amount obtained from selling one additional unit of a product—this is usually the price paid for the unit. Marginal cost is the cost of producing and selling one additional unit of a product.

The cost and revenue data presented in Exhibit B–4 can be used to analyze these relationships for a hypothetical manufacturer of personalized T-shirts. The corresponding cost and revenue curves are depicted in Exhibit B–5. Note that in columns 4, Marginal Revenue,

Exhibit B–4		*Sales and cost information for personalized T-shirts*					
(1)	**(2)**	**(3)**	**(4)**	**(5)**	**(6)**	**(7)**	**(8)**
Quantity Q	Price P	Total Revenue $TR = Q \times P$	Marginal Revenue MR	Total Cost TC	Average Total Cost $ATC = \dfrac{TC}{Q}$	Marginal Cost MC	Profit $\pi = TR - TC$
0	$15	$ 0		$ 3.00	—		$ −3.00
1	14	14	$11	9.50	$9.50	$ 9.00	4.50
2	13	26	9	12.00	6.00	7.00	14.00
3	12	36	7	14.00	4.66	3.00	22.00
4	11	44	5	19.00	4.75	5.00	25.00
5	10	50	3	24.00	4.80	6.50	26.00
6	9	54	1	28.00	4.66	9.50	26.00
7	8	56	−1	47.00	6.91	21.00	9.00

Exhibit B–5	*Intersection of marginal cost and marginal revenue curves*

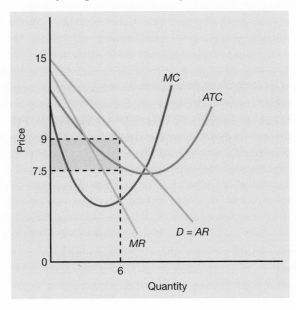

and 7, Marginal Cost, the manufacturer continues to expand output as long as marginal revenue exceeds marginal cost. Any expansion in output beyond this point would increase costs more than it would revenue. Therefore, the optimal output is six units priced at $9. Profits are maximized at that level:

$$\text{Profit} = TR - TC = \$54 - \$28 = \$26$$

Exhibit B–5 plots these findings. It shows that profits are maximized when price equals $9 and quantity equals 6. Notice that marginal costs initially decline as output increases. The shaded profit area is computed by multiplying unit profit times quantity of output:

$$\begin{aligned} \text{Profit} &= (AR - ATC) \times Q \\ &= (\$9 - \$4.66) \times 6 \\ &= \$26.04 \end{aligned}$$

In this case, unit profit is the difference between average revenue and average total cost.

Markups and Markdowns

Retail markups can be computed on either cost or the selling price. Markup as a percentage of cost is calculated as

$$\text{Markup} = \frac{\text{Selling price} - \text{Cost}}{\text{Cost}}$$

Assume, for example, that a new Wilson tennis racket costs a retailer $85 and the markup is $60. Therefore, the selling price is $145. The markups on cost and price are

$$\text{Markup on cost} = \$60/\$85 = 71\%$$
$$\text{Markup on price} = \$60/\$145 = 41\%$$

Frequently, retailers desire to convert markup percentages on cost to markup percentages on price and vice versa. The computational procedures for making these conversions are

$$\text{Markup on cost} = \frac{\text{Markup on selling price}}{100\% - \text{Markup on selling price}}$$

$$\text{Markup on price} = \frac{\text{Markup on cost}}{100\% + \text{Markup on cost}}$$

Price reductions are common practice in retailing. In these instances, the retailer may wish to know what the percentage markdown is:

$$\text{Markdown on initial selling price} = \frac{\text{Initial selling price} - \text{Reduced sale price}}{\text{Initial selling price}}$$

$$\text{Markdown on reduced sale price} = \frac{\text{Initial selling price} - \text{Reduced sale price}}{\text{Reduced sale price}}$$

Return on Inventory Investment

Retailers evaluate merchandising performance of departments using the *gross margin return on inventory investments (GMROI)*. The GMROI combines the effects of both profits and turnover. Because both are considered, the GMROI enables comparison between retail store areas that differ in turnover and gross margin. It is computed as follows:

$$GMROI = \frac{\text{Gross margin}}{\text{Net sales}} \times \frac{\text{Net sales}}{\text{Average inventory}} = \frac{\text{Gross margin}}{\text{Average inventory}}$$

Average inventory is usually expressed in terms of costs.

Inventory turnover, which is also used to evaluate how well investments in inventory are used, is the number of times inventory turns over or is sold, typically in a year. Inventory turnover is computed as

$$\text{Inventory turnover} = \frac{\text{Cost of goods sold}}{\text{Average inventory cost}}$$

where average inventory equals (Beginning inventory + Ending inventory)/2. If for example, the cost of goods sold during a year was $800,000 and the average inventory was $400,000, then inventory turnover was 2. This value can be compared with that of competitive firms to evaluate inventory investment and firm performance.

Balancing Physical Distribution Costs

One of the objectives of a distribution system is to provide adequate levels of customer service at reasonable costs. Companies would like to carry high inventories so they can fill orders promptly and maintain high service levels. As inventories increase, however, costs to the firm rise as well. These relationships are depicted graphically in Exhibit B–6.

As Exhibit B–6 shows, total costs represent the sum of two offsetting costs. Order-processing costs, which decline as average inventory increases, include setup costs, manufacturing costs, and administrative costs. Inventory-carrying costs increase as average inventory increases. Carrying costs include storage, insurance, investment, and obsoles-

| **Exhibit B–6** | *Determining optimal order quantity* |

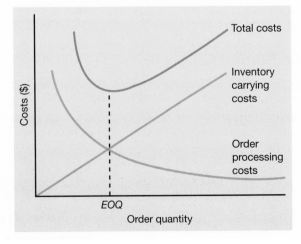

cence costs. The *economic order quantity (EOQ)* model offers one approach for determining inventory order quantities that balance these costs. Specifically, the EOQ model can be derived from the total cost relationships presented in Exhibit B–6 as follows:

$$\text{Total costs} = \text{Carrying costs} + \text{Ordering costs} = \frac{QCI}{2} + \frac{RS}{Q}$$

where

Q = order quantity
C = unit cost
I = opportunity cost (%)
R = annual demand
S = ordering, setup cost

Note that $(Q/2)$ is the average inventory and (R/S) is the number of orders required per year. The objective is to select the quantity that minimizes the total cost curve (see Exhibit B–6). Therefore, using basic calculus, the equation can be differentiated with respect to Q:

$$TC'(Q) = \frac{CI}{2} + (-1)\frac{RS}{Q^2} = 0$$

By setting this zero and solving for Q, the EOQ model is derived:

$$EOQ = \sqrt{\tfrac{2RS}{CI}}$$

The model assumes that the pattern of demand is constant, that the lead time from order to delivery is constant, that all the order is received in a batch, and that stockouts do not occur. This approach can easily be modified to include the maintenance of safety stocks to further enhance service levels.

As an example, assume a manager wishes to determine the economic order quantity for a product that costs $4 and has annual sales of 700 units. The ordering cost is $100, and the opportunity cost of capital is 25 percent.

$$EOQ = \sqrt{\frac{2(700)(\$100)}{(\$4)(.25)}} = 374 \text{ units}$$

Total inventory costs for this product then would be

$$TC = \frac{374}{2}(4)(.25) + \frac{700}{374}(100) = 187 + 187 = \$374$$

Income Statement and Performance Ratios   The income statement summarizes the firm's revenues and expenses over an accounting period, usually 12 months beginning either July 1 or January 1. The income statement shown in Exhibit B–7 is for a manufacturer and marketer of aluminum components for compact disk manufacturers. (Income statements can also be developed for specific brands or projects.) Total and net sales are shown at the top of the statement. Net sales ($861,894) are determined by subtracting returns, allowances, and discounts from total sales. Gross profit is the amount remaining after costs of goods sold are subtracted from net sales. Operating income ($75,898) is the amount of funds available after operating expenses have been subtracted from gross profits. Net income is the final amount left after nonoperating items (interest expenses) and corporate income taxes have been paid.

This statement is useful in evaluating the performance of the firm. From the income statement, a number of frequently used ratios can be determined. Performance ratios based on the income statement include gross margin ratio, net income ratio, cost-of-goods-sold ratio, operating expense ratio, sales efficiency ratio, and return on investment (ROI).

$$\text{Gross margin ratio} = \frac{\text{Gross margin}}{\text{Net sales}} = \frac{\$340,151}{\$861,894} = 39\%$$

Exhibit B-7	*Income statement for year ended December 31, 2006*		
Sales revenue			$925,476
	Less: Returns and allowances	$ 47,257	
	Discounts	16,325	
	Total		63,582
Net sales			861,894
	Less: Cost of goods sold		521,743
Gross profits on sales (gross margin)			340,151
Operating expenses			
	Salaries	$142,000	
	Rent	21,000	
	Miscellaneous office	1,874	
	Marketing	53,251	
	Depreciation	27,000	
	Insurance	2,512	
	Utilities	3,942	
	Payroll taxes	11,274	
	Bad debts	1,400	
	Total operating expenses		264,253
Operating income			75,898
Nonoperating items			
	Interest expense	$ 8,700	
	Purchase discounts lost	625	
	Total nonoperating items		9,325
Net income before corporate income taxes			66,573
	Less: Corporate income taxes		36,522
NET INCOME			$30,051
Net income per weighted share of common stock outstanding			3.347

This ratio represents the percentage of sales revenue available to cover operating expenses and profit objectives.

$$\text{Net income ratio} = \frac{\text{Net income}}{\text{Net sales}} = \frac{\$30,051}{\$861,894} = 3\%$$

The net income ratio reflects the percentage of each sales dollar that is profit before corporate income taxes.

$$\text{Cost-of-goods-sold ratio} = \frac{\text{COGS}}{\text{Net sales}} = \frac{\$521,743}{\$861,894} = 61\%$$

This ratio reflects the percentage of sales used to manufacture goods sold. If it is high, either costs are excessive or prices may be too low.

$$\text{Operating expense ratio} = \frac{\text{Total expenses}}{\text{Net sales}} = \frac{\$264,253}{\$861,894} = 31\%$$

This ratio reflects the company's operating efficiency and represents the percentage of each dollar needed to cover expenses.

$$\text{Sales efficiency ratio} = \frac{\text{Net sales}}{\text{Gross sales}} = \frac{\$861,894}{\$925,476} = 93\%$$

This ratio reflects adjustments to gross sales from returns, allowances, and discounts.

$$\text{Return on investment (ROI)} = \frac{\text{Net profit before taxes}}{\text{Total investment}}$$

Information regarding total investment from the firm's balance sheet is required to compute ROI. ROI figures can be compared with industry averages and opportunity costs of investing elsewhere to evaluate the firm's performance.

Glossary

ABILITY the consumer's knowledge about the product category sufficient to understand the advertised message (Chapter 17)

ACCEPTABLE PRICE RANGE the range of prices buyers are willing to pay for a product; prices above the range may be judged unfair, whereas prices below the range may generate concerns about quality (Chapter 12)

ACCESSIBILITY the degree to which a firm can reach intended target segments efficiently with its products and communications (Chapter 7)

ADAPTIVE SELLING a salesperson's adjustment of his or her behavior between and during sales calls to respond appropriately to the situation and address issues important to the customer (Chapter 19)

ADMINISTERED CHANNEL SYSTEM system designed to control a line or classification of merchandise; channel members agree on a comprehensive plan, but no channel member owns another member (Chapter 13)

ADOPTION PROCESS the steps consumers follow in deciding whether to use a new product (Chapter 9)

ADVERTISING the element of the marketing communications mix that is nonpersonal, paid for by an identified sponsor, and disseminated through mass channels of communication to promote the adoption of goods, services, persons, or ideas (Chapters 16 and 17)

ADVERTISING AGENCY a company that develops advertising messages and provides media planning and scheduling for marketers (Chapter 17)

ADVERTISING ALLOWANCE money paid a reseller for including the manufacturer's product, along with other products, in the reseller's advertising efforts (Chapter 18)

ADVERTISING SPECIALTY an item of useful or interesting merchandise given away free and typically carrying an imprinted name or message; for example, a pen, calendar, or coffee mug (Chapter 18)

ADVERTORIAL a special advertising section with some editorial (nonadvertising) content included in magazines (Chapter 17)

AFFECT overall consumer feeling responses (Chapter 4)

AFFECT REFERRAL a choice heuristic in which consumers elicit from memory their overall evaluation of products and choose the alternative for which they have the most positive feelings (Chapter 4)

AIDED RECALL TESTS posttesting in which consumers are given lists of ads and asked which they remembered and read (Chapter 17)

AIO STATEMENTS survey responses concerning activities, interests, and opinions (AIO), used in psychographic research (Chapter 7)

ALL-YOU-CAN-AFFORD BUDGETING a method for determining the marketing communications budget that involves spending whatever's left over after other costs without considering the firm's objectives (Chapter 16)

AMERICANS WITH DISABILITIES ACT (ADA) a U.S. law passed in 1990 to prohibit discrimination against people with disabilities (Chapter 2)

ANCHOR POSITION retail stores, often department stores, that are strategically placed in malls, shopping centers, or downtown shopping areas to attract customers and stimulate traffic flow throughout the shopping area (Chapter 14)

ARBITRAGING see **diverting**

ATMOSPHERICS a retailer's combination of architecture, layout, color scheme, sound and temperature monitoring, special events, prices, displays, and other factors that attract and stimulate customers (Chapter 14)

ATTENTION the consumer's mental notice directed at a marketing communication (such as an ad), often stimulated by its physical characteristics; the second step in the information-processing model (Chapter 17)

ATTITUDES learned predispositions to respond favorably or unfavorably to a product or brand; based on beliefs about its attributes (price, service level, quality) (Chapter 4)

AUCTION HOUSE a company that sells merchandise at a given time and place to the highest bidder (Chapter 15)

AUTOMATIC NUMBER IDENTIFICATION a system that identifies incoming phone numbers of respondents to an ad or promotion at the beginning of the call without the caller's knowledge (Chapter 20)

B2B EXCHANGES electronic marketplace exchanges (Chapter 5)

BACKWARD INTEGRATION a corporate marketing channel system in which the channel member owns one or more of its suppliers upstream (as opposed to **forward integration,** where it owns buyers downstream) (Chapter 13)

BAIT AND SWITCH advertising a product at an attractively low price to get customers into the store but not making it available, so customers must trade up to a more expensive version (Chapter 12)

BALANCED MATRIX ORGANIZATION an approach to new product development in which a project manager oversees the project and shares responsibility and authority with functional managers

BANNER ADVERTISING ads on a Web site that are "clickable" should a viewer want more information about the product or service being advertised (Chapter 17)

BAR CODING a computer-coded bar pattern that identifies a product; see also **Universal Product Code** (Chapter 15)

BASES OF SEGMENTATION the distinguishing characteristics of market segments (such as demographics, benefits sought) within a firm's overall product or service market (Chapter 7)

BASIC PRICE MIX the basic components that define the size and means of payment exchanged for goods and services; less comprehensive than the price promotion mix (Chapter 11)

BATTLE OF THE BRANDS intense competition between manufacturer and distributor brands (Chapter 8)

BEHAVIOR-BASED PERSPECTIVE a way of evaluating salesperson performance that defines the sales behaviors expected, such as how many calls to make or which presentation tactics to use; see also **outcome-based perspective** (Chapter 19)

BENCHMARKING a market-based learning process by which a firm seeks to identify best practices that produce superior results in other firms and to replicate the processes to enhance its own competitive advantage (Chapter 3)

BENEFIT what a product feature can do for a particular customer; for example, a speaker-phone built into a fax machine is a feature, but the fact that it allows hands-free conversation is a benefit (Chapter 19)

BENEFIT SEGMENTATION segmenting the market by the attributes or benefits consumers need or desire, such as quality, service, or unique features (Chapter 7)

BEST-VALUE STRATEGY purchasing the lowest-cost brand available with the desired level of quality (Chapter 11)

BIDS in government markets, written proposals from qualified suppliers in response to published governmental requirements or specifications (Chapter 5)

BRAND a name, term, sign, symbol, design, or combination that a firm uses to identify its products and differentiate them from those of competitors (Chapter 8)

BRAND AWARENESS when target consumers know about a brand and it comes to mind when thinking about the product category; for example, Kleenex comes to mind when thinking about tissues (Chapter 8)

BRAND COMPETITORS direct competitors that offer the same types of products (for example, Domino's Pizza and Pizza Hut) (Chapter 2)

BRAND EQUITY the value a brand has in the marketplace due to reputation and goodwill (Chapter 8)

BRAND EXPERIENCE consumer experience as a result of the received benefits offered by a brand promise (Chapter 8)

BRAND IDENTITY the brand concept from the brand owner's viewpoint; the specific aspects of the brand that the marketer wants to communicate to consumers (Chapter 8)

BRAND IMAGE consumers' impression about a brand (Chapter 8)

BRAND LOYALTY when consumers purchase a specific brand all or most of the time (Chapter 8)

BRAND MARK the element of a brand that cannot be vocalized (for example, the MGM lion or the Texaco star) (Chapter 8)

BRAND NAME the element of a brand that can be vocalized (for example, IBM, Tide, Coke) (Chapter 8)

BRAND PROMISE represents the benefits customers should expect from purchasing and using a brand (Chapter 8)

BRANDING identifying a firm's products to distinguish them from competitors' similar products (Chapter 8)

BREAK-EVEN ANALYSIS calculation of the number of units that must be sold at a certain price for the firm to cover costs (break even); revenues earned past the break-even point contribute to profits (Chapter 12)

BROADBAND INTERNET TECH-NOLOGY a superfast connection to the Web via cable modem, digital subscriber lines, or satellites (Chapter 16)

BROKER an intermediary that brings buyers and sellers together and is paid a commission by whichever party it represents in a given transaction (Chapter 15)

BUNDLING marketing two or more products in a single package at one price (for example, computer systems or ski weekends) (Chapter 12)

BUSINESS ANALYSIS the stage of new product development where initial marketing plans are prepared, including a tentative marketing strategy and estimates of sales, costs, and profitability (Chapter 9)

BUSINESS FIRMS manufacturers of tangible goods and firms that provide services such as health care, entertainment, and transportation (Chapter 5)

BUSINESS LEVEL the smaller units within a complex organization that are managed as self-contained businesses (Chapter 3)

BUSINESS NETWORKS strategic alliances among suppliers, distributors, and the marketing firm (Chapter 3)

BUSINESS PRODUCTS goods and services purchased by a firm for its own use (as opposed to consumer products) (Chapter 8)

BUSINESS STRATEGIC PLAN a plan for how each business unit in the corporate family intends to compete in the marketplace, given the vision, objectives, and growth strategies of the corporate strategic plan (Chapter 3)

BUSINESS-TO-BUSINESS ADVERTISING promoting products or services directly to other firms, often through print ads in trade periodicals or direct-mail promotions to targeted potential buyers (Chapter 17)

BUSINESS-TO-BUSINESS BUYING BEHAVIOR the decision making and other activities of organizations as buyers (Chapter 5)

BUYING ALLOWANCE payment of a specified amount of money to a reseller for purchasing a certain amount of a product during a particular period (Chapter 18)

BUYING CENTER business purchasing decision makers made up of people throughout all levels of the organization, not just the purchasing department; the buying center makeup may vary as purchasing decisions change (Chapter 5)

BUYING LOADER a dealer premium in the form of a gift, such as a free trip, for buying, displaying, and selling a certain amount of a product within a specified time (Chapter 18)

BUYING POWER INDEX (BPI) a measure of a particular market's relative ability to buy, based on population, effective buying income, and retail sales and expressed as a percentage of the total U.S. potential (Appendix B)

CALLER ID INTRUSION see **automatic number identification** (Chapter 20)

CANNED SALES PRESENTATION a fully scripted presentation that the sales rep memorizes, or even an audiovisual presentation, that is not adaptable to individual customers (Chapter 19)

CANNIBALIZATION when a new product takes sales away from existing products, which leads merely to a shift in the company's sales instead of a gain (Chapter 10)

CAPITAL PRODUCTS expensive items that are used in business operations but do not become part of any finished product; examples include physical facilities (office buildings) and accessory equipment (copiers and forklifts) (Chapter 8)

CASH-AND-CARRY WHOLESALER a limited-function wholesaler that does not extend credit for or deliver the products it sells; its primary customers are small retailers (Chapter 15)

CATALOG WHOLESALER a limited-function wholesaler that offers a wide range of competitively priced products that customers order by phone or fax (Chapter 15)

CATEGORY an assortment of items seen by the customer as reasonable substitutes for each other (Chapter 14)

CATEGORY KILLERS discount retailers that offer a complete assortment and can thus dominate a product category, giving them the clout to negotiate excellent prices from suppliers and be assured of dependable sources of supply (Chapter 14)

CAUSAL RESEARCH experiments in which researchers manipulate independent variables and observe the dependent variable(s) of interest to identify cause-and-effect relationships (Chapter 6)

CAUSE-RELATED MARKETING (CRM) companies aligning themselves with causes, such as drug-abuse prevention and environmental conservation (Chapter 17)

CELEBRITY ENDORSEMENT the use of a famous spokesperson, say a sports or movie star, to promote a product (Chapters 4 and 17)

CENTRAL BUSINESS DISTRICT (CBD) a downtown area representing a city's greatest concentration of office buildings and retail stores (Chapter 14)

CENTS-OFF DEAL an offering of a brand at less than the regular price (Chapter 18)

CHANNEL CONFLICT conflict between members of a marketing channel, which may stem from poor communication, a power struggle, or incompatible objectives (Chapter 13)

CHANNEL COOPERATION a cooperative spirit among members of a marketing channel that helps reduce and resolve conflicts (Chapter 13)

CHANNEL LEADER a marketing channel member with enough power to control others in the channel (Chapter 13)

CHANNEL OBJECTIVES specific, measurable goals of a marketing channel that are consistent with the firm's marketing objectives and are often stated in terms of sales volume, profitability, market share, cost, number of wholesale or retail outlets, or geographic expansion (Chapter 13)

CHANNEL OF DISTRIBUTION see **marketing channel** (Chapter 13)

CHANNEL POWER ways marketing channel members can gain control to enhance their position, including reward power, legitimate power, expert power, and referent power (Chapter 13)

CHANNEL STRATEGY an expression of a general action plan and guidelines for allocating resources to achieve the objective of a marketing channel (Chapter 13)

CHECKOUT DISPENSERS devices that make coupons available to customers in supermarkets; although they are more expensive than newspaper coupons, they tend to be redeemed at a higher rate (Chapter 18)

CHILD PROTECTION ACT a U.S. law passed in 1990 to regulate advertising on children's TV programs (Chapter 2)

CHILD SAFETY ACT a U.S. law passed in 1966 that prohibits the marketing of dangerous products to children (Chapter 2)

CHILDHOOD CONSUMER SOCIALIZATION the process by which young people acquire skills, knowledge, and attitudes to help them function as consumers in the marketplace (Chapter 4)

CLASSIFIED ADVERTISING advertising that typically promotes transactions for a single item or service and usually appears in newspapers (Chapter 17)

CLAYTON ACT a U.S. law passed in 1914 that prohibits anticompetitive activities (Chapter 2)

CLUSTER SAMPLING a probability sampling technique in which units are organized into similar clusters, such as neighborhoods; clusters are then selected randomly, and each house in the selected clusters is included in the sample (Chapter 6)

COACHING the leadership function of providing guidance and feedback on a regular basis to direct salespeople's activities (Chapter 19)

CO-BRANDING when two brand names appear on the same product; for example, a VISA card with your university's name (Chapter 8)

COERCIVE POWER power a member of a marketing channel uses to pressure another member to do something; for example, a manufacturer threatens to cut off a distributor's credit unless the distributor pays its bills more promptly (Chapter 13)

COGNITION thinking or mental consumer responses (Chapter 4)

COGNITIVE DISSONANCE a consumer's postpurchase doubt about the appropriateness of a purchase decision; caused by an imbalance of information because each alternative has attractive features; most likely to occur when the purchase is important and visible, the perceived risk is high, and the decision involves a long-term commitment (Chapter 4)

COLLABORATIVE VENTURE an arrangement in which two or more firms share the rights to market specified products; may take the form of a strategic partnership, strategic alliance, joint venture, or licensing agreement (Chapter 9)

COMARKETING ALLIANCES contractual arrangements between different companies offering complementary products in the marketplace or possessing complementary technology (Chapter 3)

COMBINATION STRATEGY aiming marketing communications at both resellers and ultimate consumers in a push–pull approach (Chapter 16)

COMMERCIAL ZAPPING changing the channels during TV commercials (Chapter 17)

COMMERCIALIZATION the stage of new product development after the product tests successfully and the firm introduces it on a full-scale basis (Chapter 9)

COMMISSION MERCHANT a wholesaler that provides a wider range of services than do agents or brokers, often engaging in inventory management, physical distribution, and promotional activities and offering credit and market feedback to the companies it represents (Chapter 15)

COMMUNICATION the process of establishing shared meaning, exchanging ideas, or passing information between a source and a receiver (Chapter 16)

COMPARATIVE ADVERTISING advertising that compares a sponsored brand with a competitive brand on at least one product attribute (such as MCI versus AT&T services) (Chapters 16 and 17)

COMPETITIVE ADVANTAGE trying to get consumers to purchase one's products instead of competitors' products, through either lower prices or differentiation (Chapter 3)

COMPETITIVE ENVIRONMENT all the organizations that attempt to serve the same customers, including both brand competitors and product competitors (Chapter 2)

COMPETITIVE PARITY BUDGETING a budgeting method for marketing communications based on the percentage allocated by other companies in the industry (Chapter 16)

COMPETITIVE PRICING STRATEGIES pricing strategies based on a firm's position in relation to its competition; include penetration pricing, limit pricing, and price signaling (Chapter 12)

COMPETITIVE STRATEGY-POSITIONING CONTINUUM competitive strategies are described as existing on a continuum anchored by "low cost leadership" on one end and "differentiation" on the other (Chapter 11)

COMPOSITE OF SALES FORCE ESTIMATES a means of forecasting sales in which sales reps give forecasts for their territories, which can then be combined (Chapter 7)

CONCENTRATED STRATEGY a strategy in which a firm seeks a large share of one or a few profitable segments of the total market, often concentrating on serving the selected segments innovatively and creatively (Chapter 7)

CONCEPT DEVELOPMENT the process of shaping and refining the idea for a new product into a complete description (Chapter 9)

CONCEPT TESTS having the concept for a new product evaluated by potential customers (Chapter 9)

CONSOLIDATED METROPOLITAN STATISTICAL AREA (CMSA) the largest designation of geographic areas based on census data; the 20 largest market areas in the United States that contain at least two PMSAs (Chapter 7)

CONSUMER ATTITUDES learned predispositions to respond favorably or unfavorably to a product or brand (Chapter 4)

CONSUMER BEHAVIOR the mental and emotional processes and the physical activities people engage in when they select, purchase, use, and dispose of products or services to satisfy particular needs and desires (Chapter 4)

CONSUMER CREDIT PROTECTION ACT a U.S. law passed in 1968 that requires full disclosure of financial charges for loans (Chapter 2)

CONSUMER DECISION PROCESS a four-step process: (1) recognizing a need or problem, (2) searching for information, (3) evaluating alternative products or brands, and (4) purchasing a product (Chapter 4)

CONSUMER INFORMATION PROCESSING the cognitive processes by which consumers interpret and integrate information from the environment (Chapter 4)

CONSUMER LEARNING a process that changes consumers' knowledge or behavior patterns through marketing communications or experience (Chapter 4)

CONSUMER PRODUCT SAFETY COMMISSION (CPSC) an agency of the U.S. government that protects consumers from unsafe products (Chapter 2)

CONSUMER PRODUCTS goods and services purchased by consumers for their own personal use (as opposed to business products) (Chapter 8)

CONSUMER PROTECTION LAWS laws that state what firms must do to give consumers the information they need to make sound purchasing decisions or to make sure the products they buy are safe (Chapter 2)

CONSUMER RIGHTS four inherent rights of consumers: (1) to safety, (2) to be informed, (3) to choose, and (4) to be heard (Chapter 2)

CONSUMER SALES PROMOTION sales promotion directed at ultimate users of the product or service (as opposed to trade sales promotion) (Chapter 18)

CONSUMERISM a social movement in which consumers demand better consumer information, quality, service, and dependability, as well as fair prices (Chapter 2)

CONTEST a sales promotion that offers prizes based on the skill of contestants (Chapter 18)

CONTINUAL TRAINING ongoing sales training that helps firms stay current and competitive in an ever-changing environment (Chapter 19)

CONTRIBUTION MARGIN is the quantity P - VC where P = unit price and VC = variable cost (Chapter 12)

CONVENIENCE PRODUCTS consumer may prefer a specific brand but does not want to spend much time shopping for it; will buy another brand if preferred one is not available; normally low-priced, often-purchased goods (Chapter 8)

CONVENIENCE STORE retail store that carries a modest variety and shallow assortment of products and has high prices but offers a convenient location and hours (Chapters 2 and 14)

CONVERSION RATES statistical measurement that is used to describe the percentage of shoppers who are converted into buyers (Chapter 4)

COOKIES tiny computer files, stored on users' PCs, that Web sites use to track visitors to their sites (Chapter 20)

COOPERATIVE ADVERTISING advertising for a local dealer or retailer whose expense is contributed to by the manufacturer (Chapter 17)

CORE COMPETENCY the unique bundle of skills that are possessed by individuals across the organization and that provide the basis for competitive advantage (Chapter 3)

CORE PURPOSE the company's reason for being or its idealistic motivation for doing work (Chapter 3)

CORE VALUES the small set of guiding principles that represent the enduring tenets of the organization (Chapter 3)

CORPORATE ADVOCACY ADVERTISING advertising that announces a stand on some issue related to the firm's operation, often one threatening the company's well-being (Chapter 17)

CORPORATE IMAGE ADVERTISING advertising directed toward the general public or investors and stockholders promoting an organization's image and role in the community as a corporate citizen, independent of any product or service (Chapter 17)

CORPORATE LEVEL the highest level in any organization, at which managers address issues concerning the overall organization and their decisions and actions affect all other organizational levels (Chapter 3)

CORPORATE STRATEGIC PLAN a plan that determines what a company is and wants to become and that guides strategic planning at all organizational levels; it involves developing a corporate vision, formulating corporate objectives, allocating resources, determining how to achieve desired growth, and establishing business units (Chapter 3)

CORPORATE VISION the basic values of an organization, specifying what it stands for, where it wants to go, and how it plans to get there, and addressing the organization's markets, principal products or services, geographic domain, core technologies, objectives, basic philosophy, self-concept, and desired public image (Chapter 3)

CORRECTIVE ADVERTISING advertising the FTC mandates to remedy misleading impressions and information in an ad (Chapter 17)

COST PER THOUSAND (CPM) a factor in evaluating the cost effectiveness of a particular outlet for reaching desired market audiences (Chapter 17)

COUNTERSEGMENTATION combining market segments to appeal to a broad range of consumers and assuming an increasing consumer willingness to accept fewer product and service variations for lower prices (Chapter 7)

COUNTERTRADE trade between developed and less developed countries that involves barter and exchanges instead of just currency (Chapter 11)

COUPON a printed certificate giving the bearer a stated price reduction or special value on a specific product, generally for a specific time period; especially useful in encouraging new product trials; may be distributed in an ad, in a freestanding insert, or on the store shelf (Chapter 18)

CREATIVE STRATEGY combining what is said in an ad with how it is said; typically the marketer specifies the general theme of the message and the ad agency develops the presentation (Chapter 17)

CROSS ELASTICITY OF DEMAND the relation of the percentage change in quantity demanded for one product to percentage price changes for other products; a price increase for one brand of cola will increase demand for a substitute brand, but a price increase for computers will decrease demand for printers, a complementary product (Chapter 12)

CROSS-FUNCTIONAL TEAMWORK having employees from different functional areas of a firm work together to satisfy customer needs (Chapters 3 and 5)

CROSS-PROMOTION the collaboration of two or more firms in a sales promotion; also called a **tie-in** (Chapter 18)

CROSS-SECTIONAL STUDY a survey of customers administered at a given time to assess, for example, perceived satisfaction with service (Chapter 6)

CULTURAL ENVIRONMENT factors and trends related to how people live and behave, including the values, ideas, attitudes, beliefs, and activities of specific population subgroups; a component of the social environment (Chapter 2)

CULTURE the values, ideas, attitudes, and symbols people adopt to communicate, interpret, and interact as members of a society; a society's way of life, learned and transmitted from one generation to the next, that includes both abstract and material elements. Culture determines the most basic values that influence consumer behavior patterns and can be used to distinguish subcultures that represent substantial market segments and opportunities (Chapter 4)

CUSTOMARY PRICE pricing strategies that modify the quality, features, or service of a product without adjusting the price; customary price beliefs reflect consumers' strongly held expectations about what the price of a product should be (Chapter 12)

CUSTOMER EQUITY CONCEPT a focus beyond customer satisfaction toward customer retention as a way to generate sales and profit growth (Chapters 1 and 3)

CUSTOMER PRIVACY any way in which data is protected from unauthorized viewing on a Web site (Chapter 2)

CUSTOMER RELATIONSHIP MANAGEMENT (CRM) designed to achieve a continuing dialogue with customers, across all contact and access points, with personalized treatment of the most valuable customers designed to increase customer retention and the effectiveness of marketing strategies (Chapter 1)

CUSTOMER SERVICE the assistance a firm provides to help a customer with the purchase or use of a product or service; providing exceptional customer service can give a firm a marketing advantage (Chapter 8)

CUSTOMER VALUE what a customer gets (benefits from product use, related

services) for what a customer gives (price paid, time to shop) (Chapter 1)

CUSTOMER VALUE PERSPECTIVE an emphasis on giving customers more of what they want for less than they have to give (Prologue)

CUSTOMIZED MARKETING STRATEGY implementing a different marketing mix for each target market country in international marketing (Chapter 3)

CYCLE TIME the total elapsed time to complete a business process (Chapter 5)

DATA MINING the process by which market cells are derived from company databases by the use of sophisticated analytical and statistical procedures that discover interesting patterns within company data sets (Chapter 6)

DATABASE MARKETING the collection and use of individual customer-specific information stored on a computer to make marketing more efficient (Chapters 6 and 20)

DEALER LOADER a premium given to a reseller to encourage development of a special display or product offering (Chapter 18)

DECEPTIVE ADVERTISING communications intended to mislead consumers by making false claims or failing to disclose important information (Chapter 16)

DECLINE STAGE the fourth and final stage of the product life cycle, when falling sales and profits persist (Chapter 10)

DECODING the process in communications by which the receiver deciphers the meaning of the words, pictures, and other symbols used in the message (Chapter 16)

DECONGLOMERATION refers to the divestiture behavior of a conglomerate firm and the transformation of its business portfolio to one composed of relatively fewer and related businesses (Chapter 3)

DEMAND CURVE relationship that shows how many units a market will purchase at a given price in a given time period; generally, customers buy more units as prices drop and fewer units as prices rise (Chapter 12)

DEMOGRAPHIC ENVIRONMENT the size, distribution, and growth rate of groups of people with different traits that relate to buying behavior; a component of the social environment (Chapter 2)

DEPARTMENT STORE a retail store characterized by a wide variety of merchandise and extensive depth of assortment; typically organized around sales departments like apparel, cosmetics, and housewares (Chapter 14)

DEREGULATION promotes free competition, in some cases by means of legislation; one aspect of the legal environment (Chapter 15)

DERIVED DEMAND demand for business-to-business products that is dependent on demand for other products in consumer markets, as when increased consumer demand for new automobiles causes the demand for products used to make them to also go up (Chapter 5)

DESCRIPTIVE RESEARCH research directed by one or more formal research questions or hypotheses, usually involving a survey or questionnaire (Chapter 6)

DIFFERENTIAL PRICING selling the same product to different buyers at a variety of prices; such price discrimination works because there are differences in reactions to price among consumers or consumer segments (Chapter 12)

DIFFERENTIAL RESPONSIVENESS the degree to which market segments exhibit varying responses to different marketing mix combinations (Chapter 7)

DIFFERENTIATED STRATEGY using different marketing strategies for different segments: either marketing a unique product and communications campaign to each segment, or marketing a common product to different segments with various communication strategies (Chapter 7)

DIFFERENTIATION offering consumers products or services that are better than the competition; one way to gain a competitive advantage (Chapter 3)

DIFFUSION PROCESS the adoption of an innovative product form over time (Chapter 10)

DIRECT CHANNEL the movement of the product from the producer to the user without intermediaries (Chapter 13)

DIRECT INVESTMENT investing in production, sales, distribution, and/or other operations in a foreign country; requires a large investment of resources but gives the marketer much control over operations (Chapter 3)

DIRECT MAIL any form of advertising addressed to prospects through public or private delivery services, including everything from a simple flyer to a package that contains a letter, multipage brochure, video, and response card (Chapter 20)

DIRECT MARKETING distributing goods, services, information, or promotional benefits to carefully targeted consumers through interactive (two-way) communication while tracking response, sales, interests, or desires through a computer database (Chapter 14)

DIRECT MARKETING CHANNEL a way to move the product from producer to user without intermediaries (Chapter 14)

DIRECT MARKETING COMMUNI-CATIONS a process of communications directly with target customers to encourage response by telephone, mail, electronic means, or personal visit; examples of DMC methods include direct mail, telemarketing, computer shopping services, TV shopping networks, and infomercials (Chapters 16 and 20)

DIRECT-RESPONSE ADVERTISING advertising intended to elicit immediate purchase; for example, TV commercials that show a toll-free phone number (Chapter 17)

DIRECT-RESPONSE RADIO ADVERTISING radio ads that provide a phone number or address to elicit immediate feedback from the consumer (Chapter 20)

DIRECT-RESPONSE TELEVISION ADVERTISING TV ads that include an 800 or 900 phone number and an address for placing orders in an attempt to get an immediate answer from the consumer (Chapter 20)

DIRECT RETAILING the portion of direct marketing in which ultimate consumers, not business consumers, do the buying (see also **direct marketing**) (Chapter 14)

DIRECT SELLING a method in which salespeople reach consumers directly or by telephone primarily at home or at work and sell through personal demonstration and explanation (Chapter 14)

DIRECT-TO-CONSUMER SALES-PEOPLE sales reps who sell to individuals who personally use the products and services; they include retail salespeople, real estate agents, and financial securities agents (Chapter 19)

DISCOUNTS reductions from the market price; for example, cash discounts for prompt payment or quantity discounts for large orders. See also **trade sales promotion allowances** (Chapter 12)

DISPLAY ALLOWANCE money or a product provided to a retailer for featuring the manufacturer's brand in an agreed-on in-store display (Chapter 18)

DISPLAY LOADER a dealer premium that lets the reseller keep some or all of the display when the promotion ends (Chapter 18)

DISTRIBUTION CENTER an automated "superwarehouse" that serves a large geographic area and receives, processes, and ships customer orders in addition to storing products (Chapter 15)

DISTRIBUTOR BRAND a brand sponsored by a distributor such as a wholesaler

or retailer; the distributor is responsible for the product's quality and marketing. Also called a **store brand, private brand,** or **private label** (Chapter 8)

DIVERSIFICATION STRATEGY expanding into new products and new markets; the riskiest growth strategy because the company cannot build directly on its strengths in its current markets or products (Chapter 3)

DIVERTING secretly purchasing a product where it is less expensive, usually due to a trade promotion, and reselling it where prices are higher (Chapter 18)

DOWNWARD-STRETCH STRATEGY adding products to the lower end of a product line; for example, IBM entered the market with high-priced microcomputers and later added lower-priced ones (Chapter 10)

DROP SHIPPER a limited-function wholesaler that arranges for shipments directly from the factory to the customer; it does not physically handle the product but does take title and all associated risks while the product is in transit, as well as providing sales support (Chapter 15)

DUMPING selling a product in a foreign country at a price lower than in the home country and lower than its marginal cost of production (Chapter 11)

DURABILITY the stability of market segments and whether distinctions between them will diminish or disappear as the product category or the markets mature (Chapter 7)

EARLY ADOPTERS the second group to adopt a new product (after innovators); they represent about 13.5 percent of a market (Chapter 10)

EARLY MAJORITY the third group to adopt a new product (after innovators and early adopters); they represent about 34 percent of a market (Chapter 10)

ECONOMIC ENVIRONMENT factors and trends that are related to the production of goods and services and population incomes and that affect the purchasing power of markets (Chapter 2)

EFFICIENT ASSORTMENT the practice of reducing the number of brands or sizes without affecting sales or consumers' perceptions of variety (Chapter 7)

ELABORATION LIKELIHOOD MODEL a theory of persuasion that includes individual motivation and the ability to elaborate information in advertisements as determinants of two different "routes" of persuasion (Chapter 17)

ELASTIC DEMAND demand for a product that changes substantially in response to small changes in price; when demand is elastic, a small decrease in price may substantially increase total revenues (Chapter 12)

ELECTRONIC BUSINESS (E-BUSINESS) use of the Internet to conduct business activities (Chapter 20)

ELECTRONIC COMMERCE (E-COMMERCE) use of the Internet for buying and selling products that are transported either physically or digitally from location to location (Chapter 5)

ELECTRONIC DATA INTER-CHANGE (EDI) a computerized system that allows exchange of information between parties; part of a quick-response inventory control system (Chapter 15)

ELECTRONIC MARKETING (E-MARKETING) use of the Internet to perform marketing activities (Chapter 20)

EMOTIONAL APPEALS ad message strategies that attempt to evoke feelings, moods, and memories to sell a product (Chapter 17)

ENCODING the process in communications by which the source chooses the words, pictures, and other symbols used to transmit the intended message (Chapter 16)

ENTREPRENEURIAL PERSPECTIVE an emphasis on innovation, risk taking, and proactiveness in all marketing activities (Prologue)

ENTRY STRATEGY the approach used to begin marketing products internationally; options run the gamut from exporting to joint ventures to direct investment (Chapter 3)

ENVIRONMENTAL PROTECTION AGENCY (EPA) agency of the U.S. government whose goal is to protect the environment (Chapters 2 and 15)

ENVIRONMENTAL SCANNING identifying relevant factors and trends and assessing their potential impact on the organization's markets and marketing activities (Chapter 2)

E-RETAILING retail sales over the Internet (Chapter 14)

ETHICS PERSPECTIVE addressing the morality of marketing decisions and practicing social responsibility (Prologue)

ETHNIC PATTERNS the norms and values of specific groups or subcultures, which may be formed around nationality, religion, race, or geographic factors (Chapter 4)

ETHNOGRAPHIC RESEARCH technique in which market researchers record how consumers actually use products, brands, and services from day to day by entering their homes, observing consumption behavior, and recording pantry and garbage content (Chapter 6)

EUROPEAN UNION (EU) the world's largest consumer market, consisting of 25 European nations: Austria, Belgium, Cyprus, Czech Republic, Denmark, Estonia, Finland, France, Germany, Greece, Hungary, Ireland, Italy, Latvia, Lithuania, Luxembourg, Malta, The Netherlands, Poland, Portugal, Slovakia, Slovenia, Spain, Sweden, and the United Kingdom (Chapter 2)

EVERYDAY-LOW-PRICING (EDLP) suppliers reduce discounts and promotions to retailers; and retailers demand low prices from suppliers and minimize advertising and sales promotions to keep prices consistently low (Chapter 14)

EXCHANGE the transfer of something tangible or intangible, actual or symbolic, between two or more social actors (Chapter 1)

EXCHANGE RATE the price of one country's currency in terms of another country's currency (Chapter 11)

EXCLUSIVE DEALING AGREEMENT a marketing channel arrangement between producer and reseller that restricts the reseller from carrying a competing product line (Chapter 13)

EXCLUSIVE DISTRIBUTION using only one outlet in a geographic marketplace (Chapter 13)

EXCLUSIVE TERRITORIES a marketing channel arrangement between a producer and a reseller that prohibits other resellers from selling a particular brand in a given geographic area (Chapter 13)

EXISTING-BUSINESS SALES-PEOPLE sales reps who work with established customers, writing up fairly routine orders, to provide a steady stream of sales revenue (Chapter 19)

EXPANSION ADVERTISING advertising designed to increase usage by current customers with high awareness and high penetration (Chapter 17)

EXPERT OPINION a qualitative approach to forecasting sales in which analysts ask executives within the company or other experts to provide forecasts based on their own judgments (Chapter 7)

EXPERT POWER power a member of a marketing channel gains by accumulating expertise and knowledge; for example, large retailers have gained much expert power using point-of-sale scanners to gauge product

movements, price sensitivities, and trade promotion effectiveness (Chapter 13)

EXPLICIT COMMUNICATIONS a distinct, clearly stated message conveyed through personal selling, advertising, public relations, sales promotion, direct marketing, or some combination of these methods (Chapter 16)

EXPLORATORY RESEARCH research carried out to gain greater understanding or develop preliminary background and suggest hypotheses for a detailed follow-up study; may involve literature reviews, case analyses, interviews, and focus groups (Chapter 6)

EXPORT AGENT a wholesaler that locates and develops markets abroad for products manufactured in its home country, operating on commission (Chapter 15)

EXPORTING selling products to buyers in international markets, either directly or through intermediaries (Chapter 3)

EXTERNAL REFERENCE PRICES prices charged by other retailers or comparison prices a retailer provides to enhance perceptions of the advertised price (Chapter 11)

EXTERNAL SECONDARY DATA secondary data that are collected from outside the firm and may be proprietary (provided by commercial marketing research firms) or nonproprietary (available from public sources) (Chapter 6)

EXTERNAL SOURCING acquiring specific brands from another firm or purchasing the entire firm to obtain ownership of its products (Chapter 9)

FAD a subcategory of fashion that has a very short product life (Chapter 10)

FAIR CREDIT REPORT ACT a U.S. law passed in 1970 to regulate the reporting and use of credit information (Chapter 2)

FAIR DEBT COLLECTIONS PRACTICE ACT a U.S. law passed in 1970 to regulate methods for collecting on debts (Chapter 2)

FAIR PACKAGING & LABELING ACT a U.S. law passed in 1965 to regulate the packaging and labeling of products (Chapter 2)

FAMILY BRAND NAME STRATEGY branding all items in a product line or even the entire product mix with a family name or the company name (Chapter 10)

FAMILY LIFE CYCLE the sequence of steps a family goes through, from young single adults to the married couple whose children have left home; household consump-

tion patterns vary greatly across the family life cycle (Chapter 4)

FASHION a component of style whose products reflect what is currently popular (Chapter 10)

FAX-ON-DEMAND SYSTEMS allow instant response to 800-number requests for information. In these systems, a fax machine receives the request for information and immediately faxes the information back to the requester (Chapter 20)

FEAR APPEAL a type of emotional appeal used in an ad message strategy; for example, Michelin's "baby in a tire" theme (Chapter 17)

FEATURE a statement of fact about some aspect of a product or service (as opposed to a benefit, which is what the feature can do for the customer) (Chapter 19)

FEDERAL COMMUNICATIONS COMMISSION (FCC) agency of the U.S. government that regulates the interstate communications industry (Chapter 2)

FEDERAL TRADE COMMISSION (FTC) agency of the U.S. government that regulates business practices; established by the Federal Trade Commission Act of 1914 (Chapter 2)

FEEDBACK the part of the receiver's response that is communicated to the sender (Chapter 16)

FIELDWORK the process of contacting respondents, conducting interviews, and completing surveys in market research (Chapter 6)

FIVE CS OF PRICING five critical influences on pricing decisions—costs, customers, channels of distribution, competition, and compatibility (Chapter 11)

FIXED COSTS costs that cannot be changed in the short run and do not vary with the quantity produced; they include plant investments, interest, and the costs of production facilities. See also **variable costs** (Chapter 12)

FLYER a single-page piece of direct mail printed on one or both sides of 8 1/2 × 11-inch paper and folded (Chapter 20)

FOB ORIGIN PRICING a form of geographic pricing in which buyers are charged the unit cost of goods plus shipping costs, which vary with location; in FOB (free on board), the goods are placed on a carrier and shipped to the customer, who pays the transportation charges (Chapter 12)

FOCUS GROUP an exploratory research method in which a moderator leads 8 to 12 people in a focused, in-depth discussion on a specific topic; used most for examining new product concepts and advertising themes, investigating the criteria underlying purchase decisions, and generating information for developing consumer questionnaires (Chapter 6)

FOOD AND DRUG ADMINISTRATION (FDA) an agency of the U.S. government that regulates the food, drug, and cosmetics industries; established by the Food, Drug & Cosmetic Act of 1938 (Chapter 2)

FORWARD BUYING when distributors or consumers stock up on enough of a product at a deal price to carry them over to the next sale (Chapter 18)

FORWARD INTEGRATION a corporate marketing channel system in which a channel member owns one or more of its buyers downstream (as opposed to **backward integration**, where it owns suppliers upstream) (Chapter 13)

FRANCHISE SYSTEM a contractual marketing channel system where the franchisor grants a franchisee the right to distribute and sell specified goods and services and the franchisee agrees to operate according to marketing guidelines set forth by the franchisor under a recognized trademark or trade name (Chapter 13)

FRANCHISEE a party that is granted rights (by the franchisor) to distribute and sell specified goods and services (Chapter 13)

FRANCHISOR a parent company that grants rights to a franchisee to distribute and sell its goods and services (Chapter 13)

FREESTANDING INSERT (FSI) a preprinted ad, usually containing a coupon, placed in a separate publication, such as a newspaper (Chapter 18)

FREESTANDING SITES retail outlets that are not adjoined to other structures, but are often located adjacent to other retail locations (Chapter 14)

FREIGHT ABSORPTION PRICING a form of geographical pricing in which the seller absorbs freight costs (Chapter 12)

FREQUENCY the number of times a person or household is exposed to a communication vehicle such as an ad (Chapter 17)

FULL-SERVICE WHOLESALER a wholesaler that performs a wide range of services for its customers and the parties from which it purchases (Chapter 15)

FUNCTIONAL LEVEL the various functional areas within a business unit, where most of the unit's work is performed (for example, marketing and accounting are functional areas) (Chapter 3)

FUNCTIONAL MIDDLEMAN a wholesaler that does not take title to the products it sells (Chapter 15)

GAME a sales promotion that offers prizes like sweepstakes but covers a longer time period (Chapter 18)

GATEKEEPERS decision makers who control the flow of information and communication among buying center participants (Chapter 5)

GENERAL AGREEMENT ON TARIFFS AND TRADE (GATT) an agreement under which countries meet periodically to negotiate matters related to trade and tariffs; in 1993 GATT was signed by 108 countries representing 80 percent of all global trade (Chapter 2)

GENERAL MERCHANDISE WHOLESALER a wholesaler that carries a wide variety of products and provides extensive services for its customers (Chapter 15)

GENERICS products that are not branded; they are labeled only by their generic name (tomato soup) and usually cost less and may be of lower quality than their branded competitors (Chapter 8)

GEODEMOGRAPHICS the combination of geographic information and demographic characteristics; used in segmenting and targeting specific segments (Chapter 7)

GLOBAL PERSPECTIVE a view of the marketplace that includes searching for marketing opportunities around the world, competing internationally, and working with multicultural suppliers, employees, channel participants, and customers (Prologue)

GLOBAL STRATEGY a corporate-level strategy that views the whole world as a global market (Chapter 3)

GOING-RATE PRICING pricing at or near industry averages; strategy often used when companies compete on the basis of attributes or benefits other than price (Chapter 12)

GOODS physical products such as cars, golf clubs, soft drinks, or other concrete entities (in contrast to **services**, which are nonphysical products) (Chapter 8)

GOVERNMENT MARKET federal, state, and local government organizations that purchase goods and services for use in many activities (Chapter 5)

GROSS DOMESTIC PRODUCT (GDP) the total size of a country's economy measured in the amount of goods and services produced (Chapter 2)

GROSS MARGIN sales revenue minus the retailer's cost of goods sold (Chapter 14)

GROWTH STAGE the second stage in the product life cycle, when sales and profits increase rapidly (Chapter 10)

HIERARCHY OF EFFECTS see **information-processing model** (Chapter 17)

HIGH-INVOLVEMENT DECISIONS purchasing decisions that involve high levels of importance or personal relevance, thorough information processing, and substantial differences between alternatives (Chapter 4)

HYPERMARKET market format that combines a discount store with an oversized supermarket (Chapter 14)

IDEA GENERATION the initial stage of the new product development process, requiring creativity and innovation to generate ideas for potential new products (Chapter 9)

IDEA SCREENING evaluating the pool of new product ideas to reduce it to a smaller, more attractive set, based on consistency with the company vision and strategic objectives, potential market acceptance, fit with the firm's capabilities, and possible long-term contribution to profit (Chapter 9)

IMPLICIT COMMUNICATIONS what the marketing message connotes about the product, its price, or the places it is sold (Chapter 16)

IMPORT AGENT a wholesaler that finds products in foreign countries to sell in its home country; in many countries, it is illegal to sell imported products without going through an import agent or similar intermediary (Chapter 15)

IMPULSE PURCHASES impulse purchases are decisions made with little or no cognitive effort; choices made on the spur of the moment without prior problem recognition, but possibly with strong positive feelings (Chapter 4)

INCENTIVE PAY commissions, bonuses, or both; about 75 percent of U.S. firms use a combination pay plan for salespeople, less than 15 percent pay a straight salary, and 10 percent pay straight commission (Chapter 19)

INCOME-BASED PRICING the determination of price based on the income to be generated by the product under consideration (Chapter 12)

INDEPENDENT RETAILERS retailers that own and operate only one retail outlet; they account for more than three-fourths of all U.S. retail establishments (Chapter 14)

INDIRECT CHANNEL a way to move the product from producer to user with the help of intermediaries that perform functions related to buying or selling the product (Chapter 13)

INDIVIDUAL BRAND NAME STRATEGY establishing specific and different brand names for each individual product in a product line (Chapter 10)

INDIVIDUAL PRODUCT any brand or variant of a brand in a company's product line (Chapter 10)

INELASTIC DEMAND the demand that exists when price changes do not result in significant changes in the quantity of a product demanded (Chapter 12)

INFOMERCIAL a program-length TV ad that resembles a talk show or news program (Chapters 17 and 20)

INFORMATION-PROCESSING MODEL the sequence of advertising's effects: (1) exposure, (2) attention, (3) comprehension, (4) acceptance, and (5) retention; also called the **hierarchy of effects** (Chapter 17)

INFORMATIONAL INFLUENCE an interpersonal process, based on consumers' desire to make informed choices and reduce uncertainty, in which they seek information and advice from people they trust (Chapter 4)

INITIAL TRAINING sales training that focuses on product knowledge and sales techniques (Chapter 19)

INNOVATORS consumers who are most willing to try new products (about the first 2.5 percent of product adopters) (Chapter 9)

INQUIRY EVALUATION posttesting of an ad based on the number of consumers responding to requests in it, such as using coupons or asking for samples or more product information (Chapter 17)

INSTITUTIONAL ENVIRONMENT all the organizations involved in marketing products and services, including marketing research firms, ad agencies, wholesalers, retailers, suppliers, and customers (Chapter 2)

INSTITUTIONAL MARKET includes organizations such as profit or nonprofit hospitals, educational and religious institutions, and trade associations (Chapter 5)

INTEGRATED MARKETING COMMUNICATIONS (IMC) the strategic integration of multiple means of communicating with target markets to form a comprehensive, consistent message; communications are integrated horizontally (across various methods of communications) and vertically (from the marketer down through the marketing channel) (Chapter 16)

INTENSIVE DISTRIBUTION distributing a product or service through every available outlet (Chapter 13)

INTERACTIVE COMPUTER KIOSKS an electronic marketing medium, usually located in retail stores, that uses touch-screen technology to let the consumer access information of interest (Chapter 20)

INTERACTIVE COMPUTER NETWORKS systems that allow consumers and marketers to communicate with each other through phone lines and a personal computer (Chapter 20)

INTERACTIVE MARKETING that portion of electronic business that is communicating directly with target customers to encourage response (Chapter 20)

INTERCEPTOR LOCATION a location between a residential area and the closest supermarket, where a convenience store does business (Chapter 14)

INTERMARKET SEGMENTS well-defined, similar clusters of customers across national boundaries that let firms standardize marketing programs and offerings for each segment globally (Chapter 7)

INTERMEDIARIES middlemen directly involved in the purchase or sale of products as they flow from originator to user; they include retailers and wholesalers (Chapter 13)

INTERMODAL SHIPPING using two or more modes of transportation to ship products; for example, loaded trailers may travel piggyback on railcars (Chapter 15)

INTERNAL DEVELOPMENT a way to generate new products in which a firm creates the products itself, possibly subcontracting product design, engineering, or test marketing or working in partnership with another firm (Chapter 9)

INTERNAL REFERENCE PRICES comparison price standards that consumers remember and use to judge the fairness of prices; they include the expected price, the price last paid, the average retail price, and the price the consumer would like to pay now (Chapter 11)

INTERNAL SECONDARY DATA secondary data collected within a firm, including accounting records, sales force reports, and customer feedback (Chapter 6)

INTERSTATE COMMERCE COMMISSION (ICC) agency of the U.S. government that regulates interstate transportation (Chapter 2)

INTERTYPE COMPETITION competition among retailers that use different business formats to sell the same products; for example, McDonald's intertype competitors include all food retailers, from vending machines to fine restaurants (Chapter 14)

INTRATYPE COMPETITION competition among retailers that use the same business format (Chapter 14)

INTRODUCTION STAGE the first stage in the product life cycle, when a new product is launched into the marketplace; it continues the commercialization stage of the new product development process (Chapter 6)

INVENTORY TURNOVER the number of times a retailer sells its average inventory during the year, or how quickly merchandise is sold (Chapter 14)

INVOLVEMENT the level of importance, interest, or personal relevance generated by a product or a decision, which varies by the decision at hand and by the person's needs or motives (Chapter 4)

ISOLATED LOCATIONS freestanding retail sites where there are no adjoining buildings; best suited for large retailers that can attract a customer base on their own or for convenience businesses (Chapter 15)

JOINT VENTURE an arrangement between two or more organizations to market products internationally, through licensing agreements, contract manufacturing deals, or equity investments in strategic partnerships (Chapter 3)

JUST-IN-TIME (JIT) INVENTORY CONTROL SYSTEM a system that delivers raw materials, subassemblies, and component parts to manufacturers shortly before the scheduled manufacturing run that will consume the incoming shipment (Chapter 15)

LABEL a printed description of a product on a package (Chapter 8)

LAGGARDS the final group to adopt a new product; they represent about 16 percent of a market (Chapter 10)

LANHAM TRADEMARK ACT a U.S. law passed in 1946 that protects trademarks and brand names (Chapter 2)

LATE MAJORITY the fourth group to adopt a new product; they represent about 34 percent of a market (Chapter 10)

LEASED DEPARTMENTS sections in a retail store that the owner rents to another party; typically department stores rent their jewelry, shoe, hairstyling, and cosmetics departments (Chapter 14)

LEGITIMATE POWER power a member of a marketing channel gains through ownership or contractual agreements (Chapter 13)

LICENSING the right to use a trademark in exchange for paying royalties on the sale of the licensed product (Chapter 8)

LIFESTYLE RESEARCH a person's pattern of living, as expressed in activities, interests, and opinions; lifestyle traits are more concrete than personality traits and more directly linked to the acquisition, use, and disposition of goods and services. See also **psychographic research** (Chapter 7)

LIFETIME VALUE OF A LOYAL CUSTOMER the sales or profits generated from a customer who purchases a firm's product throughout his or her lifetime or some other extended period (Chapter 1)

LIMIT PRICING a competitive pricing strategy that involves setting prices low to discourage new competition (Chapter 12)

LIMITED-FUNCTION WHOLE-SALER a truck jobber, drop shipper, cash-and-carry wholesaler, catalog wholesaler, or wholesale club that does not offer the comprehensive service of a full-service wholesaler (Chapter 15)

LIMITED-LINE WHOLESALER a full-service wholesaler that does not stock as many products as a general merchandise wholesaler but has more depth in its product offering (Chapter 15)

LINE-FILLING STRATEGY adding products in various places within a product line to fill gaps that may not be at either the high or the low end (Chapter 10)

LISTS databases of current or potential customers that include their names, addresses, telephone numbers, and perhaps data on demographics, lifestyles, brand and media preferences, and consumption patterns (Chapter 20)

LOGISTICS MANAGEMENT planning, implementing, and moving raw materials and products from point of origin to point of consumption (Chapter 15)

LONGITUDINAL RESEARCH research conducted over time, typically on a panel of consumers or stores (Chapter 6)

LOW-INVOLVEMENT DECISIONS purchase decisions that involve fairly little personal interest, relevance, or importance and simple decision processes (Chapter 4)

MAGNUSSON-MOSS ACT a U.S. law passed in 1975 to regulate warranties (Chapter 2)

MAIL SURVEYS marketing research method that involves sending questionnaires via mail, often to large, geographically diverse groups of people (Chapter 6)

MAJOR ACCOUNTS key, high-potential customers (Chapter 19)

MAJORITY FALLACY pursuing large "majority" market segments because they offer potential gains while overlooking the fact that they also may attract overwhelming competition (Chapter 7)

MALL INTERCEPT INTERVIEWS market research method in which consumers are interviewed one-on-one while shopping (Chapter 6)

MANUFACTURER BRAND a brand sponsored by the product's manufacturer, who is responsible for its quality and marketing; also called a **national brand** or **regional brand** (Chapter 8)

MANUFACTURERS' AGENT a merchant wholesaler that sells related but noncompeting product lines for various manufacturers; also called *manufacturers' rep* (Chapter 15)

MANUFACTURER'S SALES BRANCH a manufacturer-owned wholesaler that maintains inventory and performs a wide range of functions for the parent company (Chapter 15)

MANUFACTURER'S SALES OFFICE a producer-owned wholesaler that differs from the manufacturer's sales branch in that it does not maintain inventory or perform as many functions for the parent company (Chapter 15)

MARGINAL COSTS costs that are incurred in producing one additional unit of output; they typically decline early due to economies of scale but increase as the firm approaches capacity (Chapter 12)

MARGINAL REVENUE the additional revenue a firm will receive if one more unit of product is sold (MR is usually the price of the product) (Chapter 12)

MARKET a group of people or organizations with needs to satisfy or problems to solve, the money to satisfy needs or solve problems, and the authority to make expenditure decisions (Chapter 2)

MARKET COVERAGE the number of outlets used to market a product; may involve intensive, selective, or exclusive distribution (Chapter 13)

MARKET EXPANSION STRATEGY a corporate growth strategy of marketing existing products to new markets (different market segments in the same geographic area or the same target market in different geographic areas) (Chapter 3)

MARKET FORECAST the amount of sales predicted based on the marketing effort (expenditures) put forth by all the companies competing to sell a particular product or service in a specific period (Chapter 7)

MARKET MAVENS people who share with other consumers their knowledge about kinds of products, places to shop, and other facets of the market (Chapter 4)

MARKET ORIENTATION used to describe firms implementing the marketing concept (Chapter 1)

MARKET PENETRATION STRATEGY achieving corporate growth objectives with existing products within existing markets, by persuading current customers to purchase more of the product or by capturing new customers (Chapter 3)

MARKET POTENTIAL the maximum amount of industry sales possible for a product or service for a specific period (Chapter 7)

MARKET SCOPE how broadly a business views its target market (Chapter 3)

MARKET SEGMENTATION dividing the market for a product into subsets of customers who behave in the same way, have similar needs, or have similar characteristics that relate to purchase behavior (Chapter 7)

MARKET SHARE a firm's percentage of the total market or total industry sales of a product (Chapter 11)

MARKET TESTS marketing a new product in test locations using the planned promotion, pricing, and distribution strategies (Chapter 7)

MARKETING the process of planning and executing the conception, pricing, promotion, and distribution of ideas, goods, and services to create exchanges that satisfy individual and organizational goals (Chapter 1)

MARKETING AS A SOCIETAL PROCESS a process that facilitates the flow of goods from producers to consumers in a society (Chapter 1)

MARKETING CHANNEL a combination of organizations and individuals (channel members) who perform the activities required to link producers to users to products to accomplish marketing objectives; also called **channel of distribution** (Chapter 13)

MARKETING COMMUNICATIONS marketer-initiated techniques directed to target audiences in an attempt to influence attitudes and behaviors; its three main objectives are to inform, persuade, and remind consumers; also called *promotion* (Chapter 16)

MARKETING COMMUNICATIONS ACTIVITIES activities that include advertising and public relations, sales promotion, personal selling, and direct marketing (Chapter 16)

MARKETING COMMUNICATIONS MESSAGE what the company is trying to convey about its products (Chapter 16)

MARKETING COMMUNICATIONS MIX the combination of advertising, public relations, sales promotion, personal selling, and direct marketing; also called the *promotional mix* (Chapter 16)

MARKETING COMMUNICATIONS PLANNING a seven-step process: (1) marketing plan review, (2) situation analysis, (3) communications process analysis, (4) budget development, (5) program development, (6) integration and implementation of the plan, and (7) monitoring, evaluating, and controlling the marketing communications program (Chapter 16)

MARKETING CONCEPT the interrelated principles that (1) an organization's basic purpose is to satisfy customer needs, (2) satisfying customer needs requires integrated, coordinated efforts throughout the organization, and (3) organizations should focus on long-term success (Chapter 1)

MARKETING DECISION SUPPORT SYSTEM (MDSS) a comprehensive entity that encompasses all data, activities, and computerized elements used to process information relevant to marketing decisions; designed to enhance managerial decision making and firm performance by providing timely, relevant internal and external information (Chapter 6)

MARKETING ENVIRONMENT the uncontrollable environment within which marketers must operate, encompassing social, economic, competitive, technological, legal/political, and institutional environments; all factors outside an organization that can affect its marketing activities (Chapter 2)

MARKETING MANAGEMENT specific strategic decisions for individual products and the day-to-day activities needed to execute these strategies successfully (Chapter 3)

MARKETING MIX the overall marketing effort to appeal to the target market, consisting of decisions in four basic areas: product, pricing, communications, and distribution (Chapter 1)

MARKETING PHILOSOPHY an organization's emphasis on satisfying customers' needs; a focus on the marketing concept (Chapter 1)

MARKETING PUBLIC RELATIONS public relations functions designed to support marketing activities (e.g., creating advertising news, introducing a new product with little advertising) (Chapter 17)

MARKETING RESEARCH activities linking marketer, customer, and public through information used to identify marketing opportunities; generate, refine, and evaluate marketing actions; monitor marketing performance; and improve understanding of marketing as a process. Marketing research specifies the information required to address these issues, designs the methods for collecting information, manages and implements the data collection process, analyzes the results, and communicates the findings and implications (Chapter 6)

MARKETING RESEARCH DESIGNS general strategies or plans of action for addressing research problems, data collection, and analysis (Chapter 6)

MARKETING RESEARCH PROCESS a six-step sequence: (1) problem definition, (2) determination of research design, (3) determination of data collection methods, (4) development of data collection forms, (5) sample design, and (6) analysis and interpretation (Chapter 6)

MARKETING STRATEGIC PLAN a functional plan for how marketing managers will execute the business strategic plan, addressing the general target market and marketing mix (Chapter 3)

MARKETING STRATEGIES selecting a target market and developing a marketing mix to satisfy that market's needs (Chapter 1)

MARKUP PRICING pricing where markup is the difference between the cost of an item and the retail price, expressed as a percentage (Chapter 12)

MASS CUSTOMIZATION the ability of complex manufactured products to be made to order; possible because of advances in manufacturing and information technology (Chapter 7)

MATURITY STAGE the third stage of the product life cycle, when competition intensifies and sales growth slows (Chapter 10)

MEASURABILITY the degree to which the size and purchasing power of market segments can be assessed (Chapter 7)

MEDIA CLASS one of seven classes of advertising media: TV, magazines, newspapers, radio, outdoor, transit, and direct mail (Chapter 17)

MEDIA SCHEDULE the frequency and timing of ads and commercials; see also **reach** and **frequency** (Chapter 17)

MEDIA VEHICLE a specific TV program, magazine, or the like in any of the seven media classes (Chapter 17)

MERCHANT WHOLESALER an independent distributor that takes title to the products it sells; may be either a full-service or a limited-function wholesaler (Chapter 15)

MESSAGE ACCEPTANCE the point where the consumer develops favorable attitudes about the advertised product and subsequent purchase; step 4 in the information-processing model (Chapter 17)

MESSAGE CHANNEL the means by which a company conveys its message about its products; for example, advertising vehicles like newspapers, TV, and billboards (Chapter 16)

MESSAGE COMPREHENSION the point where the consumer understands an ad's meaning; step 3 in the information-processing model (Chapter 17)

MESSAGE EXPOSURE what a marketer achieves by placing ads in appropriate media, giving consumers the opportunity to process the message; step 1 in the information-processing or hierarchy of effects model (Chapter 17)

MESSAGE PRESENTER a person, perhaps a salesperson, actor, or TV personality, who actually delivers a message (Chapter 16)

MESSAGE RETENTION the point where a consumer stores ad information in long-term memory, which is critical for affecting later purchase decisions and behavior; step 5 in the information-processing model (Chapter 17)

MESSAGE SPONSOR the organization that is attempting to market its goods, services, or ideas (Chapter 16)

METROPOLITAN STATISTICAL AREA (MSA) a geographic area identified by census data to contain a city with a population of at least 50,000 or be an urbanized area with 50,000 people that is part of a county of at least 100,000 residents (Chapter 7)

MICROMARKETING using computer analysis of census and demographic data to identify clusters of households that share similar consumption patterns (for example, the PRIZM market segmentation system) (Chapter 7)

MIDDLEMEN see **intermediaries**

MISSION STATEMENT an element in the strategic planning process that expresses the company's basic values and specifies the boundaries within which business units, marketing, and other functions must operate (Chapter 3)

MISSIONARY SALESPEOPLE sales support personnel who work at the grassroots level to promote their company's products; especially important in the grocery and pharmaceutical markets (Chapter 19)

MODIFIED REBUY DECISIONS business purchasing decisions that call for the evaluation of new alternatives; could involve considering new suppliers for current purchase needs or new products offered by current suppliers; an example is the purchase of complex component parts from a new supplier (Chapter 5)

MOTIVATION the desire to process ad information; a state or condition within a person that prompts goal-directed behavior; it generally occurs when some need or problem is recognized, and it can affect information search, information processing, and purchase behavior (Chapter 19)

MULTINATIONAL STRATEGY recognizes national differences and views other countries as a portfolio of markets (Chapter 3)

MULTIPLE-CHANNELS STRATEGY distributing a product through more than one channel to reach customers (for example, Prell shampoo is widely available at discount, drug, and grocery stores) (Chapter 13)

NATIONAL BRAND see **manufacturer brand** (Chapter 8)

NEGATIVE DISCONFIRMATION an experience where a purchase does not turn out as well as the consumer expected (Chapter 4)

NEGOTIATED PRICING pricing in which negotiation between vendor and supplier replaces multiple bids; common for large investments. See also **sealed-bid pricing** (Chapter 12)

NETWORK ORGANIZATIONS firms involved in many different types of organizational partnerships, including strategic alliances, joint ventures, and vendor partnering (Chapter 3)

NEURAL NETWORKS sophisticated statistical techniques that can use a database to calculate weights for such traits as age, income, education, or time on the job (Chapter 20)

NEW-BUSINESS SALESPEOPLE members of the sales force who concentrate on selling new products or selling to new customers (Chapter 19)

NEW-TASK DECISIONS business purchasing decisions that occur when the buying problem is new and a great deal of information must be gathered; relatively infrequent decisions for a company, and the cost of making a wrong decision is high (Chapter 5)

NOISE any distraction or distortion during the communications process that prevents the message from being communicated effectively (Chapter 16)

NONPRICE COMPETITION competition between brands for sales based on factors other than price, such as quality, service, or specific product features (Chapter 11)

NONPROBABILITY SAMPLING market research in which selection of the sample is based on the researcher's or field worker's judgment (Chapter 6)

NONPROPRIETARY SECONDARY DATA secondary data that are available from libraries, computer databases, and other public sources (Chapter 6)

NONSTORE RETAILING the selling of products and services outside a physical structure through, for example, direct marketing, direct selling, or vending machine sales (Chapter 14)

NORMATIVE INFLUENCE a strategy in which marketers show consumers the favorable conditions that can occur when their brands are used or the unfavorable consequences that can occur when not used (Chapter 4)

NORMS the expectations, real or imagined, of other individuals or groups of people (Chapter 1)

NORTH AMERICAN FREE TRADE AGREEMENT (NAFTA) a treaty that eliminates many trade barriers among the United States, Mexico, and Canada (Chapter 11)

NORTH AMERICAN INDUSTRY CLASSIFICATION SYSTEM (NAICS) a numerical scheme developed by the federal government for categorizing businesses (Chapter 5)

OBJECTIONS buyer concerns about a product (Chapter 19)

OBJECTIVE CLAIMS advertising messages that describe product features or performance in measurable terms, often reflecting a quality/value perspective (Chapter 17)

OBJECTIVE PRICE see **price** (Chapter 11)

OBJECTIVE-TASK BUDGETING a budgeting method for marketing communications based on achieving stipulated objectives, identifying tasks to meet those objectives, and evaluating results (Chapter 16)

OBSERVATION RESEARCH market research technique where a researcher or a video camera monitors customer behavior, or anonymous shoppers evaluate the quality of services offered (Chapter 6)

ODD–EVEN PRICING setting prices at just below an even amount (for example, contact lenses for $199.95 instead of $200) (Chapter 12)

ONLINE AUCTION COMPANY a firm that uses a computer network, typically the Internet, to bring buyers and sellers together (Chapter 15)

ONLINE COUPONING distribution of coupons on the Internet (Chapter 18)

ON-SHELF COUPONING distributing coupons via a dispenser mounted near the manufacturer's product on a store shelf (Chapter 18)

OPERATIONAL PRODUCTS products that are used in a firm's activities but do not become part of any finished product; examples include lightbulbs, cleaning materials, and services (such as accounting or advertising) (Chapter 8)

OPINION LEADERS people who influence consumer behavior through word-of-mouth communications based on their interest or expertise in particular products (Chapter 4)

OPPORTUNITIES areas where a company's performance might be improved; typically ranked by managers so the most important can be addressed first in the next strategic planning stage (Chapter 3)

OPPORTUNITY the extent to which distractions or limited exposure time affect the buyer's attention to brand information in an ad (Chapter 17)

ORDER in order processing, either a customer's purchase order or an order transmitted by a sales rep (Chapter 15)

ORDER TAKERS see **existing-business salespeople**

ORGANIZATION OF PETROLEUM EXPORTING COUNTRIES (OPEC) a loose federation of many of the oil-producing countries, designed to influence market prices and short-term profits for crude oil (Chapter 11)

ORGANIZED SALES PRESENTATION a mental or written outline developed by the salesperson that is flexible enough to allow adaptive selling (Chapter 19)

OUTCOME-BASED PERSPECTIVE a way of evaluating salesperson performance that focuses on the results of sales behavior, such as total sales volume; see also **behavior-based perspective** (Chapter 19)

OUTSOURCING a firm's decision to purchase products and services from other companies rather than to make the products or perform the services internally; examples include components for computers, shipping, telecommunications, payroll administration (Chapter 5)

PACKAGE the container or wrapper for a product, including the label (Chapter 8)

PARTITIONED PRICING a pricing strategy in which a firm divides the price of a product or service into parts in lieu of charging a single price; the parts are often termed *base price* and *surcharge* (Chapter 12)

PAY-FOR-PERFORMANCE TRADE PROMOTION a sales promotion in which retailers are rewarded for making sales to consumers rather than purchases from manufacturers (Chapter 18)

PENETRATION PRICING setting a low initial price to encourage initial product trial, stimulate sales growth and lower unit production costs, increase total revenues, and enhance profits (Chapters 11 and 12)

PERCEIVED MONETARY PRICE the consumer's subjective perception of whether the price of a product is high or low, fair or unfair (in contrast to **objective price**) (Chapter 11)

PERCEIVED VALUE the buyer's overall assessment of a product's utility based on what is received and what is given; the quality per dollar (Chapter 11)

PERCENTAGE OF SALES BUDGETING a budgeting method for marketing communications based on the preceding year's or forecast coming year's sales (Chapter 16)

PERCEPTUAL MAPS spatial representations of consumer perceptions of products or brands, used to evaluate brand positions in a market (Chapter 7)

PERIODIC DISCOUNTING offering occasional discounts to take advantage of consumer segments' differing price sensitivity; includes price skimming (Chapter 12)

PERMISSION MARKETING marketing that occurs when the customer grants the marketer permission to send regular updates of interest to the consumer via e-mail (Chapter 16)

PERSONAL INTERVIEWS one-on-one interactions—between a consumer, customer, or respondent and a market researcher—to gather data (Chapter 6)

PERSONAL SELLING the element of the marketing communications mix that involves face-to-face interactions between seller and buyer to satisfy buyer needs for their mutual benefit (Chapters 16 and 19)

PERSONALITY a person's consistent response to his or her environment, linked to susceptibility to persuasion and social influence and thereby to purchase behavior (Chapter 4)

PERSUASION KNOWLEDGE helps consumer understand why and how marketers are trying to persuade us and to adaptively respond to these attempts (Chapter 4)

PLUS-ONE DIALING method of telephone interview where a phone number is randomly selected from the local directory and a digit or digits added to it; allows inclusion of unlisted numbers in the sample (Chapter 6)

POINT-OF-PURCHASE DISPLAY a sales promotion, often provided free by the manufacturer to the retailer, to call customer attention to a featured product (Chapter 18)

POLITICAL/LEGAL ENVIRONMENT factors and trends related to governmental activities and specific laws and regulations that affect marketing practice (Chapter 2)

PORTALS search engines that offer general Internet functions and that direct visitors to additional sites (Chapter 14)

POSITIONING developing an overall image for a product or brand by designing a marketing program, including the product mix, that a market segment will perceive as desirable (Chapter 7)

POSITIVE DISCONFIRMATION an experience where a purchase turns out better than a consumer expected (Chapter 4)

POSTTESTING recall and attitude tests and inquiry evaluations marketers use to assess the effectiveness of an ad campaign (Chapter 17)

PRECALL PLANNING focusing on learning more about the customer's situation before making a sales call (Chapter 19)

PREDATORY DUMPING dumping intended to drive rivals out of business (Chapter 11)

PREDATORY PRICING charging very low prices to drive competition from the market and then raising prices once a monopoly has been established (Chapter 12)

PREDICTIVE DIALING SYSTEMS automated dialing machines that make telemarketing more productive by passing over answering machines, busy signals, and no answers and passing live calls on to a live telemarketer (Chapter 20)

PREDICTIVE MODELING manipulating a customer database to reach a desired target more effectively, using neural networks and other technologies (Chapter 20)

PRELAUNCH ACTIVITIES marketing research studies conducted before commercialization of a new product (Chapter 9)

PREMIUM an item given free or at a bargain price to encourage the consumer to buy (Chapter 18)

PREMIUM PRICING setting higher prices on one or more product versions; a popular strategy for beer, clothing, appliances, and cars (Chapter 12)

PRESTIGE PRICING keeping prices high to maintain an image of product quality and appeal to buyers who associate premium prices with high quality (Chapter 11)

PRETESTING evaluating consumer reactions to proposed ads through focus groups and direct questioning, based on overall likability, consumer recall of information, message communication, and effects on purchase intentions and brand attitudes (Chapter 17)

PRICE the amount of money a buyer pays a seller in exchange for products and services (Chapter 11)

PRICE-AVERSION STRATEGY buying the lowest-priced brand (in contrast to the best-value strategy, which takes quality into account) (Chapter 11)

PRICE COMPETITION competition between brands for sales based on price alone; most common for similar brands and for customers with limited budgets and weak brand loyalties; see also **nonprice competition** (Chapter 11)

PRICE DEAL a temporary reduction in the price of a product, in the form of a cents-off or price-pack deal, used to introduce a new brand, convince current users to purchase more, or encourage new users to try an established brand (Chapter 18)

PRICE DISCRIMINATION selling the same product to different customers at different prices; restricted in the United States by the Robinson-Patman Act; see also **differential pricing** (Chapter 11)

PRICE ELASTICITY OF DEMAND the responsiveness of customer demand to changes in a product's price (Chapter 11)

PRICE-PACK DEAL a product that offers consumers something extra through the packaging itself; for example, a box of cereal with 20 percent more cereal for the regular price (Chapter 18)

PRICE PROMOTION MIX the basic price plus such supplemental components as sale prices, temporary discounts, coupons, and favorable payment and credit terms; encourages purchase behavior by strengthening the basic price during relatively short periods of time (Chapter 11)

PRICE–QUALITY RELATIONSHIP the extent to which a consumer associates a higher product price with higher quality (Chapter 11)

PRICE-SEEKING STRATEGY purchasing the highest-priced brand to maximize expected quality (Chapter 11)

PRICE SIGNALING a competitive pricing strategy that puts high prices on low-quality products (Chapter 12)

PRICE SKIMMING setting prices high initially to appeal to consumers who are not price sensitive, then lowering prices sequentially to appeal to the next market segments (Chapters 11 and 12)

PRICE THRESHOLD the point at which buyers notice a price increase or decrease; the threshold level depends on a product's average price (for example, a 10¢ reduction on a 50¢ product is more meaningful than on a $10 product) (Chapter 12)

PRIMARY DATA data collected for a particular research problem—for example, survey information; typically more current and relevant than secondary data but more expensive to gather (Chapter 6)

PRIMARY DEMAND general demand for a new product form, which marketing tries to generate at the introduction stage of the product life cycle (Chapter 10)

PRIMARY METROPOLITAN STATISTICAL AREA (PMSA) a major urban area, often located within a CMSA, that has at least 1 million inhabitants (Chapter 7)

PRIVATE BRAND see **distributor brand** (Chapter 8)

PRIVATE EXCHANGES electronic marketplace that link invitation-only buyers and sellers (Chapter 5)

PRIVATE LABEL see **distributor brand** (Chapter 8)

PRIVATE RESPONSE a complaint in which a dissatisfied consumer badmouths a product to friends or family (Chapter 4)

PRIVATE WAREHOUSE a warehouse operated by the company that uses it (Chapter 15)

PRIZM potential rating index by zip markets, which divides every neighborhood in the United States into one of 40 distinct cluster types that reveal consumer data; PRIZM14 uses ZIP14 codes for even greater detail covering individual demographics, individual credit records, model-specific auto registration, and

purchase behavior data from private sources (Chapter 7)

PROACTIVE PR a form of public relations that is positive and opportunity seeking, such as product release announce-ments, event sponsorship, and placement of articles in the business press (Chapter 17)

PROBABILITY SAMPLING market research in which each person in the popula-tion has a known, nonzero chance of being selected by some objective procedure; such unbiased selection increases the sample's representativeness (Chapter 6)

PROBLEM DEFINITION the first step in the marketing research process; identifying the difference between the way things should be and the way they are or identifying the issues that need to be investigated (Chapter 6)

PRODUCT an idea, a physical entity (a good), a service, or any combination that is an element of exchange to satisfy individual or business objectives (Chapter 8)

PRODUCT COMPETITORS companies that offer different kinds of products to satisfy the same basic need (for example, Domino's Pizza and Kentucky Fried Chicken both attempt to satisfy a consumer need for fast food but offer somewhat different products and services from each other) (Chapter 2)

PRODUCT DESIGN the styling, aesthetics, and function of a product, which affect how it works, how it feels, and how easy it is to assemble, fix, and recycle (Chapter 8)

PRODUCT DIFFERENTIATION circumstance in which a firm's offerings differ or are perceived to differ from those of competing firms on any attribute, including price (Chapter 7)

PRODUCT EXPANSION STRATEGY marketing new products to the same customer base (Chapter 3)

PRODUCT LIFE CYCLE (PLC) the advancement of a product through the stages of introduction, growth, maturity, and decline (Chapter 10)

PRODUCT LINE a group of individual products that are closely related in some way (Chapter 10)

PRODUCT LINE CONTRACTION deleting individual products from a product line (Chapter 10)

PRODUCT LINE LENGTH the number of products in any one product line (Chapter 10)

PRODUCT-LINE PRICING offering multiple versions of the same product, with those priced at the low end used to build traffic

and those at the high end creating a quality image for the entire product line (Chapter 12)

PRODUCT MARKETING PLANS plans within each business unit that focus on specific target markets and marketing mixes for each product and include both strategic decisions (what to do) and execution decisions (how to do it) (Chapter 3)

PRODUCT MIX the total assortment of products and services marketed by a firm (Chapter 10)

PRODUCT MIX CONSISTENCY the relatedness of the different product lines in a product mix; for example, all of Schwab's product lines are investment-related, but J&J sells everything from contact lenses to baby powder (Chapter 10)

PRODUCT MIX WIDTH the number of product lines in a company's product mix (Chapter 10)

PRODUCT PLACEMENT ADVER-TISING the combined efforts of marketers with moviemakers, such that product exposure is obtained among moviegoers (Chapter 17)

PRODUCTION PHILOSOPHY an organization's emphasis on the production function, valuing activities related to improving production efficiency or producing sophisti-cated products and services (Chapter 1)

PRODUCTION PRODUCTS raw materials and components that become part of some finished product (for example, steel and paper) (Chapter 8)

PRODUCTIVITY PERSPECTIVE getting the most output for each marketing dollar spent, by doing the same things better and/or doing different things (Prologue)

PROJECTIVE TECHNIQUES market research methods, such as word association or sentence completion, that let researchers elicit feelings that normally go unexpressed (Chapter 6)

PROMOTIONAL INTERACTIVE COMPUTER DISKS a relatively new format for direct-mail campaigns in which the information is presented on disk and the consumer can respond (Chapter 20)

PROPRIETARY SECONDARY DATA data provided by commercial marketing research firms that sell their services to other firms; examples are diary panels and scanner data (Chapter 6)

PROSPECTING the seller's search for and identification of qualified buyers, defined as buyers who are reasonably accessible to the seller, able to afford the purchase, and willing to consider making it (Chapter 19)

PROTOTYPE DEVELOPMENT converting the concept for a new product into an actual product, using the information obtained from concept tests to design a tangible product that can be tested further (Chapter 9)

PSYCHOGRAPHIC RESEARCH a concept for dividing a market into lifestyle segments on the basis of consumer interests, values, opinions, personality traits, attitudes, and demographics to develop marketing communications and product strategies (Chapter 7)

PSYCHOLOGICAL PRICING the recognition that buyers' perceptions and beliefs affect their evaluations of prices (Chapter 12)

PUBLIC RELATIONS (PR) the element of the marketing communications mix that identifies, establishes, and maintains mutually beneficial relations between an organization and the various publics on which its success or failure depends—for example, customers, employees, stockholders, community members, and the government (Chapters 16 and 17)

PUBLIC RELATIONS FUNCTIONS press relations; product promotions; internal and external corporate communications; lobbying to promote, defeat, or circumvent legislation and regulations; advising management about public issues and company positions and image; and overall responding to various occurrences in the marketplace, either reactively or proactively (Chapter 17)

PUBLIC SERVICE ADVERTISING (PSAS) advertising donated by the ad industry to promote activities for some social good (Chapter 17)

PUBLIC WAREHOUSE a for-hire facility available to any business that requires storage or handling of goods (Chapter 15)

PUBLICITY information about the company or product that appears, unpaid for, in the news media; primary publicity techniques are news releases, press conferences, and feature articles, often presented in the business press (Chapters 16 and 17)

PUFFERY advertising that contains claims including acceptable exaggeration (Chapter 17)

PULL STRATEGY concentrating marketing communications on consumers to stimulate demand in an attempt to get consumers to "pull" a product from the manufacturing company through the marketing channel (Chapter 16)

PUSH MONEY what a manufacturer pays retail salespeople to encourage them to promote its products over competitive brands or to sell specific products in the manufacturer's line (Chapter 18)

PUSH STRATEGY directing marketing communications toward intermediary channel members to "push" a product through the channel to the ultimate consumer (Chapter 16)

QUALITATIVE DATA open-ended responses obtained from in-depth interviews, focus groups, and some observation studies; characterized by depth of response and richness of description (Chapter 6)

QUALITY the totality of features and characteristics of a product or service that bear on its ability to satisfy stated or implied needs (Chapter 8)

QUALITY FUNCTION DEPLOYMENT (QFD) a procedure in the new product development process that links specific consumer requirements with specific product characteristics (Chapter 9)

QUANTITATIVE DATA information collected using more structured response formats that can be more easily analyzed and projected to larger populations (Chapter 6)

QUICK-RESPONSE (QR) INVENTORY CONTROL SYSTEM a system for providing retailers with finished goods in which inventory is restocked according to what has just been sold, based on small but frequent orders (Chapter 15)

QUOTAS the quantitative outcomes (such as total sales volume, gross margin, market share, number of new accounts added, and accounts retained) used to assess sales reps' performance and effectiveness (Chapter 19)

RACK JOBBER a specialty-line wholesaler that sells to retail stores, setting up and maintaining attractive store displays and stocking them with goods sold on consignment (Chapter 15)

RADIO FREQUENCY IDENTIFICATION (RFID) allows the printing of radio antennas that can be affixed to products in place of a bar code, enabling entire containers of diverse items to be scanned instantly at a distance (Chapter 15)

RANDOM-DIGIT DIALING a method of telephone interviewing where, for example, four random digits are added to three-digit telephone exchanges to reach consumers (Chapter 6)

REACH the number of different people or households exposed to an ad or campaign over a specified time period (usually four weeks) (Chapter 17)

REACTIVE PR a form of public relations that addresses negative events or changes in the marketplace that adversely affect the firm, such as negative publicity from product defects or employee behavior (Chapter 17)

READER-RESPONSE CARDS card inserts in magazines, used in conjunction with ads, that make it easy for readers to send for more information on a product (Chapter 20)

REBATE cash reimbursement for purchasing a product, in which the buyer must mail a rebate form, the receipt, and proof of purchase to the manufacturer within a certain time (Chapter 18)

RECEIVER the intended target for any basic communication; for example, a purchasing agent listening to a sales presentation or a consumer reading a magazine ad (Chapter 16)

RECIPROCITY when firm A purchases from supplier B who in turn buys A's own products and services (Chapter 5)

REFERENCE GROUPS interpersonal influences beyond the family, including friends and coworkers (Chapter 4)

REFERENT POWER power a member of a marketing channel gains through another member's desire to be associated with it (Chapter 13)

REGIONAL BRAND see **manufacturer brand**

RELATED DIVERSIFICATION branching out into new products and markets that have something in common with existing operations (for example, a video rental store diversifying into music retailing) (Chapter 3)

RELATIONSHIP MARKETING developing, maintaining, and enhancing long-term profitable relationships with customers (Chapter 19)

RELATIONSHIP PERSPECTIVE building partnerships with firms outside the organization and encouraging teamwork among different functions within the organization to develop long-term customer relationships (Prologue)

RELATIONSHIP SELLING see **relationship marketing** (Chapter 19)

RELATIONSHIP STRATEGY a framework for working with customers based on relationship selling; it includes the counselor strategy, the supplier strategy, and the systems-designer strategy (Chapter 19)

RELIABILITY reflects the consistency of responses or the extent to which results are reproducible (Chapter 6)

REPOSITIONING developing new marketing programs to shift consumer beliefs and opinions about an existing brand; see also **positioning** (Chapter 7)

RESELLER MARKET firms that purchase goods and in turn sell them to others at a gain; includes wholesalers and retailers (Chapter 5)

RESERVATION PRICE the highest price a person is willing to pay for a product; one form of a consumer's internal reference price (Chapter 11)

RETAIL CHAIN a retailer that owns and operates multiple retail outlets; chains represent 20 percent of all retailers and account for 50 percent of all retail sales (Chapter 14)

RETAIL COOPERATIVE a group of stores that remain independently owned but adopt a common name and storefront and band together to increase their buying power (Chapter 14)

RETAIL FRANCHISING a form of chain ownership in which a franchisee pays the franchisor (parent company) fees or royalties and agrees to run the franchise by prescribed norms in exchange for use of the franchisor's name (Chapter 14)

RETAIL SALES sales to final consumers, as opposed to wholesale sales; a firm's retail sales must be at least half of its total revenues for it to be classified as a retailer (Chapter 14)

RETAIL STRATEGY MIX the controllable variables of location, products and services, pricing, and marketing communications (Chapter 14)

RETAILER-OWNED COOPERATIVE GROUP a contractual marketing channel system in which the retailers own the wholesaler (Chapter 13)

RETAILING all of the activities involved in selling products and services to the final consumer; retailers include independents, chains, franchises, leased departments, cooperatives, and various forms of nonstore retailers (Chapter 14)

RETURN ON INVESTMENT (ROI) ratio of income before taxes to total operating assets associated with a product, such as plant and equipment and inventory (Chapter 11)

REVERSE AUCTIONS auctions in which sellers bid instead of buyers and prices fall instead of rise, enabling buyers to negotiate lower prices from multiple suppliers (Chapter 12)

REWARD POWER power a member of a marketing channel gains when it can offer another member widespread distribution, special credit terms, or some other reward (Chapter 13)

ROBINSON-PATMAN ACT a U.S. law passed in 1936 to prohibit price discrimination (Chapter 2)

ROLLOUT STUDIES marketing research studies performed on a new product after it has been introduced (Chapter 9)

SALES AUTOMATION SYSTEMS computerized systems sales managers use for routine supervisory chores such as processing sales reps' call reports, itineraries, and expense reports (Chapter 19)

SALES CHANNEL STRATEGY addresses how a company initiates and maintains contact with customer through the use of a company field sales force, telemarketing, independent sales reps, distributors, or trade shows (Chapter 19)

SALES EFFECTIVENESS EVALUATIONS the most stringent tests of advertising efficiency, they assess whether the advertising resulted in increased sales (Chapter 17)

SALES FORCE EFFECTIVENESS how well the entire sales organization is performing, including an evaluation of individual salespeople's performance (Chapter 19)

SALES FORCE TURNOVER the proportion of salespeople who leave their jobs (Chapter 19)

SALES MANAGEMENT managers who oversee the personal selling function, managing sales personnel and developing and implementing sales strategy (Chapter 19)

SALES POTENTIAL the maximum amount of sales a specific firm can obtain for a specified time period (Chapter 7)

SALES PROCESS the process of initiating, developing, and enhancing long-term, mutually satisfying relationships with customers (Chapter 19)

SALES PROMOTION the element of the marketing communications mix that provides extra value or incentives to consumers, wholesalers, retailers, or other organizational customers to stimulate product interest, trial, or purchase; media and nonmedia marketing communications employed for a predetermined, limited time to stimulate trial, increase consumer demand, or improve product availability (Chapters 16 and 18)

SALES RESISTANCE customer concerns about a product, both spoken (objections) and unspoken (Chapter 19)

SALES SUPPORT SALESPEOPLE employees who support the personal selling function by promoting a product or providing technical support, working in coordination with the salespeople who actually solicit customer purchases (Chapter 19)

SALES TERRITORY usually defined geographically, a territory consists of specific customers assigned to a specific salesperson (Chapter 19)

SALESPERSON PERFORMANCE how well individual salespeople meet job expectations, evaluated from a behavior-based perspective, an outcome-based perspective, or a combination of the two (Chapter 19)

SAMPLE a small size of a product made available to prospective purchasers, usually free, to demonstrate a product's value or use and encourage future purchase (Chapter 18)

SAMPLE SIZE the size of a sample in market research, based on the anticipated response rate, variability in the data, cost and time considerations, and desired level of precision (Chapter 6)

SAMPLING FRAME the outline or working description of the population used in sample selection for market research (Chapter 6)

SANCTIONS restrictions imposed by the UN or individual governments to limit trade with specific countries

SCANNER DATA a type of proprietary data derived from UPC bar codes (Chapter 6)

SCRAMBLED MERCHANDISING adding unrelated product categories to existing product lines (Chapter 14)

SEALED-BID PRICING pricing in which sellers submit sealed bids for providing their products or services and the buyer chooses among them. See also **negotiated pricing** (Chapter 12)

SEASONALITY product demand fluctuations related to the time of year, which may be affected by unpredictable changes in weather and in consumer preferences (Chapter 14)

SECOND-MARKET DISCOUNTING a form of differential pricing in which different prices are charged in different market segments (for example, foreign markets) (Chapter 12)

SECONDARY DATA proprietary and nonproprietary data already collected for some other purpose and available from various sources (such as library research); typically cheaper than collecting primary data but may be less current or relevant (Chapter 6)

SECONDARY DEMAND demand for a specific brand of new product form, which marketing tries to generate after competing brands are introduced (Chapter 10)

SELECTING choosing the candidates to be hired for a sales job (Chapter 19)

SELECTIVE DISTRIBUTION involves selling a product in only some of the available outlets; commonly used when after-the-sale service is necessary, such as in the home appliance industry (Chapter 13)

SELECTIVE PERCEPTION information is only partially processed or is misinterpreted due to limited exposure, attention, or comprehension; caused most often by the consumer's limited ability and motivation to see and process everything (Chapter 17)

SELF-CONCEPT a person's overall perception and feelings about himself or herself; consumers buy products that are consistent with or that enhance their self-concept (Chapter 4)

SELLING PHILOSOPHY an organization's emphasis on the selling function to the exclusion of other marketing activities (Chapter 1)

SELLING STRATEGY an overall plan for a salesperson's course of action, developed at three levels: sales territory, customer, and individual sales call (Chapter 19)

SERVICE MERCHANDISER see **rack jobber**

SERVICE RETAILERS all retailers that sell services, from rental businesses to movie theaters, hotels, and car repair shops (Chapter 14)

SERVICES nonphysical products such as a haircut, a football game, or a doctor's diagnosis (in contrast to **goods,** which are physical products) (Chapter 8)

SHERMAN ACT a U.S. law passed in 1890 to prohibit monopolistic practices (Chapter 2)

SHIPPING CONTAINER MARKING (SCM) feeds information into a computerized tracking system to facilitate shipping of products (Chapter 15)

SHOPPING MALL a concentration of retail stores enclosed under one roof and designed for more pedestrian flow (Chapter 14)

SHOPPING PRODUCTS categories of items within which consumers do not know exactly what they want and are willing to spend time shopping; usually expensive items such as cars, TVs (Chapter 8)

SIMPLE RANDOM SAMPLING a probability sampling approach in which each unit has an equal chance of being selected (Chapter 6)

SIMULATED TEST MARKETING evaluating a new product prototype in situations set up to be similar to those where consumers would actually purchase or use the product (for example, intercepting shoppers at a high-traffic location in a mall) (Chapter 9)

SINGLE-CHANNEL STRATEGY using only one means to reach customers (for example, Nexxus shampoo is distributed exclusively through hair care professionals) (Chapter 13)

SINGLE-SOURCE DATA data produced by proprietary systems that combine information on product purchase behavior with TV viewing behavior (Chapter 6)

SLOTTING ALLOWANCES fees manufacturers pay to retailers or wholesalers to obtain shelf or warehouse space for their products (Chapter 14)

SOCIAL CLASSES relatively homogeneous divisions within a society that contain people with similar values, needs, lifestyles, and behavior; usually divided into four classes: upper, middle, working, and lower (Chapter 4)

SOCIAL ENVIRONMENT all factors and trends related to groups of people, including their number, characteristics, behavior, and growth projections (Chapter 2)

SOCIAL RESPONSIBILITY minimizing social costs, such as environmental damage, and maximizing the positive impact of marketing decisions on society (Chapter 3)

SOCIALIZATION absorbing a culture, a process that continues throughout life and produces many specific preferences of products and services, shopping patterns, and interactions with others (Chapter 4)

SOURCE the message sender; in marketing communications, the marketer (Chapter 16)

SOURCE CREDIBILITY the state in which a customer perceives that its needs are satisfied by the combination of the sales rep, the product or service, and the rep's company (Chapter 19)

SOURCES companies or individuals who sell products and services directly to buying organizations; also called **suppliers** or **vendors** (Chapter 5)

SPAM unsolicited e-mail (Chapter 20)

SPECIALTY-LINE WHOLESALER a wholesaler that sells only a single product line or part of a line but is an expert regarding those products (Chapter 15)

SPECIALTY PRODUCTS items for which consumers want a specific brand and are willing to hunt for it; they won't switch brands (as with convenience products) or shop to evaluate alternatives (as for shopping products) (Chapter 8)

SPIFF see **push money** (Chapter 18)

SPONSORSHIP investments in causes and events to support overall corporate and marketing objectives (Chapter 16)

STANDARD TEST MARKETING testing a new product prototype and its marketing strategy in actual market situations (Chapter 9)

STANDARDIZED MARKETING STRATEGY implementing the same product, price, distribution, and communications programs in all international markets (Chapter 3)

STATEMENT STUFFERS promotional pieces that are included in other mail, such as bank or credit card statements (Chapter 20)

STATISTICAL DEMAND ANALYSIS forecasting sales from equations in which price, promotion, distribution, competitive, and economic factors are independent variables (Chapter 7)

STEALTH MARKETING involves a wide range of publicity generators, from product placement in movies and television to the naming of sports facilities, such as the United Center in Chicago (Chapter 16)

STORE BRAND see **distributor brand** (Chapter 8)

STORE IMAGE the picture shoppers have of a store's identity, composed of their perceptions of its location, goods and services sold, and atmospherics (Chapter 14)

STRAIGHT REBUY DECISIONS most common type of business purchasing decision in which products and services are simply repurchased; delivery, performance, and price are critical considerations (Chapter 5)

STRATEGIC BUSINESS UNIT (SBU) a unit of a company that focuses on a single product or brand, a line of products, or a mix of related products that meet a common market need and whose management oversees the basic business functions (Chapter 3)

STRATEGIC MARKETING marketing activities that encompass three functions: (1) helping to orient everyone in the organization toward markets and customers; (2) helping to gather and analyze information needed to examine the current situation, identify trends in the marketing environment, and assess their potential impact; and (3) helping to develop corporate, business, and marketing strategic plans (Chapter 3)

STRATEGY MIX one way by which retailers differentiate themselves from one another; consists of the following (all controllable) elements—location, product and services, pricing, and marketing mixes (Chapter 14)

STRATIFIED SAMPLING a probability sampling technique in which the population is divided into mutually exclusive groups, such as consumers with different income levels, and random samples are taken from each group (Chapter 6)

STRIP CENTERS retail shopping districts that are not enclosed under one roof and usually feature parking in front of the stores (Chapter 14)

STYLE a unique form of expression that is defined by a product's characteristics and has a fluctuating life cycle (Chapter 10)

SUBJECTIVE CLAIMS advertising claims that are not measurable and often stress image enhancement (Chapter 17)

SUBLIMINAL ADVERTISING initially related to ad messages presented at a rate or level below thresholds of conscious awareness, this practice today most often involves the embedding of hidden symbols in advertisements (Chapter 17)

SUBSTANTIALNESS the degree to which identified target segments are large enough and have sufficient sales and profit potential to warrant separate marketing programs (Chapter 7)

SUPPLIERS see **sources** (Chapter 5)

SUPPLY CHAIN MANAGEMENT the "effort involved in producing and delivering a final product from the supplier's supplier to the customer's customer," usually by cutting across organizational and company boundaries, to better serve the customer and gain a competitive advantage (Chapter 5)

SURROGATE SHOPPERS those who are a commercial enterprise, consciously engaged and paid, by a consumer or other interested partner on behalf of the consumer, to perform any or all of the activities involved in consumer decision making (Chapter 4)

SURVEY OF BUYERS' INTENTIONS sales forecast based on surveys of what either consumers or organizational buyers say they will do; such surveys are most reliable when the buyers have well-formed intentions and are willing to disclose them accurately (Chapter 7)

SWEEPSTAKES a sales promotion that offers prizes based on a chance drawing of participants' names (Chapter 18)

TARGET COSTING a pricing process that combines both cost and customer input into pricing decisions; determines what the manufacturing costs must be to achieve desired profits and customer features, as well as acceptable market prices (Chapter 11)

TARGET-COST PRICING concept in which new products are developed on what the market wants and the price it will accept (Chapter 12)

TARGET MARKET a defined group of consumers or organizations with whom a firm wants to create marketing exchanges (Chapter 1)

TARGET-RETURN PRICING a cost-oriented approach that sets prices to achieve a desired rate of return, with cost and profit estimates based on some expected volume or sales level (Chapter 12)

TARGETING selecting which segments in a market are appropriate to focus on and designing the means to reach them (Chapter 7)

TEAM SELLING a sales approach in which a company assigns accounts to sales teams of specialists according to the customers' purchase information needs (Chapter 19)

TECHNICAL SUPPORT SALESPEOPLE the people in sales support who have expertise in areas such as design and installation of complex equipment and may provide specialized training to customer employees (Chapter 19)

TECHNOLOGICAL ENVIRONMENT factors and trends related to innovations that affect the development of new products or the marketing process (Chapter 2)

TECHNOLOGICAL PERSPECTIVE using new and emerging technologies as sources for new products and services and to improve marketing practice (Prologue)

TELEMARKETING an interactive direct marketing communications approach that uses the phone to initiate, develop, and enhance relationships with customers (Chapter 20)

TEST MARKETING testing the prototype of a new product and its marketing strategy in simulated or actual market situations (Chapter 9)

TESTIMONIALS third-party evidence, such as letters from satisfied customers, that enhance source credibility (Chapter 19)

THIRD-PARTY RESPONSE a complaint about a product in which the consumer takes legal action or files a complaint with a consumer affairs agency instead of dealing just with the company (Chapter 4)

THREATS trends in the marketing environment that might adversely affect a company's situation; typically ranked by managers so the most important threats can be addressed first in the next strategic planning stage (Chapter 2)

TIE-IN see **cross-promotion** (Chapter 18)

TOTAL COSTS the sum of variable costs and fixed costs (Chapter 12)

TOTAL REVENUE total sales, or unit price multiplied by the quantity of the product sold; (before-tax) profits equal total revenue minus total costs (Chapter 12)

TRADE ALLOWANCE the amount a manufacturer contributes to a local dealer or retailer's advertising expense (Chapter 18)

TRADE CONTEST a sales promotion at the reseller level that associates prizes with sales of the sponsor's product (Chapter 18)

TRADE SALES PROMOTION sales promotion directed at retailers, wholesalers, or other business buyers to help push products through the marketing channel (Chapter 18)

TRADE SALES PROMOTION ALLOWANCES concessions a manufacturer allocates to wholesalers or retailers to promote its products (for example, supermarkets' cooperative advertising) (Chapter 12)

TRADE SHOW a periodic, semipublic event sponsored by a trade, professional, or industrial association at which suppliers rent booths to display products and provide information to potential buyers (Chapter 18)

TRADEMARK a brand or part of a brand that is registered with the U.S. Patent and Trademark Office, giving the owner exclusive rights to use the brand (Chapter 8)

TRANSACTION VALUE the perceived merits of the deal itself; retailers provide comparison pricing in an effort to boost products' transaction value by raising shoppers' internal price standard (Chapter 11)

TREND ANALYSIS a quantitative forecasting approach that examines historical sales data for predictable patterns (also known as time-series analysis) (Chapter 7)

TRUCK JOBBER a limited-function wholesaler that delivers within a small geographic area to ensure freshness of goods (for example, bakery, meat, dairy) (Chapter 15)

TWO-WAY-STRETCH STRATEGY adding products at both the low and the high ends of a product line (Chapter 10)

TYING CONTRACT   a marketing channel arrangement in which a manufacturer requires a reseller to buy products in addition to the one it really wants (Chapter 13)

UNAIDED RECALL TESTS   posttesting in which consumers are questioned with no prompting about ads (Chapter 17)

UNDIFFERENTIATED STRATEGY marketing a single product using a single promotional mix for the entire market; most often used early in the life of a product category (Chapter 7)

UNIFORM DELIVERED PRICE   a form of geographical pricing in which each customer, no matter where located, is charged the same average freight amount (Chapter 12)

UNIT PRICING   price information presented on a per-unit weight or volume basis so shoppers can compare prices across brands and across package sizes within brands (Chapter 12)

UNIVERSAL PRODUCT CODE (UPC)   bar code that is scanned at grocery checkouts and can provide secondary data for marketing research (Chapter 6)

UNRELATED DIVERSIFICATION branching out into products or services that have nothing in common with existing operations (Chapter 3)

UPWARD-STRETCH STRATEGY adding products at the higher end of a product line; for example, Japanese carmakers entered the U.S. market at the low end and gradually added higher-priced cars (Chapter 10)

U.S.–CANADA TRADE ACT   a law passed in 1988 to allow free trade between the United States and Canada (Chapter 2)

UTILITARIAN INFLUENCE   compliance with the expectations of others to achieve rewards or avoid punishments (for example, peer disapproval) (Chapter 4)

VALIDITY   refers to the extent to which the measures or questions used in a study truly reflect the concepts being studied (Chapter 6)

VALUE-ADDED RESELLERS (VARS) intermediaries that add value to goods and services as they pass through the marketing channel (Chapter 15)

VALUE-EXPRESSIVE INFLUENCE   a desire to enhance self-concept through identification with others (for example, by purchasing a product endorsed by a celebrity) (Chapter 4)

VALUE IN USE (VIU)   an approach for determining the economic value that a product has relative to an existing competitive offering (Chapter 12)

VALUE-IN-USE PRICING   basing pricing on customer estimates of the costs if the service could not be obtained (for example, downtime costs if a computer could not be repaired) (Chapter 11)

VALUES   shared beliefs or cultural norms about what is important or right, which directly influence how consumers view and use products, brands, and services (Chapter 4)

VALUES AND LIFESTYLES PROGRAM (VALS)   a lifestyle program from SRI International that segments consumers into eight groups: actualizers, fulfillers, believers, achievers, strivers, experiencers, makers, and strugglers (Chapter 7)

VARIABLE COSTS   costs that change with the level of output, such as wages and raw materials; see also **fixed costs** (Chapter 12)

VENDORS   see **sources** (Chapter 16)

VERTICAL MARKETING SYSTEMS centrally coordinated, highly integrated operations in which the product flows down the channel from producer to ultimate consumer; the basic vertical types are corporate, contractual, and administered channel systems (Chapter 13)

VIDEO CATALOG   a direct-mail catalog in videocassette or DVD form (Chapter 20)

VOICE RESPONSE   a complaint about a product in which the customer seeks satisfaction directly from the seller (Chapter 4)

WHOLESALE CLUB   a club whose members pay an annual fee that entitles them to make tax-free purchases at lower-than-retail prices (Chapter 15)

WHOLESALE SALES   sales to other businesses that resell the product or service or use it in running their own businesses (as opposed to retail sales) (Chapter 14)

WHOLESALER-SPONSORED VOLUNTARY GROUP   a contractual marketing channel system consisting of independent retailers that operate under the name of a sponsoring wholesaler (Chapter 13)

WHOLESALERS   firms that sell to manufacturers and industrial customers, retailers, government agencies, other wholesalers, and institutional customers such as schools and hospitals (Chapter 15)

WHOLESALING   refers to the marketing activities associated with selling products to purchasers who resell the products, use them to make another product, or use them to conduct business activities (Chapter 15)

WRITTEN SALES PROPOSAL   a detailed written presentation of a product's capabilities, benefits, and costs, often tailored to the individual customer (Chapter 19)

ZONE PRICING   a form of geographical pricing in which customers within one area (say, the Northeast) are charged one freight price and more distant zones are charged higher freight amounts (Chapter 12)

Notes

Prologue

[1]David Goetz, "New Name Reflects Tricon's Culture," *The Courier-Journal,* March 22, 2002, p. E3.

[2]Bruce Schreiner, "KFC Looks to Be Great Chain of China," *USA Today,* January 1, 2005, pp. B8, B9.

[3]Ron Insana, "Yum Brands Builds Dynasty in China," *USA Today,* February 7, 2005, p. 4B.

[4]Schreiner, "KFC Looks to Be Great Chain of China."

[5]Ibid.

[6]Ken Blanchard, Jim Ballard, and Fred Finch, *Customer Mania!* (New York: Free Press, 2004).

[7]Ibid.

[8]Insana, "Yum Brands Builds Dynasty."

[9]Kate MacArthur, "Games People Play: Looking for Lift, Taco Bell Stakes $70 Mil on Xbox," *Advertising Age,* October 1, 2001, pp. 3, 59 (accessed through *www.proquest.com*).

[10]Khanh T. L. Tran, "Microsoft Teams Up with SoBe, Taco Bell, Vans to Promote Xbox Video-Game System," *The Wall Street Journal,* September 5, 2001, p. B4 (accessed from *www.proquest.com*).

[11]David Goetz, "Yum Keeps China Focus," *The Courier-Journal,* February 3, 2005, pp. D1, D2.

Chapter One

[1]Peter D. Bennett, ed., *Dictionary of Marketing Terms* (Chicago: American Marketing Association, 1988), p. 54.

[2]The new definition of marketing is available at the American Marketing Association Web site: *www.marketingpower.com.*

[3]Jessi Hempel, "Nonprofit Drugs for the Poor," *BusinessWeek,* May 9, 2005, p. 16.

[4]Becky Bohrer, "Farmers Join Marketing Clubs to Grow Profits," *Marketing News,* March 1, 2005, p. 13.

[5]Steve Jarvis, "Theater's Rebranding Efforts Take a Bow," *Marketing News,* June 10, 2002, pp. 6–8.

[6]Mara Der Hovanesian, Heather Timmons, and Chris Palmeri, "For Small Banks, It's a Wonderful Life," *BusinessWeek,* May 6, 2002, pp. 83–84.

[7]Eilene Zimmerman, "So, You Wanna Be a CEO," *Sales and Marketing Management,* January 2002, pp. 31–35.

[8]Dana James, "Marketing's a Good Place to Start That Next Career," *Marketing News,* June 10, 2002, pp. 4–5.

[9]Chad Rubel, "Managers Buy into Quality When They See That It Works," *Marketing News,* March 25, 1996, p. 14.

[10]For different perspectives concerning the marketing concept, see Franklin S. Houston, "The Marketing Concept: What It Is and What It Is Not," *Journal of Marketing,* April 1986, pp. 81–87; Frederick E. Webster Jr., "The Rediscovery of the Marketing Concept," *Business Horizons,* May–June 1988, pp. 29–39; Lynn W. McGee and Rosann L. Spiro, "The Marketing Concept in Perspective," *Business Horizons,* May–June 1988, pp. 40–45; and Ajay K. Kohli and Bernard J. Jaworski, "Market Orientation: The Construct, Research Propositions, and Managerial Implications," *Journal of Marketing,* April 1990, pp. 1–18.

[11]James L. Heskett, Thomas O. Jones, Gary W. Loveman, W. Earl Sasser, Jr., and Leonard A. Schlesinger, "Putting the Service–Profit Chain to Work," *Harvard Business Review,* March–April 1994, pp. 165–66.

[12]Ahmet H. Kirca, Satish Jayachandran, and William O. Bearden, "Market Orientation: A Meta-Analytic Review and Assessment of Its Antecedents and Impact on Performance," *Journal of Marketing,* April 2005, pp. 24–41.

[13]Don Peppers and Martha Rogers, *Managing Customer Relationships* (Hoboken, NJ: John Wiley & Sons, 2004), pp. 1–8.

[14]Ranjay Gulati and James B. Oldroyd, "The Quest for Customer Focus," *Harvard Business Review,* April 2005, pp. 92–101.

[15]Peppers and Rogers, *Managing Customer Relationships,* p. 5.

[16]Robert C. Blattberg, Gary Getz, and Jacquelyn S. Thomas, *Customer Equity* (Boston: Harvard Business School Press, 2001).

[17]Roland T. Rust, Katherine Lemon, and Valarie A. Zeithaml, "Return on Marketing: Using Customer Equity to Focus Marketing Strategy," *Journal of Marketing,* January 2004, pp. 109–27.

[18]Werner Reinartz and V. Kumar, "The Mismanagement of Customer Loyalty," *Harvard Business Review,* July 2002, pp. 86–94.

[19]Werner J. Reinartz and V. Kumar, "The Impact of Customer Relationship Characteristics on Profitable Lifetime Duration," *Journal of Marketing,* January 2003, pp. 77–99.

[20]Laura Struebling, "Customer Loyalty: Playing for Keeps," *Quality Progress,* February 1996, pp. 25–26.

[21]Thomas O. Jones and Earl Sasser, Jr., "Why Satisfied Customers Defect," *Harvard Business Review,* November–December 1995, pp. 91–93.

[22]Heskett et al., "Putting the Service–Profit Chain to Work," pp. 166–67.

[23]David Fairlamb with Bogdan Turek, "Poland and the EU," *BusinessWeek,* May 10, 2004, pp. 54–56.

[24]Robyn Meredith, "Middle Kingdom, Middle Class," *Forbes,* November 15, 2004, pp. 188–82.

[25]William L. Wilkie and Elizabeth S. Moore, "Marketing's Contribution to Society," *Journal of Marketing,* Special Issue 1999, pp. 198–218.

[26]See Franklin S. Houston and Jule B. Gassenheimer, "Marketing and Exchange," *Journal of Marketing,* October 1987, pp. 3–18, for a more complete discussion of exchange and marketing.

[27]Richard P. Bagozzi, "Toward a Formal Theory of Marketing Exchange," in *Conceptual and Theoretical Developments in Marketing,* eds. O. C. Ferrell, Stephen W. Brown, and Charles W. Lamb Jr. (Chicago: American Marketing Association, 1979), p. 434.

Chapter Two

[1]Andrew Park and Spencer E. Ante, "Who Will Master the Server Biz," *BusinessWeek,* June 24, 2002, pp. 92–93.

[2]U.S. Census Bureau, International Database, *www.census.gov,* May 23, 2005.

[3]*The World Almanac and Book of Facts 2005* (New York: World Almanac Books, 2005).

[4]*The World Almanac and Book of Facts 2005.*

[5]Libby Quaid, "Producing Easy-to-Eat Food," *The Courier-Journal,* May 2, 2005, p. A3.

[6]Kristina Dell, "Just for Dudes," *Time Inside Business,* March 2005, p. B22.

[7]David Welch, "Later for You, Mom," *BusinessWeek,* February 21, 2005, p. 43.

[8]Dody Tsiantar, "The War on Wrinkles," *Time Inside Business,* May 2005, pp. A16–A19.

[9]Michelle Conlin, "UnMarried America," *BusinessWeek,* October 20, 2003, pp. 106–16.

[10]Michael Fielding, "Accrued Interest," *Marketing News,* May 15, 2005, pp. 41–43.

[11]Joseph Weber, "What's Not Cookin' at Campbell's," *BusinessWeek,* September 23, 1996, p. 40.

[12]Sean Gregory, "Diapers for Fatima," *Time Inside Business,* February 2005, pp. B6–B12.

[13]Maria Puente and Martin Kasindorf, "Blended Races Make a True Melting Pot," *USA Today,* September 7, 1999, pp. 1A, 13A.

[14]Deborah L. Vence, "You Talkin' to Me?" *Marketing News,* March 1, 2004, pp. 1, 9–11.

[15]Lisa M. Keefe, "P&G's multiculti marketing DNA," *Marketing News,* March 1, 2004, pp. 13–14 and 18.

[16]Deborah L. Vence, "Pick Up the Pieces," *Marketing News,* March 15, 2005, pp. 13–15.

[17]Deborah L. Vence, "Top Niche," *Marketing News,* June 1, 2004, pp. 11–13.

[18]Deborah L. Vence, "The Next Big Thing," *Marketing News,* May 15, 2005, pp. 11, 45.

[19]Tim Triplett, "Increase in Women Golfers Sparks Marketing Interest," *Marketing News,* June 3, 1996, pp. 2, 14.

[20]Richard C. Morais, "The Gnomes of Cocoa," *Forbes,* April 11, 2005, pp. 110–12.

[21]Kathryn Kranhold and Jeffrey Ball, "General Electric Plans Broad Push on Green Issues," *The Wall Street Journal Online,* May 9, 2005, pp. 1–3.

[22]Carol Matlack, Michael Arndt, and Adrienne Carter, "Time to Cut Losses," *BusinessWeek,* May 23, 2005, p. 56.

[23]Michael Fielding, "Slow but Steady," *Marketing News,* January 15, 2005, pp. 20, 27.

[24]Kathryn Kranhold, "GE Pins Hopes on Emerging Markets," *The Wall Street Journal Online,* March 2, 2005, pp. 1–3.

[25]Pete Engardio and Dexter Roberts, "The China Price," *BusinessWeek,* December 6, 2004, pp. 102–12.

[26]Christopher Rhoads and Marc Champion, "As Europe Expands, New Union Faces Problems of Scale," *The Wall Street Journal Online,* April 29, 2004, pp. 1–5.

[27]*www.wto.org.*

[28]Margaret Popper, "The Payoff from Free Trade," *BusinessWeek,* June 24, 2002, p. 26.

[29]Paul Magnusson, "Bush: What Price Fast Track?" *BusinessWeek,* June 3, 2002, p. 38.

[30]John Rossant, Jack Ewing, and Brian Bremmer, "The Corporate Cleanup Goes Global," *BusinessWeek,* May 6, 2002, pp. 80–81.

[31]John Carey with Amy Barrett, " 'Off-Label'—And Out of Bounds?" *BusinessWeek,* October 18, 2004, p. 39.

[32]Daren Fonda and Barbara Kiviat, "Curbing the Drug Marketers," *Time,* July 5, 2004, pp. 40–42.

[33]Bart A. Lazar, "Can SPAM Creates Quandary, Opportunities," *Marketing News,* June 15, 2004, pp. 6, 10.

[34]"FTC Announces First 'Do Not Call' Settlements," *Marketing Matters,* March 17, 2005, pp. 1–2.

[35]"The List: Adapt or Die," *BusinessWeek,* July 26, 1999, p. 6.

[36]Michael Fitzgerald, "The Next Wave," *Business 2.0,* July 2002, pp. 53–58.

[37]Ian Wylie, "Green Giant," *Fast Company,* June 2002, p. 64.

[38]Catherine Yang, "The Pulse of the Future," *BusinessWeek,* April 22, 2002, pp. 92–93.

[39]Ronald Glover, "DVDs at ATMs," *BusinessWeek,* May 23, 2005, p. 14; John Heilemann, "Showtime for Netflix," *Business 2.0,* March 2005, pp. 36–38.

[40]Jay Solomon and Kathryn Kranhold, "In India's Outsourcing Boom, GE Played a Starring Role," *The Wall Street Journal Online,* March 23, 2005, pp. 1–5.

[41]Pete Engardio and Bruce Einhorn, "Outsourcing Innovation," *BusinessWeek,* March 21, 2005, pp. 84–94.

Chapter Three

[1]Aixa M. Pascual, "Four's a Crowd," *BusinessWeek Online,* February 25, 2002.

[2]Anil Menon, Sundar G. Bharadwaj, Phani Tej, and Steven W. Edison, "Antecedents and Consequences of Marketing Strategy Making: A Model and Test," *Journal of Marketing,* April 1999, p. 19.

[3]Rajdeep Grewal and Patriya Tansuhaj, "Building Organizational Capabilities for Managing Economic Crisis: The Role of Market Orientation and Strategic Flexibility," *Journal of Marketing,* April 2001, p. 67.

[4]Roland T. Rust, Katherine N. Lemon, and Valarie A. Zeithaml, "Return on Marketing: Using Customer Equity to Focus Marketing Strategy," *Journal of Marketing,* January 2004, p. 109.

[5]Keith H. Hammonds, "Michael Porter's Big Ideas," *Fast Company,* March 2001, pp. 152–54, 156.

[6]Michael H. Morris and Leyland F. Pitts, "The Contemporary Use of Strategy, Strategic Planning, and Planning Tools by Marketers: A Cross-National Comparison," *European Journal of Marketing,* 1993, pp. 36–57.

[7]Michael Krauss, "Marketing Department Organization Is Destiny," *Marketing News,* February 18, 2002, p. 14.

[8]Eric Dash, "A Merger in Search of a Home: Yours," *The New York Times,* January 29, 2005, p. C1; Claudia Deutsch, "Deal Can Only Raise the Level of Competition, from the Boardroom to Aisle 5," *The New York Times,* January 29, 2005, p. C2.

[9]Emily Nelson, "Marketing & Media: Colgate Net Rose 12% in 1st Quarter on Toothpaste Sales," *The Wall Street Journal,* April 20, 2001, p. B8.

[10]Francy Blackwood, "Dissecting the Service," *Selling,* March 1996, pp. 26–28; *Hoover's Company Profile Database* (Austin, TX: The Reference Press, 1996); and Malcolm Fleschner, "Copy This, Copy This, Copy This," *Selling Power,* March 1996, pp. 22–26.

[11]Nanette Byrnes, Robert Berner, and William C. Symonds, "Branding: Five New Lessons," *BusinessWeek,* February 14, 2005, pp. 26–28.

[12]Arjun Chaudhuri and Morris Holbrook, "The Chain of Effects from Brand Trust and Brand Affect to Brand Performance: The Role of Brand Loyalty," *Journal of Marketing,* April 2001, pp. 81–93.

[13]David A. Aaker, *Managing Brand Equity* (New York: The Free Press, 1991), p. 17; Kevin Lane Keller, *Strategic Brand Management* (Upper Saddle River, NJ: Prentice Hall, 1998), p. 7; Kevin Lane Keller, "Value Emerges through a Unique Chain of Events," *Marketing Management,* May/June 2003, p. 29.

[14]Katherine N. Lemon, Roland T. Rust, and Valarie A. Zeithaml, "What Drives Customer Equity," *Marketing Management,* Spring 2001, p. 21.

[15]Lee G. Cooper, "Strategic Marketing Planning for Radically New Products," *Journal of Marketing,* January 2000, p. 1.

[16]Douglas W. Vorhies and Neil A. Morgan, "Benchmarking Marketing Capabilities for Sustainable Competitive Advantage," *Journal of Marketing,* January 2005, p. 81.

[17]J. Chris White, P. Rajan Varadarajan, and Peter A. Dacin, "Market Situation Interpretation and Response: The Role of Cognitive, Organizational Culture, and Information Use," *Journal of Marketing,* July 2003, p. 68.

[18]"Some Utilities Rake in Revenue Amid Crisis," *The Wall Street Journal,* January 23, 2001, *www.djinteractive.com.*

[19]Philip Kotler, *Marketing Management,* The Millennium Edition (Upper Saddle River, NJ: Prentice Hall, 2000); Anil Menon, Sundar G. Bharadwaj, Phani Tej Adidam, and Steve W. Edison, "Antecedents and Consequences of Marketing Strategy Making: A Model and a Test," *Journal of Marketing,* April 1999, pp. 18–40; and Charles H. Noble and Michael P. Mokwa, "Implementing Marketing Strategies: Developing and Testing a Managerial Theory," *Journal of Marketing,* October 1999, pp. 57–73.

[20]Charles H. Noble and Michael P. Mokwa, "Implementing Marketing Strategies: Developing and Testing a Managerial Strategy," *Journal of Marketing,* October 1999, pp. 57–73.

[21]Frederick E. Webster, Jr., "The Changing Role of Marketing in the Corporation," *Journal of Marketing,* October 1992, pp. 1–17.

[22]Stanley F. Slater, Eric M. Olson, and G. Tomas M. Hult, "Proper Pairs," *Marketing Management,* March/April 2005, p. 24.

[23]Webster, Jr., "The Changing Role of Marketing in the Corporation," p. 10.

[24]Ravi S. Achrol and Philip Kotler, "Marketing in the Network Economy," *Journal of Marketing,* Special Issue 1999, pp. 146–47.

[25]George S. Day and David B. Montgomery, "Charting New Directions for Marketing," *Journal of Marketing,* Special Issue 1999, pp. 3–13.

[26]Christine Moorman and Roland T. Rust, "The Role of Marketing," *Journal of Marketing,* Special Issue 1999, p. 180.

[27]Michael E. Porter, "Strategy and the Internet," *Harvard Business Review,* March 2001, 63–78.

[28]Tim Coltman, Timothy M. Devinney, Alopi Latukefu, and David F. Midgley, "E-Business: Revolution, Evolution, or Hype," *California Management Review* 44 (1), pp. 57–86; Sydney Finkelstein, "Internet Startups: So Why Can't They Win?" *Journal of Business Strategy,* July/August 2001, pp. 18–21; Michael E. Porter, "Strategy and the Internet," *Harvard Business Review,* March 2001, pp. 63–78.

[29]Adapted from John A. Pearce II and Fred David, "Corporate Mission Statements: The Bottom Line," *Academy of Management Executive,* May 1987, p. 109.

[30]James C. Collins and Jerry I. Porras, "Building Your Company's Vision," *Harvard Business Review,* September–October 1996, pp. 65–77.

[31]http://www.benjerry.co.uk/aboutbj/mission.htm.

[32]http://www.whirlpool.com/whr/ics/story/vision.html.

[33]Gilbert Fuchsberg, "'Visioning' Missions Becomes Its Own Mission," *The Wall Street Journal,* January 7, 1994, pp. B1, B4.

[34]http://www.boeing.com/companyoffices/aboutus/mission/index.html.

[35]Cecily Fluke and Kurt Badenhausen, "Power Brands," *Forbes,* April 19, 2004, p. 59.

[36]Claes Fornell, "Customer Satisfaction, Capital Efficiency, and Shareholder Value," *Managing Customer Relationships,* Cambridge, MA: Marketing Science Institute, Report No. 00–107, 2000, pp. 9–12.

[37]George S. Day, "Capabilities for Forging Customer Relationships," Report No. 00–118, Cambridge, MA: Marketing Science Institute, 2000; George S. Day, "The Capabilities of Market-Driven Organizations," *Journal of Marketing,* October 1994, pp. 37–52.

[38]Anupam Agarwal, David P. Harding, and Jeffrey R. Schumacher, "Organizing for CRM," *The McKinsey Quarterly,* no. 3, 2004, pp. 81–91; Chekitan S. Dev and Don E. Schultz, "Simply SIVA," *Marketing Management,* March/April 2005, p. 38; Sudhir H. Kale, "CRM Failure and the Seven Deadly Sins," *Marketing Management,* September/October 2004, pp. 42–46; Jagdish N. Sheth and Rajendra S. Sisodia, "High-Performance Marketing," *Marketing Management,* September/October 2001, pp. 18–23.

[39]Linda Himelstein, "The Soul of a New Nike," *BusinessWeek,* June 17, 1996, pp. 70–71.

[40]Ian P. Murphy, "Survey Finds Safe Growth Is Priority for New Products," *Marketing News,* July 15, 1996, p. 15.

[41]Terry Lefton, "Nike's New Golf Balls Aim Straight up Fairway," *Brandweek,* January 18, 1999, p. 5; and Chuck Stogel, "Nike Restages Golf Push for '00," *Brandweek,* June 28, 1999, p. 34.

[42]Rajesh K. Chandy and Gerard J. Tellis, "The Incumbent's Curse? Incumbency, Size, and Radical Product Innovation," *Journal of Marketing,* July 2000, pp. 1–17.

[43]Chad Holliday, "Sustainable Growth, the DuPont Way," *Harvard Business Review,* September 2001, pp. 129–134.

[44]Lawrence A. Crosby and Sheree L. Johnson, "Do Your Metrics Reflect Your Market Strategy?" *Marketing Management,* September/October 2003, p. 10.

[45]David W. Cravens, *Strategic Marketing* (Homewood, IL: Richard D. Irwin, 1994), pp. 46–47.

[46]"The Genesis of a Giant's Stumble," *The New York Times,* January 21, 2001, pp. 1, 13.

[47]"Technology: Ricoh Tries to Put Multiple Brands under One Roof," *The New York Times,* February 5, 2001, www.nytimes.com/archives.

[48]Webster, "The Changing Role of Marketing in the Corporation," p. 10.

[49]George S. Day, *Analysis for Strategic Marketing Decisions* (St. Paul, MN: West Publishing Company, 1995), pp. 202–5.

[50]Philip Kotler, *Marketing Management: Analysis, Planning, Implementation, and Control,* 8th ed. (Englewood Cliffs, NJ: Prentice Hall, 1994), p. 76.

[51]John A. Byrne, "Strategic Planning," *BusinessWeek,* August 26, 1996, pp. 46–52; Peter Elstrom, "Did Motorola Make the Wrong Call?" *BusinessWeek,* July 29, 1996, pp. 66–68; Gary Hamel and C. K. Prahalad, *Competing for the Future* (Boston: Harvard Business School Press, 1994); Webster, "The Changing Role of Marketing," pp. 1–17; and John O. Whitney, "Strategic Renewal for Business Units," *Harvard Business Review,* July–August 1996, pp. 84–98.

[52]Jay Barney, "Firm Resources and Sustained Competitive Advantage," *Journal of Management* 17 (1), 1991, pp. 99–120.

[53]P. Rajan Varadarajan, Satish Jayachandran, and J. Chris White, "Strategic Interdependence in Organizations: Deconglomeration and Marketing Strategy," *Journal of Marketing,* January 2001, pp. 15–28.

[54]C. K. Prahalad and Richard A. Bettis, "The Dominant Logic: A New Linkage between Diversity and Performance," *Strategic Management Journal* 7, 1986, pp. 485–501.

[55]Susan Carey, "Rough Climate on Airlines Takes Toll on Midwest Express—Extraordinary Service, Loyal Following Don't Shield Carrier from Industry Woes," *The Wall Street Journal,* July 9, 2001, p. B4; Amy Goldwasser, "Something Stylish, Something Blue," *Business 2.0,* February 2002, pp. 94–96; James Ott, "Cautionary Tale of Two Texas Airlines," *Aviation Week and Space Technology,* November 19, 2001, pp. 60–63; Pierre Sparaco, "British Carrier Expands Operation in France," *Aviation Week and Space Technology,* December 17, 2001, pp. 86–87; "The Pluck of the Irish: Low-Cost Airlines," *The Economist,* January 26, 2002, pp. 58–59.

[56]"General Excellence: Southwest Airlines," *Sales & Marketing Management,* August 1993, p. 38.

[57]Kevin Kelly, Wendy Zellner, and Aaron Bernstein, "Suddenly Big Airlines Are Saying, 'Small Is Beautiful,' " *BusinessWeek,* January 17, 1994, p. 37.

[58]Pierre Sparaco, "Swissair Expands Partnership Network," *Aviation Week and Space Technology,* August 23, 1999, p. 56.

[59]Jagdish Sheth and Rajendra Sisodia, *The Rule of Three: Surviving and Thriving in Competitive Markets* (New York: The Free Press, 2002) p. 2.

[60]Christine Bittar, "Gillette's Edge: Male-Skewing Razor Backed by $60M," *Brandweek,* May 28, 2001, p. 5.

[61]Philip Kotler, "Is Marketing Ethics an Oxymoron?" *Marketing Management,* November/December 2004, p. 35.

[62]Vijay Mahajan, Marcos V. Pratini De Moraes, and Jerry Wind, "The Invisible Global Market," *Marketing Management,* Winter 2000, pp. 31–35.

[63]Edmund Faltermayer, "Competitiveness: How U.S. Companies Stack Up Now," *Fortune,* April 18, 1994, pp. 52–64.

[64]Gary McWilliams, "Wang's Great Leap out of Limbo," *BusinessWeek,* March 7, 1994, pp. 68–69.

[65]"Cadbury Buys Spanish Concern," *The Wall Street Journal,* April 22, 1994, p. A6.

[66]Kathy Rebello and Neil Gross, "A Juicy New Apple?" *BusinessWeek,* March 7, 1994, pp. 88–90; "Ciba-Geigy Plans China Venture," *The Wall Street Journal,* April 22, 1994, p. A6; and Brian Coleman and Bridget O'Brian, "Delta Airlines, Virgin Atlantic Forge Alliance," *The Wall Street Journal,* April 13, 1994, p. A4.

[67]David M. Szymanski, Sundar G. Bharadwaj, and P. Rajan Varadarajan, "Standardization versus Adaptation of International Marketing Strategy: An Empirical Investigation," *Journal of Marketing,* October 1993, pp. 1–17; Subhash C. Jain, "Standardization of International Marketing Strategy: Some Research Hypotheses," *Journal of Marketing,* January 1989, pp. 70–79; and John A. Quelch and Edward J. Hoff, "Customizing Global Marketing," *Harvard Business Review,* May–June 1986, pp. 59–68.

[68]Quelch and Hoff, "Customizing," p. 59.

[69]Theresa Howard, "Global Ads Aim for One Brand, Image," *USA Today,* June 24, 2004, p. 6B.

[70]John A. Quelch, "Does Globalization Have Staying Power?" *Marketing Management,* March/April 2002, pp. 20–21.

[71]Richard A. Melcher and Stewart Toy, "On Guard, Europe," *Business-Week,* December 14, 1992, pp. 54–55.

[72]James E. Ellis, "Why Overseas? 'Cause That's Where the Sales Are," *BusinessWeek,* January 10, 1994, p. 63.

[73]Sally Solo, "How to Listen to Consumers," *Fortune,* January 11, 1993, pp. 77–78.

[74]Michael R. Czinkota and Ilka A. Ronkainen, *International Marketing,* 4th ed. (Fort Worth, TX: Dryden Press, 1995), pp. 263–65; and Jean-Pierre Jeannet and H. David Hennessey, *Global Marketing Strategies,* 3rd ed. (Boston: Houghton Mifflin Company, 1995), p. 336.

[75]David A. Aaker and Erich Joachimsthaler, "The Lure of Global Branding," *Harvard Business Review,* November–December 1999, p. 138.

[76]Carlos Ghosn, "Saving the Business without Losing the Company," *Harvard Business Review,* January 2002, pp. 37–45.

[77]Rajesh Sethi, Daniel C. Smith, and C. Whan Park, "Cross-Functional Product Development Teams, Creativity, and the Innovativeness of New Consumer Products," *Journal of Marketing Research,* February 2001, pp. 73–85.

[78]Ginger Trumfio, "Kodak Adjusts Its Focus," *Sales & Marketing Management,* January 1994, p. 20.

[79]Maricris G. Briones, "Strange Bedfellows," *Marketing News,* August 17, 1998, p. 2.

[80]Louis Bucklin and Sanjit Sengupta, "Organizing Successful Co-Marketing Alliances," *Journal of Marketing,* April 1993, pp. 32–46; Manohar U. Kalwani and Narakesari Narayandas, "Long-Term Manufacturer–Supplier Relationships: Do They Pay Off for Supplier Firms?" *Journal of Marketing,* January 1995, pp. 1–16; and Robert M. Morgan and Shelby D. Hunt, "The Commitment–Trust Theory of Relationship Marketing," *Journal of Marketing,* July 1994, pp. 20–38.

[81]"Making New Friends at Procter & Gamble; With Whirlpool, Trying to Change Consumer Habits," *The New York Times,* March 16, 2001, pp. C1, C4.

[82]Briones, "Strange Bedfellows," p. 2.

[83]Bernard Simonin and Julie Ruth, "Is a Company Known by the Company It Keeps? Assessing the Spillover Effects of Brand Alliances on Consumer Brand Attitudes," *Journal of Marketing Research,* February 1998, pp. 30–42; "Credit Card Co-Branding on the Rise: Survey," *Supermarket News,* June 5, 1998, p. 21; Harriet Marsh, "P&G Enters the Age of Alliances," *Marketing,* February 11, 1999, p. 18; R. Venkatesh and Vijay Mahajan, "Products with Branded Components: An Approach for Premium Pricing and Partner Selection," *Marketing Science* 16, no. 2 (1997), pp. 146–65.

[84]Aric Rindfleisch and Christine Moorman, "The Acquisition and Utilization of Information in New Product Alliances: A Strength-of-Ties Perspective," *Journal of Marketing,* April 2001, pp. 1–18.

Chapter Four

[1]Sherrie E. Wehner, "10 Things to Know about Customers," *Marketing News,* December 4, 2000, pp. 20, 22.

[2]David Whelan, "A Tale of Two Consumers," *American Demographics,* September 2001, pp. 54–55.

[3]Wayne D. Hoyer and Deborah J. MacInnis, *Consumer Behavior,* 3rd ed. (New York: Houghton Mifflin, 2003), p. 8.

[4]http://www.Ebea.doc.gov/.

[5]Annetta Miller, "The Millennial Mind-Set: It's Here, It's Clear, Get Used to It," *American Demographics,* January 1999, pp. 60–65; and Cheryl Russell, "The New Consumer Paradigm," *American Demographics,* April 1999, pp. 51–58.

[6]Frank Solis, "The Next Big Market," *Success,* October 2000, pp. 36, 38.

[7]Joseph Weber and Ann Therese, "How the Net Is Remaking the Mall," *BusinessWeek,* May 9, 2005, p. 60.

[8]Dave Carpenter, "Diets Force Kraft to Change Marketing Approach," *Marketing News,* September 15, 2004, p. 37.

[9]Michael Silverstein and Neil Fiske, "Luxury for the Masses," *Harvard Business Review,* April 2003, pp. 48–57.

[10]*What the Customer Wants: The Wall Street Journal's Guide to Marketing in the 1990s* (New York: Dow Jones, 1990), p. vi.

[11]Sunil Gupta, Donald R. Lehmann, and Jennifer Ames Stuart, "Valuing Customers," MSI Report No. 01-119 (Cambridge, MA: Marketing Science Institute, 2001).

[12]Bernard J. Jaworski and Ajay K. Kohli, "Market Orientation: Antecedents and Consequences," *Journal of Marketing,* July 1993, p. 53.

[13]Peter R. Dickson, "Toward a General Theory of Competitive Rationality," *Journal of Marketing,* January 1992, p. 70.

[14]Jill Griffin and Michael Lowenstein, "Winning Back Lost Customers," Retailing Issues Letter, March 2001 (Texas A&M University, College Station, TX: Center for Retailing Studies).

[15]David J. Reibstein, "Who's Buying on the Internet and How Long Will They Be Loyal?" MSI Report 00-102 (Cambridge, MA: Marketing Science Institute, December 1999), p. 33.

[16]Subir Bandyopadhyay, Guangbo Lin, and Yan Zhong, "Smart Marketers Are Sold on Online Auctions," *Marketing Management,* November/December 2001, pp. 25–28; Michael J. Weiss, "Online America," *American Demographics,* March 2001, pp. 53–60.

[17]Saul Hansell, "An Ambitious Internet Grocer Is Out of Both Cash and Ideas," *The New York Times,* July 12, 2001, p. A1.

[18]Merrie Brucks, "The Effects of Product Class Knowledge on Information Search Behavior," *Journal of Consumer Research,* June 1985, pp. 1–16; Patricia M. West, Christina L. Brown, and Stephen J. Hoch, "Consumption Vocabulary and Preference Formation," *Journal of Consumer Research,* September 1996, pp. 120–135.

[19]Robert Hof, Heather Green, and Paul Judge, "Going, Going, Gone," *BusinessWeek,* April 12, 1999, pp. 30–32; Sloane Lucas, "Lycos, mySimon Tout New User Guides," *Brandweek,* August 9, 1999, p. 31; Michael Schrage, "The Tangled Web of E-Deception," *Fortune,* September 27, 1999, p. 296; Erica Goode, "The On-Line Consumer? Tough, Impatient, and Gone in a Blink," *The New York Times,* September 22, 1999, p. 22; and Edward C. Baig, "The Biggest Used-Car Lot of All," *BusinessWeek,* August 9, 1999, pp. 96–98.

[20]J. Jeffrey Inman and Russell S. Winer, "Where the Rubber Meets the Road: A Model of In-Store Decision Making," Report No. 98–122 (Cambridge, MA: Marketing Science Institute, October 1998), p. v.

[21]Stanley C. Hollander and Kathleen M. Rassuli, "Shopping with Other People's Money: The Marketing Management Implications of Surrogate-Mediated Consumer Decision-Making," *Journal of Marketing* 63 (April 1999), pp. 102–18; Paco Underhill, "What Shoppers Want," *Inc.,* July 1999, pp. 72–82.

[22]J. Paul Peter and Jerry C. Olson, *Consumer Behavior and Marketing Strategy,* 3rd ed. (Homewood, IL: Richard D. Irwin, Inc., 1993), p. 57.

[23]James F. Engel, Roger D. Blackwell, and Paul W. Miniard, *Consumer Behavior,* 7th ed. (Ft. Worth, TX: Dryden Press, 1993), pp. 276–77.

[24]Thomas S. Robertson, "Low-Commitment Consumer Behavior," *Journal of Advertising Research,* April 1976, pp. 19–24.

[25]Jeffrey J. Stoltman, James W. Gentry, Kenneth A. Anglin, and Alvin C. Burns, "Situational Influences on the Consumer Decision Sequence," *Journal of Business Research,* November 1990, p. 196.

[26]Emily Nelson, "Too Many Choices," *The Wall Street Journal,* April 20, 2001, p. B1.

[27]Marcia Mogelonsky, "America's Hottest Markets," *American Demographics,* January 1996, p. 22.

[28]Wayne D. Hoyer and Deborah J. MacInnis, *Consumer Behavior,* 3rd ed. (New York: Houghton Mifflin, 2003), p. 265; J. Paul Peter and Jerry C. Olson, *Consumer Behavior and Marketing Strategy* (Burr Ridge, IL: McGraw-Hill/Irwin, 2004), p. 42.

[29]Chester Dawson and David Welch, "Honda's First U.S. Bruiser," *BusinessWeek,* December 27, 2004, pp. 58–59.

[30]John C. Mowen, *Consumer Behavior,* 2nd ed. (New York: Macmillan Publishing Company, 1990), pp. 332–33; Dennis W. Rook, "The Buying Impulse," *Journal of Consumer Research,* September 1987, pp. 189–99.

[31]Stephen J. Hoch and George F. Lowenstein, "Time-Inconsistent Preferences and Consumer Self-Control," *Journal of Consumer Research,* March 1991, pp. 492–502.

[32]Robert B. Cialdini, "The Science of Persuasion," *Scientific American,* January 2004, Special Edition, pp. 70–77; Robert B. Cialdini, *Influence: Science and Practice,* 4th ed. (Boston: Allyn & Bacon, 2001); D. T. Kenrick, S. L. Neuberg, and Robert B. Cialdini, *Social Psychology: Unraveling the Mystery,* 2nd ed. (Boston: Allyn & Bacon, 2002).

[33]Hans Baumgartner, "Toward a Personology of the Consumer," *Journal of Consumer Research,* September 2002, pp. 286–92.

[34]Geert Hofstede, "Culture and Organizations," *International Studies of Management and Organizations* 10, no. 4 (1981), pp. 15–41; Martin S. Roth, "The Effects of Culture and Socioeconomics on the Performance of Global Brand Image Strategies," *Journal of Marketing Research,* May 1995, p. 172; and Mikael Sandergaard, "Hofstede's Consequences: A Study of Reviews, Citations, and Replications," *Organizational Studies* 15, no. 3 (1994), pp. 447–56.

[35]Jan-Benedict E. M. Steenkamp, Frenkel ter Hofstede, and Michael Wedel, "A Cross-National Investigation into the Individual and National Cultural Antecedents of Consumer Innovativeness," *Journal of Marketing,* April 1999, pp. 55–69.

[36]Lynn R. Kahle, Sharon E. Beatty, and Pamela Homer, "Alternative Measurement Approaches to Consumer Values: The List of Values (LOV) and Values and Life Style (VALS)," *Journal of Consumer Research,* December 1986, p. 406.

[37]Engel et al., *Consumer Behavior,* p. 87.

[38]Joel Garreau, *The Nine Nations of North America* (Boston: Houghton Mifflin, 1981).

[39]Mowen, *Consumer Behavior,* pp. 618–19.

[40]Michael M. Phillips, "Selling by Evoking What Defines a Generation," *The Wall Street Journal,* August 13, 1996, p. B1.

[41]Haidee E. Allerton, "Generation Why," *T + D,* November 2001, pp. 56–60; Pamela Paul, "Getting Inside Gen Y," *American Demographics,* September 2001; Joyce M. Wolburg and James Pokyrwczynski, "A Psychographic Analysis of Generation Y College Students," *Journal of Advertising Research,* September/October 2001, pp. 33–52.

[42]Alan B. Krueger, "Women Are Less Likely to Negotiate and It Can Be Costly to Them," *The New York Times,* August 21, 2003, p. C2.

[43]Richard P. Coleman, "The Continuing Significance of Social Class to Marketing," *Journal of Consumer Research,* December 1983, pp. 265–80.

[44]Jerry C. Olson, *Consumer Behavior and Marketing Strategy,* 3rd ed. (Homewood, IL: Richard D. Irwin, 1993), p. 490.

[45]Felicia R. Lee, "Does Class Count in Today's Land of Opportunity?" *The New York Times,* January 18, 2003, p. B7.

[46]Greg J. Duncan, Timothy M. Smeeding, and Willard Rogers, "The Incredible Shrinking Middle Class," *American Demographics,* May 1992, p. 38.

[47]Rebecca Piirto Health, "The New Working Class," *American Demographics,* January 1998, p. 52.

[48]Mowen, *Consumer Behavior,* p. 527; Scott Ward, "Consumer Socialization," *Journal of Consumer Research,* September 1974, pp. 1–14.

[49]Gregory M. Rose, "Consumer Socialization, Parental Style, and Developmental Timetables in the United States and Japan," *Journal of Marketing,* July 1999, p. 116.

[50]Sonia Reyes, "Into the Mouths of Babes," *Brandweek,* May 6, 2002, pp. 27–30.

[51]Robert Bontilier, "Pulling the Family's Strings," *American Demographics,* August 1993, p. 46.

[52]Chip Walker, "Can TV Save the Planet?" *American Demographics,* May 1996, pp. 42–48.

[53]William D. Danko and Charles M. Schaninger, "An Empirical Evaluation of the Gilly-Enis Updated Household Life Cycle Model," *Journal of Business Research,* August 1990, p. 39; Mary C. Gilly and Ben M. Enis, "Recycling the Family Life Cycle: A Proposal for Redefinition," in *Advances in Consumer Research,* vol. 9, ed. Andrew Mitchell (Ann Arbor, MI: Association for Consumer Research, 1982), pp. 271–76; Patrick Murphy and William Staples, "A Modernized Family Life Cycle," *Journal of Consumer Research,* June 1979, pp. 12–22; and Charles M. Schaninger and William D. Danko, "A Conceptual and Empirical Comparison of Alternative Household Life Cycle Models," *Journal of Consumer Research,* March 1993, pp. 580–94.

[54]Tom W. Smith, "The Emerging 21st Century American Family," *GSS Social Exchange Report No. 42* (Chicago, IL: National Opinion Research Center, University of Chicago, November 24, 1999), p. 28.

[55]Diane Crispell, "Dual-Earner Diversity," *American Demographics,* July 1995, pp. 32–37, 55; and Marcia Mogelonsky, "The Rocky Road to Adulthood," *American Demographics,* May 1996, pp. 26–35, 56.

[56]Hal Espen, "Levi's Blues," *New York Times Magazine,* March 21, 1999, p. 54.

[57]Robert B. Cialdini, "Harnessing the Science of Persuasion," *Harvard Business Review,* October 2001, pp. 75–76.

[58]Hilary Cassidy, "College Guys Get Carded," *Brandweek,* November 12, 2001, p. 31.

[59]Lawrence F. Feick and Linda L. Price, "The Market Maven: A Diffuser of Marketplace Information," *Journal of Marketing,* January 1987, pp. 83–97.

[60]Chip Walker, "Word of Mouth," *American Demographics,* July 1995, p. 38.

[61]"Poor College Students Ain't What They Used to Be," *Marketing News,* August 16, 1999, p. 3.

[62]Douglas R. Pruden and Terry G. Vavra, "Controlling the Grapevine," *Marketing Management,* July/August 2004, pp. 24–30.

[63]Malcolm Gladwell, "The Coolhunt," *The New Yorker,* March 17, 1997, *www.gladwell.com.*

[64]Nicholas Thompson, "More Companies Pay Heed to Their 'Word of Mouse' Reputation," *The New York Times,* June 23, 2003, p. C4.

[65]M. Joseph Sirgy, "Self-Concept in Consumer Behavior: A Critical Review," *Journal of Consumer Research,* December 1982, pp. 287–88.

[66]Beth A. Walker and Jerry L. Olson, "Means–End Chains: Connecting Products with Self," *Journal of Business Research,* March 1991, p. 111.

[67]Stephen J. Hoch and George F. Lowenstein, "Time-Inconsistent Preferences and Consumer Self-Control," *Journal of Consumer Research,* March 1991, pp. 492–502; Sirgy, "Self-Concept in Consumer Behavior," pp. 288–89.

[68]Harold H. Kassarjian and Mary Jane Sheffet, "Personality and Consumer Behavior: An Update," in *Perspectives in Consumer Behavior,* 4th ed., eds. H. H. Kassarjian and T. S. Robertson (Englewood Cliffs, NJ: Prentice Hall, 1990), pp. 281–363.

[69]John L. Lastovicka, "On the Validation of Lifestyle Traits: A Review and Illustration," *Journal of Marketing Research,* February 1982, p. 126.

[70]William L. Wilkie, *Consumer Behavior* (New York: John Wiley Sons, 1986), p. 307.

[71]Abraham H. Maslow, *Motivation and Personality,* 2nd ed. (New York: Harper and Row, 1970).

[72]Adrian Slywotzky and Richard Wise, "Growing Pains," *Marketing Management,* May/June 2003, pp. 39–44.

[73]Russell W. Belk, "An Exploratory Assessment of Situational Effects in Buyer Behavior," *Journal of Marketing Research,* May 1974, p. 156.

[74]Gordon C. Brunner, "Music, Mood, and Marketing," *Journal of Marketing,* October 1990, pp. 94–104; Ronald E. Milman, "Using Background Music to Affect the Behavior of Supermarket Shoppers," *Journal of Marketing,* Summer 1982, pp. 86–91.

[75]Brian Wansink and Michael L. Ray, *How Expansion Advertising Affects Brand Usage Frequency: A Programmatic Evaluation,* MSI Report Summary, Report No. 93–126 (Cambridge, MA: Marketing Science Institute, 1993), p. 1.

[76]Stephen J. Hoch and John Deighton, "Managing What Consumers Learn from Experience," *Journal of Marketing,* April 1989, pp. 1–20.

[77]Walter R. Nord and J. Paul Peter, "A Behavior Modification Perspective on Marketing," *Journal of Marketing,* Spring 1980, p. 41; Michael L. Rothschild and William C. Gaidis, "Behavioral Learning Theory: Its Relevance to Marketing and Promotions," *Journal of Marketing,* Spring 1981, pp. 70–78.

[78]Fred Reichheld and Christine Detrick, "Loyalty: A Prescription for Cutting Costs," *Marketing Management,* September/October 2003, pp. 24–25.

[79]Marian Friestad and Peter Wright, "The Persuasion Knowledge Model: How People Cope with Persuasion Attempts," *Journal of Consumer Research,* June 1994, pp. 1–31.

[80]Susan Fournier and David Glen Mick, "Rediscovering Satisfaction," *Journal of Marketing* 63 (October 1999), pp. 5–23.

[81]Richard L. Oliver, "A Cognitive Model of the Antecedents and Consequences of Satisfaction Decisions," *Journal of Marketing Research,* November 1980, pp. 460–61.

[82]Jonathan Gutman and George Miaoulis, Jr., "Past Experience Drives Future CS Behavior," *Marketing News,* October 22, 2001, p. 45.

[83]John A. Larson, "The Importance of Expectations," *Marketing Management,* Winter 2000, pp. 4–5.

[84]Stephen W. Brown, "The Leadership Experience," *Marketing Management,* May/June 2003, pp. 12–13.

[85]Richard L. Oliver, "Cognitive, Affective, and Attribute Bases of the Satisfaction Response," *Journal of Consumer Research,* December 1993, p. 419.

[86]Marsha L. Richins and Peter H. Bloch, "Post-Purchase Product Satisfaction: Incorporating the Effects of Involvement and Time," *Journal of Business Research,* September 1991, pp. 145–58.

[87]Kelly Shermach, "Don't Grow Complacent When Your Customers Are 'Satisfied,'" *Marketing News,* May 20, 1996, p. 7.

[88]Timothy L. Keiningham, Melinda K. M. Goddard, Terry G. Vavra, and Andrew J. Iaci, "Customer Delight and the Bottom Line," *Marketing Management,* Fall 1999, pp. 57–63; Steve Lewis, "All or Nothing: Customers Must Be 'Totally Satisfied,'" *Marketing News,* March 2, 1998, p. 11; and Don Peppers and Martha Rogers, "When Extreme Isn't Enough," *Sales & Marketing Management,* February 1999, p. 26.

[89]Fournier and Mick, "Rediscovering Satisfaction," pp. 5–23.

[90]Thomas Gruca and Lopo Rego, "Customer Satisfaction, Cash Flow, and Shareholder Value," MSI Report No. 03–106 (Boston: Marketing Science Institute, 2003).

[91]Jagdip Singh, "Consumer Complaint Intentions and Behavior: Definitional and Taxonomical Issues," *Journal of Marketing,* January 1988, pp. 93–107.

[92]For a detailed discussion of managerial reactions to complaint behavior, see Alan J. Resnik and Robert R. Harmon, "Consumer Complaints and Managerial Response: A Holistic Approach," *Journal of Marketing,* Winter 1983, pp. 86–97; see also Howard Schlossberg, "Customer Satisfaction: Not a Fad, but a Way of Life," *Marketing News,* June 10, 1991, p. 18; and Judith Waldrop, "Educating the Customer," *American Demographics,* September 1991, p. 45.

[93]Waldrop, "Educating the Customer," p. 45.

[94]Stephanie Anderson Forest, "Customers 'Must Be Pleased, Not Just Satisfied,'" *BusinessWeek,* August 3, 1992, p. 52.

[95]Waldrop, "Educating the Customer," p. 44.

[96]For additional explanation regarding the role of cognitive dissonance in marketing and consumer behavior, see William H. Cummings and M. Venkatesan, "Cognitive Dissonance and Consumer Behavior: A Review of the Evidence," *Journal of Marketing Research,* August 1976, pp. 303–8; and Pradeep K. Korgaonkar and George P. Moschis, "An Experimental Study of Cognitive Dissonance, Product Involvement, Expectations, Performance, and Consumer Judgments of Product Performance," *Journal of Advertising* 11, no. 3 (1982), pp. 32–44.

[97]Mowen, *Consumer Behavior,* p. 764.

[98]Carolyn Gatten, "Social Issues Guide Consumer Buying," *Marketing News,* December 9, 1991, p. 80.

[99]Kirk Davidson, "Like Marketers, Consumers Have Responsibilities," *Marketing News,* March 3, 1998, p. 24.

[100]John E. Richardson and David L. Ralph, "The Ethical Treatment of Consumers," *Annual Editions: Business Ethics 00/01* (Guilford, CT: Duskin/McGraw-Hill), p. 50.

Chapter Five

[1]Martha C. Cooper, Douglas M. Lambert, and Janus D. Pugh, "Supply Chain Management: More Than a New Name for Logistics," *The International Journal of Logistics Management* 8, no. 1 (1997), p. 2.

[2]Roberta J. Duffy, "Defining Supply Management," *Inside Supply Management,* January 2002, pp. 30–32.

[3]"BellSouth: Electronic Education Program," accessed at Accenture Web site at *www.accenture.com,* May 5, 2005.

[4]Mark G. Dotzour, "Outsource: Outwit, Outplay, Outlast," *Terre Grande,* January 2005, pp. 1–3.

[5]From Michael F. Corbett & Associates Web site at *www.corbettassociates.com/content,* accessed on April 13, 2005.

[6]"Supply Strategy in Tough Times," *Inside Supply Management,* March 2002, p. 6.

[7]Leslie Hansen Harps, "Optimization: Gearing up for Growth," *Inbound Logistics,* January 2005, pp. 134–38.

[8]Janet Adamy, "Retail Exchanges to Vie with Wal-Mart," *The Wall Street Journal,* April 26, 2005, p. B7.

[9]"Ariba Opens Global Supplier Network with New Supplier Connectivity Offering," from Ariba, Inc., Web site at *www.arriba.com,* accessed on May 6, 2005.

[10]Peter Burrows, "Cisco's Comeback," *BusinessWeek,* November 23, 2003, pp. 116–24.

[11]Lee Hawkins, Jr., "GM Pushing Its U.S. Suppliers to Reduce Prices," *The Wall Street Journal,* April 7, 2005, p. A2.

[12]John Yuva, "Collaborative Logistics: Building a Collaborative Network," *Inside Supply Management,* May 2002, pp. 42–53.

[13]Susan Avery, "Advanced Partnering," *Purchasing Magazine Online,* available at *www.manufacturing.net,* accessed on July 27, 2004.

[14]"Design for the Environment," from Herman Miller's Web site, *www.hermanmiller.com,* accessed on May 7, 2005.

[15]For a revised and expanded version of this typology, see Michele D. Bunn, "Taxonomy of Buying Decision Approaches," *Journal of Marketing,* January 1993, pp. 38–56; see also Patrick J. Robinson, Charles W. Faris, and Yoram Wind, *Industrial Buying and Creative Marketing* (Boston: Allyn and Bacon, 1967).

[16]"Wal-Mart Stores, Inc., Supplier Proposal Packet," available at *www.walmartstores.com.*

[17]Elizabeth Wilson, Gary L. Lillien, and David T. Wilson, "Developing and Testing a Contingency Paradigm of Group Choice in Organizational Buying," *Journal of Marketing Research,* November 1991, pp. 452–53.

[18]Penny M. Simpson, Judy A. Siguaw, and Susan C. White, "Measuring the Performance of Suppliers: An Evaluation Process," *The Journal of Supply Chain Management,* Winter 2002, pp. 29–41.

[19]Kevin R. Fitzgerald, "What Makes a Superior Supplier?" *Velocity,* Spring 1999, pp. 22–24, 49.

[20]"Budget of the United States Government, Fiscal Year 2006," Office of Management and Budget, as presented at *www.white-house.gov/omb/budget/fy2006/tables.html.*

[21]Information from online version of *Commerce Business Daily* (Washington, DC: U.S. Department of Commerce), May 7, 2005, at *www.cbdnet.access.gpo.gov.*

[22]Gregory T. Gundlach and Patrick E. Murphy, "Ethical and Legal Foundations of Relational Marketing Exchanges," *Journal of Marketing,* October 1993, pp. 35–46; Craig Smith and John A. Quelch, *Ethics in Marketing* (Homewood, IL: Richard D. Irwin, 1983), pp. 40–43.

Chapter Six

[1]Vincent P. Barabba, "The Market Research Encyclopedia," *Harvard Business Review,* January–February 1990, p. 105.

[2]"AMA Board Approves New Marketing Definition," *Marketing News,* March 1, 1985, pp. 1, 14.

[3]John Tarsa, "Ocean Spray Marketing Research: Delivering Insights in a Customer–Supplier Relationship," *Marketing Research: A Magazine of Management and Application,* September 1991, p. 8.

[4]Saul Hansell, "Some Hard Lessons for Online Grocers," *The New York Times,* February 19, 2001, pp. C1, C5; David Miller, "McDonald's Is Missing the Mark," *Brandweek,* November 12, 2001, pp. 20, 23.

[5]Hilton Barrett, "Ultimate Goal Is to Anticipate the Needs of Market," *Marketing News,* October 7, 1996, p. 10; Paul Gerhold, "Defining Marketing (or Is It Market?) Research," *Marketing Research: A Magazine of Management and Application* 5, no. 4, p. 67.

[6]Ty Albert, "Mindset Clearly Has Changed," *Marketing News,* December 6, 1999, p. 17.

[7]Sara Eckel, "Intelligence Agents," *American Demographics,* March 1999, p. 53; Ann M. Raider, "Programs Make Results out of Research," *Marketing News,* June 21, 1999, p. 14; Jagdish Sheth and Rajendra S. Sisodia, "Feeling the Heat—Part 2," *Marketing Management* 3, no. 4 (Winter 1995), p. 22.

[8]Simon Chadwick, "The Research Industry Grows Up and Out," *Marketing News,* June 8, 1998, p. 9.

[9]Adapted from Gilbert A. Churchill, Jr., *Marketing Research: Methodological Foundations,* 5th ed. (Chicago: Dryden Press, 1991), p. 9.

[10]Nino DeNicola, "Casting Finer Net Not Necessary," *Marketing News,* March 4, 2002, p. 46.

[11]Earl Babbie, *The Practice of Social Research,* 5th ed. (Belmont, CA: Wadsworth, 1989), p. 80.

[12]See William R. Dillon, Thomas J. Madden, and Neil A. Firtle, *Marketing Research in a Marketing Environment,* 2nd ed. (Homewood, IL: Richard D. Irwin, 1990), p. 29; and Churchill, *Marketing Research,* pp. 130–43.

[13]Maria F. Flores Letelier, Charles Spinosa, and Bobby J. Calder, "Taking an Expanded View of Customers' Needs: Qualitative Research for Aiding Innovation," *Marketing Research,* Winter 2000, pp. 4–11.

[14]Duncan Simester, "Finally, Market Research You Can Use," *Harvard Business Review,* February 2004, p. 21.

[15]Jack Honomichl, "U.S. Total Spending and Segments," *Marketing News,* June 10, 2002, p. H3.

[16]See, for example, Johan K. Johansson and Ikujiro Nonaka, "Market Research the Japanese Way," *Harvard Business Review,* May–June 1987, pp. 16–18, 22; and Tim Powell, "Despite Myths, Secondary Research Is Valuable Tool," *Marketing News,* September 2, 1991, p. 28.

[17]Alvin C. Burns and Ronald F. Bush, *Marketing Research,* 2nd ed. (Upper Saddle River, NJ: Prentice Hall), p. 143.

[18]Ed Campbell, "CD-ROMs Bring Census Data In-House," *Marketing News,* January 1992, p. 15.

[19]Lawrence N. Gold, "The Coming of Age of Scanner Data," *Marketing Research: A Magazine of Management and Application,* Winter 1993, p. 23.

[20]For several descriptions, see Joseph M. Winski, "Gentle Rain Turns to Torrent," *Advertising Age,* June 3, 1991, p. 34; Blair Peters, "The 'Brave New World' of Single Source Information," *Marketing Research: A Magazine of Management and Applications,* December 1990, pp. 13–21; and "Nielsen, NPD Start Single Source Service," *Marketing News,* August 28, 1987, p. 1.

[21]Thomas G. Exter, "The Next Step Is Called GIS," *American Demographics,* May 1992, p. 2.

[22]Jack Szergold, "Getting the GIS of Things," *Management Review,* July 1993, p. 6.

[23]David Churbuck, "Geographics," *Forbes,* January 6, 1992, pp. 262–67; Eric Schine, "Computer Maps Pop Up All over the Map," *BusinessWeek,* July 26, 1993, p. 75.

[24]See Bobby J. Calder, "Focus Groups and the Nature of Qualitative Marketing Research," *Journal of Marketing Research,* August 1977, pp. 353–64; and Edward F. Fern, "The Use of Focus Groups for Idea Generation: The Effects of Group Size, Acquaintanceship, and Moderator on Response Quantity and Quality," *Journal of Marketing Research,* February 1982, pp. 1–13.

[25]Judith Langer, "15 Myths of Qualitative Research: It's Conventional, But Is It Wisdom," *Marketing News,* March 1, 1999, pp. 13–14.

[26]Catherine Forrest, "Research with a Laugh Track," *Marketing News,* March 2, 2002, p. 48.

[27]Emily Nelson, "P&G Keeps Focus Groupies of Cincinnati Busy as Guinea Pigs in Product Studies," *The Wall Street Journal,* http://interactive.wsj.com/archive/retrieve.cgi?id = SB1011821805284938360.djm.

[28]Allison Stein Wellner, "The New Science of Focus Groups," *American Demographics,* March 2003, pp. 29–33.

[29]Michael Fielding, "Survival Skills," *Marketing News,* March 1, 2005, p. 12.

[30]Jack Honomichl, "Legislation Threatens Research by Phone," *Marketing News,* June 24, 1991, p. 4.

[31]Stephen W. McDaniel, Perry Verille, and Charles S. Madden, "The Threats to Marketing Research: An Empirical Reappraisal," *Journal of Marketing Research,* February 1985, pp. 74–80; Howard Gershowitz, "Entering the 1990s—The State of Data Collection— Telephone Data Collection," *Applied Marketing Research,* Spring 1990, pp. 16–19.

[32]Michael P. Cronin, "On-the-Cheap Market Research," *Inc.,* June 1992, p. 108.

[33]Pamela Rogers, "One-on-Ones Don't Get the Credit They Deserve," *Marketing News,* January 2, 1991, p. 9.

[34]Susan Kraft, "Who Slams the Door on Research?" *American Demographics,* September 1991, p. 9.

[35]Alan J. Bush and Joseph F. Hair, Jr., "Mall Intercept versus Telephone Interviewing Environment," *Journal of Marketing Research,* May 1985, pp. 158–68.

[36]Howard Schlossberg, "Shoppers Virtually Stroll through Store Aisles to Examine Packages," *Marketing News,* June 6, 1993, p. 2.

[37]"Big Bytes," Marketing News, March 18, 2002, p. 3.

[38]Robert Hayes, "Internet-Based Surveys Provide Fast Results," *Marketing News,* April 13, 1998, p. 13; Dana James, "Precision Decision," *Marketing News,* September 27, 1999, pp. 23–25; Phil Levine, Bill Ahlauser, Dale Kulp, and Rick Hunter, "Internet Interviewing," *Marketing Research: A Magazine of Management and Application,* Summer 1999, pp. 33–36; Seymour Sudman and Edward Blair, "Sampling in the Twenty-First Century," *Journal of the Academy of Marketing Science* 27, no. 2, p. 275.

[39]Catherine Arnold, "Cast Your Net," *Marketing News,* November 12, 2003, p. 15; Jacob Brown, "Survey Metrics Ward Off Problems," *Marketing News,* November 24, 2003, p. 17; Michael Fielding, "Recent Converts," *Marketing News,* November 15, 2004, pp. 21–22; Arundhati Parmar, "Net Research Is Not Quite Global," *Marketing News,* March 3, 2003, pp. 51–52.

[40]Sharon Hollander, "Projective Techniques Uncover Real Consumer Attitudes," *Marketing News,* January 4, 1988, p. 34.

[41]Stephen Groves and Raymond P. Fisk, "Observational Data Collection Methods for Services Marketing: An Overview," *Journal of the Academy of Marketing Science,* Summer 1992, pp. 217–24.

[42]Stephanie Wilkinson, "Mystery Shoppers Going High Tech," *Investor's Business Daily,* May 3, 2002, p. A5.

[43]William B. Helmreich, "Louder Than Words: On-Site Observational Research," *Marketing News,* March 1, 1999, p. 16.

[44]James McQuivey, "Technology Monitors People in New Ways," *Marketing News,* September 15, 2004, p. 23.

[45]Rebecca Piirto, "Socks, Ties, and Videotape," *American Demographics,* September 1991, p. 6.

[46]Sandra Yin, "Marketing Tools," *American Demographics,* November 2001, pp. 32–33.

[47]Debra Goldman, "Consumer Republic: Marketers Discover Surveillance Is Socially Acceptable," *Adweek,* June 4, 2001, p. 24; Gerry Khermouch, "Consumers in the Mist," *BusinessWeek,* February 26, 2001, pp. 92, 94.

[48]Shelby D. Hunt, Richard D. Sparkman, Jr., and James B. Wilcox, "The Pretest in Survey Research: Issues and Preliminary Findings," *Journal of Marketing Research,* May 1982, pp. 269–73.

[49]James D. Lenskold, "Marketing ROI: Playing to Win," *Marketing Management,* May/June 2002, pp. 31–35.

[50]Diane Schmalensee, "One Researcher's Rules of Thumb for B-to-B Arena," *Marketing News,* November 19, 2001, pp. 17–18.

[51]Steve Jarvis, "CMOR Finds Survey Refusal Rate Still Rising," *Marketing News,* February 4, 2002, p. 4.

[52]Sudman and Blair, "Sampling in the Twenty-First Century," *Journal of the Academy of Marketing Science* 27, no.2, p. 275.

[53]Gershowitz, "Entering the 1990s."

[54]Peter S. Tuckel and Harry W. O'Neil, "Call Waiting," *Marketing Research: A Magazine of Management and Application,* Spring 1995, p. 7.

[55]Thomas L. Greenbaum, "Focus Group by Video Next Trend of the 90s," *Marketing News,* July 29, 1996, p. 4; Leslie M. Harris, "Technology, Techniques Drive Focus Group Trends," *Marketing News,* February 27, 1995, p. 8; Beth Schneider, "Using Interactive Kiosks for Retail Research," *Marketing News,* January 2, 1995, p. 13; Barbara A. Schuldt and Jeff W. Totten, "Electronic Mail vs. Mail Response Rates," *Marketing Research: A Magazine of Management and Application* 6, no. 1, p. 36; and Gary S. Vazzana and Duane Bachmann, "Fax Attracts," *Marketing Research: A Magazine of Management and Application* 6, no. 2, p. 19.

[56]Daphre Chandler, "Eight Common Pitfalls of International Research," in *The Resurgence of Research in Decision Making: 1992 CASRO Annual Journal* (Port Jefferson, NY: The Council of American Survey Research Organizations, 1992), pp. 81–85.

[57]Elizabeth Loken, "Probing Japanese Buyers' Minds," *Business Marketing* 72, no. 11, November 1987, pp. 85–90.

[58]Neil Helgeson, "Research Isn't Linear When Done Globally," *Marketing News,* July 19, 1999, p. 13.

[59]Catherine Arnold, "Global Perspective," *Marketing News,* May 15, 2004, p. 43.

[60]Arundhati Parmar, "Tailor Techniques to Each Audience in Latin Market," *Marketing News,* February 3, 2003, pp. 4, 6.

[61]William R. Dillon, Thomas J. Madden, and Neil Firtle, *Essentials of Marketing Research* (Homewood, IL: Richard D. Irwin, Inc., 1993), pp. 293–95.

[62]Bruce H. Clark, "Bad Examples," *Marketing Management,* November/December 2003, pp. 34–38.

[63]Howard N. Gundee, "Council Joins Industrial Effort to Support Research," *Marketing News,* January 4, 1993, p. 22.

[64]McDaniel, Verille, and Madden, "Threats to Marketing Research."

[65]Wade Lettwich, "How Researchers Can Win Friends and Influence Politicians," *American Demographics,* August 1993, p. 9.

[66]"The Persistence of Surveying," *Marketing News,* September 2, 1992, p. 4.

[67]Ishmael P. Akaah and Edward A. Riordan, "Judgments of Marketing Professionals about Ethical Issues in Marketing Research: Replication and Extension," *Journal of Marketing Research,* February 1989, p. 113.

[68]Patrick E. Murphy and Gene R. Laczniak, "Emerging Ethical Issues Facing Marketing Researchers," *Marketing Research,* June 1992, pp. 6–7.

[69]Tom Eisenhart, "After 10 Years of Marketing Decision Support Systems, Where's the Payoff?" *Business Marketing,* June 1990, pp. 46–48, 50.

[70]Alan J. Greco and Jack T. Hogue, "Developing Marketing Decision Support Systems," *Journal of Business and Industrial Marketing,* Summer–Fall 1990, p. 28; and Alan J. Greco and Jack T. Hogue, "Developing Marketing Decision Support Systems in Consumer Goods Firms," *Journal of Consumer Marketing,* Winter 1990, pp. 56–64.

[71]Rajerdra S. Sisodia, "Marketing Information and Decision Support Systems for Services," *Journal of Services Marketing,* Winter 1992, p. 53.

[72]Randolph E. Bucklin, Donald R. Lehmann, and John D. C. Little, *From Decision Support to Decision Automation: A 2020 Vision,* Marketing Science Institute, Report no. 98–119 (Cambridge, MA: June 1998).

[73]Joe Ashbrook Nickell, "Data Mining: Welcome to Harrah's," *Business 2.0,* April 2002, p. 48.

[74]Doug Grisaffe, "See about Linking CRM and MR Systems," *Marketing News,* January 21, 2002, p. 13; Gordon A. Wyner, "Customer Relationship Management," *Marketing Research,* Summer 1999, pp. 39–41.

[75]James Heckman, "You Have Tools to Boost Your Budget," *Marketing News,* September 13, 1999, p. 4.

[76]Jagdish Sheth and Rajendra S. Sisodia, "Feeling the Heat— Part 2," p. 22.

[77]George R. Milne and Maria-Eugenia Boza, *A Business Perspective on Database Marketing and Consumer Privacy Practices,* Marketing Science Institute, Report no. 98–110 (Cambridge, MA: June 1998); and Joseph Phelps, Glen Nowak, and Elizabeth Ferrell, *Marketers' Information Practices and Privacy Concerns: How Willing Are Consumers to Provide Personal Information for Shopping Benefits?* Marketing Science Institute, Report no. 99–112, (Cambridge, MA: June 1999).

Chapter Seven

[1]Gordon A. Wyner, "Segmentation Architecture," *Marketing Management,* March/April 2000, pp. 6–7.

[2]Nora A. Aufreiter, David Elzinga, and Jonathan W. Gordon, "Better Branding," *The McKinsey Quarterly,* no. 4, 2003, p. 30.

[3]For an in-depth review, see Gary L. Lilien and Philip Kotler, *Marketing Decision Making: A Model Building Approach* (New York: Harper and Row, 1983); and Peter R. Dickson and James L. Ginter, "Market Segmentation, Product Differentiation, and Marketing," *Journal of Marketing,* April 1987, pp. 1–10.

[4]Faye Brookman, "Companies Invest in Customer Loyalty," *Marketing News,* March 2, 1998, p. 12.

[5]Suzanne Vranica, "McDonald's Ad Goes Presidential," *The Wall Street Journal,* February 8, 2005, p. B7.

[6]Harper W. Boyd Jr. and Orville C. Walker Jr., *Marketing Management: A Strategic Approach* (Homewood, IL: Richard D. Irwin, 1990), p. 186.

[7]Brian Grow, Ronald Grover, Arlene Weintraub, Christopher Pameri, Mara Der Hovanesian, and Michael Eidam, "Hispanic Nation," *BusinessWeek,* March 15, 2004, pp. 58–65.

[8]Robert Sharoff, "Diversity in the Mainstream," *Marketing News,* May 21, 2001, pp. 1, 13.

[9]Daniel F. Hansler and Donald R. Riggin, "Geodemographics: Targeting the Market," *Fund Raising Management;* December 1989, pp. 35–43.

[10]Saeed Samiee, "A Conceptual Framework for International Marketing," in *International Business: Inquiry: An Emerging Vision,* eds. B. Toyne and Douglas Nigh (Columbia, SC: USC Press, 1994); see also Theodore Leavitt, "The Globalization of Markets," *Harvard Business Review,* May–June 1983, pp. 99–102; and Saeed Samiee and Kendall Roth, "The Influence of Global Marketing Standardization on Performance," *Journal of Marketing,* April 1992, pp. 1–17.

[11]Ugar Yavas, Bronislaw J. Verhage, and Robert T. Green, "Global Consumer Segmentation versus Local Market Orientation: Empirical Findings," *Marketing International Review,* 1992, pp. 266–68.

[12]Alpa Agarwal, "Profiting from India's Strong Middle Class," *Marketing News,* October 7, 1996, p. 6; and Cyndee Miller, "Teens Seen as the First Truly Global Consumers," *Marketing News,* March 27, 1995, p. 9.

[13]Peter D. Bennett, ed., *Dictionary of Marketing Terms* (Chicago: American Marketing Association, 1988), p. 199.

[14]Deborah L. Vence, "Win Hispanic Market with Proper Research," *Marketing News,* July 7, 2003, p. 7.

[15]Gordon A. Wyner, "Risky Business," *Marketing Management,* September/ October 2004, p. 9.

[16]James H. Gilmore and B. Joseph Pine, II, "The Four Faces of Mass Customization," *Harvard Business Review,* January–February 1997, pp. 91–101; and Suresh Kotha, "From Mass Production to Mass Customization: The Case of the National Industrial Bicycle Company of Japan," *European Management Journal,* October 1996, pp. 442–50.

[17]Jerry Wind and Arvind Rangaswamy, "Customerization: The Next Revolution in Mass Customization," Marketing Science Report No. 00–108, Marketing Science Institute, Boston, MA, pp. 25–26.

[18]Gary L. Berman, "The Hispanic Market: Getting Down to Cases," *Sales & Marketing Management,* October 1991, p. 66.

[19]Shirley Young, Leland Ott, and Barbara Feign, "Some Practical Considerations in Market Segmentation," *Journal of Marketing Research,* August 1978, pp. 405–12.

[20]Jennifer Barron and Jim Hollingshead, "Making Segmentation Work," *Marketing Management,* January/February 2002, p. 25.

[21]"A Long Wait: Population Growth," *The Economist,* December 21, 2000, p. 69.

[22]Ronald Grover, "Old Rockers Never Die—They Just Switch to CDs," *BusinessWeek,* August 17, 1992, p. 54.

[23]Cyndi W. Greenglass, "It's All about People," *1 to 1,* September 2000, p. 44.

[24]"Multicultural Marketing Experts Give Their Two Cents on Census Data," *BrandWeek,* May 14, 2001, p. 25.

[25]Deborah Vence, "Top Niche," *Marketing News,* July 1, 2004, p. 11.

[26]Roger J. Calantone and Alan G. Sawyer, "The Stability of Benefit Segments," *Journal of Marketing Research,* August 1978, pp. 395–404.

[27]Henry Assael, "Segmenting Markets by Response Elasticity," *Journal of Advertising Research,* April 1976, pp. 27–35.

[28]Hartmarx, *Annual Report* (Chicago: Hartmarx Corporation, 1992).

[29]"The American Dream Is Alive and Well—In Mexico," *BusinessWeek,* September 30, 1991, p. 102.

[30]Rebecca Gardyn, "Habla English," *American Demographics,* 2001, pp. 54–57.

[31]Paula Lyon Andruss, "Show Boat to China: Worth Eyeing Now More Than Ever—Carefully," *Marketing News,* September 10, 2001, pp. 1, 11.

[32]Philip Kotler, *Marketing Management: Analysis, Planning Implementation and Control,* 8th ed. (Englewood Cliffs, NJ: Prentice Hall, 1994), p. 265.

[33]See Yoram Wind and Richard Cardoza, "Industrial Market Segmentation," *Industrial Marketing Management,* March 1974, pp. 153–66, for a similar outline of business-to-business segmentation bases.

[34]June Lee Risser, "Come First," *Marketing Management,* November/ December, p. 25.

[35]Peter Francese, "America at Mid-Decade," *American Demographics,* February 1995, pp. 23–31; Peter Zollo, "Talking to Teens," *American Demographics,* November 1995, pp. 22–28.

[36]Michael J. Silverstein and Neil Fiske, "Luxury for the Masses," *Harvard Business Review,* April 2003, pp. 48–57.

[37]Susan Mitchell, *American Generations: Who They Are and How They Live,* 2nd ed. (Ithaca, NY: New Strategist Publications, 1998).

[38]David Welch, "Not Your Father's . . . Whatever," *BusinessWeek,* March 15, 2004, pp. 82–83.

[39]Laura Koss-Feder, "Want to Catch Gen X? Try Looking on the Web," *Marketing News,* June 8, 1998, p. 20.

[40]Francese, "America at Mid-Decade"; Cyndee Miller, "Boomers Come of Age," *Marketing News,* January 15, 1996, pp. 1, 6; Karen Ritchie, "Marketing to Generation X," *American Demographics,* April 1995, pp. 34–39; and Zollo, "Talking to Teens."

[41]Wendy Bounds, "Rushing to Cash In on the New Baby Boom," *The Wall Street Journal,* pp. B1, B4; Pamela Paul, "Childless by Choice," *American Demographics,* November 2001, pp. 45–50.

[42]Clark Crowdus, "Pay Your Respects," *Marketing News,* March 15, 2005, p. 22.

[43]Lisa Modisette and Steve Huson, "Customer Knowledge Is Power," *Cellular Business,* September 1996, p. 98.

[44]Daniel F. Hansler and Don L. Riggen, "Geodemographics: Targeting the Market," *Fund Raising Management,* December 1989, p. 35.

[45]Eric A. Cohen, "Demos Alone Don't Sell Products," *Marketing News,* June 21, 1999, p. 16.

[46]Nick Fuller, "Finding Cable's Target," *Marketing,* February 18, 1992, p. 27.

[47]Susan Mitchell, "Birds of a Feather," *American Demographics,* February 1995, pp. 40–41.

[48]Geert Hofstede, *Culture's Consequences: Comparing Values, Behaviors, Institutions, and Organizations across Nations,* 2nd ed. 2003 (Thousand Oaks, CA: Sage Publications); and V. Kumar and Anish Nagpal, "Segmenting Global Markets: Look Before You Leap," *Marketing Research,* Spring 2001, pp. 8–13.

[49]William D. Wells and Douglas J. Tigert, "Activities, Interests, and Opinions," *Journal of Advertising Research,* August 1971, pp. 27–35; and William D. Wells, "Psychographics: A Critical Review," *Journal of Marketing Research,* May 1975, pp. 196–213. See also Allen M. Clark, "'Trends' That Will Impact New Products," *Journal of Consumer Marketing,* Winter 1991, pp. 29–34; P. Valette-Florence and A. Jolibert, "Social Values, AIO, and Consumption Patterns: Exploratory Findings," *Journal of Business Research,* March 1990, pp. 109–22; and Steven Hoch, "Who Do We Know: Predicting the Interests and Opinions of the American Consumer," *Journal of Consumer Research,* December 1988, pp. 315–24.

[50]Joanna L. Krotz, "Divide and Conquer Your Customers with Psychographics," *http://www.bcentral.com/articles/krotz/108.asp.*

[51]Wells and Tigert, "Activities, Interests, and Opinions," p. 30.

[52]Marvin Schoenwald, "Psychographic Segmentation: Used or Abused?" *Brand Week,* January 22, 2001, pp. 34–38.

[53]Brian Davis and Warren A. French, "Exploring Advertising Usage Segments among the Aged," *Journal of Advertising Research,* February–March 1989, pp. 22–29.

[54]Pamela Paul, "Getting Inside Gen Y," *American Demographics,* September 2001, pp. 43–49.

[55]Michael Gates, "VALS Changes with the Times," *Incentive,* June 1989, p. 27.

[56]Martha Farnsworth Riche, "Psychographics for the 1990s," *American Demographics,* July 1989, p. 30.

[57]Russell I. Haley, "Benefit Segmentation: A Decision-Oriented Tool," *Journal of Marketing,* July 1968, pp. 30–35.

[58]Ibid.; and Paul E. Green, Abba M. Krieger, and Catherine M. Schagger, "Quick and Simple Benefit Segmentation," *Journal of Advertising Research,* June–July 1985, pp. 9–17.

[59]Michael Anthony, "More Customers or Right Customers: Your Choice," *Marketing News,* August 31, 1998, p. 13.

[60]Diane Brady, "Why Service Stinks," *BusinessWeek,* October 23, 2000, pp. 118–28.

[61]Gerald E. Smith, "Segmenting B2B Markets with Economic Value Analysis," *Marketing Management,* March/April 2002, pp. 35–39.

[62]Kristaan Helson, Kamel Jedidi, and Wayne S. DeSarbo, "A New Approach to Country Segmentation Utilizing Multinational Diffusion Patterns," *Journal of Marketing,* October 1993, p. 61.

[63]V. Kumar and Anish Nagpal, "Segmenting Global Markets: Look before You Leap," *Marketing Research,* Spring 2001, p. 813.

[64]Karl Greenberg, "Nissan Clears 2002 Maxima for Takeoff," *BrandWeek,* November 12, 2001, p. 8.

[65]Michael E. Raynor and Howard S. Weinberg, "Beyond Segmentation," *Marketing Management,* November/December 2004, p. 23.

[66]Robert H. Waterman, Jr., "Successful Small- and Medium-Sized Firms Stress Creativity, Employ Niche Strategy," *Marketing News,* March 15, 1984, p. 24.

[67]Michael E. Raynor and Howard S. Weinberg, "Beyond Segmentation," *Marketing Management*, November/December 2004, p. 23.

[68]Boyd and Walker, *Marketing Management*, p. 294.

[69]John B. Mahaffie, "Why Forecasts Fail," *American Demographics*, March 1995, pp. 34–40.

[70]Raymond Serafin and Cleveland Horton, "Buick Ads Target Zip Codes," *Advertising Age*, April 1, 1991, pp. 1, 36.

[71]Lisa Napoli, "Staying with the Pitch," *The New York Times*, February 23, 1998, p. 5; Joseph Pereira, "Sneaker Company Targets Out-of-Breath Baby Boomers," *The Wall Street Journal*, January 16, 1998, p. B1; and B. G. Yovovich, "Scanners Reshape Grocery Business," *Marketing News*, March 16, 1998, pp. 1, 11.

[72]Martin R. Lautman, "The ABCs of Positioning," *Marketing Research: A Magazine of Management and Application*, Winter 1993, p. 12.

[73]Judann Pollack, "Snackwell's Rallies with New Focus," *Advertising Age*, January 25, 1999, p. 16.

[74]Mita Sujan and James R. Bettman, "The Effects of Brand Positioning Strategies on Consumers' Brand and Category Perceptions: Some Insights from Schema Research," *Journal of Marketing Research*, November 1989, p. 454.

[75]Arundhati Parmar, "Where Are They Now," *Marketing News*, April 14, 2003, pp. 1, 13–14.

[76]Jason M. Sherman, "Reducing the Risks of Target Marketing," *Marketing News*, November 11–18, 1996, p. 12.

[77]Paula Munier Lee, "The Micromarketing Revolution," *Small Business Reports*, February 1990, pp. 73–82.

[78]James Heckman, "Today's Game Is Keep-Away," pp. 1, 7; Allyson L.Stewart-Allen, "Rules for Reaching Euro Kids Are Changing," *Marketing News*, June 7, 1999, p. 10.

[79]Marcia Mogelonsky, "Product Overload?" *American Demographics*, August 1998, pp. 65–69; "What's New," *Marketing News*, March 2, 1998, p. 2.

[80]Barbara Kahn and Leigh McAlister, *Grocery Revolution: The New Focus on the Consumer* (Reading, MA: Addison Wesley, 1997) pp. 66–67.

Chapter Eight

[1]Adapted from Peter D. Bennett, ed., *Dictionary of Marketing Terms* (Chicago: American Marketing Association, 1988), p. 153.

[2]"Business-to-Business Product: Hewlett-Packard," *Sales & Marketing Management*, August 1993, p. 42.

[3]Stephen L. Vargo and Robert L. Lusch, "Evolving to a New Dominant Logic for Marketing," *Journal of Marketing*, January 2004, pp. 1–17; C. K. Prahalad, "The Cocreation of Value," *Journal of Marketing*, January 2004, p. 23.

[4]Aixa M. Pascual, "Striking the Right Chord," *BusinessWeek*, June 10, 2002, p. 98.

[5]Tom Peters, *Liberation Management* (New York: Alfred A. Knopf, 1992), p. 295.

[6]Norihiko Shirouzu, "BMW, Mercedes Make Big Comebacks in Quality," *The Wall Street Journal Online*, May 19, 2005, pp. 1–3.

[7]David Welch, "Nissan: The Squeaks Get Louder," *BusinessWeek*, May 17, 2004, p. 44.

[8]Moon Ihlwan with Larry Armstrong and Michael Eidam, "Hyundai: Kissing Clunkers Goodbye," *BusinessWeek*, May 17, 2004, p. 45.

[9]Gail Edmondson, "Mercedes' Head-On Collision with a Quality Survey," *BusinessWeek*, July 21, 2003, p. 27.

[10]Ted C. Fishman, "How Ed Zander Honed Razr's Edge," *Business 2.0*, June 2005, pp. 47–49.

[11]Bruce Nussbaum, "The Power of Design," *BusinessWeek*, May 17, 2004, pp. 85–94.

[12]Seanna Browder, "In This Dogfight, Boeing's Gutsy Maneuver Paid Off," *BusinessWeek*, December 2, 1996, p. 46.

[13]G. Pascal Zachary, "Invasion of the Gadget Snatchers," *Business 2.0*, May 2005, pp. 49–51.

[14]Faith Keenan and Adam Aston, "Building 'Easy' into Technology," *BusinessWeek*, December 3, 2001, pp. 92B–92D.

[15]Elizabeth Esfahani, Susanna Hamner, Monica Khemsurov, Matthew Maier, and Matt Palmquist, "The First Annual Bottom Line Design Awards," *Business 2.0*, April 2005, pp. 89–96.

[16]Lisa Keefe, ed., "Panda, and Still Champion," *Marketing News*, April 1, 2002, p. 3.

[17]Maxine Lans Retsky, "New Law Protects Marks Worldwide," *Marketing News*, April 14, 2003, pp. 10, 12.

[18]Arundhati Parmar, "The Name Game," *Marketing News*, March 17, 2003, p. 3.

[19]Gerry Khermouch, Bruce Einhorn, and Dexter Roberts, "Breaking into the Name Game," *BusinessWeek*, April 7, 2003, p. 54.

[20]Roland T. Rust, Valerie A. Zeithaml, and Katherine N. Lemon, "Customer-Centered Brand Management," *Harvard Business Review*, September 2004, pp. 110–18.

[21]Bob Lamons, "Create Focused Expectations with Brand Image," *Marketing News*, September 29, 2003, pp. 7–8.

[22]Kevin J. Clancy and Jack Trout, "Brand Confusion," *Harvard Business Review*, March 2002, p. 22.

[23]Catherine Arnold, "New Brand Image Sharpens IT Firm's Focus," *Marketing News*, May 12, 2003, pp. 5–6.

[24]Clint Willis, "Leaping Loyalty," *Business 2.0*, July 2002, p. 87.

[25]Michael Fielding, "Unchartered Territory," *Marketing News*, November 1, 2004, pp. 7–8.

[26]Gardiner Harris and Joanna Slater, "Bitter Pill: 'Branded Generics' Eat into Drug Makers' Profits," *The Wall Street Journal Online*, April 17, 2003, pp. 1–5.

[27]Matthew Boyle, "Brand Killers," *Fortune*, August 11, 2003, pp. 89–100.

[28]Michael Arndt, "Why Kraft Is on a Crash Diet," *BusinessWeek*, November 29, 2004, p. 46.

[29]Alex Frankel, "The New Science of Naming," *Business 2.0*, December 2004, pp. 53–55.

[30]Mark Lasswell, "Lost in Translation," *Business 2.0*, August 2004, pp. 68–70.

[31]Joann Muller, "Apple Strudel and Chevrolet," *Forbes*, November 1, 2004, p. 56.

[32]Bruce Horovitz, "P&G Licenses Its Brand Names to Boost Income," *The Courier-Journal*, April 20, 2003, p. E2.

[33]Jeremy Caplan, "Strange Bedfellows," *Time*, March 7, 2005.

[34]Deborah Vence, "The Lowdown on Trans Fats," *Marketing News*, March 15, 2004, pp. 13–14.

[35]Kelly Shermach, "Proper Design Aids Sales of Do-It-Yourself Products," *Marketing News*, September 11, 1995, p. 12.

[36]Tara Siegel Bernard, "Winning a Place on Grocery Store Shelves," *The Wall Street Journal Online*, March 29, 2005, pp. 1–3.

[37]Catherine Arnold, "Way Outside the Box," *Marketing News*, June 23, 2003, pp. 13, 15.

[38]Elizabeth Esfahani, "Packaging as Entertainment," *Business 2.0*, June 2005, p. 73.

[39]Greg Morago, "Cans Are Calling Out to Consumers with Their Unique Shapes," *The Courier-Journal*, October 24, 2004, p. E8.

[40]James B. Miller, "Bailing Out Customer," *Sales & Marketing Management*, January 1994, p. 29.

Chapter Nine

[1]Christopher Power, Kathleen Kerwin, Ronald Glover, Keith Alexander, and Robert D. Hof, "Flops," *BusinessWeek*, August 16, 1993, p. 82.

[2]"Try It, They May Buy It," *The Wall Street Journal*, November 14, 1996, p. A1.

[3]Alan Farnham, "America's Most Admired Company," *Fortune*, February 7, 1994, pp. 50–54.

[4]Bridget Finn, "Scoring the Salad Wars," *Business 2.0*, December 2003, p. 34.

[5]Ashwin W. Joshi and Sanjay Sharma, "Customer Knowledge Management: Antecedents and Impact on New Product Performance," *Journal of Marketing,* October 2004, pp. 47–59; Eugene Sivadas and F. Robert Dwyer, "An Examination of Organizational Factors Influencing New Product Success in Internal and Alliance-Based Processes," *Journal of Marketing,* January 2000, pp. 31–49.

[6]Rahul Jacob, "Beyond Quality and Value," *Fortune,* Autumn–Winter 1993, pp. 8–11.

[7]"Shortening the Product Pipeline," *Sales and Marketing Management,* January 1999, p. 71.

[8]Cyndee Miller, "Little Relief Seen for New Product Failure," *Marketing News,* June 21, 1993, pp. 1, 10.

[9]Roger Van Bakel, "The Art of Brand Revival," *Business 2.0,* September 2002, pp. 45–48.

[10]*www.newellco.com* and *www.rubbermaid.com,* January 12, 2000.

[11]Amy Barrett, "A Drug Company on Growth Hormones," *BusinessWeek,* March 7, 2005, p. 40.

[12]Don Clark and Charles Forelle, "Sun Microsystems to Buy Storage Tek for $4.1 Billion," *The Wall Street Journal Online,* June 3, 2005, pp. 1–3.

[13]Michelle Pacelle, "Citigroup to Buy 2 Card Lines," *The Wall Street Journal Online,* June 3, 2005, pp. 1–2.

[14]Paul Kaihla, "Why China Wants to Scoop Up Your Company," *Business 2.0,* June 2005, pp. 29–30.

[15]Sividas and Dwyer, "An Examination of Organizational Factors."

[16]David Bank, "Microsoft, SAP Plan a Joint Product," *The Wall Street Journal Online,* April 26, 2005, pp. 1–2.

[17]Bradford L. Goldense, John R. Power, and Anne R. Schwartz, "Two-Step Solution Process Helps Limit NPD Products in Pipeline, According to Study," *Visions,* April 2004, accessed at *www.pdma.org* on June 5, 2005.

[18]*www.3M.com,* January 14, 2000.

[19]Stephanie Clifford, "How to Get the Geeks and the Suits to Play Nice," *Business 2.0,* May 2002, pp. 92–93.

[20]Anne Fisher, "Get Employees to Brainstorm Online," *Fortune,* November 29, 2004, p. 72.

[21]Jennifer Esty, "Those Wacky Customers!" *Fast Company,* January 2004, p. 40.

[22]Amy Borrus, "Click Here to Pay Your Parking Ticket," *BusinessWeek,* January 17, 2000, pp. 76, 78.

[23]Dantar Oosterwal and Anthony Reese, "Harley-Davidson's Formula for NPD," *Visions,* January 2004, accessed at *www.pdma.org* on June 5, 2005.

[24]Kevin Kelleher, "A Site Stickier Than a Barroom Floor," *Business 2.0,* June 2005, pp. 74–76.

[25]Thomas M. Burton, "By Learning from Failures, Lilly Keeps Drug Pipeline Full," *The Wall Street Journal Online,* April 21, 2004, pp. 1–5.

[26]Lisa Bannon, "Mattel's Project Platypus Aims to Inspire Creative Thinking," *The Wall Street Journal Online,* June 6, 2002, pp. 1–3.

[27]Kathleen Devery, "Failure of Its Oven Lovin' Cookie Dough Shows Pillsbury Pitfalls of New Products," *The Wall Street Journal,* July 17, 1993, pp. B1, B8.

[28]Jerry Flint, "The Car Chrysler Didn't Build," *Forbes,* August 12, 1996, pp. 89–91.

[29]Christopher Power, "Will It Sell in Podunk? Hard to Say," *BusinessWeek,* August 10, 1992, p. 46.

[30]Ian P. Murphy, "Ameritech Test Towns Market Innovation," *Marketing News,* November 18, 1996, pp. 2, 12.

[31]"Up Front," *BusinessWeek,* April 19, 1999, p. 8.

[32]Fernando Suarez and Gianvito Lanzolla, "The Half-Truth of First-Mover Advantage," *Harvard Business Review,* April 2005, pp. 121–27.

[33]Yuhong Wu, Sridhar Balasubramanian, and Vijay Mahajan, "When Is a Preannounced New Product Likely to Be Delayed?" *Journal of Marketing,* April 2004, pp. 101–13.

[34]Ken Kono, "Planning Makes Perfect," *Marketing Management,* April 2005, pp. 31–34.

[35]"Winning the New Product Launch," *On Target Research,* 1999, pp. 14–15.

[36]Kono, "Planning Makes Perfect."

[37]This section draws heavily from Robert G. Cooper and Elko J. Kleinschmidt, "Stage Gate Systems for New Product Success," *Marketing Management* 1, no. 4, pp. 20–26.

[38]Rajesh Sethi, "New Product Quality and Product Development Teams," *Journal of Marketing,* April 2000, pp. 1–14.

[39]Subin Im and John P. Workman Jr., "Market Orientation, Creativity, and New Product Performance in High-Technology Firms," *Journal of Marketing,* April 2004, pp. 114–132; Kevin Zheng Zhou, Chi Kin (Bennett) Yim, and David K. Tse, "The Effects of Strategic Orientations on Technology- and Market-Based Breakthrough Innovations," *Journal of Marketing,* April 2005, pp. 42–60.

[40]Oosterwal and Reese, "Harley-Davidson's Formula."

[41]Kurt Swogger, " 'Speed' Philosophy Helps Dow Win OCI Award," *Visions,* January 2004, accessed at *www.pdma.org* on June 5, 2005.

[42]Richard Gibson, "A Cereal Maker's Quest for the Next Grape-Nuts," *The Wall Street Journal,* January 23, 1997, pp. B1–2.

[43]Larry Armstrong, "The Best Products of 2004," *BusinessWeek,* December 13, 2004, pp. 131–40.

Chapter Ten

[1]*www.geappliances.com,* June 8, 2005.

[2]Peter Bennett, *Dictionary of Marketing Terms* (Chicago: American Marketing Association, 1988), p. 156.

[3]*www.palm.com,* January 17, 2000.

[4]Louise Lee, "Why Levi's Still Looks Faded," *BusinessWeek,* July 22, 2002, pp. 54–55.

[5]Robert Berner, "Why P & G's Smile Is So Bright," *BusinessWeek,* August 12, 2002, pp. 58–60.

[6]Tim Morrison, "Attack of the Anti-iPods," *Time Inside Business,* May 2005, p. A22.

[7]Peter Lewis, "Play That Funky Music, White Toy," *Fortune,* February 7, 2005, pp. 38–40.

[8]Dana James, "Rejuvenating Mature Brands Can Be Stimulating Exercise," *Marketing News,* August 16, 1999, pp. 16–17.

[9]Youngme Moon, "Break Free from the Product Life Cycle," *Harvard Business Review,* May 2005, pp. 86–95.

[10]Scott McCartney, "Airlines Face Implications of Dusseldorf Experiment," *The Wall Street Journal Online,* July 31, 2002, pp. 1–3.

[11]Joseph B. White, "Honda Looks to Break Truck Rules," *The Wall Street Journal Online,* February 28, 2005, pp. 1–4.

[12]Owen Thomas, "Hits & Misses," *Business 2.0,* June 2005, p. 156; Christopher Lawton, "Anheuser's New Brew May Confuse," *The Wall Street Journal Online,* February 28, 2005.

[13]Robert Berner with Diane Brady and Wendy Zellner, "There Goes the Rainbow Nut Crunch," *BusinessWeek,* July 19, 2004, p. 38.

[14]Stanley Holmes, "Nike's New Advice? Just Strut It," *BusinessWeek,* November 3, 2003, p. 40.

[15]Kathleen Kerwin, "Fixing the Engine Trouble at Ford Credit," *BusinessWeek,* July 15, 2002, p. 116.

[16]Dean Foust, "Whipping a Behemoth into Shape," *BusinessWeek,* January 21, 2002, p. 84.

[17]The Associated Press, "Bristol-Myers May Sell OTC Pain Relievers," *Marketing News,* February 1, 2005, p. 63.

[18]Julia Boorstin, "Mickey Drexler's Second Coming," *Fortune,* May 2, 2005, pp. 101–4.

[19]Allen D. Shocker, Rajendra K. Srivastava, and Robert W. Ruekert, "Challenges and Opportunities Facing Brand Management: An Introduction to the Special Issue," *Journal of Marketing Research*, May 1994, pp. 149–58.

[20]Mary Agnes Carey, "Popcorn at Movies Gets Thumbs Down for Being Full of Fat," *The Wall Street Journal*, April 26, 1994, p. A5.

[21]Frederik Balfour, "Fakes!" *BusinessWeek*, February 7, 2005, pp. 54–64.

[22]Gene R. Laczniak and Patrick E. Murphy, *Ethical Marketing Decisions: The Higher Road* (Boston, MA: Allyn and Bacon, 1993), p. 103.

Chapter Eleven

[1]Michael V. Marn, Eric V. Roegner, and Craig C. Zawada, "The Power of Pricing," *The McKinsey Quarterly*, no. 1, 2003, p. 27.

[2]"That Falling Feeling," *The Economist*, March 17, 2001, p. 60.

[3]Stuart Sinclair, "A Guide to Global Pricing," *Journal of Business Strategy*, May–June 1993, p. 16.

[4]Rick Brooks, "Package Carriers Deliver Bad News to Shippers: Heap of Higher Prices," *The Wall Street Journal*, http://interactive.wsj.com/archive/retrie...00754067404440.djm.

[5]Walter van Waterschoot and Christophe Van den Butle, "The 4P Classification of the Marketing Mix Revisited," *Journal of Marketing*, October 1992, p. 90.

[6]Michael V. Marn and Robert Rosiello, "Managing Price, Gaining Profit," *Harvard Business Review*, September–October 1992, p. 86.

[7]David R. Bell and James M. Lattin, "Shopping Behavior and Consumer Preference for Store Price Format: Why 'Large Basket' Shoppers Prefer EDLP," Marketing Science Institute, Report no. 98–114 (Cambridge, MA: 1998); and Susan Keane, "Beyond EDLP/HiLo: A New Look at Retailer Pricing," *Insights from MSI*, Marketing Science Institute (Cambridge, MA: 1999), pp. 7–8.

[8]Kathleen Seiders and Glenn B. Voss, "From Price to Purchase," *Marketing Management*, November/December 2004, pp. 38–40.

[9]Marn and Rosiello, "Managing Price, Gaining Profit," p. 84.

[10]Hermann Simon, "Pricing Opportunities and How to Exploit Them," *Sloan Management Review*, Winter 1992, p. 56; Gerard J. Tellis, "The Price Elasticity of Selective Demand: A Meta-Analysis of Econometric Models of Sales," *Journal of Marketing Research*, November 1988, p. 331–41.

[11]Virginia Postrel, "When It Comes to Books, Internet Selling Has Not Led to Uniformly Low Prices," *The New York Times*, September 11, 2003, p. C2.

[12]Kent B. Monroe, *Pricing: Making Profitable Decisions* (New York: McGraw-Hill, 1990), pp. 8–10; Paul W. Farris and John A. Quelch, "In Defense of Price Promotion," *Sloan Management Review*, Fall 1987, p. 63.

[13]Nick Wreden, "How to Think about Pricing Strategies in a Downturn," *Harvard Business Update*, March 2002, pp. 9–10.

[14]John G. Lynch and Dan Ariely, "Electronic Shopping for Wine: How Search Costs Affect Consumer Price Sensitivity, Satisfaction with Merchandise, and Retention," Marketing Science Institute, Report no. 99–104 (Cambridge, MA: 1999).

[15]Pam Black, "All the World's an Auction," *BusinessWeek*, February 8, 1999, pp. 120–21; and Gene Koretz, "Inflation's New Adversary," *BusinessWeek*, October 4, 1999, p. 30.

[16]Walter Baker, Mike Marn, and Craig Zawada, "Price Smarter on the Net," *Harvard Business Review*, February 2001, pp. 122–27; Scott McNealy, "Welcome to the Bazaar," *Harvard Business Review*, March 2001, pp. 18–19; Peter Coy and Pamela L. Moore, "A Revolution in Pricing? Not Quite," *BusinessWeek*, November 20, 2000, pp. 48–49; Kimberly Weisul, "Sucker Prices—But Who's the Sucker?" *BusinessWeek*, March 18, 2002, p. 16.

[17]Tommy Hanrahan, "Price Isn't Everything," *The Wall Street Journal*, July 12, 1999, p. R20; Gene Koretz, "Inflation's New Adversary," *BusinessWeek*, October 4, 1999, p. 30; Gary McWilliams, "Dealer Loses?" *The Wall Street Journal*, July 12, 1999, p. R20.

[18]George E. Cressman Jr., "Reaping What You Sow," *Marketing Management*, March/April 2004, pp. 37–38.

[19]Jack Ewing, "A Cold Shoulder for Coca-Cola," *BusinessWeek*, May 2, 2005, p. 52.

[20]Anne-Marie Crawford, "Our Money Message for Euro's Ad Campaign," *Ad Age Global*, September 2001, p. 8; Christopher Rhoads, "Euro Launch Reaches Its Final Crucial Phase," *The Wall Street Journal*, December 17, 2001, p. A8; Michael R. Sesit, "Euro's Launch Helps Consumers Easily Compare Cost of Goods," *The Wall Street Journal*, January 18, 2002, p. C11.

[21]Maricris G. Briones, "The Euro Starts Here," *Marketing News*, July 20, 1998, pp. 1, 39.

[22]Michael D. Mondello, "Naming Your Price," *Inc.*, July 1992, p. 80.

[23]Thomas T. Nagle, *The Strategy and Tactics of Pricing: A Guide to Profitable Decision Making* (Englewood Cliffs, NJ: Prentice Hall, 1989), p. 8.

[24]"Cruise Lines Deep in Discounts," *Advertising Age*, February 3, 1992, p. 16.

[25]Zachary Schiller, "Procter & Gamble Hits Back," *BusinessWeek*, July 19, 1993, p. 20.

[26]Alison Rea, "Why Rising Bank Fees Are Backfiring," *BusinessWeek*, August 19, 1996, p. 66.

[27]Reed K. Holden and Thomas T. Nagle, "Kamikaze Pricing," *Marketing Management*, Summer 1998, pp. 30–39.

[28]Holden and Nagle, "Kamikaze Pricing."

[29]Peter R. Dickson, *Marketing Management* (Fort Worth, TX: Dryden Press, 1994), p. 476.

[30]Robert Jacobson and David A. Aaker, "Is Market Share All That It's Cracked Up to Be?" *Journal of Marketing*, Fall 1985, pp. 11–22.

[31]Greg Bowers, "Wiping the Mess from Gerber's Chin," *BusinessWeek*, February 1, 1993, p. 32.

[32]Richard Gibson, "Kellogg's Cutting Prices on Some Cereals in Bid to Check Loss of Market Share," *The Wall Street Journal*, June 10, 1996, p. A3.

[33]Monroe, *Pricing*, p. 8.

[34]Michael V. Marn, Eric V. Roegner, and Craig C. Zawada, "The Power of Pricing," *The McKinsey Quarterly*, no. 2, 2001, p. 40.

[35]Walter L. Baker, Eric Lin, Michael V. Marn, and Craig C. Zawada, "Getting Prices Right on the Web," *The McKinsey Quarterly*, no. 2 (2001), p. 57.

[36]Marn and Rosiello, "Managing Price, Gaining Profit," pp. 84–85.

[37]Nagle, *Strategy and Tactics of Pricing*, pp. 114–15.

[38]Simon, "Pricing Opportunities," p. 64.

[39]"Sheraton's New Pricing Makes Rivals Cry Foul," *Advertising Age*, May 11, 1992, p. 6.

[40]Michael Porter, *Competitive Strategy* (New York, NY: Free Press, 1980); Joel E. Urbany, "Pricing Strategies and Determination," *Marketing: Best Practices* (Fort Worth, TX: The Dryden Press, 2000), p. 510.

[41]Bob Francis, "Luxury for the Masses," *BrandWeek*, June 25, 2001, pp. 16–20.

[42]Mondello, "Naming Your Price," p. 80.

[43]Doug Carroll, "Price Wars Make Airlines Shrink," *USA Today*, November 24, 1993, p. 18B.

[44]Allan J. McGrath, "Ten Timeless Truths about Pricing," *Journal of Business and Industrial Marketing*, Summer–Fall 1991, p. 17.

[45]Jack Neff, "Value Positioning Becomes a Priority," *Advertising Age*, February 23, 2004, pp. 24–25.

[46]Ralph G. Kauffman, "The Future of Purchasing and Supply: Strategic Cost Management," *Purchasing*, September 1999, pp. 33–35; Leslie Kaufman, "Downscale Moves Up," *Newsweek*, July 27, 1998, pp. 32–33; Zachary Schiller, Greg Burns, and Karen Lowry Miller, "Make It Simple," *BusinessWeek*, September 9, 1996, pp. 96–104.

[47]Raymond Serafin, "U.S. Cars Build Share with Value Pricing," *Advertising Age*, July 12, 1993, p. 4; and Wendy Zeller, "Penney's Rediscovers Its Calling," *BusinessWeek*, April 5, 1993, p. 51.

[48]Donald F. Blurnberg, "What Is Your Service Really Worth?" *Success,* July–August 1992, p. 13.

[49]Robert Hales and David Staley, "Mix Target Costing, QFD for Successful New Products," *Marketing News,* January 2, 1995, p. 18.

[50]David Wessel, "How Technology Tailors Price Tags," *The Wall Street Journal, http://interactive.wjs.com/archive/retrie. . .81676486297602.djm.*

[51]Stephen J. Hoch, Byung-Do Kim, Alan L. Montgomery, and Peter E. Rossi, "Determinants of Store-Level Price Elasticity," *Journal of Marketing Research* 32 (February 1995), pp. 17–29; Barbara E. Kahn and Leigh McAlister, *Grocery Revolution: The Focus on the Consumer* (Reading, MA: Addison-Wesley, 1997), pp. 185–92.

[52]Monroe, *Pricing,* p. 204.

[53]Gerard P. Cachon and Martin A. Lariviere, "Turning the Supply Chain into a Revenue Chain," *Harvard Business Review,* March 2001, pp. 20–21.

[54]Peggy Simpson, "Poles Shop till Prices Drop," *BusinessWeek,* August 19, 1996, p. 4.

[55]Gene Koretz, "Inflation's New Adversary," *BusinessWeek,* October 4, 1999, p. 30.

[56]Makoto Abe, "Behavioral Explanations for Asymmetric Price Competition," Marketing Science Institute, Report no. 98–123 (Cambridge, MA: 1998); George Cressman Jr., "Utility Pricing: It's All in the Packaging," *Marketing News,* May 24, 1999, p. 12; Nikhilm Deogun, "Coke and Pepsi Call Off Pricing Battle," *The Wall Street Journal,* June 12, 1997, p. A3.

[57]Susan M. Broniarczyk and Joseph W. Alba, "The Importance of the Brand in Brand Extension," *Journal of Marketing Research,* May 1994, pp. 214–25. For reviews, see David A. Aaker and Kevin Lane Keller, "Consumer Evaluations of Brand Extensions," *Journal of Marketing,* January 1990, pp. 27–41; and C. Whan Park, Sandra Milberg, and Robert Lawson, "Evaluation of Brand Extensions: The Role of Product Feature Similarity and Brand Concept Consistency," *Journal of Consumer Research,* September 1991, pp. 185–93.

[58]Joseph Weber, "Drug Prices: So Much for Restraint," *BusinessWeek,* March 4, 1996, p. 40.

[59]Christopher Elliott, "Car-Rental Agencies Talk of Realistic 'Total Pricing,'" *The New York Times,* February 10, 2004, p. C7.

[60]Kent B. Monroe and Susan M. Petroshius, "Buyers' Perceptions of Price: An Update of the Evidence," in *Perspectives in Consumer Behavior,* 3rd ed., ed. H. H. Kassarjian and T. S. Robertson (Glenview, IL: Scott, Foresman, 1991), p. 44.

[61]Valarie Zeithaml, "Consumer Perceptions of Price, Quality, and Value: A Means-End Model and Synthesis of Evidence," *Journal of Marketing,* July 1988, p. 10; Peter R. Dickson and Alan G. Sawyer, "The Price Knowledge and Search of Supermarket Shoppers," *Journal of Marketing,* July 1990, pp. 42–53.

[62]Eric V. Roegner, Michael V. Marn, and Craig C. Zawada, "Pricing Gets Creative," *Marketing Management,* January/February 2005, pp. 25–30.

[63]Zeithaml, "Consumer Perceptions," p. 14.

[64]Kent B. Monroe and R. Krishnan, "The Effect of Price on Subjective Product Evaluations," *Perceived Quality: How Consumers View Stores and Merchandise,* ed. Jacob Jacoby and Jerry Olson (Lexington, MA: Lexington Books, 1985), pp. 209–32.

[65]Gary Levin, "Price Rises as Factor for Consumers," *Advertising Age,* November 8, 1993, p. 37.

[66]Leonard Berry, "Strengthening the Service Brand," *Marketing Science Institute Review* (Cambridge, MA: Marketing Science Institute, Spring 1998), p. 4.

[67]Jay E. Klompmaker, William H. Rodgers, and Anthony E. Nygren, "Value, Not Volume," *Marketing Management,* May/June 2004, pp. 45–48.

[68]Robert A. Peterson and William R. Wilson, "Perceived Risk and Price-Reliance Schema and Price–Perceived-Quality Mediators," in *Perceived Quality: How Consumers View Stores and Merchandise,* ed. Jacob Jacoby and Jerry Olson (Lexington, MA: Lexington Books, 1985), pp. 247–68. Studies of firm behavior reveal that pursuit of product-quality strategies can improve profitability and that price and quality are related at the firm level. See Robert Jacobson and David A. Aaker, "The Strategic Role of Product Quality," *Journal of Marketing,* October 1987, pp. 31–44.

[69]Donald R. Lichtenstein and Scot Burton, "The Relationship between Perceived and Objective Price Quality," *Journal of Marketing Research,* November 1989, pp. 429–43.

[70]Gerard J. Tellis and Gary J. Gaeth, "Best Value, Price Seeking, and Price Aversion: The Impact of Information and Learning on Consumer Choices," *Journal of Marketing,* April 1990, pp. 34–45.

[71]Niraj Dawar, "The Signaling Impact of Low Introductory Price on Perceived Quality and Trial," *Marketing Letters* 8, no. 3, p. 252.

[72]Robert Jacobson and Carl Obermiller, "The Formation of Expected Future Price: A Reference Price for Forward-Looking Consumers," *Journal of Consumer Research,* March 1990, p. 421.

[73]Noreen M. Klein and Janet E. Oglethorpe, "Cognitive Reference Points in Consumer Decision Making," in *Advances in Consumer Research,* vol. 14, ed. M. Wallendorf and J. Anderson (Provo, UT: Association for Consumer Research, 1987), pp. 183–97.

[74]Margaret C. Campbell, "Perceptions of Price Unfairness: Antecedents and Consequences," *Journal of Marketing Research* 36 (May 1999), pp. 187–99.

[75]Joel E. Urbany and Peter R. Dickson, *Consumer Knowledge of Consumer Prices: An Exploratory Study and Framework,* Marketing Science Institute, Report no. 90–112 (Cambridge, MA: 1990), p. 18.

[76]Dickson and Sawyer, "Price Knowledge and Search," pp. 42–53.

[77]Kent B. Monroe and Jennifer L. Cox, "Pricing Practices That Endanger Profits," *Marketing Management,* September/October 2001, pp. 42–46.

[78]Aradha Krishna, "Effect of Dealing Patterns on Consumer Perceptions of Deal Frequency and Willingness to Pay," *Journal of Marketing Research,* November 1991, pp. 441–51.

[79]Abhijit Biswas and Edward A. Blair, "Contextual Effects of Reference Prices in Retail Advertisements," *Journal of Marketing,* July 1991, p. 4.

[80]Richard Thaler, "Mental Accounting and Consumer Choice," *Marketing Science,* Summer 1985, pp. 199–214.

[81]Dhruv Grewal, Kent B. Monroe, and R. Krishnan, "The Effects of Price-Comparison Advertising on Buyers' Perceptions of Acquisition Value, Transaction Value, and Behavioral Intentions," *Journal of Marketing* 62 (April 1998), pp. 46–59.

Chapter Twelve

[1]Shantanu Dutta, Mark Bergen, and Mark Zbaracki, "Pricing Process as a Capability," MSI Report No. 01–117 (Cambridge, MA: Marketing Science Institute, 2001).

[2]Tim Matanovich, "The Competitive Advantage," *Marketing Management,* November/December 2004, p. 16.

[3]Harper W. Boyd Jr., Orville C. Walker Jr., John Mulling, and Jean-Clarde Larreche, *Marketing Management: A Strategic Decision-Making Approach,* 4th ed. (New York: McGraw-Hill/Irwin, 2002), p. 283.

[4]Trichy V. Krishnan, Frank M. Bass, and Dipak C. Jain, "Optimal Pricing Strategy for New Products," *Management Science,* December 1999, p. 1650.

[5]Thomas T. Nagle and George E. Cressman Jr., "Don't Just Set Prices, Manage Them," *Marketing Management,* November/December 2002, p. 30.

[6]Allan B. Krueger, "Seven Lessons about Super Bowl Tickets," *The New York Times,* February 1, 2001, p. C2.

[7]Scott C. Friend and Patricia H. Walker, "Welcome to the New World of Merchandising," *Harvard Business Review,* November 2001, p. 134.

[8]Michael Parkin, *Microeconomics,* 2nd ed. (Reading, MA: Addison-Wesley, 1992), p. 109.

[9]Philip Kotler, *Marketing Management: Analysis, Planning, Implementation, and Control,* 8th ed. (Englewood Cliffs, NJ: Prentice Hall, 1994), p. 495.

[10]Tammo H. A. Bijmolt, Harald J. Van Heerde, and Rik G. M. Pieters, "New Empirical Generalizations on the Determinants of Price Elasticity," *Journal of Marketing Research*, May 2005, p. 153.

[11]Rockney G. Walters, "Assessing the Impact of Retail Price Promotions on Product Substitution, Complementary Purchase, and Interstore Sales Displacement," *Journal of Marketing*, April 1991, p. 17.

[12]Paul A. Samuelson and William D. Nordhaus, *Economics*, 14th ed. (New York: McGraw-Hill, 1992), p. 210.

[13]Ford S. Worthy, "Japan's Smart Secret Weapon," *Fortune*, August 12, 1991, pp. 72–73.

[14]Stephan A. Butscher and Michael Laker, "Market-Driven Product Development," *Marketing Management*, Summer 2000, pp. 48–52.

[15]Allen L. Appell, "Income-Based Pricing: An Additional Approach to Teaching the Subject of Pricing in Marketing Courses," *Marketing Education Review* 7 (Summer), pp. 61–64.

[16]Kathleen Seiders and Glenn B. Voss, "From Price to Purchase," *Marketing Management*, November/December 2004, p. 40.

[17]Klaus Wertenbroch and Bernd Skiera, "Measuring Consumer Willingness to Pay at the Point of Purchase," *Journal of Marketing Research*, May 2002, p. 230.

[18]Timothy Matanovich, Gary L. Lilien, and Arvind Rangaswamy, "Engineering the Price–Value Relationship," *Marketing Management*, Spring 1999, pp. 48–53.

[19]The organization and content of this section are based on the typology and discussion of Gerard J. Tellis, "Beyond the Many Faces of Price: An Integration of Pricing Strategies," *Journal of Marketing*, October 1986, pp. 146–60.

[20]Kent B. Monroe, *Pricing: Making Profitable Decisions*, 2nd ed. (New York: McGraw-Hill, 1990), p. 490.

[21]Evan I. Schwartz, *Digital Darwinism: 7 Breakthrough Business Strategies for Surviving in the Cutthroat Web Economy* (New York: Broadway Books, 1999).

[22]Kotler, *Marketing Management*, p. 512.

[23]Gerard J. Tellis and Gary J. Gaeth, "Best Value, Price-Seeking, and Price Aversion: The Impact of Information and Learning on Consumer Choices," *Journal of Marketing*, April 1990, p. 36.

[24]Tellis, "Beyond the Many Faces of Price," p. 153.

[25]Teresa Andreoli, "Value Retailers Take the Low-Income Road to New Heights," *Discount Store News*, February 19, 1996, pp. 1, 19.

[26]Monroe, *Pricing*, p. 304.

[27]John Gourville and Dilip Soman, "Pricing and the Psychology of Consumption," *Harvard Business Review*, September 2002, p. 94.

[28]Stefan Stemersch and Gerard J. Tellis, "Strategic Bundling of Products and Prices: A New Synthesis for Marketing," *Journal of Marketing*, January 2002, p. 57.

[29]David Barboza, "A Weed Killer Is a Block for Monsanto to Build On," *The New York Times*, August 2, 2001, p. C1.

[30]Tim Clark, "Four H-P Success Story Strategies," *Business Marketing*, July 1993, pp. 18, 20.

[31]Normandy Madden and Jack Neff, "P&G Adapts Attitude toward Local Markets," *Advertising Age*, February 23, 2004, p. 28.

[32]Vicki Morwitz, Eric A. Greenleaf, and Eric J. Johnson, "Divide and Prosper: Consumers' Reactions to Partitioned Prices," *Journal of Marketing Research* 35 (November 1998), pp. 453–63.

[33]Eric Anderson and Duncan Simester, "Mind Your Pricing Cues," *Harvard Business Review*, September 2003, p. 99.

[34]Robert Schindler, "How to Advertise Price," in *Attention, Attitude, and Affect in Response to Advertising*, ed. E. M. Clark, T. C. Brock, and D. W. Stewart (Hillsdale, NJ: Lawrence Erlbaum Associates, 1994), pp. 251–69.

[35]"Package Ploy Not Fair Play," *Advertising Age*, May 28, 2001, p. 20; and Sonia Reyes, "Honey, They Shrunk the Bag," *BrandWeek*, October 23, 2000, pp. 1, 60.

[36]Cornelia Pechmann, "Do Consumers Overgeneralize One-Sided Comparative Price Claims, and Are More Stringent Regulations Needed?" *Journal of Marketing Research* 33 (May 1996), pp. 150–62.

[37]Peter M. Noble and Thomas S. Cruca, "Industrial Pricing: Theory and Managerial Practice," *Marketing Science* 18, no. 3 (1999), pp. 435–54.

[38]Bob Donath, "Dispel Major Myths about Pricing Strategy," *Marketing News*, February 3, 2003, p. 10.

[39]Donald V. Potter, "Discovering Hidden Pricing Power," *Business Horizons*, November/December 2000, p. 41.

[40]Dean Forest, Michael Ardnt, Robert Berner, and Amy Barrett, "Raising Price Won't Fly," *BusinessWeek*, June 3, 2002, pp. 34–36.

[41]Kotler, *Marketing Management*, p. 514.

[42]Charles Fishman, "Which Price Is Right?" *Fast Company*, March 2003, p. 94.

[43]Barbara E. Kahn and Leigh McAlister, *Grocery Revolution: New Focus on the Consumer* (Reading, MA: Addison-Wesley, 1997), pp. 69–72.

[44]Robert Berner and William C. Symonds, "Welcome to Procter & Gadget," *BusinessWeek*, February 7, 2005, p. 76.

[45]For research regarding acceptable price limits, see Peter R. Dickson and Alan G. Sawyer, "The Price Knowledge and Search of Supermarket Shoppers," *Journal of Marketing*, July 1990, pp. 42–53; Rustan Kosenko and Don Rahtz, "Buyer Market Price Knowledge on Acceptable Price Range and Price Limits," in *Advances in Consumer Research*, vol. 15, ed. Michael J. Houston (Provo, UT: Association for Consumer Research, 1987), pp. 328–33; and Patricia Sorce and Stanley M. Widrick, "Individual Differences in Latitude of Acceptable Prices," in *Advances in Consumer Research*, vol. 18, ed. Rebecca H. Holman and Michael R. Soloman (Provo, UT: Association for Consumer Research, 1991), pp. 802–5.

[46]Margaret C. Campbell, "Perceptions of Price Unfairness: Antecedents and Consequences," *Journal of Marketing Research* 36 (May 1999), pp. 187–99; Daniel Kahneman, Jack L. Knetsch, and Richard Thaler, "Fairness and the Assumptions of Economics," *Journal of Business* 59, no. 4 (1986), pp. S285–S300; and Wendy Zeller, "Straightened Up and Flying Right," *BusinessWeek*, April 5, 1999, p. 42.

[47]Kate Fitzgerald, "Target Accuses Wal-Mart in Ads," *Advertising Age*, March 29, 1993, pp. 1, 50.

[48]"A Merger's Bitter Harvest," *BusinessWeek*, February 5, 2001, p. 112.

[49]Alan Radding, "Big Blue Takes Aim at Toshiba, Compaq," *Advertising Age*, March 25, 1991, pp. 1, 48; Kathy Rebello and Stephanie Anderson, "They're Slashing as Fast as They Can," *BusinessWeek*, February 17, 1992, p. 40; Hal Lancaster and Michael Allen, "Compaq Computer Finds Itself Where It Once Put IBM," *The Wall Street Journal*, January 13, 1992, p. B4.

[50]Kathleen Madigan, Joseph Weber, and Geoffrey Smith, "The Latest Mad Plunge of the Price Slashers," *BusinessWeek*, May 11, 1992, p. 36.

[51]Akshay R. Rao, Mark E. Bergen, and Scott Davis, "How to Fight a Price War," *Harvard Business Review*, March–April 2000, p. 109; Mike Troy, "Kmart: Drop EDLP and Continue Promoting the Value Message," *Dsn Retailing Today*, March 11, 2002, p. 33.

[52]Robert C. Blattberg, Richard Briesch, and Edward J. Fox, "How Promotions Work," *Marketing Science* 14, no. 3, pp. G123–4.

[53]Michael J. Zenor, Bart J. Bronnenberg, and Leigh McAlister, *The Impact of Marketing Policy on Promotional Price Elasticities and Baseline Sales*, Marketing Science Institute, Report no. 98–101 (Cambridge, MA: 1998).

[54]Hugh M. Cannon and Fred W. Morgan, "A Strategic Pricing Framework," *Journal of Business and Industrial Marketing*, Summer–Fall 1991, p. 62.

[55]Monroe, *Pricing*, p. 427.

[56]Michael L. Mellot, "Systematic Approach to Pricing Increases Profits," *Marketing News*, May 24, 1993, p. 3.

[57]"Going, Going, Gone! The B2B Tool That Really Is Changing the World," *Fortune*, March 20, 2000, pp. 132–45.

[58]Jim Hansen, "Fees for Loans: Just Part of the Marketing Equation," *Credit Union Executive*, November–December 1992, pp. 42–45; Clifford

L. Ratza, "A Client-Driven Model for Service Pricing," *Journal of Professional Services Marketing* 8, no. 2 (1993), pp. 55–64; Madhav N. Segal, "An Empirical Investigation of the Pricing of Professional Services," *Journal of Professional Services Marketing,* 1991, pp. 169–81.

[59]Tim Matanovich, "Pricing Services vs. Pricing Products," *Marketing Management,* July/August 2003, pp. 12–13.

[60]Joseph P. Guiltinan, "The Price Bundling of Services: A Normative Framework," *Journal of Marketing,* April 1987, p. 74.

[61]Russell G. Bundschuh and Theodore M. Dezvane, "How to Make After Sales Services Pay Off," *The McKinsey Quarterly* no. 4 (September 2003), p. 1.

[62]Zachary Schiller, Susan Garland, and Julia Flynn Siler, "The Humana Flap Could Make All Hospitals Feel Sick," *BusinessWeek,* November 4, 1991, p. 34.

[63]Gwendolyn K. Ortmeyer, "Ethical Issues in Pricing," in *Ethics in Marketing,* ed. N. Craig Smith and John A. Quelch (Homewood, IL: Richard D. Irwin, 1993), p. 401; Andrea Rothman, "The Airlines Get Out the Good China," *BusinessWeek,* February 3, 1992, p. 66.

[64]Marc Rice, "Profiteering Claimed as Wood Prices Rise," *The Commercial Appeal,* August 28, 1992, pp. B4–B5; "Home Depot Offers Storm Victims Break," *The Commercial Appeal,* August 29, 1992, p. B4.

[65]*Code of Federal Regulations,* 16, 233.0 FTC, Office of the Federal Register, National Archives and Records Administration, Washington, DC, pp. 26–30.

[66]"News Release," Colorado Department of Law, Attorney General, June 21, 1989, pp. 2–3.

[67]Dan Morse, "Breakthrough Product Visits Funeral Homes," *The Wall Street Journal,* January 7, 2000, p. A1.

[68]Nagle, *Strategy and Tactics of Pricing,* p. 324.

[69]Adam Bryant, "Aisle Seat Bully," *Newsweek,* May 24, 1999, p. 56; Anna Wilde Mathews and Scott McCartney, "U.S. Sues American Air in Antitrust Case," *The Wall Street Journal,* May 15, 1999, pp. A3, A6; Wendy Zeller, "Straightened Up and Flying Right," *BusinessWeek,* April 5, 1999, p. 42.

[70]Ortmeyer, "Ethical Issues in Pricing," pp. 396–97.

Chapter Thirteen

[1]Adapted from Peter D. Bennett, ed., *Dictionary of Marketing Terms,* 2nd ed. (Chicago: American Marketing Association, 1995), p. 167.

[2]Information from National Presto Industries Inc. overview on Hoover's Online at *www.hoovers.com,* May 16, 2005.

[3]Nanette Byrnes, Robert Berner, Wendy Zellner, and William C. Symonds, "Branding: Five New Lessons," *BusinessWeek,* February 14, 2005, pp. 26–28; Anthony Bianco and Wendy Zellner, "Is Wal-Mart Too Powerful?" *BusinessWeek,* October 6, 2003, pp. 101–110; and "In Hollywood, Best Buy Calls the Shots," *Fortune,* November 29, 2004, p. 56.

[4]Information from Building Materials Distributors' Web site at *www.bmdusa.com,* May 16, 2005.

[5]Kevin Coupe, "No April Fool's for Fleming: It Files for Bankruptcy, Deals with Repercussions," as published at *www.morningnewsbeat.com,* April 2, 2003.

[6]Information from SUPERVALU Inc. overview on Hoover's Online at *www.hooversonline.com,* May 16, 2005.

[7]Bennett, *Dictionary of Marketing Terms,* p. 300.

[8]Bridget Finn, "A More Profitable Harvest," *Business 2.0,* May 2005, pp. 66–67.

[9]Phillip Britt, "Manufacturing Builds on Customer Relationships," *Customer Relationship Management,* May 2005, pp. 44–49.

[10]"Lexus Brand Marketing Case," from Persona Web site at *www.personako.com,* May 17, 2005; "The Lexus Covenant" from the Lexus Web site at *www.lexus.com,* May 17, 2005.

[11]Marcia Savage, "McAfee Gives Channel a Lift," *CRN,* February 4, 2002, p. 8.

[12]"In Bow to Retailers' New Clout, Levi Strauss Makes Alterations," *The Wall Street Journal,* June 17, 2004, pp. A1, A15.

[13]Elizabeth Souder, "Independence Air Tests Direct Sales," *The Wall Street Journal,* July 21, 2004, p. B2.

[14]Betsy McKay, "Coke Reaches Pact with Danone for U.S. Distribution of Evian," *The Wall Street Journal,* April 26, 2002, p. B4.

[15]Information from Amazon.com Web site at *www.amazon.com,* May 18, 2005.

[16]Jordan Robertson, "Toe the Line between Corporate and Cool," *Business 2.0,* November 2004, p. 86.

[17]Matthew Haeberle, "An Industry Changes Its Tune," *Chain Store Age,* February 2005, pp. 38–39.

[18]Information from the AutoNation Web site at *www.corp.autonation.com,* May 18, 2005.

[19]Ronald Grover, "Cinema Scope: DVDs at ATMs," *BusinessWeek,* May 23, 2005, p. 14.

[20]"Investment Guide 2005 20 Best Bargains: Tupperware," *Fortune,* December 27, 2004, p. 37.

[21]Elizabeth Montalbano, "Sun Engages Channel," *CRN,* May 16, 2005, p. 5.

[22]Steven Burke, "Thumbs Up for IBM, Cisco, Sony," from the April 22, 2005, issue of *CRN Magazine,* posted online at *www.crn.com,* accessed May 17, 2005.

[23]The types of power discussed in this section can be traced back to John French Jr. and Bertram Raven, "The Bases of Social Power," in *Studies in Social Power,* ed. D. Cartwright (Ann Arbor, MI: University of Michigan Press, 1959), pp. 150–67.

[24]Betsy McKay and David Luhnow, "Mexico Finds Coke and Its Bottlers Guilty of Abusing Dominant Position in Market," *The Wall Street Journal,* March 8, 2002, p. B3.

[25]Anne Dinnocenzio, "Apparel Suppliers, Retailers Spar over Finances," *The Coloradoan,* April 24, 2005, p. E3.

[26]Shelly Branch, "Hershey Turns to Convenience Stores to Sweeten Revenue," *The Wall Street Journal,* March 29, 2002, p. B4.

Chapter Fourteen

[1]*Statistical Abstract of the United States* (Washington, D.C.: U.S. Department of Commerce, 2001), p. 480.

[2]Tenisha Mercer, "Kohl's Takes Page from Rivals' Expansion Playbook," *The Coloradoan,* May 1, 2005, p. E1.

[3]Parija Bhatnagar, "Wal-Mart, the Bank?" from CNN Web site at *www.money.cnn.com,* January 26, 2005.

[4]Bruce Horowitz, "A Whole New Ballgame in Grocery Shopping," *USA TODAY,* March 9, 2005, pp. 1–2B.

[5]Information from Mall of America's Web site at *www.mallofamerica.com,* May 24, 2005.

[6]Information from *www.franchiseinfomall.com,* May 24, 2005.

[7]*McDonald's Annual Report: 2004,* available online at *www.mcdonalds.com,* May 23, 2005.

[8]Information from *www.franchiseinfomall.com,* May 24, 2005.

[9]Information from *Entrepreneur* magazine Web site at *www.entrepreneur.com/franzone,* May 10, 2005.

[10]Information from *www.franchiseinfomall.com,* May 23, 2005.

[11]Mya Frazier, "New JCPenney CEO Announces Five-Year Re-Invigoration Plan," from *Advertising Age* Web site at *www.adage.com,* April 25, 2005; and Dan Scheraga, "Sounds Like a Plan," *Chain Store Age,* March 2005, pp. 65–66.

[12]Bruce Horowitz and Lorrie Grant, "Changes in Store for Department Stores?" *USA TODAY,* January 21, 2005, pp. 1–2B; Julie Schlosser, "Federated's 76-Year Shopping Spree," *Fortune,* March 21, 2005, p. 36; John Eckberg, "Federated Plans to Buy May for $11B," *USA TODAY,* February 28, 2005, p. 1B.

[13]Information from Carrefour's Web site at *www.carrefour.com,* May 20, 2005.

[14]"U.S. Cities Set Up Wireless Networks," furnished by Reuters as posted on the CNN Web site at *www.cnn.com,* May 24, 2005.

[15]"100 Best Companies to Work For," *Fortune,* January 24, 2005, p. 60; information from The Container Store Web site at *www.containerstore. com,* May 26, 2005.

[16]Stan Rapp, "Getting the Words Right," *Direct,* July 1993, p. 98.

[17]Information from the Direct Marketing Association Web site at *www.the-dma.org,* May 17, 2005.

[18]Louise Lee, "Retail: There Goes the Gravy Train," *BusinessWeek Online,* January 10, 2005, at *www.businessweek.com.*

[19]"The Multi-Channel Retail Report," from *www.shop.org/research/ tmcrr2.html,* June 13, 2002.

[20]"The Multi-Channel Retail Report."

[21]Information from Yahoo! Web site at *www.smallbusiness.yahoo.com/ merchant,* May 24, 2005.

[22]Information from the Direct Selling Association Web site at *www.dsa. org,* May 24, 2005.

[23]Ibid.

[24]Information from the National Automatic Merchandising Association Web site at *www.vending.org,* May 15, 2005.

[25]Julia Borstin, "Mickey Drexler's Second Coming," *Fortune,* May 2, 2005, pp. 101–4.

[26]Kathleen Hickey, "Radio Shack's Supply Chain Tune-Up," *Inbound Logistics,* November 2004, pp. 55–61; and information from Radio Shack Web site at *www.corporate-ir.net/ireye/,* May 24, 2005.

[27]Kirsten Orsini-Meinhard, "New Day, New Dollar Store," *The Coloradoan,* February 21, 2005, p. E1.

[28]Connie Robbins Gentry, "Small Chains with Big Growth Plans," *Chain Store Age,* March 2005, pp. 121–24.

[29]Information from Amazon.com's Web site at *www.amazon.com,* May 9, 2005.

[30]Information from the National Association of Convenience Stores Web site at *www.nacsonline.com/NACS/News/,* May 24, 2005.

[31]Ibid.

[32]Noah Rothaum, "Unhappy Returns," *Smart Money,* January 2005, p. 109; and Barney Gimbel, "Sorry. Your Return Is No Good Here," *Fortune,* October 6, 2004, p. 16.

[33]Aaron Bernstein, "A Major Swipe at Sweatshops," *BusinessWeek,* May 23, 2005, pp. 98–100; David J. Lynch, "Cambodia's Sales Pitch: Sweatshop-Free Products," *USA TODAY,* April 4, 2005, pp. 1–2B.

[34]"Retail Theft and Inventory Shrinkage," from About.com Web site at *www.retailindustry.com/od/statistics_loss_prevention,* May 16, 2005.

[35]Stephen Bitsoli, "The Practice and Money behind Displaying Goods," *The Macomb Daily,* December 12, 1999, p. 1C; and Paul N. Bloom, Gregory T. Gundlach, and Joseph P. Cannon, *Slotting Allowances and Fees: Schools of Thought and the Views of Practicing Managers,* Marketing Science Institute working paper no. 99-106 (1999).

[36]Julie Forster, "The Hidden Cost of Shelf Space," *BusinessWeek,* April 15, 2002, p. 103.

[37]Marianne Wilson, "Taking the LEED," *Chain Store Age,* March 2005, pp. 45–52.

[38]Information from Home Depot's Web site at *www.homedepot.com,* May 24, 2005.

Chapter Fifteen

[1]*1997 Economic Census of Wholesale Trade, summary section* (Washington, DC: U.S. Census Bureau), pp. 7–24.

[2]Alex Halperin, "Going, Going, Gone Online," *The Wall Street Journal,* May 25, 2005, p. D12; information from eBay Web site at *www.eBay.com,* May 27, 2005.

[3]Erick Schonfeld, "The World According to eBay," *Business 2.0,* January/ February 2005, pp. 79–84.

[4]Information from DoveBid's Web site at *www.dovebid.com,* May 27, 2005.

[5]"Office Depot Expands Its Successful European Services Division into Germany," *Business Wire,* June 24, 2002, as presented at Hoover's Online at *www.hoovers.com;* and information from Office Depot's Web site at *www.officedepot.com,* May 29, 2005.

[6]Information from Ingram Micro's Web site at *www.ingrammicro.com,* May 29, 2005.

[7]Jenny McTaggart, "The A-Team," *Progressive Grocer,* February 1, 2005, pp. 42–45.

[8]Lisa Harrington, "Small Companies Take on the World," *Inbound Logistics,* March 2005, pp. 43–49.

[9]Peter D. Bennett, ed., *Dictionary of Marketing Terms* (Chicago: American Marketing Association, 1998), p. 213.

[10]"Integrating Warehouses: A Game Like No Other," *Inbound Logistics,* January 2002, pp. 194–98.

[11]"Logistics Planner 2005: Big Dog Logistics," from *Inbound Logistics* Web site at *www.inboundlogistics.com,* May 27, 2005.

[12]Mark Roberti, "Your Inventory Wants to Talk to You," *Business 2.0,* May 2002, pp. 84–87.

[13]"Xicor Enables Centralized Worldwide Sales and Order-Tracking Process with Acom's Solution: EZConnect for EDI-XML," from Acom Solution's Web site at *www.acom.com,* May 27, 2005.

[14]Amy Tsao, "Where Retailers Shop for Savings," *BusinessWeek Online,* at *www.businessweek.com/technology/,* April 15, 2002.

[15]James Cooke, "EDI-Electronic Data Interchange, What Lies Ahead . . ." *Modern Materials Handling,* March 2002, pp. 59–61; James Cooke, "Is XML the Next Big Thing?" *Logistics Management & Distribution Report,* May 2002, p. 53.

[16]Chris Woodyard, "Ford to Bail Out Parts Supplier," *USA TODAY,* May 26, 2005, p. 1B.

[17]Information from the Association of American Railroads Web site at *www.aar.org,* May 29, 2005.

[18]Dean Foust and Michael Eidam, "Transport: Putting the Pedal to the Metal," *BusinessWeek Online,* January 10, 2005, at *www.businessweek. com;* "Truck-Driver Shortage Worsens," from the *Railway Age* magazine Web site at *www.railwayage.com/breaking_news.shtml,* May 29, 2005.

[19]Information from the Association of American Railroads Web site at *www.aar.org,* May 29, 2005.

[20]Robert Block, "In Terrorism Fight, Government Finds a Surprising Ally: FedEx," *The Wall Street Journal,* May 26, 2005, pp. A1, A5.

[21]Joseph O'Reilly, "Seeing Green," *Inbound Logistics,* January 2005, pp. 199–208.

[22]"Railroads Go Green," from the *Railway Age* magazine Web site at *www.railwayage.com/breaking_news.shtml,* May 29, 2005.

Chapter Sixteen

[1]Chris Woodyard, "Outside-the-Box Scion Scores with Young Drivers," *USA Today,* May 2, 2005, p. 1B.

[2]Dana James, "Cricket Plans Nationally, Acts Locally," *Marketing News,* May 13, 2002, pp. 5–6.

[3]Jeremy Smith, "European Union Blackens Smoking's Image," *USA Today,* May 31, 2005, p. 6D.

[4]Ken Belson, "Verizon Wireless Makes an Appeal to Rival's Subscribers," from the online version of *The New York Times* at *www.nytimes.com,* November 12, 2004.

[5]Examples of ads from the Partnership for a Drug-Free America as presented at *www.mediacampaign.org,* May 31, 2005.

[6]Information from *Advertising Age* Web sites at *www.adage.com,* May 1, 2005.

[7]George E. Belch and Michael A. Belch, *Introduction to Advertising and Promotion: An Integrated Marketing Communications Perspective,* 5th ed. (New York: McGraw-Hill/Irwin, 2001), p. 21.

[8]Tom Duncan, *Principles of Advertising and IMC,* 2nd ed. (New York: McGraw-Hill/Irwin, 2005), p. 464.

[9]Don E. Schultz, "New Media, Old Problem: Keeping Marcom Integrated," *Marketing News,* March 25, 1999, p. 12.

[10]Rich Thomaselli, "NBA Eyes Sale of Advertising Space on Uniforms," from *Advertising Age* Web site at *www.adage.com,* May 26, 2005.

[11]Thomas Mucha, "Luring Gamers Like Bees to Honey," *Business 2.0,* January/February 2005, p. 62.

[12]Brad Stone, "No Place Left to Hide," *Newsweek,* May 2005, p. E32; Merissa Marr, "Fox to Pitch Movies at the Mall," *The Wall Street Journal,* July 15, 2004; Justin Dickerson, "Tattoos Quickly Becoming the Latest Form of Advertising," *The Coloradoan,* March 10, 2005, p. B7; "Wyoming Man Offers Ads on Mud Flaps," *The Coloradoan,* January 9, 2005, p. E4.

[13]T. Bettina Cornwell, "Sponsorship-Linked Marketing Development," *Sport Marketing Quarterly* 4, no. 4 (1995), pp. 13–24.

[14]Lesa Ukman, "Naming Rights: Not Just for Stadiums Anymore," from the IEG Inc. Web site at *www.sponsorship.com,* May 30, 2005.

[15]"How Sponsorship's Growth Compares to Advertising and Sales Promotion," from the IEG Inc. Web site at *www.sponsorship.com,* May 30, 2005.

[16]Barry Janoff, "Ford Pumps Ironman Circuit," from the online version of *Brandweek* at *www.brandweek.com,* May 31, 2005; Michael McCarthy, "Ford Joins Forces with Ironman for Tough Sell," *USA Today,* May 19, 2005, p. 3B; and information from Ford Motor Company Web site at *www.media.ford.com,* May 31, 2005.

[17]Rich Thomaselli, "Coke Ponies Up $500 Million for NCAA," from the *Advertising Age* Web site at *www.adage.com,* June 28, 2002.

[18]"China Bans James Ad, Says It Insults Dignity," *USA Today,* December 7, 2004, p. 12C.

[19]Rukmini Callimachi, "Nike's Controversial Ads in Asia; Faux Pas or Score?" *USA Today,* December 9, 2004, p. 4B.

[20]Kate McArthur, "Wendy's Overhauls Marketing Strategies," from *Advertising Age* Web site at *www.adage.com,* May 20, 2005.

[21]Geoffrey A. Fowler, "Shoppers Choose Convenience over Ecological Benefits; Landfills Piled with Plastic," *The Wall Street Journal,* March 6, 2002, pp. B1, B4.

[22]Kipp Cheng, "Mixed Messages: How Ethnic Ads Succeed With, Then Transcend, Niche Markets," from Diversity Inc. Web site at *www.diversityinc.com,* May 8, 2002.

[23]Kipp Cheng, "Does Diversity-Conscious Advertising Prove a Diversity Commitment?" from Diversity Inc. Web site at *www.diversity.com,* May 14, 2002.

[24]Cheng, "Mixed Messages."

[25]Mark Hyman, "Branding the Course," *BusinessWeek,* May 30, 2005, pp. 97–100.

[26]George S. Low and Jakki J. Mohr, *Brand Managers' Perceptions of the Marketing Communications Budget Allocation Process,* Marketing Science Institute (Cambridge, MA: 1998), pp. 35–38.

[27]Dagmar Mussey, "Mars Goes Local," from the global section of the *Advertising Age* Web site at *www.adageglobal.com,* June 28, 2002.

[28]Vanessa O'Connell, "Drug Czar Says Ad Campaign Has Flopped," *The Wall Street Journal,* May 11, 2002, pp. B1, B10.

[29]Stephanie Clifford, "Most Bang for the Buck," *Business 2.0,* May 2002, p. 102.

[30]Information from Target's Web site at *www.target.com,* May 31, 2005.

[31]David Kiley, "A Green Flag for Booze," *BusinessWeek,* March 7, 2005, p. 95.

[32]Chris Jenkins, "Hard Liquor Ads Get Green Flag from NASCAR," *USA Today,* November 10, 2004, p. 12C.

[33]Kiley, "A Green Flag for Booze."

[34]Ann Zimmerman and David Armstrong, "FTC Asked to Study Promotion of More Costly Brands of Drugs," *The Wall Street Journal,* May 6, 2002, p. B6.

[35]Julie Schmit, "FDA Races to Keep Up with Drug Ads That Go Too Far," from *USA Today* Web site at *www.usatoday.com,* May 31, 2005.

[36]Julie Schmit, "Drugmakers Likely to Lob Softer Pitches," from *USA Today* Web site at *www.usatoday.com,* March 17, 2005.

[37]"Bogus Weight Loss Products Do Not Work," from the Federal Trade Commission Web site at *www.ftc.gov/opa/2005/05/selfworx.htm,* June 1, 2005.

[38]"FTC Flexes Its Muscle in Ab Energizer Case," from the Federal Trade Commission Web site at *www.ftc.gov/opa/2005/04/abenergizer.htm,* June 1, 2005; and "Defective HIV Kit Marketer Settles FTC Charges," from the Federal Trade Commission Web site at *www.ftc.gov/opa/2005/06/seville.htm,* June 1, 2005.

[39]For more on deceptive advertising, see the Better Business Bureau site at *www.bbb.org,* and the Federal Trade Commission site at *www.ftc.gov.*

[40]"Guidance for Food Advertising Self-Regulation," published by the National Advertising Review Council, available on the Children's Advertising Review Unit (CARU) Web site at *www.caru.org,* June 1, 2005.

Chapter Seventeen

[1]Charles H. Patti and Charles F. Frazer, *Advertising: A Decision-Making Approach* (Chicago: Dryden Press, 1988), p. 4.

[2]Laurie Petersen, "A Short-Sighted View of Advertising," *Adweek's Marketing Week,* November 11, 1991, p. 9.

[3]John Kenneth Galbraith, "Economics and Advertising: Exercise in Denial," *Advertising Age,* November 9, 1988, p. 81.

[4]John Deighton, Caroline M. Henderson, and Scott A. Nelson, "The Effects of Advertising on Brand Switching and Repeat Purchasing," *Journal of Marketing Research,* February 1994, p. 28.

[5]Amit Joshi and Dominique Hanssens, "Advertising Spending and Marketing Capitalization," MSI Report No. 04-110 (Cambridge, MA: Marketing Science Institute), pp. 1–15.

[6]Dana L. Alden, Jan-Benedict E. M. Steenkamp, and Rajeev Batra, "Brand Positioning through Advertising in Asia, North America, and Europe: The Role of Global Consumer Culture," *Journal of Marketing,* January 1999, pp. 75–87.

[7]"Top 200 Brands," *Advertising Age,* May 6, 1996, p. 34.

[8]Dean M. Krugman and Roland T. Rust, "The Impact of Cable and VCR Penetration on Network Viewing: Assessing the Decade," *Journal of Advertising Research,* January–February 1993, pp. 67–73; Joe Mandese, "Nets Get Less for More," *Advertising Age,* March 2, 1992, p. 1.

[9]Mel Mandell, "Getting the Word Out," *World Trade,* November 1993, p. 30.

[10]Frederik Balfour and David Kiley, "Ad Agencies Unchained," *BusinessWeek,* April 25, 2005, pp. 50–51.

[11]Iris Cohen Selinger, "Big Profits, Risks with Incentive Fees," *Advertising Age,* May 15, 1995, p. 3; Mark Gleason, "Driver's Mart Pacing Agency Pay to Sales," *Advertising Age,* May 6, 1996, p. 3.

[12]Paul Allen, "New Ad Agency Model Needed to Cope with Info Overload," *Marketing News,* August 31, 1998, p. 4; Sarah Lorge, "Paying Ad Agencies Their Due," *Sales & Marketing Management,* November 1999, p. 13; Daniel McGinn, "Pour on the Pitch," *Newsweek,* May 31, 1999, pp. 5–51.

[13]Robert Berner, "How Unilever Scored with Young Guys," *BusinessWeek,* May 23, 2005, p. 39.

[14]Allan J. Magrath, "The Death of Advertising Has Been Greatly Exaggerated," *Sales & Marketing Management,* February 1992, p. 23.

[15]Sergey Frank, "Avoiding the Pitfalls of Business Abroad," *Sales & Marketing Management,* March 1992, p. 57.

[16]James M. Kolts, "Adaptive Marketing," *Journal of Consumer Marketing,* Summer 1990, pp. 39–40.

[17]C. Anthony Di Benedetto, Marik Tamate, and Rajan Chandran, "Developing Creative Advertising Strategy for the Japanese Marketplace," *Journal of Advertising Research,* January–February 1992, pp. 39–48.

[18]Fred S. Zufryden, James H. Pendrick, and Avu Sankaralingam, "Zapping and Its Impact on Brand Purchase Behavior," *Journal of Advertising Research,* January–February 1993, p. 58.

[19]Joanne Lipman, "TV Ad Deals to Set Big Price Increases," *The Wall Street Journal,* June 25, 1992, p. B8.

[20]Judith Waldrap, "And Now a Break from Our Sponsor," *American Demographics,* August 1993, pp. 16–18.

[21]Michael Krauss, "Television Advertising in a Time of TiVo," *Marketing News,* January 6, 2003, p. 4.

[22]Amy Harmon, "Skip-the-Ads TV Has Madison Ave. Upset," *The New York Times,* May 23, 2002, pp. A1, C3.

[23]Dana Wechsler Linden and Vicki Contavespi, "Media Wars," *Forbes,* August 19, 1991, p. 38.

[24]"Numbers Game," *Marketing Management,* April 2005, p. 7.

[25]Michael Krauss, "Google Changes the Context of Advertising," *Marketing News,* June 1, 2004, p. 6.

[26]Lauren Gard, "The Business of Blogging," *BusinessWeek,* December 13, 2004, pp. 118–19.

[27]David Kiley, "New Generations Steal the Show," *BusinessWeek,* January 10, 2005, pp. 118–19.

[28]John Gaffney, "The Online Advertising Comeback," *Business 2.0,* June 2002, pp. 118–19; Sandeep Krishnamurthy, "Deciphering the Internet Advertising Puzzle," *Marketing Management,* Fall 2000, pp. 35–39; "Looking beyond Banner Ads to Revive Web Advertising," *The Wall Street Journal,* February 26, 2001, www.djinteractive.com; Lynda Richardson, "Window Seat," *AdWeek,* July 23, 2001, p. 15; Hillary Rosner, "Reality Check," *AdWeek,* February 4, 2002, pp. IQ9–Q11; Deborah Szynal, "Next Step in Taming Net Frontier," *Marketing News,* March 4, 2002, p. 4; Deborah L. Venice, "B-to-C Advertisers Learn Online Tricks from Biz Colleagues," *Marketing News,* June 24, 2002, p. 4.

[29]William F. Arens and Courtland L. Bovée, *Contemporary Advertising,* 5th ed. (Burr Ridge, IL: Richard D. Irwin, 1994), p. 8.

[30]Peggy Conlon, "Letter from the President," *AdWeek,* June 10, 2002, p. 24.

[31]Jim Garner, "Sneakers, Soap, and Semiconductors," *Marketing News,* March 1, 1999, p. 55; Bob Lamons, "Resolve to Promote Your Firm's Brand Image in the New Millennium," *Marketing News,* January 17, 2000, p. 4.

[32]Bob Lamons, "The Brand Battlefield Resides in the Customers' Minds," *Marketing News,* January 15, 2004, p. 8.

[33]Richard Brunelli, "B2B and Beyond," *Trade Media,* May 7, 2001, pp. SR14–SR15; Bob Lamons, "Tips for Distinguishing Your Ads from Bad Ads," *Marketing News,* November 19, 2001, p. 10; Mark McMaster, "Advertising B-to-B Brands on TV," *Sales and Marketing Management,* November 2001, p. 11.

[34]Catherine Arnold, "Cooperative Effort," *Marketing News,* March 3, 2003, p. 4.

[35]Scott B. MacKenzie, "The Role of Attention in Mediating the Effect of Advertising on Attribute Importance," *Journal of Consumer Research,* September 1986, pp. 174–95.

[36]Rik Pieters and Michel Wedel, "Attention Capture and Transfer in Advertising: Brand, Pictorial, and Text-Size Effects," *Journal of Marketing,* April 2004, p. 48.

[37]Demetrios Vakratsas and Tim Ambler, "How Advertising Works: What Do We Really Know," *Journal of Marketing,* January 1999, pp. 26–43.

[38]Ibid.

[39]Deborah J. MacInnis, Christine Moorman, and Bernard J. Jaworski, "Enhancing and Measuring Consumers' Motivation, Opportunity, and Ability to Process Brand Information from Ads," *Journal of Marketing,* October 1991, pp. 32–53.

[40]Robert J. Kent, "Competitive Interference Effects in Consumer Memory for Advertising: The Role of Brand Familiarity," *Journal of Marketing,* July 1994, pp. 97–105.

[41]James F. Engel, Roger D. Blackwell, and Paul W. Miniard, *Consumer Behavior,* 7th ed. (Fort Worth, TX: Dryden Press, 1993), p. 277.

[42]Richard E. Petty, John T. Cacioppo, and David Schumann, "Central and Peripheral Routes to Advertising Effectiveness: The Moderating Role of Involvement," *Journal of Consumer Research* 10 (September 1983), pp. 135–46.

[43]Jeff Manning and Kevin Lane Keller, "Got Advertising That Works," *Marketing Management,* January/February 2004, pp. 16–20.

[44]Seema Nayyar and Jennifer Lach, "We're Being Watched," *American Demographics,* October 1998, pp. 53–58; Bill Stoneman, "Beyond Rocking the Ages," *American Demographics,* May 1998, pp. 45–49.

[45]Stuart Elliot, "A Wave of Spending to Try to Restore Aging Brands," *The New York Times,* November 12, 2004, p. C6.

[46]Don E. Schultz, "Make Communications Worth the Profits," *Marketing News,* January 15, 2001, p. 13.

[47]Joann Lublin, "As VCRs Advance, Agencies Fear TV Viewers Will Zap More Ads," *The Wall Street Journal,* January 4, 1991, p. B3.

[48]Deborah L. Vence, "Ad Campaign, Simplicity Drive Sales of Apple iPod," *Marketing News,* December 15, 2004, p. 16.

[49]Tom Dougherty, "Create Great Advertising for the Millennium," *Marketing News,* March 15, 1999, p. 2; Jean Halliday, "Chrysler Officials Admit to Flubbing the Intrepid Relaunch," *Advertising Age,* June 18, 1998, p. 10; George F. Will, "The Perils of Brushing," *Newsweek,* May 10, 1999, p. 92.

[50]Sandra Dolbow, "Levi's Leaning on Past Tactics to Design Jean Maker's Future," *BrandWeek,* June 24, 2002, p. 9.

[51]Gary T. Ford, Darlene B. Smith, and John L. Swasy, "Consumer Skepticism of Advertising Claims: Testing Hypotheses from Economics of Information," *Journal of Consumer Research,* March 1990, pp. 433–41.

[52]Brian Wansik and Michael L. Ray, "Advertising Strategies to Increase Usage Frequencies," *Journal of Marketing,* January 1996, pp. 31–46.

[53]Ajay Karla and Ronald C. Goodstein, "The Impact of Advertising Positioning Strategies on Consumer Price Sensitivity," *Journal of Marketing Research,* May 1998, pp. 210–24.

[54]Thomas E. Barry, "Comparative Advertising: What Have We Learned in Two Decades?" *Journal of Advertising Research,* March–April 1993, p. 20.

[55]Daniel Golden and Suzanne Vranica, "Duracell's Duck Ad Will Carry Disclaimer," *The Wall Street Journal,* February 7, 2002, p. B7.

[56]Ad-Vantage: The Williams Sisters, *BusinessWeek,* February 5, 2001, p. 71.

[57]Arlene Weintraub, "Marketing Champ of the World," *BusinessWeek,* December 20, 2004, pp. 64–65.

[58]"Humor Remains Top Tool for Ad Campaign," *USA Today,* September 30, 1996, p. 3B.

[59]Adrienne Carter, "Making Lite of the King," *BusinessWeek,* March 28, 2005, p. 105: Josephine L. C. M. Woltman Elpers, Ashesh Mukerjee, and Wayne Hoyer, "Humor in Television Advertising: A Moment-to-Moment Advertising," *Journal of Consumer Research,* December 2004, pp. 592–98.

[60]Timothy E. Moore, "Subliminal Advertising: What You See Is What You Get," *Journal of Marketing,* Spring 1982, pp. 27–47; Terence A. Shimp, *Advertising, Promotion, and Supplemental Aspects of Integrated Marketing Communications,* 4th ed. (Fort Worth, TX: Dryden Press, 1997), pp. 310–12.

[61]Scott Donaten, "Advertorials Are Like a Drug," *Advertising Age,* March 9, 1992, p. S16.

[62]Ronald Grover and Gerry Khermouch, "The Trouble with Tie-Ends," *BusinessWeek,* June 3, 2002, p. 63.

[63]David Leonhardt, Peter Burrows, and Bill Vlasic, "Cue the Soda Can," *BusinessWeek,* June 24, 1996, pp. 64–65.

[64]Don E. Schultz, "Big Marketing Firms Try 'Reversing Flow' as a Way to Fix Marcom," *Marketing News,* November 15, 2004, p. 7.

[65]"Stiff Competition," *Marketing News,* December 15, 2005, p. 9.

[66]Alison Stein Wellner, "The Female Persuasion," *American Demographics,* February 2002, pp. 24–29.

[67]Brad Edmonson, "In the Driver's Seat," *American Demographics,* March 1998, pp. 46–52.

[68]Deborah Vence, "Shed Some Light," *Marketing News,* September 15, 2004, p. 11.

[69]Constance Hayes, "Wal-Mart Is Upgrading Its Vast In-Store Television Network," *The New York Times,* February 21, 2005, p. C1.

[70]Giles D'Souza and Ram C. Rao, "Can Repeating an Advertisement More Frequently Than the Competition Affect Brand Preference in a Mature Market?" *Journal of Marketing,* April 1995, p. 39.

[71]Vicki R. Lane, "The Impact of Ad Repetition and Ad Content on Consumer Perceptions of Incongruent Extensions," *Journal of Marketing,* April 2000, pp. 80–91.

[72]Joe Mandese, "Revisiting Ad Reach, Frequency," *Advertising Age,* November 27, 1995, p. 46.

[73]Gerard J. Tellis, "Effective Frequency: One Exposure or Three Factors," *Journal of Advertising Research,* July–August 1997, pp. 75–80.

[74]Leonard M. Lodish, et al., "How TV Advertising Works: A Meta-Analysis of 389 Real World Split Cable TV Advertising Experiments," *Journal of Marketing Research,* May 1995, p. 138.

[75]Dwight R. Riskey, "How TV Advertising Works: An Industry Response," *Journal of Marketing Research,* May 1997, pp. 202–3.

[76]Chris Grindem, "The Whole Truth," *AdWeek,* June 24, 2002, p. 16.

[77]Diane Brady and David Kiley, "Making Marketing Measure Up," *BusinessWeek,* December 13, 2004, pp. 112–113.

[78]Cyndee Miller, "Study Says 'Likability' Surfaces as Measure of TV Ad Success," *Marketing News,* January 7, 1991, p. 14.

[79]Laurence N. Gold, "Advertising Tracking: New Tricks of the Trade," *Marketing Research: A Magazine of Practice and Application* 5, p. 42.

[80]Faye Rice, "A Cure for What Ails Advertising?" *Fortune,* December 16, 1991, p. 121.

[81]Lorraine Calvacca, "Making a Case for the Glossies," *American Demographics,* July 1999, p. 36; Juliana Koranteng, "A. C. Nielsen to Offer Data on Net Ad Effectiveness," *Advertising Age International,* October 1999, p. 4; "Net Ads on Pace for $4 Billion Year," *Content Factory,* November 4, 1999, http://www.comtexnews.com; "Net Newbie @ Plan: Still Undiscovered," *BusinessWeek,* January 17, 2000, p. 115.

[82]Gerard J. Tellis, Rajesh K. Chandy, and Pattana Thaivanich, *Decomposing the Effects of Direct TV Advertising: Which Ad Works, When, Where, and How Often?* Marketing Science Institute, MSI Working Paper No. 99–118 (Cambridge, MA: 1999).

[83]Demetrios Vakratsas and Tim Ambler, "How Advertising Works: What Do We Really Know," *Journal of Marketing,* January 1999, pp. 30–31.

[84]D. Kirk Davidson, "Marketing This 'Hope' Sells Our Profession Short," *Marketing News,* July 20, 1998, p. 6.

[85]Raymond Serafin and Gary Levin, "An Industry Suffers Crushing Blow," *Advertising Age,* November 12, 1990, pp. 1, 76, 77.

[86]"Misleading Advertising," *The New York Times,* February 18, 2001, p. C1.

[87]Jim Edwards, "The Book," *BrandWeek,* April 15, 2002, pp. 19–20.

[88]David A. Aaker, Rajeev Batra, and John G. Myers, *Advertising Management,* 4th ed. (Englewood Cliffs, NJ: Prentice Hall, 1992), p. 557.

[89]Michel Arndt, Wendy Zellner, and Peter Coy, "Too Much Corporate Power," *BusinessWeek,* September 11, 2000, p. 154.

[90]"Anything for a Ratings Boost," *Marketing News,* September 13, 1999, p. 2; Kathryn C. Montgomery, "Gov't Must Take the Lead in Protecting Children," *Advertising Age,* June 22, 1998, p. 40.

[91]Wendy Melillo, "Paper Chase," *AdWeek,* April 13, 2001, p. 12.

[92]Maxine Lans Retsky, "Junk Faxes Subject to Telemarketing Laws," *Marketing News,* April 26, 1999, p. 7.

[93]Minette E. Drumwright, "Company Advertising with a Social Dimension," Report #96–110, Marketing Science Institute (Cambridge, MA: 1996), p. i; Bob Garfield, "This Heavy-Handed Ad Exploits Someone New," *Advertising Age,* May 10, 1993, p. 50.

[94]Allyson L. Stewart-Allen, "Europe Ready for Cause-Related Campaigns," *Marketing News,* July 6, 1998, p. 9; and "Why P&G Is Linking Brands to Good Causes," *Marketing,* August 26, 1999, p. 11.

[95]Kirk Davidson, "Look for Abundance of Opposition to TV Liquor Ads," *Marketing News,* January 6, 1997, pp. 4, 30; Ian P. Murphy, "Competitive Spirits: Liquor Industry Turns to TV Ads," *Marketing News,* December 12, 1996, pp. 1, 17; Tar Parker-Pope, "Tough Tobacco-Ad Rules Light Creative Fires," *The Wall Street Journal,* October 9, 1996, p. B1.

[96]George E. Belch and Michael A. Belch, *Advertising and Promotion: An Integrated Marketing and Communications Perspective,* 6th ed. (New York: McGraw-Hill/Irwin, 2004), p. 564.

[97]Tim Johnson, "Audits Aren't Just for the Accountants," *Marketing News,* March 18, 2002, p. 13.

[98]Donald P. Robin and R. Eric Reidenbach, "Social Responsibility, Ethics, and Marketing Strategy: Closing the Gap between Concept and Application," *Journal of Marketing,* January 1987, pp. 44–58.

[99]Sue Duris, "To Ensure PR's ROI, Make It a Valuable Resource," *Marketing News,* April 14, 2003, p. 22.

[100]Patricia Winters, "Drugmakers Portrayed as Villains, Worry about Image," *Advertising Age,* February 22, 1993, p. 1; Kate Fitzgerald, "Health Concerns Don't Slow Down Cellular Phones," *Advertising Age,* February 8, 1993, p. 4; Annetta Miller, "Do Boycotts Work?" *Newsweek,* July 6, 1992, p. 56; Howard Schlossberg, "Members Only to Introduce Homeless in Cause Marketing," *Marketing News,* July 20, 1992, p. 6.

[101]Caleb Solomon, "Exxon Attacks Scientific Views of *Valdez* Oil Spill," *The Wall Street Journal,* April 15, 1993, p. B1.

[102]Philip Kotler, *Marketing Management: Analysis, Planning, Implementation, and Control,* 8th ed. (Englewood Cliffs, NJ: Prentice Hall, 1994), pp. 676–77.

[103]George E. Belch and Michael A. Belch, *Advertising and Promotion: An Integrated Marketing and Communications Perspective,* 6th ed. (New York: McGraw-Hill/Irwin), p. 566.

[104]Adriana Cento, "7 Habits for Highly Effective Public Relations," *Marketing News,* March 16, 1999, p. 8; Dana James, "Dot-Coms Demand New Kind of Publicity," *Marketing News,* November 22, 1999, p. 6; Kathleen V. Schmidt, "Public Relations," *Marketing News,* January 17, 2000, p. 13.

[105]Dana James, "Code Blue: How Crisis Management Has Changed," *Marketing News,* November 6, 2000, pp. 1, 15.

[106]Joseph B. Cahill, "Net Chats: Big Business Is Listening," *Crain's Chicago Business,* April 8, 1996, pp. 1, 53; Helen Roper, "Letters from Cyberhell," *Inc. Technology,* September 1995, pp. 67–70.

[107]Joan McGrath and Myrna Pedersen, "Don't Wait for Disaster; Have a Crisis Plan Ready," *Marketing News,* December 2, 1996, p. 6.

Chapter Eighteen

[1]Adapted from Peter D. Bennett, ed., *Dictionary of Marketing Terms* (Chicago: American Marketing Association, 1988), p. 179.

[2]Pierre Chandon, Brian Wansink, and Gilles Laurent, "A Benefit Congruency Framework of Sales Promotion Effectiveness," *Journal of Marketing,* October 2000, pp. 65–81.

[3]Information from Overstock.com Web site at *www.overstock.com,* June 3, 2005.

[4]Chandon et al., "A Benefit Congruency Framework."

[5]"FSI-Distributed Coupons Up 7.7%; CPGs Lead the Way," from the *PROMO Magazine* Web site at *www.promomagazine.com,* June 3, 2005.

[6]Kathleen M. Joyce, "No Nickel and Dime," from the *PROMO Magazine* Web site at *www.promomagazine.com,* April 1, 2005.

[7]"FSI-Distributed Coupons."

[8]Natalie Schwartz, "Clipping Path," from the *PROMO Magazine* Web site at *www.promomagazine.com,* April 1, 2005.

[9]"FSI-Distributed Coupons."

[10]"Yahoo Gives Away Scoops of Baskin-Robbins Ice Cream," from the *PROMO Magazine* Web site at *www.promomagazine.com,* March 3, 2005.

[11]Kathryn Williams, "Coupons Clip-Free," *Newsweek,* April 18, 2005.

[12]Information from RebatePlace Web site at *www.rebateplace.com,* June 3, 2005.

[13]Information from CyberRebate Web site at *www.cyberrebate.com,* June 3, 2005.

[14]"2005 Reggie Awards: Promotion Marketing Association," from the Promotion Marketing Association Web site at *www.pmalink.org*, June 1, 2005.

[15]Chris Woodyard, "Camera Phones Click with Contests," *USA Today*, March 3, 2005, p. 4B.

[16]Amy Johannes, "LA Gear Launches Interactive Campaign, Sweeps," from the *PROMO Magazine* Web site at *www.promomagazine.com*, May 26, 2005.

[17]Amy Johannes, "Jack in the Box Launches Instant-Win Game," from the *PROMO Magazine* Web site at *www.promomagazine.com*, April 26, 2005.

[18]Tim Parry, "All in the Game," from the *PROMO Magazine* Web site at *www.promomagazine.com*, April 1, 2005.

[19]Information from the Jeep Web site at *www.jeep.com*, June 3, 2005.

[20]"2005 Reggie Awards."

[21]Shirley Leung, "Happy Meals Angle for Little Girls' Loyalty with Well-Dressed Dolls," *The Wall Street Journal*, April 5, 2002, pp. B1, B4.

[22]David Vaczek, "Hard, Cold Merchandise," *PROMO Magazine*, May 1999, pp. S3–S5.

[23]"2005 Reggie Awards."

[24]Miriam Jordan, "Fuel and Freebies," *The Wall Street Journal*, June 10, 2002, pp. B1, B6.

[25]"The 2004 Estimate of Promotional Products Distributor Sales," from the Promotional Products Association International Web site at *www.ppa.org*, June 4, 2005.

[25]Information from the Promotional Products Association International Web site at *www.ppa.org*, June 1, 2005.

[26]Adapted from Robert C. Blattberg and Scott A. Neslin, *Sales Promotion, Concepts, Methods, and Strategies* (Englewood Cliffs, NJ: Prentice Hall, 1990), p. 314.

[27]Information from the Promotional Products Association International Web site at *www.ppa.org*, July 9, 2002.

[28]Information from the Promotional Products Association International Web site at *www.ppa.org*, June 4, 2005.

[29]Tara J. Radin and Carolyn E. Predmore, "The Myth of the Salesperson: Intended and Unintended Consequences of Product-Specific Sales Incentives," *Journal of Business Ethics*, March 2002, pp. 79–92.

[30]Bill Werde, "Major-Label Payola Probe," *Rolling Stone*, November 2004, pp. 15–16; Julie Schmit, "FDA Races to Keep Up with Drug Ads That Go Too Far," from *USA Today* Web site at *www.usatoday.com*, May 31, 2005; Julie Schmit, "Drugmakers Likely to Lob Softer Pitches," from *USA Today* Web site at *www.usatoday.com*, March 17, 2005.

[31]"Games, Contests, Sweeps: Front and Center," *PROMO Magazine*, June 1, 2002, as presented at *www.promomagazine.com*.

Chapter Nineteen

[1]Derrick C. Schnebelt, "Turning the Tables," *Sales & Marketing Management*, January 1993, pp. 22–23.

[2]David Topus, "Keep It Short . . . and Smart," *Selling*, August 1993, p. 30.

[3]Betsy Cummings, "Hearing Them Out," *Sales & Marketing Management*, January 2005, p. 10.

[4]Jennifer Gilbert, "Promoting Productivity," *Sales & Marketing Management*, February 2005, p. 9; "Salespeople Don't Spend a Lot of Time Actually Selling," *The Courier-Journal*, February 21, 2005, p. D6.

[5]Betsy Cummings, "Open for Business," *Sales & Marketing Management*, February 2005, pp. 27–31.

[6]Betsy Wiesendanger, "Temp Reps," *Selling Power*, May 2004, pp. 68–71.

[7]Jon M. Hawes, Kenneth E. Mast, and John E. Swan, "Trust Earning Perceptions of Sellers and Buyers," *Journal of Personal Selling and Sales Management*, Spring 1989, pp. 1–8.

[8]Thomas N. Ingram, Raymond W. LaForge, Ramon A. Avila, Charles H. Schwepker Jr., and Michael R. Williams, *Professional Selling: A Trust-Based Approach*, 3rd ed. (Mason, OH: Thomson/South-Western, 2006), p. 14.

[9]Linda Strand, "Top of Their Class," *Sales & Marketing Management*, February 2004, p. 58.

[10]Ibid., p. 58.

[11]Mark McNaster, "Connecting with Customers," *Sales and Marketing Management*, May 2002, pp. 59–60.

[12]Rosann L. Spiro and Barton A. Weitz, "Adaptive Selling: Conceptualization, Measurement, and Nomological Validity," *Journal of Marketing Research*, February 1990, pp. 61–69.

[13]Thomas N. Ingram, Raymond W. LaForge, and Thomas W. Leigh, "Selling in the New Millennium: A Joint Agenda," *Industrial Marketing Management* 31 (2002), pp. 559–67.

[14]Ibid.

[15]Chad Kaydo, "You've Got Sales," *Sales & Marketing Management*, October 1999, pp. 30–34.

[16]Ibid., pp. 36–38.

[17]Erin Stout, "Planning to Profit from National Accounts," *Sales & Marketing Management*, October 1999, p. 107.

[18]"Microsoft Boosts Sales Force by 450," *USA Today*, June 25, 2002, p. 1B.

[19]Sheree Curry, "Coping With the Ever-Enlarging Sales Territory," *Sales and Marketing Management*, March 2002, p. 11.

[20]Thomas N. Ingram, Raymond W. LaForge, Ramon A. Avila, Charles H. Schwepker Jr., and Michael R. Williams, *Sales Management: Analysis and Decision Making*, 6th ed. (Mason, OH: Thomson/South-Western, 2006), p. 132.

[21]Ron Loback, "Our Revamped Hiring Strategy Brought the Best Salespeople Aboard," *What's Working in Sales Management*, March 29, 2004, p. 5.

[22]Christine Galea, "2002 Sales Training Survey," *Sales & Marketing Management*, July 2002, pp. 34–37.

[23]Strand, "Top of Their Class," pp. 56–57.

[24]Christine Galea, "2004 Salary Survey," *Sales & Marketing Management*, May 2004, pp. 28–34.

[25]Ibid.

[26]Kathleen Cholewka, "Motivating Mentors," *Sales and Marketing Management*, June 2002, p. 61.

[27]Karl A. Boedecker, Fred W. Morgan, and Jeffrey J. Stoltman, "Legal Dimensions of Salespersons' Statements: A Review and Managerial Suggestions," *Journal of Marketing*, January 1991, pp. 70–80.

[28]I. Frederick Trawick, John E. Swan, Gail McGee, and David R. Rink, "Influence of Buyer Ethics and Salesperson Behavior on Intention to Choose a Supplier," *Journal of the Academy of Marketing Science*, Winter 1991, pp. 17–23.

[29]Reported in Bernard L. Rosenbaum, "What You Need for Success in the 21st Century," *Selling*, November 1999, pp. 8–9.

Chapter Twenty

[1]"Economic Impact: U.S. Direct Marketing Today Executive Summary," from the Direct Marketing Association's Web site at *www.the-dma.org*, June 3, 2005.

[2]Ibid.

[3]Ibid.

[4]Jean Halliday, "Dodge Brings Back the Muscle Car" from the online version of *Advertising Age* at *www.adage.com*, May 18, 2005.

[5]Peter D. Bennett, ed., *Dictionary of Marketing Terms*, 2nd ed. (Chicago: American Marketing Association, 1995), p. 75.

[6]"Focus on Small Business" at the Focus USA Web site at *www.focus-usa-1.com/business_lists_smbiz.html*, June 5, 2005.

[7]"CDSxpress Moves" at the MKTG Services Web site at *www.mktgserviceslists.com/datacard.cfm?list_id=20392*, June 5, 2005.

[8]Jane E. Zarem, "From the Store to the Web . . . and Back Again," *1 to 1 Magazine*, January/February 2002, pp. 22–26.

[9]Richard H. Levey, "Child's Play for KinderCare," *Direct,* January 2005, p. 12.

[10]"Economic Impact: U.S. Direct Marketing Today Executive Summary."

[11]Ibid.

[12]Melissa Campanelli, "British Tourist Authority Targets U.S. Seniors," from *www.dmnews.com,* July 8, 2002.

[13]"Economic Impact: U.S. Direct Marketing Today Executive Summary."

[14]Ibid.

[15]Susanne Khawand, "Adaptation Is Critical," *Direct,* May 15, 2005, p. 40.

[16]Allison McCoy, "Advancing CRM around the World," *1 to 1 Magazine,* April 2002, pp. 41–45.

[17]"Economic Impact: U.S. Direct Marketing Today Executive Summary."

[18]"2001 Reggie Award Winners: BMW Films," from *www. pmalink.org,* July 2, 2002.

[19]Scott Hovanyetz, "Xerox Aims to Duplicate 2004's Success Using Theme, Packaging and Prize" from *DMNEWS* at *www.dmnews.com,* May 31, 2005.

[20]Stephen Barrett, "Misleading Infomercials" at Infomercial Watch Web site at *www.infomercialwatch.org,* June 6, 2005; Stephen Barrett, "NAD Concludes That Lorraine Day Infomercial Is Misleading" at Infomercial Watch Web site at *www.infomercialwatch.org,* June 6, 2005; information from *www.infomercialscams.com,* June 6, 2005.

[21]Thomas Mucha, "Stronger Sales in Just 28 Minutes," *Business 2.0,* June 2005, pp. 56–60; information from Hawthorne Direct Web site at *www.hawthornedirect.com,* June 8, 2005.

[22]Richard H. Levey, "Chicago Tribune Returns to DRTV," *Direct,* February 2002, p. 12.

[23]"Economic Impact: U.S. Direct Marketing Today Executive Summary."

[24]"JunkBusters Anti-Telemarketing Script," from the JunkBusters Web site at *www.junkbusters.com,* June 6, 2005.

[25]"Are You Getting Telephone Calls You Don't Want? Here's How to Stop Them" from the Federal Trade commission Web site at *www.ftc.gov,* June 6, 2005.

[26]"Do Not Call List Protection" at *www.donotcallprotection.com,* June 6, 2005.

[27]"Bryan Texas Utilities Relies on FOD" from FaxBack Web site at *www.faxback.com,* June 6, 2005.

[28]Bob Chatham, "Online Privacy Concerns: More Than Hype" from Forrester Web site at *www.forrester.com,* June 6, 2005; "Privacy Survey Results" from Center for Democracy & Technology Web site at *www.cdt.org/privacy/survey/findings/,* June 6, 2005.

[29]"Congress Turns Hard Eye toward Identity Theft, Data Brokers," *Marketing Matters,* e-mail newsletter published by the American Marketing Association, June 3, 2005.

[30]"Legislation Affecting the Internet" from Center for Democracy & Technology Web site at *www.cdt.org/legislaton/108th/privacy/,* June 6, 2005.

[31]From the National Consumers League Web site at *www.natlconsumersleague.org,* June 4, 2005; "Children and Electronic Commerce" from the Trans Atlantic Consumer Dialogue Web site at *www.tacd.org,* June 6, 2005.

[32]Steve Jarvis, "U.S., EU Still Don't Agree on Data Handling," *Marketing News,* August 13, 2001, p. 5.

[33]"The CAN-SPAM Act: Requirements for Commercial E-mailers" from the Federal Trade Commission Web site at *www.ftc.org,* June 6, 2005.

[34]"Summary of State Spam Laws" from The Direct Marketing Association Web site at *www.the-dma.org/antispam/statespamlaws.shtml,* June 6, 2005.

Source Notes

Prologue

Reprinted with the permission of The Free Press, a Division of Simon & Schuster Adult Publishing Group, from *CUSTOMER MANIA!: It is Never Too Late to Build a Customer-Focused Company* by Ken Blanchard, Jim Ballard and Fred Finch. Copyright © 2004 by Blanchard Family Partnership, Fred Finch and Jim Ballard. All rights reserved.

Chapter One

Page 3: Amazon: Heather Green, "How Hard Should Amazon Swing?" *BusinessWeek,* January 14, 2002, p. 38; Robert D. Hof, "Amazon: 'We've Never Said We Had to Do It All,'" *BusinessWeek,* October 15, 2001, p. 53; Leslie Kaufman, "Amazon II: Will This Smile Last?" *New York Times On the Web,* May 19, 2002, pp. 1–5; Mylene Mangalindan, "Who's Selling What on Amazon," *The Wall Street Journal Online,* April 28, 2005, pp. 1–4; James B. Stewart, "Internet Big Four: Worth a Look as Growth Stocks," *Smart Money,* May 4, 2005, p. D3; "Comeback Kid? Amazon Revival Could Shake Up Industry," *Publishers Weekly,* April 14, 2005, accessed on *www.hoovers.com.*

Exhibit 1–1: Adapted from James L. Heskett, Thomas O. Jones, Gary W. Loveman, W. Earl Sasser, Jr., and Leonard A. Schlesinger, "Putting the Service–Profit Chain to Work," *Harvard Business Review,* March–April 1994, pp. 164–74; and Frederick F. Reichheld, *The Loyalty Effect: The Hidden Force behind Growth, Profits, and Lasting Value* (Boston: Harvard Business School Press, 1996).

Exhibit 1–2: Frederick F. Reichheld, *The Loyalty Effect: The Hidden Force behind Growth, Profits, and Lasting Value* (Boston: Harvard Business School Press, 1996), pp. 39–50.

Exhibit 1–3: Frederick E. Webster, Jr., "Executing the New Marketing Concept," *Marketing Management,* Vol. 3, No. 1. p. 10. Reprinted by permission of American Marketing Association.

Exhibit 1–8: Rolph E. Anderson, *Professional Personal Selling.* © 1991, p. 105. Reprinted by permission of the author.

Exhibit 1–11: Reprinted with permission from American Marketing Association Web site, *www.marketingpower.com.*

Case 1–1: Dean Foust, Geri Smith, and David Rocks, "Man on the Spot," *BusinessWeek,* May 3, 1999, pp. 142–51; Dean Foust, David Rocks, and Mark L. Clifford, "Is Douglas Daft the Real Thing?" *BusinessWeek,* December 20, 1999, pp. 44–45; Patricia Sellers, "Who's in Charge Here," *Fortune,* December 24, 2001 (accessed from *www.fortune.com*); Lee Clifford, "Winning in the Water Fight," *Fortune,* March 4, 2002 (accessed from *www.fortune.com*). Dean Foust, "Things Go Better With . . . Juice," *BusinessWeek,* May 17, 2004, pp. 81–82; Dean Foust, "Gone Flat," *BusinessWeek,* December 20, 2004, pp. 76–82; Chad Terhune, "Coke's Profit Falls 11% as Sales Remain Weak in North America," *The Wall Street Journal Online,* April 20, 2005, pp. 1–2.

Case 1–2: Hugh Filman, "Happy Meals for a McDonald's Rival," *BusinessWeek,* July 29, 1996, p. 77; "King of Fast Food at Home, Jollibee Plans Six More Stores in the U.S.," *Fox Market Wire,* March 12, 1999, pp. 1–3; *www.jollibee.com.ph,* June 6, 2002. *www.jollibee.com* accessed on May 18, 2005.

Chapter Two

Page 25: *www.dell.com,* June 20, 2002; Andrew Park and Spencer E. Ande, "Who Will Master the Server Biz?" *BusinessWeek,* June 24, 2002, pp. 92–93; Andy Serwer, "The Education of Michael Dell," *Fortune,* March 7, 2005, pp. 74–82; John Battelle, "Still Giving 'Em Dell," *Business 2.0,* May 2004, pp. 99–101.

Exhibit 2–3: Excerpt from *The World Almanac and Book of Facts 2000* (World Almanac Books, 1999), pp. 878–79. Used with permission of the publisher. All rights reserved.

Exhibit 2–4: *The World Almanac and Book of Facts 2000* (World Almanac Books, 1999), p. 878.

Exhibit 2–5: Data from United Nations Population Division.

Exhibit 2–6: Sean Gregory, "Diapers for Fatima," *Time Inside Business,* February 2005, pp. B6–B12; Deborah L. Vence, "Top Niche," *Marketing News,* June 1, 2004, pp. 11–13; Deborah L. Vence, "The next best thing," *Marketing News,* May 15, 2005, pp. 11–45.

Creating Customer Value, p. 34: Elizabeth Esfahani, "7-Eleven Gets Sophisiticated," *Business 2.0,* January/February 2005, pp. 93–100; J. M. Hirsch, "Convenience stores add upscale eats, dining areas," *The Courier-Journal,* May 25, 2005, pp. D3.

Being Entrepreneurial, p. 35: C. K. Prahalad and Allen Hammond, "Serving the World's Poor, Profitably," *Harvard Business Review,* September 2002, pp. 48–57; Cris Prystay, "With Loans, Poor South Asian Women Turn Entrepreneurial," *The Wall Street Journal Online,* May 25, 2005, pp. 1–3.

Case 2–1: Margaret Littman, "Sponsors Take to the Court with New Women's NBA," *Marketing News,* March 3, 1997, pp. 1–6; Gigi Barnett and Skip Rozin, "A Lot of Leagues of Their Own," *BusinessWeek,* March 3, 1997, pp. 54–56; *www.wnba.com,* accessed on May 25, 2005.

Case 2–2: Geoffrey Smith and Faith Keenan, "Kodak Is the Picture of Digital Success," *BusinessWeek,* January 14, 2002, p. 39; Unmesh Kher, "Getting Kodak to Focus," *Time Inside Business,* March 2005, pp. B9–B14; William C. Symonds with Peter Burrows, "A Digital Warrior for Kodak," *BusinessWeek,* May 23, 2005, p. 42.

Chapter Three

Page 47: *http://disney.go.com/park/homepage/today/flash/index.html;* "Business: Disney or Doesn't He?" *The Economist,* January 12, 2002, p. 61; Marc Gunther, "Has Eisner Lost the Disney Magic?" *Fortune,* January 7, 2002, pp. 64–69; Richard Linnett and Wayne Friedman, "Disney Picks Starcom Strategy," *Advertising Age,* December 31, 2001, pp. 3, 28; Bruce Orwall, "Disney CEO Acknowledges Woes, Stresses Confidences in a Rebound," *The Wall Street Journal,* January 4, 2002, p. A; Ronald Grover, "Disney: First the Good News . . .", *BusinessWeek Online,* February 3, 2005, AN 16002963; Ronald Grover, "Disney: Top Bet for No. 1? No. 2," *Business Week Online,* January 19, 2005, AN 15855018; David J. Jefferson, "A Guided Tour of Disney's Horrors," *Newsweek,* November 8, 2004, p. 46; Patricia Sellers, "Disney's Mr. Calm Unreels Miramax," *Fortune,* March 21, 2005, p. 30.

Exhibit 3–5: Reprinted by permission of *Harvard Business Review.* Exhibit from "Building a Company's Vision," by James C. Collins and Jerry I. Porras, September–October 1996, p. 69. Copyright © 1996 by the Harvard Business School Publishing Corporation; all rights reserved.

Exhibit 3–6: Reprinted by permission of Harvard Business School Press. Exhibit from *Competing for the Future,* by Gary Hamel and C.K. Prahalad. Copyright © 1994 by the Harvard Business School Publishing Corporation; all rights reserved.

Exhibit 3–7: Shelby D. Hunt and Robert M. Morgan, "The Comparative Advantage Theory of Competition," *Journal of Marketing,* April 1995, pp. 1–15; and Gary Hamel and C. K. Prahalad, *Competing for the Future* (Boston: Harvard Business School Press, 1994), p. 223.

Exhibit 3–9: B. Heldey, "Strategy and the Business Portfolio," *Long Range Planning,* February 1977, p. 12; and George S. Day, "Organizing the Product Portfolio," *Journal of Marketing,* April 1977, p. 34.

Creating Customer Value, p. 62: Mathew Boyle, "Why FedEx Is Flying High," *Fortune,* November 1, 2004, p. 145; Ginger Conlon, "CRM Delivers for FedEx," *Customer Relationship Management,* January 2005, p. 45; Mary Ellen Podmolik, "FedEx Campaign Touts New Unit," *B to B,* October 25, 2004, p. 6; Ted Samson, "FedEx Kinko's Delivers Remote Printing," *Infoworld.com,* November 15, 2004, p. 52; Mike Savage, "FedEx Moves Local Markets to Regionwide Loyalty Plan," *Media Asia,* October 9, 2004, p. 4; Amy Tsao, "Can FedEx Deliver More Than UPS?" *BusinessWeek Online,* September 10, 2004, *web15.epnet.com.*

Being Entrepreneurial, p. 64: Ross Snel, "Small-Cap Fund Seeks Postattack Bargains," *The Wall Street Journal,* October 23, 2001, p. C21; Chantal Tode, "Evolution of Tweens Tastes Keeps Retailers on their Toes," *Advertising Age,* February 12, 2001, p. 56; Erik Torkells, "Abercrombie & Fitch," *Fortune,* June 25, 2001, p. 198; Erin White, "Abercrombie Seeks to Send Teeny-Boppers Packing—to Keep Juveniles from Marring Its Image, A&F Lures Them to Its New 'Surferish' Chain," *The Wall Street Journal,* August 30, 2001, p. B1; Jim Edwards, "Court Oversees A&F's Ads," *Brandweek,* November 29, 2004, p. 6; Jean Palmieri and David Lipke, "The Ruehl of Expansion: A&F Plans Growth," *WWD: Women's Wear Daily,* September 13, 2004, p. 8; Emily Scardino, "Ruehl: A&F's Hip New Retail Concept," *DSNRetailing Today,* September 20, 2004, p. 4; Roos Tucker, "A&F's Growing Pains: Retailer Eyes Global, Multibrand Strategy," *WWD: Women's Wear Daily,* August 11, 2004, p. 1.

Case 3–1: Jeff Cioletti, "That's No Bull," *Beverage World,* June 15, 2004, p. 10; Wilfried Eckl-Dorna, "Red Bull Lightens Up," *Fortune,* September 6, 2004, p. 23; Bob Phillips, "A Beverage to Call Their Own," *Convenience Store News,* October 16, 2004, p. 133; Andrew Purvis, "Dietrich Mateschitz," *Time,* December 20, 2004, p. 146; Samuel Solley, "How Can Red Bull Move on from Energy Roots," *Marketing,* November 5, 2004, p. 13.

Case 3–2: "Advantages of the Versatile Voucher," *Marketing: Incentive 95 Preview,* April 27, 1995, pp. 5–6; Edmond Lawler, "How Underdogs Outmarket Leaders," *Advertising Age,* November 13, 1995, p. 24; Becky Ebenkamp, "JB, Virgin Unite Again for U.K. Trip," *Brandweek,* March 8, 1999, p. 14; Julia Flynn, Wendy Zeller, Larry Light, and Joseph Weber, "Then Came Branson," *BusinessWeek,* October 26, 1998, pp. 116–20; "Virgin Atlantic Ads Take Aim at United, American," *Brandweek,* October 11, 1999, p. 8; "Virgin Aims to 'Shag' Greater Awareness in U.S.," *Adweek,* June 7, 1999, p. 5; Matthew Arnold, "Airlines Fight to Survive Crisis," *Marketing,* September 27, 2001, p. 15; Rafer Guzman, "Takeoffs and Landings," *The Wall Street Journal,* November 23, 2001, p. W.11C; Stephen Power, "British Air-AMR Plan Is Dealt a Setback—U.S. Antitrust Officials Say Tie-Up Should Be Pared to Protect Competition," *The Wall Street Journal,* December 18, 2001, p. A3; "Best Use of E-Mail," *New Media Age,* November 11, 2004, p. 27; Douglas Barrie, "Virgin Territory," *Aviation Week & Space Technology,* December 13, 2004, p. 52.

Chapter Four

Page 75: Hilary Cassidy, "Cards Seek More 'You' in Usage," *BrandWeek,* June 4, 2001, p. S44; Kevin Higgins, "Marketing Visa Everywhere It Wants to Be," *Marketing Management,* November/December 2001, pp. 14–17; *www.usa.visa.com/personal/about_visa/who/index.html;* Anne Chen, "Visa Upgrades Mean Business," *EWEEK,* November 15, 2004, p. 54; Lavonne Kuykendall, "Visa Reports Transaction Volume Hike," *American Banker,* February 9, 2005, p. 7; Kate Maddox, "Visa Effort Aims to Raise B-to-B Profile," *B to B,* July 19, 2004, p. 4; Amy White, "Visa Unveils Olympic Credit Card with BOC," *Media Asia,* December 17, 2004, p. 10.

Exhibit 4–1: "Emerging and Burgeoning," by Allan Magrath, *Across the Board,* January 2000, pp. 38-41. Reprinted by permission of The Conference Board and Allan Magrath.

Acting Ethically, p. 78: Lorenza Muñoz, "Blockbuster Sued over Late-Fee Claims," *Los Angeles Times,* February 19, 2005.

Exhibit 4–3: From J. Paul Peter and Jerry C. Olson, *Understanding Consumer Behavior* 5/e, 1999, p. 250. Copyright © 1999 The McGraw-Hill Companies. Reprinted with permission.

Exhibit 4–4: Adapted from Robert Boutilier, "Pulling the Family Strings," *American Demographics,* August 1993, p. 46.

Exhibit 4–5: *America's Families and Living Arrangements: 2003,* U.S. Department of Commerce, Economics and Statistics Division, U.S. Census Bureau, November 2004, p. 4.

Creating Customer Value, p. 94: Sara Calabro, "Word on the Street," *Sales and Marketing Management,* December 2004, p. 12; Angeld Fernando, "Creating Buzz: New Media Tactics Have Changed the PR and Advertising Game," *Communication World,* November/December 2004, p. 10; Nat Ives, "Marketing's Flip Side Is the 'Determined Detractor,' " *The New York Times,* December 27, 2004, p. C1.

Case 4–1: Jeffrey Ball, "Daimler-Chrysler Turnaround Seems to Be Going in Reverse," *The Wall Street Journal,* October 11, 2002, p. B.4; Karl Greenberg, "Overdrive," *Brandweek,* January 14, 2002, pp. 19–24; Scott Miller and Karen Lundegaard," *The Wall Street Journal,* February 4, 2002, p. B.1; Alex Taylor III, "A Mercedes for the Masses," *Fortune Small Business,* December 2001/January 2002, p. 98; Curtis Brown, "Mercedes-Benz to Draw in Youth with 'Elements' Blitz," *Precision Marketing,* August 20, 2004, p. 6; Alan Deutschman and John A. Byrne, *Fast Company,* February 2005, pp. 60–61; Alex Taylor III and Doris Burke, "The Nine Lives of Jürgen Schrempp," *Fortune (Europe),* January 24, 2005, pp. 44–48; David Welch, "Sexy Enough to Seduce Europe?" *BusinessWeek,* February 28, 2005, pp. 94–95.

Case 4–2: "Daddy Gap," *BusinessWeek,* January 11, 1999, p. 63; Hal Espen, "Levi's Blues," *New York Times Magazine,* March 21, 1999, p. 54; Bob Garfield, "Gap Secretes Sweet Smell of Ad Success," *Advertising Age,* August 16, 1999, p. 55; Alan Treadgold, "The Outlook for Asian Retailing," *Discount Merchandiser,* May 1999, pp. 45–46; Louise Lee and Nanette Byrnes, "More Than Just a Bad Patch at Gap," *BusinessWeek,* February 11, 2002; Amy Merrick, "Gap Posts Losses, Reshuffles Executives," *The Wall Street Journal,* February 27, 2002, p. B7; "The Goods on the Gap," *Advertising Age,* December 17, 2001, p. 10; "U.S., International Units Separated at the Gap Inc.," *The Wall Street Journal,* January 17, 2002, p. B4; Cheryl Dahle, "Gap's New Look: The See-Through," *Fast Company,* September 2004, pp. 69–70; Meredith Derby, "Gap Looking Abroad, Will Set Up Banana Republics in Japan," *WWD: Women's Wear Daily,* November 19, 2004, pp. 1–2.

Chapter Five

Page 105: Mark Bernstein, "Office Depot Harvests Untapped Potential by Stretching Its Supply Chain," *World Trade,* March 2005, pp. 34–39; Brian Quinton, "Office Depot's Multichannel Challenge," *Direct,* May 1, 2005, pp. 10, 22.

Exhibit 5–2: United States Census Bureau, *www.ntis.gov/naics,* May 9, 2005.

Exhibit 5–3: Phillip L. Carter, Joseph R. Carter, Robert M. Monczka, Thomas H. Slaight, and Andrew J. Swan, *The Future of Purchasing and Supply: A Five- and Ten-Year Forecast* (Arizona State University: The Center for Advanced Purchasing Studies, 1998), pp. 27–36; Roberta J. Duffy, "18 Initiatives: Following the Trends, Combining Elements, and Progressing Forward," *Purchasing Today,* November 2000, pp. 1–2.

Exhibit 5–4: Jennifer Mears, "Study: Outsourcing Losing Luster," *Network World,* April 25, 2005, p. 10; "The Ins and Outs of Outsourcing," *Management Training and Development,* May 2005, pp. 1, 13; Mark G. Dotzour, "Outsource: Outwit, Outplay, Outlast," *Terre Grande,* January 2005, pp. 1–3; From Alex Brown, Kristopher K. Andrew, Connie R. Mullins, and Kenneth D. Lipton Jr., "What Are the Key Factors You Use to Determine If Outsourcing Is Appropriate?" *Inside Supply Management,* May 2002, p. 60.

Using Technology, p. 110: Ken Kenjale and Arnie Phatak, "B2B Exchanges: How to Move Forward from Here," *World Trade,* June 1, 2003, pp. 26–27.

Exhibit 5–6: A. T. Kearney, as reported in Phillip P. Carter, Joseph R. Carter, Richard M. Monczka, Thomas H. Slaight, and Andrew J. Swan,

"The Future of Purchasing and Supply: A Five- and Ten-Year Forecast," p. 23. Copyright the Center for Advanced Purchasing Studies, Arizona State University, 1998.

Creating Customer Value, p. 113: "Dell Recognizes Six Suppliers in Annual Awards Program," from Dell Inc. Web site at *www.dell.com,* accessed on April 14, 2005.

Exhibit 5–7: Erin Anderson, Wujin Shu, and Barton Weitz, "Industrial Purchasing: An Empirical Examination of the Buyclass Framework," *Journal of Marketing,* July 1987, p. 72. © 1987 by the American Marketing Association. Reprinted with permission.

Case 5–1: Doug Barney, "Harley-Davidson: All-American Supply Chain Hero," from the online version of *Chief Supply Chain Officer Magazine,* January 19, 2005, available at *www.cscomagazine.com;* Joel L. Smith, "All Hail, Harley Davidson," *Detroit News,* February 22, 2002, p. B1; Lara Lee, "Hogging the Market (Best Practices)," *Sales and Marketing Management,* April 2002, p. 70.

Case 5–2: Lee Hawkins Jr., "GM Pushing Its U.S. Suppliers to Reduce Prices," *The Wall Street Journal,* April 7, 2005, p. A2; "Ford Renews Agreement to Use Compuware Covisint Supplier Portal," press release dated May 4, 2005, Covisint Web site at *www.covisint.com;* Christopher Koch, "Motorcity Shakeup," *Darwin,* January 2002, pp. 46–51; "Auto Suppliers Will Be Pressured to Be e-Quipped," *Solutions,* February 2002, p. 12; "Top 250 Purchasing Departments," *Supply Chain Management Review,* March 30, 2002, p. 88.

Chapter Six

Page 125: Jack Honomichl, "2004 Business Report of the Marketing Research Industry," *Marketing News,* June 15, 2004, p. H10; *www.imsglobal.com/about/about.htm,* April 30, 2005.

Using Technology, p. 133: Gilbert A. Churchill Jr. and Dawn Iacobucci, *Marketing Research: Methodological Foundations,* 8th ed. (Fort Worth, TX: Harcourt College Publishers, 2002), pp. 748–62; David J. Lipke, "Product by Design," *American Demographics,* February 2001, pp. 38–41.

Being Entrepreneurial, p. 135: Maria Nguyen, "Online Market Research Poised for Even Bigger Growth," *B&T,* January 14, 2005, p. 7; Paul Vriend, "Technical Writers Turn to Web Surveys," *Intercom,* February 2005, p. 13.

Case 6–1: Aaron Barr, "Aleve Gets in the Fighting Spirit," *Adweek,* March 25, 2002, p. 6; Sara Eckel, "Road to Recovery," *American Demographics,* March 2001, p. S8; Rosie Cortes, "Bayer Launches New Advertising Campaign for Aleve," *Caribbean Business,* August 5, 2004; Christine Gorman, "What Risks Lurk in Your Medicine Cabinet?" *Time,* March 15, 2005, *web18.epnet.com;* Kate MacArthur, "Aleve Goes Back to Roots," *Advertising Age,* November 4, 2002, p. 6.

Case 6–2: Jeremy Caplan, "Strange Brandfellows," *Time,* March 7, 2005, v165, i10, p. 25; Atifa Hargrave-Silk, "Adidas Toasts Win with National Blitz," *Media Asia,* February 11, 2005, p. 8; Stanley Holmes, "The Machine of a New Sole," *BusinessWeek,* March 14, 2005, pp. 99–100.

Chapter Seven

Page 153: Richard Behar, "Never Heard of Acxiom? Chances Are It's Heard of You," *Fortune,* February 23, 2004, pp. 140–45; Emily Cubitt, "Orr Gets Stuck in for Acxiom," *Precision Marketing,* April 16, 2004, p. 12; David Myron, "Clean and Compliant," *Business Process Outsourcing: Knowledge Services,* April 2004, pp. 4–5; *http://www.acxiom.com.*

Acting Ethically, p. 162: Caron Carlson, "Congress Acts on Privacy," *eweek,* March 14, 2005, p. 12; Todd Davenport, "Momentum on Data Privacy," *American Banker,* March 16, 2005; David M. Raab, "Privacy Technologies," *DM Review,* March 2005, pp. 62–63.

Exhibit 7–4: SRI International.

Exhibit 7–6: From "Teen Segment Bases" by Elissa Moses, The $100 Billion Allowance: Accessing the Global Teen Market, 2000. Copyright © John Wiley & Sons, Inc. Reprinted with permission of John Wiley & Sons, Inc.

Exhibit 7–9: From Joseph P. Guiltinian, Gordon W. Paul, and Thomas J. Madden, *Marketing Management: Strategies and Programs,* 6th Edition,

1997, p. 111. Copyright © 1997 The McGraw-Hill Companies. Reprinted with permission

Creating Customer Value, p. 175: *http://www.mastercardintl.com/about/press/factsheet.html* downloaded June 20, 2002; Lisa Bertagnoli, " 'Priceless' a Hit with Hispanic Audiences," *Marketing News,* January 15, 2001, p. 5; Cris Prystay, "MasterCard Hopes to Score in Asia with Prepaid Plastic," *The Wall Street Journal,* May 21, 2002, p. D2; Mary Shacklett, "MasterCard Positions Itself for m-Commerce," *Credit Union Magazine,* March 2002, pp. 70–73; Anne Chen, "MasterCard Cashes in on Web Services," *eweek,* February 7, 2005, pp. 52–53; Gregory Solomon, "Regal, MasterCard Star in Double Bill," *Adweek,* February 28, 2005, p. 18.

Exhibit 7–10: James H. Meyers, *Segmentation and Positioning for Strategic Marketing Decisions,* American Marketing Association, 1996, p. 209. © 1996 by American Marketing Association. Reprinted with permission.

Case 7–1: "A Higher Profile for Audience Measurement," *Broadcasting & Cable,* December 1, 1997, p. S20; "The PRIZM Advantage," *The Frame* (Fairfield, CT: Survey Sampling, Inc.), August 1999, p. 1; *http://yawl.claritas.com/about.asp,* December 12, 1999; Deborah D. McAdams, "Micro-Marketing," *Broadcasting & Cable,* July 17, 2000, p. 50; Amy Merrick, "The 2000 Count: Counting on the Census," *The Wall Street Journal,* February 14, 2001, p. B1; Evan St. Lifer, "Tapping into the Zen of Marketing," *Library Journal,* May 1, 2001, pp. 44–46; "Claritas Introduces PRIZM Segmentation System," *Retail Merchandiser,* November 2003, p. 7; "Cruise Line: Boosting Bookings with Segmentation," *Retail, Restaurant, and Real Estate,* March 26, 2003, *www.clusterbigip1.claritas.com.*

Case 7–2: Christina Brinkley, "Marriott Outfits an Old Chain for a Brand-New Market," *The Wall Street Journal,* October 13, 1998, *http://interactive.wsj.com/articles/;* "Marriott's New View of Downtown," *BusinessWeek,* July 26, 1999, p. 78; Marty Whitford, "Marriott International Restructures Management," *Hotel & Management,* October 18, 1999, p. 23; Marty Whitford, "Old and New Flags Vanish with Rebranding Strategy," *Hotel & Management,* October 4, 1999, p. 30; *http://www.Marriott.com/corporate-info,* downloaded June 20, 2002; Jeff Higley, "Marriott Focuses on Building Portfolio, Rebranding Spas," *H&MM,* June 21, 2004, p. 11; John P. Walsh, "The Good and the Bad," *H&HM,* March 1, 2004, p. 26.

Chapter Eight

Page 183: The Frito-Lay Web site, *http://www.fritolay.com,* July 7, 2002; Chad Terhune, "Frito-Lay Plans New Ad Push," *The Wall Street Journal Online,* May 27, 2005, pp. 1–2; Diane Brady, "A Thousand and One Noshes," *BusinessWeek,* June 14, 2001, pp. 54–56; *www.fritolay.com,* May 27, 2005.

Using Technology, p. 185: Julie Schlosser, "Cashing in on the World of Me," *Fortune,* December 13, 2004, pp. 244–50.

Exhibit 8–7: Reported in Diane Brady with Robert D. Hof, Andy Reinhardt, Moon Ihlwan, Stanley Holmes, and Kerry Capell, "Cult Brands," *BusinessWeek,* August 2, 2004, p. 64.

Creating Customer Value, p. 199: Excerpt from "The Pay Off for Trying Harder," by Thomas Mucha, *Business 2.0,* July 2002, pp. 84-86.

Case 8–1: From Michael Behar, "Computer Heal Thyself," *Business 2.0,* July 2002, pp. 100-101. Copyright © 2002 Time Inc. All rights reserved.

Case 8–2: Stanley Holmes, "Gert Gets the Last Laugh," *BusinessWeek,* June 10, 2002, p. 100. Reprinted with permission.

Chapter Nine

Page 205: *www.3m.com,* July 15, 2002. Michael Arndt, "3M: A Lab for Growth?" *BusinessWeek,* January 21, 2002, pp. 50–51; *www.3m.com,* accessed on June 3, 2005.

Exhibit 9–1: Adapted from C. Merle Crawford, *New Products Management* 4th edition, Richard D. Irwin, 1994, p. 11.

Exhibit 9–4: James J. McKeown, "New Products from New Technologies," *Journal of Business and Industrial Marketing,* Winter–Spring 1990, p. 70. Reprinted with permission.

Exhibit 9–5: Merle Crawford and Anthony Di Benedetto, *New Products Management* (Burr Ridge, IL: McGraw-Hill/Irwin, 2003), p. 188.

Acting Ethically, p. 212: Danielle Sacks, "It's Easy Being Green," *Fast Company,* August 2004, pp. 50–51.

Using Technology, p. 215: Michael V. Copeland and Andrew Tilin, "The New Instant Companies," *Business 2.0,* June 2005, pp. 84–86.

Exhibit 9–8: Adapted from Robert G. Cooper and Elko J. Kleinschmidt, "Stage Gate Systems for New Product Success," *Marketing Management* 1, no. 4, pp. 20–29. Reprinted by permission of the American Marketing Association.

Exhibit 9–9: William R. Dillon, Thomas J. Madden, and Neil H. Firtle, *Essentials of Marketing Research* (Homewood, IL: Richard D. Irwin, 1993), p. 50. Copyright © 1993 The McGraw-Hill Companies. Reprinted with permission.

Case 9–1: J. Lynn Lunsford, "New Jet Promises to Be Cheaper to Buy, Fly; Unveiling 'Air Taxi,'" *The Wall Street Journal Online,* July 12, 2002, pp. 1–2; *www.eclipseaviation.com.*

Case 9–2: Siri Schubert, "Bound to Succeed," *Business 2.0,* April 2005, p. 50; Wendy Cole, "The Stapler Wars," *Time Inside Business,* April 2005, p. A5.

Chapter Ten

Page 225: *www.starbucks.com,* July 16, 2002; Jeff Schlegel, "Something Brewin'," *Individual Investor,* February 2000, pp. 60–61; "How Much Starbucks Is Too Much," *Business 2.0,* July 2002, p. 35; Company Fact Sheet, June 2005, accessed at *www.starbucks.com* on June 8, 2005; Patricia Sellers, "Starbucks: The Next Generation," *Fortune,* April 4, 2005, p. 30.

Being Entrepreneurial, p. 228: Leslie Earnest, "Skechers Strides Away from the Competition," *The Courier-Journal,* June 30, 2002, pp. 66–68; *www.skechers.com,* accessed June 9, 2005.

Exhibit 10–4: Adapted from Eric N. Berkowitz, Roger A. Kerin, Steven W. Hartley, and William Rudelius, *Marketing,* 4th ed. (Burr Ridge IL: Richard D. Irwin, 1994), p. 327.

Creating Customer Value p. 237: Amey Stone, "Bare Bones," *BusinessWeek,* March 14, 2005, p. 88.

Case 10–1: Mike McNamee, "Don't Leave Home without a Freebie," *BusinessWeek,* November 8, 1999, pp. 150, 152; *www.americanexpress.com,* July 16, 2002; Julie Creswell, "Ken Chenault Reshuffles His Cards," *Fortune,* April 18, 2005, pp. 180–86.

Case 10–2: Peter Burrows, "What's in Store for This Happy Couple?" *BusinessWeek,* May 20, 2002, p. 45; Cliff Edwards and Andrew Park, "HP and Compaq: It's Showtime," *BusinessWeek,* June 17, 2002, pp. 76–77; Peter Burrows with Ben Elgin, "Why HP Is Pruning the Printers," *BusinessWeek,* May 9, 2005, pp. 38–39.

Chapter Eleven

Page 245: Nanessa L. Facenda, "Caught in the Squeeze?" *Retail Merchandiser,* May 2004, p. 20; Constance L. Hayes, "What's behind the Procter Deal? Wal-Mart," *The New York Times,* January 29, 2005, p. C1; Sarah Lacy, "RFID: Plenty of Mixed Signals," *BusinessWeek Online,* January 31, 2005, AN 1596172; Marilyn Much, "Wal-Mart's Low-Price Obsession Puts Suppliers through Wringer," *Investor's Business Daily,* January 30, 2004, p. A01; Jack Neff and Rich Thomaselli, "Nike Finds a Way to Go to Wal-Mart," *Advertising Age,* March 21, 2005, p. 1; Chuck Salter, "Pulling Punches," *Fast Company,* April 2005, p. 31; *www.walmartfacts.com/doyouknow/default.aspx.*

Exhibit 11–2: Adapted from John A. Farris and John A. Quelch, "In Defense of Price Promotion," *Sloan Management Review,* Fall 1989, p. 64; and Rockney G. Walters, "Assessing the Impact of Retail Price Promotions on Product Substitution, Complementary Purchase, and Interstore Displacement," *Journal of Marketing,* April 1991, p. 17.

Exhibit 11–4: Reprinted from "Pricing Opportunities—And How to Exploit Them," by Hermann Simon, *MIT Sloan Management Review,* Winter 1992, p. 59, by permission of publisher. Copyright © 1992 by Massachusetts Institute of Technology. All rights reserved.

Using Technology, p. 254 "Ebay Realizes Success in Small-Biz Arena," *Marketing News,* May 1, 2004; Rachel Konrad, "Ebay Sets Sights on China to Expand Market Presence," *Marketing News,* May 15, 2004, p. 48; Patricia Sellers, "eBay's Secret," *Fortune,* October 18, 2004, pp. 161–78.

Creating Customer Value, p. 260: Eliza Gallo, "Best Buy to Shift from CDs to DVDs," *Video Business,* March 14, 2005, p. 10; Mya Frazier, "Boy-Toy Peddler Best Buy Seeks Balance with Women's Health Store," *Advertising Age,* March 14, 2005, p. 4; Louise Lee, "What's Roiling the Selling Season," *BusinessWeek,* January 10, 2005, p. 38; Don Tapscott, "After the Customer Analysis, Then What?" *Intelligent Enterprise,* March 2005, p. 10; Allan Wolf, "Best Buy to Build 60 Next-Gen Locations," *Twice,* February 7, 2005, pp. 1, 8.

Exhibit 11–8: Adapted from Kent B. Monroe, *Pricing: Making Profitable Decisions,* 2nd ed. (New York: McGraw-Hill, 1990), p. 46; and William B. Dodds, Kent B. Monroe, and Druv Grewal, "Effects of Price, Brand, and Store Information on Buyers' Product Evaluations," *Journal of Marketing Research,* August 1991, p. 308.

Exhibit 11–9: Adapted from Joel E. Urbany and Peter R. Dickson, *Consumer Knowledge of Normal Prices: An Exploratory Study and Framework,* Marketing Science Institute, report no. 90–112 (Cambridge, MA: 1990), p. 18.

Exhibit 11–10: Adapted from Abhijit Biswas and Edward A. Blair, "Contextual Effects of Reference Prices in Retail Advertisement," *Journal of Marketing,* July 1991, p. 4. © 1991 by the American Marketing Association. Reprinted with permission.

Case 11–1: Dale Buss, Karl Greenberg, and Michael Applebaum, "Can Green Be Hummer's True Color?" *Brandweek,* January 10, 2005, p. 34; Jason Stein, "Hummer Unveils Big Plans," *Automotive News,* October 25, 2004, p. 6; Jason Stein, "Hummer Considers Alternatives for Next Vehicle," *Automotive News,* February 21, 2005, p. 8; James B. Treece, "In Godzilla's Footsteps: Hummer Takes Tokyo," *Automotive News,* October 4, 2004, p. 4; David Welch, "A Bummer for the Hummer," *BusinessWeek,* February 23, 2004, p. 49.

Case 11–2: Robert D. Hof, Heather Green, and Paul Judge, "Going, Going, Gone," *BusinessWeek,* April 12, 1999, pp. 30–32; Nick Wingfield, "Priceline Adds Three Airlines to System, Resulting in a Charge of $1.1 Billion," *The Wall Street Journal,* November 17, 1999, p. B2; Nick Wingfield, "Priceline.com Names Microsoft in Suit, Alleging Violation of One of Its Patents," *The Wall Street Journal,* October 14, 1999, p. B18; *http://www.priceline.com/PriceLineASOPourCompany?asp/company.asp;* Dan Selicaro, "Curtain Call for Priceline.com," *Upside,* February 2001, pp. 36–37; Mark Veverka, "Plugged In: Can Jay Walker Pull a New Rabbit Out of His Hat," *Barrons,* January 8, 2001, p. 41; Suh-kyung Yoon, "Priceline.com, Hutchinson Launch an Online Travel Service for Asia," *The Wall Street Journal,* April 17, 2002, p. D3; Henry Baltazar, "Database Replication Is the Ticket," *eweek,* February 21, 2005, pp. 39–40; Jerry Limone, "Priceline Launches Merchant Hotel Program," *Travel Weekly,* May 10, 2004, p. 2; Timothy J. Mullaney, "Turbulence for Online Travel," *BusinessWeek Online,* August 5, 2004, AN 14164957.

Chapter Twelve

Page 269: Sally B. Donnelly and Mitch Frank, "Auction Nation: Town Square Community Center, Social Scene—eBay Turned into Much More Than Auction," *Time,* December 27, 1999, p. 82; Michael Krantz, "The Attic of e:>> From Yesteryear's Treasures to Yesterday's Garbage, There's a Price and a Place for Everything; What Are You Collecting?" *Time,* December 27, 1999, p. 74; Kathleen Melymuka, "Internet Intuition," *Computer World,* January 10, 2000, p. 48; Jerry Adler "The eBay Way of Life," *Newsweek,* June 17, 2002, pp. 51–60; "eBay to Buy France's iBazar for $66 Million to $112 Million," *Futures World News,* May 7, 2001, p. 1008053r0738; "eBay Revenue Increases 81% as Net Surges," *The Wall Street Journal,* January 19, 2001, *www.djinteractive.com;* Collin Keefe, "Where Haves Meet Wants," *Dealerscope,* January 2002, pp. 50–54; Stephanie Clifford, "eBay Hike Irks Small Businesses," *Inc. Magazine,* April 2005, p. 26; Robert D. Hof, "How eBay Can Restore Its Luster," *BusinessWeek Online,* January 26, 2005, AN 15855854; Mylene Mangalindan, "Some Sellers Leave eBay over New Fees," *The Wall Street Journal,* January 31, 2005, p. B1.

Exhibit 12–1: Harper W. Boyd Jr., Orville C. Walker Jr., John Mulling, and Jean-Clarde Larreche, *Marketing Management: A Strategic Decision-Making Approach,* 4th ed. (New York: McGraw-Hill/Irwin, 2002), p. 283. Copyright © 2003 The McGraw-Hill Companies. Reprinted with permission.

Acting Ethically, p. 272: Theresa Howard, "Pay the Same, Get Less as Package Volume Falls," *USA Today,* March 17, 2004, p. 3B; Megan Johnson and Sangita Malhotra, "Stealth Inflation," *Money,* March 2001, p. 26.

Using Technology, p. 254: *http://www.shopzilla.com/40_-_content—about.*

Exhibit 12–5: Adapted from Ford S. Worthy, "Japan's Smart Secret Weapon," *Fortune,* August 12, 1991, p. 73. © 1991 Time Inc. All rights reserved.

Exhibit 12–6: Reprinted with permission from *Journal of Marketing Research,* published by the American Marketing Association, Klaus Wertenbach and Bernd Skiera, "Measuring Consumer Willingness to Pay at the Point of Purchase, May 2002, p. 203.

Exhibit 12–7: Reprinted with permission from *Marketing Management,* published by the American Marketing Association, Timothy Matanovich, Gary L. Lilien and Arvind Rangaswamy, "Engineering the Price-Value Relationship, Spring 1999, p. 49.

Exhibit 12–9: Reprinted by permission, Noble, Peter M., Thomas S. Gruca, "Industrial Pricing: Theory and Managerial Practice," *Marketing Science,* 18, 3, Summer 1999. Copyright 1999, the Institute for Operations Research and the Management Sciences (INFORMS), 7240 Parkway Drive, Suite 310, Hanover, MD 21076 USA.

Case 12–1: "Saturn's New Orbit," *ABRN,* March 2005, p. 68; Jason Stein, "Wagoner: Saturn Will Try to Move Upscale," *Automotive News,* November 1, 2004, p. 6; David Welch, "Will These Rockets Rescue Saturn," *BusinessWeek,* January 17, 2005, pp. 78–79.

Case 12–2: Shirley Leung, "Fast-Food Chains Vie to Carve Out Empire in Pricey Sandwiches," *The Wall Street Journal,* April 5, 2002, pp. A1, A10; James Peters, "Starbucks' Growth Still Hot; Gift Card Jolts Chain's Sales," *Nation's Restaurant News,* February 11, 2002, pp. 1, 47; Greg W. Prince, "Doubleshot of Starbucks' Love," *Beverage World,* March 15, 2002, p. 76; Terry Pristin, "Starbucks Strikes Deep in Wary Land of Pushcarts and Delis," *The New York Times,* April 29, 2002, p. B1; Howard Schultz, "Starbucks," *BusinessWeek,* January 14, 2002, p. 55; Steven Gray, "Starbucks Brews Broader Menu," *The Wall Street Journal,* February 9, 2005, p. B9; Steven Gray, "Starbucks to Raise Drink Prices by an Average of 11 Cents a Cup," *The Wall Street Journal,* September 28, 2004, p. B5; Steven Gray and Amy Merrick, "Latte Letdown: Starbucks Set to Raise Prices," *The Wall Street Journal,* September 2, 2004, p. B1; William C. Symonds, David Kiley, and Stanley Homes, "A Java Jolt for Dunkin' Donuts," *BusinessWeek,* December 20, 2004, pp. 61–63.

Chapter Thirteen

Page 295: Andrew Tiln, "Bagging the Right Customers," *Business 2.0,* May 2005, pp. 56–57; and information from Timbuk2 Web site at *www.timbuk2.com.*

Creating Customer Value, p. 306: Rochelle Garner, "SAP Makes Its Move," *CRN,* May 16, 2005, pp. 16–20.

Acting Ethically, p. 312: Sean Donahue, "Tom's of Mainstream," *Business 2.0,* December 2004, pp. 72–73.

Case 13–1: Kathy Showalter, "CarMax to Bring Tough Competition to Market," *Business First,* March 26, 2004, p. A10; information from CarMax Web site at *www.carmax.com,* May 18, 2005; Gregory J. Gilligan, "CarMax Accelerates Its Expected Earnings: Wall Street Bids Up Stock after the Firm Reports Sales Have Risen This Quarter," *Richmond Times-Dispatch,* November 17, 2004, p. C1; and Carol Hazard, "Fortune Praises CarMax: Magazine Adds Auto Dealer to List of Best Companies to Work For," *Richmond Times-Dispatch,* January 11, 2005, p. C1.

Case 13–2: "Cat Logistics: The Know-How That Helped Build the Legend," from ASCET: Achieving Supply Chain Excellence through Technology Web site at *www.ascet.com,* May 8, 2005; and information from the Caterpillar Web site at *www.cat.com,* May 19, 2005.

Chapter Fourteen

Page 319: John Gaffney, "Best Buy Pumps Up the Volume," from the Peppers and Rogers Group online newsletter, *Inside 1to1,* at *www.1to1.com,* April 25, 2005; Gary McWilliams, "Analyzing Customers, Best Buy Decides Not All Are Welcome," *The Wall Street Journal Online* at *www.online.wsj.com,* November 8, 2004; Joshua Freed, "Best Buy Maps Out Expansion," *USA TODAY,* April 28, 2005, p. 6B; Duff McDonald, "Best Buy's Brilliant Bouncer," *Business 2.0,* January/February 2005, p. 60.

Exhibit 14–1: "Fortune 1000 Ranked within Industries," *Fortune,* April 18, 2005, pp. F53–F64.

Creating Customer Value, p. 323: Matthew Boyle, "The Wegman's Way," *Fortune,* January 24, 2005, pp. 62–68; and Michael A. Prospero, "Employee Innovator: Wegman's," *Fast Company,* October 2004, p. 88.

Exhibit 14–2: Selected from "*Entrepreneur* Magazine's Top 200 International Franchises," *www.franchiseinfomall.com,* May 24, 2005.

Using Technology, p. 327: Libby Quaid, "New Computers Make Grocery Carts Smarter," *The Coloradoan,* May 15, 2005, p. E4.

Exhibit 14–3: Adapted from Michael Levy and Barton A. Weitz, *Retailing Management,* 5th ed. (Burr Ridge, IL: Richard D. Irwin, 2004), p. 620 © 2004 Irwin/McGraw-Hill. Reprinted with permission of the publisher.

Exhibit 14–5: Michael Levy and Barton A. Weitz, *Retailing Management,* 5th ed. (Burr Ridge, Illinois: McGraw-Hill Irwin, 2001) p. 250. Copyright © 2004 The McGraw-Hill Companies. Reprinted with permission.

Exhibit 14–7: Adapted from Barry Berman and Joel R. Evans, *Retail Management: A Strategic Approach,* 5th ed. (New York: Macmillan, 1992), pp. 98–99.

Exhibit 14–8: ADT Security Systems and "The Peter Berlin Report on Shrinkage Control—Store Manager's Edition," The Peter Berlin Retail Consulting Group, Jericho, New York, as presented at *www.retailindustry.about.com,* June 14, 2002.

Case 14–1: Lauren Lipton, "Too Trendy for You?" *The Wall Street Journal,* May 17, 2002, pp. W1, W14; Information from Chico's FAS management presentation at *www.chicos.com/store/SlideShow,* May 25, 2005; Anne D'Innocenzio, "Nation's Clothing Stores Struggling to Draw in 35-Plus Female Market," *The Coloradoan,* May 8, 2005, p. E4; and Olivia Barker, "Shoppers Have a Fit about Sizes," *USA Today,* May 15, 2002, pp. 1D–2D.

Case 14–2: "Home Depot Profit Up, Some Centers Closing," from AP online as it appeared on Hoover's Online at *www.hoovers.com,* May 25, 2005; "Lowe's Profits Up 30.5 Percent," from *Home Textiles Today* as it appeared on Hoovers Online at *www.hoovers.com,* May 25, 2005; information from Home Depot Web site at *www.homedepot.com,* May 25, 2005, and Lowe's Web site at *www.lowes.com,* May 25, 2005; and Pamela Sebastian Ridge, "Tool Sellers Tap Their Feminine Side, *The Wall Street Journal,* March 29, 2002, p. B1.

Chapter Fifteen

Page 345: "The 75-Year-Old Supply Chain," *Inbound Logistics,* January 2002, pp. 96–104; and information from Grainger's Web site at *www.grainger.com,* May 27, 2005; "Kudos: Grainger Industrial Supply," *Purchasing,* May 5, 2005, p. 54.

Exhibit 15–3: Adapted with permission of the International Hardware Distributors Association.

Exhibit 15–4: Mushtaq Luqmani, Donna Goehle, Zahir A. Quraeshi, and Ugur Yavas, "Tracing the Development of Wholesaling Thought and Practice," *Journal of Marketing Channels,* April 1991, p. 95. Reprinted with permission of The Hayworth Press, Inc.

Creating Customer Value, p. 354: Michael V. Copeland, "Stitching Together an Apparel Powerhouse," *Business 2.0,* April 2005, pp. 52–54.

Exhibit 15–5: Deborah Catalano, "Measuring Carrier Performance," *Inbound Logistics,* April 2002, p. 88.

Using Technology, p. 356: Dan Scheraga, "Time's Up: Wal-Mart's Mandate Met with Mixed Results," *Chain Store Age,* February 2005, p. 41; Martha Rogers, "Wal-Mart RFID Deadline Passes, Yet Development Continues," from the Peppers and Rogers Group Web site at *www.peppersandrogers. com*, January 24, 2005; Ann Keeton, "Sensors on Containers May Offer Safer Shipping, *The Wall Street Journal*, March 31, 2005, pp. B4–B5.

Exhibit 15–6: Adapted from "Quick Response: What It Is; What It's Not," *Chain Store Age Executive*, March 1991, pp. B4, B5.

Case 15–1: Thomas Claburn, "Top of the List: Recipe for a Better Winery," from the online version of *Information Week* magazine at *www. informationweek.com*, September 20, 2004; Liza B. Zimmerman, "Reinventing Gallo," *Market Watch*, November/December 2004, pp. 36–46; Jo Bennett, "Gallo Connects with Customers," *1 to 1 magazine*, May/June 2002, pp. 16–17; information from E & J Gallo Winery Web site at *www.gallo.com*, May 27, 2005.

Case 15–2: William Atkinson, "Urban, Rural, or In-Between: Which Location Works for You?" supplement to *Logistics Management*, April 2005, pp. S75–S76; and information from Columbia Sportswear Company Web site at *www.columbia.com*, May 29, 2005.

Chapter Sixteen

Page 367: Tom Weir, "When You Absolutely, Positively Need $$$," *USA Today*, December 29, 2004, p. 3C; information from FedEx Web site at *www.fedex.com*, May 30, 2005.

Using Technology, p. 373: Kate McArthur, "Pepsi Smash TV Show Moves to Yahoo," from the online version of *Advertising Age* at *www.adage.com*, June 3, 2005; Kevin J. Delaney, "CNET Offers TV Junkies a New Fix as It Chases Online Ads," *The Wall Street Journal*, June 2, 2005, p. B1.

Exhibit 16–5: "2004 Advertising to Sales Ratios for 200 Largest Ad Spending Industries," from *Advertising Age* Web site at *www.adage.com*, June 1, 2005.

Acting Ethically, p. 385: "FTC Puts Squeeze on Tropicana's Orange Juice Claims," from the Federal Trade Commission Web site at *www.ftc. gov/opa/2005/06/tropicana.htm*; Jeff Neff, "Court Rules Gillette Razor Ad Claim Is False," from the online version of *Advertising Age* at *www.adage. com*, June 3, 2005.

Case 16–1: David Kiley, "A Green Flag for Booze," *BusinessWeek*, March 7, 2005, p. 95; Zak Brown, "NASCAR's New Spirit," from the *PROMO Magazine* Web site at *www.promomagazine.com*, January 1, 2005; Joe Flint and Shelly Branch, "In Face of Widening Backlash, NBC Gives Up Plan to Run Liquor Ads," *The Wall Street Journal*, March 21, 2002, pp. B1, B3; Theresa Howard, "Liquor Ad Outlets Sought," *USA Today*, April 8, 2002, p. 2B; Vanessa O'Connell, "Landmark TV Liquor Ad Created by D.C. Insiders," *The Wall Street Journal*, January 3, 2002, pp. B1, B3.

Case 16–2: Maureen Tkacik, "As Extreme Goes Mass, Nike Nips at Skate-Shoe Icon," *The Wall Street Journal*, April 24, 2002, pp. A1, A6; information from Savier Inc. Web site at *www.savier.com*, July 2, 2002; Vans Web site at *www.vans.com*, July 2, 2002.

Chapter Seventeen

Page 391: Matt Carmichael, "British Airways Pops Up in Most Unobtrusive Way," *Advertising Age*, October 11, 1999, p. 64; Ian Darby, "Joshua Fights for the Battle of BA Long-Haul," *Marketing*, September 2, 1999, p. 11; Janet Guyon, "British Airways Takes," *Fortune*, September 27, 1999, pp. 214–17; Danny Rogers, "Will BA Take Off Again?" *Marketing*, August 26, 1999, pp. 18–19; "BA Opts for PR to Retain Full-Service 'Premium' Image," *Marketing*, May 23, 2002, p. 6; "Business: AA = No-No; BA Thwarted," *The Economist*, February 2, 2002, pp. 58–59; Daniel Michaels, "British Airways Posts Loss, Says Cost Cuts Help," *The Wall Street Journal*, May 21, 2002, p. D5; Daniel Rogers and Matthew Arnold, "BA to Challenge 'Expensive' Tag with Tactical Ads," *Marketing*, February 14, 2002, p. 3; "A Whiff of Wapping?" *The Economist*, March 12, 2005, p. 60; Finian Davern, "BA Cut: The Reaction," *Travel Trade Gazette*, January 21, 2005, p. 2; Daniel Michaels, "British Airways Plans to Refocus on Service While Cutting Costs," *The Wall Street Journal*, March 2, 2005, p. A6; Sarah Thomas, "Know Your Worth," *Travel Weekly*, February 11, 2005, p. 36.

Exhibit 17–1: Bradley Johnson, "Ad Spending Rose 9.8% for 2004, TNS Reports," *AdAge.com*, March 8, 2005, AAQ38P.

Exhibit 17–2: "2004 Agency Benchmarks," *ADWEEK*, April 25, 2005, p. 57.

Acting Ethically, p. 403: Aaron Baar, "A Healthy Skepticism," *Adweek*, February 7, 2005, p. 18; Sarah Ellison, "Kraft Limits on Kids' Ads May Cheese Off Rivals," *The Wall Street Journal*, January 13, 2005, p. B3; Andrew Grossman, "Primed for Victory," *Multichannel News*, March 7, 2005, pp. 18–19; "Kraft Takes Lead in Responsibility," *Advertising Age*, January 24, 2005, p. 24; Wendy Melillo and Aaron Baar, "Battle Lines Are Drawn Over What Makes Kids Fat," *Adweek*, January 31, 2005, p. 8.

Being Entrepreneurial, p. 408: Michael Abshire, "The Business Case for Philanthropy," *Corporate Philanthropy Report*, February 2004, pp. 1–5; Vinay Bhagat, "The New Marketing Model for Nonprofits," *Nonprofit World*, November–December 2004, pp. 17–18; Nat Ives, "Advertising," *The New York Times*, February 20, 2004, p. C4.

Case 17–1: Michael A. Cusamano, "Google: What It Is and What It Is Not," *Communication of the ACM*, February 2005, pp. 15–17; Kevin Delaney, "Your Ad Here, 10 Words Max: Automated Search Ads Can Serve Up Nonsense: 'Great Deals on Sewage,' " *The Wall Street Journal*, March 24, 2005, p. B1; Ben Elgin and Robert D. Hof, "Keywords for Ad Buyers Pay Up," *BusinessWeek*, February 21, 2005, p. 40; John Markoff and Nat Ives, "Web Search Sites See Clicks Add Up to Big Ad Dollars," *The New York Times*, February 4, 2005, p. A1; Brian Morrissey, "MSN Draws Its Sword in Search Battle with Google," *Adweek*, February 7, 2005, p. 10; Brian Morrissey, "The Race Is On: MSN Raises Stakes in Search Advertising," *Adweek*, March 21, 2005, p. 12.

Case 17–2: "Bates Saatchi to Open Kosovo Agency," *Advertising Age*, August 2, 1999, p. 41; David Kiley, "A New Set of Wheels," *American Demographics*, August 1999, pp. 38–39; Diana T. Kurylko, "Toyota to Consolidate Its Dealers in Europe," *Automotive News*, December 6, 1999, p. 55; Jo-Anne Walker, "Toyota Poaches Director of Marketing from Ford," *Marketing Week*, March 29, 1996, p. 9; Matthew Arnold, "Toyota Backs U.K. Style Show to Boost Corolla," *Marketing*, May 30, 2002, p. 6; Chester Dawson, Larry Armstrong, Joann Muller, and Kathleen Kerwin, "The Americanization of Toyota," *BusinessWeek*, April 15, 2002, pp. 52–54; Ken Gofton, "Toyota Uses Humor to Change Perceptions," *Marketing*, June 6, 2002, p. 25; Jules Grant, "Toyota to Blitz Commuter Railway Sites," *Marketing*, February 28, 2002, p. 8; Jean Halliday, "Young Buyers Increasingly Critical to Toyota Efforts," *Advertising Age*, April 1, 2002, p. S10.

Chapter Eighteen

Page 421: Kris Oser, "Inside McDonald's Branded Online-Game Success," from the online version of *Advertising Age* at *www.adage.com*, November 22, 2004; from the *PROMO Magazine* Web site at *www.promomagazine. com*, April 1, 2005.

Exhibit 18–1: Adapted with permission from William F. Arens, *Contemporary Advertising*, 8th ed. (New York: McGraw-Hill/Irwin, 2002), p. 323.

Creating Customer Value, p. 429: Amy Johannes, "Big Idea Cooks Up *Veggie Tales* Promo with Applebee's, Tyson Foods," from the *PROMO Magazine* Web site at *www.promomagazine.com*, March 16, 2005.

Exhibit 18–6: From Yumiko Ono, "Wobblers & Sidekicks Clutter Stores, Ink Retailers," *Wall Street Journal*, Sept. 8, 1998, B, B3. Copyright © 1998 by Dow Jones & Co. Inc. Reproduced with permission of Dow Jones & Co. Inc. via Copyright Clearance Center.

Acting Ethically, p. 437: Amy Johannes, "FTC Fingers CompUSA in Rebate Complaints," from the *PROMO Magazine* Web site at *www.promomagazine.com*, March 16, 2005.

Exhibit 18–7: Christopher Power, "Coupon Scams Are Clipping Companies," *BusinessWeek*, June 15, 1992, pp. 110–11. Reprinted by permission.

Case 18–1: Information from Wyndham's Women on Their Way Web site at *www.womenbusinesstravelers.com*, July 10, 2002; and Sonia Reyes, "Tapping Girl Power," *Brandweek*, April 22, 2002, pp. 26–30.

Case 18–2: Daniel Pearl and Steve Stecklow, "Drug Firms' Incentives to Pharmacists in India Fuel Mounting Abuse," *The Wall Street Journal*, August 16, 2001, pp. A1, A5; P. T. Jyothi Datta, "Patents for Pharma Companies Must be Dealt with Cautiously," *Global News Wire—Asia Africa Intelligence Wire*, February 15, 2002, Copyright 2002 Kasturi & Sons Ltd,

Business Line; Ravi Dyal, "Doctors Turn Their Backs on Hippocratic Oath," February 1, 2002, *Global News Wire,* Copyright 2002, *The Times of India,* Bennett, Coleman & Co., Ltd; information from the GlaxoSmith-Kline Web site at *www.gsk.com/about/about.htm,* July 10, 2002; information from the Pharmaceutical Research and Manufacturers of America at *www.phrma.org,* July 10, 2002.

Chapter Nineteen

Page 445: *www.pfizer.com,* July 17, 2002; Malcolm Campbell, "Fantastic Pfizer," *Selling Power,* May 1999, pp. 50–56; Amy Barrett and Michael Arudt, "Can Pfizer Stay This Robust?" *BusinessWeek,* March 18, 2002, pp. 68–69; Amy Barrett, "Pfizer's Funk," *BusinessWeek,* February 28, 2005, pp. 72–82; Scott Nensley, "As Drug-Sales Teams Multiply, Doctors Start to Tune Them Out," *The Wall Street Journal Online,* June 13, 2003, p. 4.

Exhibit 19–1: Linda Corman, "The World's Toughest Customers," *Selling,* September 1993, p. 53.

Exhibit: 19–3: From *Sales Management: Analysis and Decision Making,* 3rd Edition by Thomas N. Ingram, Raymond W. LaForge, and Charles H. Schwepker, Jr. Copyright © 1997. Reprinted with permission of South-Western, a division of Thomson Learning: *www.thomsonrights.com.* Fax 800 730-2215.

Exhibit 19–4: From Thomas N. Ingram, Michael D. Hartline, and Charles A. Schwepker, "Gatekeeper Perceptions: Implications for Improving Sales Ethics and Professionalism," *Proceedings of the Academy of Marketing Science,* 1992, pp. 238-42. Reprinted by permission of the Academy of Marketing Science.

Exhibit 19–5: Phillip Schembra, "Often Overlooked Listening Habits," *The Selling Advantage,* January 1991, p. 3; Phillip Schembra, "A Checklist on Asking Questions," *The Selling Advantage,* July 1991, p. 3. Reprinted by permission of the publisher.

Exhibit 19–6: Adapted from: *Making . . . Serving . . . Keeping Customers* by permission of the The Dartnell Corporation, 1990.

Using Technology, p. 452: Alan Horowitz, "Doing Your Homework," *Sales & Marketing Management,* March 2005, p. 19; Jeanette Borzo, "Monetizing the Handshake," *Business 2.0,* May 2005, p. 32; Daniel Terdiman, "Service Warms Cold Calls," *The Courier-Journal,* April 4, 2005, pp. D1–D2.

Exhibit 19–7: From *Sales Management: Analysis and Decision Making,* 3rd Edition by Thomas N. Ingram, Raymond W. LaForge, and Charles H. Schwepker, Jr. Copyright © 1997. Reprinted with permission of South-Western, a division of Thomson Learning: *www.thomsonrights.com.* Fax 800 730-2215.

Exhibit 19–8: From *Sales Management: Analysis and Decision Making,* 3rd Edition by Thomas N. Ingram, Raymond W. LaForge, and Charles H. Schwepker, Jr. Copyright © 1997. Reprinted with permission of South-Western, a division of Thomson Learning: *www.thomsonrights.com.* Fax 800 730-2215.

Being Entrepreneurial, p. 456: Michael Weinreb, "Power to the People," *Sales & Marketing Management,* April 2003, pp. 29–35.

Exhibit 19–9: From S*ales Management: Analysis and Decision Making,* 3rd Edition by Thomas N. Ingram, Raymond W. LaForge, and Charles H.

Schwepker, Jr. Copyright © 1997. Reprinted with permission of South-Western, a division of Thomson Learning: *www.thomsonrights.com.* Fax 800 730-2215.

Exhibit 19–10: Excerpted from *Sales and Marketing Executives International Certified Professional Salesperson Code of Ethics* by permission of Sales and Marketing Executives International, 1994.

Exhibit 19–11: Rosemary R. Lagace, Thomas N. Ingram, and Michael Borom, "An Exploratory Study of Salesperson Unethical Behavior: Scale Development and Validation," *Proceedings,* American Marketing Association Summer Educators' Conference, 1994.

Case 19–1: "STEP . . . Training to Integrate the Saturn Difference," *Marketing Journal,* Winter 1993, pp. 1–2; Dorothy Cottrell, Larry Davis, Pat Detrick, and Marty Raymond, "Sales Training and the Saturn Difference," *Training and Development,* December 1992, pp. 38–43; Andrea Sawyers, "No-Haggle Pricing Hits Full Throttle," *Advertising Age,* March 22, 1992, p. S10; Saturn Web site (*http://www.saturncars.com*), July 17, 2002; *www.saturn.com,* accessed on June 13, 2005.

Case 19–2: John A. Byrne, "Main Street Trumps Wall Street," *Business-Week,* June 10, 2002, pp. 134–38; *www.edwardjones.com,* accessed on June 13, 2005.

Chapter Twenty

Page 469: Laura Cococcia, "Skechers Changes E-mail Strategy to Reach Customers," *Inside 1 to 1,* January 31, 2005; information from Skechers's Web site at *www.skx.com/index.php,* April 25, 2005.

Exhibit 20–1: First appeared in *Success,* February 1993. Written by Jody Hewgill. Reprinted with permission of *Success* magazine. Copyright © 1993 by Hal Holdings Corporation.

Using Technology, p. 471: Brian Quinton, "E-Mailings Boost Boston Dry Cleaner's Business," *Direct,* May 1, 2005.

Exhibit 20–4: Adapted from Bill Furlong, "Reach All Levels of the Decision-Making Process" from *www.DMNews.com.* June 27, 2002. Reprinted with permission of Courtney Communications, Copyright © 2002.

Being Entrepreneurial, p. 479: Thomas Mucha, "Stronger Sales in Just 28 Minutes," *Business 2.0,* June 2005, pp. 56–60; and information from Hawthorne Direct Web site at *www.hawthornedirect.com,* June 8, 2005.

Exhibit 20–5: The National Consumers League's National Fraud Information Center at *www.natlconsumersleague.org,* July 25, 2002. Reprinted by permission.

Exhibit 20–6: "Complying with the Telemarketing Sales Rule," available from the Federal Trade Commission Web site at *www.ftc.gov,* June 1, 2005.

Case 20–1: Larry Riggs, "Cisco Scuttles Postal Mail," *Direct,* June 2002, p. 16; Larry Riggs, "Cisco Starts Major DM Effort," *Direct,* February 2002, p. 18; Steven Burke, "Thumbs Up for IBM, Cisco, Sony" from the *CRN* magazine Web site at *www.crn.com,* April 25, 2005.

Case 20–2: Jim Emerson, "Turnaround: Sam Goody Revives and Expands Sagging Loyalty Program," *Direct,* November 1999, pp. 1, 11; information from Group 3 Marketing's Web site at *www.group3marketing.com,* July 25, 2002; information from Musicland's Web site at *www.musicland.com.,* June 8, 2005.

Photo Credits

Prologue

Chapter One

Chapter Two

Chapter Three

Chapter Four

Chapter Five

Chapter Six

Chapter Seven

Courtesy Acxiom, p. 153

Courtesy Ford Motor Company, p. 154

Courtesy Evian; Agency: Paradiset DDB/Sweden, p. 156

Courtesy Univision Communications, Inc., p. 159

Courtesy Hartmarx Corporation, p. 159

Courtesy Hartmarx Corporation, p. 159

Courtesy Corlison Pte. Ltd.; Agency: Impiric Singapore, p. 163

Courtesy Kilmer & Kilmer, Inc./Albuquerque, N.M, p. 165

Courtesy Johnson & Johnson, p. 166

Courtesy Claritas, p. 173

Courtesy Aimaq Rapp Stolle/Berlin, p. 174

Courtesy Martin Agency, p. 175

Kinko's Inc. 2000. Kinko's is a registered trademark of Kinko's Corporation and is used by permission. All copyrights and trademarks are the property of the respective owners and are used by permission. All rights reserved, p. 175

Chapter Eight

© 2005 PepsiCo, Inc. Used with permission, p. 183

Courtesy The Gillette Company, p. 184

Courtesy Singapore Airlines, Ltd, p. 186

Courtesy Komatsu, p. 189

Courtesy United Parcel Service of America, Inc., p. 190

Courtesy American Honda Motor Co., Inc., p. 192

Courtesy Motorola, Inc., p. 192

Courtesy Maytag Corporation, p. 192

© The Procter & Gamble Company. Used by permission, p. 193

© M. Hruby, p. 197

Courtesy Acushnet Company, p. 198

Courtesy The Black & Decker Corporation, p. 198

Courtesy Marriott Corporation, p. 200

Chapter Nine

Courtesy 3M, p. 205

Courtesy Apple Computer, Inc., p. 206

Courtesy Kelly-Springfield Tire Company, p. 207

© NTT/Verio, p. 208

© Ted Rice, p. 211

© Ted Rice, p. 211

© Ted Rice, p. 211

Courtesy Electrovaya, Inc., p. 216

Courtesy LG Electronics, p. 217

© James Schnepf, p. 218

Courtesy Lufthansa German Airlines; Agency: Gotham/New York, p. 219

Chapter Ten

AP Photo/Achmad Ibrahim, p. 225

Courtesy Pfizer, p. 226

Courtesy Nokia Corporation, p. 232

Courtesy General Mills, Inc., p. 233

Courtesy General Mills, Inc., p. 233

Reprinted by permission Hilton Hospitality, Inc., p. 235

Courtesy EMCOR Group, Inc., p. 236

Courtesy Coty, Inc. and Coty USA, Inc., p. 238

Courtesy Xerox Corporation, p. 239

Corbis, p. 240

Chapter Eleven

AP Photo/April L. Brown, p. 245

Courtesy Verizon Wireless, p. 247

Courtesy European Central Bank, p. 252

Courtesy ADT Security Services, Inc.; Agency: Grey Worldwide Northwest, p. 254

Courtesy Jaguar Cars, Inc., p. 256

Courtesy Bartle, Bogel Hegarty/New York, p. 258

Courtesy The Richards Group, p. 261

DeVito/Verdi, p. 263

AP Photo/Jim Mone, p. 264

Chapter Twelve

These materials have been reproduced with the permission of eBay Inc. COPYRIGHT © EBAY INC. ALL RIGHTS RESERVED, p. 269

Courtesy Norwegian Cruise Line, p. 273

Courtesy DDB/Berlin, p. 273

Courtesy United Airlines, p. 278

Courtesy DDB/London, p. 279

Courtesy Dell, Inc., p. 281

© M. Hruby, p. 281

Courtesy General Mills, p. 286

Courtesy Progress Energy, p. 288

Chapter Thirteen

Images provided by Timbuk2 Designs, Inc., p. 295

Courtesy Target Corporation, p. 299

Courtesy Avon, p. 300

Courtesy Spiker Communications, p. 302

Mary Beth Camp/Matrix, p. 303

Courtesy General Motors Corporation, p. 307

© M. Hruby, p. 309

Photo by Mario Tama/Getty Images, p. 309

© John Abbott, p. 311

Chapter Fourteen

Photo by Tim Boyle/Getty Images, p. 319

Courtesy Mall of America, p. 321

Courtesy Mall of America, p. 321

John Roberts, p. 322

Courtesy 7-11 of Japan, p. 322

Photo by Piotr Malecki/Liaison/Getty Images, p. 324

Greg Girard/Contact Press, p. 324

Courtesy of Evolution Robotics, p. 325

Courtesy Amazon.com, p. 327

© John Madere, p. 328

© Red Morgan, p. 332

Chuck Solomon, p. 333

Photo by Justin Sullivan/Getty Images, p. 335

© Marc Joseph, p. 335

Chapter Fifteen

Courtesy W.W. Grainger, p. 345

Courtesy Ingram Micro, Inc., p. 346

Courtesy W.W. Grainger, p. 348

Photo by Tim Boyle/Getty Images, p. 350

Courtesy DoveBid, Inc., p. 350

Courtesy United Parcel Service of America, Inc., p. 354

Courtesy Knight-Ridder, Inc., p. 354

Courtesy Unilever, P.L.C., p. 355

© Jeff Zaruba, p. 358

Courtesy TRANSFLO Corporation, p. 358

© Lester Lefkowitz, p. 359

Chapter Sixteen

Photo by Jamie Squire/Getty Images, p. 367

Courtesy Benjamin Moore & Co., p. 369

Courtesy Wisconsin Milk Marketing Board, Inc., p. 369

Courtesy Samsung Electronics North America, p. 370

Courtesy WNBA Enterprises, LLC, p. 371

© Flip Chalfant, p. 372

Used with permission of Memorial Sloan-Kettering Cancer Center, p. 374

Courtesy Omega Ltd, p. 374

Courtesy Bailey's Nursery; Art Director: Tim Ward; Creative Director/Copywriter/Photographer: Michael La Monica, p. 378

Courtesy Timex Corporation, p. 381

Courtesy Liberty Mutual Insurance Company, p. 384

© 2002 Wyeth Consumer Healthcare, p. 385

Chapter Seventeen

Courtesy British Airways, p. 391

Courtesy A.T. Cross, p. 394

Courtesy Courtroom Television Network LLC, p. 395

Courtesy Outdoor Channel Holdings, Inc., p. 395

Courtesy Master Comunicacáo/Brazil, p. 396

Courtesy Penn Racquet Sports, p. 401

Courtesy Ogilvy & Mather/New Delhi, p. 402

© M. Hruby, p. 403

Courtesy The Gillette Company, p. 404

Courtesy Nike, Inc., p. 406

Courtesy Ogilvy & Mather/London, p. 414

Chapter Eighteen

Courtesy McDonald's Corporation; Agency: The Market Store, p. 421

Courtesy OmB Agency/New York, p. 422

© The Procter & Gamble Company. Used by permission, p. 424

Courtesy Duraflame, p. 425

Courtesy Catalina Marketing, p. 427

Courtesy Fiskars, p. 428

Courtesy CNN/Sports Illustrated for Kids, p. 429

Courtesy Lamb Weston, Inc.; Agency: Strahan Advertising, Inc., p. 433

© M. Hruby, p. 434

© Einzig Photographers, Inc., p. 435

Keith Dennemiller/CORBIS, p. 435

Chapter Nineteen

Courtesy Pfizer, Inc., p. 445

Marc Bolster/ImageState, p. 446

Courtesy Hunt Wesson, Inc., p. 448

Photo by Tim Boyle/Getty Images, p. 449

Mark Tuschman/The Stock Market/CORBIS, p. 450

Melanie Carr/Custom Medical Stock, p. 451

Images Colour Library/ImageState, p. 457

Courtesy Terr Align, p. 458

Image Bank, p. 459

Courtesy Panasonic Corporation of North America, p. 460

Chapter Twenty

Photo by Chris Hondros/Getty Images, p. 469

Photo by Mario Tama/Getty Images, p. 470

Courtesy R.R. Donnelley & Sons Company, p. 471

Courtesy Johnson & Hayward, p. 474

© M. Hruby, p. 475

Courtesy Callaway Golf Company, p. 476

© M. Hruby, p. 477

Courtesy Lincoln Logs International LLC, p. 479

Name Index

Company Index

Subject Index